Everyday Mathematics®

The University of Chicago School Mathematics Project

Teacher's Lesson Guide
Volume 1

Grade 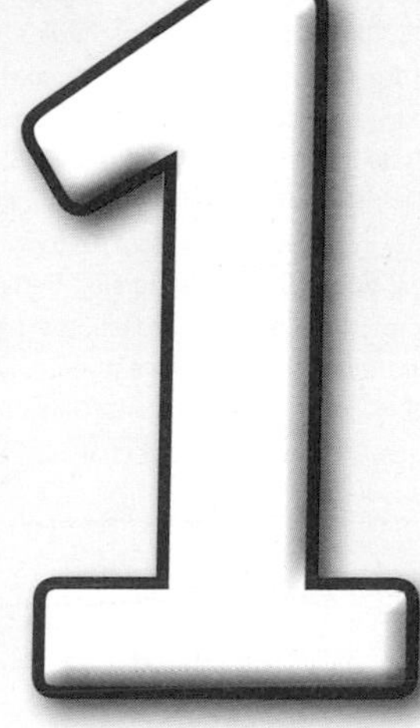

Chicago, IL • Columbus, OH • New York, NY

The University of Chicago School Mathematics Project (UCSMP)

Max Bell, Director, UCSMP Elementary Materials Component, Director, *Everyday Mathematics* First Edition; James McBride, Director, *Everyday Mathematics* Second Edition; Andy Isaacs, Director, *Everyday Mathematics* Third Edition; Amy Dillard, Associate Director, *Everyday Mathematics* Third Edition; Rachel Malpass McCall, Associate Director, *Everyday Mathematics* Common Core State Standards Edition

Authors

Max Bell, Jean Bell, John Bretzlauf, Amy Dillard, Robert Hartfield, Andy Isaacs, James McBride, Rachel Malpass McCall, Kathleen Pitvorec, Peter Saecker

Technical Art

Diana Barrie

UCSMP Editorial

Rossita Fernando
Lila K. Schwartz

ELL Consultant

Kathryn B. Chval

Mathematics and Technology Advisor

James Flanders

Third Edition Teachers in Residence

Jeanine O'Nan Brownell, Andrea Cocke, Brooke A. North

Contributors

Regina Littleton (Office Manager), Kriszta Miner (Project Manager), Allison Greer, Meg Schleppenbach, Cynthia Annorh, Amy DeLong, Debra Fields, Jenny Fischer, Nancy Glinka, Serena Hohmann, Robert Balfanz, Judith Busse, Mary Ellen Dairyko, Lynn Evans, James Flanders, Dorothy Freedman, Nancy Guile Goodsell, Pam Guastafeste, Nancy Hanvey, Murray Hozinsky, Deborah Arron Leslie, Sue Lindsley, Mariana Mardrus, Carol Montag, Elizabeth Moore, Kate Morrison, William D. Pattison, Joan Pederson, Erenda Penix, June Ploen, Herb Price, Danette Riehle, Ellen Ryan, Marie Schilling, Sheila Sconiers, Susan Sherrill, Patricia Smith, Kimberli Sorg, Robert Strang, Jaronda Strong, Kevin Sweeney, Sally Vongsathorn, Esther Weiss, Francine Williams, Michael Wilson, Izaak Wirzup

Photo Credits

Cover (l)C Squared Studios/Getty Images, (r)Tom & Dee Ann McCarthy/CORBIS, (bkgd)Ralph A. Clevenger/CORBIS; **Back Cover** C Squared Studios/Getty Images; **ii xx** The McGraw-Hill Companies; **xxv** (t)Simon Brown/Digital Vision/Getty Images, (others)The McGraw-Hill Companies; **xxvi xxvii** The McGraw-Hill Companies; **xxviii** BrandXPictures/Punchstock; **xxix** The McGraw-Hill Companies; **xxx** (t)Dorling Kindersley/Getty Images, (others)Siede Preis/Photodisc/Getty Images; **xxxi** The McGraw-Hill Companies; **xxxii** (t)The McGraw-Hill Companies, (b)Zedcor Wholly Owned/PhotoObjects.net/Jupiterimages; **xxxiii** (t)C Squared Studios/Photodisc/Getty Images, (b)The McGraw-Hill Companies; **xxiv xxvi xxxvii** The McGraw-Hill Companies; **2** (t)Petra Roeder/Alamy, (b)f1.2/Alamy; **3** Mark Steinmetz **14** The McGraw-Hill Companies; **80** (l)The McGraw-Hill Companies, (r)C Squared Studios/Getty Image; **81** The McGraw-Hill Companies; **92** Jim Vecchi/CORBIS; **93 111 153** The McGraw-Hill Companies; **166** (1 to r) (1 4)GK Hart/Vikki Hart/Getty Images, (2 3 5 6)Lana Langlois; **177** Jules Frazier/Photodisc/Getty Images; **179 180** The McGraw-Hill Companies; **181** William Andrew/Getty Images; **260** (l)Dorling Kindersley/Getty Images, (r)Jilly Wendell/Getty Images; **271 272** The McGraw-Hill Companies; **273** Digital Vision/Getty Images; **309 337** The McGraw-Hill Companies; **344** Comstock/PunchStock; **345 376 446 449** The McGraw-Hill Companies; **460** Image Source/Alamy; **464 465 467** The McGraw-Hill Companies; **Icons** (NCTM l-r)Sharon Hoogstraten/Courtesy of Dave Wyman, Jules Frazier/Photodisc/Getty Images, Comstock/PunchStock, Sundell Larsen/Getty Images, PhotoAlto/PunchStock, Four Elements/V262/CORBIS, Juan Silva/Stockbyte/Getty Images, Digital Vision/Getty Images; (iTLG)C Squared Studios/Getty Images; (Online Content Support)Image Source; (Objective)Brand X Pictures/PunchStock/Getty Images.

---

everyday**math**.com

Send all inquiries to:
McGraw-Hill Education
STEM Learning Solutions Center
P.O. Box 812960
Chicago, IL 60681

ISBN: 978-0-07-623381-6
MHID: 0-07-623381-2

Printed in the United States of America.

1 2 3 4 5 6 7 8 9 RMN 17 16 15 14 13 12 11

STEM

McGraw-Hill is committed to providing instructional materials in Science, Technology, Engineering, and Mathematics (STEM) that give all students a solid foundation, one that prepares them for college and careers in the 21st century.

The University of Chicago School Mathematics Project (UCSMP)

Acknowledgements

The first edition of *Everyday Mathematics* was made possible by sustained support over several years from the GTE Corporation and the National Science Foundation; additional help came from the Amoco Foundation through its support of the University of Chicago School Mathematics Project (UCSMP). Earlier projects supported by the National Science Foundation, the National Institute of Education, and the Benton Foundation provided us with insights into the surprising capabilities of young children.

Development of the second edition of *Everyday Mathematics* was funded by the Everyday Learning Corporation and the authors; development of the third edition was supported by McGraw-Hill, the University of Chicago, and the authors. For all of these editions, many University of Chicago and UCSMP colleagues have been helpful. For this Common Core State Standards edition, Deborah Arron Leslie, Rachel Malpass McCall, Cheryl G. Moran, Mary Ellen Dairyko, Rebecca W. Maxcy, Denise Porter, and Sarah R. Burns formed a committee that provided invaluable guidance on many key issues. Rachel Malpass McCall's work as Associate Director of the Common Core State Standards Edition was especially important to the success of the project. We also acknowledge dedicated and resourceful assistance on production and technical tasks by many people at the University of Chicago and at the McGraw-Hill School Education Group.

Over the years that UCSMP has been working in schools, feedback and advice from teachers willing to take risks in trying development versions of our materials have been essential and enormously helpful. There are too many such teachers to list, but their contributions are gratefully acknowledged.

Andy Isaacs
Director, Third Edition and Common Core State Standards Edition

James McBride
Director, Second Edition

Max Bell
Director, First Edition

Contents

Everyday Mathematics

A Mission to Improve Mathematics

The University of Chicago School Mathematics Project

Everyday Mathematics was developed by the University of Chicago School Mathematics Project (UCSMP) in order to enable students in elementary grades to learn more mathematical content and become life-long mathematical thinkers.

- The National Science Foundation and Amoco, GTE, and other leading corporations supported the project through substantial, long-term funding.
- A strong partnership among researchers, mathematics educators, classroom teachers, students, and administrators was developed.
- A consistent, core author team at the University of Chicago School Mathematics Project collaborated on all grade levels to provide a cohesive and well-articulated Pre-K through Grade 6 curriculum.
- The *Everyday Mathematics* curriculum is completely aligned to the NCTM Curriculum Focal Points and the Connections to the Curriculum Focal Points for Grades Pre-K through 6.

"We, our funders, and our users believe strongly that even the best curricula of decades ago are not adequate for today's youth."

University of Chicago School Mathematics Project

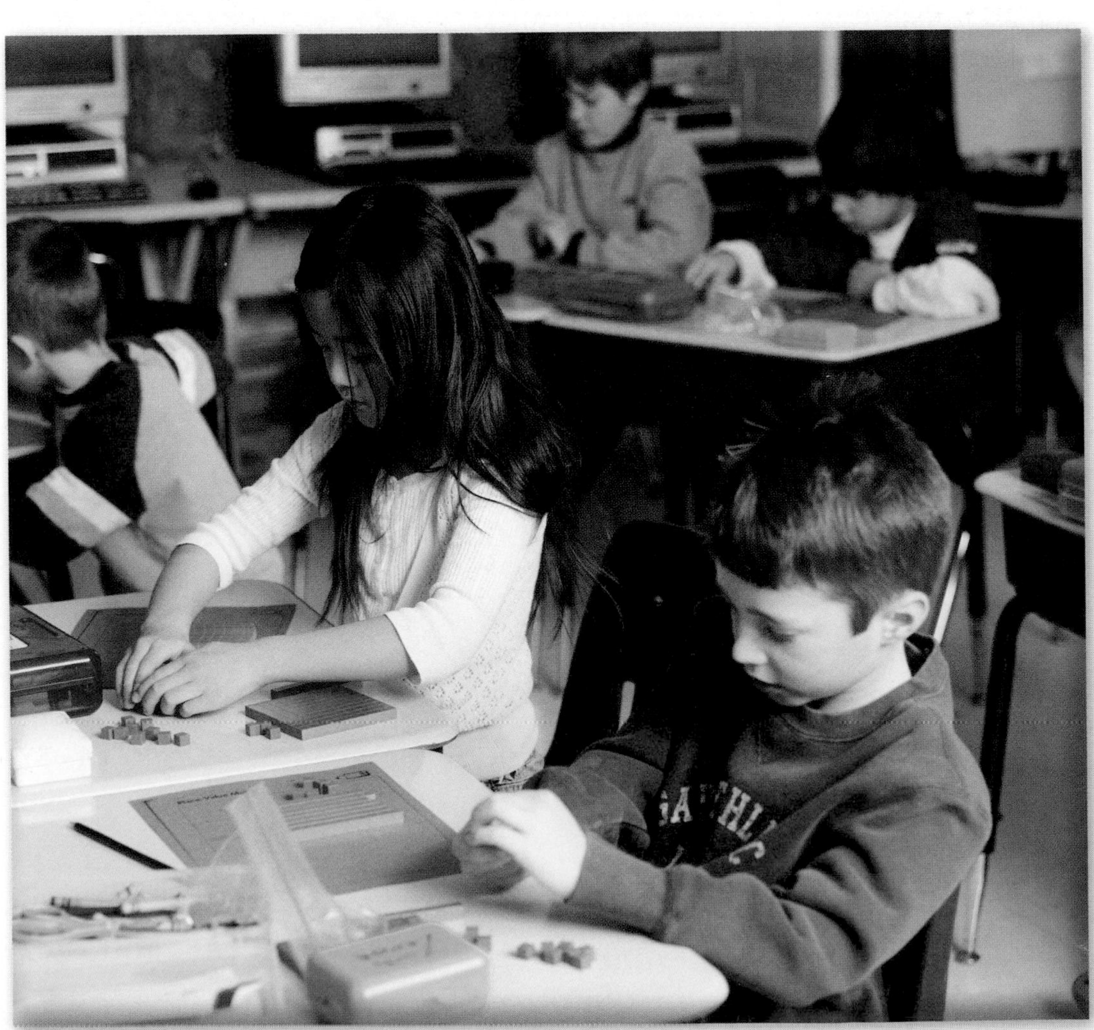

Research Foundation

Everyday Mathematics began with the premise that students can, and must, learn more mathematics than has been expected from them in the past. This premise is based on research the UCSMP author team and others undertook prior to writing the curriculum. Following are some major findings of this research:

- The typical U.S. mathematics curriculum is arithmetic-driven, slow-paced, isolated in its instruction, and broad—rather than deep—in its content.
- International studies show that U.S. students learn much less mathematics than students in other countries.
- Children are capable of learning more mathematics in a richer curriculum.
- All children can be successful mathematical thinkers.
- Mathematics is meaningful to children when it is varied, rich, and rooted in real-world problems and applications.

Instructional Design

The *Everyday Mathematics* instructional design was carefully crafted to capitalize on student interest and maximize student learning. Among its features are the following:

- High expectations for all students
- Concepts and skills developed over time and in a wide variety of contexts
- Balance among mathematical strands
- Dynamic applications
- Multiple methods and strategies for problem solving
- Concrete modeling as a pathway to abstract understanding
- Collaborative learning in partner and small-group activities
- Cross-curricular applications and connections
- Built-in professional development for teachers

"Our teachers in Grades 6–8 tell me that students using the *Everyday Mathematics* program in earlier grades are arriving in their classrooms with a deeper understanding of mathematical concepts and are ready to start the year at a much higher level."

Principal Kenneth Tucker,
Pre-K to 8

Meeting Standards, Achieving Results

The *Everyday Mathematics* program is celebrating more than 25 years of research and development. The program offers schools results unmatched by any other elementary mathematics program.

Research, Validation, Results

As part of the research for *Everyday Mathematics,* the authors at the University of Chicago School Mathematics Project examined successful curricula from around the world, researched how children learn mathematics, and studied the actual use of mathematics by people in their everyday lives. The results of this research were used to establish the scope and sequence for the mathematical content of the *Everyday Mathematics* program.

Field Testing

The program was written and field tested one grade-level at a time, beginning with kindergarten. Field tests gathered information from classroom teachers and students in three main areas: teacher preparation of materials, student response to materials, and student achievement. Based on teacher and student feedback, the authors revised the curriculum before *Everyday Mathematics* was published.

Learner Verification

The best way to show the effectiveness of a program is to study it over time. Several independent research studies have been conducted which provide evidence for the effectiveness of *Everyday Mathematics*. For example, *Everyday Mathematics* was the focus of a five-year longitudinal study conducted by researchers at Northwestern University. Reports from this study and others are available through the University of Chicago School Mathematics Project or McGraw-Hill.

Everyday Mathematics **Timeline of Research and Development**

	Pre-1989	1989	1990	1991	1992	1993	1994	1995	1996	1997
Pre-K										
Kindergarten	PUBLISH								FEEDBACK • WRITE • FIELD-TEST	
Grade 1	WRITE • FIELD-TEST REWRITE • PUBLISH									◆
Grade 2		WRITE • FIELD-TEST • REWRITE • PUBLISH								◆
Grade 3			WRITE • FIELD-TEST • REWRITE • PUBLISH							◆
Grade 4					WRITE • FIELD-TEST • REWRITE • PUBLISH					
Grade 5						WRITE • FIELD-TEST • REWRITE • PUBLISH				
Grade 6							WRITE • FIELD-TEST • REWRITE • PUBLISH			

Tri-State Student Achievement Study

The ARC Center, a National Science Foundation (NSF) funded project, located at the Consortium for Mathematics and its Applications (COMAP), has carried out a study of the effects of standards-based mathematics programs on student performance on state-mandated standardized tests in Massachusetts, Illinois, and Washington.

The findings of the study are based on the records of over 78,000 students: 39,701 who had used the *Everyday Mathematics* curriculum for at least two years, and 38,481 students from comparison schools. The students were carefully matched by reading level, socioeconomic status, and other variables.

Results showed that the average scores of students in the *Everyday Mathematics* schools were consistently higher than the average scores of students in the comparison schools. (A complete report is available from COMAP or McGraw-Hill.)

A report based on 78,000 students showed that average standardized test scores were significantly higher for students in *Everyday Mathematics* schools than for students in comparison schools.

What Works Clearinghouse

Everyday Mathematics is the only elementary math program found by the What Works Clearinghouse to have potentially positive effects on students' math achievement, among those with a medium to large extent of evidence. The studies of *Everyday Mathematics* cited in the What Works Clearinghouse findings included a total of approximately 12,600 students in Grades 3–5. The students were from a range of socioeconomic backgrounds and attended schools in urban, suburban, and rural communities in multiple states.

Closing the Gap

Many districts, by using the *Everyday Mathematics* program, have helped minority students increase achievement, reducing the minority/majority achievement gap while maintaining growth for all students. This helps schools and districts meet adequate yearly progress requirements set forth by No Child Left Behind legislation. District information is available by contacting McGraw-Hill.

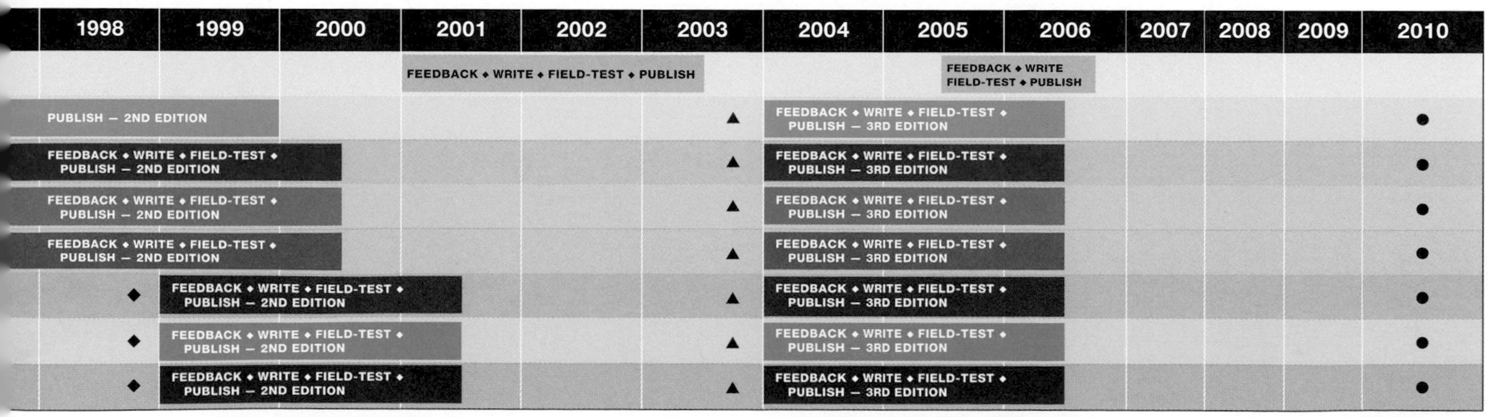

1998	1999	2000	2001	2002	2003	2004	2005	2006	2007	2008	2009	2010
			FEEDBACK ◆ WRITE ◆ FIELD-TEST ◆ PUBLISH				FEEDBACK ◆ WRITE FIELD-TEST ◆ PUBLISH					
PUBLISH – 2ND EDITION					▲	FEEDBACK ◆ WRITE ◆ FIELD-TEST ◆ PUBLISH – 3RD EDITION						●
FEEDBACK ◆ WRITE ◆ FIELD-TEST ◆ PUBLISH – 2ND EDITION					▲	FEEDBACK ◆ WRITE ◆ FIELD-TEST ◆ PUBLISH – 3RD EDITION						●
FEEDBACK ◆ WRITE ◆ FIELD-TEST ◆ PUBLISH – 2ND EDITION					▲	FEEDBACK ◆ WRITE ◆ FIELD-TEST ◆ PUBLISH – 3RD EDITION						●
FEEDBACK ◆ WRITE ◆ FIELD-TEST ◆ PUBLISH – 2ND EDITION					▲	FEEDBACK ◆ WRITE ◆ FIELD-TEST ◆ PUBLISH – 3RD EDITION						●
◆	FEEDBACK ◆ WRITE ◆ FIELD-TEST ◆ PUBLISH – 2ND EDITION				▲	FEEDBACK ◆ WRITE ◆ FIELD-TEST ◆ PUBLISH – 3RD EDITION						●
◆	FEEDBACK ◆ WRITE ◆ FIELD-TEST ◆ PUBLISH – 2ND EDITION				▲	FEEDBACK ◆ WRITE ◆ FIELD-TEST ◆ PUBLISH – 3RD EDITION						●
◆	FEEDBACK ◆ WRITE ◆ FIELD-TEST ◆ PUBLISH – 2ND EDITION				▲	FEEDBACK ◆ WRITE ◆ FIELD-TEST ◆ PUBLISH – 3RD EDITION						●

◆ = 1st edition update ▲ = 2nd edition update ● = 3rd edition update

Everyday Mathematics Grade-Level Goals for Grade 1

Everyday Mathematics structures content into Grade-Level Goals and Program Goals. Grade-Level Goals are then organized by content strand and are carefully articulated across the grades. The content in each grade provides all children with a balanced mathematics curriculum that is rich in real-world problem-solving opportunities. The success of this approach to teaching mathematics is evident in children's improved scores on standardized tests.

The Program Goals and Grade-Level Goals for Grade 1 are listed in the chart below.

Number and Numeration	
Program Goal: Understand the meanings, uses, and representations of numbers.	
Rote counting	**Goal 1** Count on by 1s, 2s, 5s, and 10s past 100 and back by 1s from any number less than 100 with and without number grids, number lines, and calculators.
Rational counting	**Goal 2** Count collections of objects accurately and reliably; estimate the number of objects in a collection.
Place value and notation	**Goal 3** Read, write, and model with manipulatives whole numbers up to 1,000; identify places in such numbers and the values of the digits in those places.
Meanings and uses of fractions	**Goal 4** Use manipulatives and drawings to model halves, thirds, and fourths as equal parts of a region or a collection; describe the model.
Number theory	**Goal 5** Use manipulatives to identify and model odd and even numbers.
Program Goal: Understand equivalent names for numbers.	
Equivalent names for whole numbers	**Goal 5** Use manipulatives, drawings, tally marks, and numerical expressions involving addition and subtraction of 1- or 2-digit numbers to give equivalent names for whole numbers up to 100.
Program Goal: Understand common numerical relations.	
Comparing and ordering numbers	**Goal 7** Compare and order whole numbers up to 1,000.

Operations and Computation

Program Goal: Compute accurately.	
Addition and subtraction facts	**Goal 1** Demonstrate appropriate fluency with addition and subtraction facts through 10 + 10.
Addition and subtraction procedures	**Goal 2** Use manipulatives, number grids, tally marks, mental arithmetic, and calculators to solve problems involving the addition and subtraction of 1-digit whole numbers with 2-digit whole numbers; calculate and compare the values of combinations of coins.
Program Goal: Make reasonable estimates.	
Computational estimation	**Goal 3** Estimate reasonableness of answers to basic fact problems (e.g., Will 7 + 8 be more or less than 10?).
Program Goal: Understand meanings of operations.	
Models for the operations	**Goal 4** Identify change-to-more, change-to-less, comparison, and parts-and-total situations.

Data and Chance

Program Goal: Select and create appropriate graphical representations of collected or given data.	
Data collection and representation	**Goal 1** Collect and organize data to create tally charts, tables, bar graphs, and line plots.
Program Goal: Analyze and interpret data.	
Data analysis	**Goal 2** Use graphs to answer simple questions and draw conclusions; find the maximum and minimum of a data set.
Program Goal: Understand and apply basic concepts of probability.	
Qualitative probability	**Goal 3** Describe events using *certain, likely, unlikely, impossible,* and other basic probability terms.

Measurement and Reference Frames

Program Goal: Understand the systems and processes of measurement; use appropriate techniques, tools, units, and formulas in making measurements.	
Length, weight, and angles	**Goal 1** Use nonstandard tools and techniques to estimate and compare weight and length; measure length with standard measuring tools.
Money	**Goal 2** Know and compare the value of pennies, nickels, dimes, quarters, and dollar bills; make exchanges between coins.
Program Goal: Use and understand reference frames.	
Temperature	**Goal 3** Identify a thermometer as a tool for measuring temperature; read temperatures on Fahrenheit and Celsius thermometers to the nearest 10°.
Time	**Goal 4** Use a calendar to identify days, weeks, months, and dates; tell and show time to the nearest half and quarter hour on an analog clock.

Geometry

Program Goal: Investigate characteristics and properties of two- and three-dimensional geometric shapes.	
Plane and solid figures	**Goal 1** Identify and describe plane and solid figures including circles, triangles, squares, rectangles, spheres, cylinders, rectangular prisms, pyramids, cones, and cubes.
Program Goal: Apply transformations and symmetry in geometric situations.	
Transformations and symmetry	**Goal 2** Identify shapes having line symmetry; complete line-symmetric shapes or designs.

Patterns, Functions, and Algebra

Program Goal: Understand patterns and functions.	
Patterns and functions	**Goal 1** Extend, describe, and create numeric, visual, and concrete patterns; solve problems involving function machines, "What's My Rule?" tables, and Frames-and-Arrows diagrams.
Program Goal: Use algebraic notation to represent and analyze situations and structures.	
Algebraic notation and solving number sentences	**Goal 2** Read, write, and explain expressions and number sentences using the symbols +, −, and = and the symbols > and < with cues; solve equations involving addition and subtraction.
Properties of the arithmetic operations	**Goal 3** Apply the Commutative and Associative Properties of Addition and the Additive Identity to basic addition fact problems.

Common Core State Standards

Everyday Mathematics fully aligns with the national Common Core State Standards for Mathematics. Both are founded on cross-disciplinary skills such as critical thinking and problem solving. The Standards for Mathematical Practice, described in the Common Core State Standards, form a cohesive match with the already-proven instructional design of *Everyday Mathematics*. Both require students to:

- Make sense of problems and persevere in solving them.
- Reason abstractly and quantitatively.
- Construct viable arguments and critique the reasoning of others.
- Model with mathematics.
- Use appropriate tools strategically.
- Attend to precision.
- Look for and make use of structure.
- Look for and express regularity in repeated reasoning.

In *Everyday Mathematics*, the Grade-Level Goals, which state the core content that is assessed at each grade level, align with the Standards for Mathematical Content. *Everyday Mathematics* has a long track record of success resulting from constant revision based on evidence of what works. *Everyday Mathematics* is a world-class mathematics curriculum that fully meets the Common Core State Standards for Grades K–6.

***Everyday Mathematics* fully meets all of the Common Core State Standards for Mathematics, Grades K–6.**

Instruction and Planning

The *Teacher's Lesson Guide* includes a comprehensive grade-level correlation that shows the *Everyday Mathematics* lessons that cover each of the Standards for Mathematical Content. Correlation documents for the complete *Everyday Mathematics* program are available at everydaymathonline.com.

Everyday Mathematics offers a variety of print and technology materials to meet instructional needs and to help incorporate these standards in the classroom curriculum.

Assessment

Everyday Mathematics provides many opportunities and tools for assessment. Assessment results show students' progress toward the *Everyday Mathematics* Grade-Level Goals and the Common Core State Standards.

Professional Development

Professional Development is offered at implementation, for continued support, and is built into the program materials to help teachers successfully implement the Common Core State Standards with the *Everyday Mathematics* program.

Everyday Mathematics

Common Core State Standards and *Everyday Mathematics*

The *Everyday Mathematics* curriculum is completely aligned to the *K-12 Common Core State Standards* for Kindergarten through Grade 6.

Common Core State Standards for Grade 1	*Everyday Mathematics* Grade 1 Lessons*
OPERATIONS AND ALGEBRAIC THINKING 1.OA	
Represent and solve problems involving addition and subtraction.	
1.OA.1. Use addition and subtraction within 20 to solve word problems involving situations of adding to, taking from, putting together, taking apart, and comparing, with unknowns in all positions, e.g., by using objects, drawings, and equations with a symbol for the unknown number to represent the problem.	**1•5, 1•13,** 2•6, **2•7, 2•8, 2•11, 2•12, 2•13, 3•6, 3•11, 3•12, 3•13, 3•14, 4•3, 4•6,** 4•7, 4•9, **5•5, 5-6, 5•7, 5•8,** 5•10, **6•3,** 6•9, **6•10,** 10•3, **10•4,** Project 8
1.OA.2. Solve word problems that call for addition of three whole numbers whose sum is less than or equal to 20, e.g., by using objects, drawings, and equations with a symbol for the unknown number to represent the problem.	**2•13, 3•10, 8•4**
Understand and apply properties of operations and the relationship between addition and subtraction.	
1.OA.3. Apply properties of operations as strategies to add and subtract. *Examples: If $8 + 3 = 11$ is known, then $3 + 8 = 11$ is also known. (Commutative property of addition.) To add $2 + 6 + 4$, the second two numbers can be added to make a ten, so $2 + 6 + 4 = 2 + 10 = 12$. (Associative property of addition.)*	**2•13, 3•10, 4•11, 4•12, 5•5, 5•8, 5•11, 6•1, 6•3, 6•4**
1.OA.4. Understand subtraction as an unknown-addend problem. *For example, subtract $10 - 8$ by finding the number that makes 10 when added to 8.*	**2•13, 4•11, 5•7, 5•8, 6•3, 6•5, 8•5,** 10•4
Add and subtract within 20.	
1.OA.5. Relate counting to addition and subtraction (e.g., by counting on 2 to add 2).	**2•1, 2•11, 2•13, 3•6, 3•8, 3•9, 3•10,** 6•3, **6•8,** 8•5
1.OA.6. Add and subtract within 20, demonstrating fluency for addition and subtraction within 10. Use strategies such as counting on; making ten (e.g., $8 + 6 = 8 + 2 + 4 = 10 + 4 = 14$); decomposing a number leading to a ten (e.g., $13 - 4 = 13 - 3 - 1 = 9$); using the relationship between addition and subtraction (e.g., knowing that $8 + 4 = 12$, one knows $12 - 8 = 4$); and creating equivalent but easier or known sums (e.g., adding $6 + 7$ by creating the known equivalent $6 + 6 + 1 = 12 + 1 = 13$).	**1•5,** 1•10, **1•13, 2•1, 2•2, 2•3, 2•8, 2•11, 2•12, 2•13, 3•6, 3•9, 3•14,** 4•2, 4•6, **4•7,** 4•8, **4•11, 4•12,** 5•5, **5•7, 5•9, 5•10, 5•11,** 5•12, 5•13, **6•1, 6•2, 6•3, 6•4, 6•5,** 6•6, **6•7, 6•8,** 7•1, **7•2,** 7•3, 7•7, 8•2, 8•3, **8•5,** 8•7, 8•8, 8•9, 9•1, 9•7, 10•2

***Bold lesson numbers indicate that content from the standard is being taught. Lesson numbers not in bold indicate that content from the standard is being reviewed or practiced.**

Common Core State Standards for Grade 1	*Everyday Mathematics* Grade 1 Lessons
Work with addition and subtraction equations.	
1.OA.7. Understand the meaning of the equal sign, and determine if equations involving addition and subtraction are true or false. *For example, which of the following equations are true and which are false?* $6 = 6$, $7 = 8 - 1$, $5 + 2 = 2 + 5$, $4 + 1 = 5 + 2$.	**2•11, 3•6,** 4•12, **5•3, 5•10, 6•2,** 8•2
1.OA.8. Determine the unknown whole number in an addition or subtraction equation relating to three whole numbers. *For example, determine the unknown number that makes the equation true in each of the equations* $8 + ? = 11$, $5 = \_\_ - 3$, $6 + 6 = \_\_$.	**3•8, 3•9, 4•11, 4•12, 5•8, 5•10, 5•11, 5•12, 5•13, 6•3, 6•4,** 6•5, 6•6, 6•8
NUMBER AND OPERATIONS IN BASE TEN 1.NBT	
Extend the counting sequence.	
1.NBT.1. Count to 120, starting at any number less than 120. In this range, read and write numerals and represent a number of objects with a written numeral.	***Number of the Day Routine,* 1•1,** 1•2, **1•4,** 1•5, 1•7, 1•8, 1•9, 1•10, 1•12, 1•13, **2•1, 2•2, 2•3, 2•4,** 2•5, 2•6, 2•7, 2•11, 2•13, 3•6, **4•10, 5•1,** 6•4, 6•9, **9•1, 9•3,** 10•7, **Project 3, Project 5**
Understand place value.	
1.NBT.2. Understand that the two digits of a two-digit number represent amounts of tens and ones. Understand the following as special cases:	***Number of the Day Routine,* 5•1, 5•2, 5•3, 5•5,** 5•6, 5•8, 5•9, 6•6, **8•3,** 8•5, **10•7**
1.NBT.2a. 10 can be thought of as a bundle of ten ones — called a "ten."	***Number of the Day Routine,* 5•1, 5•3, 5•5,** 5•9, 6•6, **8•2, 8•3,** 8•4, **10•4,** 10•7
1.NBT.2b. The numbers from 11 to 19 are composed of a ten and one, two, three, four, five, six, seven, eight, or nine ones.	***Number of the Day Routine,* 5•1, 5•2, 5•5**
1.NBT.2c. The numbers 10, 20, 30, 40, 50, 60, 70, 80, 90 refer to one, two, three, four, five, six, seven, eight, or nine tens (and 0 ones).	***Number of the Day Routine,* 5•1, 5•2, 5•5,** 6•6, 8•3
1.NBT.3. Compare two two-digit numbers based on meanings of the tens and ones digits, recording the results of comparisons with the symbols $>$, $=$, and $<$.	**1•6, 5•3, 5•6,** 5•7, 8•1, 8•2, 10•3

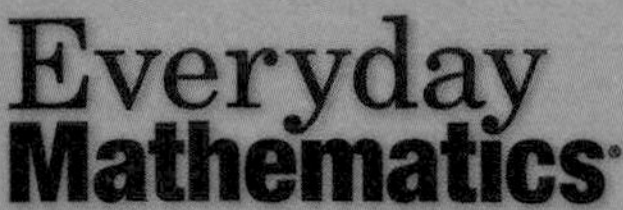

Common Core State Standards for Grade 1	*Everyday Mathematics* Grade 1 Lessons
Use place value understanding and properties of operations to add and subtract.	
1.NBT.4. Add within 100, including adding a two-digit number and a one-digit number, and adding a two-digit number and a multiple of 10, using concrete models or drawings and strategies based on place value, properties of operations, and/or the relationship between addition and subtraction; relate the strategy to a written method and explain the reasoning used. Understand that in adding two-digit numbers, one adds tens and tens, ones and ones; and sometimes it is necessary to compose a ten.	**2•1, 2•13,** 3•9, 4•2, **5•5, 5•8, 8•4,** 8•5, **9•2, 9•3, 9•4, 10•3, 10•4,** 10•6, **Project 9**
1.NBT.5. Given a two-digit number, mentally find 10 more or 10 less than the number, without having to count; explain the reasoning used.	3•9, 8•5, 8•6, **9•1, 9•2, 9•3,** 9•5, **10•4,** 10•6, **10•7**
1.NBT.6. Subtract multiples of 10 in the range 10–90 from multiples of 10 in the range 10–90 (positive or zero differences), using concrete models or drawings and strategies based on place value, properties of operations, and/or the relationship between addition and subtraction; relate the strategy to a written method and explain the reasoning used.	8•4, 8•6, **9•2, 9•3, 9•4, 10•4,** 10•6, **Project 9**
MEASUREMENT AND DATA 1.MD	
Measure lengths indirectly and by iterating length units.	
1.MD.1. Order three objects by length; compare the lengths of two objects indirectly by using a third object.	2•7, **4•2, 4•4,** 4•5, **6•6**
1.MD.2. Express the length of an object as a whole number of length units, by laying multiple copies of a shorter object (the length unit) end to end; understand that the length measurement of an object is the number of same-size length units that span it with no gaps or overlaps. *Limit to contexts where the object being measured is spanned by a whole number of length units with no gaps or overlaps.*	**4•2, 4•3, 4•4, 4•5, 4•6, 4•7, 6•6,** 6•11, **9•5, Project 2**
Tell and write time.	
1.MD.3. Tell and write time in hours and half-hours using analog and digital clocks.	**2•5, 2•6, 3•7,** 3•8, **4•4, 4•8,** 4•9, 4•10, **6•10,** 6•11, 7•2, 8•1, 10•1, **10•2,** 10•5
Represent and interpret data.	
1.MD.4. Organize, represent, and interpret data with up to three categories; ask and answer questions about the total number of data points, how many in each category, and how many more or less are in one category than in another.	**1•7, 1•8, 1•12, 2•11, 3•13,** 4•5, **4•7, 5•9, 6•12,** 7•3, **7•4, 8•1, 9•2, 9•6, 10•1, 10•3, Project 2**

Common Core State Standards for Grade 1	*Everyday Mathematics* Grade 1 Lessons
GEOMETRY 1.G	
Reason with shapes and their attributes.	
1.G.1. Distinguish between defining attributes (e.g., triangles are closed and three-sided) versus non-defining attributes (e.g., color, orientation, overall size); build and draw shapes to possess defining attributes.	6•7, **7•1, 7•2, 7•3, 7•4, 7•5, 7•6, 10•5**
1.G.2. Compose two-dimensional shapes (rectangles, squares, trapezoids, triangles, half-circles, and quarter-circles) or three-dimensional shapes (cubes, right rectangular prisms, right circular cones, and right circular cylinders) to create a composite shape, and compose new shapes from the composite shape.	**3•4, 7•1,** 7•2, **7•3, 7•4, 7•5, 7•6,** 7•7, 9•3, **10•5, Project 1, Project 10**
1.G.3. Partition circles and rectangles into two and four equal shares, describe the shares using the words *halves, fourths,* and *quarters,* and use the phrases *half of, fourth of,* and *quarter of.* Describe the whole as two of, or four of the shares. Understand for these examples that decomposing into more equal shares creates smaller shares.	**8•6, 8•7, 8•9, 9•6, 9•7, 9•8,** 10•7

Components at a Glance

▶ Student Materials

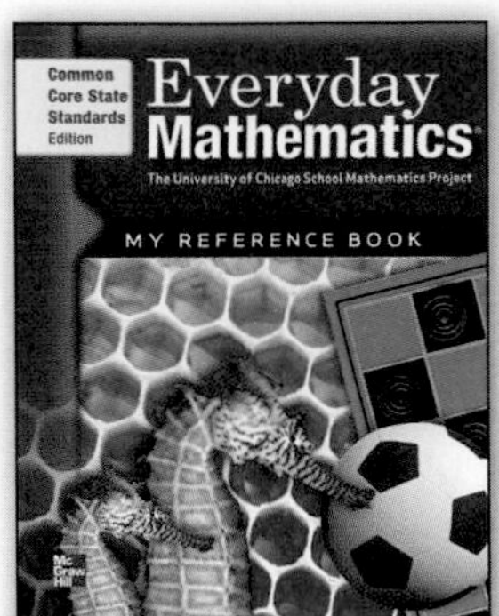

My Reference Book (Grades 1 and 2)
This hardcover book is a child's first mathematical reference book. *My Reference Book* contains explanations of key concepts as well as directions for games.

Student Reference Book (Grades 3–6)
Contains explanations of key mathematical content, along with directions for the *Everyday Mathematics* games. This hardbound book supports student learning in the classroom and at home.

Student Math Journal, Volumes 1 & 2 (Grades 1–6)
These consumable books provide daily support for classroom instruction. They provide a long-term record of each child's mathematical development.

▶ Teacher Materials

Teacher's Lesson Guide, Volumes 1 & 2 (Grades 1–6)
The core of the *Everyday Mathematics* program, the *Teacher's Lesson Guide* provides teachers with easy-to-follow lessons organized by instructional unit, as well as built-in mathematical content support. Lessons include planning and assessment tips and multilevel differentiation strategies to support all learners.

Math Masters (Grades 1–6)
Blackline masters that support daily lesson activities. Includes Home/Study Links, lesson-specific masters, game masters, and project masters.

Minute Math®+ (Grades 1–3) 5-Minute Math (Grades 4–6)
Brief activities for transition time and for spare moments throughout the day.

▶ Teacher Resources

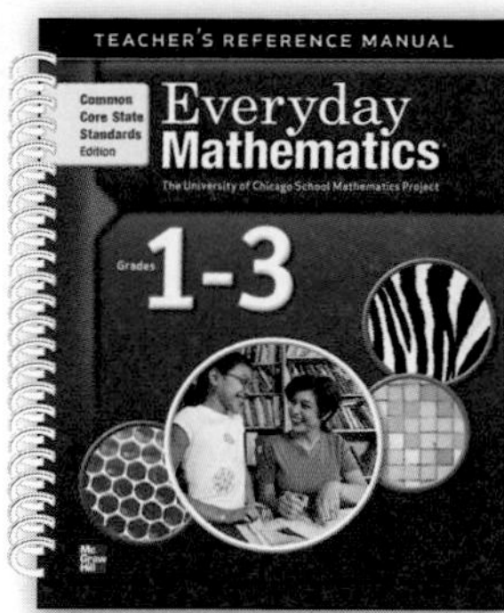

Teacher's Reference Manual Contains comprehensive background information about mathematical content and program management for grades Early Childhood, 1–3, and 4–6.

Home Connection Handbook Enhances home-school communication for teachers and administrators. Includes masters for easy planning for grades Early Childhood, 1–3, and 4–6.

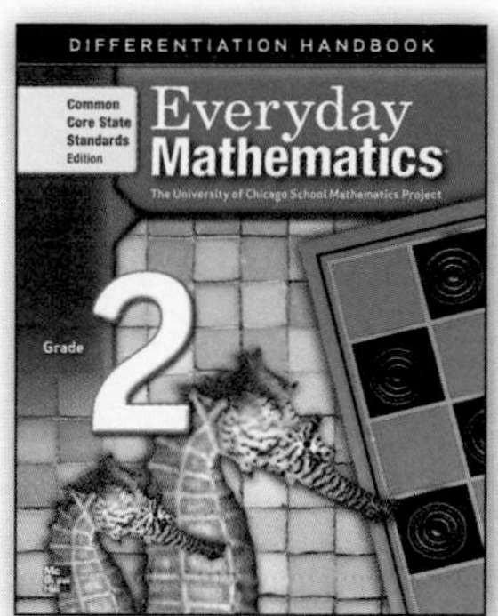

Differentiation Handbook (Grades 1–6)
Grade-specific handbooks that help teachers plan strategically in order to reach the needs of diverse learners.

Assessment Handbook (Grades 1–6)
Grade-specific handbooks provide explanations of key features of assessment in the *Everyday Mathematics* program. Includes all assessment masters.

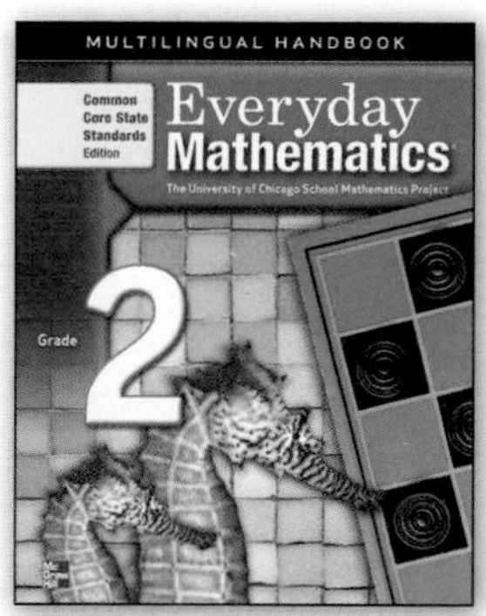

Multilingual Handbook (Grades 1–6) Grade-specific component provides lesson-specific support to help meet the needs of a multilingual classroom. Includes a brief summary and an example for each lesson. Content provided in English, Spanish, traditional Chinese, Vietnamese, Arabic, and Hmong.

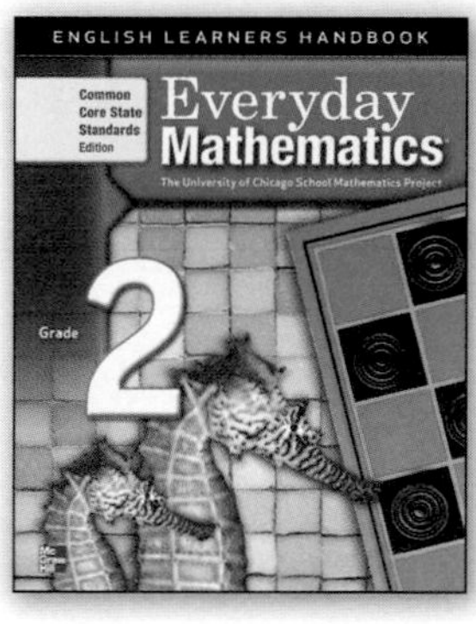

English Learners Handbook (Grades 1–6)
Grade-specific component provides lesson-specific comprehension strategies to aid in meeting the needs of a multilingual classroom. Also included are language development notes.

Content by Strand Poster
To help with pacing, the Key Concepts and Skills for each content strand are presented by month. Provides overview of program content for each grade level. Reverse side is a poster of the Grade-Level Goals.

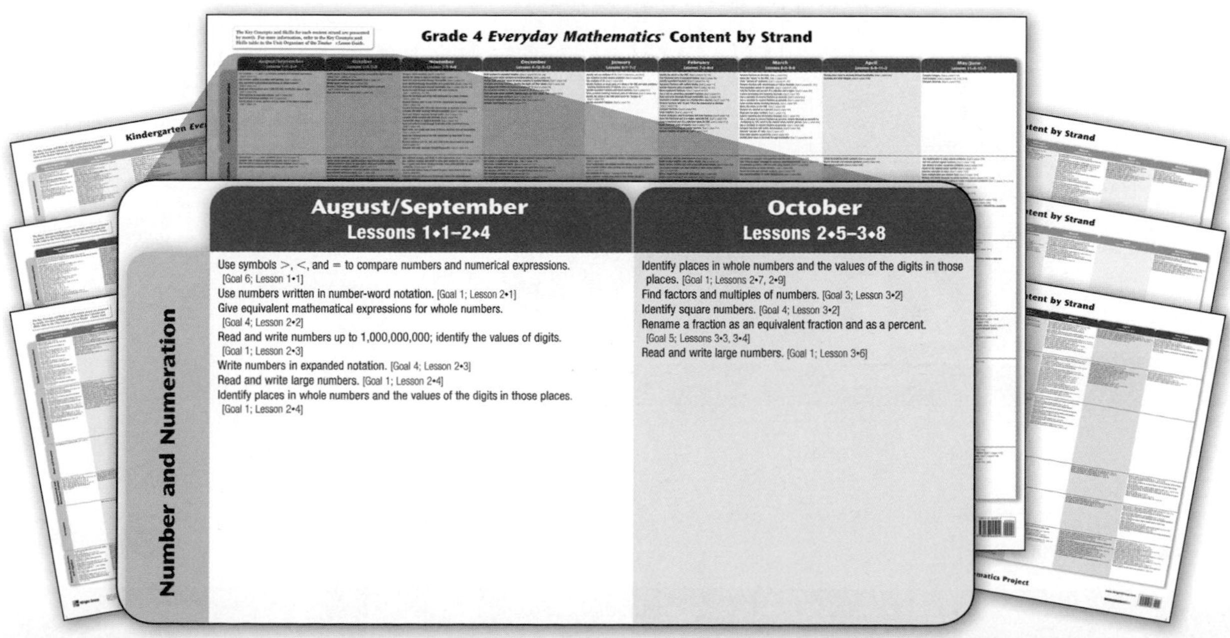

Technology at a Glance

Integrated technology enhances instruction and engages learners. *Everyday Mathematics* offers integrated technology for planning and teaching, practice, assessment, and home connections. Learn more and access all technology resources online at **www.everydaymathonline.com**.

Planning and Teaching

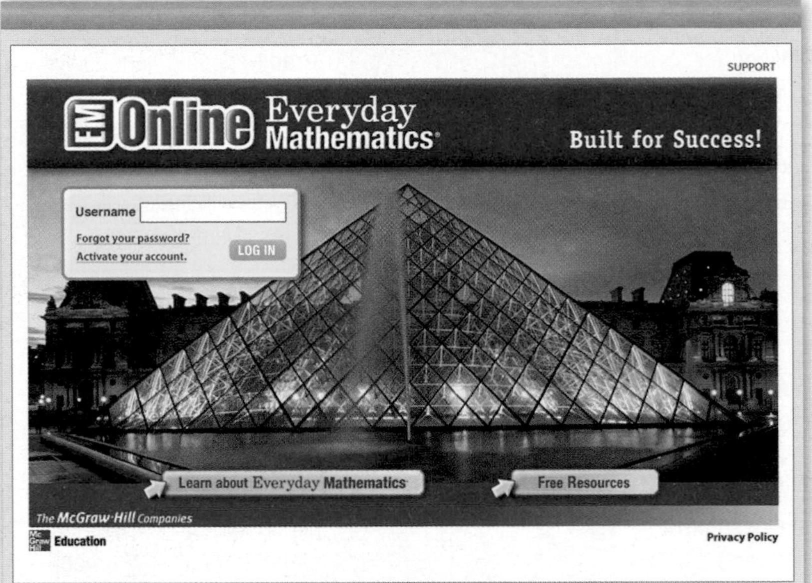

everydaymathonline.com

Offers an eSuite of fully integrated online tools that provide rich, interactive classroom experiences and solutions for students and teachers.

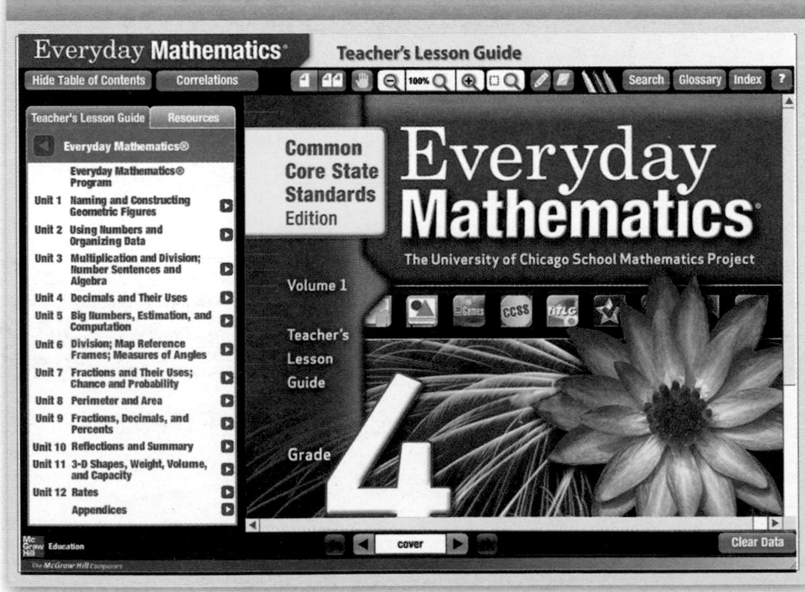

Interactive Teacher's Lesson Guide (iTLG)*

Enables digital access to the entire *Everyday Mathematics* program. Includes access to all components found in the Classroom Resource Package. Content is searchable by word or phase so all pages related to a specific topic can be found quickly and easily. Available online or on CD-ROM.

*Available as separate purchase

Planning and Teaching continued

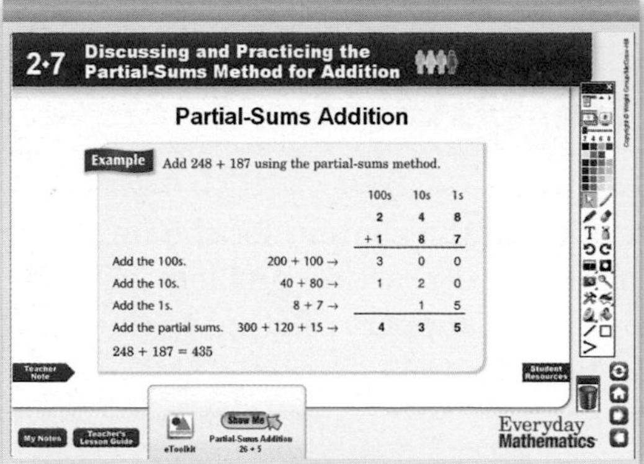

ePresentations*
Provide engaging lessons on your favorite interactive whiteboard for every lesson, except for the Progress Checks. Available online through the ePlanner Deluxe.

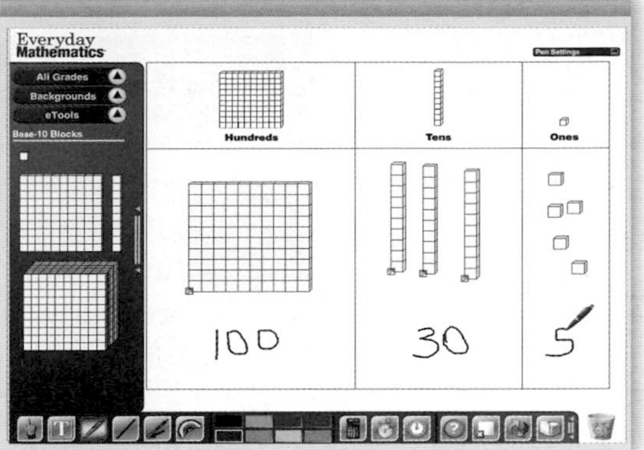

eToolkit*
Includes all the online tools and virtual manipulatives necessary to teach an *Everyday Mathematics* lesson. Available online through the ePlanner Deluxe.

Home Connections

Family Letters** Support students at home by sharing each unit's key content and vocabulary, directions to games, Do-Anytime Activities, and answers to most Home Links/Study Links. Available online in nine different languages.

Practice

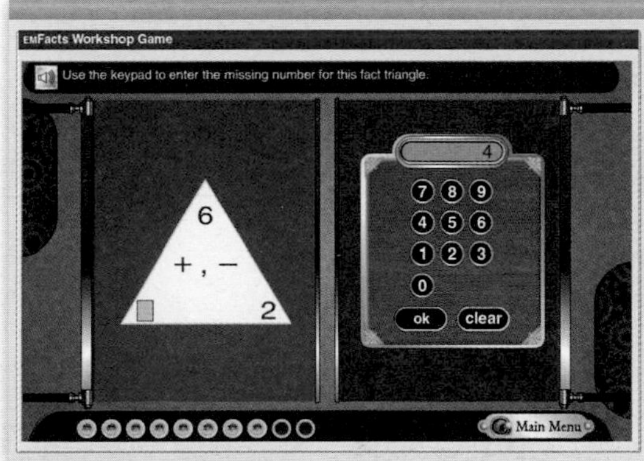

EM Facts Workshop Game
Provides interactive practice for students on basic facts and computation. Available online only.

Assessment

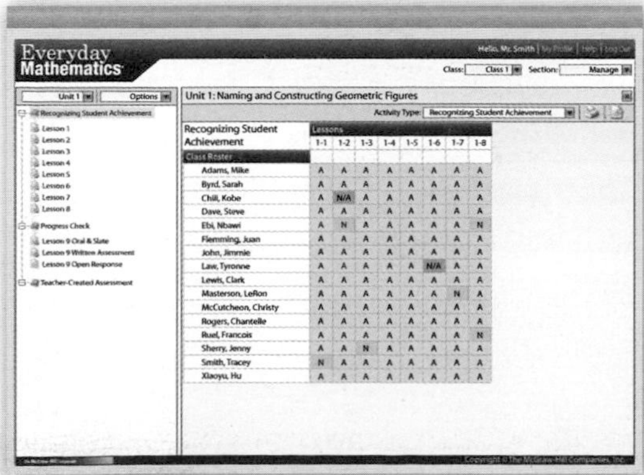

Assessment Management Spreadsheets
This electronic tool can be used to monitor and record students' progress.

After information on student performance is entered, the Assessment Management Spreadsheets provide reports showing students' progress toward Grade-Level Goals. Available online only.

*Available as separate purchase
**Languages other than English and Spanish available as separate purchase

Everyday Mathematics

Planning and Instructional Support

Each unit organizer provides an overview of the content for the unit. Also included is support for ongoing learning and practice, problem solving, and differentiated instruction. Detailed content support relating to the unit instruction is provided in Mathematical Background.

Overview

Describes concepts and ideas that are the focus of the unit.

Contents

Includes the objective for every lesson.

Unit 1 Organizer

Naming and Constructing Geometric Figures

Overview

The principal focus of Unit 1 is geometry. Opening with geometry enables a relatively relaxed beginning of the school year and allows teachers and students to get acquainted and establish yearlong routines. Starting the year with geometry also makes the point that mathematics is more than numbers and is strongly linked to language and art. Unit 1 has five main areas of focus:

- To introduce students to the *Student Reference Book*,
- To practice using geometry tools,
- To classify quadrangles,
- To explore and identify polygons, and
- To review and practice addition and subtraction fact extensions.

Linking to the Common Core State Standards

The content of Unit 1 addresses the Common Core State Standards for Mathematics in *Geometry*. The correlation of the Common Core State Standards to the *Everyday Mathematics* Grade 4 lessons begins on page CS1.

2 Unit 1 Naming and Constructing Geometric Figures

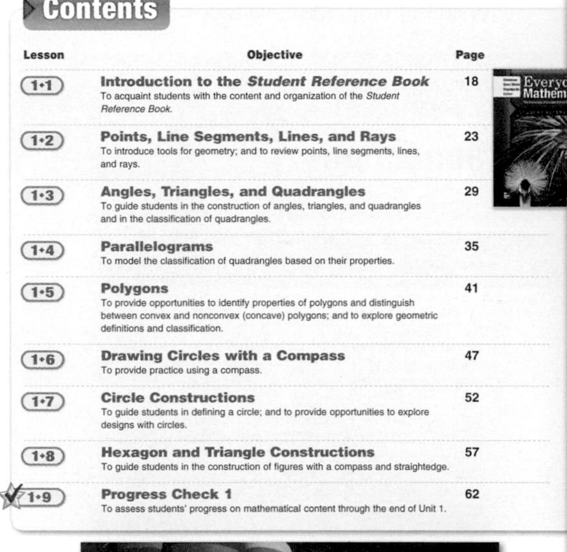

Contents

Unit 1 Organizer

Learning In Perspective

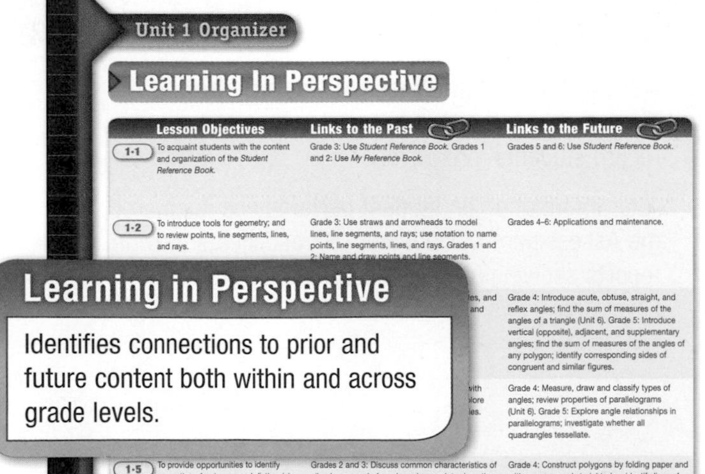

	Lesson Objectives	Links to the Past	Links to the Future
1•1	To acquaint students with the content and organization of the *Student Reference Book.*	Grade 3: Use *Student Reference Book.* Grades 1 and 2: Use *My Reference Book.*	Grades 5 and 6: Use *Student Reference Book.*
1•2	To introduce tools for geometry; and to review points, line segments, lines, and rays.	Grade 3: Use straws and arrowheads to model lines, line segments, and rays; use notation to name points, line segments, lines, and rays. Grades 1 and 2: Name and draw points and line segments.	Grades 4–6: Applications and maintenance.
		...es, and ... and	Grade 4: Introduce acute, obtuse, straight, and reflex angles; find the sum of measures of the angles of a triangle (Unit 6). Grade 5: Introduce vertical (opposite), adjacent, and supplementary angles; find the sum of measures of the angles of any polygon; identify corresponding sides of congruent and similar figures.
		...with ...lore ...les.	Grade 4: Measure, draw and classify types of angles; review properties of parallelograms (Unit 6). Grade 5: Explore angle relationships in parallelograms; investigate whether all quadrangles tessellate.
1•5	To provide opportunities to identify properties of polygons and distinguish between convex and nonconvex (concave) polygons; and to explore ... classification.	Grades 2 and 3: Discuss common characteristics of all polygons and of regular polygons; introduce the term *parallel.* Grades 1–3: Explore polygons with straws, geoboards, and dot paper. Name the parts of a polygon: side, vertex, and angle.	Grade 4: Construct polygons by folding paper and with compass and straightedge; identify lines of symmetry for polygons, and introduce congruent figures (Units 6, 10, and 11). Grades 5 and 6: ... polygons in a plane;

Learning in Perspective

Identifies connections to prior and future content both within and across grade levels.

Key Concepts and Skills

Lists the Key Concepts and Skills, the important mathematical ideas that are covered in each lesson.

	Key Concepts and Skills	Grade 4 Goals*
1•1	Use the symbols >, <, and = to compare numbers and numerical expressions.	Number and Numeration Goal 6
	Solve simple +, −, ×, and ÷ problems.	Operations and Computation Goals 1 and 3
	Describe relationships among U.S. customary units of length.	Measurement and Reference Frames Goal 3
1•2	Identify and draw line segments, lines, and rays.	Geometry Goal 1
	Describe characteristics of line segments, lines, and rays.	Geometry Goal 1
	Use letter and symbol notation to name line segments, lines, and rays.	Geometry Goal 1
1•3	Use letter notation to name angles.	Geometry Goal 1
	Construct angles, triangles, and quadrangles.	Geometry Goals 1 and 2
	Describe properties of and compare quadrangles.	Geometry Goal 2
	Identify types of quadrangles.	Geometry Goal 2
1•4	Develop definitions for *parallel* and *intersecting line segments, lines,* and *rays.*	Geometry Goal 1
	Develop a definition for *perpendicular line segments.*	Geometry Goal 1
	Describe characteristics of parallelograms.	Geometry Goal 2
	Classify quadrangles based on side and angle properties.	Geometry Goal 2
1•5	Construct convex and nonconvex (concave) polygons.	Geometry Goal 2
	Develop definitions for *convex* and *nonconvex* (*concave*) *polygons.*	Geometry Goal 2
	Describe properties of polygons and regular polygons.	Geometry Goal 2
	Identify types of polygons according to the number of sides.	Geometry Goal 2

Ongoing Practice

Highlights essential activities that provide review and practice for maintaining skills. These activities include Math Boxes, Home/Study Links, games, and Extra Practice.

Unit 1 Organizer

A Balanced Curriculum

Ongoing Practice

Everyday Mathematics provides numerous opportunities for ongoing practice. These activities are embedded throughout the lessons:

Mental Math and Reflexes activities promote speed and accuracy in mental computation.

Math Boxes offer mixed practice and are paired across lessons as shown in the brackets below. This makes them useful as assessment tools. The last one or two boxes on each page preview the next unit's content.

Mixed practice [1•1, 1•3], [1•2, 1•4], [1•5, 1•7], [1•6, 1•8]
Mixed practice with multiple choice 1•1, 1•4, 1•5, 1•8
Mixed practice with writing/reasoning opportunity 1•3, 1•4, 1•6, 1•7

Study Links are daily homework assignments that review the content of the lesson and often contain ongoing facts practice or computation practice.

5-Minute Math problems are offered for additional practice in Lesson 1•3.

EM Facts Workshop Game provides online practice of basic facts and computation.

EXTRA PRACTICE **Extra Practice** activities are included in Lessons 1•3, 1•6, and 1•8.

Daily Assessments

Includes the assessment opportunities in each lesson to assess progress toward Grade-Level Goals.

Assessment Support

Identifies useful pages in the *Assessment Handbook* for each unit.

Unit 1 Organizer

Balanced Assessment

Daily Assessments

- **Recognizing Student Achievement** – A daily assessment that is included in every lesson to evaluate students' progress toward the Grade 4 Grade-Level Goals.
- **Informing Instruction** – Notes that appear throughout the unit to help anticipate students' common errors and suggest appropriate problem-solving strategies.

Lesson	Recognizing Student Achievement	Informing Instruction
1•1	Demonstrate automaticity with addition fact extensions. [OC Goal 1]	
1•2	Describe a line segment and a line. [GEO Goal 1]	Connect points to other points.
1•3	Compare and contrast plane figures. [GEO Goal 2]	Consider the measures of angles rather than the lengths of rays.
1•4	Understand parallel line segments. [GEO Goal 1]	
1•5	Explain the properties of polygons. [GEO Goal 2]	Distinguish regular polygons from other polygons.
1•6	Understand right angles. [GEO Goal 1]	
1•7	Construct circles with a compass. [GEO Goal 2]	
1•8	Demonstrate automaticity with subtraction fact extensions. [OC Goal 1]	Connect consecutive marks to form a regular hexagon.

[NN] Number and Numeration [OC] Operations and Computation [DC] Data and Chance
[MRF] Measurement and Reference Frames [GEO] Geometry [PFA] Patterns, Functions, and Algebra

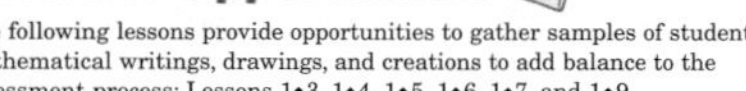

Portfolio Opportunities

The following lessons provide opportunities to gather samples of students' mathematical writings, drawings, and creations to add balance to the assessment process: Lessons 1•3, 1•4, 1•5, 1•6, 1•7, and 1•9.

See pages 16 and 17 in the *Assessment Handbook* for more information about portfolios and how to use them.

Unit Assessment

Progress Check 1 – A cumulative assessment of concepts and skills taught in Unit 1, providing information for evaluating students' progress and planning for future instruction. These assessments include oral/slate, written, and open-response activities, as shown below in the sample Progress Check lesson opener.

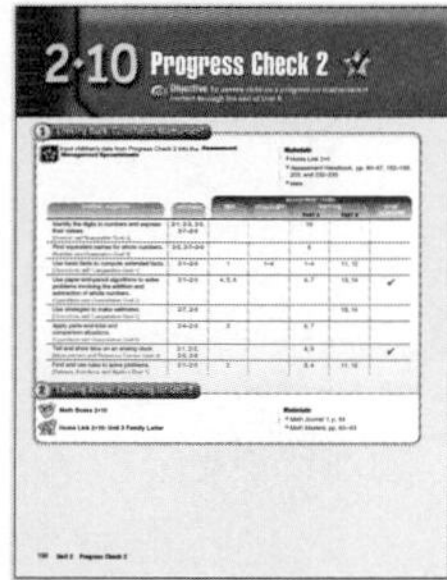

Core Assessment Resources

Assessment Handbook

- **Unit 1 Assessment Overview,** pages 52–59
- **Unit 1 Assessment Masters,** pages 154–158
- **Unit 1 Individual Profiles of Progress,** pages 246, 247, and 302
- **Unit 1 Class Checklists,** pages 248, 249, and 303
- **Beginning-of-Year Assessment,*** pages 227A–227D
- **Math Logs,** pages 306–308
- **Exit Slip,** page 311
- **Other Student Assessment Forms,** pages 304, 305, 309, and 310

*The Beginning-of-Year Assessment is one of the screening tools that can be used to help identify which concepts and skills students have learned and to help plan instruction for the upcoming year.

Assessment Management Spreadsheets

The Assessment Management Spreadsheets consist of the Digital Class Checklists and Individual Profile of Progress Checklists. Use them to monitor, record, and report student progress.

Unit 1 Organizer

Addressing All Needs

Differentiated Instruction

Adjusting the Activity – suggests adaptations that target advanced learners, English language learners, or learners who need additional instructional support.

ELL SUPPORT / ELL – provides lesson-specific suggestions to help English language learners understand and process the mathematical content.

READINESS – accesses students' prior knowledge or previews content that prepares students to engage in the lesson's Part 1 activities.

EXTRA PRACTICE – provides additional opportunities to apply the mathematical content of the lesson.

ENRICHMENT – enables students to apply or further explore the mathematical content of the lesson.

Lesson	Adjusting the Activity	ELL Support/ ELL	Readiness	Extra Practice	Enrichment
1•1	•	•	•		•
1•2	•	•	•		•
1•3	•	•	•	•	•
1•4	•	•	•		•
1•5	•	•	•		•
1•6	•			•	•
1•7	•	•			•
1•8	•		•	•	•

Differentiated Instruction

Highlights the many facets of differentiated instruction in each unit. Includes English language learner support, as well as Enrichment, Readiness, and Extra Practice activities.

3-Part Lesson Plan

3-Part Lesson

① **Teaching the Lesson** Provides main instructional activities for the lesson.

② **Ongoing Learning and Practice** Supports previously introduced concepts and skills; essential for maintaining skills.

① **Differentiation Options** Includes options for supporting the needs of all students; usually an extension of Part 1, Teaching the Lesson.

Technology Resources

Suggests appropriate digital resources that support instruction of the lesson.

Lesson Opener

At-a-glance view of the 3-part lesson, highlighting materials, vocabulary, assessment, and more!

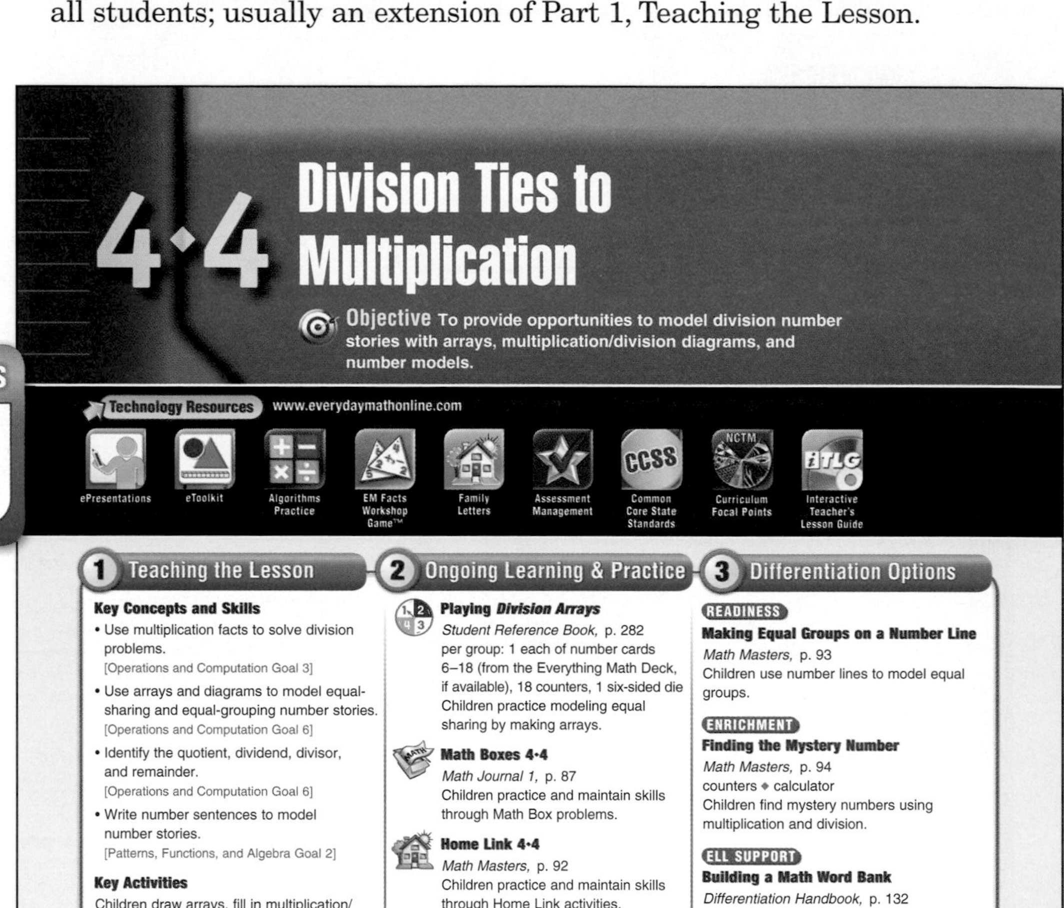

4•4 Division Ties to Multiplication

Objective To provide opportunities to model division number stories with arrays, multiplication/division diagrams, and number models.

Technology Resources www.everydaymathonline.com

ePresentations | eToolkit | Algorithms Practice | EM Facts Workshop Game™ | Family Letters | Assessment Management | Common Core State Standards | Curriculum Focal Points | Interactive Teacher's Lesson Guide

1 Teaching the Lesson

Key Concepts and Skills

- Use multiplication facts to solve division problems. [Operations and Computation Goal 3]
- Use arrays and diagrams to model equal-sharing and equal-grouping number stories. [Operations and Computation Goal 6]
- Identify the quotient, dividend, divisor, and remainder. [Operations and Computation Goal 6]
- Write number sentences to model number stories. [Patterns, Functions, and Algebra Goal 2]

Key Activities

Children draw arrays, fill in multiplication/division diagrams, and write number models to solve division number stories.

Ongoing Assessment: Recognizing Student Achievement Use the Math Message. [Operations and Computation Goal 6]

Ongoing Assessment: Informing Instruction See page 263.

Key Vocabulary

quotient • dividend • divisor • remainder

Materials

Math Journal 1, p. 86
Student Reference Book, p. 250 (optional)
Home Link 4•3
Math Masters, p. 406 (optional); pp. 407 and 419
pennies or other counters • calculator (optional)

2 Ongoing Learning & Practice

Playing *Division Arrays*
Student Reference Book, p. 282
per group: 1 each of number cards 6–18 (from the Everything Math Deck, if available), 18 counters, 1 six-sided die
Children practice modeling equal sharing by making arrays.

Math Boxes 4•4
Math Journal 1, p. 87
Children practice and maintain skills through Math Box problems.

Home Link 4•4
Math Masters, p. 92
Children practice and maintain skills through Home Link activities.

3 Differentiation Options

READINESS
Making Equal Groups on a Number Line
Math Masters, p. 93
Children use number lines to model equal groups.

ENRICHMENT
Finding the Mystery Number
Math Masters, p. 94
counters • calculator
Children find mystery numbers using multiplication and division.

ELL SUPPORT
Building a Math Word Bank
Differentiation Handbook, p. 132
Children add the term *quotient* to their Math Word Banks.

Advance Preparation

Post the Guide to Solving Number Stories. Make multiple copies of *Math Masters,* page 419 for each child to use during Part 1.

***Teacher's Reference Manual,* Grades 1–3** p. 84

260 Unit 4 Multiplication and Division

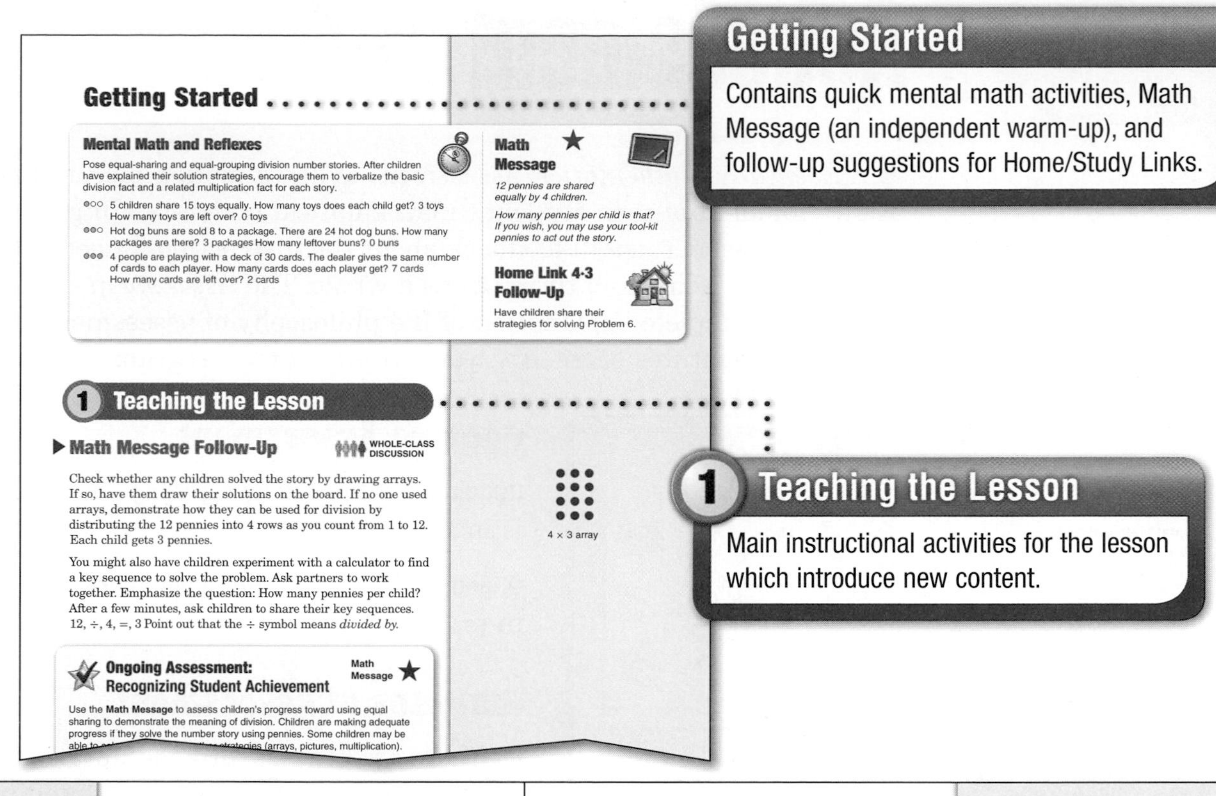

Getting Started

Mental Math and Reflexes

Pose equal-sharing and equal-grouping division number stories. After children have explained their solution strategies, encourage them to verbalize the basic division fact and a related multiplication fact for each story.

- 5 children share 15 toys equally. How many toys does each child get? 3 toys How many toys are left over? 0 toys
- Hot dog buns are sold 8 to a package. There are 24 hot dog buns. How many packages are there? 3 packages How many leftover buns? 0 buns
- 4 people are playing with a deck of 30 cards. The dealer gives the same number of cards to each player. How many cards does each player get? 7 cards How many cards are left over? 2 cards

Math Message

12 pennies are shared equally by 4 children.

How many pennies per child is that? If you wish, you may use your tool-kit pennies to act out the story.

Home Link 4-3 Follow-Up

Have children share their strategies for solving Problem 6.

1 Teaching the Lesson

▶ Math Message Follow-Up

WHOLE-CLASS DISCUSSION

Check whether any children solved the story by drawing arrays. If so, have them draw their solutions on the board. If no one used arrays, demonstrate how they can be used for division by distributing the 12 pennies into 4 rows as you count from 1 to 12. Each child gets 3 pennies.

You might also have children experiment with a calculator to find a key sequence to solve the problem. Ask partners to work together. Emphasize the question: How many pennies per child? After a few minutes, ask children to share their key sequences. 12, ÷, 4, =, 3 Point out that the ÷ symbol means *divided by.*

4 × 3 array

Ongoing Assessment: Recognizing Student Achievement

Math Message

Use the **Math Message** to assess children's progress toward using equal sharing to demonstrate the meaning of division. Children are making adequate progress if they solve the number story using pennies. Some children may be

Getting Started

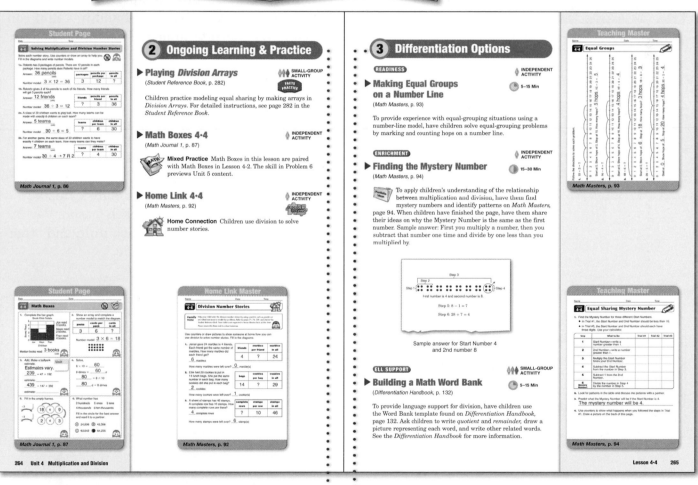

Contains quick mental math activities, Math Message (an independent warm-up), and follow-up suggestions for Home/Study Links.

1 Teaching the Lesson

Main instructional activities for the lesson which introduce new content.

Student Page — Math Journal 1, p. 86

2 Ongoing Learning & Practice

▶ Playing *Division Arrays*

SMALL-GROUP ACTIVITY

(*Student Reference Book*, p. 282)

Children practice modeling equal sharing by making arrays in *Division Arrays*. For detailed instructions, see page 282 in the *Student Reference Book*.

▶ Math Boxes 4·4

INDEPENDENT ACTIVITY

(*Math Journal 1*, p. 87)

Mixed Practice Math Boxes in this lesson are paired with Math Boxes in Lesson 4-2. The skill in Problem 6 previews Unit 5 content.

▶ Home Link 4·4

INDEPENDENT ACTIVITY

(*Math Masters*, p. 92)

Home Connection Children use division to solve number stories.

Student Page — Math Journal 1, p. 87

Home Link Master — Math Masters, p. 92

3 Differentiation Options

READINESS

▶ Making Equal Groups on a Number Line

INDEPENDENT ACTIVITY 5–15 Min

(*Math Masters*, p. 93)

To provide experience with equal-grouping situations using a number-line model, have children solve equal-grouping problems by marking and counting hops on a number line.

ENRICHMENT

▶ Finding the Mystery Number

INDEPENDENT ACTIVITY 15–30 Min

(*Math Masters*, p. 94)

To apply children's understanding of the relationship between multiplication and division, have them find mystery numbers and identify patterns on *Math Masters*, page 94. When children have finished the page, have them share their ideas on why the Mystery Number is the same as the first number. Sample answer: First you multiply a number, then you subtract that number one time and divide by one less than you multiplied by.

Step 5: 8 − 1 = 7

Step 6: 28 ÷ 7 = 4

Sample answer for Start Number 4 and 2nd number 8

ELL SUPPORT

▶ Building a Math Word Bank

SMALL-GROUP ACTIVITY 5–15 Min

(*Differentiation Handbook*, p. 132)

To provide language support for division, have children use the Word Bank template found on *Differentiation Handbook*, page 132. Ask children to write *quotient* and *remainder,* draw a picture representing each word, and write other related words. See the *Differentiation Handbook* for more information.

Teaching Master — Math Masters, p. 93

Teaching Master — Math Masters, p. 94

264 Unit 4 Multiplication and Division — Lesson 4·4 265

2 Ongoing Learning & Practice

Activities provide essential review and practice for maintaining skills. Includes *Everyday Mathematics* games appropriate for revisiting mathematics skills, as well as Math Boxes and Home/Study Links.

3 Differentiation Options

Includes Readiness activities which cover mathematical content necessary for student success in the lesson. English Language Learner Support, Enrichment, and Extra Practice are also key features of the Differentiation Options.

Assessment

In *Everyday Mathematics,* assessment is like a motion picture revealing the development of each student's mathematical understanding over time, while giving the teacher useful feedback about the instructional needs of both individual students and the class as a whole. The *Assessment Handbook* contains a complete explanation of the philosophy of assessment and assessment features of the *Everyday Mathematics* program.

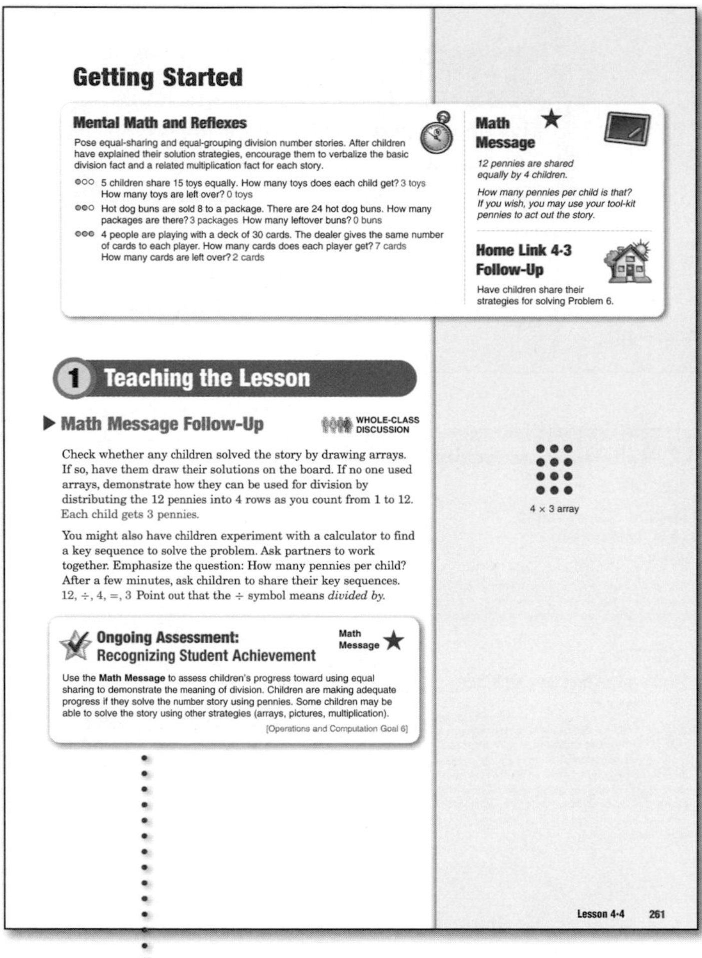

Getting Started

Mental Math and Reflexes

Pose equal-sharing and equal-grouping division number stories. After children have explained their solution strategies, encourage them to verbalize the basic division fact and a related multiplication fact for each story.

●○○ 5 children share 15 toys equally. How many toys does each child get? 3 toys How many toys are left over? 0 toys

●●○ Hot dog buns are sold 8 to a package. There are 24 hot dog buns. How many packages are there? 3 packages How many leftover buns? 0 buns

●●● 4 people are playing with a deck of 30 cards. The dealer gives the same number of cards to each player. How many cards does each player get? 7 cards How many cards are left over? 2 cards

Math Message

12 pennies are shared equally by 4 children.

How many pennies per child is that? If you wish, you may use your tool-kit pennies to act out the story.

Home Link 4-3 Follow-Up

Have children share their strategies for solving Problem 6.

1 Teaching the Lesson

▶ Math Message Follow-Up WHOLE-CLASS DISCUSSION

Check whether any children solved the story by drawing arrays. If so, have them draw their solutions on the board. If no one used arrays, demonstrate how they can be used for division by distributing the 12 pennies into 4 rows as you count from 1 to 12. Each child gets 3 pennies.

You might also have children experiment with a calculator to find a key sequence to solve the problem. Ask partners to work together. Emphasize the question: How many pennies per child? After a few minutes, ask children to share their key sequences. 12, ÷, 4, =, 3 Point out that the ÷ symbol means *divided by.*

4 × 3 array

Ongoing Assessment: Recognizing Student Achievement Math Message

Use the **Math Message** to assess children's progress toward using equal sharing to demonstrate the meaning of division. Children are making adequate progress if they solve the number story using pennies. Some children may be able to solve the story using other strategies (arrays, pictures, multiplication).

[Operations and Computation Goal 6]

Lesson 4-4 261

Recognizing Student Achievevment

Each lesson contains a Recognizing Student Achievement note. The notes highlight tasks that can be used to monitor student progress.

Ongoing Assessment

Ongoing Assessment: Recognizing Student Achievement is included in every lesson.

Ongoing Assessment: Informing Instruction is included in many lessons to help you guide instruction.

Purposes of Assessment

Formative Assessments provide information about students' current knowledge and abilities that can be used to plan or inform instruction. Information from almost any assessment task in *Everyday Mathematics* might be useful for planning future instruction.

Summative Assessments measure student growth and achievement and provide information that may be used to assign grades or otherwise evaluate students' performance. Summative assessments in *Everyday Mathematics* include the Recognizing Student Achievement tasks in each lesson, Part A of the written assessments in each unit, and other assessments labeled "fair to grade."

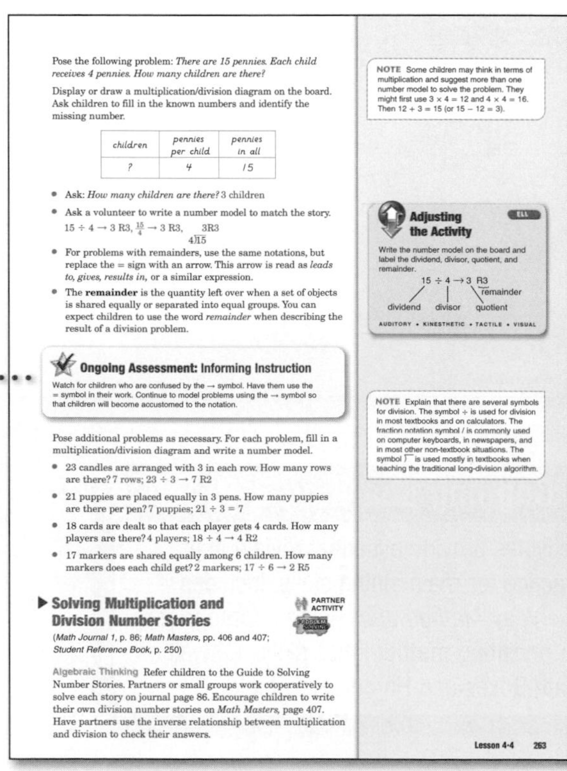

Pose the following problem: *There are 15 pennies. Each child receives 4 pennies. How many children are there?*

Display or draw a multiplication/division diagram on the board. Ask children to fill in the known numbers and identify the missing number.

children	pennies per child	pennies in all
?	4	15

- Ask: *How many children are there?* 3 children
- Ask a volunteer to write a number model to match the story. 15 ÷ 4 → 3 R3, $\frac{15}{4}$ → 3 R3, 4)15 3R3
- For problems with remainders, use the same notations, but replace the = sign with an arrow. This arrow is read as *leads to, gives, results in,* or a similar expression.
- The **remainder** is the quantity left over when a set of objects is shared equally or separated into equal groups. You can expect children to use the word *remainder* when describing the result of a division problem.

Ongoing Assessment: Informing Instruction

Watch for children who are confused by the → symbol. Have them use the = symbol in their work. Continue to model problems using the → symbol so that children will become accustomed to the notation.

Pose additional problems as necessary. For each problem, fill in a multiplication/division diagram and write a number model.

- 23 candles are arranged with 3 in each row. How many rows are there? 7 rows; 23 ÷ 3 → 7 R2
- 21 puppies are placed equally in 3 pens. How many puppies are there per pen? 7 puppies; 21 ÷ 3 = 7
- 18 cards are dealt so that each player gets 4 cards. How many players are there? 4 players; 18 ÷ 4 → 4 R2
- 17 markers are shared equally among 6 children. How many markers does each child get? 2 markers; 17 ÷ 6 → 2 R5

▶ Solving Multiplication and Division Number Stories PARTNER ACTIVITY

(*Math Journal 1,* p. 86; *Math Masters,* pp. 406 and 407; *Student Reference Book,* p. 250)

Algebraic Thinking Refer children to the Guide to Solving Number Stories. Partners or small groups work cooperatively to solve each story on journal page 86. Encourage children to write their own division number stories on *Math Masters,* page 407. Have partners use the inverse relationship between multiplication and division to check their answers.

NOTE Some children may think in terms of multiplication and suggest more than one number model to solve the problem. They might first use 3 × 4 = 12 and 4 × 4 = 16. Then 12 + 3 = 15 (or 15 − 12 = 3).

Adjusting the Activity ELL

Write the number model on the board and label the dividend, divisor, quotient, and remainder.

15 ÷ 4 → 3 R3 (dividend, divisor, quotient, remainder)

AUDITORY • KINESTHETIC • TACTILE • VISUAL

NOTE Explain that there are several symbols for division. The symbol ÷ is used for division in most textbooks and on calculators. The fraction notation symbol / is commonly used on computer keyboards, in newspapers, and in most other non-textbook situations. The symbol)‾ is used mostly in textbooks when teaching the traditional long-division algorithm.

Lesson 4-4 263

Informing Instruction

Suggests how to use observation of students' work to effectively adapt instruction.

Periodic Assessment

The Progress Check lessons, included for each unit, provide several types of periodic assessment.

Online Assessment Tools

The Assessment Management Spreadsheets provide additional opportunities to monitor student progress and inform instruction.

Written Assessment

Each Written Assessment has two parts: Part A Recognizing Student Achievement (summative assessment), and Part B Informing Instruction (formative assessment).

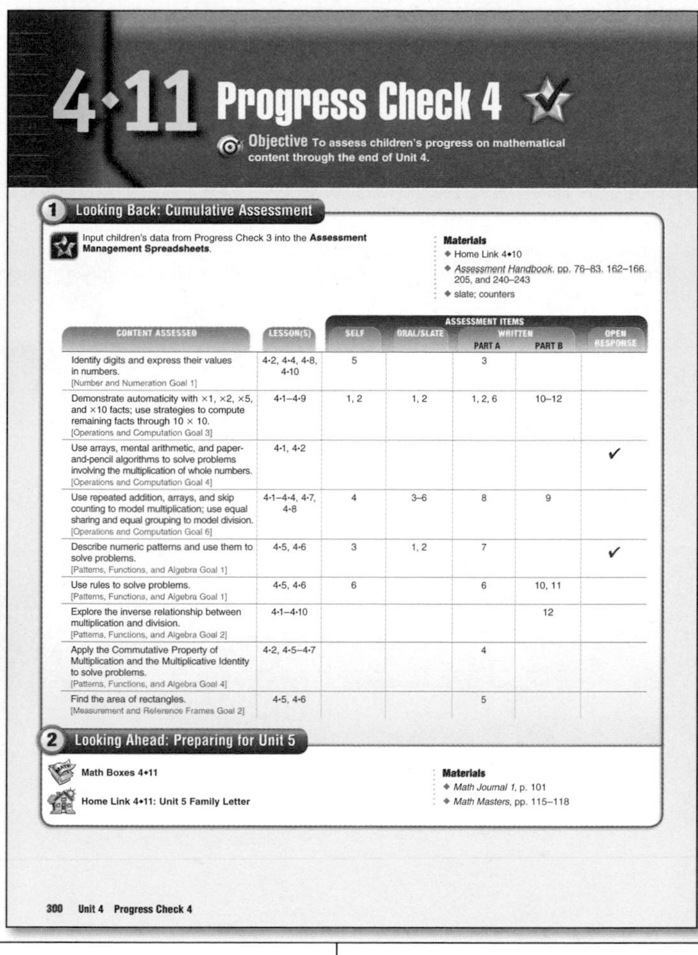

4·11 Progress Check 4

Objective To assess children's progress on mathematical content through the end of Unit 4.

1 Looking Back: Cumulative Assessment

Input children's data from Progress Check 3 into the **Assessment Management Spreadsheets**.

Materials
- Home Link 4•10
- *Assessment Handbook*, pp. 76–83, 162–166, 205, and 240–243
- slate; counters

CONTENT ASSESSED	LESSON(S)	ASSESSMENT ITEMS: SELF	ORAL/SLATE	WRITTEN PART A	WRITTEN PART B	OPEN RESPONSE
Identify digits and express their values in numbers. [Number and Numeration Goal 1]	4·2, 4·4, 4·8, 4·10	5		3		
Demonstrate automaticity with ×1, ×2, ×5, and ×10 facts; use strategies to compute remaining facts through 10 × 10. [Operations and Computation Goal 3]	4·1–4·9	1, 2	1, 2	1, 2, 6	10–12	
Use arrays, mental arithmetic, and paper-and-pencil algorithms to solve problems involving the multiplication of whole numbers. [Operations and Computation Goal 4]	4·1, 4·2					✓
Use repeated addition, arrays, and skip counting to model multiplication; use equal sharing and equal grouping to model division. [Operations and Computation Goal 6]	4·1–4·4, 4·7, 4·8	4	3–6	8	9	
Describe numeric patterns and use them to solve problems. [Patterns, Functions, and Algebra Goal 1]	4·5, 4·6	3	1, 2	7		✓
Use rules to solve problems. [Patterns, Functions, and Algebra Goal 1]	4·5, 4·6	6		6	10, 11	
Explore the inverse relationship between multiplication and division. [Patterns, Functions, and Algebra Goal 2]	4·1–4·10				12	
Apply the Commutative Property of Multiplication and the Multiplicative Identity to solve problems. [Patterns, Functions, and Algebra Goal 4]	4·2, 4·5–4·7			4		
Find the area of rectangles. [Measurement and Reference Frames Goal 2]	4·5, 4·6			5		

2 Looking Ahead: Preparing for Unit 5

Math Boxes 4•11

Home Link 4•11: Unit 5 Family Letter

Materials
- *Math Journal 1*, p. 101
- *Math Masters*, pp. 115–118

300 Unit 4 Progress Check 4

Progress Check

Provides multiple assessment options. Includes Oral and Slate Assessments, Written Assessment, Open Response, and Self-Assessment.

Open Response

Each unit provides an Open Response question. Sample student responses as well as rubrics for every Open Response question are found in the *Assessment Handbook.*

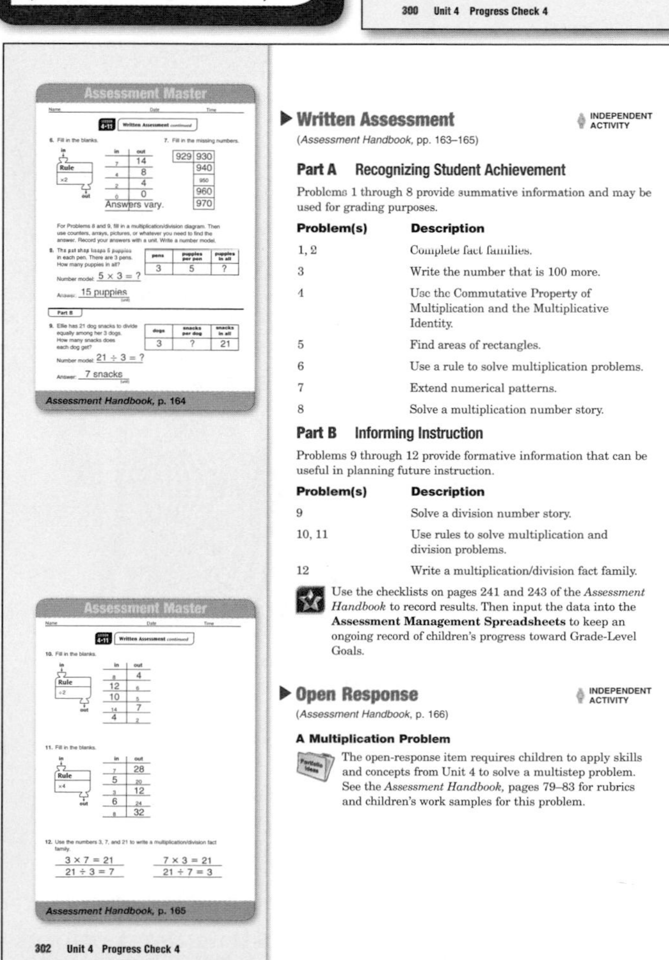

Assessment Master

Assessment Handbook, p. 164

▶ Written Assessment INDEPENDENT ACTIVITY

(*Assessment Handbook*, pp. 163–165)

Part A Recognizing Student Achievement

Problems 1 through 8 provide summative information and may be used for grading purposes.

Problem(s)	Description
1, 2	Complete fact families.
3	Write the number that is 100 more.
4	Use the Commutative Property of Multiplication and the Multiplicative Identity.
5	Find areas of rectangles.
6	Use a rule to solve multiplication problems.
7	Extend numerical patterns.
8	Solve a multiplication number story.

Part B Informing Instruction

Problems 9 through 12 provide formative information that can be useful in planning future instruction.

Problem(s)	Description
9	Solve a division number story.
10, 11	Use rules to solve multiplication and division problems.
12	Write a multiplication/division fact family.

Use the checklists on pages 241 and 243 of the *Assessment Handbook* to record results. Then input the data into the **Assessment Management Spreadsheets** to keep an ongoing record of children's progress toward Grade-Level Goals.

▶ Open Response INDEPENDENT ACTIVITY

(*Assessment Handbook*, p. 166)

A Multiplication Problem

The open-response item requires children to apply skills and concepts from Unit 4 to solve a multistep problem. See the *Assessment Handbook*, pages 79–83 for rubrics and children's work samples for this problem.

Assessment Master

Assessment Handbook, p. 165

302 Unit 4 Progress Check 4

2 Looking Ahead: Preparing for Unit 5

▶ Math Boxes 4·11 INDEPENDENT ACTIVITY

(*Math Journal 1*, p. 101)

Mixed Practice This Math Boxes page previews Unit 5 content.

▶ Home Link 4·11: Unit 5 Family Letter INDEPENDENT ACTIVITY

(*Math Masters*, pp. 115–118)

Home Connection The Unit 5 Family Letter provides parents and guardians with information and activities related to Unit 5 topics.

Home Link Masters

Unit 5: Family Letter

Place Value in Whole Numbers and Decimals

Math Masters, pp. 115–118

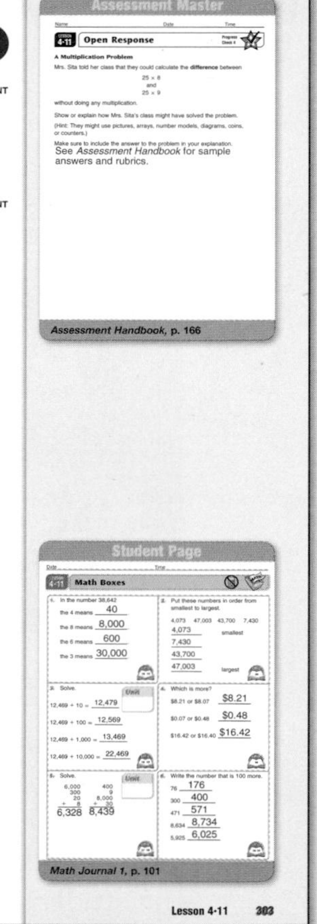

Assessment Master

Open Response

A Multiplication Problem

See Assessment Handbook for sample answers and rubrics.

Assessment Handbook, p. 166

Student Page

Math Boxes

Math Journal 1, p. 101

Lesson 4·11 303

Everyday Mathematics

Professional Development

Everyday Mathematics believes it is critical to support teachers with the materials necessary to enable students to meet higher expectations of mathematical achievement. In addition to district-specific training offered at implementation and for continued support, numerous professional development opportunities are built into the *Everyday Mathematics* program. Additional support is also available at **www.everydaymathonline.com**.

Teacher's Reference Manual

An invaluable resource that contains comprehensive background information about mathematical content as well as a guide to help organize the curriculum, the students, and the program materials.

Teacher's Lesson Guide

Professional development is embedded throughout, including Mathematical Background in each unit organizer to highlight the major content ideas presented and to help establish instructional priorities.

Supporting Students and Home

Family Involvement

Within *Everyday Mathematics* there are several opportunities for supporting the home-school connection.

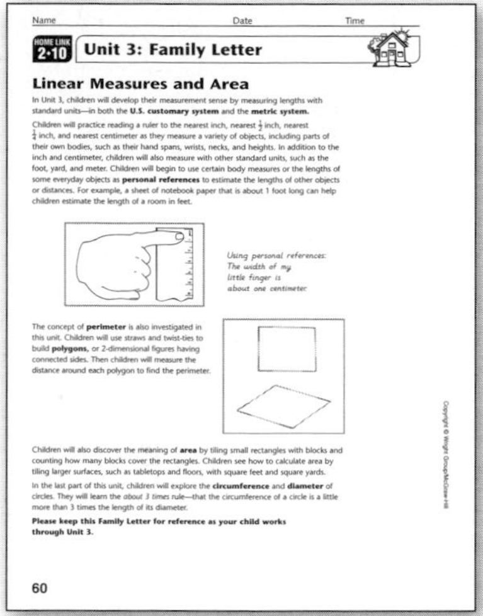

Name Date Time

HOME LINK 2·10 **Unit 3: Family Letter**

Linear Measures and Area

In Unit 3, children will develop their measurement sense by measuring lengths with standard units—in both the **U.S. customary system** and the **metric system.**

Children will practice reading a ruler to the nearest inch, nearest $\frac{1}{2}$ inch, nearest $\frac{1}{4}$ inch, and nearest centimeter as they measure a variety of objects, including parts of their own bodies, such as their hand spans, wrists, necks, and heights. In addition to the inch and centimeter, children will also measure with other standard units, such as the foot, yard, and meter. Children will begin to use certain body measures or the lengths of some everyday objects as **personal references** to estimate the lengths of other objects or distances. For example, a sheet of notebook paper that is about 1 foot long can help children estimate the length of a room in feet.

Using personal references: The width of my little finger is about one centimeter.

The concept of **perimeter** is also investigated in this unit. Children will use straws and twist-ties to build **polygons,** or 2-dimensional figures having connected sides. Then children will measure the distance around each polygon to find the perimeter.

Children will also discover the meaning of **area** by tiling small rectangles with blocks and counting how many blocks cover the rectangles. Children see how to calculate area by tiling larger surfaces, such as tabletops and floors, with square feet and square yards.

In the last part of this unit, children will explore the **circumference** and **diameter** of circles. They will learn the *about 3 times* rule—that the circumference of a circle is a little more than 3 times the length of its diameter.

Please keep this Family Letter for reference as your child works through Unit 3.

Copyright © Wright Group/McGraw-Hill

60

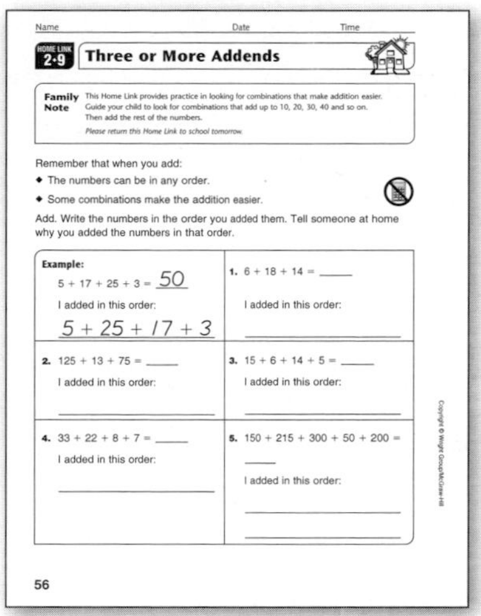

Name Date Time

HOME LINK 2·9 **Three or More Addends**

Family Note This Home Link provides practice in looking for combinations that make addition easier. Guide your child to look for combinations that add up to 10, 20, 30, 40 and so on. Then add the rest of the numbers.

Please return this Home Link to school tomorrow.

Remember that when you add:

- The numbers can be in any order.
- Some combinations make the addition easier.

Add. Write the numbers in the order you added them. Tell someone at home why you added the numbers in that order.

Example: 5 + 17 + 25 + 3 = 50 I added in this order: 5 + 25 + 17 + 3	**1.** 6 + 18 + 14 = _____ I added in this order: _____
2. 125 + 13 + 75 = _____ I added in this order: _____	**3.** 15 + 6 + 14 + 5 = _____ I added in this order: _____
4. 33 + 22 + 8 + 7 = _____ I added in this order: _____	**5.** 150 + 215 + 300 + 50 + 200 = _____ I added in this order: _____

Copyright © Wright Group/McGraw-Hill

56

Family Letters

Each unit's Family Letter explains the unit's key content and vocabulary and provides directions for appropriate games, Do-Anytime Activities, and answers to most Home/Study Links for the unit.

Home Links/Study Links

Each lesson has a Home/Study Link. They show families what students are doing in mathematics.

Student Reference Book and My Reference Book

These books are resources that can be sent home to provide parents with support on lesson content. The reference books include explanations and examples of mathematical topics, as well as directions for *Everyday Mathematics* games.

Home Connection Handbook

This teacher- and administrator-focused handbook provides support for communicating with families. Includes blackline masters for easier communication.

EM Online Access all technology resources online at everydaymathonline.com

Everyday Mathematics

NCTM Curriculum Focal Points and *Everyday Mathematics*

The *Everyday Mathematics* curriculum is completely aligned to the NCTM Curriculum Focal Points and the Connections to the Curriculum Focal Points for Pre-Kindergarten through Grade 6.

NCTM Curriculum Focal Points for Grade 1	*Everyday Mathematics* Grade 1 Lessons
Number and Operations and Algebra: Developing understandings of addition and subtraction and strategies for basic addition facts and related subtraction facts.	
Children develop strategies for adding and subtracting whole numbers on the basis of their earlier work with small numbers.	3•14, 4•11, 4•12, 5•10, 5•11, 6•8, 8•1, 8•5, 9•2, 9•4, 10•4, 10•6
Children use a variety of models, including discrete objects, length-based models (e.g., lengths of connecting cubes), and number lines, to model "part-whole," "adding to," "taking away from," and "comparing" situations to develop an understanding of the meanings of addition and subtraction and strategies to solve such arithmetic problems.	1•2, 1•5, 1•13, 2•1, 2•3, 2•9, 2•10, 2•11, 2•12, 2•13, 3•5, 3•6, 3•8, 3•9, 3•14, 4•11, 4•12, 5•7, 5•8, 5•9, 6•1, 6•3, 6•5, 8•5, 10•3, 10•4 Project 8
Children understand the connections between counting and the operations of addition and subtraction (e.g., adding two is the same as "counting on" two).	2•11, 3•6, 3•8, 3•9, 3•10, 8•3
Childern use properties of addition (commutativity and associativity) to add whole numbers, and they create and use increasingly sophisticated strategies based on these properties (e.g., "making tens") to solve addition and subtraction problems involving basic facts.	4•11, 5•5, 5•10, 6•3, 6•4, 6•5
By comparaing a variety of solution strategies, children relate addition and subtraction as inverse operations.	6•3, 6•4, 6•5, 6•8, 7•2, 7•3, 8•4, 9•4, 10•6
Number and Operations: Developing an understanding of whole number relationships, including grouping in tens and ones.	
Children compare and order whole numbers (at least to 100) to develop an understanding of and solve problems involving the relative sizes of these numbers.	1•2, 1•6, 1•9, 1•10, 4•10, 5•3, 5•6, 5•7, 10•4
Children think of whole numbers between 10 and 100 in terms of groups of tens and ones (especially recognizing the numbers 11 to 19 as 1 group of ten and particular numbers of ones).	5•1, 5•2, 5•5, 8•2, 8•3, 9•1, 9•3, 10•7
Children understand the sequential order of the counting numbers and their relative magnitudes and represent numbers on a number line.	1•2, 1•5, 2•1, 2•6, 3•5, 6•10
Geometry: Composing and decomposing geometric shapes.	
Children compose and decompose plane and solid figures (e.g., by putting two congruent isosceles triangles together to make a rhombus), thus building an understanding of part-whole relationships as well as the properties of the original and composite shapes.	3•4, 7•3, 7•5, 7•6, 8•6, 8•7, 9•6, 9•7, 9•8, 10•4
As children combine figures, they recognize them from different perspectives and orientations, describe their geometric attributes and properties, and determine how they are alike and different, in the process developing a background for measurement and initial understandings of such properties as congruence and symmetry.	7•5, 7•6, 7•7

NCTM Connections to the Curriculum Focal Points for Grade 1	*Everyday Mathematics* Grade 1 Lessons
Number and Operations and Algebra	
Children use mathematical reasoning, including ideas such as commutativity and associativity and beginning ideas of tens and ones, to solve two-digit addition and subtraction problems with strategies that they understand and can explain.	5•5, 9•2, 9•3, 9•4, 10•3, 10•4, 10•6
Children solve both routine and nonroutine problems.	2•6, 2•13, 5•5, 5•12, 5•13, 6•8, 8•4, 8•5, 8•8, 9•4, 10•3, 10•4, 10•6 Project 8
Measurement and Data Analysis	
Children strengthen their sense of number by solving problems involving measurements and data.	1•7, 1•12, 3•13, 4•5, 4•6, 4•7, 5•4, 6•6, 6•12, 9•5, 10•1 Projects 3, 4, 5
Measuring by laying multiple copies of a unit end to end and then counting the units by using groups of tens and ones supports children's understanding of number lines and number relationships.	4•2, 4•3, 4•4, 6•6 Project 6
Representing measurements and discrete data in picture and bar graphs involves counting and comparisons that provide another meaningful connection to number relationships.	1•7, 1•12, 2•11, 3•13, 4•7, 6•12, 7•3 Projects 2, 5
Algebra	
Through identifying, describing, and applying number patterns and properties in developing strategies for basic facts, children learn about other properties of numbers and operations, such as odd and even (e.g., "Even numbers of objects can be paired, with none left over"), and 0 as the identity element for addition.	3•2, 3•3, 3•5, 3•8, 3•9, 3•10, 3•14, 4•12, 5•11, 6•10

The Curriculum Focal Points identify key mathematical ideas for these grades. They are not discrete topics or a checklist to be mastered; rather, they provide a framework for the majority of instruction at a particular grade level and the foundation for future mathematics study.

Contents

Volume 1

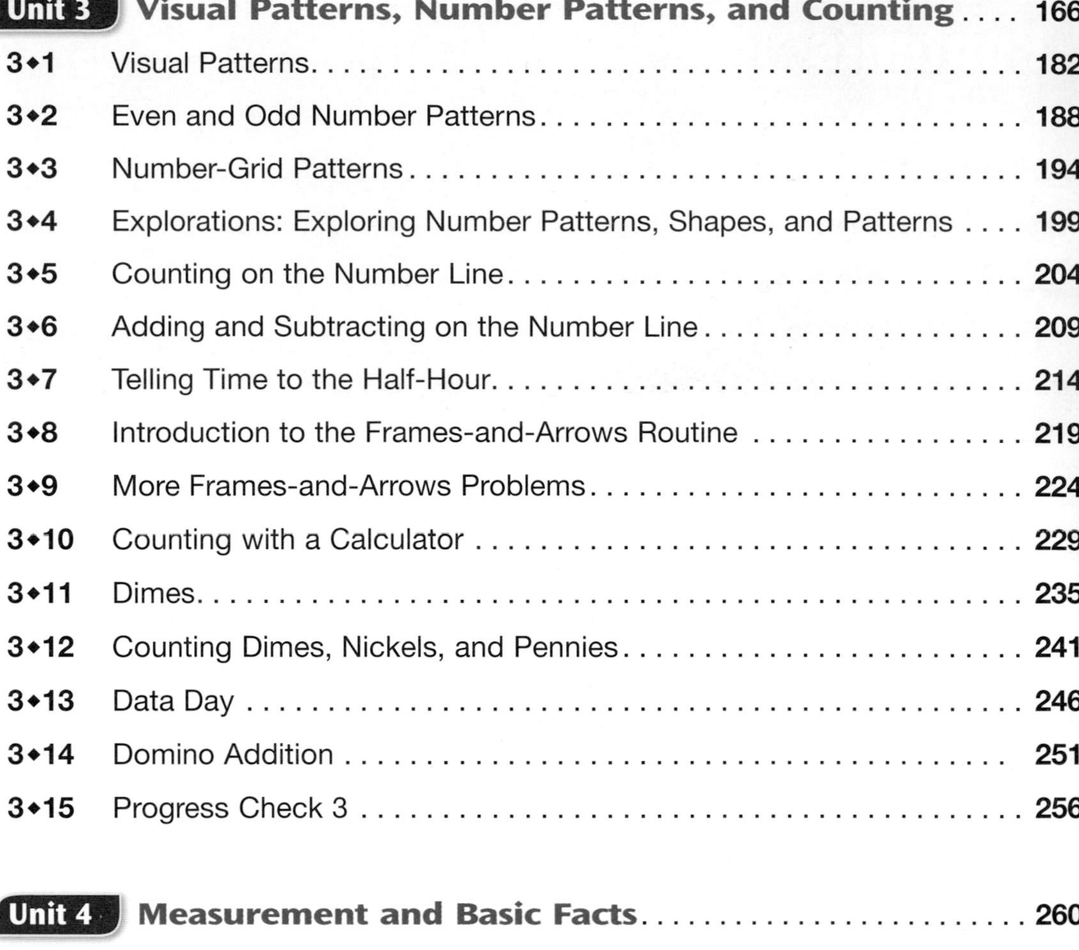

Everyday® Mathematics

0.
+/–
%
÷
MRC
M–
M+
×
7
8
9
–
4
5
6
+
1
2
3
=
ON/C
0
.

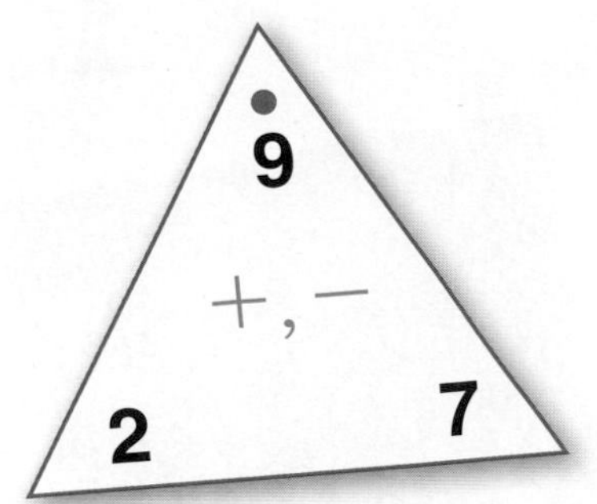

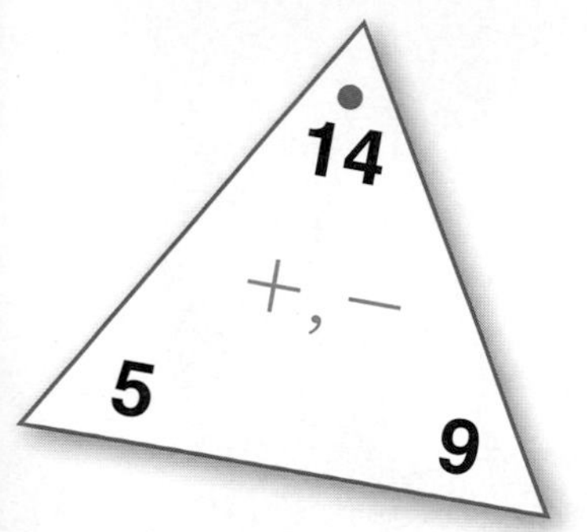

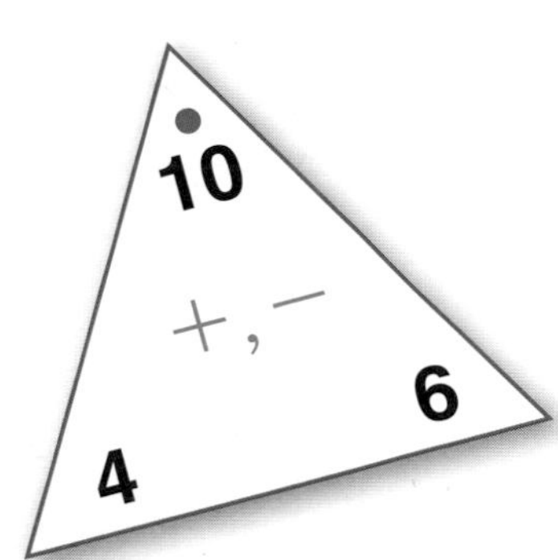

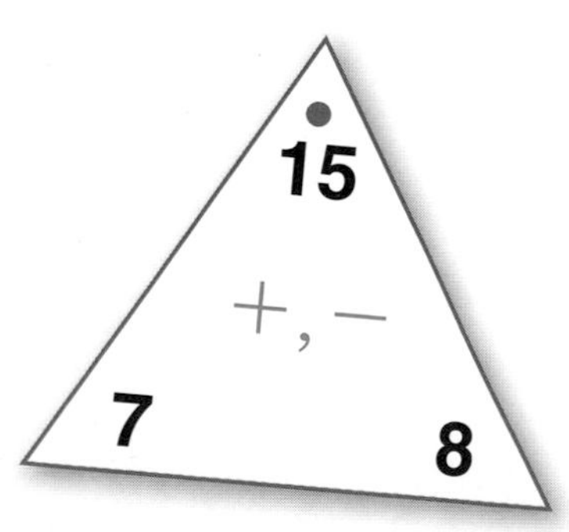

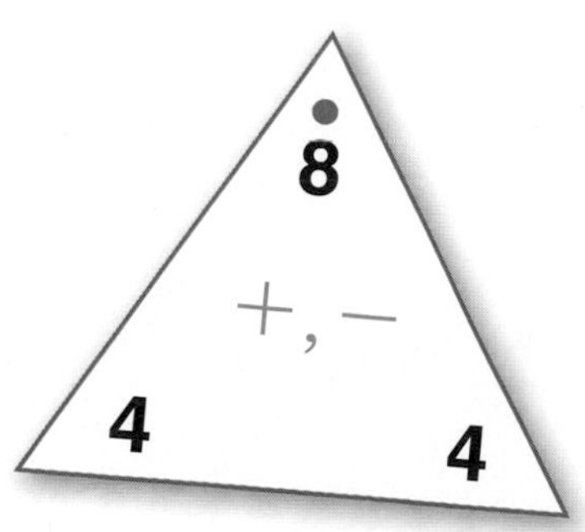

Volume 2

50
40
30
20
10
0
-10
-20
-30
-40
120
100
80
60
40
20
0
-20
-40
°C
°F

Welcome to *Everyday Mathematics*, the elementary school mathematics curriculum developed by the University of Chicago School Mathematics project (UCSMP). *Everyday Mathematics* offers you and your children a broad, rich, and balanced experience in mathematics.

September						
1	2	3	4	5	6	7
8	9	10	11	12	13	14
15	16	17	18	19	20	21
22	23	24	25	26	27	28
29	30					

First Grade Everyday Mathematics emphasizes the following content strands, skills, and concepts:

- **Number and Numeration** Counting; reading, writing, and modeling whole numbers; investigating whole number place value; exploring fractions; using ordinal numbers.
- **Operations and Computation** Learning addition and subtraction facts and exploring fact families; beginning informal work with properties of numbers and operations; exploring the values of coin combinations.
- **Data and Chance** Collecting, organizing, and displaying data using tally charts, tables, line plots, and graphs; exploring concepts of chance.
- **Measurement and Reference Frames** Using tools to measure length and weight; using clocks, calendars, timelines, and thermometers.
- **Geometry** Exploring 2- and 3-dimensional shapes.
- **Patterns, Functions, and Algebra** Exploring attributes, patterns, sequences, relations, and functions; finding missing numbers and rules in Frames-and-Arrows and "What's My Rule?" problems.

Throughout *Everyday Mathematics,* emphasis is placed on:

- A realistic approach to problem solving in everyday situations, other applications, and purely mathematical contexts.
- Frequent and distributed practice of basic skills through ongoing program routines and mathematical games.
- An instructional approach that revisits topics regularly to ensure full concept development and long-term retention of learning.
- Activities that explore a wide variety of mathematical content and offer opportunities for students to apply their skills and understandings to geometry, measurement, and algebra.

During your first year, you will become increasingly comfortable with the content, components, and strategies of *First Grade Everyday Mathematics.* During your first months with the program, focus on Parts 1 and 2 of the lessons; these parts are the core of the program. As the year progresses, incorporate activities from Part 3 of the lesson as appropriate for your children. You and your children will experience mathematical processes as a part of everyday work and play. These processes will gradually shape children's ways of thinking about mathematics and will foster the development of their mathematical intuitions and understandings. By the end of the year, we think you will agree that the rewards are worth the effort.

Have an exciting year!

Professional Preparation

Components for *First Grade Everyday Mathematics*

Go to...	When you need...	
Teacher's Lesson Guide	• daily lessons • unit support information • daily assessment suggestions • English language learners support	• readiness, enrichment, and extra practice suggestions • key vocabulary • scope and sequence • Grade-Level Goals
Teacher's Reference Manual	• background on mathematical content	• ideas for curriculum and classroom management
Assessment Handbook	• suggestions for ongoing and periodic assessment • Grade-Level Goals across all grades	• assessment masters • sample rubrics for open-response items
Differentiation Handbook	• suggestions for meeting diverse needs	• unit specific ideas
Minute Math®+	• brief activities for transition time and extra practice	
Content-by-Strand Poster	• key concepts and skills organized by content strand and paced by month	• Program Goals and Grade-Level Goals
Home Connection Handbook	• suggestions for home-school communication	• masters for easy planning
My Reference Book	• concise explanations of mathematical concepts • worked examples	• game directions • a reference for children to read with teachers, parents, and others
Student Math Journal	• a year-long record of each child's mathematical development	• paired "Math Boxes" for mixed practice • activity sheets
Math Masters	• blackline masters for lessons, Home Links, projects, teaching aids, and games	
English Learners Handbook	• comprehensive instructional strategies that maximize understanding	• methods that accelerate the acquisition of academic language and improve students' comprehension
Multilingual Handbook	• brief lesson summaries with examples in 6 languages	• lesson vocabulary in 11 languages

Suggested Reading & Lesson Preparation

In order to prepare for effective classroom and curriculum management, we suggest the following before you teach *Everyday Mathematics* for the first time.

- ☐ Review each component in your Classroom Resource Package (CRP). Determine where information and materials are located so that you can find them as needed throughout the school year. See the chart on the previous page.
- ☐ Read the Management Guide in the *Teacher's Reference Manual*, which has many useful tips and explanations.
- ☐ Read the Unit 1 Organizer and the first three to four lessons in this *Teacher's Lesson Guide,* noting the Advance Preparation sections in each lesson.
- ☐ Prepare a general daily math schedule. This schedule should include time for morning routines (calendar, weather, attendance, etc.), Teaching the Lesson, and Ongoing Learning and Practice activities such as games and Math Boxes.
- ☐ Make a list of coins for each child to bring from home (10 pennies, 5 nickels, 10 dimes, 2 quarters). Suggest that children bring the coins in a small plastic bag. An additional class collection of pennies is also useful.
- ☐ Create tool kits.
- ☐ Prepare slates for student use. See page 29.
- ☐ Prepare a supply of paper:
  Blank $8\frac{1}{2}$ inch by 11 inch paper (full-, half-, and quarter-size sheets)
  Primary grade handwriting paper
  Colored construction paper
  Graph paper (1-inch)

Before you teach subsequent units, you should read the Unit Organizer in the *Teacher's Lesson Guide* and the relevant sections of the *Teacher's Reference Manual*, the *Assessment Handbook*, and the *Differentiation Handbook*.

Organizing Your Classroom

Items for Display

Before the school year begins, we suggest that you prepare the following items for classroom display. By taking time to prepare these items your first year and laminating them if possible, you will be able to reuse them year after year. See the given sections of the Management Guide of your *Teacher's Reference Manual* for more information and suggestions.

- ☐ Number Line (235 to 180) (Section 5.4)
- ☐ Class Data Pad (Section 5.3)
- ☐ Number-Grid Poster (in your CRP)
- ☐ Thermometer Posters (in your CRP)
- ☐ Monthly Calendar (Section 5.2)
- ☐ Weather/Temperature Recording Chart (Section 5.8)
- ☐ Attendance Chart (Section 5.1)
- ☐ Daily Class Schedule (Section 5.6)
- ☐ Job Chart (Section 5.5)
- ☐ N, S, E, W directional indicators

Classroom Setup

The following items should be considered as you set up your classroom for *Everyday Mathematics.* Try several arrangements until you find one that is comfortable and effective for you and your children. Visit other classrooms in your building to observe and discuss what works for your colleagues.

- ☐ Prepare and label a location in the classroom where children can deposit their written work such as Math Messages, Home Links, Exit Slips, and so on.
- ☐ Arrange classroom desks/tables to allow for easy access to manipulatives and to facilitate efficient transitions for individual, partner, and small-group activities.
- ☐ Organize class and individual manipulatives for easy access and efficient use of storage space.
- ☐ Allow (table) space for math center(s). Selected games and activities can then be left in this space for ongoing practice or free exploration.
- ☐ One or more computers with Internet access can let children use software and Web sites that are recommended in *First Grade Everyday Mathematics.*

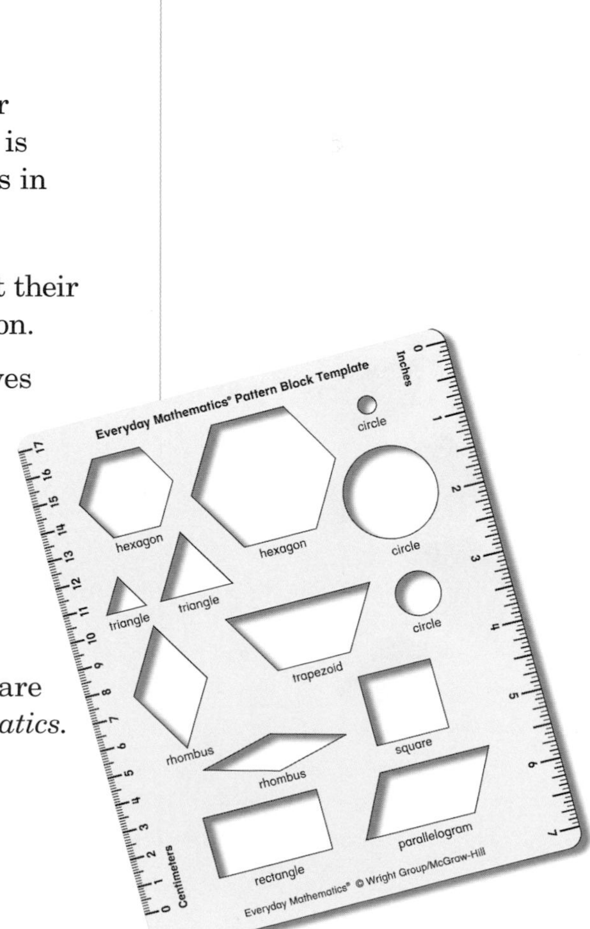

Manipulatives

The table below lists the materials that are used on a regular basis throughout *First Grade Everyday Mathematics*. Some lessons call for minor additional materials, which you or your children can bring in at the appropriate time.

Additional Valuable Classroom Resources

- Number Cards 0–100 with numerals and words
- Overhead Projector Materials
- Demonstration Clock
- Class Data Pad (12 inch by 15 inch spiral flip chart)
- Supply of Coins

Quantity	Item
2 sets	Attribute Blocks
1 set	Base-10 Blocks
1 per student	Calculators (Texas Instruments TI-108 or Casio SL-450 recommended)
1 per student	Clock Face
1	Clock Face Stamp
1 package (2,000)	Connectors (Twist-Ties)
1 package (450)	Counters
1 package (1,000)	Counting (Craft) Sticks
2 packages (16)	Dice, Blank
1 per student	Dice, Dot
3 packages (18 total)	Dice, Polyhedral
5 sets	Dominoes, Double-9
15 decks	Everything Math Decks
8	Geoboards, Two-Sided, 7" x 7"
10	Metersticks, Dual Scale
1	Number Line, –35 to 180
2 sets	Pattern Blocks
2 sets	Play Money Coin Set
10 sets	Play Money Bill Set
1	Rocker (Pan) Balance
1 package (400)	Rubber Bands (for geoboards)
1 per student	Rulers, 6 in./15 cm
1 per student	Slates (chalk or marker boards)
10	Spinners, Clear
1 package (500)	Straws
15	Tape Measures, Retractable
1	Thermometer, Classroom
1 per student	Tool-Kit Bags

All of the items above are available from McGraw-Hill. They may be purchased either as a comprehensive classroom manipulatives kit or by individual components. The manipulatives kit provides multiple classroom quantities and comes packaged in durable plastic tubs with labels.

Instruction

The following sections introduce instructional procedures and suggestions for implementing *Everyday Mathematics.* Teachers are encouraged to read these pages and refer to them as needed throughout the school year.

Daily Routines

In *Everyday Mathematics,* children learn a great deal of mathematics through daily individual and class routines. These daily activities may include tracking attendance, calendar, weather, temperature, and choral counting. Numerous mathematical concepts are reinforced on a daily basis so that children become aware of how mathematics pervades our everyday lives.

Most of the daily routines in *First Grade Everyday Mathematics* are introduced in Unit 1 and should be maintained throughout the school year. Refer to Unit 1 lessons and the Management Guide of the *Teacher's Reference Manual* for more information.

Program Routines

Everyday Mathematics uses a number of program routines that are incorporated throughout all grade levels. These allow for ongoing developmental practice in a number of skill and content areas. Below is a list of the routines you will encounter in *First Grade Everyday Mathematics.* The lesson in which each routine is first used has been noted. Refer to the Management Guide in the *Teacher's Reference Manual* for more information.

Mental Math and Reflexes (Lesson 1-1)
Games (Lesson 1-2)
Home Links (Lesson 1-8)*
Math Boxes (Lesson 2-3)
Frames and Arrows (Lesson 3-8)
Math Message (Lesson 4-1)
What's My Rule?"/Function Machines (Lesson 5-12)*
Name-Collection Boxes (Lesson 6-2)
Fact Families (Lesson 6-3)
Fact Triangles (Lesson 6-4)
My Reference Book (Lesson 6-11)

* Routine used in *Kindergarten Everyday Mathematics*

50

25 + 25

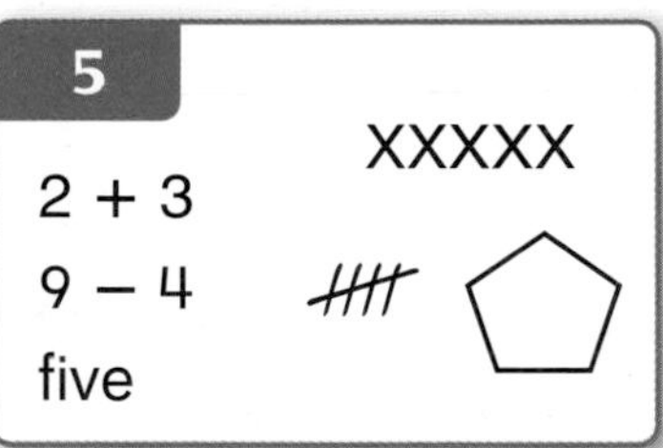

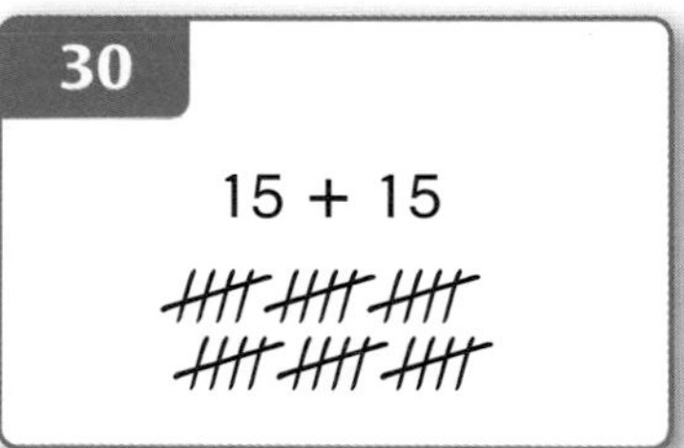

Name-Collection Boxes

Games

Everyday Mathematics games are important because they make learning fun for children, help them develop the ability to think critically and solve problems, and provide an enjoyable way for them to practice and master basic skills. Establish a games routine during the first unit and maintain it throughout the year. Make sure that all children are afforded time to play the games, especially those children who require the most practice.

Suggestions for building games into your instructional program:

- ◆ Include games as part of your daily morning routine.
- ◆ Devote the first or last 10 minutes of each math class to playing games from the current unit.
- ◆ Designate one math class per week as "Games Day." Set up stations that feature the unit games. Ask parent volunteers to assist in the rotation of children through these stations.
- ◆ Set up a Games Corner that features some of the children's favorite games. Encourage children to visit this corner during free time. Change the games frequently to maintain children's interest.

Explorations

You will find an Explorations lesson in every unit in *First Grade Everyday Mathematics.* These lessons include several independent, small-group activities that are informal and open-ended. The Explorations lessons have been designed so that you can place the activities at stations around the room and have small groups rotate among them.

Each Explorations lesson suggests up to three exploratory activities, with the option of adding other familiar activities as desired. In each lesson, Exploration A contains the main content and requires the most teacher facilitation, especially at the outset.

Explorations are not intended as optional activities for children to do when they have finished their other work, so be sure to set aside enough class time so that all children can experience them. Explorations provide critical initial exposure to content that is developed later in *Everyday Mathematics*.

Refer to the Management Guide in the *Teacher's Reference Manual* for more information.

Museums

Everyday Mathematics encourages the development of classroom museums using a bulletin board or table where related items can be collected, categorized, and labeled. For example, beginning in Lesson 2-2, first graders assemble a Numbers All Around Museum using examples of uses of numbers from home.

Refer to the Management Guide in the *Teacher's Reference Manual* for more information.

Projects

First Grade Everyday Mathematics provides ten projects, each of which includes an array of mathematics activities that focus on a theme that interests children. Projects are suggested in the Unit Organizers in the *Teacher's Lesson Guide* at appropriate times throughout the year. They typically take one to two days to complete, depending upon how many of the suggested activities are used. Projects involve a range of concepts and skills; integrate mathematics with science, social studies, art, and language arts; and allow the teacher to assess children's abilities to apply the mathematics they have learned in cross-curricular contexts. Projects are also often memorable events for children.

Refer to the Management Guide in the *Teacher's Reference Manual* and Unit Organizers in the *Teacher's Lesson Guide* for more information.

Assessment

Everyday Mathematics supports a balanced approach to assessment, one that provides information both for guiding instruction and for evaluating student performance. Assessment takes place on an ongoing basis as children complete their everyday work and in special periodic assessments, such as the assessment lesson at the end of each unit. Information for assessment is gathered both through teacher observations while children are working and through children's written products.

Refer to the *Assessment Handbook* and the Unit Organizers in the *Teacher's Lesson Guide* for detailed information regarding student assessment.

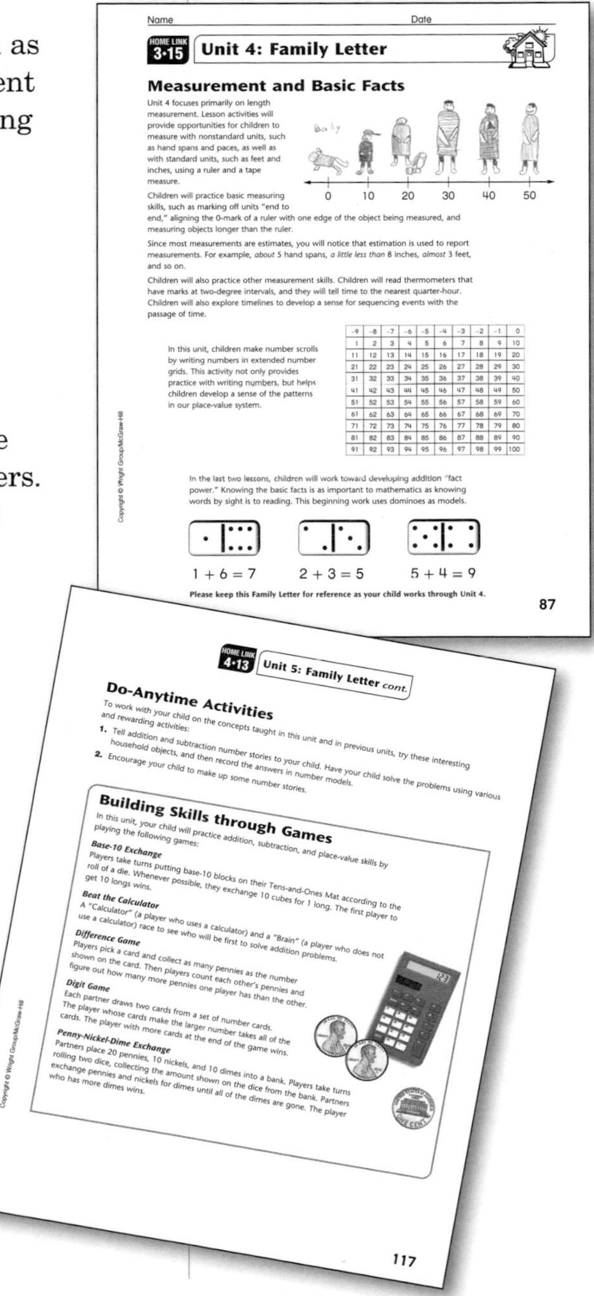

Name Date

HOME LINK 3•15 **Unit 4: Family Letter**

Measurement and Basic Facts

Unit 4 focuses primarily on length measurement. Lesson activities will provide opportunities for children to measure with nonstandard units, such as hand spans and paces, as well as with standard units, such as feet and inches, using a ruler and a tape measure.

Children will practice basic measuring skills, such as marking off units "end to end," aligning the 0-mark of a ruler with one edge of the object being measured, and measuring objects longer than the ruler.

Since most measurements are estimates, you will notice that estimation is used to report measurements. For example, *about* 5 hand spans, *a little less than* 8 inches, *almost* 3 feet, and so on.

Children will also practice other measurement skills. Children will read thermometers that have marks at two-degree intervals, and they will tell time to the nearest quarter-hour. Children will also explore timelines to develop a sense for sequencing events with the passage of time.

In this unit, children make number scrolls by writing numbers in extended number grids. This activity not only provides practice with writing numbers, but helps children develop a sense of the patterns in our place-value system.

-9	-8	-7	-6	-5	-4	-3	-2	-1	0
1	2	3	4	5	6	7	8	9	10
11	12	13	14	15	16	17	18	19	20
21	22	23	24	25	26	27	28	29	30
31	32	33	34	35	36	37	38	39	40
41	42	43	44	45	46	47	48	49	50
51	52	53	54	55	56	57	58	59	60
61	62	63	64	65	66	67	68	69	70
71	72	73	74	75	76	77	78	79	80
81	82	83	84	85	86	87	88	89	90
91	92	93	94	95	96	97	98	99	100

In the last two lessons, children will work toward developing addition "fact power." Knowing the basic facts is as important to mathematics as knowing words by sight is to reading. This beginning work uses dominoes as models.

$1 + 6 = 7$ $2 + 3 = 5$ $5 + 4 = 9$

Please keep this Family Letter for reference as your child works through Unit 4.

87

HOME LINK 4•13 **Unit 5: Family Letter** *cont.*

Do-Anytime Activities

To work with your child on the concepts taught in this unit and in previous units, try these interesting and rewarding activities:

1. Tell addition and subtraction number stories to your child. Have your child solve the problems using various household objects, and then record the answers in number models.
2. Encourage your child to make up some number stories.

Building Skills through Games

In this unit, your child will practice addition, subtraction, and place-value skills by playing the following games:

Base-10 Exchange
Players take turns putting base-10 blocks on their Tens-and-Ones Mat according to the roll of a die. Whenever possible, they exchange 10 cubes for 1 long. The first player to get 10 longs wins.

Beat the Calculator
A "Calculator" (a player who uses a calculator) and a "Brain" (a player who does not use a calculator) race to see who will be first to solve addition problems.

Difference Game
Players pick a card and collect as many pennies as the number shown on the card. Then players count each other's pennies and figure out how many more pennies one player has than the other.

Digit Game
Each partner draws two cards from a set of number cards. The player whose cards make the larger number takes all of the cards. The player with more cards at the end of the game wins.

Penny-Nickel-Dime Exchange
Partners place 20 pennies, 10 nickels, and 10 dimes into a bank. Players take turns rolling two dice, collecting the amount shown on the dice from the bank. Partners exchange pennies and nickels for dimes until all of the dimes are gone. The player who has more dimes wins.

117

Differentiation

Everyday Mathematics has been designed to accommodate a wide range of student backgrounds and abilities, including English language learners. The program also includes many tools and suggestions to help teachers differentiate instruction to meet children's diverse needs, including Enrichment, Readiness, ELL Support, and Extra Practice activities in Part 3 of the lessons and Adjusting the Activity suggestions in Parts 1 and 2.

Refer to the *Differentiation Handbook* and the Unit Organizers in the *Teacher's Lesson Guide* for detailed information about differentiation in *Everyday Mathematics*.

Providing for Home-School Connections

Comprehensive and consistent home-school communication is essential for successful implementation of *Everyday Mathematics*. The *Home Connection Handbook* has many suggestions and tools that can help you introduce parents and primary caregivers to the *Everyday Mathematics* curriculum. Grade-specific Family Letters and Home Links facilitate ongoing communication and engage parents as partners in the learning process.

Refer to the *Home Connection Handbook* for more information.

K–2 Games Correlation Chart

Game	Grade K Activity	Grade 1 Lesson	Grade 2 Lesson	Skill and Concept Areas: Numeration	Mental Math	Basic Facts	Operations	Patterns	Geometry	Money	Time	Probability	Calculator
Addition Card Draw			12•5		●	●	●						
Addition Spin		*	4•2		●	●	●						
Addition Top-It	4•2	6•1	1•4	●	●	●	●						
Animal Weight Top-It		5•5		●	●	●	●						
Array Bingo			6•9	●	●	●	●						
Attribute Spinner Game	5•14								●				
Attribute Train Game		7•2						●	●				
Base-10 Exchange		5•3	3•4	●									
Base-10 Trading Game			6•5	●		●	●						
Basketball Addition			7•3		●	●	●						
Beat the Calculator (Addition)		5•11	2•2		●	●	●						●
Beat the Calculator (Multiplication)			11•9		●	●	●						●
Before and After		3•1	*	●									
Bunny Hop		1•5		●									
Clear the Board	7•12			●	●	●	●						
Coin-Dice		3•12		●						●			
Coin Exchange		6•10	*				●			●			
Coin Top-It		2•13	1•4	●						●			
Count and Sit	2•6			●									
Cover Half	6•11							●					
Cover the Board	7•12			●	●	●	●						
Dice Addition	7•6			●	●	●	●						
Dice Subtraction	7•6			●	●	●	●						
Dice Race	3•3			●								●	
Difference Game		5•7	2•12	●	●	●	●			●			
Digit Game		5•1	3•1	●	●	●							
Dime-Nickel-Penny Grab		3•13		●			●			●			
Disappearing Train Game	3•13			●	●	●	●						
Dollar Rummy			3•6	●	●	●	●			●			
Domino Concentration	3•5			●									
Domino Top-It		3•14	2•2	●	●	●	●						
Doubles or Nothing			2•3	●	●	●	●						
Equivalent Fractions Game			8•5	●									
Fact Extension Game		*	4•8		●	●	●	●					
Fact Power Game		6•4			●	●	●						
Find the Block	5•3							●	●				
Follow the Leader	2•6			●									
Fraction Top-It			8•6	●									
Give the Next Number	1•12			●	●			●					
Go Forward, Back Up	4•1			●	●								
Growing Train Game	3•13			●	●	●	●						
Growing and Disappearing Train Game	3•13			●	●	●	●						
Guess My Number	5•4			●	●			●					
High Low	7•14			●								●	
High Roller	8•4	2•12	3•7	●	●	●	●						
Hit the Target		*	7•2		●		●						●
I Spy	2•1	10•5						●	●				
Make My Design		7•1							●				
Match Up	1•5			●									
Matching Coin Game	2•8									●			
Money Cube	7•1									●			
Money Exchange Game			1•5	●						●			

Number indicates first exposure at grade level. *Available in the Games section of *My Reference Book* or the *Student Reference Book*

Games Correlation Chart *continued*

Game	K Activity	Grade 1 Lesson	Grade 2 Lesson	Numeration	Mental Math	Basic Facts	Operations	Patterns	Geometry	Money	Time	Probability	Calculator
				Skill and Concept Areas									
Money Grid	7•1									●			
Monster Squeeze	3•6	1•2		●									
Name that Number		*	2•9		●	●	●						
Nickel-Penny Grab		2•11		●			●			●			
Number-Grid Difference		*	2•12	●		●	●	●					
Number-Grid Game	5•16	9•2	1•8	●			●	●					
Number-Grid Grab	7•13			●		●	●	●					
Number-Grid Search	5•16			●				●					
Number Gymnastics	8•6			●	●	●	●						
Number-Line Squeeze			1•1	●									
Number Top-It			1•11	●									
One-Dollar Exchange		8•2	*	●						●			
One Dollar Game	8•8			●						●			
$1, $10, $100 Exchange Game		10•4	1•5	●	●	●	●			●			
Ones, Tens, Hundreds Game	8•1			●									
Paper Money Exchange Game	8•1			●						●			
Pattern Cover Up	4•5							●					
Penny-Dice Game		1•3		●						●			
Penny-Dime-Dollar Exchange			3•2	●						●			
Penny-Dime Exchange	6•7			●						●			
enny Grab		2•8		●		●	●			●			
enny-Nickel-Dime Exchange		5•13		●						●			
enny-Nickel Exchange	5•10	2•10	1•5	●						●			
enny Plate		2•8	1•6	●	●					●			
ick-a-Coin			10•3							●			●
uarter-Dime-Nickel-Penny Grab		6•9		●			●			●			
he Raft Game	5•10			●									
ead My Mind	6•12								●				
ock, Paper, Scissors		1•8										●	
olling for 50		2•1		●									
haker Addition Top-It		4•12		●	●	●	●						
occer Spin			7•8									●	
pin a Number	2•4			●									
pinning for Money			3•2	●						●			
tand Up If...	6•3								●				
tick Pick-Up	3•11											●	
ubtraction Top-It		*	2•6	●	●	●	●						
een Frame	3•16			●	●								
een Tangle	2•10			●									
n-Frame Top-It		2•3		●									
ree Addends			6•1	●	●	●							
2, 1 Game		8•5	*	●	●	●	●	●					
me Match	8•12	4•4	*								●		
p-It	4•2	1•6	*	●									
icky Teens	2•10			●									
ic-Trac		6•8	*	●	●	●	●						
vo-Fisted Penny Addition			1•6	●	●	●	●						
alk Around the Clock	8•3										●		
hat's My Rule?" Fishing	4•14							●					
ho Am I Thinking Of?	4•14							●					

Number indicates first exposure at grade level. *Available in the Games section of *My Reference Book* or the *Student Reference Book*

Unit 1 Organizer

Establishing Routines

Overview

In this unit, an active learning environment is established in which children will build mathematical knowledge in cooperation with you and their classmates. Routines are introduced that will be followed both throughout the school year and in later grades. These routines provide a structure within which you and the children will begin work on a number of rich mathematical activities. Unit 1 has four main areas of focus:

- To practice counting on a number line,
- To practice comparing pairs of numbers,
- To practice daily routines for marking on slates and making and recording weather observations, and
- To learn how to represent data using tally counts.

Linking to the Common Core State Standards

The content of Unit 1 addresses the Common Core State Standards for Mathematics in *Numbers and Operations in Base Ten.* The correlation of the Common Core State Standards to the *Everyday Mathematics* Grade 1 lessons begins on page CS1.

Contents

Learning In Perspective

	Lesson Objectives	Links to the Past	Links to the Future
1·1	To introduce the count-the-days-of-school and job-management routines.	In Kindergarten, children practice counting up and back, including doing countdowns and counting on from numbers.	Counting up is reviewed throughout first grade.
1·2	To introduce number-line routines; and to provide practice counting up on the number line.	In Kindergarten, children practice counting up.	Counting up is reviewed throughout first grade.
1·3	To introduce and provide practice using mathematical tools for drawing and counting.	In Kindergarten, children use mathematical tools for drawing. They practice counting objects.	In Units 2–10, children use mathematical tools to draw, count objects, and work with fractions.
1·4	To introduce and provide practice with a slate routine; and to provide practice writing the numbers 1 and 2.	In Kindergarten, children begin writing numbers.	In Units 1 and 2, children practice writing the numbers 3–9 and 0.
1·5	To provide practice finding the number that is 1 more or 1 less than a given number.	In Kindergarten, children begin ordering and comparing numbers.	In Units 1–9, children compare numbers and quantities.
1·6	To provide practice comparing pairs of numbers.	In Kindergarten, children begin ordering and comparing numbers.	In Units 1–9, children compare numbers and quantities.
1·7	To introduce tally marks for data representation.	In Kindergarten, children use tally marks to count and record numbers of things.	Children use tallies to record data throughout Grades 1–6.
1·8	To provide experiences with equal-chance events.	In Kindergarten, children are introduced to probability situations and language, using visual cues and teacher-led discussions.	In Grades 1–6, children use probability language and explore equal- and unequal-chance events with dice, coin tosses, and spinners.
1·9	To introduce the calendar as a device for keeping track of the days in a month.	In Kindergarten, children are introduced to the day, month, and date as a part of a monthly calendar routine.	Children complete daily calendar routines throughout Grade 1. In Grade 2, children complete monthly calendars as part of the calendar routine.
1·10	To discuss and provide practice with rules for working in small groups.	In Kindergarten, children work in small groups throughout the school year.	In Grades 1–6, children work in small groups throughout the school year.
1·11	To introduce Explorations with manipulative materials.	In Kindergarten, children are introduced to a variety of manipulative materials.	Children participate in Explorations throughout Grades 1–3.
1·12	To introduce the routines for recording the day's weather and approximate temperature; and to teach how a thermometer works.	In Kindergarten, children work with temperatures as a part of daily routines.	Throughout Grade 1, children work with temperatures as a part of daily routines and solve problems involving temperature change.
1·13	To provide practice telling and solving number stories.	In Kindergarten, children begin telling and solving number stories.	Children tell and solve number stories throughout Grades 1–6.

	Key Concepts and Skills	Grade 1 Goals*
1·1	Count forward and backward by 1s.	Number and Numeration Goal 1
	Identify plane and solid figures.	Geometry Goal 1
	Identify patterns.	Patterns, Functions, and Algebra Goal 1
1·2	Find numbers that are larger than and smaller than a given number.	Number and Numeration Goal 7
	Describe numbers using comparison vocabulary, such as *more than, smaller than, bigger than,* and *less than.*	Number and Numeration Goal 7
	Count up from a smaller number to a larger number.	Operations and Computation Goal 2
	Use a tally chart to collect data.	Data and Chance Goal 1
1·3	Count objects by 1s.	Number and Numeration Goal 2
	Recognize dot patterns on dice as representations of numbers.	Number and Numeration Goal 6
	Compare quantities using *more* and *fewer.*	Number and Numeration Goal 7
	Name and draw plane figures using the Pattern-Block Template.	Geometry Goal 1
1·4	Write numbers to represent quantities.	Number and Numeration Goal 3
	Draw pictures to represent the numbers 1 and 2.	Number and Numeration Goal 3
	Name the numbers before and after a given number.	Number and Numeration Goal 7
1·5	Count objects by 1s.	Number and Numeration Goal 2
	Locate numbers on a number line.	Number and Numeration Goal 7
	Name numbers that are one more and one less than a given number.	Operations and Computation Goal 1
	Use a number line to solve number stories.	Operations and Computation Goal 1
1·6	Read whole numbers.	Number and Numeration Goal 3
	Order whole numbers from smallest to largest.	Number and Numeration Goal 7
	Compare pairs of whole numbers.	Number and Numeration Goal 7
	Name numbers that are one more and one less than a given number.	Operations and Computation Goal 1
1·7	Count forward by 1s and 5s.	Number and Numeration Goal 1
	Represent numbers using tally marks.	Number and Numeration Goal 6
	Create a tally chart to organize data.	Data and Chance Goal 1
	Make predictions based on data organized in a tally chart.	Data and Chance Goal 2
1·8	Represent numbers using tally marks.	Number and Numeration Goal 6
	Create a tally chart to organize data.	Data and Chance Goal 1
	Answer questions and make predictions based on data organized in a tally chart.	Data and Chance Goal 2
	Make predictions about the outcomes of dice rolls.	Data and Chance Goal 3
1·9	Count forward by 1s.	Number and Numeration Goal 1
	Order whole numbers.	Number and Numeration Goal 7
	Use a calendar to answer questions about days, weeks, months, and dates.	Measurement and Reference Frames Goal 4
1·10	Count objects by 1s and 5s.	Number and Numeration Goal 2
	Represent numbers using tally marks.	Number and Numeration Goal 6
	Compare pairs of whole numbers.	Number and Numeration Goal 7
1·11	Identify base-10 blocks.	Number and Numeration Goal 3
	Use a number line to solve number-line problems.	Operations and Computation Goal 1
	Identify geoboards and the plane shapes of pattern blocks.	Geometry Goal 1
	Create designs using the plane shapes of pattern blocks.	Patterns, Functions, and Algebra Goal 1
1·12	Count forward by 2s and 10s.	Number and Numeration Goal 1
	Create a tally chart to organize data.	Data and Chance Goal 1
	Read temperature ranges on a Fahrenheit thermometer.	Measurement and Reference Frames Goal 3
1·13	Tell simple number stories using up to 10 counters and a variety of strategies.	Operations and Computation Goal 4
	Solve number stories.	Operations and Computation Goal 4

*See the Appendix for a complete list of Grade 1 Goals.

A Balanced Curriculum

Ongoing Practice

Everyday Mathematics provides numerous opportunities for ongoing practice. These activities are embedded throughout the lessons:

Mental Math and Reflexes activities promote speed and accuracy in mental computation.

Home Links are daily homework assignments that review the content of the lesson and often contain ongoing facts practice.

Minute Math+ problems are offered for additional practice in Lessons 1•1, 1•2, 1•7, and 1•10.

EM Facts Workshop Game provides online practice of basic facts and computation.

EXTRA PRACTICE **Extra Practice** activities are included in Lessons 1•1, 1•2, 1•6, and 1•10.

Practice through Games

Games are an essential component of practice in the *Everyday Mathematics* program. Games offer skills practice and promote strategic thinking. See the *Differentiation Handbook* for ways to adapt games to meet children's needs.

Lesson	Game	Skill Practiced
1•2, 1•3, 1•6, 1•10	*Monster Squeeze*	Comparing numbers [NN Goal 7]
1•3, 1•4, 1•5, 1•6, 1•13	*Penny-Dice Game*	Counting objects and comparing quantities [NN Goals 2 and 7]
1•5, 1•12	*Bunny Hop*	Counting on a number line [NN Goal 1]
1•6, 1•7, 1•10, 1•11	*Top-It*	Comparing numbers [NN Goal 7]
1•8	*Rock, Paper, Scissors*	Recording data with tally marks [DC Goal 1]

[NN] Number and Numeration
[MRF] Measurement and Reference Frames
[OC] Operations and Computation
[GEO] Geometry
[DC] Data and Chance
[PFA] Patterns, Functions, and Algebra

Problem Solving 

Good problem solvers use a variety of strategies, including the following:

- Draw a picture.
- Act out the problem.
- Make a table, chart, or list.
- Look for a pattern.
- Try a simpler version of the problem.
- Make a guess and try it out.

The table below lists some of the opportunities in this unit for children to practice these strategies.

Lesson	Activity
1•2	Play *Monster Squeeze.*
1•2	Find the number of children who are absent.
1•5	Tell "One More" and "One Less" number stories.
1•8	Do the Dice-Roll and Tally activity.
1•13	Tell simple number stories.

Lessons that teach *through* problem solving, not just *about* problem solving

See Chapter 18: Problem Solving in the *Teacher's Reference Manual* for more information.

The Language of Mathematics

Everyday Mathematics provides lesson-specific suggestions to help all children acquire, process, and express mathematical ideas. Throughout Unit 1, there are lesson-specific language development notes that address the needs of English language learners, indicated by ELL.

ELL SUPPORT Activities to support English language learners are in Part 3 of Lessons 1•1, 1•3, 1•5, 1•9, 1•10, and 1•12.

The *English Learners Handbook* and the *Differentiation Handbook* have suggestions for promoting language development and acquisition of mathematics vocabulary. See Unit 1 in each handbook.

Unit 1 Vocabulary

base-10 blocks
calendar
date
degree
Exploration
Fahrenheit
geoboard
number line
number story
pattern blocks
Pattern-Block Template
slate
tally mark
temperature
thermometer
tool kit

Literacy Connection

Lesson 1•4 *Anno's Counting Book,* by Mitsumasa Anno, HarperCollins Publishers, 1986

Lesson 1•4 *City by Numbers,* by Stephen T. Johnson, Viking, 2003

For more literacy connections, see the *Home Connection Handbook,* Grades 1–3.

Cross-Curricular Links 

Literature and Reading

Lesson 1•1 Children recite and act out action rhymes and finger plays.

Lesson 1•4 Children review counting objects and writing numbers using *Anno's Counting Book.*

Lesson 1•4 Children identify numbers using *City by Numbers.*

Lesson 1•13 Children find numbers represented in classroom library books.

Science

Lesson 1•12 Children learn how a thermometer works.

Balanced Assessment

Daily Assessments

- **Recognizing Student Achievement** – A daily assessment that is included in every lesson to evaluate children's progress toward the Grade 1 Grade-Level Goals.
- **Informing Instruction** – Notes that appear throughout the unit to help anticipate children's common errors and suggest appropriate problem-solving strategies.

Lesson	Recognizing Student Achievement	Informing Instruction
1•1	Count by 1s to 20. [NN Goal 1]	
1•2	Count by 1s and 5s. [NN Goal 1]	Play *Monster Squeeze.*
1•3	Compare groups of pennies and tell which group has more. [NN Goal 7]	
1•4	Write the numbers 1 and 2 legibly. [NN Goal 3]	
1•5	Name numbers before and after a given number using a number line. [NN Goal 7]	Count beginning with 0.
1•6	Tell the number that is one more and one less than any number up to 10. [NN Goal 7]	
1•7	Write the numbers 3 and 4 legibly. [NN Goal 3]	Make tally marks.
1•8	Represent numbers using tally marks. [NN Goal 6]	
1•9	Write the numbers 5 and 6 legibly. [NN Goal 3]	
1•10	Count hops on a number line. [OC Goal 1]	
1•11	Compare numbers and tell which is greater. [NN Goal 7]	
1•12	Count by 2s to 8. [NN Goal 1]	
1•13	Solve simple number stories. [OC Goal 4]	Share simple number stories.

[NN] Number and Numeration [OC] Operations and Computation [DC] Data and Chance
[MRF] Measurement and Reference Frames [GEO] Geometry [PFA] Patterns, Functions, and Algebra

Portfolio Opportunities

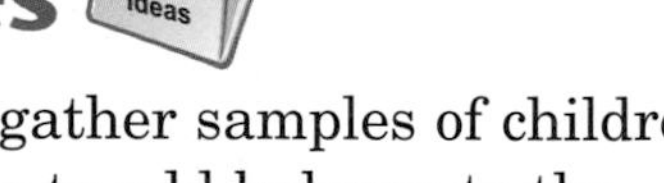

The following lessons provide opportunities to gather samples of children's mathematical writings, drawings, and creations to add balance to the assessment process: Lessons 1•2, 1•3, 1•12, 1•13, and 1•14.

See pages 16 and 17 in the *Assessment Handbook* for more information about portfolios and how to use them.

Unit Assessment

Progress Check 1 – A cumulative assessment of concepts and skills taught in Unit 1, providing information for evaluating children's progress and planning for future instruction. These assessments include oral/slate, written, and open-response activities, as shown below in the sample Progress Check lesson opener.

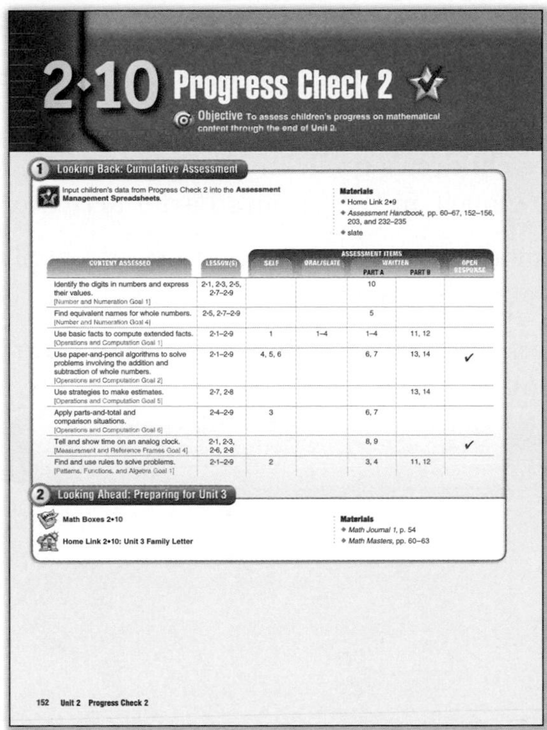

2•10 Progress Check 2

Objective To assess children's progress on mathematical content through the end of Unit 2.

1 Looking Back: Cumulative Assessment

Input children's data from Progress Check 2 into the **Assessment Management Spreadsheets.**

Materials
- Home Link 2•9
- *Assessment Handbook*, pp. 60–67, 152–156, 203, and 232–235
- slate

Content Assessed	Lesson(s)	Assessment Items: Self	Oral/Slate	Written: Part A	Written: Part B	Open Response
Identify the digits in numbers and express their values. [Number and Numeration Goal 1]	2·1, 2·3, 2·5, 2·7–2·9			10		
Find equivalent names for whole numbers. [Number and Numeration Goal 4]	2·5, 2·7–2·9			5		
Use basic facts to compute extended facts. [Operations and Computation Goal 1]	2·1–2·9	1	1–4	1–4	11, 12	
Use paper-and-pencil algorithms to solve problems involving the addition and subtraction of whole numbers. [Operations and Computation Goal 2]	2·1–2·9	4, 5, 6		6, 7	13, 14	✓
Use strategies to make estimates. [Operations and Computation Goal 5]	2·7, 2·8				13, 14	
Apply parts-and-total and comparison situations. [Operations and Computation Goal 6]	2·4–2·9	3		6, 7		
Tell and show time on an analog clock. [Measurement and Reference Frames Goal 4]	2·1, 2·3, 2·6, 2·8			8, 9		✓
Find and use rules to solve problems. [Patterns, Functions, and Algebra Goal 1]	2·1–2·9	2		3, 4	11, 12	

2 Looking Ahead: Preparing for Unit 3

Math Boxes 2•10

Home Link 2•10: Unit 3 Family Letter

Materials
- *Math Journal 1*, p. 54
- *Math Masters*, pp. 60–63

152 Unit 2 Progress Check 2

Core Assessment Resources

Assessment Handbook

- **Unit 1 Assessment Overview,** pages pages 52–59
- **Unit 1 Assessment Masters,** pages 138–140
- **Unit 1 Individual Profiles of Progress,** pages 200, 201, and 248
- **Unit 1 Class Checklists,** pages 202, 203, and 249
- **Beginning-of-Year Assessment,*** pages 51A, 51B, 186A, and 186B
- **Math Logs,** pages 254–256
- **Exit Slip,** page 251
- **Other Student Assessment Forms,** pages 252, 253, 257, and 258

*The Beginning-of-Year Assessment is one of the screening tools that can be used to help identify which concepts and skills children have learned and to help plan instruction for the upcoming year.

Assessment Management Spreadsheets

The Assessment Management Spreadsheets consist of the Digital Class Checklists and Individual Profile of Progress Checklists. Use them to monitor, record, and report children's progress.

Addressing All Needs

Differentiated Instruction

Adjusting the Activity – suggests adaptations that target advanced learners, English language learners, or learners who need additional instructional support.

ELL SUPPORT / **ELL** – provides lesson-specific suggestions to help English language learners understand and process the mathematical content.

READINESS – accesses children's prior knowledge or previews content that prepares children to engage in the lesson's Part 1 activities.

EXTRA PRACTICE – provides additional opportunities to apply the mathematical content of the lesson.

ENRICHMENT – enables children to apply or further explore the mathematical content of the lesson.

Lesson	Adjusting the Activity	ELL Support/ ELL	Readiness	Extra Practice	Enrichment
1•1	•	•	•	•	
1•2	•	•	•	•	•
1•3		•	•		•
1•4	•		•		•
1•5	•	•	•		
1•6	•		•	•	•
1•7	•	•	•		•
1•8	•	•	•		•
1•9	•	•	•		•
1•10		•	•	•	
1•11			•		•
1•12	•	•	•		•
1•13			•		•

Additional Resources

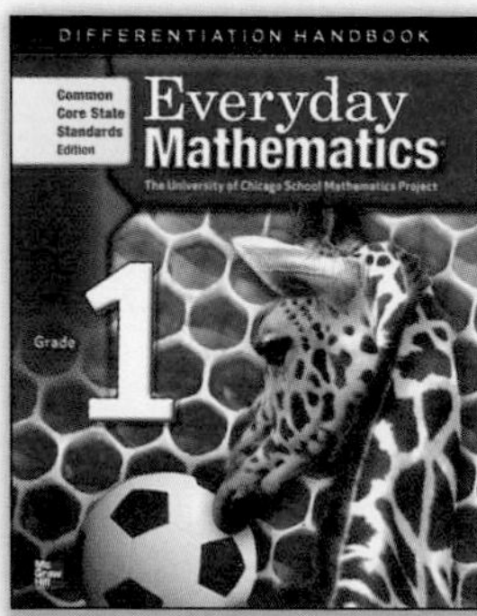

Differentiation Handbook
Provides ideas and strategies for differentiating instruction.
Pages 50–56

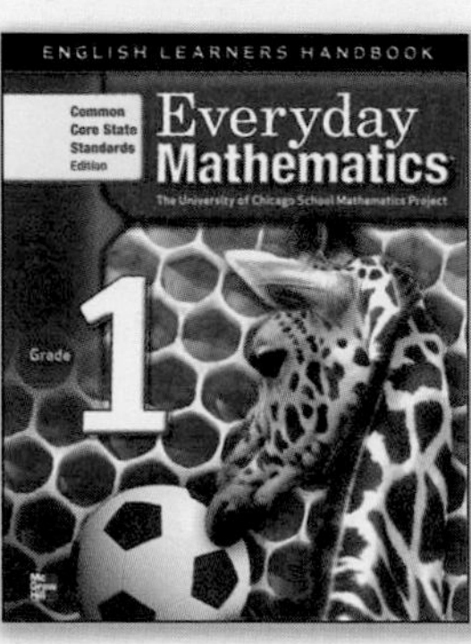

English Learners Handbook
Contains lesson-specific comprehension strategies.
Pages 1–13

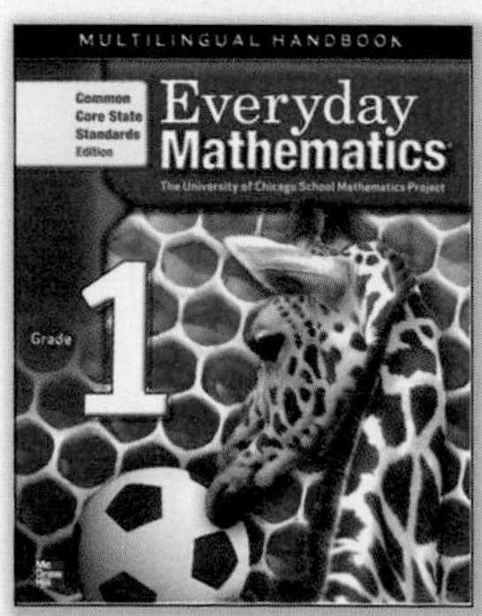

Multilingual Handbook
Previews concepts and vocabulary. It is written in six languages.
Pages 1–26

Planning Tips

Multiage Classroom

Companion Lessons from Grades K and 2 can help you meet instructional needs of a multiage classroom. The full Scope and Sequence can be found in the Appendix.

Grade K	Routines 1–8	1•5, 1•12, 4•1		2•7, 2•9	1•12, 7•12	6•9	5•9	3•10, 3•11	Routine 4			Routines 6 and 7	2•14, 4•15
Grade 1	**1•1**	**1•2**	**1•3**	**1•4**	**1•5**	**1•6**	**1•7**	**1•8**	**1•9**	**1•10**	**1•11**	**1•12**	**1•13**
Grade 2		1•1	1•2		1•11	1•11	1•5		1•3	1•4	1•12	4•3, 4•4	2•1, 4•1, 4•2

Pacing for Success

Pacing depends on a number of factors, such as children's individual needs and how long your school has been using *Everyday Mathematics*. At the beginning of Unit 1, you may want to use tools available at www.everydaymathonline.com to help you set your pace.

Home Support

Unit 1 Family Letter (English/Spanish) provides families with an overview, Do-Anytime Activities, Building Skills through Games, a list of vocabulary, and answers to the daily homework (Home Links). Family Letters in English, Spanish, and seven other languages are also available online.

Home Links are the daily homework assignments. They consist of active projects and ongoing review problems.

Home Support Resources

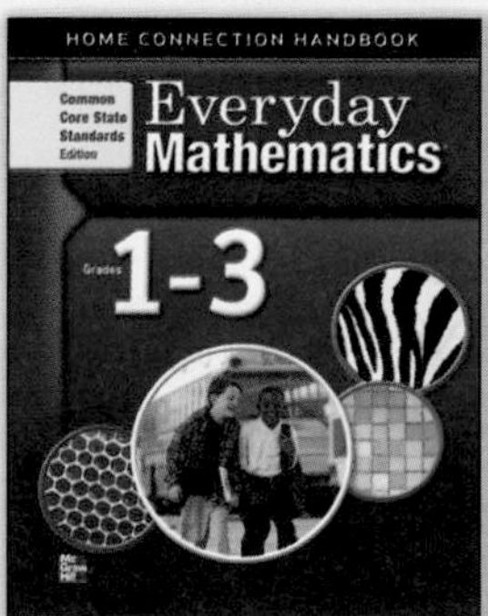

Home Connection Handbook
Offers ideas and reproducible masters for communicating with families. See Table of Contents for unit information.

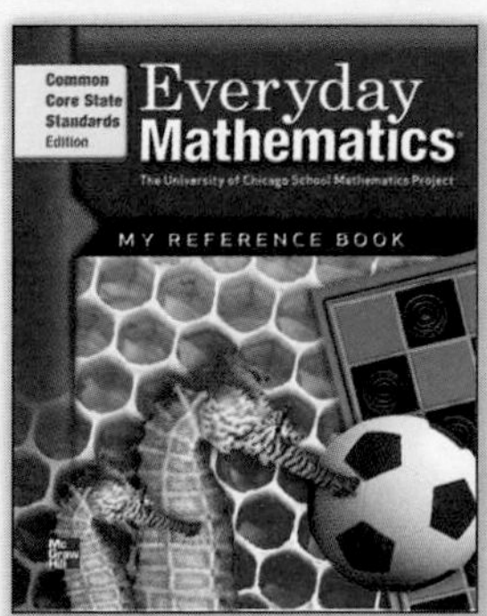

My Reference Book
Beginning in Unit 6, *My Reference Book* provides a resource for children and parents.

Technology Resources

Materials

Technology Resources www.everydaymathonline.com

ePresentations

eToolkit

Algorithms Practice

EM Facts Workshop Game™

Family Letters

Assessment Management

Common Core State Standards

Curriculum Focal Points

Interactive Teacher's Lesson Guide

Lesson	Masters	Manipulative Kit	Other Items
1•1	Home Link Masters, pp. 2 and 3		materials for ongoing classroom routines; Job Chart; index cards
1•2	Teaching Masters, pp. 4 and 5* Home Link Masters, pp. 6 and 7	Class Number Line	"fences" to bracket number-line intervals*; numbered sheets of paper; stapler
1•3	Teaching Master, p. 8	pattern blocks*; dice; tool kit	pennies; Class Data Pad; Pattern-Block Template
1•4		Class Number Line; per group: 1 die; slate	chalk or dry-erase marker; eraser (sock or facial tissue); per group: 20 pennies; *Anno's Counting Book; City by Numbers*
1•5	Game Master, p. 341 Teaching Aid Master, p. 304 *Differentiation Handbook,* p. 126	Class Number Line; per group: 1 die; slate	pennies; basket
1•6	Teaching Aid Master, p. 305 *Monster Squeeze* (*Math Masters,* p. 8) Teaching Master, p. 9	per group: 1 die; number cards 0–15; slate	4" by 6" index cards*; counters and/or pennies; envelope, paper clip, or rubber band
1•7		Class Number Line; number cards 0–15; slate	Class Data Pad; pennies; can or other container
1•8	Home Link Master, p. 10 Teaching Aid Master, p. 304 Game Master, p. 352	per group: 1 die; craft sticks*; number cards 1–10; slate	per group: tally cards
1•9	Transparency of *Math Masters,* p. 306* Home Link Master, p. 11		Class Calendar; calendar pages
1•10	Teaching Master, p. 8 Teaching Aid Master, p. 304 Home Link Master, p. 12	number cards 0–22; slate	Rules for Small Groups Poster*; per group: 2 pennies; overhead counters in 2 colors (10 of each); per child: 2 squares of paper in colors of counters
1•11	Teaching Aid Master, 305 Home Link Master, p. 13	pattern blocks; base-10 blocks; geoboard; rubber bands; number cards 0–15; slate	Rules for Explorations Poster; color and shape word cards
1•12	Teaching Aid Master, p. 307 Game Master, p. 341 Home Link Master, p. 14 *Differentiation Handbook,* p. 126	per group: 1 die; classroom thermometer	Class Data Pad; Class Weather Chart; Class Thermometer Poster (°F); per child: 7 sheets of blank construction paper; 4 foot length of red ribbon or crepe paper; removable tape; calculator*
1•13	Teaching Aid Masters, pp. 304 and 305 Home Link Master, p. 15	per group: 1 die; number cards 0–10; slate; tool-kit pennies	picture books; stick-on notes
1•14	Assessment Masters, pp. 138–140 Home Link Masters, pp. 16–19	slate	

*Denotes optional materials

Mathematical Background

The discussion below highlights the major content ideas presented in Unit 1 and helps establish instructional priorities.

Daily Routines (Lesson 1•1 and following)

If children used *Kindergarten Everyday Mathematics,* many of the routines in Grade 1, Unit 1 and later units may be familiar to them.

To help you become acquainted with the routines, background information is provided in the **Management Guide** section of the *Teacher's Reference Manual.* Occasionally, the Mathematical Background section will have additional references to the Mathematical Topics essays in the *Teacher's Reference Manual.* It is important that you read about these topics in advance so that you feel comfortable making decisions about these daily routines.

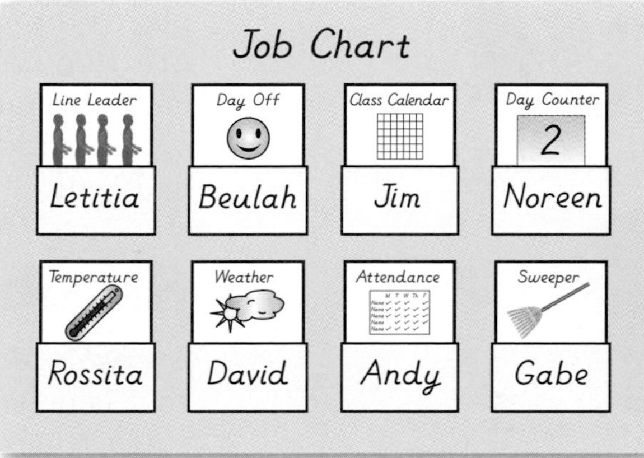

Children's jobs are displayed on the Job Chart.

The time needed to fully develop the routines will vary from group to group. If you or the children begin to feel overwhelmed by the number of routines, delay introducing some of them, or omit some, especially if this is your first year using the program.

If you have an experienced group, move through these first lessons more rapidly. The routines become habitual as they are put into practice over and over.

Investigating the Number Line (Lesson 1•2)

Young children need to develop the ability to count by rote as a prerequisite to rational counting (the counting of objects). The number line provides a visual display for such rote-counting activities. It may also be used for other numeration activities, such as comparing pairs of numbers and finding numbers between two numbers. Children practice the latter activity by playing *Monster Squeeze.* Later, children will use number lines in their work with number patterns, addition, and subtraction.

The **Management Guide** (Section 1.3.4) in the *Teacher's Reference Manual* provides more information about number lines.

Routines	Lesson
Choral Counting	1•1
*Class Number Line	1•1
*Managing classroom jobs	1•1
Mental Math and Reflexes	1•1
*Keeping track of attendance	1•2
Tool kits and identification numbers	1•3
Working with a Partner	1•3
Using slates	1•4
Home Links	1•8
*Calendars	1•9
Working in small groups	1•10
Explorations	1•11
*Keeping a weather record	1•12
Keeping a temperature record	1•12

*Denotes a routine introduced in *Kindergarten Everyday Mathematics*

The table lists the routines that are introduced in Unit 1 and the lessons in which they first occur.

Tools for Doing Mathematics
(Lesson 1•3)

In this lesson, children begin to use three mathematical tools: pennies, which are used for counting practice and for modeling number problems; dice, which are usually used in games and probability experiments; and Pattern-Block Templates, which are used for drawing shapes. More mathematical tools will be added later on.

See the *Teacher's Reference Manual,* Section 3.2, for more information about mathematical tools.

In this lesson, children play the *Penny-Dice Game,* the first of many games played throughout *Everyday Mathematics.* Games are an integral part of *Everyday Mathematics.* They help children build and reinforce a variety of mathematical skills. In addition, games provide children with opportunities to build intuition about probability, chance, patterns, and logic.

Number-Writing Practice (Lesson 1•4)

Everyday Mathematics encourages the recording and writing of numbers, so it is important that children practice correct number writing. At this stage, children's small-motor skills vary greatly, so you will need to determine how rapidly children work through these activities.

Additional information about number-writing practice can be found in the *Teacher's Reference Manual,* Section 5.7.

In this lesson, children begin to use two recording devices: slates, which, when used in whole class activities, make it possible for everyone to display answers quietly and at the same time; and journals, which will comprise a record of children's work for the entire year.

One More, One Less (Lesson 1•5)

Children solve "one-more" and "one-less" number stories, which provide concrete experiences in preparation for later work with addition and subtraction.

Comparing Numbers (Lesson 1•6)

Having had a certain amount of rote-counting practice, children should be ready to begin comparing small numbers. They practice this skill by playing *Top-It.*

For more information about comparing numbers, see Section 9.6 in the *Teacher's Reference Manual.*

Recording Tally Counts
(Lessons 1•7 and 1•8)

Tally counts are a good way to keep track of counts and data collected over time. Tally counts improve a child's ability to count by 5s and show each number between 5 and 10 as five *plus* one or more. Tallies may serve as a way for children to represent numbers they can count to and say but cannot yet write.

Tally marks can also be used to collect data. Throughout the year, children will often record the data they collect using tally marks.

Home Links are sent home for the first time in Lesson 1-8. The purpose of Home Links is to involve families in children's mathematical activities.

See the *Teacher's Reference Manual,* Section 12.2.2, for more information about collecting and recording data.

The Calendar (Lesson 1•9)

By using the calendar on a daily basis, children gradually acquire calendar skills. Throughout the year, there will be many opportunities to use the calendar to record such data as special days and events.

You can learn more about calendar concepts by reading Chapter 15, Reference Frames, in the *Teacher's Reference Manual.*

Working in Small Groups (Lessons 1•10 and 1•11)

For cooperative work to be effective, children need to observe small-group etiquette and rules. Be prepared to spend extra time reinforcing these principles.

See the *Teacher's Reference Manual,* Section 4.1, for additional information about cooperative grouping.

Explorations give children opportunities to share manipulatives in small groups. Explorations are usually informal and open ended. Children are encouraged to verbalize their discoveries and follow the rules for cooperative behavior.

See the **Management Guide,** Section 1.2.1, in the *Teacher's Reference Manual* for more information about Explorations.

Weather and Temperature Routines (Lesson 1•12)

These routines involve collecting, recording, and analyzing data. Working with various sets of data is an important part of *Everyday Mathematics* at every grade level. Through these activities, children experience real-world applications of mathematics.

You can read more about daily routines in the **Management Guide,** Section 1.1, which is located in the *Teacher's Reference Manual.*

Number Stories (Lesson 1•13)

Throughout *Everyday Mathematics,* number stories emphasize the use of a variety of solution strategies, including concrete, pictorial, and verbal strategies, as well as solution strategies with number models. It is important that children verbalize their thought processes when solving number stories.

See the *Teacher's Reference Manual,* Section 18.4, for additional information about number stories and problem solving.

1•1 Daily Routines

Objective To introduce the count-the-days-of-school and job-management routines.

www.everydaymathonline.com

ePresentations

eToolkit

Algorithms Practice

EM Facts Workshop Game™

Family Letters

Assessment Management

Common Core State Standards

Curriculum Focal Points

Interactive Teacher's Lesson Guide

1 Teaching the Lesson

Key Concepts and Skills

- Count forward and backward by 1s.
  [Number and Numeration Goal 1]
- Identify plane and solid figures.
  [Geometry Goal 1]
- Identify patterns.
  [Patterns, Functions, and Algebra Goal 1]

Key Activities

Children describe what they think mathematics is and what they expect to do in mathematics class in first grade. They are introduced to at least one count-the-days-of-school routine and to a routine for managing classroom jobs.

Ongoing Assessment: Recognizing Student Achievement
Use Mental Math and Reflexes.
[Number and Numeration Goal 1]

Key Vocabulary

number line

Materials

materials for ongoing classroom routines ◆ Job Chart ◆ index cards (optional)

2 Ongoing Learning & Practice

Revisiting Rhymes and Songs
Children revisit favorite rhymes, songs, and games from Kindergarten that promote counting and emphasize positional words.

Home Link 1•1
Math Masters, pp. 2 and 3
Children take home the Family Letter introducing *First Grade Everyday Mathematics*.

3 Differentiation Options

READINESS

Making Number Collections
index cards
Children make and label number collections.

EXTRA PRACTICE

Minute Math+
Minute Math®+, pp. 5 and 60
Children practice skip counting and identifying shapes.

ELL SUPPORT

Labeling the Room
Children label visual routines.

Advance Preparation

You may use either the Growing Number Line or Class Number Line routine.

***Teacher's Reference Manual,* Grades 1–3** pp. 4, 8–19, 40, 50, 51, 53–55, 70–75

Getting Started

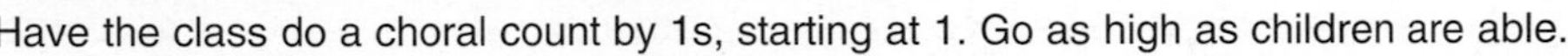

Mental Math and Reflexes ★

Have the class do a choral count by 1s, starting at 1. Go as high as children are able.

Ongoing Assessment: Recognizing Student Achievement — Mental Math and Reflexes ★

Use **Mental Math and Reflexes** to assess children's ability to count by 1s. Children are making adequate progress if they can count by 1s to 20. Some children may be able to count by 1s to 100.

[Number and Numeration Goal 1]

NOTE **Readiness** activities help children gain prerequisite skills so that they can be successful in the lesson. Some children may benefit from doing the Readiness activity before you begin Part 1 of the lesson. See the Readiness activity in Part 3 for details.

Interactive whiteboard-ready ePresentations are available at www.everydaymathonline.com to help you teach the lesson.

1 Teaching the Lesson

Introducing *First Grade Everyday Mathematics*

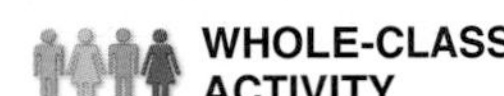

WHOLE-CLASS ACTIVITY

Ask children to describe what they think mathematics is and what they think they might do in mathematics class in first grade.

Mention that mathematics is used in counting and measuring things, in exploring shapes and patterns, and in solving all kinds of problems.

Have children find numbers, shapes, and patterns in the classroom; for example, the numbers on the number line, the classroom clock, and the calendar; the shapes of the door and the clock; and the patterns made by floor or ceiling tiles.

Showing the first day of school on the Growing Number Line

Counting the Days of School

WHOLE-CLASS ACTIVITY

Tell children that they will start daily math routines today. One daily routine is to use the **number line** to count the days of school. Use one of the following number-line routines for designating this first day of the school year:

▷ *Growing Number Line:* Post the "1" card.

▷ *Class Number Line:* Place an arrow on, or a frame around, the number 1 on the Class Number Line.

Showing the first day of school on the Class Number Line

Adjusting the Activity

The Class Number Line can be used as a timeline for recording special events. Help children record each event using words or pictures on an index card and attach it to the number of the day on which it occurs. For example, "Susie lost a tooth!" or "Field trip to the zoo!"

AUDITORY ◆ KINESTHETIC ◆ TACTILE ◆ VISUAL

By the end of today, children will have been in first grade for 1 day.

- Which number represents the *next* day of first grade? 2
- Which number represents the day *before* school started? 0

Remember to reserve time to complete the number-line routine.

Consider also using one (or both) of the following routines:

NOTE The first routine requires approximately 5 pennies, 2 nickels, 2 dimes, and 7 quarters for the entire year. Some teachers use coins with magnets or tape.

If you use the second routine, set up your ONES, TENS, and HUNDREDS cups from the beginning. This is one way to develop a sense of magnitude and place value.

Count the Days Using Coins

Display a penny to designate **Day 1.** Then add a penny each day. On **Day 5,** add a penny, but then trade the 5 pennies for a nickel. On **Day 10,** trade the nickel and 5 pennies for a dime. On **Day 20,** trade the dime, nickel, and 5 pennies for 2 dimes. On **Day 25,** trade the 2 dimes and 5 pennies for a quarter, and so on.

Count the Days Using Straws

Put a straw in the ONES cup to designate **Day 1.** Then add a straw each day. On **Day 10,** take the 10 straws out of the ONES cup, bundle them, and put them in the TENS cup. On **Day 20,** put another bundle of 10 straws into the TENS cup, and so on. On **Day 100,** take the 10 bundles out of the TENS cup, bundle them, and put them in the HUNDREDS cup.

▶ Assigning Classroom Jobs

WHOLE-CLAS DISCUSSION

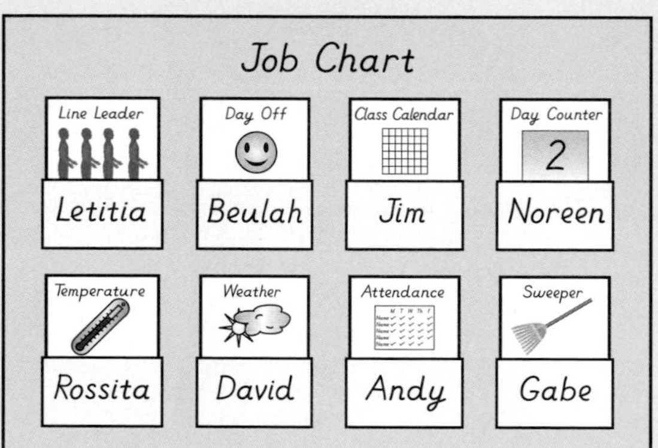

Job Chart
Line Leader
Day Off
Class Calendar
Day Counter
2
Letitia
Beulah
Jim
Noreen
Temperature
Weather
Attendance
Sweeper
Rossita
David
Andy
Gabe

Children's classroom jobs can be displayed on a Job Chart.

Although setting up and teaching a Job Chart routine can be tim consuming, the rewards are well worth the effort. As children learn independence and responsibility, less time will be spent on housekeeping tasks.

The following "math" jobs will be introduced throughout Unit 1: Day Counter, Class Calendar, Weather, and Temperature. The calendar routine will be introduced in Lesson 1-9, and the weath and temperature routines will be introduced in Lesson 1-12. Consider including these jobs as part of your classroom routines.

Take time today to introduce the Day Counter job (the person wh designates the number of days children have attended school so far). Explain your expectations for the job and have children demonstrate how to do the job.

2 Ongoing Learning & Practice

▶ Revisiting Rhymes and Songs

WHOLE-CLAS ACTIVITY

One, Two, Buckle My Shoe

1
2 Buckle my shoe.

3
4 Shut the door.

5
6 Pick up sticks.

7
8 Lay them straight.

9
10 A big fat hen.

Children practice their rote-counting skills as they recite well-known counting rhymes in unison.

Revisit some rhymes, songs, or games that promote counting (for example, "One, Two, Buckle My Shoe") or emphasize positional language (for example, "Simon Says" or "Hokey Pokey").

Home Link 1·1

INDEPENDENT ACTIVITY

(*Math Masters,* pp. 2 and 3)

Home Connection Distribute copies of the beginning-of-the-year Family Letter for children to take home. This letter introduces families to *First Grade Everyday Mathematics*. A Family Letter will be sent home after Lesson 1-2 that introduces Unit 1 in particular. Home Links are provided for every lesson beginning with Lesson 1-8.

Home Link Master

Name Date

HOME LINK 1·1 Unit 1: Family Letter

Introduction to *First Grade Everyday Mathematics*

Welcome to *First Grade Everyday Mathematics*. It is part of an elementary school mathematics curriculum developed by the University of Chicago School Mathematics Project (UCSMP). *Everyday Mathematics* offers children a broad background in mathematics.

Several features of the program are described below to help familiarize you with *Everyday Mathematics*.

A problem-solving approach based on everyday situations By making connections between their own knowledge and experiences, children learn basic skills in meaningful contexts so that mathematics becomes "real."

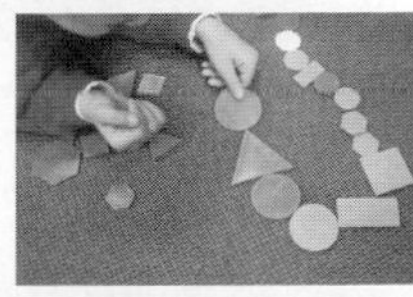

A variety of formats for frequent practice of basic skills Instead of practice presented only in a tedious drill format, children practice basic skills in a variety of engaging ways. In addition to completing daily mixed practice pages, finding patterns on the number grid, and working with addition and subtraction fact families, children will play games designed to develop basic skills.

An instructional approach that revisits concepts regularly To enhance the development of basic skills and concepts, children revisit previously learned concepts and practice skills encountered earlier. The lessons take advantage of previously learned concepts and skills and build on them throughout the year.

A curriculum that explores mathematical content beyond basic arithmetic Mathematics standards in the United States, as well as around the world, indicate that basic arithmetic skills are only the beginning of the mathematical knowledge children will need. In addition to basic arithmetic, *First Grade Everyday Mathematics* emphasizes the topics discussed on the following page.

***Math Masters,* p. 2**

3 Differentiation Options

READINESS

SMALL-GROUP ACTIVITY

Making Number Collections

5–15 Min

To provide experience with counting objects, have children make and label number collections for objects in the room. For example, one group makes a collection for the number 5 by displaying five crayons and labeling an index card with the number 5. Encourage children to move about the room and find interesting objects for their collections. They can display the collections at their desks or at a math station.

EXTRA PRACTICE

SMALL-GROUP ACTIVITY

Minute Math +

5–15 Min

Use *Minute Math+*, pages 5 and 60, to provide practice skip counting and identifying shapes.

ELL SUPPORT

SMALL-GROUP ACTIVITY

Labeling the Room

5–15 Min

To provide language support through classroom routines, label all visual routines in the room with the appropriate words. For example, display the words *Number Line* over the class number line; add the word *Calendar* above the calendar; add the words *Number Grid* over the Number-Grid Poster, and so on. Having this vocabulary displayed in the room near its visual representation will provide English language learners with a reference when working on journal pages and during whole-class discussions.

Literature and Reading Link Using posters while children recite and act out action rhymes and finger plays helps them bridge the gap between spoken and written language as they practice their rote-counting skills.

Home Link Master

HOME LINK 1·1 Unit 1: Family Letter *cont.*

- **Number and Numeration** Counting; reading and writing numbers; investigating place value of whole numbers; exploring fractions and money
- **Operations and Computation** Learning addition and subtraction facts, fact families, and extended facts; beginning informal work with properties of numbers and problem solving
- **Data and Chance** Collecting, organizing, and displaying data using tables, charts, and graphs
- **Measurement and Reference Frames** Using tools to measure length, capacity (quarts, liters), and weight; using clocks, calendars, timelines, thermometers, and ordinal numbers such as *fifth* and *tenth*
- **Geometry** Exploring 2-dimensional shapes (squares, triangles, rectangles) and 3-dimensional shapes (pyramids, cones, prisms)
- **Patterns, Functions, and Algebra** Exploring attributes, patterns, sequences, relations, and functions; finding missing numbers and rules in problems; studying properties of operations (addition and subtraction)

Everyday Mathematics will provide you with ample opportunities to monitor your child's progress and to participate in your child's mathematics experiences. Throughout the year, you will receive Family Letters to keep you informed of the mathematical content your child will be studying in each unit.

You will enjoy seeing your child's confidence and comprehension soar as he or she connects mathematics to everyday life.

We look forward to an exciting year!

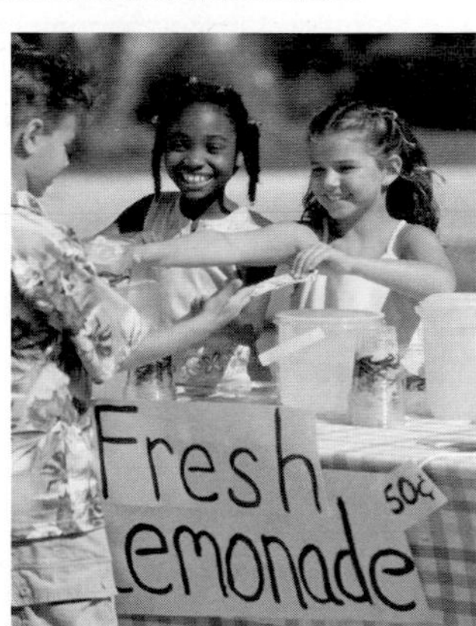

***Math Masters,* p. 3**

Planning Ahead

In Lesson 1-3, have enough pennies available so that each child can put 10 pennies in his or her tool kit.

1·2 Investigating the Number Line

Objectives To introduce number-line routines; and to provide practice counting up on the number line.

www.everydaymathonline.com

ePresentations

eToolkit

Algorithms Practice

EM Facts Workshop Game™

Family Letters

Assessment Management

Common Core State Standards

Curriculum Focal Points

Interactive Teacher's Lesson Guide

1 Teaching the Lesson

Key Concepts and Skills

- Find numbers that are larger than and smaller than a given number. [Number and Numeration Goal 7]
- Describe numbers using comparison vocabulary, such as *more than, smaller than, bigger than,* and *less than.* [Number and Numeration Goal 7]
- Count up from a smaller number to a larger number. [Operations and Computation Goal 2]
- Use a tally chart to collect data. [Data and Chance Goal 1]

Key Activities

Children play *Monster Squeeze.* They also use the Class Number Line to find the number of children who are absent.

Ongoing Assessment: Recognizing Student Achievement Use Mental Math and Reflexes. [Number and Numeration Goal 1]

Ongoing Assessment: Informing Instruction See page 22.

Materials

Math Masters, pp. 4 and 5 (optional)
Class Number Line ◆ "fences" to bracket number-line intervals (optional)

2 Ongoing Learning & Practice

Revisiting Rhymes and Songs

Children revisit favorite rhymes, songs, and games from Kindergarten that promote counting and emphasize positional words.

Home Link 1·2: Unit 1 Family Letter

Math Masters, pp. 6 and 7
Children take home the Family Letter introducing Unit 1.

3 Differentiation Options

READINESS

Ordering Numbers

numbered sheets of paper
Children sequence sets of numbers to provide experience with ordering numbers.

ENRICHMENT

Making Counting Books

stapler
Children illustrate their own counting books.

EXTRA PRACTICE

Minute Math+

Minute Math®+, p. 28
Children practice counting.

Advance Preparation

See page 21 for directions on making brackets or frames for *Monster Squeeze.*

***Teacher's Reference Manual,* Grades 1–3** pp. 9–11, 42, 43, 57, 58

Getting Started

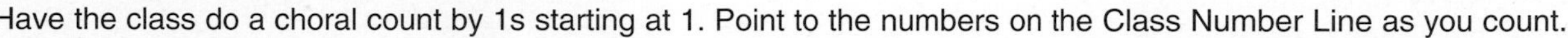
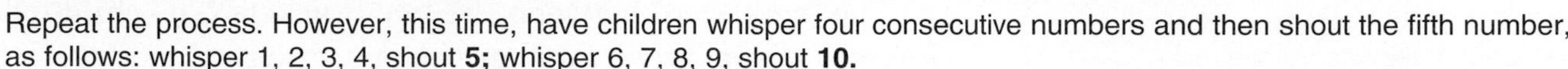

Mental Math and Reflexes ★

Have the class do a choral count by 1s starting at 1. Point to the numbers on the Class Number Line as you count.

Repeat the process. However, this time, have children whisper four consecutive numbers and then shout the fifth number, as follows: whisper 1, 2, 3, 4, shout **5;** whisper 6, 7, 8, 9, shout **10.**

Do not expect all children to know when to shout. This choral-counting routine will be repeated many times in subsequent lessons. To help children, point to the numbers on the number line with one hand and show the count with fingers on your other hand. When five fingers are up, shout the number.

Ongoing Assessment: Recognizing Student Achievement

Mental Math and Reflexes ★

Use **Mental Math and Reflexes** to assess children's ability to count by 1s and 5s. Children are making adequate progress if they can count by 1s. Some children may shout at appropriate times, indicating that they have some knowledge of counting by 5s.

[Number and Numeration Goal 1]

NOTE Some children may benefit from doing the **Readiness** activity before you begin Part 1 of the lesson. See the Readiness activity in Part 3 for details.

Interactive whiteboard-ready ePresentations are available at www.everydaymathonline.com to help you teach the lesson.

1 Teaching the Lesson

Playing *Monster Squeeze*

WHOLE-CLASS ACTIVITY

Remind children that they used the number line to count the days of school. Tell them that they will learn to use the number line for other math routines and games.

For this game, the leader thinks of a mystery number and then calls out two numbers such that the mystery number is somewhere between the two numbers. The other children then try to guess the mystery number.

Take the part of the leader and play a demonstration round with the class.

Sample Game

1. The leader chooses 5 as the mystery number and says: *I am thinking of a number between 1 and 9. What's my number?*
2. Two children are the bracket holders. (You might also call the brackets *fences* or *monsters.*) One child covers the 1 on the number line with a bracket; the other child covers the 9.
3. The leader calls on someone to make a guess. The child guesses 7. The leader says: *No, my number is smaller than* (or *less than*) *7,* or *7 is more than* (or *bigger than* or *greater than*) *my number.* The right bracket is then moved to cover the 7.

NOTE Prepare two brackets or frames for *Monster Squeeze*. Either make two "creatures" to use as brackets or use the monsters on *Math Masters,* pages 4 and 5. You can attach each bracket to one end of a yardstick or you can use flyswatters (with their centers cut out) as frames.

Monster Squeeze is a favorite game from *Kindergarten Everyday Mathematics.*

Games are an integral part of the *Everyday Mathematics* program like the Math Boxes and Home Links. They are an effective and interactive way to reinforce skills identified in the Grade-Level Goals, especially for children who find traditional drill and practice tedious and not motivating. Establish a games routine and maintain it throughout the year. Once established, the routine becomes self-sustaining. Make sure that all children are given time to play the games. *Suggestions:*

- ▷ Include games as part of your daily morning routine.
- ▷ Devote the first or last 10 minutes of each math class to playing games.
- ▷ Designate one math class per week as "Games Day." Set up stations that feature the unit's games. Ask parent volunteers to assist children at these stations.
- ▷ Set up a Games Corner with favorite games. Encourage children to visit this corner during free time. Change the games frequently to maintain interest.

Attendance Chart

25	*children are in our class.*
23	*children are here today.*
2	*children are absent today.*

4. Another child guesses 4. The leader says that the mystery number is greater than 4. The left bracket is then moved to cover the 4.
5. Children continue to guess. Eventually, the mystery number will be "squeezed" between the two brackets. The child who guesses the mystery number becomes the next leader.

NOTE The game leader may write down the mystery number so as not to forget it when responding to children's guesses.

Adjusting the Activity

Have children label the left and right sides of the number line with words such as *smaller* or *less* and *larger* or *more.* At first, you might limit the range to numbers up to 15. Extend the range as appropriate to assess children's knowledge of numbers.

AUDITORY ◆ KINESTHETIC ◆ TACTILE ◆ VISUAL

Ongoing Assessment: Informing Instruction

Watch for children who are confused about which bracket to move. Tell them that one of the brackets will move to the guessed number. Discuss how to decide which bracket to move.

▶ Finding the Number of Children Who Are Absent

ELL

Explain your attendance-recording procedure, and have children demonstrate the correct way to gather and display the attendance information. Write the words *present* and *absent* on the board. Discuss the meanings of these words within the context of attendance to support English language learners.

On the board, write the total number of children who are enrolled in your class. With the class, count the number of children who are present and write that number on the board. Ask: *How would you find the number of children who are absent today?*

After children have discussed strategies for finding the number of absentees, model the following strategy on the Class Number Line:

1. Find the number of children present.
2. Find the number of children enrolled.
3. Use the Class Number Line to count up from the smaller number to the larger number. For example, if 23 children are present and there are 25 children enrolled in your class, start at 23 and count up 2 to 25. This, of course, means that two children are absent today.

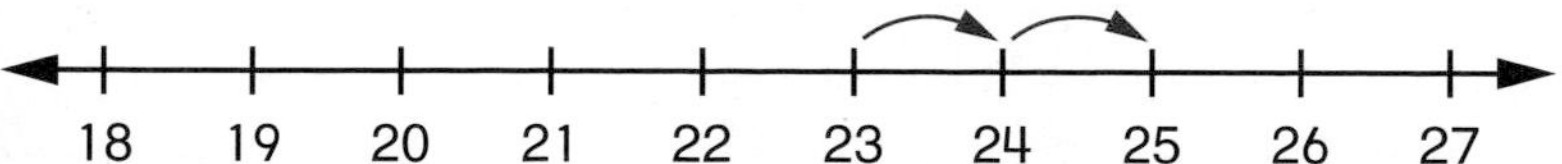

Repeat this procedure, using the attendance data from the previous day(s).

Consider including the following procedure as part of your attendance-taking routine.

▷ Make a table such as the one shown below.

▷ Each day, make a tally mark in the appropriate column of the table.

▷ About once a week, find the total number of tallies in each column and the grand total of tallies in all five columns.

▷ Compare this grand total to the total number of school days so far. (The two numbers should be the same. Do not expect children to do this activity independently at this time.)

Number of Children Who Are Absent (1 tally mark for each school day)				
1 is absent.	2 are absent.	3 are absent.	4 or more are absent.	Everyone is present.
////	//	//	/	~~////~~ //

NOTE Tallying is addressed more extensively in Lesson 1-7.

NOTE Remember to reserve time every day to complete the number-line and attendance routines.

2 Ongoing Learning & Practice

Revisiting Rhymes and Songs

WHOLE-CLASS ACTIVITY

Review counting and positional language by revisiting children's favorite rhymes, songs, or games. For games like "Simon Says," include directions such as: *Place your hand on top of your head* or *Stand to the left of your desk*. Choral reading posters can also be used.

Home Link 1•2

INDEPENDENT ACTIVITY

(*Math Masters,* pp. 6 and 7)

Home Connection Distribute copies of the Family Letter for children to take home. This letter introduces families to Unit 1.

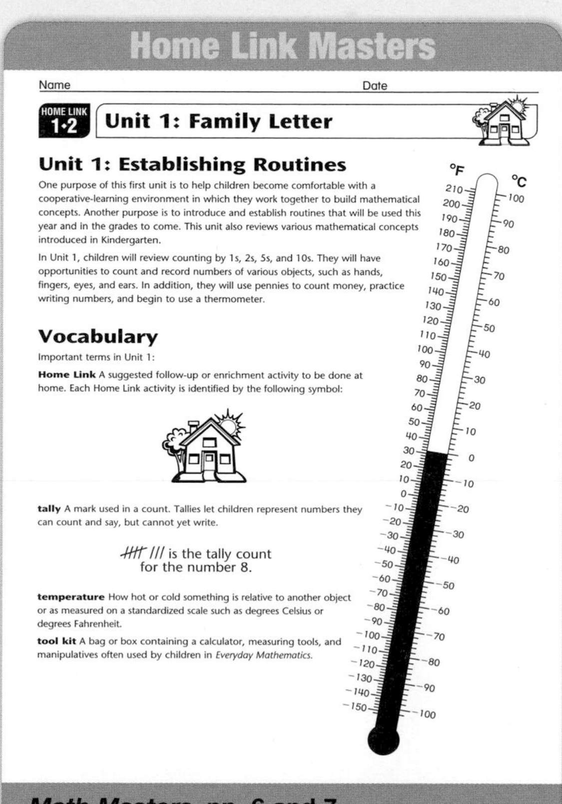

Home Link Masters

Name Date

HOME LINK 1•2 **Unit 1: Family Letter**

Unit 1: Establishing Routines

One purpose of this first unit is to help children become comfortable with a cooperative-learning environment in which they work together to build mathematical concepts. Another purpose is to introduce and establish routines that will be used this year and in the grades to come. This unit also reviews various mathematical concepts introduced in Kindergarten.

In Unit 1, children will review counting by 1s, 2s, 5s, and 10s. They will have opportunities to count and record numbers of various objects, such as hands, fingers, eyes, and ears. In addition, they will use pennies to count money, practice writing numbers, and begin to use a thermometer.

Vocabulary

Important terms in Unit 1:

Home Link A suggested follow-up or enrichment activity to be done at home. Each Home Link activity is identified by the following symbol:

tally A mark used in a count. Tallies let children represent numbers they can count and say, but cannot yet write.

~~////~~ /// is the tally count for the number 8.

temperature How hot or cold something is relative to another object or as measured on a standardized scale such as degrees Celsius or degrees Fahrenheit.

tool kit A bag or box containing a calculator, measuring tools, and manipulatives often used by children in *Everyday Mathematics.*

Math Masters, pp. 6 and 7

3 Differentiation Options

READINESS

▶ Ordering Numbers

5–15 Min

To provide experience with ordering numbers, have children put number pages in order. On sheets of paper, write an appropriate sequence of numbers for the level of each group (for example, eleven pieces of paper each labeled with a different number from 0 to 10). Give each child one sheet of paper. Children work together to put the numbers in order. The final order can be displayed on the board or children can hold up their numbers in order.

ENRICHMENT

▶ Making Counting Books

5–15 Min

Portfolio Ideas

To further explore number relationships, have children create counting books on a particular theme of their choice; for example, fish, flowers, or geometric shapes. On half-sheets of paper, children write a number and draw that number of things. You may want to have children put their pages in numerical order. Staple the pages to make counting books.

EXTRA PRACTICE

SMALL-GROU
ACTIVITY

▶ 

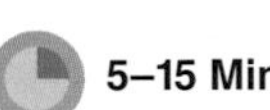
5–15 Min

Use *Minute Math+,* page 28, to provide practice counting.

Planning Ahead

Send a note home asking each child to bring one clean sock to school. Children will use these socks as erasers for their slates, starting in Lesson 1-4.

1•3 Tools for Doing Mathematics

Objective To introduce and provide practice using mathematical tools for drawing and counting.

Technology Resources www.everydaymathonline.com

resentations

eToolkit

Algorithms Practice

EM Facts Workshop Game™

Family Letters

Assessment Management

Common Core State Standards

Curriculum Focal Points

Interactive Teacher's Lesson Guide

1 Teaching the Lesson

Key Concepts and Skills

- Count objects by 1s. [Number and Numeration Goal 2]
- Recognize dot patterns on dice as representations of numbers. [Number and Numeration Goal 6]
- Compare quantities using *more* and *fewer*. [Number and Numeration Goal 7]
- Name and draw plane figures using the Pattern-Block Template. [Geometry Goal 1]

Key Activities

Distribute tool kits and discuss children's tool kit identification numbers. Children use their Pattern-Block Templates to practice drawing shapes. After discussng the guiding principles for working with partners (Guide, Check, Praise), children play the *Penny-Dice Game* to practice counting.

Ongoing Assessment: Recognizing Student Achievement
Use the *Penny-Dice Game.*
[Number and Numeration Goal 7]

Key Vocabulary

tool kit ◆ Pattern-Block Template

Materials

tool kit ◆ Pattern-Block Template ◆ 10 pennies ◆ 1 die

2 Ongoing Learning & Practice

Playing *Monster Squeeze*
Math Masters, p. 8
per partnership: 2 pennies
Children practice comparing numbers.

3 Differentiation Options

READINESS

Exploring Dice-Dot Patterns
per partnership: dice, half-sheet of paper folded into sixths
Children explore and draw dice-dot patterns.

ENRICHMENT

Making Geometric Patterns
Pattern-Block Template ◆ pattern blocks (optional)
Children create colored shape patterns using their Pattern-Block Templates.

ELL SUPPORT

Discussing Mathematical Tools
Class Data Pad
Children make a list of tools used in mathematics.

Advance Preparation

For Part 1, you will be using numbers to identify children's tool kits and Pattern-Block Templates. For Part 2, you will be making number lines. See Part 2 for details.

***Teacher's Reference Manual,* Grades 1–3** pp. 36–40, 152

Getting Started

Mental Math and Reflexes

As in Lesson 1-2, do a choral count by 1s, in which children shout every fifth number and whisper the numbers in between.

NOTE Some children may benefit from doing the **Readiness** activity before you begin Part 1 of the lesson. See the Readiness activity in Part 3 for details.

Interactive whiteboard-ready ePresentations are available at www.everydaymathonline.com to help you teach the lesson.

1 Teaching the Lesson

▶ Exploring the Tool Kits

Ask children to give examples of tools and describe their uses. Te them that they will use tools to do mathematics and that they wi each keep their tools in a little bag called a **tool kit.**

Distribute the tool kits. After children have had a chance to examine the kit contents, tell them that they will keep their tool kits for the entire school year. Other children will use the tool kit next year, so children should take good care of them. Tell childre that they will be adding tools to their kits throughout the year. They should keep their tools in their tool kits when they are not using them.

Ask children to count the pennies to check that each kit has 10 pennies.

Point out that each child has been assigned a number and that t number appears both on the tool kit and on the **Pattern-Block Template.**

NOTE Children who used *Kindergarten Everyday Mathematics* will be familiar with these templates.

Show children the Lost-and-Found Box and tell them that if they find someone else's tool kit or template, they should put it in the box. The number on the tool kit will identify its owner.

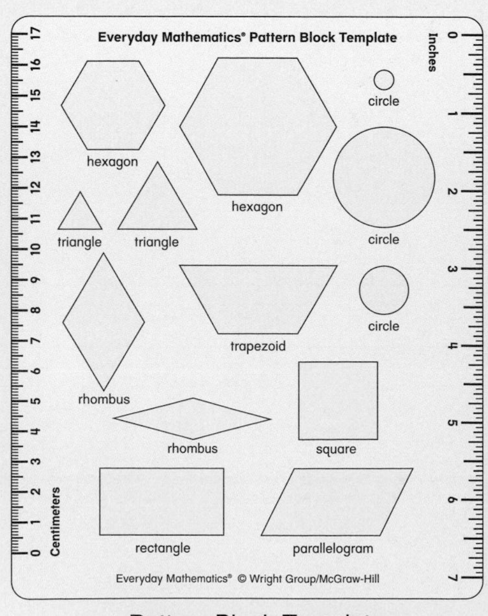

Pattern-Block Template

▶ Using the Pattern-Block Template

Hold up a template (or display it on the overhead projector). Ask children to identify the shapes they recognize, but do not dwell o the shapes that are unfamiliar. Then discuss other places childre may have seen the template shapes. To support English language learners, write the name of each shape next to its picture on the board.

To practice using the Pattern-Block Template, ask children to draw a row of shapes on a half-sheet of paper. Remind them to pu their templates back in their tool kits when they have finished.

Playing the *Penny-Dice Game*

PARTNER ACTIVITY

This game involves rolling a die, so demonstrate how to keep the noise level down while preventing the die from rolling away. Shake the die in both hands, open your hands within 4 or 5 inches of the tabletop, and let the die drop.

Before starting the game, discuss and demonstrate the principles of being a good partner: Guide, Check, Praise.

Partnership Principles

1. Guide
2. Check
3. Praise

At this point, limit the number of players in a game to two. Later, three or four players can play the game.

Demonstrate how to play the game. Partners pool their tool-kit pennies so that they have 20 pennies. They take turns rolling the die and picking up as many pennies as indicated on the die until all of the pennies have been picked up. To pick up the last pennies, the number on the die must match the number of pennies remaining. Either the player with more pennies wins the game, or partners flip a penny to determine whether the player with more or fewer pennies wins.

HEADS: The player with more pennies wins.

TAILS: The player with fewer pennies wins.

NOTE The *Coin-Dice Game,* introduced in Lesson 3-12, is a more advanced version of the *Penny-Dice Game.* In the *Coin-Dice Game,* children will begin exchanging pennies for nickels, dimes, and later, quarters.

Ongoing Assessment: Recognizing Student Achievement

Penny-Dice Game

Use the ***Penny-Dice Game*** to assess children's ability to compare numbers. Children are making adequate progress if they are able to compare groups of pennies and tell which group has more. Some children may be able to compare numerals without using pennies.

[Number and Numeration Goal 7]

NOTE Some teachers line coffee-can lids with felt to make dice pads. The dice can be rolled inside the lid. They do not fall out if rolled correctly, and the felt lining reduces the noise level. Other teachers use plastic foam meat trays that have been thoroughly washed and cleaned.

NOTE To provide practice estimating quantities of objects, show the class a clear container filled with 100 pennies. Have children estimate the number of pennies in the container. Discuss their estimates. Then show a similar container filled with 20 pennies. Tell children that there are 20 pennies in this container. Discuss possible revisions to children's first estimates in light of the new information.

NOTE Copy *Math Masters,* page 8 to make number lines. Cut out the sections and write appropriate sets of numbers under the dots. Save these number-line sections to use in later lessons.

NOTE Remember to reserve time every day to complete the number-line and attendance routines.

2 Ongoing Learning & Practice

▶ Playing *Monster Squeeze*

(*Math Masters,* p. 8)

In Lesson 1-2, children played *Monster Squeeze* as a whole-class activity. In this lesson, the game is adapted for two players.

Give each partnership a number-line section. Children use penni as brackets and take turns choosing and guessing the mystery number. After a few games, partnerships trade number-line sections with other partnerships.

3 Differentiation Options

READINESS

▶ Exploring Dice-Dot Patterns

Portfolio Ideas

To explore the numbers represented by dice patterns, have children examine the patterns of dots on dice by counting the number of dots on each side and then comparing their dice with others. On a half-sheet of paper folded into six sections, have children draw each dot pattern and write the corresponding number.

ENRICHMENT

▶ Making Geometric Patterns

Portfolio Ideas

To further explore geometric patterns, have children use Pattern-Block Templates to create patterns on half-sheet of paper. Consider having them build their patterns first with pattern blocks and then use the template to record their patterns. Children color their shapes according to a pattern. You might collect children's patterns for a bulletin-board display.

NOTE After children make patterns, have them describe the patterns. Encourage the use of positional words or phrases; for example, "There is a triangle to the right of the square."

ELL SUPPORT

▶ Discussing Mathematical Tools

5–15 Min

To provide language support for mathematical tools, explain that there are tools that help us, such as hammers, wrenches, and screwdrivers, but there are also "mathematical tools." This distinction may be important for English language learners. Ask children to generate a list of mathematical tools they talked abou in this lesson and other mathematical tools they may know. Record the list on the Class Data Pad.

Teaching Master

Name Date

LESSON 1·3 **Number-Line Sections**

TAB TAB TAB TAB

Math Masters, p. 8

1•4 Number-Writing Practice

Objectives To introduce and provide practice with a slate routine; and to provide practice writing the numbers 1 and 2.

Technology Resources www.everydaymathonline.com

esentations

eToolkit

Algorithms Practice

EM Facts Workshop Game™

Family Letters

Assessment Management

Common Core State Standards

Curriculum Focal Points

Interactive Teacher's Lesson Guide

1 Teaching the Lesson

Key Concepts and Skills

- Write numbers to represent quantities. [Number and Numeration Goal 3]
- Draw pictures to represent the numbers 1 and 2. [Number and Numeration Goal 3]
- Name the numbers before and after a given number. [Number and Numeration Goal 7]

Key Activities

Children practice a slate routine by writing numerical answers to questions. They begin *Math Journal 1*. Children also write the numbers 1 and 2 on their slates and in their journals.

Ongoing Assessment: Recognizing Student Achievement
Use journal page 1.
[Number and Numeration Goal 3]

Key Vocabulary

slate

Materials

Math Journal 1, p. 1
Class Number Line ◆ slate or marker board ◆ chalk or dry-erase marker ◆ eraser (sock or facial tissue)

2 Ongoing Learning & Practice

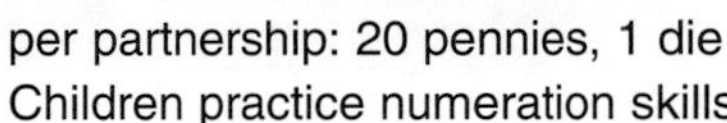
Playing the *Penny-Dice Game*
per partnership: 20 pennies, 1 die
Children practice numeration skills.

3 Differentiation Options

READINESS

Counting Objects and Tracing Numbers
Children count objects and trace numbers while reading *Anno's Counting Book.*

ENRICHMENT

Tracing Hidden Numbers
Children find hidden numbers in *City by Numbers.*

Advance Preparation

Decide how you will manage the slates. Some teachers number the slates so they can be kept in the children's tool kits. Others keep the slates stacked somewhere in the room, so children can use them when they need them. Or passing out slates can be a classroom job.

For the optional Readiness activity in Part 3, obtain a copy of ***Anno's Counting Book*** by Mitsumasa Anno (HarperCollins Publishers, 1986). For the optional Enrichment activity in Part 3, obtain a copy of ***City by Numbers*** by Stephen T. Johnson (Viking, 2003).

***Teacher's Reference Manual,* Grades 1–3** pp. 15, 16, 47

Getting Started

Mental Math and Reflexes

Repeat the whisper-and-shout count for multiples of 5. Count up to at least 20. Then do a choral chant of only the "shout" numbers (5, 10, 15, 20, ...) while pointing to the numbers on the Class Number Line.

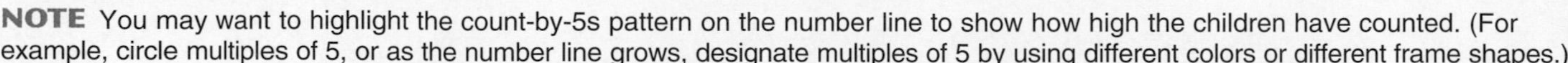

NOTE You may want to highlight the count-by-5s pattern on the number line to show how high the children have counted. (For example, circle multiples of 5, or as the number line grows, designate multiples of 5 by using different colors or different frame shapes.)

Reminder: If you are doing counts for the days of school using coins, you will soon need to exchange 5 pennies for a nickel. Emphasize that the exchange makes it easier to count the days: Instead of counting 5 pennies, you know that a nickel represents 5 days. Then, for days 6, 7, 8, and 9, you begin your counts at 5 and count up by 1s.

NOTE Some children may benefit from doing the **Readiness** activity before you begin Part 1 of the lesson. See the Readiness activity in Part 3 for details.

Interactive whiteboard-ready ePresentations are available at www.everydaymathonline.com to help you teach the lesson.

How to Use Slates to Answer Questions

- *Listen*
- *Think*
- *Write*
- *Show*
- *Erase*

1 Teaching the Lesson

▶ Introducing Slates as a Classroom Tool

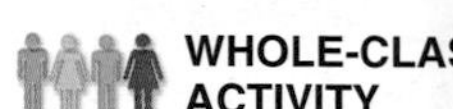

WHOLE-CLAS ACTIVITY

Distribute the **slates** and chalk (or dry-erase markers). Children will use the socks they brought to school as erasers and as storag "containers" for their chalk. Give children a chance to draw and erase freely.

NOTE Distribute facial tissue to any child who has not brought a sock.

Explain that the slates give everyone a chance to answer quietly and at the same time.

Suggest that children follow the steps shown in the margin wher using slates to answer questions. Ask children to erase their slat completely between problems.

Use some of the following questions, or make up your own, to hel children practice the slate routine. Children write their answers on their slates.

- How old are you?
- How old were you last year?
- How old will you be next year?
- How many girls are in our room?
- How many boys are in our room?
- How many teachers are in our room?
- How many swimming pools are in our room?
- What number comes after 4? 5
- What number comes before 7? 6

Finally, have children practice writing the numbers 1 and 2 on their slates.

Introducing *Math Journal 1*

WHOLE-CLASS ACTIVITY

Pass out copies of *Math Journal 1* and have children write their names on the back covers. Give them time to look through their journals. Remind them that they should write in their journals only when directed to do so.

Discuss that the reason for the number 1 in the title is that this is the first of two math journals that children will use this year. Explain that all of the pages, except a few in the back, will stay in the journal, so that when children finish their journals, they (and their families) will be able to see what they have learned in first grade.

Writing the Numbers 1 and 2

INDEPENDENT ACTIVITY

(*Math Journal 1,* p. 1)

Children write the numbers 1 and 2 in their journals. Remind them that speed is not important. Keep in mind that many children may not feel confident about writing numbers at this time. Encourage them; help them to feel good about their beginning efforts.

Explain that the arrows on the numbers are there to remind them of the strokes needed for efficient number writing. These strokes will help them become better writers.

Have children circle what they think are their best numbers. As children finish their writing practice, have them draw a picture to represent each number; for example, an apple for the number 1 and two fish for the number 2.

Adjusting the Activity

Suggest items that children can draw for the numbers 1 or 2. You might draw children's suggestions on the board.

AUDITORY ◆ KINESTHETIC ◆ TACTILE ◆ VISUAL

When most children have finished, they can display their drawings and describe them to one another.

Ongoing Assessment: Recognizing Student Achievement

Journal page 1 ★

Use **journal page 1** to assess children's progress in number writing. Children are making adequate progress if they are able to write the numbers 1 and 2 legibly. Some children may have more advanced fine motor skills.

[Number and Numeration Goal 3]

NOTE Children can practice writing numbers in shaving cream, finger paint, on a friend's back, or on trays of salt.

Children draw pictures to represent the numbers 1 and 2.

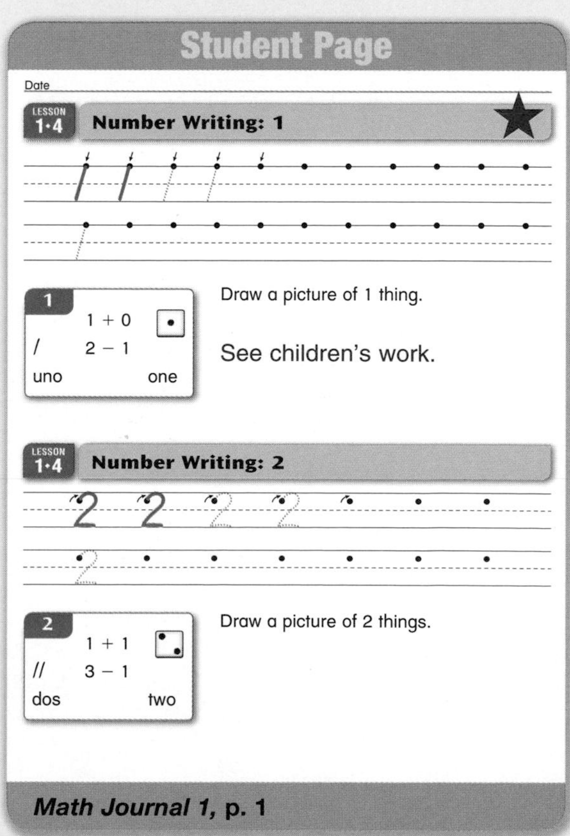

Student Page

Date

LESSON 1·4 **Number Writing: 1** ★

1: 1 + 0, 2 − 1, /, uno, one

Draw a picture of 1 thing.

See children's work.

LESSON 1·4 **Number Writing: 2**

2: 1 + 1, 3 − 1, //, dos, two

Draw a picture of 2 things.

Math Journal 1, p. 1

NOTE Remember to reserve time every day to complete the number-line and attendance routines.

2 Ongoing Learning & Practice

▶ Playing the *Penny-Dice Game*

Children practice numeration skills by playing the *Penny-Dice Game.* For detailed instructions, see Lesson 1-3. Remind children of the partnership principles.

3 Differentiation Options

READINESS

5–15 Min

▶ Counting Objects and Tracing Numbers

Literature Link To review counting objects and writing numbers, use copies of ***Anno's Counting Book*** by Mitsumasa Anno (HarperCollins Publishers, 1986) and have children point to each object as they count the total number of objects. Then have them trace the numeral on the page. Encourag children to say each number as they trace it.

ENRICHMENT

5–15 Min

▶ Tracing Hidden Numbers

Literature Link To further explore standard notation for the numbers 1–20, use copies of ***City by Numbers*** by Stephen T. Johnson (Viking, 2003) and have children identify each of the numbers 1–20. Each number is hidden in a richly textured painting of a city scene. For each page, have children identify and trace the hidden numeral. Encourage children to say each number as they trace it.

Planning Ahead

Starting in Lesson 1-6, children will use the number cards found on Activity Sheets 1 and 2 in the back of their journals. The cards will have to be cut apart, a task that many children may not be able to perform at this stage.

Since children will sometimes combine their card decks for an activity, they should identify all of the cards in their decks with a distinctive shape, mark, letter, or color. That way, combined decks can be separated easily.

To store the number cards in their tool kits, children can put them in an envelope or put a rubber band around them. If they use envelopes, label the envelopes with the children's tool-kit numbers.

1·5 One More, One Less

Objective To provide practice finding the number that is 1 more or 1 less than a given number.

Technology Resources www.everydaymathonline.com

resentations

eToolkit

Algorithms Practice

EM Facts Workshop Game™

Family Letters

Assessment Management

Common Core State Standards

Curriculum Focal Points

Interactive Teacher's Lesson Guide

1 Teaching the Lesson

Key Concepts and Skills

- Count objects by 1s.
  [Number and Numeration Goal 2]
- Locate numbers on a number line.
  [Number and Numeration Goal 7]
- Name numbers that are one more and one less than a given number.
  [Operations and Computation Goal 1]
- Use a number line to solve number stories.
  [Operations and Computation Goal 1]

Key Activities

Children solve "one more" and "one less" number stories. They also play *Bunny Hop* to practice counting on a number line.

Ongoing Assessment: Recognizing Student Achievement Use Mental Math and Reflexes.
[Number and Numeration Goal 7]

Ongoing Assessment: Informing Instruction See page 35.

Materials

Math Journal 1, inside back cover
Math Masters, p. 341
slate ◆ Class Number Line ◆ per partnership: 1 die

2 Ongoing Learning & Practice

Playing the *Penny-Dice Game*
per partnership: 20 pennies, 1 die
Children practice numeration skills.

Writing the Numbers 1 and 2
Math Masters, p. 304
Children practice writing the numbers 1 and 2.

3 Differentiation Options

READINESS

Passing the Basket of Pennies
per group: pennies, 1 basket
Children practice counting one more and one less by collecting pennies in a basket.

ELL SUPPORT

Building a Math Word Bank
Differentiation Handbook, p. 126
Children add the terms *less* and *more* to their Math Word Banks.

Advance Preparation

***Teacher's Reference Manual,* Grades 1–3** pp. 51–53, 220, 221

Getting Started

Mental Math and Reflexes 

Ask questions such as the following, and have children write the answers on their slates. Children may use a number line to help them.

●○○ What number comes after 7? 8 After 4? 5 After 8? 9

●●○ What number comes before 10? 9 Before 6? 5 Before 1? 0

●●● What number comes before 12? 11 After 19? 20 Before 20? 19

NOTE Some children may benefit from doing the **Readiness** activity before you begin Part 1 of the lesson. See the Readiness activity in Part 3 for details.

Interactive whiteboard-ready ePresentations are available at www.everydaymathonline.com to help you teach the lesson.

Ongoing Assessment: Recognizing Student Achievement

Mental Math and Reflexes ★

Use **Mental Math and Reflexes** to assess children's ability to name numbers that come before and after a given number. Children are making adequate progress if they can name numbers before and after a given number using a number line. Some children may be able to do this without a number line.

[Number and Numeration Goal 7]

Student Page

−9	−8	−7	−6	−5	−4	−3	−2	−1	0
1	2	3	4	5	6	7	8	9	10
11	12	13	14	15	16	17	18	19	20
21	22	23	24	25	26	27	28	29	30
31	32	33	34	35	36	37	38	39	40
41	42	43	44	45	46	47	48	49	50
51	52	53	54	55	56	57	58	59	60
61	62	63	64	65	66	67	68	69	70
71	72	73	74	75	76	77	78	79	80
81	82	83	84	85	86	87	88	89	90
91	92	93	94	95	96	97	98	99	100
101	102	103	104	105	106	107	108	109	110

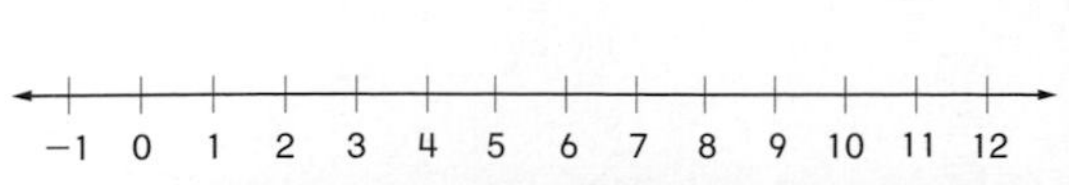

Math Journal 1, inside back cover

1 Teaching the Lesson

▶ Telling "One More" and "One Less" Stories

(*Math Journal 1,* inside back cover)

Ask children to turn to the number line on the inside back cover of their journals. Explain that they will be solving "one more" and "one less" stories using this number line.

Use the Class Number Line to demonstrate how to use the number line to figure out the answers to the questions posed by the following stories:

- Felipe walks 8 steps to get from his bathroom to the door of his bedroom. If he takes one more step, he will be inside his bedroom. How many steps does Felipe have to take in all to get from the bathroom to the inside of his bedroom? (Begin with your finger on 0 on the number line. Then move your finger 8 hops forward to model getting to the door of the bedroom. Then move your finger 1 more hop to 9 to model getting inside of the bedroom. The answer is 9 steps. The number 9 is 1 more than 8.)

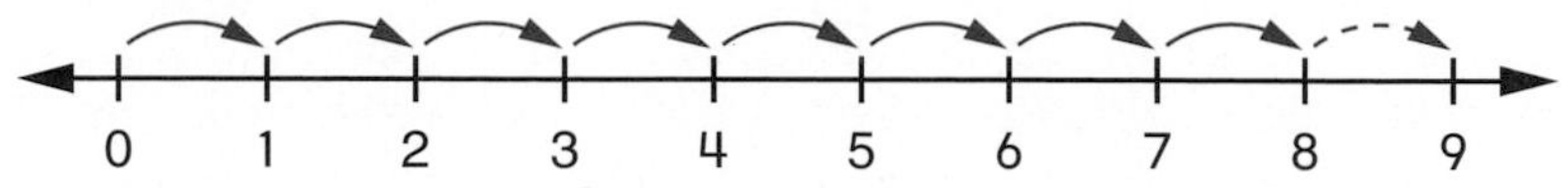

- Lisa went to the bakery. She bought 5 cookies. On the way home, she ate 1 cookie. Lisa had 1 less cookie. How many cookies did Lisa have when she got home? (Children move their fingers from 0 to 5 to show the number of cookies Lisa bought. Then they move their fingers 1 hop back to 4 to show how many cookies were left after Lisa ate 1. The answer is 4 cookies. The number 4 is 1 less than 5.)

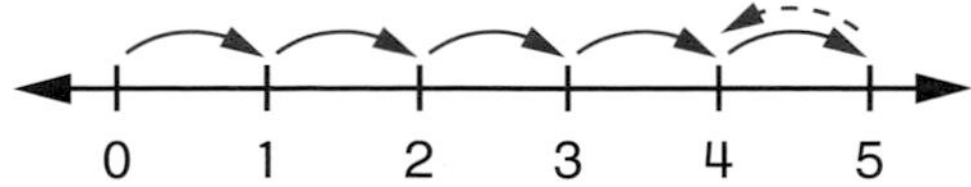

Tell more number stories as time allows.

NOTE Remind children to include the applicable unit in each of their answers. For example, the answer to the first problem is "9 steps," not simply "9."

Do not penalize or criticize children who do not use a unit; simply continue to model the preferred answer format.

Ongoing Assessment: Informing Instruction

Watch for children who begin counting at the number 1 instead of 0. Explain the importance of starting at 0 and hopping to 1.

Links to the Future

This lesson provides early preparation for children's learning of addition and subtraction facts. Facts that involve adding and subtracting 1 are among the facts that first-grade children are expected to learn. Knowing addition facts through 10 + 10 is a Grade 2 Goal.

Playing *Bunny Hop*

PARTNER ACTIVITY

(*Math Masters,* p. 341)

Children practice counting up and back on a number line by playing *Bunny Hop.*

Directions

1. Each player needs a number line and a bunny marker. Players take turns rolling the die and moving the bunny the number of spaces shown on the die.
2. Both players hop to the carrot—20—by rolling the exact number. Then they hop back to the bunny's hole—0—by rolling the exact number.
3. The first player to get to the carrot and back to the bunny hole wins.

Encourage children to talk about the movements, making statements such as, "The bunny hopped 4 spaces from 6 to 10." You may wish to have children play the game a few times.

NOTE As you move around the classroom, watch carefully to see that children are not hopping in place, but instead are hopping forward with each count.

Adjusting the Activity

Children may use a shortcut, wherein they start by putting their fingers on the first number, without first counting from 0. For example, when solving the second problem using the shortcut, children start by putting their fingers on 5, without first counting from 0 to 5.

AUDITORY ◆ KINESTHETIC ◆ TACTILE ◆ VISUAL

Game Master

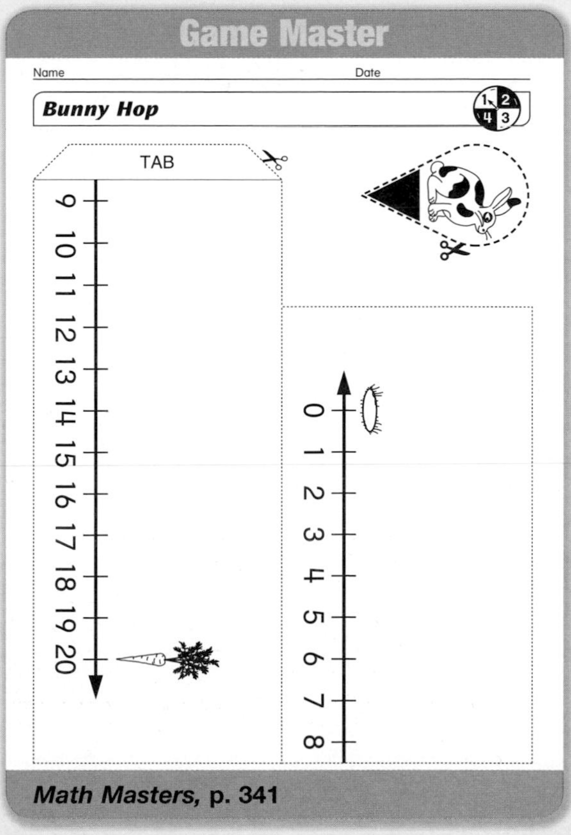

Math Masters, p. 341

Teaching Aid Master

Name Date

Number Writing

✂

Name Date

Number Writing

Math Masters, p. 304

2 Ongoing Learning & Practice

▶ Playing the *Penny-Dice Game*

PARTNER ACTIVITY

Children practice numeration skills by playing the *Penny-Dice Game.* For detailed instructions, see Lesson 1-3.

▶ Writing the Numbers 1 and 2

INDEPENDENT ACTIVITY

(*Math Masters,* p. 304)

Children practice writing the numbers 1 and 2. When children have finished their number-writing practice, have them circle their best numbers.

3 Differentiation Options

READINESS

FACTS PRACTICE

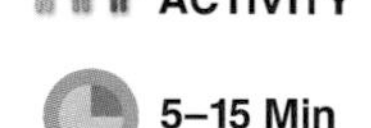

SMALL-GROUP ACTIVITY

5–15 Min

▶ Passing the Basket of Pennies

To provide experience with counting up and back, have children count pennies in a basket. Children sit in a circle. Tell children that there are zero pennies in the basket. Place one penny in the basket and say: *One more penny makes one penny*. Pass the basket to the first child and ask the group to say, "One more penny makes two pennies." After each child adds one penny, reverse the circle and take one penny out while saying: *One less penny makes ____ pennies.* You can point to the number line as children add and subtract pennies.

ELL SUPPORT

SMALL-GROUP ACTIVITY

5–15 Min

▶ Building a Math Word Bank

(*Differentiation Handbook,* p. 126)

Many children, especially English language learners, can gain additional support by building a Math Word Bank as they encounter new vocabulary. To provide language support for comparing numbers, have children use the Word Bank Template found on *Differentiation Handbook,* page 126. Ask children to write the terms *less* and *more,* draw pictures representing the terms, and write other words that describe them. See the *Differentiation Handbook* for more information.

1•6 Comparing Numbers

Objective To provide practice comparing pairs of numbers.

Technology Resources www.everydaymathonline.com

Presentations

eToolkit

Algorithms Practice

EM Facts Workshop Game™

Family Letters

Assessment Management

Common Core State Standards

Curriculum Focal Points

Interactive Teacher's Lesson Guide

1 Teaching the Lesson

Key Concepts and Skills

- Read whole numbers. [Number and Numeration Goal 3]
- Order whole numbers from smallest to largest. [Number and Numeration Goal 7]
- Compare pairs of whole numbers. [Number and Numeration Goal 7]
- Name numbers that are one more and one less than a given number. [Operations and Computation Goal 1]

Key Activities

Children use number cards to compare pairs of numbers and to order sets of numbers. They also play *Top-It.*

Ongoing Assessment: Recognizing Student Achievement Use an Exit Slip (*Math Masters,* page 305). [Number and Numeration Goal 7]

Materials

Math Masters, p. 305

slate ◆ number cards 0–15 (from *Math Journal 1,* Activity Sheet 1 or the Everything Math Deck, if available) ◆ 4" by 6" index cards (optional) ◆ envelope, paper clip, or rubber band ◆ counters and/or pennies (optional)

2 Ongoing Learning & Practice

Playing *Monster Squeeze*

Math Masters, p. 8

per partnership: 2 pennies

Children practice comparing numbers.

Ordering Numbers

Math Masters, p. 9

Children practice ordering numbers by completing a connect-the-dots picture.

3 Differentiation Options

READINESS

Matching Counters

per partnership: number cards 0–10 (from the Everything Math Deck, if available), counters

Children compare sets of counters using one-to-one correspondence.

ENRICHMENT

Flipping and Comparing

Math Journal 1, inside back cover

per partnership: number cards 0–10 (from the Everything Math Deck, if available)

Children work in pairs to determine how many hops are between two numbers.

EXTRA PRACTICE

Playing the *Penny-Dice Game*

per partnership: 20 pennies, 1 die

Children play the *Penny-Dice Game* to practice comparing numbers.

Advance Preparation

For Part 1, you will be making number cards from 0 through 15. See Part 1 for details. For Part 2, prepare number-line sections or use sections created in Lesson 1•3. (See Part 2 in Lesson 1•3.)

***Teacher's Reference Manual,* Grades 1–3** p. 68

Getting Started

Mental Math and Reflexes

Children record their answers on their slates. Remind them of the slate routine. "Listen ... think ... write ... show ... erase." Ask questions such as the following:

●○○ What number comes after 6? 7 After 4? 5 Before 9? 8

●●○ What number is 1 smaller than 12? 11 1 larger than 15? 16 After 11? 12

●●● What number is 1 more than 19? 20 1 less than 18? 17 1 fewer than 16? 15

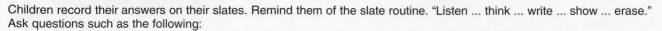

NOTE Some children may benefit from doing the **Readiness** activity before you begin Part 1. See the Readiness activity in Part 3 for details.

Interactive whiteboard-ready ePresentations are available at www.everydaymathonline.com to help you teach the lesson.

Student Page

Name Date

Number Cards 0–15

15	14	13	12
11	10	9	8
7	6	5	4
3	2	1	0

Math Journal 1, Activity Sheet 1

1 Teaching the Lesson

▶ Comparing and Ordering Numbers

WHOLE-CLASS ACTIVITY

(*Math Journal 1*, Activity Sheet 1)

Explain to children that they will be comparing two numbers to determine which one is larger. Give each child a deck of number cards, and give the class time to examine the cards. Then do several whole-class activities. *Suggestions:*

- Put the cards in a pile. Take the top two cards. Which card shows the larger number? Check your answer on the number line.

NOTE Use 4" by 6" index cards to make a large demonstration set of number cards from 0 through 15.

Each child will need a set of number cards from 0 through 15. Use cards from Activity Sheet 1 of the journal or the Everything Math Deck. Mark each child's card deck with a distinctive shape, mark, letter, or color so it can be easily identified. Decide how children will store their number cards in their tool kits.

- Order the 0–15 cards from the smallest to the largest number.

Adjusting the Activity

Have children select 10 cards at random and put those cards in order from smallest to largest. Then display a card from your demonstration set and say: *Hold up the card that shows the number that is one more (or one less) than this number.*

AUDITORY ♦ KINESTHETIC ♦ TACTILE ♦ VISUAL

Ongoing Assessment: Recognizing Student Achievement

Exit Slip 

Have children answer the following questions on an Exit Slip:

- What number is 1 more than 7? 8
- What number is 1 less than 16? 15

Use an **Exit Slip** (*Math Masters,* page 305) to assess children's understanding of *one more* and *one less.* Children are making adequate progress if they are able to tell the number that is one more and one less than any number up to 10. Some children may be able to do this for higher numbers.

[Number and Numeration Goal 7]

NOTE Exit Slips will be used periodically for children to record oral work. Should you choose not to use Exit Slips, blank paper works equally well.

▸ Introducing *Top-It*

 PARTNER ACTIVITY

Review the rules for working with a partner.

This game is for two players. If you are using an Everything Math Deck, remove the numbers 16 through 22 from the deck. If you are using the cards from Activity Sheet 1, have players combine their sets of number cards, mix them together, and put them in a pile with the number side facing down.

Directions

1. Each player takes a card from the top of the pile, turns it over, and says the number on the card.
2. The player who has the larger number takes both cards.
3. If the two cards show the same number, each player takes another card from the top of the pile. The player with the larger number then takes all of the cards facing up.
4. The game is over when all of the cards have been taken. The player with more cards wins.

NOTE When the game is over, have children estimate who has more cards before they begin counting them to determine the winner.

Variation

Another way to determine who wins at the end of the game is to flip a penny.

HEADS: The player with more cards wins.

TAILS: The player with fewer cards wins.

Teaching Aid Master

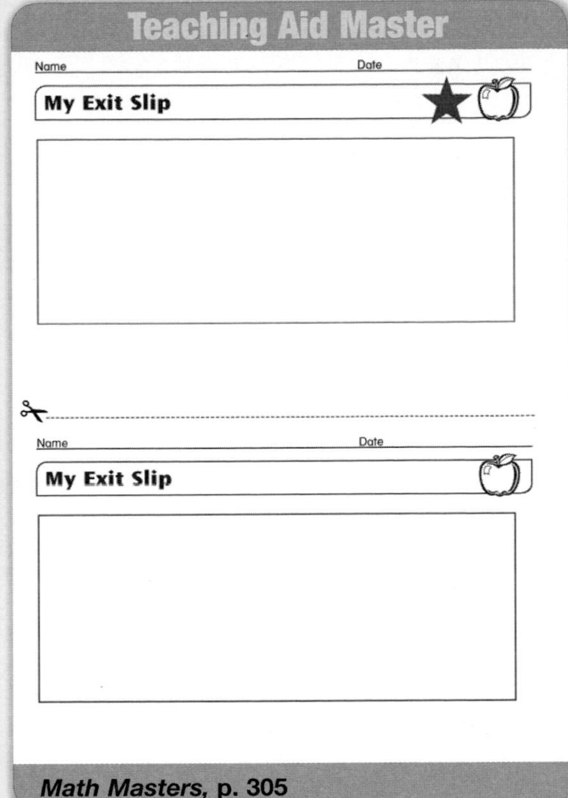
Name Date

My Exit Slip

Name Date

My Exit Slip

Math Masters, p. 305

NOTE You may wish to discuss the probability of penny flips with children by asking them if penny flipping gives each player the same chance of winning. Consider having children pursue this as a class experiment.

When finished with the activity, children sort the number cards into decks and store their decks in their tool kits.

Adjusting the Activity

Limit the range of numbers children use. For example, begin play with the 0–10 cards, increasing the range of numbers as children are ready.

AUDITORY ◆ KINESTHETIC ◆ TACTILE ◆ VISUAL

2 Ongoing Learning & Practice

▶ Playing *Monster Squeeze*

(*Math Masters,* p. 8)

Children review greater-than and less-than number relations by playing *Monster Squeeze.* For detailed instructions for playing in pairs, see Lesson 1-3.

NOTE Remember to reserve time every day to complete the number-line and attendance routines.

▶ Ordering Numbers

(*Math Masters,* p. 9)

Children practice ordering numbers by completing a connect-the-dots picture.

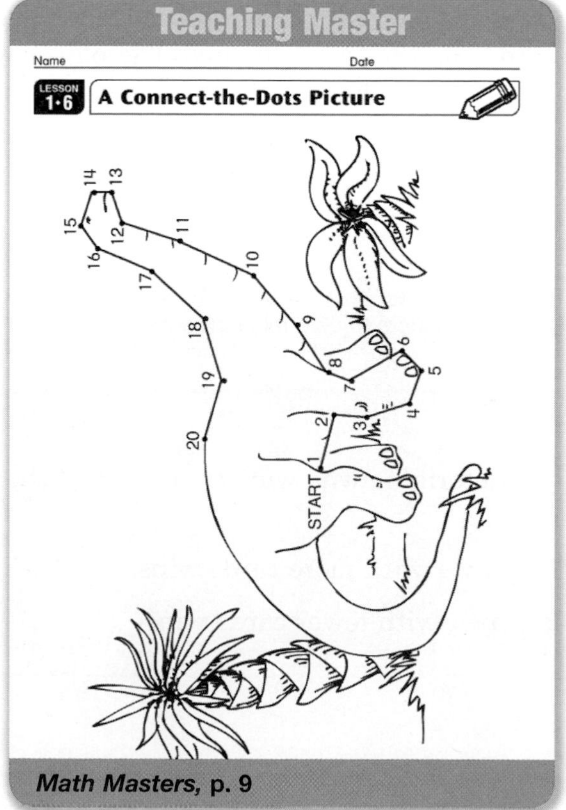

Math Masters, p. 9

3 Differentiation Options

READINESS

 PARTNER ACTIVITY

Matching Counters

5–15 Min

To explore one-to-one correspondence, have children match number cards to counters. Provide a stack of mixed number cards from 0 through 10. Children draw two number cards. For each card, they count out the indicated number of counters. Then they line up the counters from each group and match them one-to-one in order to determine which number is larger.

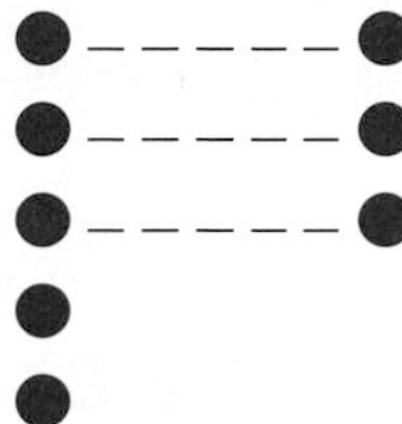

5 is larger than 3.

As a record of their exploration, children record the two numbers for each pair of cards that they draw. After counting out and comparing the counters, they circle the larger of the two numbers.

ENRICHMENT

 PARTNER ACTIVITY

Flipping and Comparing

 5–15 Min

To apply children's understanding of comparing numbers, have partners use the number line on the inside back cover of their journals to compare numbers. Have pairs of children take turns flipping over two cards. They use the number line to estimate how many hops from their number to their partner's number. Encourage children to check their estimates using the number line.

EXTRA PRACTICE

 PARTNER ACTIVITY

Playing the *Penny-Dice Game*

 5–15 Min

Children count and compare numbers by playing the *Penny-Dice Game*. For detailed instructions, see Lesson 1-3.

1•7 Recording Tally Counts

Objective To introduce tally marks for data representation.

www.everydaymathonline.com

ePresentations

eToolkit

Algorithms Practice

EM Facts Workshop Game™

Family Letters

Assessment Management

Common Core State Standards

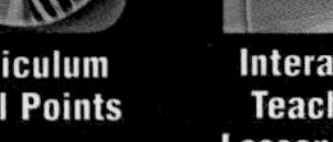
Curriculum Focal Points

Interactive Teacher's Lesson Guide

1 Teaching the Lesson

Key Concepts and Skills

- Count forward by 1s and 5s. [Number and Numeration Goal 1]
- Represent numbers using tally marks. [Number and Numeration Goal 6]
- Create a tally chart to organize data. [Data and Chance Goal 1]
- Make predictions based on data organized in a tally chart. [Data and Chance Goal 2]

Key Activities

Children read and make tally marks representing numbers. Then they collect data about pets owned by their classmates and keep track of the data using tally marks.

Ongoing Assessment: Informing Instruction See page 44.

Key Vocabulary

tally mark

Materials

Math Journal 1, inside back cover
slate ◆ Class Data Pad ◆ Class Number Line (optional) ◆ number cards (optional)

2 Ongoing Learning & Practice

Playing *Top-It*
per partnership: number cards 0–15 (from *Math Journal 1,* Activity Sheet 1 or the Everything Math Deck, if available)
Children practice comparing numbers.

Writing the Numbers 3 and 4
Math Journal 1, p. 2
Children practice writing the numbers 3 and 4.

Ongoing Assessment: Recognizing Student Achievement
Use journal page 2.
[Number and Numeration Goal 3]

Minute Math+
Minute Math®+, pp. 3, 27, and 31
Children practice counting and ordering numbers.

3 Differentiation Options

READINESS

Whisper-and-Shout Counts by 5s
Class Number Line
Children do a whisper-and-shout count by 5s to 40.

ENRICHMENT

Making a Listening Tally
pennies ◆ can or other container ◆ slate
Children use tally marks to keep track of the number of pennies dropped into a can one at a time.

Advance Preparation

For Part 1, prepare a tally chart on the Class Data Pad (see page 44). If you are using coins or straws to count the days of school, see page 43 for details. For the optional Enrichment activity in Part 3, you will need a can or other container and at least 10 pennies. Your container should be made of something that will make a loud sound when pennies are dropped into it.

***Teacher's Reference Manual,* Grades 1–3** pp. 44, 120, 121

Getting Started

Mental Math and Reflexes

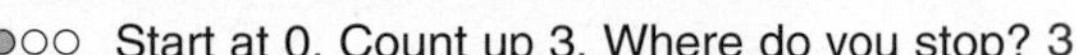

Have children use the number line on the inside back cover of their journals and record answers on their slates.

●○○ Start at 0. Count up 3. Where do you stop? 3

●●○ Start at 2. Count up 4. Where do you stop? 6

●●● Start at 7. Count back 2. Where do you stop? 5

1 Teaching the Lesson

▸ Introducing Tally Marks

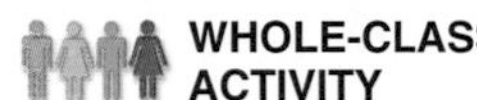

Explain to children that they will be learning a new way to record, count, and write numbers using tally marks.

Write **tally marks** and /////// on the board and ask children to count the tally marks with you. (*See margin.*)

Now count aloud, 1, 2, 3, 4, 5, 6, 7, as you write 𝍸 //. (*See margin.*)

- How are these tally marks different from the tally marks we made before? The fifth tally mark crosses the first four.
- What is the advantage of having the fifth mark cross the first four? It makes it easier to count the tally marks.

When we record numbers this way, the groups always have 5 tallies, and each group is counted as 5 (more).

Use tally marks to write other single-digit numbers greater than 5 on the board. Model the counting process starting with 5 and counting on by 1s.

Call out single-digit numbers and have children draw tally marks on their slates to represent each number. They should write the 5s first and then the 1s.

Adjusting the Activity

ELL

As you call out a number, point to it on the Class Number Line or hold up the appropriate number card.

AUDITORY ◆ KINESTHETIC ◆ TACTILE ◆ VISUAL

- Can you show the number 10 using tally marks? 𝍸 𝍸 The number 11? 𝍸 𝍸 / The number 18? 𝍸 𝍸 𝍸 ///

NOTE Some children may benefit from doing the **Readiness** activity before you begin Part 1 of the lesson. See the Readiness activity in Part 3 for details.

Interactive whiteboard-ready ePresentations are available at www.everydaymathonline.com to help you teach the lesson.

NOTE On the Class Data Pad or board, prepare a tally chart like the one shown on page 44.

NOTE If you are doing counts of days of school with coins, replace the nickel and five pennies with a dime on the 10th day of school. If you are using straws, you will need to bundle 10 straws and move them to the TENS cup on the 10th day of school. When counting each day between the 10th and 20th days, begin with the number 10 and count up.

Adjusting the Activity

ELL

As you count out loud and model drawing tallies on the board, have children draw vertical lines in the air for 1 through 4. For 5, have children draw a diagonal line in the air as you draw the fifth line across the tallies. Repeat as appropriate.

AUDITORY ◆ KINESTHETIC ◆ TACTILE ◆ VISUAL

Ongoing Assessment: Informing Instruction

Watch for children who write five tally marks and then cross another one over the group of five. Remind children that every fifth tally mark is made diagonally across a group of four vertical marks: *Four are standing tall; one takes a fall.*

▶ Making a Tally Chart to Count Children's Pets

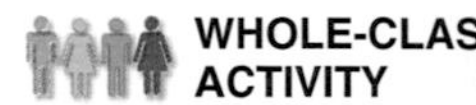

WHOLE-CLASS ACTIVITY

Explain that children are going to use a chart and tally marks to find how many pets are owned by everyone in the class. Have children come up to the Class Data Pad, a few at a time, to fill in the chart. They should make one tally mark for each pet they own. Check that every fifth tally mark is made correctly.

When all children have had a turn, have them count the tally marks in each row, in unison. Then write the total for that row. Always count the 5s first and then the 1s.

The Pets We Own		
Pet	Tallies	Total
Cat		
Dog		
Other		
No Pet		

NOTE For practice making a picture graph with the data collected on children's pets, go to www.everydaymathonline.com.

NOTE Based on the data they collected, have children make predictions such as the following:

- The total number of pets owned by all the first graders in the school
- The total number of each kind of pet owned by all the first graders in the school

Children may use calculators to help make predictions.

Links to the Future

This is the first lesson in which children use tally marks to represent data. In first grade, children will also use bar graphs and line plots to represent data. Both creating and using these representations are Grade 2 Goals.

2 Ongoing Learning & Practice

▸ Playing *Top-It*

PARTNER ACTIVITY

Children practice comparing numbers by playing *Top-It.* For detailed instructions, see Lesson 1-6.

▸ Writing the Numbers 3 and 4

INDEPENDENT ACTIVITY

(*Math Journal 1,* p. 2)

Children write the numbers 3 and 4. Remind them that they should take their time and follow the arrows that show them the most efficient ways to form the numbers. When children have finished their number-writing practice, have them circle their best numbers.

Then children draw pictures to represent the numbers.

Ongoing Assessment: Recognizing Student Achievement

Journal page 2 

Use **journal page 2** to assess children's progress in number writing. Children are making adequate progress if they are able to write the numbers 3 and 4 legibly. Some children may have more advanced fine motor skills than others.

[Number and Numeration Goal 3]

▸ *Minute Math+*

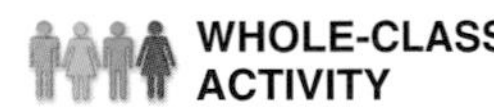

WHOLE-CLASS ACTIVITY

Use *Minute Math+,* pages 3, 27, and 31, to provide children with practice counting and ordering numbers.

3 Differentiation Options

READINESS

SMALL-GROUP ACTIVITY

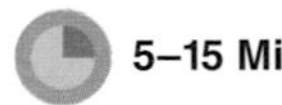

5–15 Min

▸ Whisper-and-Shout Counts by 5s

To explore skip counting, have children do whisper-and-shout counts. Point to the Class Number Line as you guide children in a whisper-and-shout count. Whisper numbers as children count by 1s and shout every fifth number (multiples of 5) up to 40. Then say only the "shout" numbers up to 40: 5, 10, 15, 20, 25, 30, 35, 40.

Student Page

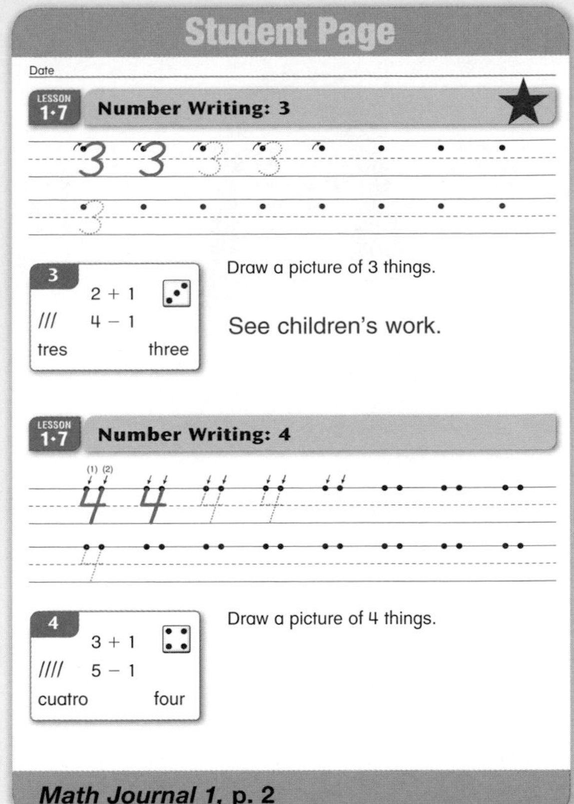

Math Journal 1, p. 2

NOTE Remember to reserve time every day to complete the number-line and attendance routines.

Children listen carefully as the teacher drops a small number of pennies into a container removed from view.

ENRICHMENT

▶ Making a Listening Tally

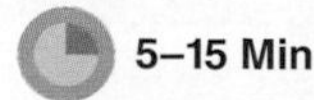

To apply children's understanding of making and counting tally marks, do the following activity:

- ▷ Tell children to make a tally mark on their slates each time they hear a penny drop.
- ▷ Drop a selected number of pennies into a container, one at a time. (Do this out of the children's view.)
- ▷ Have them count the tally marks and write the total number o pennies on their slates.

Check that children have grouped their tally marks by 5s and that the number tallied matches the number of pennies. Repeat a time allows.

1·8 Investigating Equally Likely Outcomes

Objective To provide experiences with equal-chance events.

Technology Resources www.everydaymathonline.com

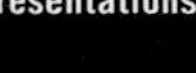

Presentations | eToolkit | Algorithms Practice | EM Facts Workshop Game™ | Family Letters | Assessment Management | Common Core State Standards | Curriculum Focal Points | Interactive Teacher's Lesson Guide

1 Teaching the Lesson

Key Concepts and Skills

- Represent numbers using tally marks. [Number and Numeration Goal 6]
- Create a tally chart to organize data. [Data and Chance Goal 1]
- Answer questions and make predictions based on data organized in a tally chart. [Data and Chance Goal 2]
- Make predictions about the outcomes of dice rolls. [Data and Chance Goal 3]

Key Activities

Children roll a die and record the results with tally marks. Then they speculate whether one number is more likely to be rolled than another. Children answer questions about the data.

Ongoing Assessment: Recognizing Student Achievement
Use journal page 3.
[Number and Numeration Goal 6]

Materials

Math Journal 1, p. 3
per partnership: die, craft sticks (optional) ◆ slate

2 Ongoing Learning & Practice

Writing the Numbers 3 and 4
Math Masters, p. 304
Children practice writing the numbers 3 and 4.

Home Link 1·8
Math Masters, p. 10
Children practice and maintain skills through Home Link activities.

3 Differentiation Options

READINESS

Matching Numbers and Tallies
per partnership: number cards 1–10 (from the Everything Math Deck, if available), tally cards
To provide experience with tallying, children match numerals and tally marks.

ENRICHMENT

Playing *Rock, Paper, Scissors*
Math Masters, p. 352
Children play *Rock, Paper, Scissors* and record the results with tally marks. They speculate whether one gesture is more likely to win than another.

Advance Preparation

For the optional Readiness activity in Part 3, you will need to make tally cards using 3" by 5" index cards.
For the optional Enrichment activity, make copies of *Math Masters,* page 352. See Part 3 for details.

***Teacher's Reference Manual,* Grades 1–3** p. 11

Getting Started

Mental Math and Reflexes

Call out single-digit numbers. Children write tallies for the numbers on their slates. After displaying their answers, children count the tally marks in unison, always beginning with 5 if the number is 5 or more.

If children are ready, try tally counts for numbers from 10 through 15.

NOTE Some children may benefit from doing the **Readiness** activity before you begin Part 1 of the lesson. See the Readiness activity in Part 3 for details.

Interactive whiteboard-ready ePresentations are available at www.everydaymathonline.com to help you teach the lesson.

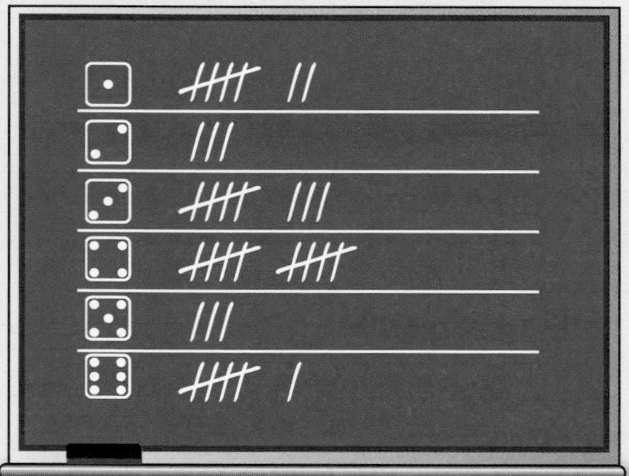

Adjusting the Activity ELL

Have children bundle craft sticks by 5s for each ~~||||~~ tally count.

AUDITORY ◆ KINESTHETIC ◆ TACTILE ◆ VISUAL

1 Teaching the Lesson

▶ Dice-Roll and Tally

PARTNER ACTIVITY

(*Math Journal 1,* p. 3)

Ask children which number they think will come up most often when they roll a die. Tell them that they will roll a die to find out. Explain that they will record the rolls using tallies.

Divide the class into partnerships and review the partnership principles: Guide, Check, Praise.

On the board, make a tally chart for the numbers 1 through 6. (*See margin.*) Then describe the activity:

Directions

1. Partners take turns rolling a die.
2. Both children make tally marks next to the appropriate die in the chart in their journals.
3. After 2 minutes, ask children to pause. Invite them to predict which number or numbers will come up most often. Record children's predictions, but do not take sides.
4. Children continue to roll a die and record the results for 3 more minutes.
5. After 3 minutes, have children record the total number of times each number was rolled.

NOTE Theoretically, each number has the same chance of being rolled. However, in practice, it is unlikely that all numbers will come up the same number of times. This is a sophisticated idea that will be discussed in later grades. At this time, children should simply observe that the results were not the same for all partnerships.

Ongoing Assessment: Recognizing Student Achievement Journal page 3 ★

Use journal page 3 to assess children's ability to make tally marks. Children are making adequate progress if they show each set of 5 as ~~||||~~.

[Number and Numeration Goal 6]

Ask partnerships questions about their results, such as the following:

- How many times did you roll 1? 2? 3? 4? 5? 6?
- How could you figure out how many times your partnership rolled the die altogether? Sample answer: Count the tally marks in all of the rows by 5s.
- Which did you roll more times, 5 or 6 (or any combination of two numbers)? How many more times?
- Which did you roll fewer times, 2 or 3 (or any combination of two numbers)? How many fewer times?

End the activity with a cumulative tally of the results for all partnerships. You can expect the numbers to come up *about* the same number of times, even though some partnerships may have had one number come up much more often than the others. Discuss the results.

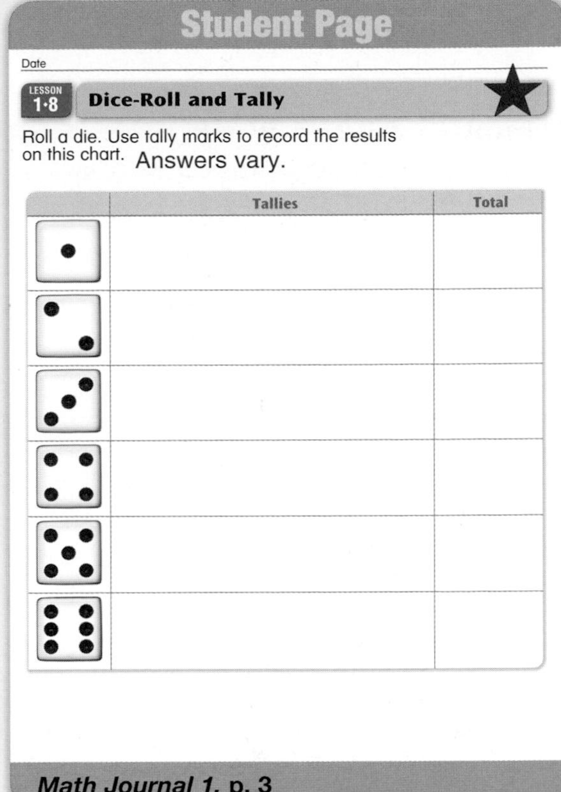
Student Page

Date

LESSON 1•8 **Dice-Roll and Tally**

Roll a die. Use tally marks to record the results on this chart. Answers vary.

	Tallies	Total

Math Journal 1, p. 3

2 Ongoing Learning & Practice

Writing the Numbers 3 and 4

(*Math Masters*, p. 304)

Use *Math Masters,* page 304 to provide more practice writing the numbers 3 and 4.

NOTE Remember to reserve time every day to complete the number-line and attendance routines.

Home Link 1•8

(*Math Masters*, p. 10)

Home Connection Have children write their names and today's date at the top of the page.

Discuss the purpose of Home Links and what children should do with them. *For example:*

- Always put your name on your Home Link.
- Be sure to take it home.
- Discuss and complete the assignment with someone at home—a parent, a guardian, a caregiver, or an older brother or sister.
- Bring the completed Home Link back to school the next school day. (Some assignments may take longer to complete. If that is the case, the Family Note in the Home Link will indicate that.)

For Home Link 1-8, children collect examples of numbers and bring them to school. They look for more examples during the next few days.

Invite children to continue bringing in examples of various numbers and their uses throughout the school year.

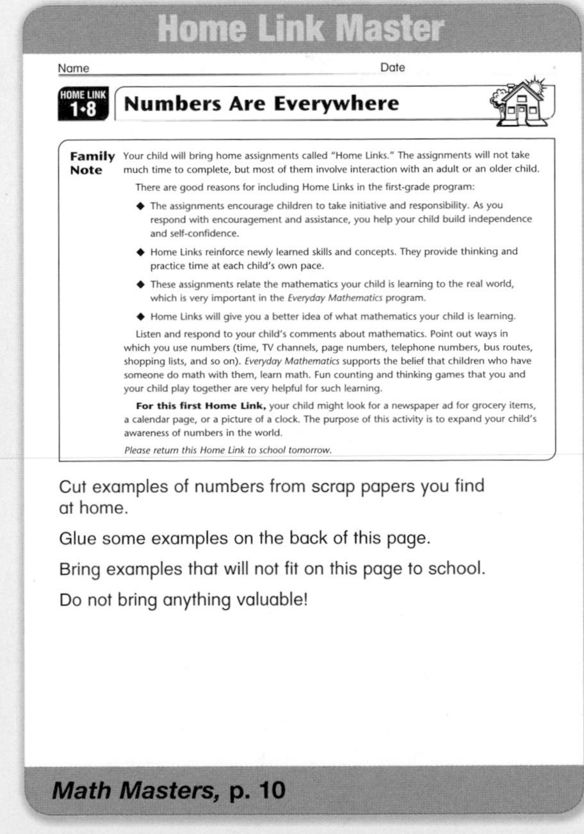
Home Link Master

Name Date

HOME LINK 1•8 **Numbers Are Everywhere**

Family Note Your child will bring home assignments called "Home Links." The assignments will not take much time to complete, but most of them involve interaction with an adult or an older child.

There are good reasons for including Home Links in the first-grade program:

- The assignments encourage children to take initiative and responsibility. As you respond with encouragement and assistance, you help your child build independence and self-confidence.
- Home Links reinforce newly learned skills and concepts. They provide thinking and practice time at each child's own pace.
- These assignments relate the mathematics your child is learning to the real world, which is very important in the *Everyday Mathematics* program.
- Home Links will give you a better idea of what mathematics your child is learning.

Listen and respond to your child's comments about mathematics. Point out ways in which you use numbers (time, TV channels, page numbers, telephone numbers, bus routes, shopping lists, and so on). *Everyday Mathematics* supports the belief that children who have someone do math with them, learn math. Fun counting and thinking games that you and your child play together are very helpful for such learning.

For this first Home Link, your child might look for a newspaper ad for grocery items, a calendar page, or a picture of a clock. The purpose of this activity is to expand your child's awareness of numbers in the world.

Please return this Home Link to school tomorrow.

Cut examples of numbers from scrap papers you find at home.

Glue some examples on the back of this page.

Bring examples that will not fit on this page to school.

Do not bring anything valuable!

Math Masters, p. 10

> **NOTE** For each partnership, cut five 3" by 5" index cards in half. Draw tally marks for the numbers 1–10 on the cards.

> **NOTE** Make enough copies of *Math Masters,* page 352, so that each child will have one half-sheet. Cut the copies in half.

Game Master

Name Date

Rock, Paper, Scissors

Tallies			
			Tied Game

Name Date

Rock, Paper, Scissors

Tallies			
			Tied Game

Math Masters, p. 352

3 Differentiation Options

READINESS

PARTNE ACTIVIT

▶ Matching Numbers and Tallies

5–15 Mi

To provide experience with tallying, have children work together to match number cards with corresponding tally cards. Spread th number cards and tally cards for 1–10 faceup on the table. Mix them up. Ask partners to work together to match the number cards to the corresponding tally cards. Have partners double-chec their work.

ENRICHMENT

PARTNE ACTIVIT

▶ Playing *Rock, Paper, Scissors*

5–15 Mir

(*Math Masters,* p. 352)

To further explore tallying as a data-collection strategy, have children use tallies to record the results of a *Rock, Paper, Scissors* game. Some children may be familiar with this well-known game It is known by many other names and is played all over the worl The game is for two players.

Three objects—a rock, a piece of paper, and scissors—are represented by the following hand gestures:

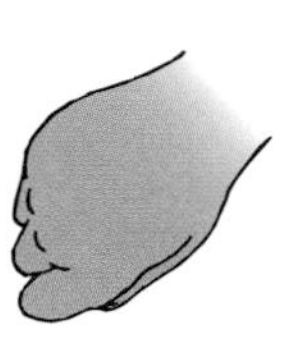

rock

paper

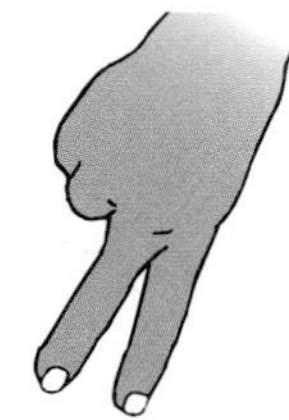

scissors

Players make one of the three hand gestures behind their backs. One player counts to 3, and then both players quickly show their hands. The following rules determine the winner of the round:

- ▷ Scissors and paper: Scissors wins because scissors can cut paper.
- ▷ Paper and rock: Paper wins because paper can be wrapped around a rock.
- ▷ Rock and scissors: Rock wins because it can blunt the scissors (make them less sharp).
- ▷ If both players choose the same gesture, it is a tie.

Players play 20 rounds. After each round, they make a tally mark in the chart on their half-sheet of paper to indicate either the winning gesture or that the round ended in a tie.

Encourage children to speculate about whether one gesture will win more often than the others, but do not take sides. You may wish to discuss the chance of winning a game compared to the chance of tying. Children can use tally marks to record the results and discover that winning happens about twice as often as tying.

NOTE Some children may think that certain gestures are more likely to win than others. Point out that if that were true, then players would choose that gesture every time and games would always end in a tie.

Planning Ahead

Starting in Lesson 1-10, children will use full decks of number cards. If you are using the cards from the back of the children's journals, you will need to prepare decks of cards from Activity Sheet 2. As before, the number cards must be cut apart and marked with the same distinctive marks, letters, shapes, or colors as the first set.

When combined with the cards from Activity Sheet 1, which you may have distributed in Lesson 1-6, each deck of number cards will consist of 22 cards, 0–22.

1·9 The Calendar

Objective To introduce the calendar as a device for keeping track of the days in a month.

www.everydaymathonline.com

ePresentations

eToolkit

Algorithms Practice

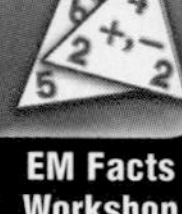

EM Facts Workshop Game™

Family Letters

Assessment Management

Common Core State Standards

Curriculum Focal Points

Interactive Teacher's Lesson Guide

1 Teaching the Lesson

Key Concepts and Skills

- Count forward by 1s.
  [Number and Numeration Goal 1]
- Order whole numbers.
  [Number and Numeration Goal 7]
- Use a calendar to answer questions about days, weeks, months, and dates.
  [Measurement and Reference Frames Goal 4]

Key Activities

The elements that make up a calendar are discussed. The class fills in the Class Calendar for the month up to and including the current day. Children then make their own calendars for the month.

Key Vocabulary

calendar ◆ date

Materials

Math Journal 1, p. 4
Home Link 1•8
transparency of *Math Masters,* p. 306 (optional) ◆ Class Calendar

2 Ongoing Learning & Practice

Writing the Numbers 5 and 6

Math Journal 1, p. 5
Children practice writing the numbers 5 and 6.

Ongoing Assessment: Recognizing Student Achievement

Use journal page 5.
[Number and Numeration Goal 3]

Home Link 1•9

Math Masters, p. 11
Children practice and maintain skills through Home Link activities.

3 Differentiation Options

READINESS

Sharing Birth Dates

classroom birth-date chart or poster (optional)
Children discuss the meanings of the words and numbers in a birth date.

ENRICHMENT

Comparing Calendars

calendar pages
Children compare calendar pages to find similarities and differences.

ELL SUPPORT

Discussing Calendar Words

calendar pages
Children discuss words and phrases associated with a calendar.

Advance Preparation

For Part 1, display your Class Calendar in a place where children can reach it. For the optional Enrichment activity in Part 3, copy pages from a variety of desk or wall calendars, if possible. Copy a different page for each child.

***Teacher's Reference Manual,* Grades 1–3** pp. 43, 44

Getting Started

Mental Math and Reflexes

Teach children the special first-grade chant—*2, 4, 6, 8, first graders are really great!*—in preparation for counting by 2s.

Do a choral count by 1s, counting up or back from a number you specify.

●○○ Start at 5 and count up by 1s. 5, 6, 7, 8, ...

●●○ Start at 12 and count up by 1s. 12, 13, 14, 15, ...

●●● Start at 18 and count back by 1s. 18, 17, 16, 15, ...

Home Link 1•8 Follow-Up

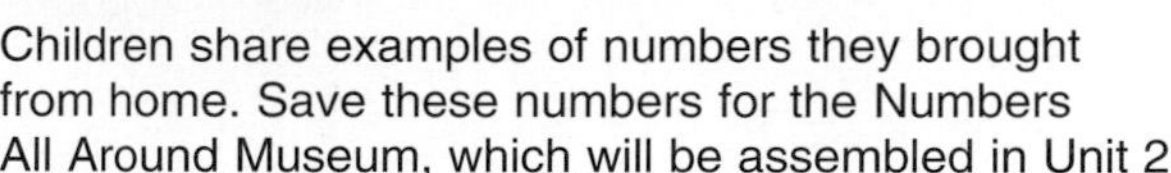

Children share examples of numbers they brought from home. Save these numbers for the Numbers All Around Museum, which will be assembled in Unit 2.

Encourage children to bring more examples of uses of numbers to school.

1 Teaching the Lesson

▸ Introducing the Class Calendar

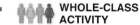

WHOLE-CLASS ACTIVITY

Discuss some uses of **calendars.** For example, calendars help us keep track of time, appointments, and special days like birth dates and holidays.

Post the Class Calendar for the month. Examine the calendar with the children as you point to its parts:

- What are the names of the months?
- What is the name of this month?
- What are the names of the days of the week?
- What day of the week is today?
- What number tells the year?
- What is today's **date?** (Write it in the appropriate cell of the Class Calendar.)

Ask children to repeat after you the complete date for today (the weekday, the month, the number of the day, and the number of the year). Sample answer: Today is Monday, September 24, 2012.

- What was yesterday's date? (Write it in the calendar. Then fill in the missing dates from the beginning of the month up to today.)

Adjusting the Activity

Have children read yesterday's, today's, and tomorrow's dates from the calendar as you or a volunteer point to the appropriate information. For example: *Today is Wednesday, September 19, 2012. Yesterday was Tuesday, September 18, 2012. Tomorrow will be Thursday, September 20, 2012.*

AUDITORY ♦ KINESTHETIC ♦ TACTILE ♦ VISUAL

NOTE Some children may benefit from doing the **Readiness** activity before you begin Part 1 of the lesson. See the Readiness activity in Part 3 for details.

Interactive whiteboard-ready ePresentations are available at www.everydaymathonline.com to help you teach the lesson.

NOTE Write the current date on the board every day. Use forms such as September 24, 2012, 9/24/12, or both. Later in the year, some children may be able to do this job. Encourage children to write the date on their work.

If appropriate, ask children if they have ever seen the date for September 24, 2012, written as 24/9/12. Explain that the month/day/year form is used in this country, while the day/month/year form is used in some other countries.

Today is Monday, September 24, 2012.
Today's date is 9/24/12.

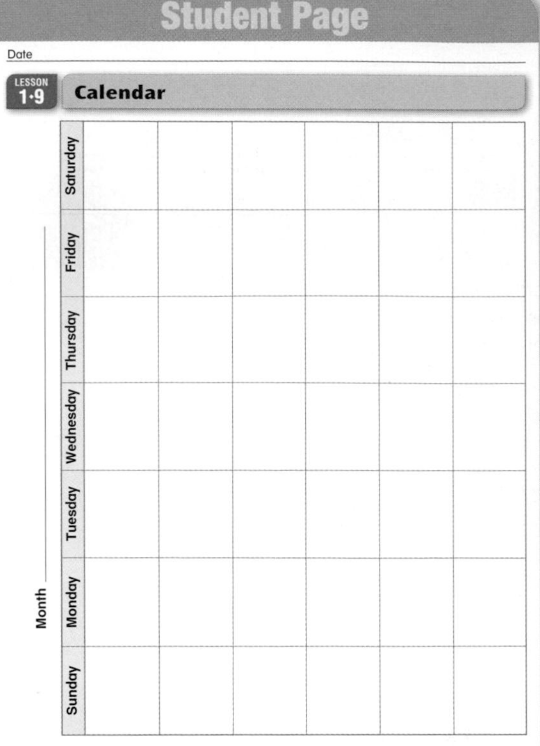
Student Page

Date

LESSON 1·9 **Calendar**

Month

Sunday	Monday	Tuesday	Wednesday	Thursday	Friday	Saturday

***Math Journal 1,* p. 4**

This journal page is also available as a Teaching Aid Master on *Math Masters,* page 306.

NOTE Remember to reserve time every day to complete the number-line, attendance, and calendar routines.

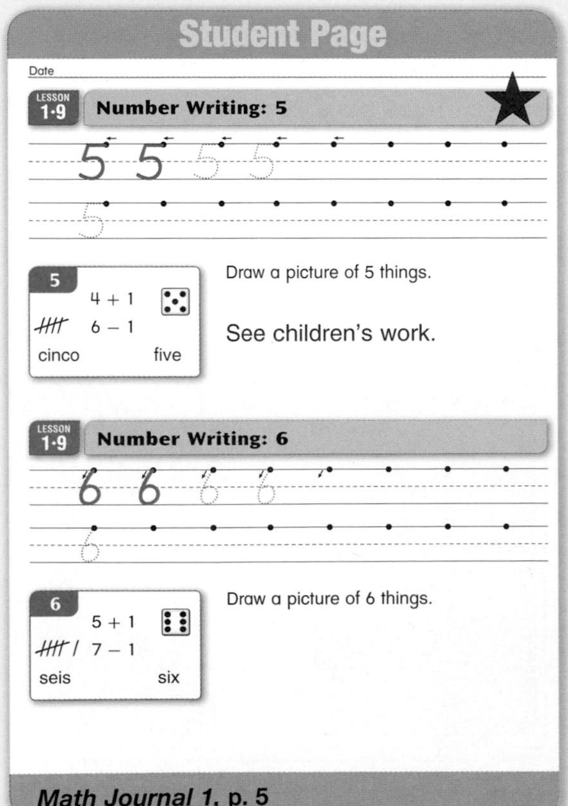
Student Page

Date

LESSON 1·9 **Number Writing: 5**

5 5

5: 4 + 1, 6 − 1, cinco, five

Draw a picture of 5 things.

See children's work.

LESSON 1·9 **Number Writing: 6**

6 6

6: 5 + 1, 7 − 1, seis, six

Draw a picture of 6 things.

***Math Journal 1,* p. 5**

If these questions can be answered using this month's calendar, ask: *What will the date be one week from today? What was the date one week ago?*

You may wish to add the calendar job to the Job Chart. The job includes filling in the date for each day and also the dates for weekends and school holidays.

Links to the Future

Do not expect children to know much about the calendar at this time. With repeated exposure through first and second grades, they will become skillful at using a calendar to keep track of time. Describing relationships between days, weeks, and months is a Grade 2 Goal.

▶ Filling in the Calendar for the Month

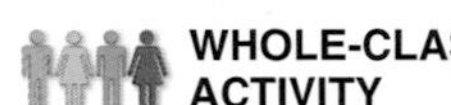
WHOLE-CLASS ACTIVITY

(*Math Journal 1,* p. 4)

Children start their own calendars for this month.

You may want to use an overhead transparency of *Math Masters,* page 306 to demonstrate where to write the words and numbers. Help children get started with this page by asking questions such as the following: *Which month goes at the top of the page? Where does the 1 go? How do you know?*

Keep this activity brief. Children can work independently or with a partner at a later time.

2 Ongoing Learning & Practice

▶ Writing the Numbers 5 and 6

INDEPENDENT ACTIVITY

(*Math Journal 1,* p. 5)

Children write the numbers 5 and 6. Remind them that they should take their time and follow the arrows that show the most efficient way to form each number.

When children have finished, have them circle their best effort for each number. Then children draw pictures to represent the numbers 5 and 6.

Ongoing Assessment: Recognizing Student Achievement

Journal page 5 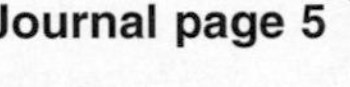

Use **journal page 5** to assess children's progress in number writing. Children are making adequate progress if they are able to write the numbers 5 and 6 legibly. Some children may have better fine motor skills than others.

[Number and Numeration Goal 3]

Home Link 1•9

INDEPENDENT ACTIVITY

(*Math Masters,* p. 11)

Home Connection Have children write their names and today's date at the top of the page. Children search their homes to find objects or places that show dates. You may want to brainstorm possible places to look.

The Practice in this and future Home Links provides a review of previously learned concepts and skills.

Remind children to keep looking for examples of numbers to bring to school.

3 Differentiation Options

READINESS

SMALL-GROUP ACTIVITY

Sharing Birth Dates

5–15 Min

To provide experience naming months, days, and years, have children discuss their birth dates. First, ask them to share their birth dates. Then discuss the meanings of the words and numbers in a birth date. If you have a birth-date chart or poster in your classroom, you can refer to it.

ENRICHMENT

PARTNER ACTIVITY

Comparing Calendars

5–15 Min

To further explore features of a calendar, have partners compare two different calendar pages to find similarities and differences. Encourage children to discuss the names of the months, how many days in the months, on what day the months begin and end, and any holidays that occur in the months. You might ask them to compare their calendar pages to the class calendar.

ELL SUPPORT

SMALL-GROUP ACTIVITY

Discussing Calendar Words

5–15 Min

To provide language support for the words and phrases associated with the calendar, have children color-code a calendar page for the current month. Ask children to color the current day with one color. Ask them to color one week with another color. If children are unfamiliar with the words *day, week, month, year,* and *date,* use the calendar to discuss the meanings of these words. You may need to discuss the differences between *week* and *weak.*

Home Link Master

Name ________ Date ________

HOME LINK 1•9 **Calendars**

Family Note Children might find dates on items like the following: watches, DVD players, newspapers, magazines, and mail with canceled stamps. Every few days, ask your child to look at a calendar and tell you that day's date.

Please return this Home Link to school tomorrow.

1. Make a list of places at home that you find the date.
   Answers vary.

Practice

2. Write the numbers from 1 through 6.
   1 2 3 4 5 6

Math Masters, p. 11

1•10 Working in Small Groups

Objective To discuss and provide practice with rules for working in small groups.

www.everydaymathonline.com

ePresentations

eToolkit

Algorithms Practice

EM Facts Workshop Game™

Family Letters

Assessment Management

Common Core State Standards

Curriculum Focal Points

Interactive Teacher's Lesson Guide

1 Teaching the Lesson

Key Concepts and Skills

- Count objects by 1s and 5s. [Number and Numeration Goal 2]
- Represent numbers using tally marks. [Number and Numeration Goal 6]
- Compare pairs of whole numbers. [Number and Numeration Goal 7]

Key Activities

Children discuss rules for working in small groups. Groups of children play *Top-It* to practice comparing numbers.

Ongoing Assessment: Recognizing Student Achievement Use Mental Math and Reflexes. [Operations and Computation Goal 1]

Materials

Math Journal 1, inside back cover
Home Link 1•9
slate ◆ Rules for Small Groups Poster (optional) ◆ number cards 0–22 (from *Math Journal 1,* Activity Sheets 1 and 2 or the Everything Math Deck, if available)

2 Ongoing Learning & Practice

Playing *Monster Squeeze*
Math Masters, p. 8
per partnership: 2 pennies
Children practice comparing numbers.

Writing the Numbers 5 and 6
Math Masters, p. 304
Children practice writing the numbers 5 and 6.

Home Link 1•10
Math Masters, p. 12
Children practice and maintain skills through Home Link activities.

3 Differentiation Options

READINESS

Comparing Quantities
overhead counters in 2 colors (10 of each) ◆ per child: 2 squares of paper in same colors as the counters
Children compare groups of objects to determine which group has more.

EXTRA PRACTICE

Minute Math+
Minute Math®+, pp. 38, 47, and 89
Children practice identifying which number is more or less.

ELL SUPPORT

Comparing Numbers
Math Journal 1, inside back cover
Children use the number line to compare numbers.

Advance Preparation

For Part 1, each child will need number cards from 0 through 22. Use the Everything Math Deck or *Math Journal 1,* Activity Sheets 1 and 2. For Part 2, prepare number-line sections or use the sections created in Lesson 1•3. (See Advance Preparation in Lesson 1•3.) *Optional:* Make a poster listing rules for working in small groups. (*See margin on page 57.*)

***Teacher's Reference Manual,* Grades 1–3** pp. 37–40

Getting Started

Mental Math and Reflexes 

Say the special first-grade chant: *2, 4, 6, 8, first graders are really great!*

Have children write answers on their slates to the following questions:

●○○ Put your finger on the number 3 on your number line. Count up 2 hops. Where do you end up? On the 5

●●○ Put your finger on the number 5 on your number line. Count up 5 hops. Where do you end up? On the 10

●●● Put your finger on the number 8 on your number line. Count up 4 hops. Where do you end up? On the 12

Home Link 1•9 Follow-Up

Have children share places at home where they found dates. If time permits, make a tally chart to determine which place was identified by most children.

Ongoing Assessment: Recognizing Student Achievement

Mental Math and Reflexes 

Use **Mental Math and Reflexes** to assess children's ability to count hops on a number line. Children are making adequate progress if they end on the correct number. Some children may be able to answer without using a number line.

[Operations and Computation Goal 1]

NOTE Some children may benefit from doing the **Readiness** activity before you begin Part 1 of the lesson. See the Readiness activity in Part 3 for details.

Interactive whiteboard-ready ePresentations are available at www.everydaymathonline.com to help you teach the lesson.

1 Teaching the Lesson

Extending Partner Expectations to Small Groups

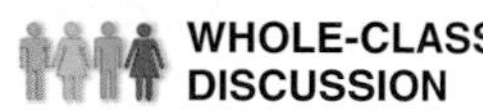

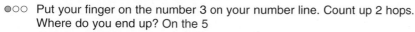

WHOLE-CLASS DISCUSSION

Discussing rules for orderly small-group interaction will encourage a cooperative attitude and reduce children's reliance on you for questions as well as answers to problems.

First, review the partner expectations: Guide, Check, Praise. Then ask the class to suggest additional rules that could help groups work together. These rules might include the ones listed on the poster shown in the margin. You might want to have children demonstrate how to follow each rule.

Post these rules where children can refer to them often.

Rules for Small Groups

1. Use quiet voices.
2. Be polite.
3. Share materials.
4. Take turns.

Playing *Top-It* in Small Groups

SMALL-GROUP ACTIVITY

(*Math Journal 1,* Activity Sheets 1 and 2)

If a group is using an Everything Math Deck, the entire deck should be used. If a group is using the Activity Sheet cards, ask two children in each group to remove all cards without numbers. Then have them combine the 0–22 cards from their respective card decks, mix the cards and put them facedown in one pile on the playing surface.

NOTE Remember to reserve time every day to complete the number-line, attendance, and calendar routines.

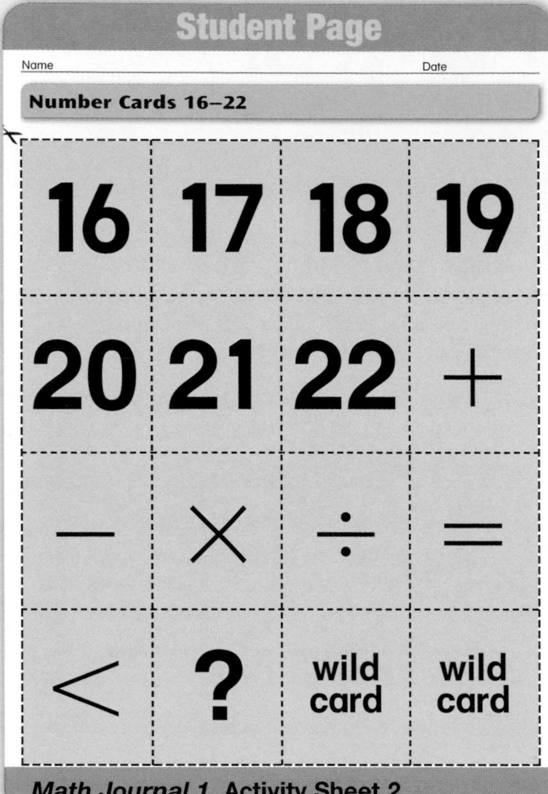

Student Page

Name Date

Number Cards 16–22

16	17	18	19
20	21	22	+
–	×	÷	=
<	?	wild card	wild card

Math Journal 1, Activity Sheet 2

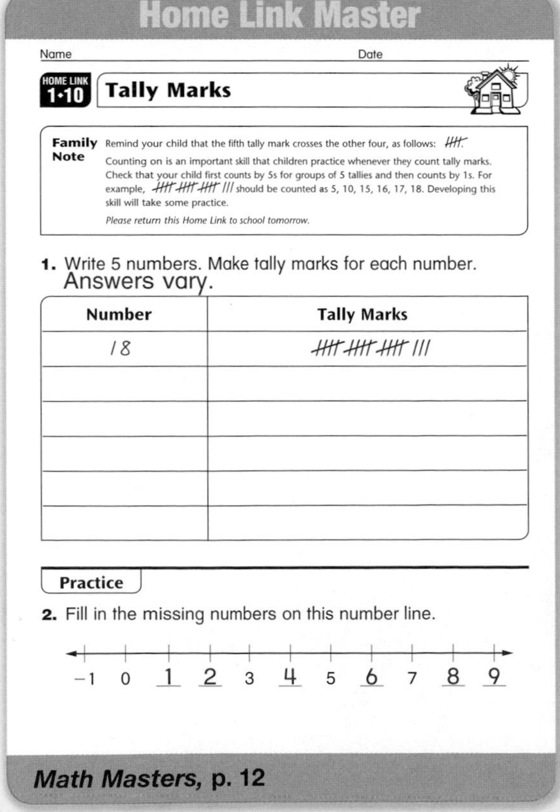

Home Link Master

Name Date

HOME LINK 1·10 **Tally Marks**

Family Note Remind your child that the fifth tally mark crosses the other four, as follows: 𝍸. Counting on is an important skill that children practice whenever they count tally marks. Check that your child first counts by 5s for groups of 5 tallies and then counts by 1s. For example, 𝍸 𝍸 𝍸 /// should be counted as 5, 10, 15, 16, 17, 18. Developing this skill will take some practice.

Please return this Home Link to school tomorrow.

1. Write 5 numbers. Make tally marks for each number.
Answers vary.

Number	Tally Marks
18	𝍸 𝍸 𝍸 ///

Practice

2. Fill in the missing numbers on this number line.

–1 0 1 2 3 4 5 6 7 8 9

Math Masters, p. 12

To play *Top-It*, each player in the group draws a card, reads the number aloud, and shows it to the other players. The player with the largest number takes all of the cards.

If two players tie with the largest number, they draw another card. The player with the larger number then takes all the cards. Play ends when there are no more cards to draw. The player who has the most cards wins.

Variation 1

The last child to win a hand wins the game.

Variation 2

Add the "wild cards" from Activity Sheet 2 to the deck. A player who draws a wild card may choose any number. The player must write the number on scratch paper or a slate so that the other players can see it.

When they have finished playing, children separate their number cards into decks. Each child then stores a complete deck of 32 cards in his or her tool kit.

2 Ongoing Learning & Practice

▶ Playing *Monster Squeeze*

(*Math Masters,* p. 8)

Children review greater-than and less-than number relationships by playing *Monster Squeeze.* For detailed instructions on playing in partnerships, see Lesson 1-3.

▶ Writing the Numbers 5 and 6

(*Math Masters,* p. 304)

Use *Math Masters,* page 304 to provide more practice writing the numbers 5 and 6.

▶ Home Link 1·10

(*Math Masters,* p. 12)

Home Connection Have children write their names and today's date at the top of the page.

Children choose five numbers and make tally marks for each of the numbers.

Remind children to keep looking for more examples of numbers to bring to school.

3 Differentiation Options

READINESS

SMALL-GROUP ACTIVITY

Comparing Quantities

5–15 Min

To explore comparing quantities using a concrete model, have children compare numbers of counters.

1. Select a different number of counters in each of two colors.
2. Arrange the selected counters on the overhead so that the number of counters in each color can be easily determined.
3. Show the counters for about 5 seconds and invite children to think about which colored set has more counters.
4. Turn off the overhead. Have children hold up a colored piece of paper to indicate their answer.
5. Turn the overhead back on. Line up each colored set of counters in a one-to-one manner to help children compare the number of counters in each set.

Repeat as appropriate.

EXTRA PRACTICE

SMALL-GROUP ACTIVITY

5–15 Min

Use *Minute Math+*, pages 38, 47, and 89 to provide practice identifying which number is more or less.

ELL SUPPORT

SMALL-GROUP ACTIVITY

Comparing Numbers

5–15 Min

To provide language support for the words *larger* and *smaller,* children use the number line on the inside back cover of their journals to compare numbers. If they have not already done so, have them draw a large circle and write the word *larger* at the right end of the number line and then draw a small circle and write the word *smaller* at the left end of the number line. Call out two numbers. Have children identify the larger (or smaller) number. Remind them that the number that is closer to the large circle is the larger number.

1•11 Exploring Math Materials

Explorations

Objective To introduce Explorations with manipulative materials.

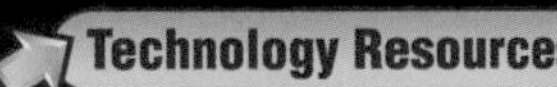

Technology Resources www.everydaymathonline.com

ePresentations

eToolkit

Algorithms Practice

EM Facts Workshop Game™

Family Letters

Assessment Management

Common Core State Standards

Curriculum Focal Points

Interactive Teacher's Lesson Guide

1 Teaching the Lesson

Key Concepts and Skills

- Identify base-10 blocks. [Number and Numeration Goal 3]
- Use a number line to solve number-line problems. [Operations and Computation Goal 1]
- Identify geoboards and the plane shapes of pattern blocks. [Geometry Goal 1]
- Create designs using the plane shapes of pattern blocks. [Patterns, Functions, and Algebra Goal 1]

Key Activities

The meaning and purpose of Explorations in *Everyday Mathematics* are discussed. Children "play" with pattern blocks, base-10 blocks, and geoboards to familiarize themselves with these materials.

Key Vocabulary

Exploration ◆ pattern blocks ◆ base-10 blocks ◆ geoboard

Materials

Math Journal 1, inside back cover
Home Link 1•10
slates ◆ Rules for Explorations poster ◆ pattern blocks ◆ base-10 blocks ◆ geoboard ◆ rubber bands (preferably colored)

2 Ongoing Learning & Practice

Playing *Top-It*
per partnership: number cards 0–15 (from *Math Journal 1,* Activity Sheet 1 or the Everything Math Deck, if available)

Ongoing Assessment: Recognizing Student Achievement
Use an Exit Slip (*Math Masters,* page 305). [Number and Numeration Goal 7]

Home Link 1•11
Math Masters, p. 13

3 Differentiation Options

READINESS

Matching Color and Shape Words to Pattern Blocks
color and shape word cards ◆ pattern blocks ◆ poster of labeled pattern blocks (optional)

ENRICHMENT

Creating Designs with Pattern Blocks and Geoboards
pattern blocks ◆ geoboards ◆ rubber bands

Advance Preparation

For Part 1, decide how you will organize the Explorations. Prepare a poster on which you will write rules for Explorations. For the optional Readiness activity in Part 3, prepare shape and color cards. See Part 3 for details.

***Teacher's Reference Manual,* Grades 1–3** pp. 8, 9, 69, 70, 153

Getting Started

Mental Math and Reflexes

Say the special first-grade chant: *2, 4, 6, 8, first graders are really great!*

Pose problems, such as those listed below, and have children write answers on their slates.

●○○ Put your finger on the number 4 on your number line. Count back 3 hops. Where do you land? On the 1

●●○ Put your finger on the number 9 on your number line. Count back 5 hops. Where do you land? On the 4

●●● Put your finger on the number 12 on your number line. Count back 12 hops. Where do you land? On the 0

Home Link 1•10 Follow-Up

Ask someone to name the largest number he or she tallied. Ask whether someone tallied an even larger number. Continue in this way until you identify the largest number in the class. Draw tally marks for that number on the board. Then count the tally marks together.

1 Teaching the Lesson

NOTE Some children may benefit from doing the **Readiness** activity before you begin Part 1 of the lesson. See the Readiness activity in Part 3 for details.

▸ Introducing Explorations

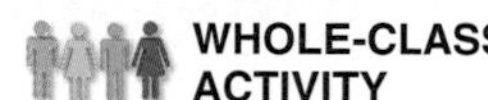

Ask children if they know who Christopher Columbus was. Tell them that Columbus was an explorer who was trying to find a route, or a way, to the East Indies. An explorer is someone who tries to find or discover something that he or she did not know before.

Interactive whiteboard-ready ePresentations are available at www.everydaymathonline.com to help you teach the lesson.

Tell children that they are going to be explorers in mathematics. They will do a mathematics **Exploration** to try to find the answer to something they did not know before, without being told how to do it.

Children will do an Exploration in small groups so that they can share ideas and help one another. They will also share materials (mathematical tools), such as pattern blocks, geoboards, dominoes, base-10 blocks, weighing scales, calculators, rulers, and attribute blocks.

Have children suggest a few rules for keeping the room relatively quiet and orderly and for sharing and caring for the materials. Refer to your Rules for Explorations Poster, and add other appropriate rules children might suggest. Post the rules along with the partnership principles: Guide, Check, Praise.

Rules for Explorations

1. *Cooperate with others.*
2. *Move about quietly.*
3. *Keep voices low.*
4. *Treat materials as tools, not as toys.*
5. *Give everyone in the group a chance to use the materials.*
6. *Straighten up when finished. Put materials back where they belong.*
7. *Try to settle disputes quietly within the group. If necessary, one person can go to the teacher for help.*

▸ Exploring with Pattern Blocks, Base-10 Blocks, and Geoboards

The purpose of the Explorations in this lesson is to familiarize children with some of the materials they will use in later lessons. It is essential that children have time to "play" with the materials before they use them in lesson activities.

Divide the class into groups of 4 or 5 children. Each group works at its own station. After 10 to 15 minutes, groups rotate to new stations.

Home Link Master

Name Date

Explorations

Family Note Time is set aside regularly in *First Grade Everyday Mathematics* for Exploration activities that involve children in data collecting, problem solving, familiarization with math manipulatives, and games in independent and small-group settings. Children will have the opportunity to participate in several activities during each Exploration session. Please ask your child about our class's mathematics Explorations.

Please return this Home Link to school tomorrow.

1. Tell someone at home about your favorite mathematics Exploration. Draw something you did in your Explorations today. Answers vary.

Practice

Write each number.

2. //// 4
3. HHT // 7
4. HHT HHT / 11

***Math Masters,* p. 13**

NOTE Before making copies of Home Link 1-11: Explorations, you might want to list on it the Explorations children did today. This will help someone at home initiate a discussion. For example, the person at home might say, "Tell me about the pattern blocks you used today."

NOTE Remember to reserve time every day to complete the number-line, attendance, and calendar routines.

Tell children to use the materials any way they want. Children who are using **pattern blocks** can create designs. Children who are working with **base-10 blocks** can build different structures. Children who are using **geoboards** can make various shapes and pictures with the rubber bands.

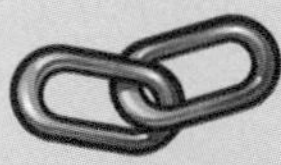

Links to the Future

This is children's first exposure to base-10 blocks. Children in first grade will use base-10 blocks to represent whole numbers through hundreds and subsequently write these numbers using place-value notation. Writing numbers to 1,000 using place-value notation is a Grade 2 Goal.

2 Ongoing Learning & Practice

▶ Playing *Top-It*

PARTNER ACTIVITY

Children practice comparing numbers by playing *Top-It.* For detailed instructions, see Lesson 1-6.

Ongoing Assessment: Recognizing Student Achievement

Exit Slip

Use an **Exit Slip** (*Math Masters,* page 305) to assess children's understanding of comparing numbers. Have children write one pair of numbers from *Top-It* on an Exit Slip. Have them circle the larger number. Children are making adequate progress if they circle the greater number.

[Number and Numeration Goal 7]

▶ Home Link 1•11

INDEPENDENT ACTIVITY

(*Math Masters,* p. 13)

Home Connection Have children write their names and today's date at the top of the page.

Children tell someone at home about the favorite Exploration they did today.

Remind children to keep looking for more examples of numbers to bring to school.

3 Differentiation Options

READINESS

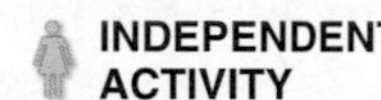

INDEPENDENT ACTIVITY

5–15 Min

Matching Color and Shape Words to Pattern Blocks

To explore colors and shapes, have children match pattern blocks to color and shape words. Provide each child with a small pile of pattern blocks and the shape and color word cards you prepared ahead of time. (*See margin.*) Ask children to pick a pattern block from the pile and to find a color word and a shape word to match that pattern block. Encourage children to count how many pattern blocks they can find with the same color or shape.

ENRICHMENT

INDEPENDENT ACTIVITY

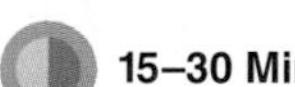

15–30 Min

Creating Designs with Pattern Blocks and Geoboards

To explore making and copying patterns, have children use pattern blocks to create simple designs. Then challenge children to copy their pattern-block designs onto their geoboards. Remind them that the size of the geoboard will dictate the size of their designs. You may want to ask children to name the shapes in their designs or tally how many of each shape they used to create their designs.

Planning Ahead

For Lesson 1-12, you will need to assemble the Class Thermometer Poster. To assemble the Class Thermometer Poster, color the various zones. Then cut along the slot in the bulb at the bottom. Insert a 4-foot length of red ribbon or crepe paper through the slot, from back to front, and pull it up to the required temperature mark. Attach the ribbon with pieces of removable tape.

NOTE For the **Readiness** activity, prepare the following materials ahead of time:

- ▷ Write the following shape words in black ink, each on a separate index card: square, triangle, trapezoid, rhombus, and hexagon.
- ▷ Write the appropriate color words in the corresponding ink colors for the pattern blocks, each on a separate index card.
- ▷ Make a set of cards for each child in the small group to use.

You may want to prepare a poster showing each pattern block labeled with its color and shape.

1•12 Weather and Temperature Routines

Objectives To introduce the routines for recording the day's weather and approximate temperature; and to teach how a thermometer works.

www.everydaymathonline.com

ePresentations

eToolkit

Algorithms Practice

EM Facts Workshop Game™

Family Letters

Assessment Management

Common Core State Standards

Curriculum Focal Points

Interactive Teacher's Lesson Guide

1 Teaching the Lesson

Key Concepts and Skills

- Count forward by 2s and 10s. [Number and Numeration Goal 1]
- Create a tally chart to organize data. [Data and Chance Goal 1]
- Read temperature ranges on a Fahrenheit thermometer. [Measurement and Reference Frames Goal 3]

Key Activities

Children are introduced to the routines for recording the day's weather and for recording the temperature from a Fahrenheit scale. They collect data and record the results with tally marks.

Ongoing Assessment: Recognizing Student Achievement
Use Mental Math and Reflexes.
[Number and Numeration Goal 1]

Key Vocabulary

thermometer ◆ degree ◆ temperature ◆ Fahrenheit

Materials

Math Journal 1, p. 6 and inside back cover
Home Link 1•11
Math Masters, p. 307
Class Weather Chart ◆ Class Data Pad ◆ classroom thermometer ◆ Class Thermometer Poster (°F) ◆ 4 feet of red ribbon or crepe paper ◆ removable tape ◆ calculator (optional)

2 Ongoing Learning & Practice

Playing *Bunny Hop*
Math Masters, p. 341
per partnership: 1 die
Children practice hopping up and back on the number line.

Home Link 1•12
Math Masters, p. 14
Children practice and maintain skills through Home Link activities.

3 Differentiation Options

READINESS
Coloring the Temperature Zones
Math Journal 1, p. 6
Children color temperature zones in their journals.

ENRICHMENT
Making a Weather Activity Booklet
per child: 7 sheets of blank paper, 2 sheets of construction paper
Children make picture booklets depicting appropriate activities for each color zone on the thermometer.

ELL SUPPORT
Building a Math Word Bank
Differentiation Handbook, p. 126 (2 copies)
Children add the terms *temperature, 80°, 80 degrees,* and *hot* to their Math Word Banks.

Advance Preparation

You may want to spend two days on this lesson. For Part 1, use the symbols on *Math Masters,* page 307 to prepare a weather chart. You will need a large outdoor thermometer. See instructions for modifying the thermometer on page 66. See assembly instructions for the Class Thermometer Poster (°F) on page 67.

***Teacher's Reference Manual,* Grades 1–3** pp. 170–172

Getting Started

Mental Math and Reflexes ★

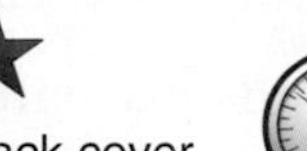

Children use the number line on the inside back cover of their journals as they count by 2s in unison. They move their fingers along the number line, using the whisper-and-shout routine: Whisper 1, shout 2, whisper 3, shout 4, ... up to 12.

Home Link 1•11 Follow-Up

Ask a few children to talk about their favorite Explorations and explain why they liked them.

Ongoing Assessment: Recognizing Student Achievement

Mental Math and Reflexes ★

Use **Mental Math and Reflexes** to assess children's ability to count by 2s. Children are making adequate progress if they shout at appropriate times up to 8. Some children may know when to shout when counting much higher numbers.

[Number and Numeration Goal 1]

NOTE Some children may benefit from doing the **Readiness** activity before you begin Part 1 of the lesson. See the Readiness activity in Part 3 for details.

- On **Day 1** of this lesson, children are introduced to the routine for recording the day's weather. Then have children complete the Part 2 activities.
- On **Day 2** of this lesson, children are introduced to the thermometer. They examine the Fahrenheit temperature scale and learn the routine for recording the temperature. They collect data and record the results with tally marks.

1 Teaching the Lesson

Introducing the Weather Routine

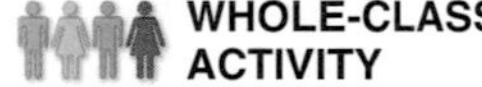

WHOLE-CLASS ACTIVITY

(*Math Masters,* p. 307)

Ask children to name words that describe the weather. Sample answers: rainy, snowy, sunny, hot, cold, freezing, cloudy, foggy Write these words on the board. Ask: *Which word (or words) describes the weather today?*

Display the Class Weather Chart and ask children to suggest weather words to describe the various symbols on the chart. Ask: *Which symbol describes the weather today?*

Tell the class that one of the class jobs will be to record on the Class Weather Chart what the weather is like each day. Model how to do this by making a tally mark under the appropriate symbol.

Expect to supervise this routine in the beginning, but with experience, children will be able to record the weather without help. The job of Weather Person can be added to the Job Chart.

NOTE Symbols that can be used on the Class Weather Chart are found on *Math Masters,* page 307.

Interactive whiteboard-ready ePresentations are available at www.everydaymathonline.com to help you teach the lesson.

Teaching Aid Master

Name Date

Weather Symbols

Math Masters, p. 307

NOTE To prepare the outdoor thermometer for classroom use, cover the Celsius scale of the thermometer with masking tape. Also, cover the marks on the Fahrenheit scale with tape so that only the numbers and marks for ten-degree intervals are visible. (Match the thermometer on journal page 6.)

NOTE The word *thermometer* is derived from *thermo,* which means *heat,* and *meter,* which means *measure.* You might ask children whether they know other words that have *thermo* in them. Sample answers: thermos, thermostat

Science Link You might want to tell the class that when the red liquid is heated, it expands (gets larger). When the air gets warmer, the expanding red liquid in a thermometer goes up.

▶ Introducing the Thermometer

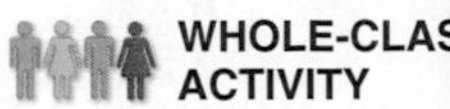

Display the outdoor **thermometer.**

- What is this device called? A thermometer
- What are some kinds of thermometers? What are they used for Sample answers: An indoor/outdoor thermometer is used to tel about how warm or cold the air is; a fever thermometer is used to check whether a person is sick; a meat thermometer is used to check whether a turkey has been in the oven long enough; a oven thermometer measures the heat in the oven.

A thermometer has a little glass tube with a bulb at the bottom that contains a liquid that is usually red in color.

- What happens to the red liquid in the thermometer when the air around it gets warmer? It goes up. When the air gets colder It goes down.
- What do you think will happen if you put your hand over the bulb? The red liquid will rise because a hand is warmer than the air around it.
- What do you think will happen if we place the bulb in cold water? The red liquid will go down because the water is colder than the air around it.

Point to the numbers on the outdoor thermometer. These numbers measure about how warm or cold it is, in **degrees.** For example, i the top of the red liquid reaches the number 60, the **temperature** is about 60 degrees. The temperature is the number of degrees indicated by the thermometer.

▶ Discussing the Fahrenheit Thermometer Scale

(*Math Journal 1,* p. 6)

Have children turn to the picture of the thermometer in their journals. Ask them to describe what they see. Sample answers: Numbers of degrees, words for colors, the letter F at the top of the thermometer with the symbol ° in front of it

Point out the following:

▷ The letter *F* stands for the word **Fahrenheit.**

▷ A Fahrenheit thermometer measures temperature in *degrees Fahrenheit.*

▷ The symbol "°" in front of the letter *F* is the symbol for *degrees* "°F" is read *degrees Fahrenheit.* Write 60 °F on the board. This is read *60 degrees Fahrenheit.*

Ask children to put their fingers on 0 and to move up the scale as they chant the numbers of degrees in unison: *0 degrees, 10 degree 20 degrees, … .*

Explain that a scale is similar to a number line. Temperature scales are made by choosing a cold point and a hot point and then marking a number of equal spaces between them.

Student Page

Date

LESSON 1·12 **A Thermometer**

°F

°F	Color
140	red
130	
120	
110	
100 (Body Temperature)	orange
90	
80	yellow
70 (Room Temperature)	
60	green
50	
40	blue
30 (Water Freezes)	
20	purple
10	
0	white
−10	
−20	
−30	
−40	

Math Journal 1, p. 6

Point out the numbers below the 0. Each is written with a little dash in front of it (–10 °, –20 °, ...). These numbers are read *10 degrees below zero, 20 degrees below zero,* and so on.

Adjusting the Activity

Point out that these numbers are negative numbers. They can also be read *negative 10 degrees, negative 20 degrees,* and so on. On the number line, negative numbers are displayed to the left of 0. On a thermometer, they are below 0.

AUDITORY ◆ KINESTHETIC ◆ TACTILE ◆ VISUAL

Introducing the Daily Temperature Routine

Prepare the Class Thermometer Poster (°F) as follows:

▷ Color the various zones of the Class Thermometer Poster (°F).

▷ To assemble the poster, cut along the slot in the bulb at the bottom.

▷ Insert a 4-foot length of red ribbon or red crepe paper through the slot from back to front, and pull it up to the required temperature mark.

▷ Attach the red ribbon to the poster with a piece of removable tape.

▷ Display the Class Thermometer Poster (°F).

Have someone place the thermometer outside for a few minutes while you discuss the Class Thermometer Poster (°F). Point out the temperature at which water freezes, the normal room temperature, and the normal body temperature. Children will soon discover that the outdoor temperature varies over time.

The Weather Person may be put in charge of the daily temperature routine, or the job may be assigned to someone else. The routine has two parts:

1. On the Class Thermometer Poster (°F), the red ribbon represents the red liquid in a regular thermometer. At about the same time each day, a child moves the red ribbon on the Class Thermometer Poster (°F) to approximately match the temperature on the outdoor thermometer.

   Model how to do this for the current day's temperature reading and ask children to describe the reading. Encourage them to use phrases such as *between __ and __ degrees Fahrenheit, almost __ degrees Fahrenheit,* and *about halfway between __ and __ degrees Fahrenheit.*

2. Describe and model the routine you plan to use for recording the current day's temperature. Record the temperature to the nearest 10 degrees. Later in the year, children will be asked to record the temperature to the nearest 2 degrees.

ELL When you use the *Everyday Mathematics* posters with English language learners, you should display either the English version only or the English and Spanish versions simultaneously.

NOTE Do not expect children to remember the °F symbol at this time. This topic will be revisited in greater detail in Lesson 4-1. You may want to take a minute to explain that there is another scale used on thermometers, especially in other countries. It is called the Celsius temperature scale.

Expect to supervise this routine in the beginning, but with experience, children will be able to do the job independently.

Links to the Future

This lesson marks the beginning of children's work with thermometers. Children should begin to recognize the relationship between the height of the red liquid and the degree of warmth or cold that it represents. Reading temperatures to the nearest degree on the thermometer is a Grade 2 Goal.

▶ Taking a Class Tally Count

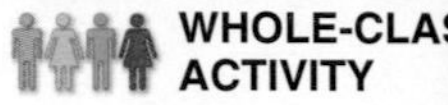

WHOLE-CLASS ACTIVITY

Remind children of the tally count of their pets that they did in Lesson 1-7. Ask them to suggest other questions they want to investigate, and record these suggestions on the Class Data Pad.

Possibilities for questions are listed below:

- How many people live with you?
- How do you get to school?
- What kind of pizza do you like best?
- How many teeth have you lost?
- Which season do you like best?

Chart children's favorite seasons. Make a tally chart on the Class Data Pad similiar to the one used in Lesson 1-7.

Save the rest of the questions for investigations at other times during the year.

NOTE After children have completed the tally chart for their classroom (see example below), have them use their data to make predictions for a larger group; for example, all the first graders in their school. Children may use their calculators to help them estimate totals.

Our Favorite Season

Seasons	Tallies	Total
Spring	~~||||~~ |	6
Summer	~~||||~~ ||	7
Fall	~~||||~~	5
Winter	~~||||~~ |||	8

NOTE You may wish to work with children to create a picture graph using this data. Have children draw pictures of their favorite seasons to add to a picture graph you have drawn on the board. When the picture graph is complete ask: *How many children altogether chose spring and summer? How many more children chose fall than winter? Which season did most children choose?*

2 Ongoing Learning & Practice

▶ Playing *Bunny Hop*

PARTNER ACTIVITY

(*Math Masters,* p. 341)

Children practice counting up and back on the number line by playing *Bunny Hop*. For detailed instructions, see Lesson 1-5.

▶ Home Link 1•12

INDEPENDENT ACTIVITY

(*Math Masters,* p. 14)

Home Connection Have children write their names and today's date at the top of the page.

Children look for thermometers and other things in their homes that tell or set a temperature.

Remind children to keep looking for more examples of numbers to bring to school.

3 Differentiation Options

READINESS

SMALL-GROUP ACTIVITY

▶ Coloring the Temperature Zones

5–15 Min

(*Math Journal 1,* p. 6)

To provide experience with *temperature zones,* have children color the temperature zones on the thermometer. This should remind them of how they recorded daily temperatures in the *Kindergarten Everyday Mathematics* program.

ENRICHMENT

INDEPENDENT ACTIVITY

▶ Making a Weather Activity Booklet

30+ Min

Portfolio Ideas

To further explore temperature and weather, have children make booklets consisting of one page for each temperature zone. Have them use construction paper for the covers. Children record each temperature zone on a page, along with the season of the year when that temperature zone might occur. Then they draw a picture of things they might do in that season. Have children describe the pictures they drew and the things they might do in each season.

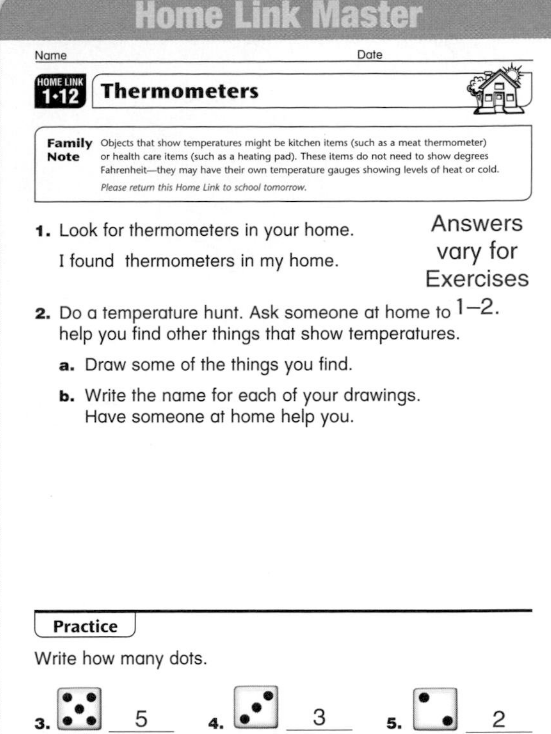

Home Link Master

Name ______ Date ______

HOME LINK 1•12 **Thermometers**

Family Note Objects that show temperatures might be kitchen items (such as a meat thermometer) or health care items (such as a heating pad). These items do not need to show degrees Fahrenheit—they may have their own temperature gauges showing levels of heat or cold.

Please return this Home Link to school tomorrow.

1. Look for thermometers in your home.

I found ___ thermometers in my home.

Answers vary for Exercises 1–2.

2. Do a temperature hunt. Ask someone at home to help you find other things that show temperatures.

a. Draw some of the things you find.

b. Write the name for each of your drawings. Have someone at home help you.

Practice

Write how many dots.

3. 5 **4.** 3 **5.** 2

***Math Masters,* p. 14**

NOTE Remember to reserve time every day to complete the number-line, attendance, calendar, weather, and temperature routines.

ELL SUPPORT

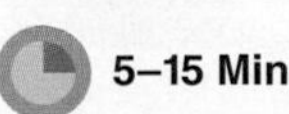

▶ Building a Math Word Bank

(*Differentiation Handbook,* p. 126)

To provide language support for temperature, have children use the Word Bank Template found on *Differentiation Handbook,* page 126. Ask children to write the terms *temperature, 80°, 80 degrees,* and *hot*, draw pictures representing the terms, and write other words that describe them. See the *Differentiation Handbook* for more information.

1•13 Number Stories

Objective To provide practice telling and solving number stories.

Technology Resources www.everydaymathonline.com

Presentations

eToolkit

Algorithms Practice

EM Facts Workshop Game™

Family Letters

Assessment Management

Common Core State Standards

Curriculum Focal Points

Interactive Teacher's Lesson Guide

1 Teaching the Lesson

Key Concepts and Skills

- Tell simple number stories using up to 10 counters and a variety of strategies. [Operations and Computation Goal 4]
- Solve number stories. [Operations and Computation Goal 4]

Key Activities

Children act out and solve number stories using various strategies. Children share their strategies and then make up and solve their own number stories.

Ongoing Assessment: Recognizing Student Achievement Use an Exit Slip (*Math Masters,* page 305). [Operations and Computation Goal 4]

Ongoing Assessment: Informing Instruction See page 73.

Key Vocabulary

number story

Materials

Math Journal 1, inside back cover
Home Link 1•12
Math Masters, p. 305
tool-kit pennies

2 Ongoing Learning & Practice

Playing the *Penny-Dice Game*
per partnership: 20 pennies, 1 die
Children practice numeration skills.

Writing Numbers
Math Masters, p. 304
Children practice writing the numbers 1–6.

Home Link 1•13
Math Masters, p. 15
Children practice and maintain skills through Home Link activities.

3 Differentiation Options

READINESS

Spying Numbers in Books
picture books ◆ stick-on notes
Children "spy" numbers in picture books.

ENRICHMENT

Telling and Solving Number Stories
number cards 0–10 (from the Everything Math Deck, if available) ◆ slate
Partners use randomly selected numbers to make up and solve number stories.

Advance Preparation

***Teacher's Reference Manual,* Grades 1–3** pp. 228, 229

Getting Started

Mental Math and Reflexes

Children use the number grid on the inside back cover of their journals as they count in unison by 2s from 1 to 20. They continue counting by 2s to 30. *What patterns do you notice when counting by 2s past 20?*

Continue counting by 2s into the 30s and 40s. If necessary, write the digits 2, 4, 6, 8, and 0 on the board and point to them as children count by 2s.

Home Link 1•12 Follow-Up

Briefly survey children to find out how many thermometers they found in their homes. Share ideas about other objects that tell temperature.

NOTE Some children may benefit from doing the **Readiness** activity before you begin Part 1. See the Readiness activity in Part 3 for details.

Interactive whiteboard-ready ePresentations are available at www.everydaymathonline.com to help you teach the lesson.

1 Teaching the Lesson

▶ Telling Simple Number Stories

WHOLE-CLASS ACTIVITY

Tell a simple **number story** about animals and draw a picture on the board or overhead to illustrate it. The picture might consist of little circles or Xs to represent the animals in the story.

Example: The zoo has 5 new tigers and 3 new lions. How many new animals does the zoo have? 8 new animals

Ask children to solve the problem in the story. Encourage them to use any strategy they choose such as the following:

- ▷ Use pennies to represent animals.
- ▷ Draw pictures similar to the one on the board.
- ▷ Use fingers to represent animals.
- ▷ Start with the number of tigers (or lions) and count on the number of lions (or tigers). For example, start with 5 tigers and count on the 3 lions.
- ▷ Count on a number line.

After a few minutes, ask children to share their answers and solution strategies. Write their strategies on the board and include correct and incorrect answers. Each time, add the unit label *animals*. As children discuss their strategies, guide them to an understanding of why certain strategies will not result in the correct answer.

Be sensitive to children with incorrect answers. Assure them that we learn as much or more by trying to understand why certain strategies do not work as by finding and using strategies that do work.

Pose several other problems such as the following and have children share their solution strategies:

- Kim belongs to a children's club. Each time she goes to the club, she pays $1. Last week, she went on Monday, Tuesday, and Friday. How much money did Kim spend last week for the club? $3

- Frank caught 7 fish last Saturday. He had to throw 6 fish back because they were too small. How many fish did Frank bring home that day? 1 fish
- Gina found 3 pennies on her walk Monday morning. She lost 1 penny on the way home. How many pennies did Gina bring home? 2 pennies
- Michael read 8 books last summer. His best friend, Brendan, read 5 books. How many more books did Michael read than Brendan? 3 more books
- Mona's dog had 3 puppies. How many dogs does Mona have now? (You may need to remind children that puppies are dogs.) 4 dogs

Ongoing Assessment: Recognizing Student Achievement

Exit Slip

Use an **Exit Slip** (*Math Masters,* page 305) to assess children's ability to solve simple number stories. Have children write the answer to one problem on an Exit Slip. Children are making adequate progress if they write the correct answer.
[Operations and Computation Goal 4]

NOTE Children love to hear their names and familiar objects, such as classroom pets, being used in the number stories you tell.

Sharing Simple Number Stories

WHOLE-CLASS ACTIVITY

Have children think of number stories for 10 pennies. Ask volunteers to share their stories. Encourage stories such as the following:

- I had 6 pennies, and my mom gave me 4 more pennies. How many pennies do I have now? 10 pennies
- I saved 9 pennies in my bank, and then I found 1 more in my pocket and added it to my bank. How many pennies do I have in my bank now? 10 pennies
- I had 10 pennies, but I lost 1 of them. How many pennies do I have now? 9 pennies

Ongoing Assessment: Informing Instruction

Watch for children who try to add to the initial 10 pennies. Tell them that they may only use 10 pennies to act out their stories. Therefore, their number stories cannot begin or end with more than 10 pennies.

Illustrate some of the stories with pennies on the overhead or draw pictures on the board.

If children suggest number models for their stories, for example, $6 + 4 = 10$, record the number models on the board. However, number models should not be emphasized at this time.

Ⓟ Ⓟ Ⓟ Ⓟ Ⓟ Ⓟ
(6 pennies)
Ⓟ Ⓟ Ⓟ Ⓟ
(4 more) How many now?

Ⓟ Ⓟ Ⓟ Ⓟ Ⓟ Ⓟ Ⓟ Ⓟ Ⓟ
(9 pennies)
Ⓟ
(1 more) How many now?

Ⓟ Ⓟ Ⓟ Ⓟ Ⓟ Ⓟ Ⓟ Ⓟ Ⓟ Ⓟ (one crossed out)
(10 pennies, lost 1) How many now?

Children use pennies to act out original problems.

Have partners pool their pennies and solve penny stories they tell to each other. Because children have pooled their pennies, number stories can now include up to 20 pennies.

Write a list of strategies for solving number stories on the board. Record how many children used each strategy today. Discuss why children selected certain strategies to solve their number stories.

2 Ongoing Learning & Practice

▶ Playing the *Penny-Dice Game*

Children practice numeration skills by playing the *Penny-Dice Game.* For detailed instructions, see Lesson 1-3.

▶ Writing Numbers

(*Math Masters,* p. 304)

Use *Math Masters,* page 304 to provide more practice writing the numbers 1 through 6.

NOTE You may wish to review number words for the numbers zero through six. Have children write each number word on the back of *Math Masters,* page 304.

▶ Home Link 1•13

INDEPENDENT ACTIVITY

(*Math Masters,* p. 15)

Home Connection Have children write their names and today's date at the top of the page.

Children find or draw a picture of a group of things and tell a number story about their picture. Children bring the pictures to school.

Remind children to keep looking for more examples of numbers to bring to school.

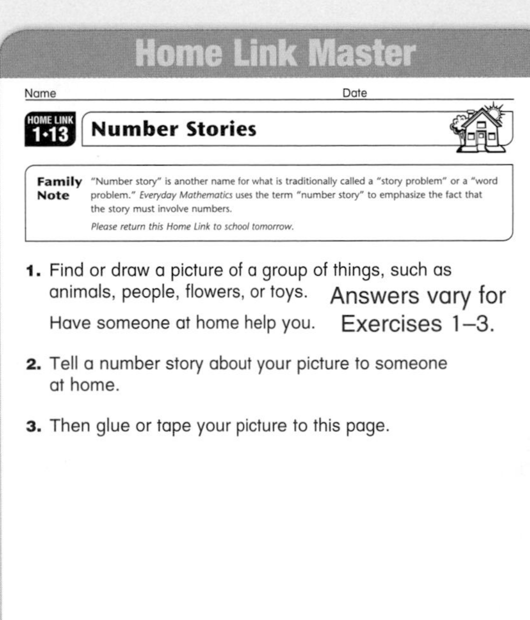

Home Link Master

Name Date

HOME LINK 1•13 **Number Stories**

Family Note "Number story" is another name for what is traditionally called a "story problem" or a "word problem." *Everyday Mathematics* uses the term "number story" to emphasize the fact that the story must involve numbers.

Please return this Home Link to school tomorrow.

1. Find or draw a picture of a group of things, such as animals, people, flowers, or toys. Have someone at home help you. Answers vary for Exercises 1–3.
2. Tell a number story about your picture to someone at home.
3. Then glue or tape your picture to this page.

Practice

Write the number that comes before each number.

4. 6 7
5. 9 10
6. 15 16
7. 1 2
8. 4 5
9. 10 11

Math Masters, p. 15

3 Differentiation Options

READINESS

INDEPENDENT ACTIVITY

Spying Numbers in Books

5–15 Min

Literature Link To provide practice with number recognition, have children find numbers represented in classroom library books. They look through the books in order to "spy" pictures that represent number situations. For example, in the story of Cinderella, children might spy the number of stepsisters that Cinderella has. Have children write the numbers they spy on a stick-on note and use it to mark the appropriate page. Allow children to share their findings.

ENRICHMENT

PARTNER ACTIVITY

Telling and Solving Number Stories

5–15 Min

To further explore children's understanding of number stories, have children write their own stories. Partners combine and mix two sets of 0–10 number cards. They put the cards facedown in a pile and take turns doing the following:

▷ One partner draws two cards from the top of the pile and tells a number story using those two numbers.

▷ Both partners solve the problem in the story, write their answers on their slates, and compare answers and solution strategies.

Some children may enjoy recording and illustrating their stories, which can be made into a class book.

1•14 Progress Check 1

Objective To assess children's progress on mathematical content through the end of Unit 1.

1 Looking Back: Cumulative Assessment

The **Beginning-of-Year Assessment** in the *Assessment Handbook* is a series of tasks that can be used to gauge children's readiness for the content they will encounter early in first grade.

Input children's data from Progress Check 1 and the Beginning-of-Year Assessment into the **Assessment Management Spreadsheets**.

Materials

- Home Link 1•13
- *Assessment Handbook,* pp. 52–59, 138–140, 177, and 200–203
- Beginning-of-Year Assessment (*Assessment Handbook,* pp. 51A, 51B, 186A, and 186B)
- slate

CONTENT ASSESSED	LESSON(S)	ASSESSMENT ITEMS				
		SELF	ORAL/SLATE	WRITTEN PART A	WRITTEN PART B	OPEN RESPONSE
Skip count with or without number grids and number lines. [Number and Numeration Goal 1]	1•1, 1•7, 1•9, 1•12	1, 2, 3	1	1	5	✓
Count collections of objects. [Number and Numeration Goal 2]	1•3, 1•5, 1•10					✓
Write whole numbers. [Number and Numeration Goal 3]	1•4, 1•9		3	4		
Represent numbers using tally marks. [Number and Numeration Goal 6]	1•7, 1•8, 1•10	4	4	3		
Order and compare whole numbers; locate them on a number line; name numbers that come before and after a given number. [Number and Numeration Goal 7]	1•2, 1•5, 1•6, 1•9, 1•10	5, 6	2	2	6	
Count forward and backward on a number line to solve number stories and number-line problems. [Operations and Computation Goal 2]	1•5, 1•11, 1•13	6				

2 Looking Ahead: Preparing for Unit 2

Home Link 1•14: Unit 2 Family Letter

Materials

- *Math Masters,* pp. 16–19

Getting Started

Home Link 1+13 Follow-Up

Have children share some of the pictures they brought from home and the number stories they made up for their pictures.

1 Looking Back: Cumulative Assessment

Self Assessment

INDEPENDENT ACTIVITY

(*Assessment Handbook,* p. 138)

The Self Assessment offers children the opportunity to reflect upon their progress.

Oral and Slate Assessments

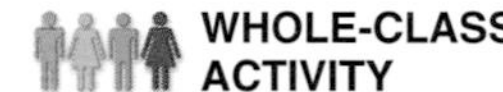

WHOLE-CLASS ACTIVITY

Problems 3 and 4 provide summative information and can be used for grading purposes. Problems 1 and 2 provide formative information that can be useful in planning future instruction.

Oral Assessment

1. Ask children to do the following counts orally.
   - Count by 1s from 20 back to 0.
   - Count by 5s to 20.
2. Ask what number comes before.
   - 1; 5; 8; 11; 13; 20 0; 4; 7; 10; 12; 19

Slate Assessment

3. Ask children to write the numeral.
   - 3; 5; 10; 14; 16
4. State a number and ask children to draw the tally marks.
   - 2; 6; 9; 12 //; 卌 /; 卌 ////; 卌卌 //

Written Assessment

INDEPENDENT ACTIVITY

(*Assessment Handbook,* p. 139)

Everyday Mathematics children are expected to master a variety of mathematical concepts and skills over time. The curriculum frequently revisits topics, concepts, and skills. For this reason, the written assessment includes items recently introduced as well as items that assess long-term retention and mastery.

The written assessment is only one part of a balanced assessment plan. Use it along with other assessment tools in the program. See the *Assessment Handbook* for additional information.

Assessment Master

Name Date

LESSON 1+14 **Self Assessment** Progress Check 1

Put a check in the box that tells how you do each skill.
Answers vary for Exercises 1–6.

Skills	I can do this by myself. I can explain how to do this.	I can do this by myself.	I can do this with help.
1. Count by 1s.			
2. Count by 2s.			
3. Count by 5s.			
4. Make tally marks.			
5. Find numbers before and after.			
6. Count on a number line.			

Assessment Handbook, p. 138

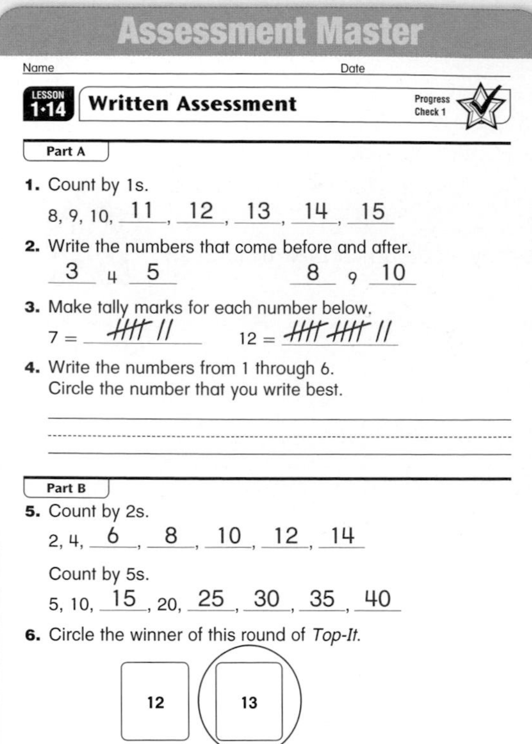
Assessment Master

Name Date

LESSON 1·14 **Written Assessment** Progress Check 1

Part A

1. Count by 1s.
8, 9, 10, 11, 12, 13, 14, 15
2. Write the numbers that come before and after.
3 4 5   8 9 10
3. Make tally marks for each number below.
7 = 𝍸 || 12 = 𝍸 𝍸 ||
4. Write the numbers from 1 through 6.
Circle the number that you write best.

Part B

5. Count by 2s.
2, 4, 6, 8, 10, 12, 14
Count by 5s.
5, 10, 15, 20, 25, 30, 35, 40
6. Circle the winner of this round of *Top-It*.
12 13

Assessment Handbook, p. 139

Part A Recognizing Student Achievement

The Recognizing Student Achievement, or *summative,* part of the written assessment is designed to help teachers assess children's progress toward Grade 1 Goals. The items in this section can be used for grading purposes since the curriculum to this point has provided multiple exposures to the content of the problems that appear in this part.

Problem(s)	Description
1	Count forward by 1s.
2	Write the numbers that come before and after a given number.
3	Write tally marks for numbers.
4	Write the numbers 1–6.

Part B Informing Instruction

The Informing Instruction, or *formative,* part of the written assessment can help teachers make decisions about how best to approach concepts and skills the next time they appear. The items in this part of the written assessment are intended to inform future instruction.

Problem(s)	Description
5	Count forward by 2s and 5s.
6	Compare pairs of numbers.

Use the checklists on pages 201 and 203 of the *Assessment Handbook* to record results. Then input the data into the **Assessment Management Spreadsheets** to keep an ongoing record of children's progress toward Grade-Level Goals.

▶ Open Response

(*Assessment Handbook,* p. 140)

Counting Buttons

The open- response item requires children to apply skills and concepts from Unit 1 to solve a multistep problem. See *Assessment Handbook,* pages 55–59 for rubrics and children's work samples for this problem.

There are two options for completing this open response. For both Option 1 and Option 2, children begin by working independently (or with a partner) to solve a multistep problem.

Option 1:
Give each child a large collection of objects. (Collections should include less than 50 objects.) Each collection must include the same number of objects; however, each child does not need to have the same objects. Have children count the objects. After children have counted the objects in their collection once, ask them to try a different, and perhaps faster, way to count the objects.

Option 2:
Distribute *Assessment Handbook*, page 140. Read the problem aloud to children. Allow children to solve the problem using manipulatives and record their solution strategy on the page.

See the *Assessment Handbook* (page 55) for more information.

After children have had a chance to complete either option, invite individual children to explain their solution strategies. Encourage them to use words and drawings to explain their strategies as you list them on the board. Be sure to discuss both successful and unsuccessful strategies.

2 Looking Ahead: Preparing for Unit 2

Home Link 1•14: Unit 2 Family Letter

INDEPENDENT ACTIVITY

(*Math Masters,* pp. 16–19)

Home Connection The Unit 2 Family Letter provides families with information and activities related to Unit 2 topics.

Assessment Master

Name Date

LESSON 1•14 **Open Response**

Counting Buttons

You have a bag of buttons, and you want to count them. Write how many buttons you have in your bag and how you counted them.

See the *Assessment Handbook* for rubrics and children's work samples.

Your friend Maria said that you could count the buttons faster if they were in groups. Draw or write how you could group the buttons to count them faster.

Assessment Handbook, p. 140

Home Link Masters

Name Date

HOME LINK 1•14 **Unit 2: Family Letter**

Everyday Uses of Numbers

In Unit 2, children will learn about three specific uses of numbers in real-world contexts: the use of numbers in telephone numbers, in telling time, and in counting money. Your child will learn how to interpret the various parts of a telephone number, how to tell time on the hour, and how to count collections of nickels and pennies.

When learning to tell time, your child will estimate the time on a clock that has no minute hand, only an hour hand. For example, when the hour hand is pointing exactly to the 4, we can say that the time is *about 4 o'clock*. When the hour hand is between the 4 and the 5, we can say that the time is *after 4 o'clock* or *between 4 and 5 o'clock*. By focusing on the hour hand, children will avoid the common mistake of giving the wrong hour reading (usually one hour off).

about 4 o'clock

between 4 o'clock and 5 o'clock

When learning to count money, it is preferred that your child use real coins. In Unit 2, the focus will be on counting nickels and pennies and on exchanging pennies for nickels. (In Unit 3, children will add dimes to their coin collections. Later, they will add quarters.)

Your child will also continue to develop counting skills with the help of a number grid, begin to do simple addition and subtraction problems, and continue to solve number stories.

Please keep this letter for reference as your child works through Unit 2.

Vocabulary

Important terms in Unit 2:

Numbers All Around Museum A routine that promotes number awareness and is used throughout the year as the class assembles examples of numbers used at home.

Math Boxes A collection of problems to practice skills.

unit box A box displaying a unit, or label, in the problems at hand. For example, in problems involving counts of children in the class, the unit box would be as shown on the right.

Unit
children

analog clock A clock that shows the time by the positions of the hour and minute hands.

digital clock A clock that shows the time with numbers of hours and minutes, usually separated by a colon.

3:00

Math Masters, pp. 16–19

Unit 2 Organizer

Everyday Uses of Numbers

Overview

Teaching the uses of numbers is an important part of the school mathematics experience. Unit 2 of *Everyday Mathematics* introduces children to several everyday uses of numbers—in particular, telling time and counting money. Understanding of these important uses will be developed throughout *First Grade Everyday Mathematics*. In Unit 2, children will also take part in many activities designed to prepare them for addition and subtraction, both as computational skills and as tools for problem solving. Unit 2 has four main areas of focus:

- To explore various uses of numbers,
- To introduce the analog clock,
- To practice finding the values of various combinations of pennies and nickels, and
- To introduce number models for change-to-more and change-to-less situations.

CCSS Linking to the Common Core State Standards

The content of Unit 2 addresses the Common Core State Standards for Mathematics in *Operations and Algebraic Thinking* and *Measurement and Data*. The correlation of the Common Core State Standards to the *Everyday Mathematics* Grade 1 lessons begins on page CS1.

Contents

Learning In Perspective

	Lesson Objectives	Links to the Past	Links to the Future
2•1	To provide practice counting up and back on the number grid.	In Unit 1, children count up and back on the number line. Children count up and back in Kindergarten. They are also introduced to the number grid.	In Units 3–6 and 8–10, children use the number grid to skip count, to find numerical patterns, and to introduce solving addition and subtraction problems.
2•2	To guide exploration of the uses of numbers; and to introduce the parts of telephone numbers.	In Unit 1 and Kindergarten, children explore the uses of numbers.	Children continue to explore different uses of numbers throughout Grades 1–6.
2•3	To guide exploration of the complements of 10; to introduce ten frames; and to introduce the Math Boxes routine.	Children work with single-digit addition in Kindergarten.	In Units 3–10, children learn sum-equals-ten addition facts and find complements of 11–18. Children complete the daily Math Boxes routine.
2•4	To introduce the need for unit labels for numbers; and to introduce calculators.	In Kindergarten, children count objects; they also learn to use calculators to count up.	Children use unit labels throughout Grades 1–6. Throughout Grades 1–3, children use calculators for various tasks of increasing complexity.
2•5	To introduce the analog clock.	Children tell time to the nearest hour in Kindergarten. The minute hand is also introduced.	In Grades 1–3, children tell time more and more precisely. By Grade 3, they can tell time to the nearest minute.
2•6	To introduce the division of the day into A.M. and P.M. times; to provide practice telling time to the hour; and to develop a sense of the duration of a minute.	Children tell time to the nearest hour in Kindergarten. The minute hand is also introduced.	In Grades 1–3, children tell time more and more precisely. By Grade 3, they can tell time to the nearest minute.
2•7	To provide experiences comparing lengths of objects; to provide practice drawing straight lines with a straightedge; and to develop familiarity with dominoes.	In Unit 1, children use mathematical tools for drawing. In Kindergarten, children compare lengths and use mathematical tools.	In Grades 1–2, children measure and compare length using standard and nonstandard units. They will also use dominoes to find patterns and solve problems.
2•8	To introduce pennies and cents notation; to provide practice recording numbers of pennies; and to reinforce comparing numbers.	In Unit 1, children compare numbers and count objects. Children are introduced to pennies in Kindergarten. They also count objects and compare numbers.	In Units 3–10, children compare numbers and quantities. They are introduced to dollars-and-cents notation and count objects.
2•9	To introduce nickels; and to provide practice exchanging pennies for nickels.	In Unit 1, children count by 1s and 5s. In Kindergarten, children are introduced to nickels and exchanging pennies for nickels.	In Units 3–6, 8, and 10, children are introduced to dimes, quarters, and dollar bills. They compare the values of coins and make exchanges between coins.
2•10	To provide practice finding the values of combinations of nickels and pennies.	In Unit 1, children count by 1s and 5s. In Kindergarten, children count by 1s and 5s. They are introduced to finding the value of coin combinations.	In Units 3–6, 8, and 10, children calculate combinations of coins, including pennies, nickels, dimes, quarters, and dollar bills.
2•11	To introduce number models for change-to-more situations.	In Unit 1, children tell and solve number stories. They tell and solve number stories that include joining situations in Kindergarten.	In Units 5, 8, and 10, children solve change-to-more number stories using a situation diagram.
2•12	To broaden experiences with extending number models to include change-to-less situations.	In Unit 1, children practice telling and solving number stories. In Kindergarten, children tell and solve number stories that include take-away situations.	In Units 5, 8, and 10, children solve change-to-less number stories using a situation diagram.
2•13	To provide practice making up and solving number stories; to review counting money; and to provide opportunities to find the sum of three 1-digit numbers.	In Unit 1, children tell and solve number stories. Children tell and solve number stories in Kindergarten and are introduced to finding the value of coin combinations.	Throughout Grades 1–6, children tell and solve number stories. Children also practice counting money.

	Key Concepts and Skills	Grade 1 Goals*
2·1	Count forward and backward by 1s from a given number.	Number and Numeration Goal 1
	Read and locate numbers on a number line and a number grid.	Number and Numeration Goal 7
	Count on a number line and a number grid to solve problems.	Operations and Computation Goal 1
2·2	Read and write numbers.	Number and Numeration Goal 3
	Create a tally chart to organize data.	Data and Chance Goal 1
	Answer questions about data.	Data and Chance Goal 2
2·3	Count objects by 1s.	Number and Numeration Goal 2
	Give equivalent names for 10; represent numbers with counters on a ten frame.	Number and Numeration Goal 6
	Compare pairs of whole numbers.	Number and Numeration Goal 7
	Find pairs of numbers with sums of 10.	Operations and Computation Goal 1
	Make predictions and check outcomes.	Data and Chance Goal 3
2·4	Count forward by 1s, labeling numbers with unit labels.	Number and Numeration Goal 1
	Count objects by 1s, labeling numbers with unit labels.	Number and Numeration Goal 2
	Use a calculator to represent numbers.	Number and Numeration Goal 6
2·5	Read whole numbers.	Number and Numeration Goal 3
	Compare the functions of the hands on a clock.	Measurement and Reference Frames Goal 4
	Estimate time on an analog clock, using only the hour hand.	Measurement and Reference Frames Goal 4
	Use language of approximation to describe times on an analog clock.	Measurement and Reference Frames Goal 4
2·6	Count forward by 1s.	Number and Numeration Goal 1
	Show a given time on an analog clock.	Measurement and Reference Frames Goal 4
	Read and record times shown on an analog clock.	Measurement and Reference Frames Goal 4
	Use language of approximation to describe times on an analog clock.	Measurement and Reference Frames Goal 4
2·7	Count forward by 2s.	Number and Numeration Goal 1
	Recognize dot patterns on dominoes as representations of numbers.	Number and Numeration Goal 6
	Compare the lengths of objects to a 6-inch ruler.	Measurement and Reference Frames Goal 1
2·8	Estimate and count the number of objects in a group.	Number and Numeration Goal 2
	Compare quantities and determine which quantity is more.	Number and Numeration Goal 7
	Identify a penny and know its value.	Measurement and Reference Frames Goal 2
	Name the value of a group of pennies using cent notation.	Measurement and Reference Frames Goal 2
2·9	Count forward by 1s and 5s from a given number.	Number and Numeration Goal 1
	Count combinations of pennies and nickels.	Operations and Computation Goal 2
	Identify a nickel and know its value.	Measurement and Reference Frames Goal 2
	Exchange pennies for nickels.	Measurement and Reference Frames Goal 2
2·10	Count forward by 5s and then on by 1s.	Number and Numeration Goal 1
	Express the value of groups of nickels and pennies using cent notation.	Operations and Computation Goal 2
	Identify and know the values of a penny and a nickel.	Measurement and Reference Frames Goal 2
	Exchange pennies for nickels.	Measurement and Reference Frames Goal 2
2·11	Count forward by 1s from a given number.	Number and Numeration Goal 1
	Solve 1-digit by 1-digit change-to-more stories.	Operations and Computation Goal 1
	Write number models for 1-digit by 1-digit change-to-more stories using the symbols + and =.	Patterns, Functions, and Algebra Goal 2
2·12	Count backward by 1s from a given number.	Number and Numeration Goal 1
	Solve 1-digit by 1-digit change-to-less stories.	Operations and Computation Goal 1
	Write number models for 1-digit by 1-digit change-to-less stories using the symbols − and =.	Patterns, Functions, and Algebra Goal 2
2·13	Count forward and backward by 1s from a given number.	Number and Numeration Goal 1
	Solve 1-digit by 1-digit addition and subtraction number stories.	Operations and Computation Goal 1
	Find sums of three 1-digit whole numbers.	Operations and Computation Goal 2
	Show amounts of money using pennies and nickels and make exchanges between them.	Measurement and Reference Frames Goal 2
	Add three numbers in different combinations using the Associative Property of Addition.	Patterns, Functions, and Algebra Goal 3

*See the Appendix for a complete list of Grade 1 Goals.

A Balanced Curriculum

Ongoing Practice

Everyday Mathematics provides numerous opportunities for ongoing practice. These activities are embedded throughout the lessons:

Mental Math and Reflexes activities promote speed and accuracy in mental computation.

Math Boxes offer mixed practice and are paired across lessons as shown in the brackets below. This makes them useful as assessment tools. The last one or two boxes on each page preview the next unit's content.

Mixed practice	[2•3, 2•5], [2•4, 2•6], [2•7, 2•9], [2•8, 2•10, 2•12], [2•11, 2•13]
Mixed practice with multiple choice	2•4, 2•5, 2•8, 2•9, 2•10, 2•13

Home Links are daily homework assignments that review the content of the lesson and often contain ongoing facts practice or computation practice.

***Minute Math*+** problems are offered for additional practice in Lessons 2•1, 2•5, and 2•13.

EM Facts Workshop Game provides online practice of basic facts and computation.

EXTRA PRACTICE **Extra Practice** activities are included in Lessons 2•4, 2•6, 2•8, and 2•13.

Practice through Games

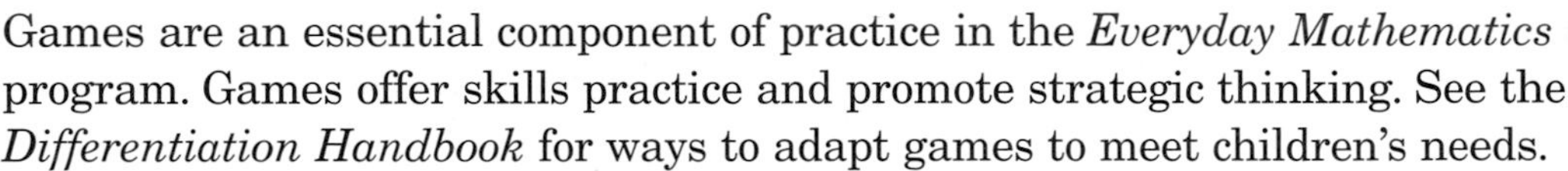

Games are an essential component of practice in the *Everyday Mathematics* program. Games offer skills practice and promote strategic thinking. See the *Differentiation Handbook* for ways to adapt games to meet children's needs.

Lesson	Game	Skill Practiced
2•1, 2•5, 2•7	*Rolling for 50*	Counting on a number grid [NN Goal 1]
2•1	*Top-It*	Comparing numbers [NN Goal 7]
2•3	*Ten-Frame Top-It*	Comparing numbers [NN Goal 7]
2•8	*Penny Grab*	Calculating and comparing the values of combinations of coins [OC Goal 2]
2•8	*Penny Plate*	Finding sums of 10 [OC Goal 1]
2•8	*Penny-Dice Game*	Counting objects and comparing quantities [NN Goals 2 and 7]
2•10	*Penny-Nickel Exchange*	Exchanging pennies for nickels [MRF Goal 2]
2•11	*Nickel-Penny Grab*	Calculating and comparing the values of combinations of coins [OC Goal 2]
2•12	*High Roller*	Comparing quantities and finding sums [NN Goal 7 and OC Goal 2]
2•13	*Coin Top-It*	Calculating and comparing the values of combinations of coins [OC Goal 2]

[NN] Number and Numeration
[MRF] Measurement and Reference Frames
[OC] Operations and Computation
[GEO] Geometry
[DC] Data and Chance
[PFA] Patterns, Functions, and Algebra

Problem Solving 

Good problem solvers use a variety of strategies, including the following:

- Draw a picture.
- Act out the problem.
- Make a table, chart, or list.
- Look for a pattern.
- Try a simpler version of the problem.
- Make a guess and try it out.

The table below lists some of the opportunities in this unit for children to practice these strategies.

Lesson	Activity
2•1	Find differences between two numbers.
2•3	Do Two-Fisted Penny Addition.
2•6, 2•13	Solve simple number stories.
2•7	Solve change-to-more number stories.
2•7	Estimate relative lengths of objects.
2•8	Solve change-to-less number stories.
2•11, 2•12	Write number models for change-to-more and change-to-less situations.

Lessons that teach *through* problem solving, not just *about* problem solving

See Chapter 18: Problem Solving in the *Teacher's Reference Manual* for more information.

The Language of Mathematics

Everyday Mathematics provides lesson-specific suggestions to help all children acquire, process, and express mathematical ideas. Throughout Unit 2, there are lesson-specific language development notes that address the needs of English language learners, indicated by ELL.

ELL SUPPORT Activities to support English language learners are in Part 3 of Lessons 2•2, 2•5, 2•6, 2•8, 2•11, and 2•12.

The *English Learners Handbook* and the *Differentiation Handbook* have suggestions for promoting language development and acquisition of mathematics vocabulary. See Unit 2 in each handbook.

Literacy Connection

Lesson 2•13 *12 Ways To Get To 11,* by Eve Merriam, Simon and Schuster Children's Publishing, 1996

For more literacy connections, see the *Home Connection Handbook,* Grades 1–3.

Cross-Curricular Links 

Social Studies – Lesson 2•2
Language Arts – Lessons 2•6, 2•9, 2•11
Science – Lesson 2•5
Music – Lesson 2•6
Literature – Lesson 2•13

Unit 2 Vocabulary

add
A.M.
analog clock
cent
clockwise
estimate
hour hand
is equal to
Math Boxes
midnight
minus
minute hand
nickel
noon
number grid
number model
penny
plus
P.M.
ruler
subtract
ten frame
unit
unit box

Balanced Assessment

Daily Assessments

- **Recognizing Student Achievement** – A daily assessment that is included in every lesson to evaluate children's progress toward the Grade 1 Grade-Level Goals.
- **Informing Instruction** – Notes that appear throughout the unit to help anticipate children's common errors and suggest appropriate problem-solving strategies.

Lesson	Recognizing Student Achievement	Informing Instruction
2•1	Compare numbers. [NN Goal 7]	Understand "counting up and down." Count hops on a number grid.
2•2	Write numbers 7 and 8 legibly. [NN Goal 3]	Write the number 8.
2•3	Represent sums of 10. [OC Goal 1]	Find sums of 10 pennies.
2•4	Write numbers 0 and 9 legibly. [NN Goal 3]	Understand the concept of zero.
2•5	Order numbers. [NN Goal 7]	
2•6	Find equivalent names for numbers. [NN Goal 6]	Distinguish between the hour and minute hands.
2•7	Count on a number grid. [OC Goal 2]	
2•8	Calculate and compare values of sets of pennies. [OC Goal 2]	
2•9	Count by 5s. [NN Goal 1]	
2•10	Count nickels and pennies. [OC Goal 2]	
2•11	Tell time to the hour. [MRF Goal 4]	
2•12	Find sums of 1-digit numbers. [OC Goal 1]	
2•13	Count nickels and pennies. [OC Goal 2]	Exchange pennies for nickels.

[NN] Number and Numeration
[MRF] Measurement and Reference Frames
[OC] Operations and Computation
[GEO] Geometry
[DC] Data and Chance
[PFA] Patterns, Functions, and Algebra

Portfolio Opportunities

The following lessons provide opportunities to gather samples of children's mathematical writings, drawings, and creations to add balance to the assessment process: Lessons 2•1, 2•3, 2•5, 2•6, 2•7, 2•11, 2•12, and 2•14.

See pages 16 and 17 in the *Assessment Handbook* for more information about portfolios and how to use them.

Unit Assessment

Progress Check 2 – A cumulative assessment of concepts and skills taught in Unit 2 and in the previous unit, providing information for evaluating children's progress and planning for future instruction. These assessments include oral/slate, written, and open-response activities, as shown below in the sample Progress Check lesson opener.

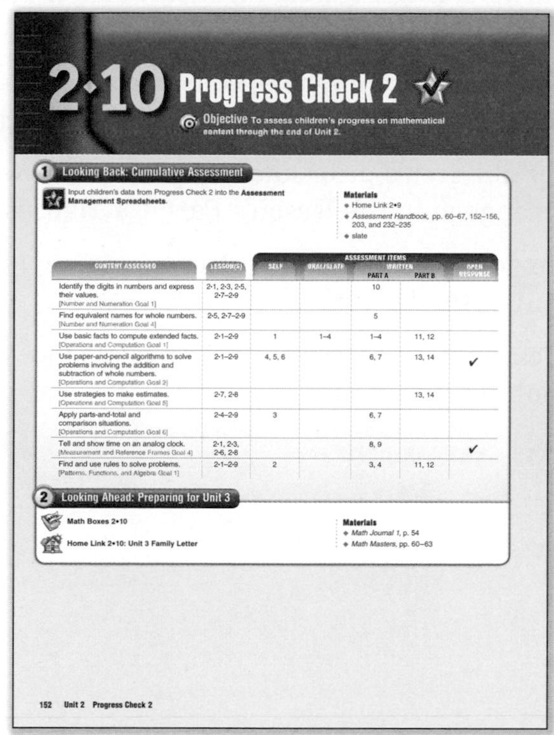

2•10 Progress Check 2

Objective To assess children's progress on mathematical content through the end of Unit 2.

1 Looking Back: Cumulative Assessment

Input children's data from Progress Check 2 into the **Assessment Management Spreadsheets**.

Materials
- Home Link 2•9
- *Assessment Handbook*, pp. 60–67, 152–156, 203, and 232–235
- slate

Content Assessed	Lesson(s)	Assessment Items: Self	Oral/Slate	Written Part A	Written Part B	Open Response
Identify the digits in numbers and express their values. [Number and Numeration Goal 1]	2•1, 2•3, 2•5, 2•7–2•9			10		
Find equivalent names for whole numbers. [Number and Numeration Goal 4]	2•5, 2•7–2•9			5		
Use basic facts to compute extended facts. [Operations and Computation Goal 1]	2•1–2•9	1	1–4	1–4	11, 12	
Use paper-and-pencil algorithms to solve problems involving the addition and subtraction of whole numbers. [Operations and Computation Goal 2]	2•1–2•9	4, 5, 6		6, 7	13, 14	✓
Use strategies to make estimates. [Operations and Computation Goal 5]	2•7, 2•8				13, 14	
Apply parts-and-total and comparison situations. [Operations and Computation Goal 6]	2•4–2•9	3		6, 7		
Tell and show time on an analog clock. [Measurement and Reference Frames Goal 4]	2•1, 2•3, 2•6, 2•8			8, 9		✓
Find and use rules to solve problems. [Patterns, Functions, and Algebra Goal 1]	2•1–2•9	2		3, 4	11, 12	

2 Looking Ahead: Preparing for Unit 3

Math Boxes 2•10

Home Link 2•10: Unit 3 Family Letter

Materials
- *Math Journal 1*, p. 54
- *Math Masters*, pp. 60–63

152 Unit 2 Progress Check 2

Core Assessment Resources

Assessment Handbook

- **Unit 2 Assessment Overview,** pages pages 60–67
- **Unit 2 Assessment Masters,** pages 141–144
- **Unit 2 Individual Profiles of Progress,** pages 204, 205, and 248
- **Unit 2 Class Checklists,** pages 206, 207, and 249
- **Math Logs,** pages 254–256
- **Exit Slip,** page 251
- **Other Student Assessment Forms,** pages 252, 253, 257, and 258

Assessment Management Spreadsheets

The Assessment Management Spreadsheets consist of the Digital Class Checklists and Individual Profile of Progress Checklists. Use them to monitor, record, and report children's progress.

Addressing All Needs

Differentiated Instruction

Adjusting the Activity – suggests adaptations that target advanced learners, English language learners, or learners who need additional instructional support.

ELL SUPPORT / **ELL** – provides lesson-specific suggestions to help English language learners understand and process the mathematical content.

READINESS – accesses children's prior knowledge or previews content that prepares children to engage in the lesson's Part 1 activities.

EXTRA PRACTICE – provides additional opportunities to apply the mathematical content of the lesson.

ENRICHMENT – enables children to apply or further explore the mathematical content of the lesson.

Lesson	Adjusting the Activity	ELL Support/ ELL	Readiness	Extra Practice	Enrichment
2•1	•		•		•
2•2		•	•		•
2•3	•	•	•		•
2•4			•	•	
2•5		•			•
2•6	•	•	•	•	•
2•7			•		•
2•8	•	•	•	•	•
2•9	•		•		•
2•10	•		•		•
2•11		•	•		•
2•12		•	•		•
2•13			•	•	•

Additional Resources

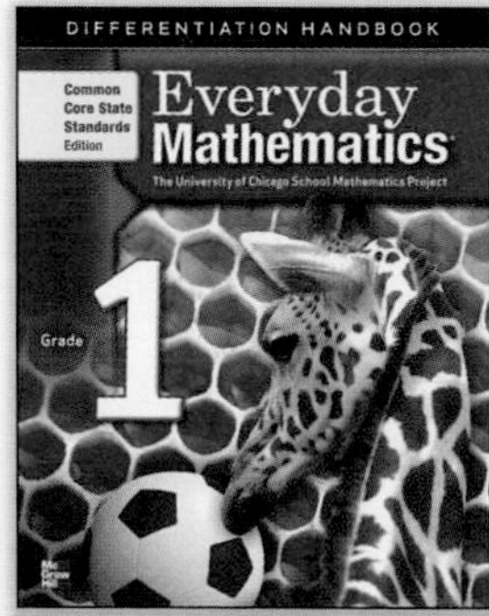

Differentiation Handbook
Provides ideas and strategies for differentiating instruction.
Pages 57–63

English Learners Handbook
Contains lesson-specific comprehension strategies.
Pages 14–26

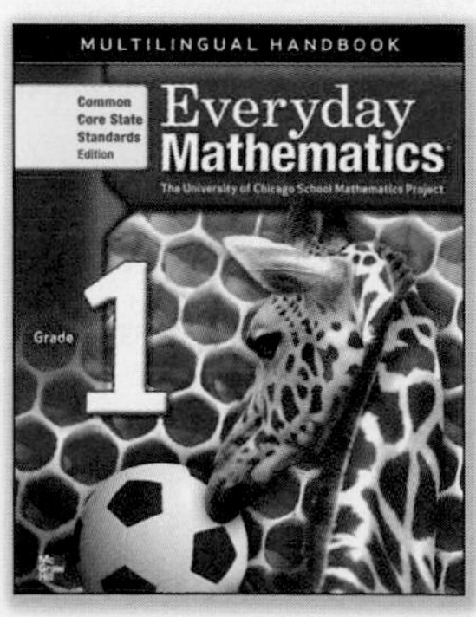

Multilingual Handbook
Previews concepts and vocabulary. It is written in six languages.
Pages 27–52

Planning Tips

Multiage Classroom

Companion Lessons from Grades K and 2 can help you meet instructional needs of a multiage classroom. The full Scope and Sequence can be found in the Appendix.

Grade K	5•15, 5•16	1•5, Project 1	1•14		6•13	8•2, 8•3	1•2, 1•13	6•1	6•2	6•1, 6•2, 6•8	4•4	4•11	2•14, 4•15
Grade 1	**2•1**	**2•2**	**2•3**	**2•4**	**2•5**	**2•6**	**2•7**	**2•8**	**2•9**	**2•10**	**2•11**	**2•12**	**2•13**
Grade 2	1•8		7•2		1•3, 3•3, 12•2	1•3, 3•3, 12•2	4•7, 9•2	3•2, 3•8, 10•1	3•2, 3•8, 10•1	3•7, 3•8, 10•1	2•1, 4•1, 11•1	2•6, 11•2	2•1, 4•2, 11•1

Pacing for Success

Pacing depends on a number of factors, such as children's individual needs and how long your school has been using *Everyday Mathematics*. At the beginning of Unit 2, you may want to use tools available at www.everydaymathonline.com to help you set your pace.

Home Support

Unit 2 Family Letter (English/Spanish) provides families with an overview, Do-Anytime Activities, Building Skills through Games, a list of vocabulary, and answers to the daily homework (Home Links). Family Letters in English, Spanish, and seven other languages are also available online.

Home Links are the daily homework assignments. They consist of active projects and ongoing review problems.

Home Support Resources

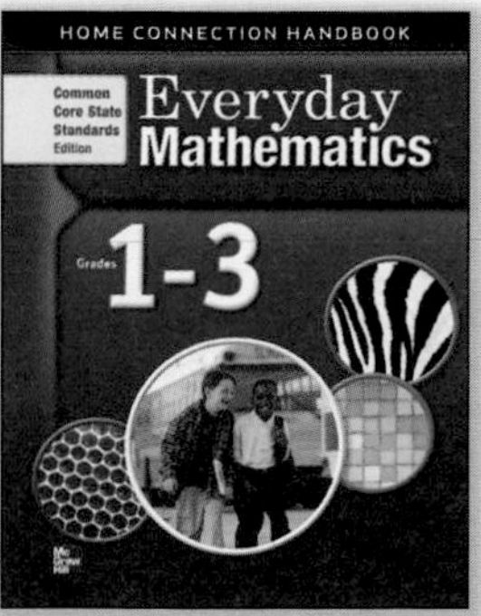

Home Connection Handbook
Offers ideas and reproducible masters for communicating with families. See Table of Contents for unit information.

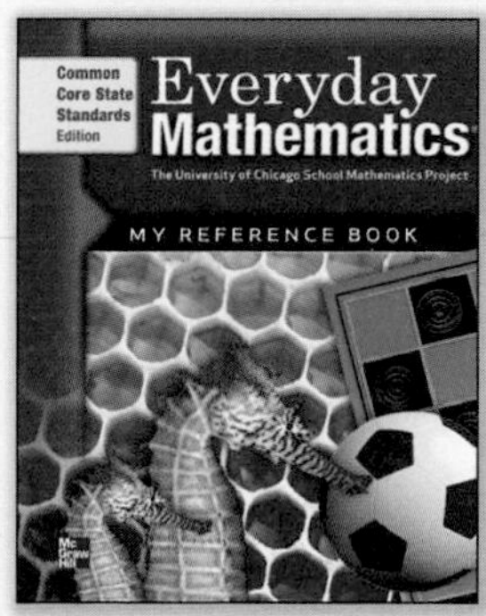

My Reference Book
Beginning in Unit 6, *My Reference Book* provides a resource for children and parents.

Technology Resources

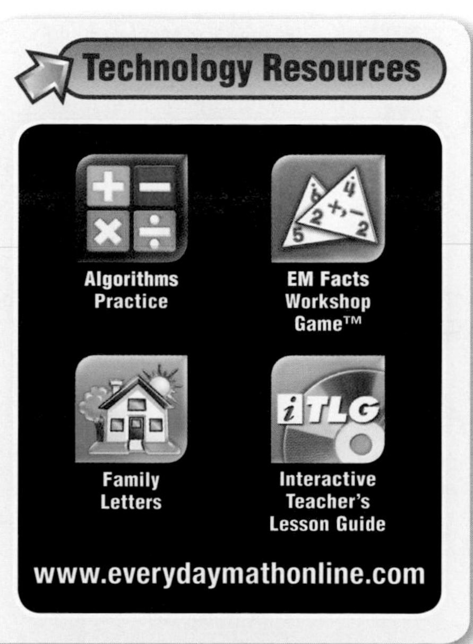

Unit 2 Organizer

Materials

Technology Resources www.everydaymathonline.com

ePresentations | eToolkit | Algorithms Practice | EM Facts Workshop Game™ | Family Letters | Assessment Management | Common Core State Standards | Curriculum Focal Points | Interactive Teacher's Lesson Guide

Lesson	Masters	Manipulative Kit	Other Items
2•1	Transparency of *Math Masters,* p. 308* Home Link Master, p. 20 Teaching Aid Master, p. 305 Teaching Master, p. 21	per group: 1 die; number cards 0–15; counters	per group: 2 game markers; Number-Grid Poster
2•2	Home Link Master, p. 22 Teaching Master, p. 23	per group: 4 numbered dice	examples of numbers from home
2•3	Teaching Master, p. 24* Teaching Aid Masters, pp. 304, 305, 336, 336A, and 336B Transparency of *Math Masters,* p. 336 Home Link Master, p. 25 Teaching Masters, pp. 26 and 27	slate	10 pennies; counters
2•4	Home Link Master, p. 28 Teaching Aid Master, p. 309	slate*	can or container; 20 pennies; mystery bags; labels on 4" by 6" cards; calculator
2•5	Teaching Masters, pp. 29 and 31 Home Link Master, p. 30 *Differentiation Handbook,* p. 126	per group: 1 die	clock or watch with second hand; demonstration clock; demonstration clock with an hour hand only; per group: 2 game markers; scissors
2•6	Teaching Masters, pp. 32 and 34 Home Link Master, p. 33 Teaching Aid Masters, pp. 304 and 310 *Differentiation Handbook,* p. 126		pennies*; demonstration clock with an hour hand only*; demonstration clock with hour and minute hands; paper plate or tagboard, scissors, glue, brad; classroom clock; paper clocks
2•7	Teaching Masters, pp. 35–37 Home Link Master, p. 38	ruler; double-nine dominoes; per group: 1 die; pattern blocks	per child: 8 objects to measure; per group: 2 game markers; string
2•8	Game Master, p. 350 Home Link Master, p. 39 Teaching Aid Master, p. 336* *Differentiation Handbook,* p. 126	slate; per group: 1 die	Class Data Pad or posterboard; magnifying lenses; per group: paper plate; pennies; Number-Grid Poster
2•9	Home Link Master, p. 41 Teaching Master, p. 40	slate	pennies and nickels; Story of Money Poster; magnifying lens; overhead coins*
2•10	Home Link Master, p. 42 Teaching Master, p. 43	slate; per group: 1 die (2 dice*)	pennies and nickels; paper bags; overhead coins*; Pattern-Block Template*
2•11	Home Link Master, p. 44 Game Master, p. 347 *Differentiation Handbook,* p. 126	slate; per group: 20 craft sticks	container; pennies and nickels; Class Data Pad
2•12	Home Link Master, p. 45 Game Master, p. 344 *Differentiation Handbook,* p. 126	slate; per group: 2 dice; number cards 0–20	12 paper cups; overhead coins*; 20 pennies; Class Number Line*
2•13	Teaching Masters, pp. 45A and 45B Home Link Master, p. 46 Teaching Aid Master, p. 305		pennies and nickels; 3" by 5" index cards; scissors; number and symbol signs; objects from home*; class bank; *12 Ways To Get To 11;* Pattern-Block Template*
2•14	Assessment Masters, pp. 141–144 Home Link Masters, pp. 47–50	slate	demonstration clock

*Denotes optional materials

Mathematical Background

Number Lines and Number Grids

(Lesson 2•1 and following)

The number line was introduced in Unit 1 as a device for developing counting skills. As children deal with larger numbers, number grids replace number lines. These grids will be used to strengthen counting, addition, subtraction, and place-value skills. The game *Rolling for 50* can be used to help children learn how to maneuver on the number grid.

See Section 1.3.4 of the Management Guide, located in the *Teacher's Reference Manual,* for additional information about number lines and number grids.

										0
	1	2	3	4	5	6	7	8	9	10
	11	12	13	14	15	16	17	18	19	20
	21	22	23	24	25	26	27	28	29	30
	31	32	33	34	35	36	37	38	39	40
	41	42	43	44	45	46	47	48	49	50
	51	52	53	54	55	56	57	58	59	60
	61	62	63	64	65	66	67	68	69	70
	71	72	73	74	75	76	77	78	79	80
	81	82	83	84	85	86	87	88	89	90
	91	92	93	94	95	96	97	98	99	100
	101	102	103	104	105	106	107	108	109	110

Numbers All Around Museum

(Lesson 2•2)

Everyday Mathematics encourages teachers to assemble classroom "museums": bulletin board or tab displays where items linked to a topic can be collected, categorized, and labeled. Such "museums" help children bridge the gap between the classroom and the outside world.

For more information about museums, see Section 1.2.8 of the Management Guide, located in the *Teacher's Reference Manual.*

Personal and Class Information

(Lesson 2•2)

Everyday Mathematics encourages children to collect and use personal numerical information and to combine it with information from their classmates. In Lesson 2-2, children analyze their own telephone numbers. Be on the lookout for opportunities to record counts, measures, dates, or other numbers that are of personal interest to children or that arise in other subject areas.

Note

Draw attention to the uses of numbers as counts, measures, money, reference frames, and codes, but don't expect children to be able to classify numbers at this time.

Developing Readiness for Addition and Subtraction (Lesson 2•2 and following)

A major first-grade goal is for children to attain fluency with addition and subtraction facts. This goal will be reached in two main ways: through the use of real-life situations to develop an understanding of the meanings of addition and subtraction and through games and activities to develop facility with the basic facts. In Lesson 2-2, children review facts within 5, which they learned in Kindergarten. In Lesson 2-3, children learn Two-Fisted Penny Addition and use ten frames. These are good starting points, because they focus on sums of 10, which are important in developing mental computation skills.

You can read more about addition and subtraction facts in Section 16.3.2 of the *Teacher's Reference Manual.*

Math Boxes (Lesson 2•3 and following)

The Math Boxes routine is one way to promote ongoing practice and review of concepts and skills over an extended period of time. At this stage, most children will need help with reading the Math Boxes directions and understanding what to do, but as children mature, they will learn to "do Math Boxes" on their own.

For more information about Math Boxes, see Section 1.2.4 of the Management Guide in the *Teacher's Reference Manual*.

Units and Unit Boxes (Lesson 2•4)

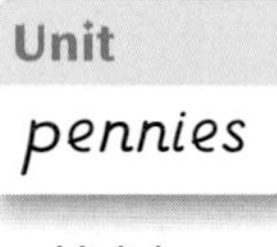

Unit box

Counts are always counts of *something* (people, buttons, elephants, and so on), and measures are meaningless unless they include one or more measurement units (inches, meters, pounds, miles per hour, and so on). For most people, numbers make the most sense when they are thought of in real-world contexts. Because it is often tedious to attach a label to every number separately, *Everyday Mathematics* encourages the use of unit boxes.

Section 1.3.6 of the Management Guide in the *Teacher's Reference Manual* has additional information about unit boxes.

Clocks and Telling Time (Lessons 2•5 and 2•6)

The development of time-telling concepts and skills in most young children takes many experiences over an extended period of time. In this unit, the focus is on telling time to the hour on an analog clock. In units to follow, children will learn to tell time to the half-hour, to the quarter-hour, and then to the nearest 5 minutes.

A common error children make is to give correct minute readings but incorrect hour readings (usually an hour off). The *Everyday Mathematics* researchers and developers have found that estimating the time with an analog clock that has an hour hand and no minute hand helps children avoid such errors. When the hour hand is pointing exactly to 3, for example, the time is 3 o'clock. When the hour hand is just before or just after a number, or between two numbers, the time is recorded as "before x o'clock," "just after x o'clock," or "between x and y o'clock."

Lesson 2-6 also gives children their first exposure to the division of the day into 24 hours and into A.M. and P.M. times. Formal lessons on digital time are postponed until children are able to understand the division of the hour into 60 minutes and the parts of an hour as fractions of 60 minutes.

You may want to read Section 15.2.1 in the *Teacher's Reference Manual* for more information about time concepts.

Money Notation, Coin Values, and Coin Exchanges (Lessons 2•8–2•10)

These lessons review and extend interactions begun in Kindergarten. If most children are comfortable with the content of the lessons, move through them at a brisk review pace; then perhaps spend more time on the history of coins.

If children lack experience with money, do not feel the need to develop mastery of the material; there will be frequent practice over an extended period of time. Dimes will be added to the set of coins in Unit 3; quarters in Unit 6. If possible, children should use and explore real coins.

Children's work with money begins with pennies and nickels.

Problem Solving (Lessons 2•7, 2•8, and 2•13)

Problem solving involves combining common sense with past experience, trial-and-error with systematic approaches. *Everyday Mathematics* encourages children to solve problems in any way they can: by using counters, by drawing pictures or doodles, by using whichever means can help them model a situation. Along with this intuitive approach, Lessons 2-7 and 2-8 begin to lay the foundation for a systematic approach to solving number stories that involve addition and subtraction. The Mental Math and Reflexes problems in these lessons consist of change-to-more and change-to-less number stories. As part of the discussion of these problems, you are encouraged to display the appropriate situation diagrams. With repeated exposure to situation diagrams, children gradually build a framework they may draw upon when solving number stories. Therefore, be sure to allow time for sharing solution strategies.

For more information about problem solving, see the Management Guide and Chapter 18, which are both found in the *Teacher's Reference Manual*.

Number Models (Lessons 2•11 and 2•12)

Mathematical symbols convey information more compactly than words, but it is important that children have the symbols clearly linked to the words and phrases they replace. In *Kindergarten Everyday Mathematics,* children learned to read the equal symbol (=) as *the same as* and to expect that whatever is on one side of the symbol balances whatever is on the other side. In these two lessons, children use number models to represent change-to-more and change-to-less situations. Mastery is not expected at this time; mastery will be achieved via repeated exposures throughout the year.

See Section 10.1 in the *Teacher's Reference Manual* for more information about number models.

2·1 Number Grids

Objective To provide practice counting up and back on the number grid.

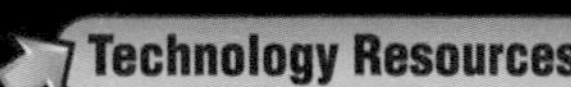

Technology Resources www.everydaymathonline.com

ePresentations

eToolkit

Algorithms Practice

EM Facts Workshop Game™

Family Letters

Assessment Management

Common Core State Standards

Curriculum Focal Points

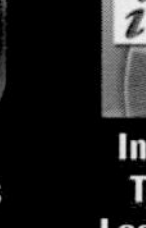
Interactive Teacher's Lesson Guide

1 Teaching the Lesson

Key Concepts and Skills

- Count forward and backward by 1s from a given number.
  [Number and Numeration Goal 1]
- Read and locate numbers on a number line and a number grid.
  [Number and Numeration Goal 7]
- Count on a number line and a number grid to solve problems.
  [Operations and Computation Goal 1]

Key Activities

Children play *Rolling for 50* to practice navigating along a number grid. Using the grid, they practice counting up and back by 1s and finding the difference between two numbers.

Ongoing Assessment: Informing Instruction See page 96.

Key Vocabulary

number grid

Materials

Math Journal 1, p. 7 and inside back cover
transparency of *Math Masters,* p. 308 (optional) ◆ Number-Grid Poster ◆
per partnership: 1 die, 2 game markers

2 Ongoing Learning & Practice

Playing *Top-It*

per partnership: 4 each of number cards 0–15 (from *Math Journal 1,* Activity Sheet 1 or the Everything Math Deck, if available)
Children practice comparing numbers.

Ongoing Assessment: Recognizing Student Achievement
Use an Exit Slip (*Math Masters,* page 305).
[Number and Numeration Goal 7]

Home Link 2·1

Math Masters, p. 20
Children practice and maintain skills through Home Link activities.

Minute Math+

Minute Math®+, pp. 88 and 94
Children practice telling and solving number stories.

3 Differentiation Options

READINESS

Coloring Return Sweeps on the Number Grid

Math Journal 1, inside back cover
Children color the return sweeps on the number grid to provide visual cues.

ENRICHMENT

Counting Up and Back

Math Masters, p. 21
Number-Grid Poster ◆ 1 counter per child
Children count up and back by 10s on a number grid.

Advance Preparation

For Part 1, color the return sweeps on the Number-Grid Poster to match the Number Grid in *My Reference Book.* Display the poster.

***Teacher's Reference Manual,* Grades 1–3** pp. 70–76, 177–182

Getting Started

Mental Math and Reflexes

Ask children to turn to the number line on the inside back cover of their journals.

Pose problems like the following:

●○○ Put your finger on 5. Count up 6 hops. Where do you land? 11

5 6 7 8 9 10 11

●●○ Put your finger on 12. Count back 3 hops. Where do you land? 9

6 7 8 9 10 11 12

●●● Put your finger on 9. Count up 2 hops. Count back 6 hops. Where do you land? 5

4 5 6 7 8 9 10 11 12

1 Teaching the Lesson

Playing *Rolling for 50*

PARTNER ACTIVITY

(*Math Journal 1,* p. 7)

When dealing with large numbers, the number line is limited as a tool for problem solving. Show children the **number grid** on the inside back cover of *Math Journal 1* to use instead. Invite them to compare the number grid to the number line.

The purpose of playing *Rolling for 50* is to provide practice navigating along a number grid. Children use the gameboard on the journal page, which is similar to a portion of a number grid.

The rules of the game are simple. Players place their markers on 0. They take turns rolling a die and moving their markers the number of spaces specified by the table. The first player to reach 50 wins.

Adjusting the Activity

Have children start at 0 and move their markers *only forward* the number of spaces shown on the die. When they are proficient at moving forward, have children start at 50 and move their markers *only backward* the number of spaces shown on the die.

AUDITORY ◆ KINESTHETIC ◆ TACTILE ◆ VISUAL

NOTE Have children color the return sweeps on the *Rolling for 50* gameboard to match the colored return sweeps on the Number-Grid Poster.

Interactive whiteboard-ready ePresentations are available at www.everydaymathonline.com to help you teach the lesson.

Student Page

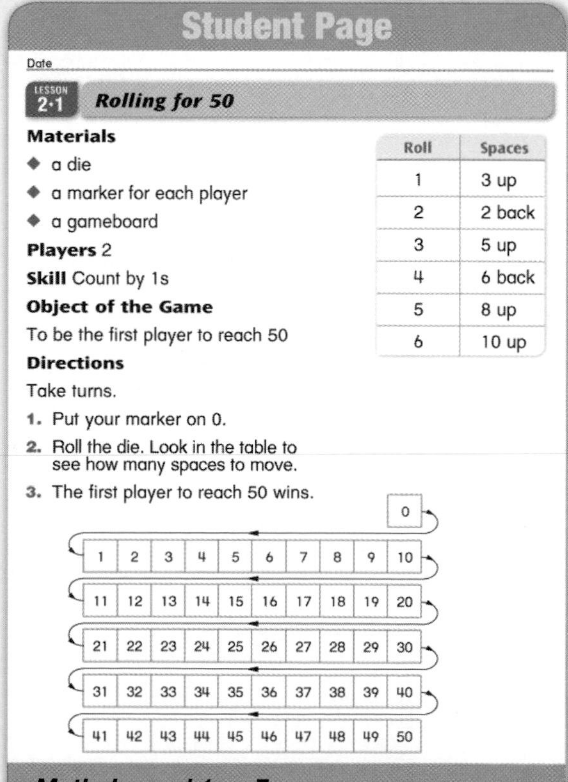

Date

LESSON 2·1 ***Rolling for 50***

Materials
- a die
- a marker for each player
- a gameboard

Players 2

Skill Count by 1s

Object of the Game

To be the first player to reach 50

Directions

Take turns.

1. Put your marker on 0.
2. Roll the die. Look in the table to see how many spaces to move.
3. The first player to reach 50 wins.

Roll	Spaces
1	3 up
2	2 back
3	5 up
4	6 back
5	8 up
6	10 up

0

1	2	3	4	5	6	7	8	9	10
11	12	13	14	15	16	17	18	19	20
21	22	23	24	25	26	27	28	29	30
31	32	33	34	35	36	37	38	39	40
41	42	43	44	45	46	47	48	49	50

Math Journal 1, p. 7

Teaching Aid Master

Name Date

Horizontal Number Grid

-9	-8	-7	-6	-5	-4	-3	-2	-1	0
1	2	3	4	5	6	7	8	9	10
11	12	13	14	15	16	17	18	19	20
21	22	23	24	25	26	27	28	29	30
31	32	33	34	35	36	37	38	39	40
41	42	43	44	45	46	47	48	49	50
51	52	53	54	55	56	57	58	59	60
61	62	63	64	65	66	67	68	69	70
71	72	73	74	75	76	77	78	79	80
81	82	83	84	85	86	87	88	89	90
91	92	93	94	95	96	97	98	99	100
101	102	103	104	105	106	107	108	109	110

Math Masters, p. 308

ELL When you use the *Everyday Mathematics* posters with English language learners, you should display either the English version only or the English and Spanish versions simultaneously.

NOTE Counting up and back on the number grid and finding the number of spaces between two numbers help prepare children to use the grid for addition and subtraction.

Ongoing Assessment: Informing Instruction

Watch for children who confuse "counting up or down" on the number grid with moving up and down on the page. Remind children to use the color-coded return sweeps to guide their movements.

▶ Introducing Number-Grid Counting

(*Math Journal 1,* inside back cover; *Math Masters,* p. 308)

Use the Number-Grid Poster (or an overhead transparency of *Math Masters,* page 308) as children follow along on the number grid on the inside back cover of their journals.

Begin by counting up by 1s. *For example:*

- Start at 12 and count up 5 spaces. Where do you land? 17
- Start at 38 and count up 9 spaces. Where do you land? 47

Next, count back by 1s. *For example:*

- Start at 26 and count back 4 spaces. Where do you land? 22
- Start at 13 and count backward 6 spaces. Where do you land? 7

Finally, count up by 1s to find the number of spaces between two numbers. *For example:*

- Start at 21 and count up to 27. How many hops did you take? 6 hops
- Start at 28 and count up to 35. How many hops did you take? 7 hops

Ongoing Assessment: Informing Instruction

When counting on the number grid, watch for children who count "1" as they put their finger on the starting number. They should put their finger on the starting number and then count "1" as they move to the next number.

Adjusting the Activity

Discuss the numbers that appear to the left of 0 on the number grid. These are called negative numbers. Remind children that they have seen negative numbers on a thermometer.

AUDITORY ◆ KINESTHETIC ◆ TACTILE ◆ VISUAL

2 Ongoing Learning & Practice

Playing *Top-It*

PARTNER ACTIVITY

Children practice comparing numbers by playing *Top-It*. For detailed instructions, see Lesson 1-6.

Ongoing Assessment: Recognizing Student Achievement

Exit Slip 

Portfolio Ideas

Use an **Exit Slip** (*Math Masters,* page 305) to assess children's ability to compare numbers. Have children write one pair of numbers from *Top-It* on an Exit Slip. Have them circle the larger number. Children are making adequate progress if they circle the larger number.

[Number and Numeration Goal 7]

Home Link 2•1

INDEPENDENT ACTIVITY

(*Math Masters,* p. 20)

Home Connection Children record their home telephone numbers and emergency daytime telephone numbers, including area codes. These numbers will be used in Lesson 2-2, so emphasize that children should bring their completed Home Links to school the next school day.

Minute Math+

SMALL-GROUP ACTIVITY

Use *Minute Math+,* pages 88 and 94 to provide more practice telling and solving number stories.

Teaching Aid Master

Name Date

My Exit Slip

Name Date

My Exit Slip

Math Masters, p. 305

NOTE Remember to reserve time every day to complete the number-line, attendance, calendar, temperature, and weather routines.

Home Link Master

Name Date

HOME LINK 2•1 **Telephone Numbers**

Family Note Work with your child to memorize important telephone numbers, including emergency daytime numbers other than your home number. Also, help your child find other examples of uses of numbers, such as:

- Measurements of length, height, weight, and volume
- Dates and times
- Tables
- Temperatures
- Counts
- Addresses and license plates
- Costs

Please return this Home Link to school tomorrow.

Answers vary for Exercises 1–3.

1. Write your area code and home telephone number.

(___ ___ ___) ___ ___ ___ – ___ ___ ___ ___

(area code) (telephone number)

2. Write an emergency number with the area code. This number could be for a relative or a neighbor. It might be the number for the local police department.

(___ ___ ___) ___ ___ ___ – ___ ___ ___ ___

(area code) (telephone number)

3. Write your first, second, and third names.

____

Practice

Write the number that comes after each number.

4. 10 11 **5.** 17 18 **6.** 19 20 **7.** 6 7

Math Masters, p. 20

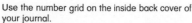

Teaching Master

Name Date

LESSON 2·1 Counting Up and Back

Use the number grid on the inside back cover of your journal.

For each problem, place a counter on the start number. Count up or back. Record the number where you end.

1. Start at 24.
   Count up 10.
   You end at 34.
2. Start at 47.
   Count up 10.
   You end at 57.
3. Start at 29.
   Count back 10.
   You end at 19.
4. Start at 88.
   Count back 10.
   You end at 78.
5. Start at 99.
   Count up 10.
   You end at 109.
6. Predict where you would end if you start at 51 and count up 10. 61

   Check your answer on the number grid.

Math Masters, **p. 21**

3 Differentiation Options

READINESS

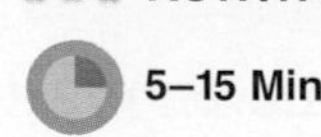

5–15 Min

▶ Coloring Return Sweeps on the Number Grid

(*Math Journal 1,* inside back cover)

To provide visual cues for navigating the number grid, have children color the return sweeps on the number grid on the inside back cover of *Math Journal 1.* They should color their grids to match the Number-Grid Poster. Children can follow the color-coded path as you ask questions that encourage them to move from row to row.

ENRICHMENT

▶ Counting Up and Back

(*Math Masters,* p. 21)

To further investigate navigating the number grid, have children count up and back by 10s on the number grid. When children hav finished the page, briefly discuss how they used patterns to predi the answer to Problem 6.

2•2 Numbers All Around

Objectives To guide exploration of the uses of numbers; and to introduce the parts of telephone numbers.

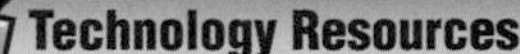

Technology Resources www.everydaymathonline.com

Presentations

eToolkit

Algorithms Practice

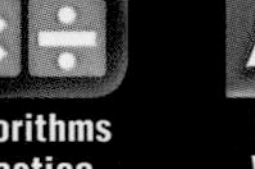
EM Facts Workshop Game™

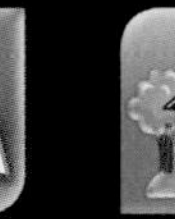
Family Letters

Assessment Management

Common Core State Standards

Curriculum Focal Points

Interactive Teacher's Lesson Guide

1 Teaching the Lesson

Key Concepts and Skills

- Read and write numbers.
  [Number and Numeration Goal 3]
- Create a tally chart to organize data.
  [Data and Chance Goal 1]
- Answer questions about data.
  [Data and Chance Goal 2]

Key Activities

Children discuss the examples of numbers they brought from home and their uses. They record personal information and important telephone numbers in their journals and discuss parts of telephone numbers.

Materials

Math Journal 1, p. 8
Home Link 2•1

2 Ongoing Learning & Practice

Reviewing Facts Within 5

Math Journal 1, pp. 8A and 8B
per small group: 4 numbered dice (see Advance Preparation for details on numbering the dice)
Children review the addition and subtraction facts within 5 and discuss strategies used to solve them.

Writing the Numbers 7 and 8

Math Journal 1, p. 9
Children practice writing the numbers 7 and 8.

Ongoing Assessment: Recognizing Student Achievement
Use journal page 9.
[Number and Numeration Goal 3]

Ongoing Assessment: Informing Instruction See page 102.

Home Link 2•2

Math Masters, p. 22
Children practice and maintain skills through Home Link activities.

3 Differentiation Options

READINESS

Categorizing Our Numbers

sample numbers from home
Children categorize the numbers they brought from home.

ENRICHMENT

Finding a Mystery Phone Number

Math Masters, p. 23
Children write combinations for the last four digits of a mystery phone number.

ELL SUPPORT

Describing Uses of Numbers

Children discuss the numbers in the Numbers All Around Museum.

Advance Preparation

For Part 1, display the Number-Grid Poster.

Beginning in Lesson 1•8, children were asked to bring examples of numbers from home. Display them on a bulletin board or in an area labeled the "Numbers All Around Museum." Group the numbers into categories; for example, counts, identification numbers, and money.

Have a list of children's home phone numbers available for those who did not complete Home Link 2•1. Include phone numbers of your school and local library.

In Part 2, you will create the beginnings of a Fact Strategy Wall that should be displayed in your classroom all year. On the wall, take care to list strategies in a way that children can understand them, along with examples of facts that can be solved using each strategy. Be sure to put the Fact Strategy Wall in a place where children can easily see it. Each time a new strategy is introduced to children or discovered by children, you will add it to the Fact Strategy Wall, so allow enough wall space to accommodate additional strategies.

Also for Part 2, each small group will need four dice, two for the addition facts review and two for the subtraction facts review. For the addition facts review, label one die 0, 1, 2, 0, 1, 2 and the other die 1, 2, 3, 1, 2, 3. For the subtraction facts review, label both dice 0, 1, 2, 3, 4, 5. Depending on the size of your class and the size of your small groups, you may need to borrow additional dice from another *Everyday Mathematics* class.

***Teacher's Reference Manual,* Grades 1–3** pp. 14, 54, 55

Getting Started

Mental Math and Reflexes

Have children say the special first-grade chant: *2, 4, 6, 8, first graders are really great!* Then have children count by 2s. You can use the following variation of the whisper-and-shout routine: The leader (you or a child) forms the front of a train. The children follow behind the leader, each child holding onto the waist of the child in front. They think *1*, hop and say "2," pause and think *3*, hop and say "4," pause and think *5*, hop and say "6," and so on.

Home Link 2•1 Follow-Up

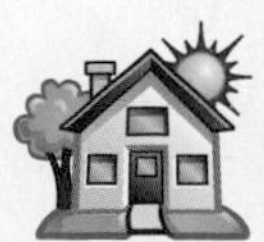

Discuss examples of numbers children brought from home. Note which children do not have Home Link 2-1 and will need to get their telephone numbers from your list.

Social Studies Link Ask children what they know about museums. A museum is a place where artistic, historic, or scientific objects are cared for and displayed.

NOTE Be sensitive to children without phones or children whose parents do not want to supply their phone numbers. In these cases, children can use fictitious phone numbers.

Student Page

Date

LESSON 2•2 **Information about Me**

Answers vary.

My first name is ______.

My second name is ______.

My last name is ______.

I am ____ years old.

Put candles on your cake.

My area code and home telephone number are

(______) ___ ___ ___ - ___ ___ ___ ___

(area code) (telephone number)

Important Phone Numbers

Emergency number: ___ ___ ___

School number:

(______) ___ ___ ___ - ___ ___ ___ ___

Local library number:

(______) ___ ___ ___ - ___ ___ ___ ___

Math Journal 1, p. 8

1 Teaching the Lesson

▶ Discussing Uses of Numbers

Tell children that they will make a Numbers All Around Museum in which they will display numbers they bring from home. Ask children to share some of the numbers they have found.

Discuss ways we use numbers in everyday life. Ask:

- How old are you? What does this number tell? Your age
- How do you call your friend on the telephone? Key in his or her telephone number How do the numbers that make up the telephone number help you? The numbers tell which buttons to press on the telephone.
- How do you know when to watch your favorite television show? Look up the time in the TV listings What does this number tell you? It tells what time the show starts.
- How do you know which tool kit is yours? Look at the identification number How does the identification number help you? It tells to whom each tool kit belongs.
- How can you find out where someone lives? Look up the person's address How does the number in the address help you? It tells in which house or building a person lives.

Remind children to keep looking for different uses of numbers to add to the Numbers All Around Museum.

▶ Recording Personal Information

(*Math Masters,* p, 20; *Math Journal 1,* p. 8)

Ask children to open their journals to page 8. Ask children to fill in personal information—their names, ages, and telephone numbers. Have them copy this information from their Home Links. They should also draw the appropriate numbers of candles on the cake.

Identifying Parts of Telephone Numbers

WHOLE-CLASS ACTIVITY

(*Math Journal 1,* p. 8)

Write the school telephone number on the board. Discuss the different parts of the telephone number: the area code, the prefix (the first three digits after the area code), and the rest of the number. Explain how each of these three parts is used.

▷ The area code identifies the section of the country in which the school is located—it may be the state, a part of the state, the city, or a part of the city.

▷ The prefix identifies a smaller part of the area code section—it may be the town or neighborhood in which the school is located.

▷ The last four digits identify the specific location of the telephone—in the school itself.

Explain to children that people usually chunk their phone numbers into groups of 3 and 4 digits so that the numbers are easier to remember.

Finally have children record the phone numbers for emergencies (911), their school, and the local library.

Social Studies Link Discuss the function of community helpers, such as firefighters, doctors, nurses, and librarians. You can have children write and illustrate simple sentences about these helpers, listing each of their advertised phone numbers.

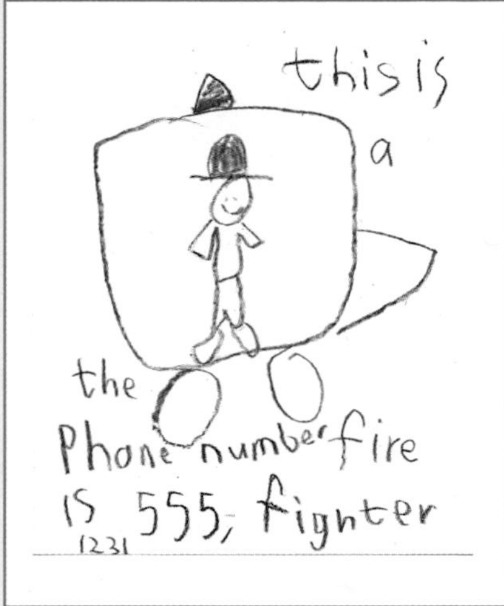

It is important for children to learn emergency numbers.

2 Ongoing Learning & Practice

Reviewing Facts Within 5

SMALL-GROUP ACTIVITY

(*Math Journal 1,* pp. 8A and 8B)

Explain that children are going to work in small groups to review some of the addition and subtraction facts that they learned in Kindergarten.

Demonstrate the addition activity using a pair of dice (one labeled 0, 1, 2, 0, 1, 2 and the other labeled 1, 2, 3, 1, 2, 3). Children take turns rolling two dice per roll. Each child records the numbers from the dice onto *Math Journal 1,* page 8A. Encourage children to recall the sums from memory or use their "quickest" strategy to find the sums. They record the sums on their journal page. You may need to suggest that children wait until others in their group have found the sum before sharing and comparing answers. Children continue rolling and recording addition facts until they have filled their Addition Facts Record with 12 different facts.

When pairs have completed the activity, bring the class together to share strategies for finding the different sums. Ask children to share addition facts they encountered during the activity. For each fact, ask several children to describe their strategies for solving the problem. Be sure to discuss a variety of facts as well as a variety of strategies.

Student Page

Date

LESSON 2·2 **Addition Facts Record**

Answers vary.

___ + ___ = ___	___ + ___ = ___
___ + ___ = ___	___ + ___ = ___
___ + ___ = ___	___ + ___ = ___
___ + ___ = ___	___ + ___ = ___
___ + ___ = ___	___ + ___ = ___
___ + ___ = ___	___ + ___ = ___

***Math Journal 1,* p. 8A**

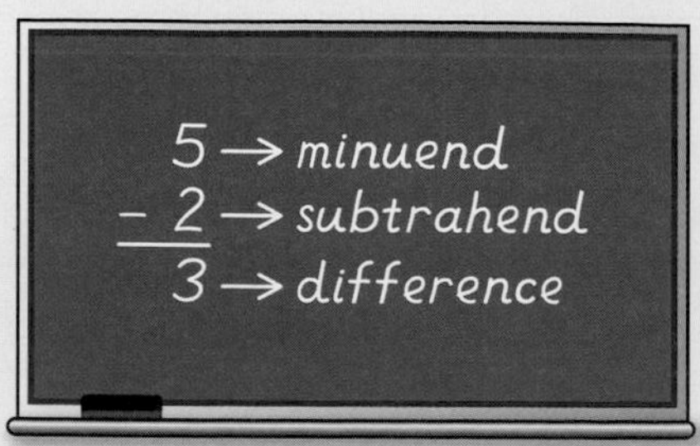

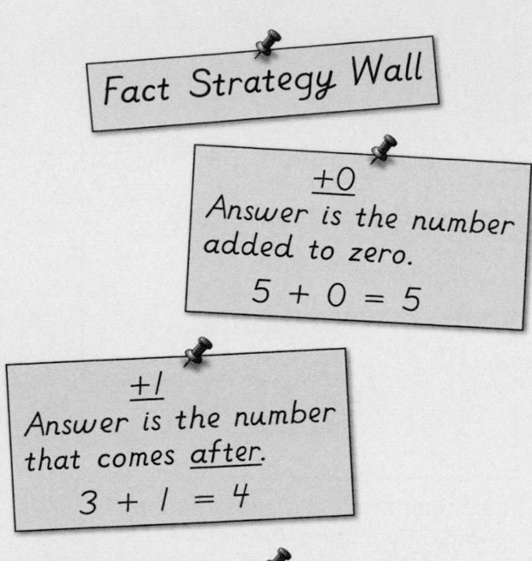

Fact Strategy Wall
+0
Answer is the number added to zero.
5 + 0 = 5
+1
Answer is the number that comes after.
3 + 1 = 4

Counting on from the larger number
Start with the larger number.
Count on the smaller number.
3 + 2 → 3 4 5
3 + 2 = 5

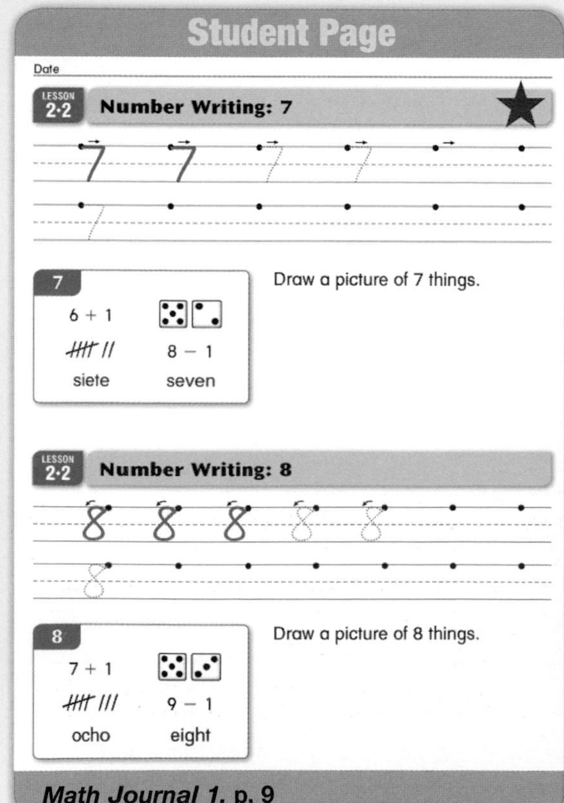
Student Page

Date

LESSON 2·2 **Number Writing: 7**

7 | 6 + 1 | 8 − 1 | siete | seven

Draw a picture of 7 things.

LESSON 2·2 **Number Writing: 8**

8 | 7 + 1 | 9 − 1 | ocho | eight

Draw a picture of 8 things.

Math Journal 1, p. 9

During this discussion, begin a Fact Strategy Wall. (*See Advance Preparation.*) If children do not mention a strategy for +0 facts, +1 facts, and counting on starting from the larger addend, introduce these strategies. (Counting on is a particularly useful strategy when adding 1, 2, and 3.) While turn-around facts are not introduced until Unit 4, if children notice that, for example, the answer to 2 + 3 is the same as the answer to 3 + 2, add this to the Fact Strategy Wall.

After discussing strategies for the addition facts within 5, have children complete the subtraction activity. Children work in pairs to roll two dice (both labeled 0, 1, 2, 3, 4, 5). Children record up to 12 different subtraction facts on their Subtraction Facts Record (*Math Journal 1,* page 8B). Remind children to write the larger number in the first space on the Subtraction Facts Record.

Once children have completed the activity, ask children to share subtraction facts recorded on their journal pages. Again, discuss a variety of different facts as well as a variety of different strategies for solving each fact. If children do not mention a strategy for −0 facts (difference is the same as the minuend), −1 facts (difference is the number that comes *before* the minuend), counting back (start at the minuend and count backwards), and counting up to subtract (start at the subtrahend and count up to the minuend), model these strategies and add them to your Fact Strategy Wall. (You do not need to use the technical terminology.)

NOTE *Kindergarten Everyday Mathematics* provides many experiences with addition and subtraction of small numbers. By the end of Kindergarten, most children will have efficient strategies for adding and subtracting within 5; many children will already have memorized the addition and subtraction facts within 5.

Writing the Numbers 7 and 8

INDEPENDENT ACTIVITY

(*Math Journal 1,* p. 9)

Children write the numbers 7 and 8. Tell them that the arrows show the most efficient way to form the numbers. When children finish, have them circle their best effort for each number. Then children draw pictures to represent the numbers 7 and 8.

Ongoing Assessment: Recognizing Student Achievement

Journal page 9

Use **journal page 9** to assess children's progress in number writing. Children are making adequate progress if they are able to write the numbers 7 and 8 legibly. Some children may have better fine motor skills than others.

[Number and Numeration Goal 3]

Ongoing Assessment: Informing Instruction

Watch for children who form an 8 by making two circles on top of each other. Show children that forming an 8 involves one continuous motion that begins and ends at the top of the 8.

Home Link 2•2

INDEPENDENT ACTIVITY

(*Math Masters,* p. 22)

Home Connection Children practice counting for someone at home. They explain how to use the number grid to help with counts.

3 Differentiation Options

READINESS

SMALL-GROUP ACTIVITY

Categorizing Our Numbers

5–15 Min

To explore numbers, have children categorize the numbers they brought from home. In each small group, children decide how to sort the numbers they brought from home into two categories. Expect to get a variety of categorization schemes—for example, numbers that have a lot of digits and numbers that have only one or two digits, numbers that have a particular digit and all other numbers, and numbers on labels and numbers from other sources. When children have finished, have them share how they sorted their numbers.

ENRICHMENT

INDEPENDENT ACTIVITY

Finding a Mystery Phone Number

5–15 Min

(*Math Masters,* p. 23)

To further explore phone numbers, explain to children that they will find a mystery phone number. Tell them that the last four digits of the phone number are missing. Have children write 4 different possible combinations on *Math Masters,* page 23. Encourage children to share the different possibilities.

ELL SUPPORT

SMALL-GROUP ACTIVITY

Describing Uses of Numbers

5–15 Min

To provide language support for numbers, have children look at the Numbers All Around Museum. Have children describe some of the kinds of numbers in the museum. Discuss ways that the numbers in the museum are being used. Sample answers: Money, an address on a door, a list of telephone numbers, the cost of something

Home Link Master

Name Date

HOME LINK 2•2 **Counting Up and Back**

Family Note To reinforce various types of counting, listen as your child counts by 1s and 10s. Counting for someone provides good practice in this essential first-grade skill.
Please return this Home Link to school tomorrow.

Answers vary.

1. Count for someone at home. Count up by 1s, starting with 1. I counted to ____.
2. Count back by 10s. Start with 50 or the highest number you can. I started with ____.
3. Explain to someone at home how to use the number grid to help with counts.

									0
1	2	3	4	5	6	7	8	9	10
11	12	13	14	15	16	17	18	19	20
21	22	23	24	25	26	27	28	29	30
31	32	33	34	35	36	37	38	39	40
41	42	43	44	45	46	47	48	49	50
51	52	53	54	55	56	57	58	59	60
61	62	63	64	65	66	67	68	69	70
71	72	73	74	75	76	77	78	79	80
81	82	83	84	85	86	87	88	89	90
91	92	93	94	95	96	97	98	99	100
101	102	103	104	105	106	107	108	109	110

Practice

Count back by 1s.

4. 10, 9, 8, 7, 6, 5, 4, 3, 2, 1

Math Masters, p. 22

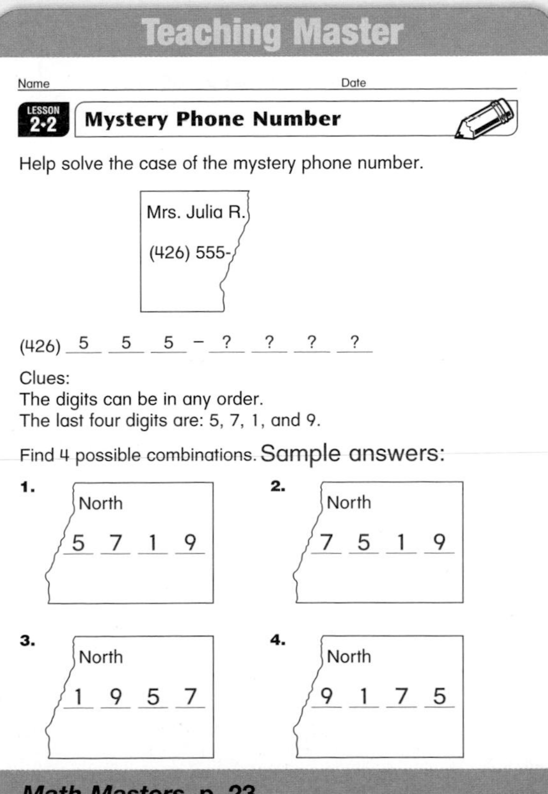

Teaching Master

Name Date

LESSON 2•2 **Mystery Phone Number**

Help solve the case of the mystery phone number.

Mrs. Julia R.
(426) 555-

(426) 5 5 5 – ? ? ? ?

Clues:
The digits can be in any order.
The last four digits are: 5, 7, 1, and 9.

Find 4 possible combinations. Sample answers:

1. North 5 7 1 9
2. North 7 5 1 9
3. North 1 9 5 7
4. North 9 1 7 5

Math Masters, p. 23

2•3 Complements of 10

Objectives To guide exploration of the complements of 10; to introduce ten frames; and to introduce the Math Boxes routine.

www.everydaymathonline.com

ePresentations

eToolkit

Algorithms Practice

EM Facts Workshop Game™

Family Letters

Assessment Management

Common Core State Standards

Curriculum Focal Points

Interactive Teacher's Lesson Guide

1 Teaching the Lesson

Key Concepts and Skills

- Count objects by 1s.
  [Number and Numeration Goal 2]
- Give equivalent names for 10; represent numbers with counters on a ten frame.
  [Number and Numeration Goal 6]
- Compare pairs of whole numbers.
  [Number and Numeration Goal 7]
- Find pairs of numbers with sums of 10.
  [Operations and Computation Goal 1]
- Make predictions and check outcomes.
  [Data and Chance Goal 3]

Key Activities

Children do Two-Fisted Penny Addition. They fill ten frames with various numbers of counters and play *Ten-Frame Top-It.* Children discuss the need for practice and complete their first Math Boxes page.

Ongoing Assessment: Informing Instruction See page 105.

Ongoing Assessment: Recognizing Student Achievement
Use Exit Slip (*Math Masters,* p. 305).
[Operations and Computation Goal 1]

Key Vocabulary

ten frame ◆ Math Boxes

Materials

Math Journal 1, p. 10 and inside back cover
Home Link 2•2
Math Masters, p. 24 (optional); pp. 305, 336, 336A, 336B ◆ transparency of *Math Masters,* p. 336 ◆ 10 pennies ◆ slate ◆ counters

2 Ongoing Learning & Practice

Practicing Writing the Numbers 7 and 8
Math Masters, p. 304
Children practice writing the numbers 7 and 8.

Home Link 2•3
Math Masters, p. 25
Children practice and maintain skills through Home Link activities.

3 Differentiation Options

READINESS
Counting Pennies
Math Masters, p. 26
per child: 10 pennies
Children divide 10 pennies into two groups.

ENRICHMENT
Making Sums of 10
Math Masters, p. 27
per partnership: 10 pennies
Children record combinations that make 10.

Advance Preparation

For Part 1, make enough copies of *Math Masters,* pages 336, 336A, and 336B on construction paper or other heavy paper so that each child has one copy of each page. Before the lesson begins, have children cut out the cards from pages 336A and 336B.
For the optional Enrichment activity in Part 3, you will need to make two copies of *Math Masters,* page 27 for each partnership.

***Teacher's Reference Manual,* Grades 1–3** pp. 11, 12

Getting Started

Mental Math and Reflexes

Children use the number grid on the inside back cover of their journals to solve the following problems:

●○○ Start at 15. Count back 8 hops. Where do you land? 7

●●○ Start at 29. Count back 5 hops. Where do you land? 24

●●● Start at 41. Count back 9 spaces. Where do you land? 32

Home Link 2·2 Follow-Up

Children share how high they counted up by 1s and where they started counting back by 10s. Invite them to explain how they used the number grid to help with their counts.

1 Teaching the Lesson

Introducing Two-Fisted Penny Addition

Ask children to name things that come in pairs. Sample answers: Socks, shoes, hands, eyes Discuss how a pair is made up of two parts. Tell children that they will be finding pairs of numbers that make 10 while doing Two-Fisted Penny Addition. Have each child take out 10 pennies. Then ask children to grab a handful of pennies with one hand and to pick up the rest with the other hand. Have volunteers identify the number of pennies in each hand as you record it on the board. Ask children to provide information using this format: "I have 3 pennies in one hand and 7 pennies in the other hand." Using such language reinforces the idea that each number is a count of objects.

Left Hand	Right Hand
3	7

NOTE This lesson provides early preparation for children's learning of addition facts. Sums of 10 are among the facts first-grade children are expected to learn. Fluency with addition facts through 10 + 10 is a Grade 1 Goal.

NOTE This lesson contains a significant amount of content; you may wish to complete it over two days.

NOTE Some teachers use this opportunity to review *right* and *left* by having children say, "I have _____ pennies in my right hand and _____ pennies in my left hand."

Ongoing Assessment: Informing Instruction

Watch for children whose pairs do not add up to 10. Help children understand that if they start with 10 pennies, then the numbers of pennies in both hands should always add up to 10.

Adjusting the Activity

ELL

Draw two large hands on the board and record the numbers of pennies inside the outlines of the hands, using both numbers and circles. Give each child a copy of *Math Masters,* page 24. Children can put the pennies on the two hands and count them.

AUDITORY ♦ KINESTHETIC ♦ TACTILE ♦ VISUAL

Adjusting the Activity

Have children predict the number of pennies in the second hand before counting them. Discuss strategies for predictions. Children can write down their predictions and then count the pennies to check them. Ask how many pennies there are in all. 10

AUDITORY ♦ KINESTHETIC ♦ TACTILE ♦ VISUAL

Have children continue this activity in partnerships, recording on their slates the number of pennies in each hand. You may need to help children record the numbers.

Ongoing Assessment: Recognizing Student Achievement

Exit Slip

Use an **Exit Slip** (*Math Masters,* page 305) to assess children's understanding of sums of 10. On an Exit Slip, have children trace their hands and then draw circles to represent pennies in each hand for a total of 10 pennies. Children are making adequate progress if the sum of the numbers of pennies drawn equals 10. Some children may show more than one combination of 10 pennies.

[Operations and Computation Goal 1]

▶ Introducing Ten Frames

WHOLE-CLASS ACTIVITY

FACTS PRACTICE

(*Math Masters,* p. 336)

Give each child a copy of *Math Masters,* page 336 and some counters. Use an overhead transparency of *Math Masters,* page 336 to demonstrate how to fill a ten frame using counters. Start at the top left and fill the top row first. Then fill the second row, beginning at the left and finishing at the bottom right. Remind children that each space can contain only one counter for a total of ten counters. Explain that this is called a **ten frame.** After children understand how to fill a ten frame, call out different numbers less than or equal to ten. Have children add or remove counters to make their ten frames match the number called. While this can be a fast-paced activity, stop every so often to discuss any patterns that children see in the layout of the counters. For example, when you have called "5," stop and ask children what they can tell about the number 5 from looking at the ten frame. Sample answer: Half of the ten frame is filled, so there are two 5s in ten. Continue this activity, calling out numbers, having children fill their ten frames, and discussing number representations on the ten frame until children seem comfortable with the ten frame.

▶ Introducing *Ten-Frame Top-It*

PARTNER ACTIVITY

FACTS PRACTICE

(*Math Masters,* pp. 336A and 336B)

This game is for two players. Prior to the game, each child should have cut 12 ten-frame cards from *Math Masters,* pages 336A and 336B. Have players combine their sets of cards, mix them together and put them in a pile with the ten frames facing down.

Directions

1. Each player takes a card from the top of the pile, turns it over, and says the number represented by the ten frame on the card.
2. The player who has the larger number takes both cards.
3. If the two cards show the same number, each player takes another card from the top of the pile. The player with the larger number takes all of the cards facing up.
4. The game is over when all of the cards have been taken. The player with more cards wins.

Variation: Players call the number represented by the blank spaces on the ten-frame cards. The player with the smaller number takes both cards.

Introducing the Math Boxes Routine

WHOLE-CLASS DISCUSSION

Ask whether anyone is learning to play a musical instrument, dance, ride a bike, or play a sport. Ask:

- What would happen if you never practiced?
- What do you think is meant by the expression "practice makes perfect"?

Explain to children that the **Math Boxes** contain problems that will help them practice important mathematics skills and become good at mathematics.

The Math Boxes routine is introduced in Part 1. Beginning in Lesson 2-4, it will appear in Part 2 of each lesson.

Math Boxes 2•3

INDEPENDENT ACTIVITY

(*Math Journal 1*, p. 10)

Mixed Practice Math Boxes in this lesson are paired with Math Boxes in Lesson 2-5. The skills in Problem 4 preview Unit 3 content.

Go over the problems so that children understand what they are to do. Then have children complete the journal page independently or with a partner. When they have solved the problems, briefly go over the answers.

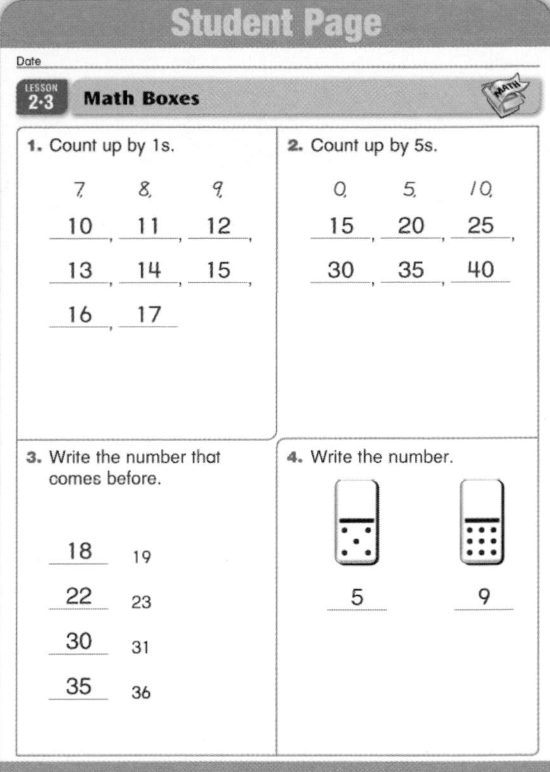
Student Page

Date

LESSON 2•3 **Math Boxes**

1. Count up by 1s.
7, 8, 9, 10, 11, 12, 13, 14, 15, 16, 17

2. Count up by 5s.
0, 5, 10, 15, 20, 25, 30, 35, 40

3. Write the number that comes before.
18 19
22 23
30 31
35 36

4. Write the number.
5 9

Math Journal 1, p. 10

Home Link Master

Name Date

HOME LINK 2•3 **Two-Fisted Penny Addition**

Family Note By doing Two-Fisted Penny Addition, you are helping your child learn the basic addition facts. These basic facts will be useful when your child solves more difficult addition and subtraction problems mentally.
Please return this Home Link to school tomorrow.

Do Two-Fisted Penny Addition with someone at home:

- On a piece of paper, draw 2 large circles.
- Place pennies on the table. Grab some pennies with one hand. Pick up the rest with the other hand.
- Place 1 pile of pennies in each circle and count them.
- Use the tables below to write how many pennies are in each circle. Sample answers:

1. Start with 10 pennies.

Number of Pennies in One Hand	Number of Pennies in the Other Hand
5	5
4	6
2	8

2. Start with 15 pennies.

Number of Pennies in One Hand	Number of Pennies in the Other Hand
8	7
9	6
12	3

Practice

3. Count up by 5s.
5, 10, 15, 20, 25, 30

Math Masters, p. 25

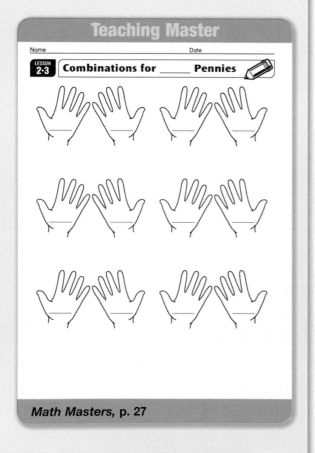

Teaching Master

Name Date

LESSON 2·3 **Number Line**

0 1 2 3 4 5 6 7 8 9 10

Math Masters, p. 26

Teaching Master

Name Date

LESSON 2·3 **Combinations for _____ Pennies**

Math Masters, p. 27

2 Ongoing Learning & Practice

▶ Practicing Writing the Numbers 7 and 8

(*Math Masters,* p. 304)

Use *Math Masters,* page 304 to provide more practice writing the numbers 7 and 8.

▶ Home Link 2·3

(*Math Masters,* p. 25)

Home Connection Children show someone at home how to do Two-Fisted Penny Addition.

3 Differentiation Options

READINESS

▶ Counting Pennies

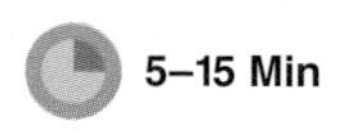

5–15 Min

(*Math Masters,* p. 26)

To provide experience with counting, have children practice lining up pennies on a number line. Children begin with 10 pennies. They grab some of the pennies and guess how many they grabbed. They line up these pennies on *Math Masters,* page 26 (one penny in each circle, starting with 1) and count how many they grabbed. Have children describe how many pennies they grabbed and how many are left.

ENRICHMENT

▶ Making Sums of 10

15–30 Min

(*Math Masters,* p. 27)

To further explore complements of ten, have children record all possible combinations while doing Two-Fisted Penny Addition. There are 11 different combinations, so each pair will need two copies of *Math Masters,* page 27.

Planning Ahead

For the optional Readiness activity in Lesson 2-4, you will need to prepare mystery bags. See Advance Preparation in Lesson 2-4 for details.

2•4 Unit Labels for Numbers

Objectives To introduce the need for unit labels for numbers; and to introduce calculators.

www.everydaymathonline.com

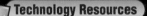

Presentations | eToolkit | Algorithms Practice | EM Facts Workshop Game™ | Family Letters | Assessment Management | Common Core State Standards | Curriculum Focal Points | Interactive Teacher's Lesson Guide

1 Teaching the Lesson

Key Concepts and Skills

- Count forward by 1s, labeling numbers with unit labels. [Number and Numeration Goal 1]
- Count objects by 1s, labeling numbers with unit labels. [Number and Numeration Goal 2]
- Use a calculator to represent numbers. [Number and Numeration Goal 6]

Key Activities

Children practice counting and using unit boxes to reinforce the idea that counting numbers always refer to units. They practice entering numbers in their calculators.

Key Vocabulary

unit box ◆ unit

Materials

Math Journal 1, inside back cover
Home Link 2•3
can or container ◆ 20 pennies ◆ calculator

2 Ongoing Learning & Practice

Writing the Numbers 9 and 0

Math Journal 1, p. 11
Children practice writing the numbers 9 and 0.

Ongoing Assessment: Recognizing Student Achievement
Use journal page 11.
[Number and Numeration Goal 3]

Ongoing Assessment: Informing Instruction See page 112.

Math Boxes 2•4

Math Journal 1, p. 12
Children practice and maintain skills through Math Box problems.

Home Link 2•4

Math Masters, p. 28
Children practice and maintain skills through Home Link activities.

3 Differentiation Options

READINESS

Labeling Items in a Mystery Bag

per child: mystery bag with 5 items, labels on 4" by 6" cards
Children count and label items from mystery bags.

EXTRA PRACTICE

Labeling Units

Math Masters, p. 309
Children practice identifying units.

Advance Preparation

For Part 1, you will need a can or container that makes a loud sound when pennies are dropped into it. Mark the calculators with children's tool-kit numbers. To prepare mystery bags for the optional Readiness activity in Part 3, you will need 1 paper bag per each type of item and 5 of each type of item. For each bag, make a label by writing the name of the items on a 4" by 6" card. Add a visual to the card—a picture, if possible.

***Teacher's Reference Manual,* Grades 1–3** pp. 18, 23–29

Getting Started

Mental Math and Reflexes

Have children say the special first-grade chant: *2, 4, 6, 8, first graders are really great!*

Then have them use the number grid on the inside back cover of their journals to solve the following problems:

●○○ Start at 11. Count up to 16. How many hops did you take? 5

●●○ Start at 14. Count up to 24. How many spaces did you move? 10

●●● Start at 35. Count up to 48. How many spaces did you move? 13

Home Link 2·3 Follow-Up

Have volunteers share their results from Two-Fisted Penny Addition.

1 Teaching the Lesson

▶ Labeling Numbers with Units

WHOLE-CLASS DISCUSSION

NOTE Numbers do not always stand for counts of objects; for example, the number 5 may refer to a measure of 5 feet; to a place in an ordered sequence, such as the 5th child in line; or to a code, such as Channel 5. Encourage children to give examples of number uses other than counts of objects.

Write the number 5 on the board and tell the class that this number can stand for many things—for example, 5 fingers, 5 desks, or 5 pennies. Have the class give other examples.

Ask children to point out 5 of something in the classroom, such as 5 crayons or 5 windows. Repeat this activity using other numbers, including those in the Numbers All Around Museum. Emphasize that numbers used to count or measure always include units, such as 5 *nickels,* 2 *eyes,* 3 *miles,* or 70 *pounds.*

▶ Introducing the Unit Box

WHOLE-CLASS ACTIVITY

In *Everyday Mathematics,* a device called a **unit box** is often used as a reminder of the **unit** to which numbers refer.

Unit
pennies

Draw a unit box on the board and write the word *pennies* in it. Tell children that they will be counting pennies and that the word *pennies* in the unit box is a reminder of what is being counted.

Start with an empty can or container. Show children that the can is empty. Then do this activity:

▷ Drop pennies into the can while children listen and count silently.

▷ After you stop, ask how many pennies are in the can.

▷ Empty the can and have someone count the pennies.

▷ Repeat this routine using different numbers of pennies.

▷ As a variation, tell children that you want to drop a certain number of pennies into the can. Tell them to say, "Stop!" when you reach that number.

Ask someone to suggest a new unit for the box. Encourage children to come up with imaginative units, such as elephants' trunks, or units they especially like, such as stickers or baseballs.

Introducing Calculators

Give a calculator to each child. Tell children that they will keep the calculators in their tool kits. Give children a few minutes to explore their calculators. Then ask children what they already know or may have discovered about calculators.

Before beginning the calculator exercises, discuss the everyday meaning of *key,* as well as its meaning in this context.

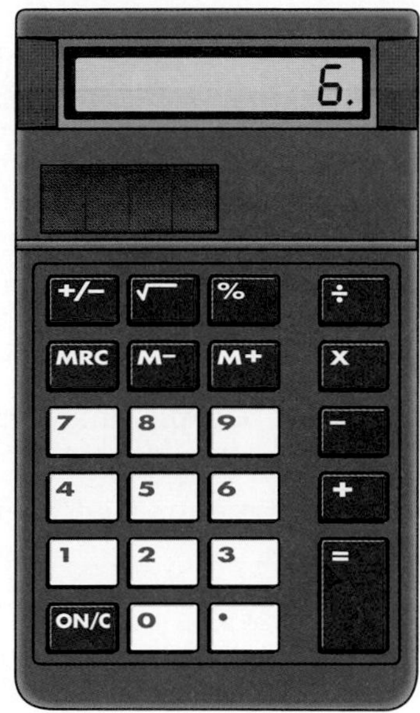

TI-108

Casio SL-450L

To practice entering and clearing numbers, direct children as follows:

- Find the Clear key on your calculator. *Clear* means "Erase the numbers in the calculator display." Clear your calculators by pressing the ON/C or C key.
- Find the number for your age on the calculator. Press that key so the calculator shows your age. Then clear your calculator.
- Enter the number of windows in the room. Clear.
- Enter the number of teachers in the room. Clear.
- Enter the number of children who are absent. Clear.
- Enter the number of puppies in the classroom. Clear.
- Enter the number 19. Clear.

Planning Tip You can use any calculator to complete the activites in *First Grade Everyday Mathematics*. For demonstration purposes, key sequences for the TI-108 and the Casio SL-450L calculators are provided. Check your calculator user's manual and adjust the instruction accordingly.

NOTE The "Clear" key may be labeled differently on your calculators. *For example:* C or ON/C.

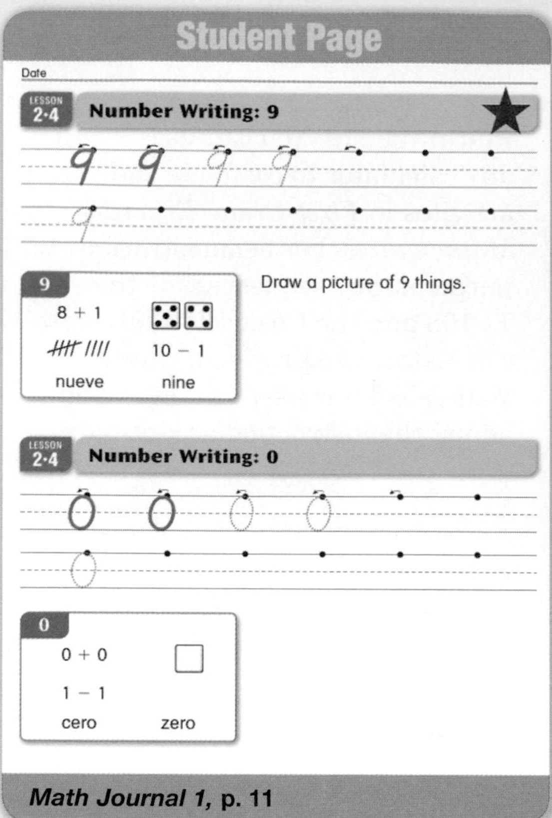

Student Page
Date
LESSON 2·4
Number Writing: 9
9
Draw a picture of 9 things.
8 + 1
10 − 1
nueve
nine
LESSON 2·4
Number Writing: 0
0
0 + 0
1 − 1
cero
zero
Math Journal 1, p. 11

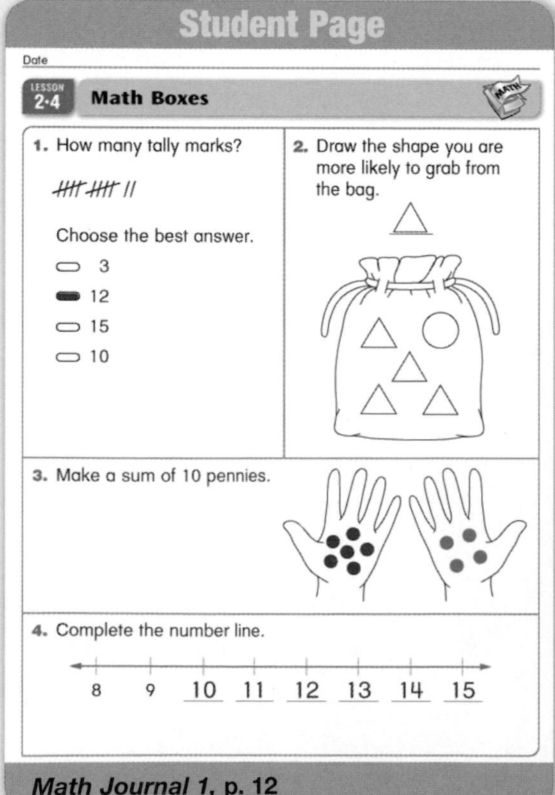

Student Page
Date
LESSON 2·4
Math Boxes
1. How many tally marks?
Choose the best answer.
3
12
15
10
2. Draw the shape you are more likely to grab from the bag.
3. Make a sum of 10 pennies.
4. Complete the number line.
8
9
10
11
12
13
14
15
Math Journal 1, p. 12

2 Ongoing Learning & Practice

▶ Writing the Numbers 9 and 0

(*Math Journal 1,* p. 11)

Have children write the numbers 9 and 0. Remind them to take their time and that the arrows show the most efficient way to form the numbers.

When children finish, have them circle their best effort for each number.

Have children draw pictures to represent the number 9.

Finally, ask:

- Can anyone make up a zero number story? Sample answer: How many children in the class have 3 ears?
- How would you draw a picture of 0 things? Sample answer: Just show a blank space because "zero things" means that there is "nothing." For example, zero apples means that there are no apples.

Ongoing Assessment: Recognizing Student Achievement

Journal page 11 

Use **journal page 11** to assess children's progress in number writing. Children are making adequate progress if they are able to write the numbers 9 and 0 legibly. Some children may be more experienced writing numbers than others.

[Number and Numeration Goal 3]

Ongoing Assessment: Informing Instruction

Watch for children who have difficulty understanding the concept of zero. Tell them that zero is used to represent nothing. Show them various numbers of items, including zero, and allow children to name and write the numbers on their slates.

▶ Math Boxes 2·4

(*Math Journal 1,* p. 12)

Mixed Practice Math Boxes in this lesson are paired with Math Boxes in Lesson 2-6. The skills in Problem 4 preview Unit 3 content.

Home Link 2•4

INDEPENDENT ACTIVITY

(*Math Masters,* p. 28)

Home Connection Children ask someone to write a number. Then they write the number that comes *before* and *after* that number.

3 Differentiation Options

READINESS

Labeling Items in a Mystery Bag

SMALL-GROUP ACTIVITY

5–15 Min

To provide concrete experiences with unit labels, have children match labels to items. Give each child a paper bag with 5 items inside. Ask children to take out the items and count them. Then have them identify the items. Have children find the label that matches their items. Have them tell what they counted and show their labels. Point out that although each bag had 5 items, the items in each bag were different. Have children ask for each other's items by number and unit. For example, "Ivan, can I have your 5 crayons?" Discuss why it is important to state both the number and the name of the item.

EXTRA PRACTICE

Labeling Units

PARTNER ACTIVITY

5–15 Min

(*Math Masters,* p. 309)

Children practice identifying units on *Math Masters,* page 309. For each problem, have children draw 3–5 of the same item. Then have them trade papers with a partner. Partners fill in unit boxes with the proper unit.

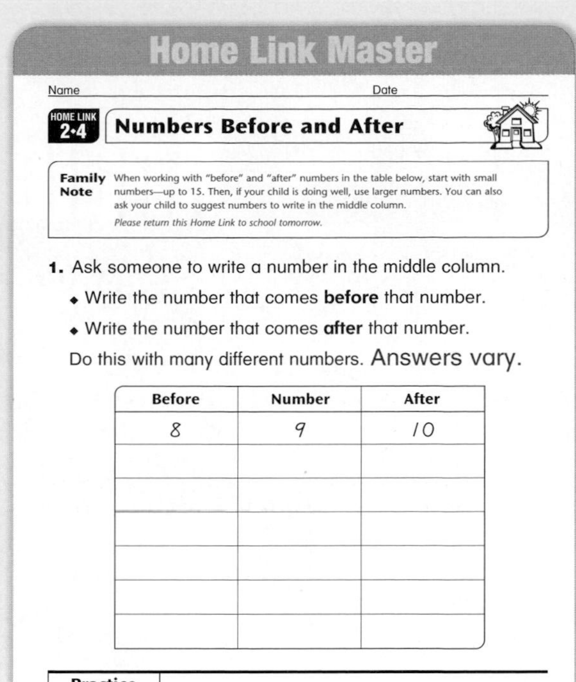

Home Link Master

Name Date

HOME LINK 2•4 **Numbers Before and After**

Family Note When working with "before" and "after" numbers in the table below, start with small numbers—up to 15. Then, if your child is doing well, use larger numbers. You can also ask your child to suggest numbers to write in the middle column.

Please return this Home Link to school tomorrow.

1. Ask someone to write a number in the middle column.
- Write the number that comes **before** that number.
- Write the number that comes **after** that number.

Do this with many different numbers. Answers vary.

Before	Number	After
8	9	10

Practice

2. Write the numbers 7–10 below. Circle the number you wrote best.

7 8 9 10

***Math Masters,* p. 28**

Teaching Aid Master

Name Date

Blank Unit Boxes

Unit

Unit

Unit

Unit

***Math Masters,* p. 309**

2•5 Analog Clocks

 Objective To introduce the analog clock.

Technology Resources www.everydaymathonline.com

ePresentations

eToolkit

Algorithms Practice

EM Facts Workshop Game™

Family Letters

Assessment Management

Common Core State Standards

Curriculum Focal Points

Interactive Teacher's Lesson Guide

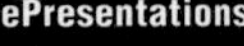

1 Teaching the Lesson

Key Concepts and Skills

- Read whole numbers. [Number and Numeration Goal 3]
- Compare the functions of the hands on a clock. [Measurement and Reference Frames Goal 4]
- Estimate time on an analog clock, using only the hour hand. [Measurement and Reference Frames Goal 4]
- Use language of approximation to describe times on an analog clock. [Measurement and Reference Frames Goal 4]

Key Activities

Children discuss some of the uses of clocks and watches. They observe the movement of the hour hand in relation to the movement of the minute hand. They estimate the time shown on a clock that has an hour hand only.

Key Vocabulary

analog clock ◆ hour hand ◆ minute hand ◆ estimate

Materials

Home Link 2•4
Math Masters, p. 29
clock or watch with second hand ◆ demonstration clock with and without a minute hand

2 Ongoing Learning & Practice

Playing *Rolling for 50*
Math Journal 1, p. 7
per partnership: 1 die, 2 game markers
Children practice navigating along a number grid.

Math Boxes 2•5
Math Journal 1, p. 13
Children practice and maintain skills through Math Box problems.

Ongoing Assessment: Recognizing Student Achievement
Use Math Boxes, Problem 3.
[Number and Numeration Goal 7]

Home Link 2•5
Math Masters, p. 30
Children practice and maintain skills through Home Link activities.

Minute Math+
Minute Math®+, pp. 9 and 22
Children practice finding compliments of 10 and counting money.

3 Differentiation Options

ENRICHMENT

Illustrating Daily Activities
Math Masters, p. 31
scissors
Children make drawings of daily activities, showing the approximate time for each activity by drawing hands on a clock face.

ELL SUPPORT

Building a Math Word Bank
Differentiation Handbook, p. 126
Children add the terms *minute hand* and *hour hand* to their Math Word Banks.

Advance Preparation

For Part 1, see page 115 for making a demonstration clock with only an hour hand. For the optional Enrichment activity in Part 3, make copies of *Math Masters,* page 31 for children to cut into quarter-sheets.

 ***Teacher's Reference Manual,* Grades 1–3** pp. 172, 173, 186–190

Getting Started

Mental Math and Reflexes

Ask children if they know about how long a minute is. Tell them to sit quietly with their eyes closed. When they think one minute is up, they raise their hands and open their eyes. When the last child has done this, tell the class which child came closest to estimating the length of a minute.

Repeat the activity. But this time, inform children when one minute is up so that they can all raise their hands at the correct time.

Help children estimate one minute by counting and then clapping in unison: 1, (clap), 2, (clap), 3, (clap), and so on, up to 60, (clap).

Home Link 2·4 Follow-Up

Briefly go over the answers.

1 Teaching the Lesson

Discussing Tools for Telling Time

WHOLE-CLASS DISCUSSION

Talk about the different ways people use time and tools for telling time. The discussions should include the following points:

▷ Clocks help us organize our day.

▷ Stopwatches help us figure out who is faster in a race or how much time a player has to take a turn.

▷ Calendars help us keep track of the days and months. They also help us remember and plan for important events.

Science Link Encourage children to talk about other ways people have kept track of time, such as observing the movement of the sun and the moon and noticing the changes from season to season.

Discussing the Position of the Hour Hand

WHOLE-CLASS ACTIVITY

Ask children to locate clocks in the classroom. It is likely that most school clocks are **analog clocks,** clocks that have an hour and a minute hand. If the subject of digital clocks comes up, point out that digital clocks have no hour or minute hand. (Digital time notation will be introduced in Lesson 6-10.)

Use a demonstration clock for the following:

▷ Identify the **hour hand** and the **minute hand.** Discuss the everyday meanings of *hand,* as well as its meaning in this context. Explain that the hour hand is shorter. Point the minute hand straight up. Ask children to describe what happens to the hour hand as you move the minute hand one full circle. The hour hand moves slower than the minute hand.

NOTE Use *Math Masters,* page 29 (see page 116) to make demonstration clocks out of tagboard or a paper plate. Attach the hour hand to it with a brad. You will need a demonstration clock with an hour hand only and one with an hour hand and a minute hand.

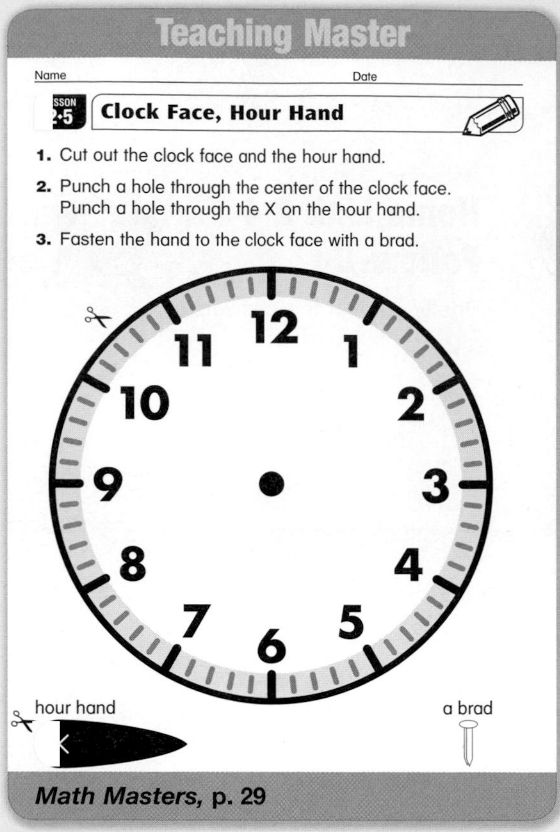

Teaching Master
Name
Date
Clock Face, Hour Hand
1. Cut out the clock face and the hour hand.
2. Punch a hole through the center of the clock face. Punch a hole through the X on the hour hand.
3. Fasten the hand to the clock face with a brad.
12
1
2
3
4
5
6
7
8
9
10
11
hour hand
a brad

Math Masters, p. 29

▷ Start with both the hour and minute hands pointing straight up. Move the minute hand clockwise around the clock face and have children call out the hours as the hour hand passes from one number to the next.

▷ Move the minute hand several more times around the clock face. Ask children to watch the hour hand only and to say, "Stop!" when they think it is exactly on a number. Ask them in which direction the minute hand is pointing when the hour hand points to a number. It's pointing straight up.

▷ *Conclusion:* When the minute hand points straight up, the hour hand points to a number. This number tells the time on the hour. For example, if the minute hand points straight up and the hour hand points to the 2, then we say that it is about 2 o'clock. Show 2 o'clock and write *2 o'clock* on the board.

▷ Move the minute hand several times around the clock face. Ask children to watch the hour hand only and to say, "Stop!" when they think it is pointing about halfway between two numbers. Repeat and ask children in which direction the minute hand is pointing when the hour hand is about halfway between two numbers. It's pointing straight down.

▶ Estimating the Time Shown on an Hour-Hand-Only Clock

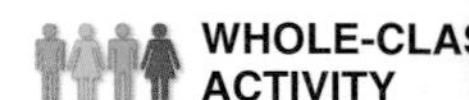

(*Math Masters,* p. 29)

Discuss the fact that as soon as you say what time it is, it is already a little later. Therefore, telling time is always an **estimate;** it is never exact.

Explain that we can estimate what time it is by looking at the hour hand only.

1. Position the hands on the demonstration clock to show about 4 o'clock. Move the minute hand so that it points to 10 minutes past 4 o'clock.
    - How would you describe the time shown? After 4 o'clock; between 4 o'clock and 5 o'clock; a little after 4 o'clock
2. Ask the class to watch the hour hand as you move the minute hand slowly around the clock face.
    - Is the time getting closer to 4 o'clock or to 5 o'clock? Closer to 5 o'clock
3. Use your hour-hand-only demonstration clock and move the hour hand so that it points to 2.
    - What time is it? About 2 o'clock
4. Move the hour hand on the hour-hand-only clock so that it points about halfway between 8 and 9.
    - How would you describe what time it is? Between 8 o'clock and 9 o'clock

5. Repeat this routine several times. Move the hour hand to various positions and ask the class to tell about what time it is. Emphasize the use of estimation language. For example, with the hour hand between two numbers, we can say the time, using words and phrases like *about* ____, *almost* ____, *just before* ____, *a little after* ____, and *between* ____ *and* ____.

2 Ongoing Learning & Practice

Playing *Rolling for 50*

PARTNER ACTIVITY

(*Math Journal 1,* p. 7)

Children practice navigating along a number grid by playing *Rolling for 50.* For detailed instructions, see Lesson 2-1.

Math Boxes 2•5

(*Math Journal 1,* p. 13)

Mixed Practice Math Boxes in this lesson are paired with Math Boxes in Lesson 2-3. The skills in Problem 4 preview Unit 3 content.

Ongoing Assessment: Recognizing Student Achievement

Math Boxes Problem 3 

Use **Math Boxes, Problem 3** to assess children's understanding of ordering numbers. Children are making adequate progress if they can use a number line or number grid to tell what number comes before another number.

[Number and Numeration Goal 7]

Home Link 2•5

(*Math Masters,* p. 30)

Home Connection Children count the numbers of clocks and watches in their homes and record the results using tally marks.

NOTE Suggest that children look at computers, cell phones, microwave ovens, and other appliances that may have clocks.

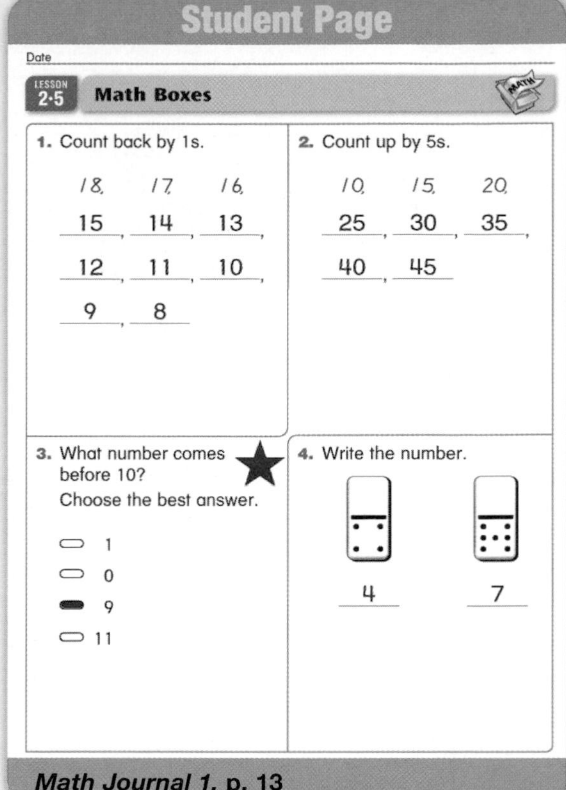

Student Page

Date

LESSON 2•5 **Math Boxes**

1. Count back by 1s.

18, 17, 16, 15, 14, 13, 12, 11, 10, 9, 8

2. Count up by 5s.

10, 15, 20, 25, 30, 35, 40, 45

3. What number comes before 10? Choose the best answer.

- 1
- 0
- 9 (filled)
- 11

4. Write the number.

4 7

Math Journal 1, p. 13

NOTE Remember to reserve time each day to complete the number-line, attendance, calendar, temperature, and weather routines.

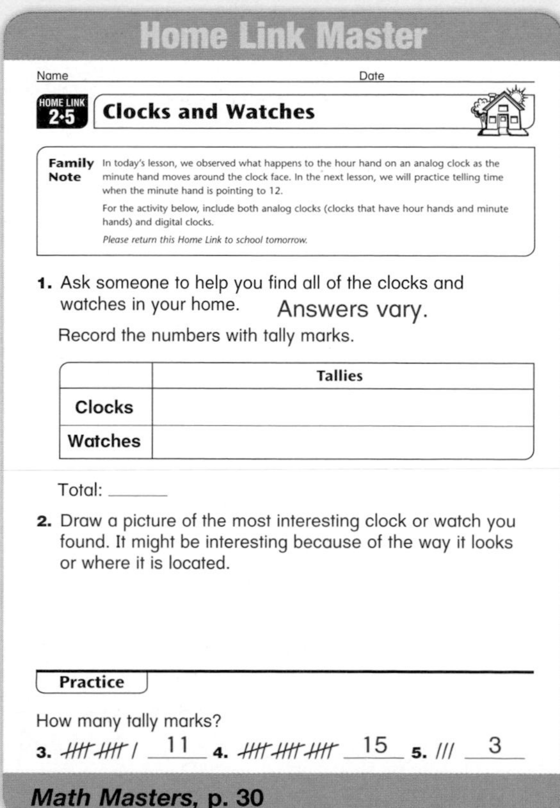

Home Link Master

Name Date

HOME LINK 2•5 **Clocks and Watches**

Family Note In today's lesson, we observed what happens to the hour hand on an analog clock as the minute hand moves around the clock face. In the next lesson, we will practice telling time when the minute hand is pointing to 12.

For the activity below, include both analog clocks (clocks that have hour hands and minute hands) and digital clocks.

Please return this Home Link to school tomorrow.

1. Ask someone to help you find all of the clocks and watches in your home. Answers vary.
Record the numbers with tally marks.

	Tallies
Clocks	
Watches	

Total: ____

2. Draw a picture of the most interesting clock or watch you found. It might be interesting because of the way it looks or where it is located.

Practice

How many tally marks?

3. HHH HHH / 11 4. HHH HHH HHH 15 5. /// 3

Math Masters, p. 30

Teaching Master

Name Date

LESSON 2·5 Clock Faces

Math Masters, p. 31

▶ *Minute Math+*

SMALL-GROU
ACTIVITY

Use *Minute Math+,* pages 9 and 22 to provide more practice with complements of 10 and counting money.

3 Differentiation Options

ENRICHMENT

INDEPENDEN
ACTIVITY

▶ Illustrating Daily Activities

15–30 Min

(*Math Masters,* p. 31)

Portfolio Ideas

To further explore children's understanding of time, have them illustrate their daily activities according to the time of day. Children cut apart *Math Masters,* page 31 into quarter-sheets and then draw pictures of daily activities on the blank sides. On the clock-face side of each sheet, they draw a minute hand pointing straight up and an hour hand pointing to th approximate hour when the activity occurs. Have children tell the time and describe the activity for each illustration.

ELL SUPPORT

SMALL-GROU
ACTIVITY

▶ Building a Math Word Bank

5–15 Min

(*Differentiation Handbook,* p. 126)

To provide language support for telling time, have children use th Word Bank Template found on *Differentiation Handbook,* page 12 Ask children to write the terms *minute hand* and *hour hand,* dra pictures representing the terms, and write other words that describe them. See the *Differentiation Handbook* for more information.

2·6 Telling Time to the Hour

Objectives To introduce the division of the day into A.M. and P.M. times; to provide practice telling time to the hour; and to develop a sense of the duration of a minute.

Technology Resources www.everydaymathonline.com

Presentations

eToolkit

Algorithms Practice

EM Facts Workshop Game™

Family Letters

Assessment Management

Common Core State Standards

Curriculum Focal Points

Interactive Teacher's Lesson Guide

1 Teaching the Lesson

Key Concepts and Skills

- Count forward by 1s. [Number and Numeration Goal 1]
- Show a given time on an analog clock. [Measurement and Reference Frames Goal 4]
- Read and record times shown on an analog clock. [Measurement and Reference Frames Goal 4]
- Use language of approximation to describe times on an analog clock. [Measurement and Reference Frames Goal 4]

Key Activities

Children are introduced to A.M. and P.M. times. Then they make paper clocks. Children use their paper clocks to practice showing and telling times to the hour.

Ongoing Assessment: Informing Instruction See page 121.

Key Vocabulary

clockwise ◆ midnight ◆ noon ◆ A.M. ◆ P.M.

Materials

Math Journal 1, p. 14 and Activity Sheet 3 (optional)
Home Link 2•5
Math Masters, p. 32
pennies (optional) ◆ demonstration clock with an hour hand only (optional) ◆ demonstration clock with hour and minute hands ◆ paper plate or tagboard ◆ scissors ◆ glue ◆ brad

2 Ongoing Learning & Practice

Practicing Writing the Numbers 0–9
Math Masters, p. 304
Children practice writing the numbers 0–9.

Ongoing Assessment: Recognizing Student Achievement
Use Math Boxes, Problem 1.
[Number and Numeration Goal 6]

Math Boxes 2·6
Math Journal 1, p. 15
Children practice and maintain skills through Math Box problems.

Home Link 2·6
Math Masters, p. 33
Children practice and maintain skills through Home Link activities.

3 Differentiation Options

READINESS

Estimating the Duration of a Minute
classroom clock
Children get a sense of the duration of one second and one minute.

ENRICHMENT

Calculating Elapsed Time in Hours
Math Masters, p. 34
paper clock
Children use their paper clocks to tell how much time has passed.

EXTRA PRACTICE

Telling Time
Math Masters, p. 310
Children practice telling time on an analog clock.

ELL SUPPORT

Building a Math Word Bank
Differentiation Handbook, p. 126
Children add the terms *noon* and *midnight* to their Math Word Banks.

Advance Preparation

For Part 1, use the two demonstration clocks from Lesson 2•5. To help children make the clocks that they will use in Part 1, pre-punch holes in paper plates, using a nail or a pencil, or copy *Math Masters,* page 32 onto tagboard. This clock is also available on Activity Sheet 3. Children will also use the paper clocks in the optional Enrichment activity in Part 3. For the optional Extra Practice in Part 3, draw hands on the clocks on *Math Masters,* page 310 that meet the needs of your children.

***Teacher's Reference Manual,* Grades 1–3** p. 173

Getting Started

Mental Math and Reflexes

Tell simple number stories. Children may use pennies to model them. Model the first story, using drawings on the chalkboard or counters on the overhead.

●○○ Maria had 5 crayons. She gave 2 crayons to David. How many crayons does Maria have now? 3 crayons

●●○ Bryant had 3 video games. For his birthday, he got 6 more video games. How many video games does Bryant have now? 9 video games

●●● Kayla and Mike went to the store. They bought a box of fruit snacks with 10 packages inside. Kayla took 3 packages, and Mike took 4 packages. How many packages were left in the box? 3 packages

Home Link 2•5 Follow-Up

Children tell about the clocks they found at home. To extend this activity, use tally marks to record the total number of clocks and watches children found. Ask someone to count the tally marks and write the total.

NOTE You may want to have children stand up and face the class clock. Ask them to raise one arm straight up (in the "o'clock" position) and slowly move that arm around in a clockwise direction.

NOTE You may want to mention that in the United States military, as well as in many other countries, time is read using hour numbers to 24. In other words, the P.M. hours are 13, 14, 15, and so on, until 24, or midnight.

Language Arts Link You may want to tell the class that A.M. and P.M. are abbreviations for *ante meridian*, which means before the middle of the day, and *post meridian*, which means after the middle of the day.

1 Teaching the Lesson

▶ Reviewing Clocks

Remind the class that the hour and minute hands always move in the same direction called the **clockwise** direction. Write *clockwise* on the board. To support English language learners, use gestures to support the discussion of the meaning of this word. Review the following facts:

▷ The numbers 1–12 are displayed on the faces of most clocks and watches.

▷ The hour hand and the minute hand move from one number to the next.

▷ It takes about one hour for the minute hand to move all the way around the clock face.

▶ Dividing the 24-Hour Day into A.M. and P.M. Hours

Ask children the following questions:

- How many hours are in 1 day? 24 hours
- About how long does it take for the hour hand to move completely around the clock face? 12 hours
- How many times does the hour hand go all the way around the clock face in 1 day? twice

Adjusting the Activity

Using the hour-hand-only clock, start with the hand pointing to the 12 and move the hand around the clock face as children count the number of hours in a day. Continue moving the hour hand until it has gone around the clock face twice and the count has reached 24.

AUDITORY • KINESTHETIC • TACTILE • VISUAL

Tell the class that each day starts at 12 o'clock at night.

- What is another name for 12 o'clock at night? **midnight**
- What do we call the time 12 hours later? 12 o'clock, or **noon**

Ask whether anyone has heard of **A.M.** and **P.M.** Point out that the first 12 hours of a day are the A.M. hours and that the second 12 hours of a day are the P.M. hours. The hours from midnight to noon are the A.M. hours, and the hours from noon to midnight are the P.M. hours.

Ask children to share some things they do during the the A.M. hours and some things they do during the P.M. hours.

NOTE This is the first time children are seeing the vocabulary for A.M. and P.M. Do not expect children to remember or use these terms at this time.

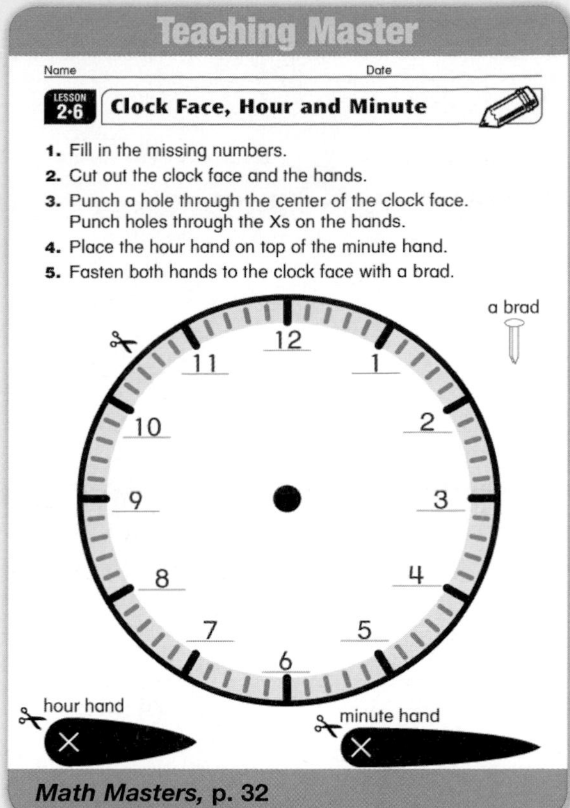

Teaching Master
Name
Date
LESSON 2·6
Clock Face, Hour and Minute
1. Fill in the missing numbers.
2. Cut out the clock face and the hands.
3. Punch a hole through the center of the clock face. Punch holes through the Xs on the hands.
4. Place the hour hand on top of the minute hand.
5. Fasten both hands to the clock face with a brad.
a brad
12
1
2
3
4
5
6
7
8
9
10
11
hour hand
minute hand

Math Masters, p. 32

Making a Clock

INDEPENDENT ACTIVITY

(*Math Masters,* p. 32)

Children write the numbers on the clock face, cut out the clock face, and glue it to a paper plate. Then they cut out the hour and minute hands and attach them to the center of the paper clock with a brad.

Music Link You may wish to play the song "Paper Clocks" from the Hap Palmer audio CD. It is one of a number of math songs children enjoy singing. For other suggestions, check with your school's music teacher or librarian.

Telling Time to the Nearest Hour

WHOLE-CLASS ACTIVITY

(*Math Journal 1,* p. 14)

Use this routine to practice telling time to the nearest hour:

1. Show a time on your demonstration clock with the minute hand pointing straight up.
2. Have children show the same time on their clocks.
3. Have children identify the time shown on the clocks.
4. Record (or have a child record) the time on the board. (Since children have not yet learned to read or write digital time notation, record each time using  o' clock notation.)

As a variation, give children a time to the hour to show on their clocks.

After a few minutes of practice, have children complete the journal page independently or with a partner. Briefly go over the answers.

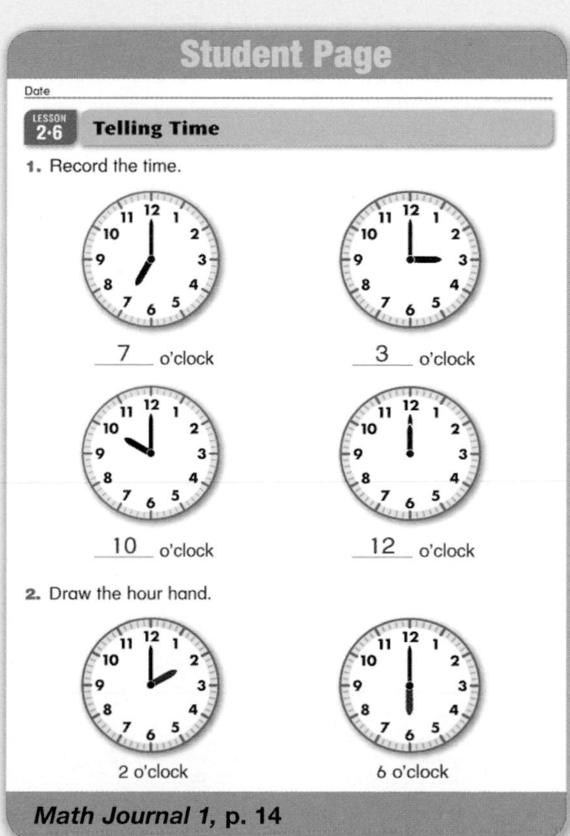

Student Page
Date
LESSON 2·6
Telling Time
1. Record the time.
7 o'clock
3 o'clock
10 o'clock
12 o'clock
2. Draw the hour hand.
2 o'clock
6 o'clock

Math Journal 1, p. 14

Ongoing Assessment: Informing Instruction

Watch for children who confuse the hour and minute hands. Remind them that the minute hand is longer than the hour hand, just as the word *minute* is longer than the word *hour.*

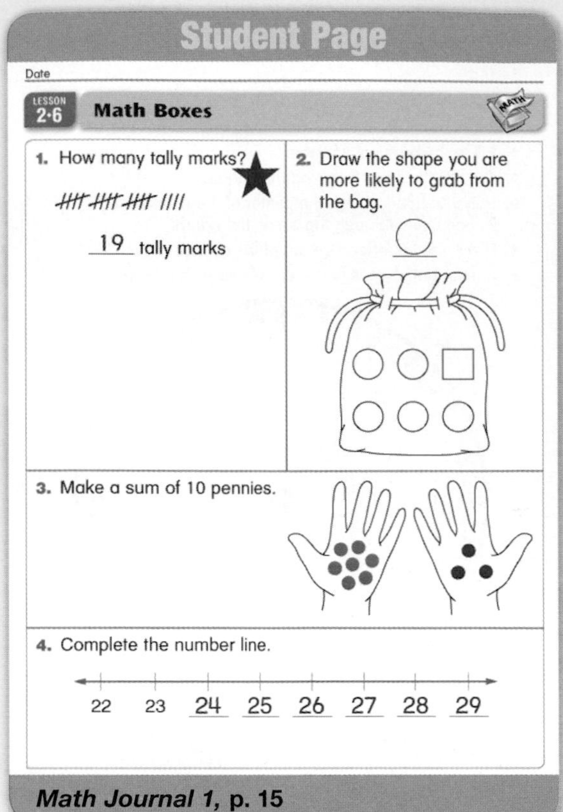

Student Page

Date

LESSON 2·6 **Math Boxes**

1. How many tally marks? ★

~~||||~~ ~~||||~~ ~~||||~~ ||||

19 tally marks

2. Draw the shape you are more likely to grab from the bag.

3. Make a sum of 10 pennies.

4. Complete the number line.

22 23 24 25 26 27 28 29

Math Journal 1, p. 15

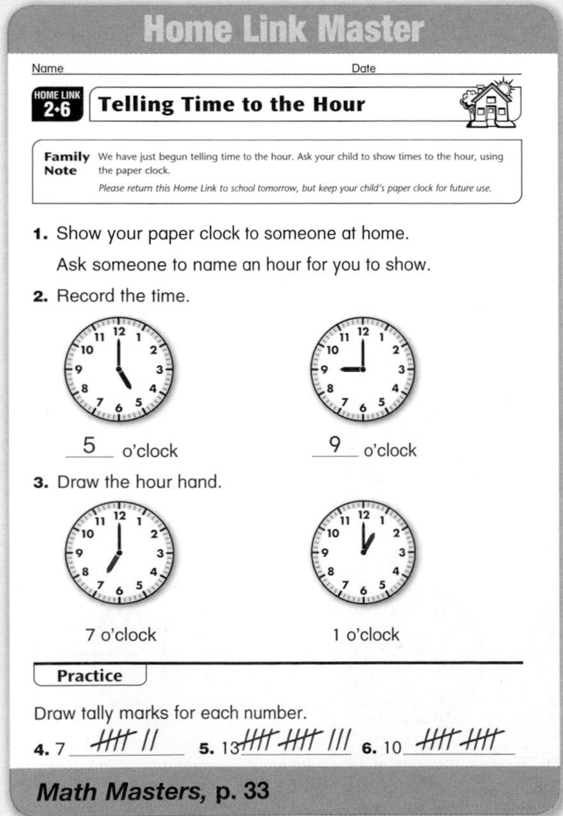

Home Link Master

Name Date

HOME LINK 2·6 **Telling Time to the Hour**

Family Note We have just begun telling time to the hour. Ask your child to show times to the hour, using the paper clock.

Please return this Home Link to school tomorrow, but keep your child's paper clock for future use.

1. Show your paper clock to someone at home. Ask someone to name an hour for you to show.
2. Record the time.

5 o'clock 9 o'clock

3. Draw the hour hand.

7 o'clock 1 o'clock

Practice

Draw tally marks for each number.

4. 7 ~~||||~~ || 5. 13 ~~||||~~ ~~||||~~ ||| 6. 10 ~~||||~~ ~~||||~~

Math Masters, p. 33

Ask children to look at the classroom clock and estimate the time to the nearest hour. Have them tell a partner the time using estimation language such as *about* ____ *o'clock, almost* ____ *o'clock, a little after* ____ *o'clock,* or *between* ____ *o'clock and* ____ *o'clock.*

NOTE Set a timer or a watch so that it will sound at a designated hour, such as 10 o'clock. Children look at the classroom clock and call out the correct time. This activity is especially effective if it is done for 2 or 3 hours in a row.

2 Ongoing Learning & Practice

▶ Practicing Writing the Numbers 0–9

INDEPENDENT ACTIVITY

(*Math Masters,* p. 304)

Use *Math Masters,* page 304 to provide more practice writing the numbers 0–9.

NOTE You may wish to review number words for the numbers zero through nine. Have children write each number word on the back of *Math Masters,* page 304.

▶ Math Boxes 2·6

INDEPENDENT ACTIVITY

(*Math Journal 1,* p. 15)

Mixed Practice Math Boxes in this lesson are paired with Math Boxes in Lesson 2-4. The skills in Problem 4 preview Unit 3 content.

Ongoing Assessment: Recognizing Student Achievement

Math Boxes Problem 1 

Use **Math Boxes, Problem 1** to assess children's ability to find equivalent names for numbers. Children are making adequate progress if they are able to correctly name the number of tally marks.

[Number and Numeration Goal 6]

▶ Home Link 2·6

INDEPENDENT ACTIVITY

(*Math Masters,* p. 33)

Home Connection Children use their paper clocks to practice telling time with someone at home. They record times on the hour and draw hour hands to show times on the hour. Remind children to keep their paper clocks at home for future use.

3 Differentiation Options

READINESS

Estimating the Duration of a Minute

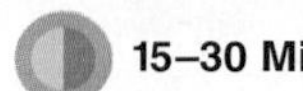

To explore the duration of seconds and minutes, have children predict and test possible activities for each unit of time. Consider demonstrating the length of a second first. Say, "Start" at the beginning and "Stop" at the end of one second. Then make a list of what children think they can do in a second; for example, blink, wink, stick out their tongue, count to five, or jump three times. Next, test the activities on the list. Time children for one second. Then repeat the process for one minute.

ENRICHMENT

Calculating Elapsed Time in Hours

(*Math Masters,* p. 34)

To apply children's understanding of the concept of time, use *Math Masters*, page 34. Have them use their paper clocks to calculate the passage of time.

EXTRA PRACTICE

Telling Time

5–15 Min

(*Math Masters,* p. 310)

Children practice telling time on an analog clock on *Math Masters,* page 310.

ELL SUPPORT

Building a Math Word Bank

5–15 Min

(*Differentiation Handbook,* p. 126)

To provide language support for times of the day, have children use the Word Bank Template found on *Differentiation Handbook,* page 126. Ask children to write the terms *noon* and *midnight,* draw pictures representing the terms, and write other words that describe them. See the *Differentiation Handbook* for more information.

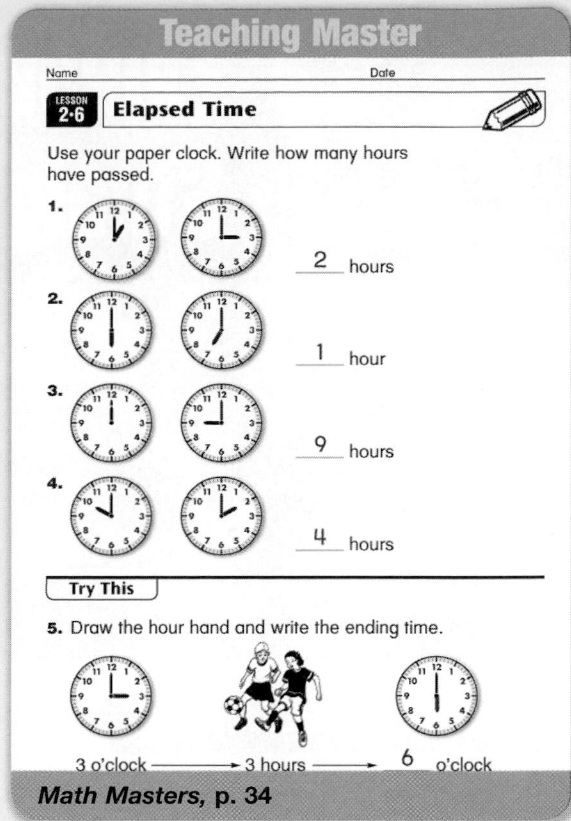

Teaching Master

Name Date

LESSON 2·6 **Elapsed Time**

Use your paper clock. Write how many hours have passed.

1. 2 hours
2. 1 hour
3. 9 hours
4. 4 hours

Try This

5. Draw the hour hand and write the ending time.

3 o'clock ——→ 3 hours ——→ 6 o'clock

Math Masters, p. 34

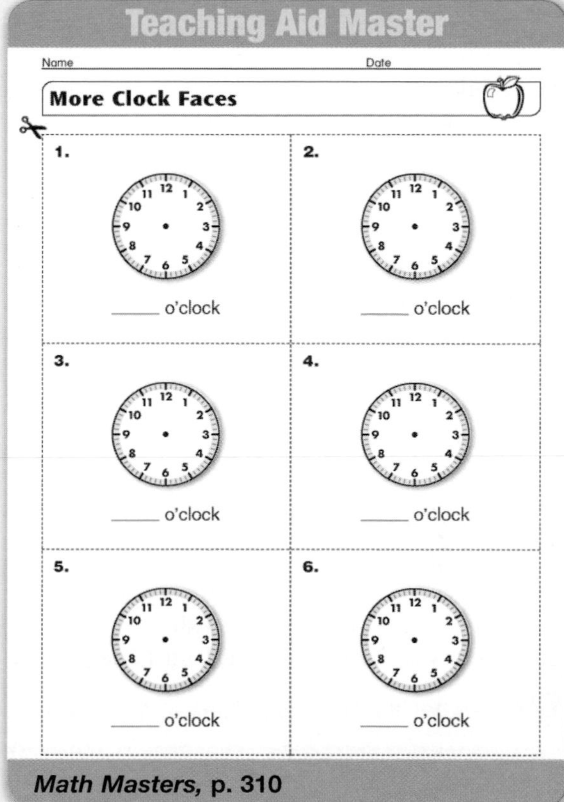

Teaching Aid Master

Name Date

More Clock Faces

1. ____ o'clock
2. ____ o'clock
3. ____ o'clock
4. ____ o'clock
5. ____ o'clock
6. ____ o'clock

Math Masters, p. 310

2•7 Exploring Lengths, Straightedges, and Dominoes

Explorations

Objectives To provide experiences comparing lengths of objects; to provide practice drawing straight lines with a straightedge; and to develop familiarity with dominoes.

Technology Resources www.everydaymathonline.com

ePresentations

eToolkit

Algorithms Practice

EM Facts Workshop Game™

Family Letters

Assessment Management

Common Core State Standards

Curriculum Focal Points

Interactive Teacher's Lesson Guide

1 Teaching the Lesson

Key Concepts and Skills

- Count forward by 2s. [Number and Numeration Goal 1]
- Recognize dot patterns on dominoes as representations of numbers. [Number and Numeration Goal 6]
- Compare the lengths of objects to a 6-inch ruler. [Measurement and Reference Frames Goal 1]

Key Activities

Exploration A: Children estimate which objects in a set are longer or shorter than their rulers. They check their estimates by comparing the objects to their rulers. Then they put the objects in order from shortest to longest.

Exploration B: Children use their straightedges to draw stars.

Exploration C: Children sort dominoes.

Key Vocabulary

ruler

Materials

Home Link Master 2•6
ruler

Exploration A: Per workstation:
Math Masters, p. 35 (optional)
per child: 8 objects to measure ◆ ruler

Exploration B: Per child:
Math Masters, p. 36
ruler

Exploration C: Per workstation:
Math Masters, p. 37 (optional)
double-nine dominoes

2 Ongoing Learning & Practice

Playing *Rolling for 50*
Math Journal 1, p. 7
per partnership: 1 die, 2 game markers

Math Boxes 2•7
Math Journal 1, p. 16

Ongoing Assessment: Recognizing Student Achievement
Use Math Boxes, Problem 2.
[Operations and Computation Goal 2]

Home Link 2•7
Math Masters, p. 38

3 Differentiation Options

READINESS

Matching Strings of Equal Lengths
string

ENRICHMENT

Drawing Pattern-Block Shapes
pattern blocks ◆ straightedge

Advance Preparation

You may wish to place copies of *Math Masters,* pages 35 and 37 at appropriate workstations for aides or volunteers. For Exploration A, mark tool-kit rulers with children's identification numbers. Each child will need about 8 objects that range in length from about 1 inch to 1 foot. For the optional Readiness activity in Part 3, cut 10 pairs of strings, each pair a different length.

***Teacher's Reference Manual,* Grades 1–3** pp. 166, 167, 196–198

Getting Started

Mental Math and Reflexes 

Tell "change-to-more" number stories and have children solve them any way they can. Have children share solution strategies after each problem. Then summarize by drawing a "change-to-more" diagram—*but only after children have had a chance to share how they solved the problem.*

●○○ Maria had 5 peaches. David gave her 3 more peaches. How many peaches does Maria have now? 8 peaches

To summarize the solution draw a "change-to-more" diagram. *How many peaches did Maria have before David gave her more peaches?* 5 *That's how many peaches Maria had to start with.* (Write 5 in the first box.)

How many peaches did David give her? 3 *That's how many more peaches Maria has now.* (Write *3 more* under the arrow.)

How many peaches does Maria have now? 8 (Write 8 in the second box.)

Start	Change	End
5	3 more	8

●●○ Berta had 7 games. She got 3 more games from her grandmother. How many games does Berta have now? 10 games

●●● When Larry woke up this morning, the temperature outside was about 5 degrees. By noon, the temperature had reached about 12 degrees. About how many degrees had the temperature gone up by noon? About 7 degrees

Reminder: Diagrams are used only for exposure at this early stage.

Home Link 2·6 Follow-Up

Briefly go over the answers.

1 Teaching the Lesson

▸ Exploring the Uses of Rulers

Tell children that they will learn to measure with a ruler another time. Today they will practice using their rulers to draw straight lines.

Distribute the rulers and ask children to check that their rulers have the correct identification numbers. Mention that a **ruler** is a mathematical tool and that they will keep their rulers in their tool kits when they are not using them. *What are rulers used for?* To measure lengths; to draw straight lines

Ask children to draw two dots on a quarter-sheet of paper. As you demonstrate, tell children to use their rulers to draw straight lines connecting the dots. Repeat until most children are fairly adept at drawing lines.

Links to the Future

Do not expect children to be able to measure with a ruler at this time. By the end of first grade, children are expected only to compare lengths. Measuring to the nearest inch is a Grade 2 Goal.

Teaching Master

Name Date

LESSON 2·7 **How Long Is It?** 

Materials ☐ ruler

☐ 8 objects

1. Look at your ruler. Try to remember how long it is. Then put it away in your tool kit.
2. Put the objects you think are longer than your ruler in one pile.

   Put the objects you think are shorter than your ruler in another pile.
3. Take out your ruler and check your guesses.
4. Now put the objects in order from shortest to longest.

***Math Masters,* p. 35**

Teaching Master

Name Date

LESSON 2·7 **Counting by 2s**

Start at 0. Count by 2s to connect the dots. Use your ruler.

Then color your finished shape.

0—Start 24 20 22 2 4 18 6 16 14 10 8 12

Math Masters, p. 36

Teaching Master

Name Date

LESSON 2·7 **Sorting Dominoes**

Materials ☐ 1 set of double-nine dominoes

1. Put all dominoes with a blank half in a pile.
2. Put all remaining dominoes that show 1 dot in a pile.
3. Put all remaining dominoes that show 2 dots in a pile.
4. Put all remaining dominoes that show 3 dots in a pile.
5. Continue until all of the dominoes are sorted into groups. Discuss the patterns you see.

Math Masters, p. 37

▶ Exploration A: Estimating the Relative Lengths of Objects

(*Math Masters,* p. 35)

Each workstation needs 8 objects of varying lengths for each child

NOTE Plan to spend most of your time working with children on **Exploration A**.

Directions

1. Look at your ruler. Try to remember how long it is. Then put it in your tool kit.
2. Put the objects you think are longer than your ruler into one pile. Put the objects you think are shorter than your ruler into another pile.
3. Take out your ruler and check your guesses.
4. Now put the objects in order from shortest to longest.

▶ Exploration B: Making a Star

(*Math Masters,* p. 36)

Ask children to use their rulers to connect the dots, starting at 0 and counting by 2s. Children then color their completed stars.

▶ Exploration C: Sorting Dominoes

(*Math Masters,* p. 37)

In this Exploration, children sort a set of double-nine dominoes by the number of dots on one half. Let children try to figure out how best to go about the task. If, after a few minutes, they are unable to come up with a plan, give them the following directions to help them get started:

Directions

1. Put all dominoes with a blank half in a pile.
2. Put all remaining dominoes that show 1 dot in a pile.
3. Put all remaining dominoes that show 2 dots in a pile.
4. Put all remaining dominoes that show 3 dots in a pile.
5. Continue until all dominoes are sorted into groups. Discuss the patterns you see.

2 Ongoing Learning & Practice

Playing *Rolling for 50*

PARTNER ACTIVITY

(*Math Journal 1,* p. 7)

Children practice navigating along a number grid by playing *Rolling for 50.* For detailed instructions, see Lesson 2-1.

Math Boxes 2•7

INDEPENDENT ACTIVITY

(*Math Journal 1,* p. 16)

Mixed Practice Math Boxes in this lesson are paired with Math Boxes in Lesson 2-9.

Ongoing Assessment: Recognizing Student Achievement

Math Boxes Problem 2

Use **Math Boxes, Problem 2** to assess children's understanding of counting on a number grid. Children are making adequate progress if they can use the number grid to solve the problem. Some children may be able to do this mentally without the use of a number grid.

[Operations and Computation Goal 2]

Home Link 2•7

INDEPENDENT ACTIVITY

(*Math Masters,* p. 38)

Home Connection Children order a set of dominoes from the least number of dots to the greatest number of dots.

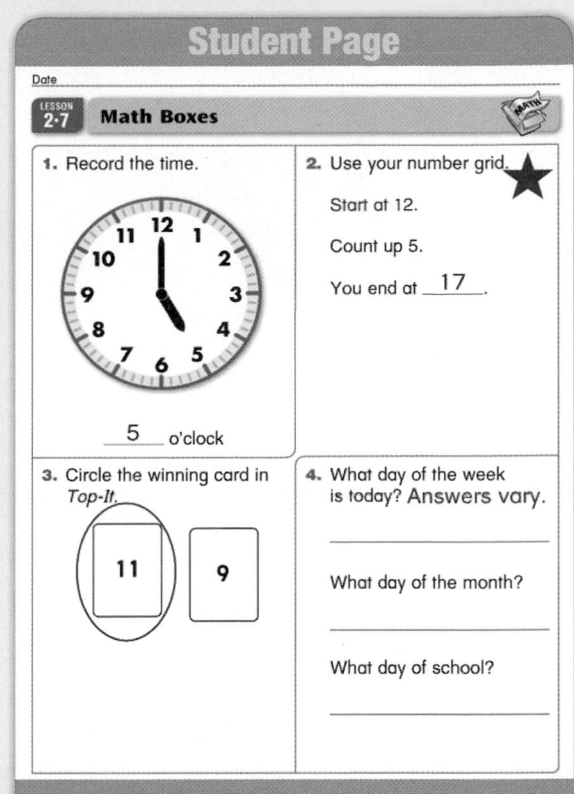

Student Page

Date

LESSON 2•7 **Math Boxes**

1. Record the time.
5 o'clock

2. Use your number grid.
Start at 12.
Count up 5.
You end at 17.

3. Circle the winning card in *Top-It.*
11 9

4. What day of the week is today? Answers vary.
What day of the month?
What day of school?

Math Journal 1, p. 16

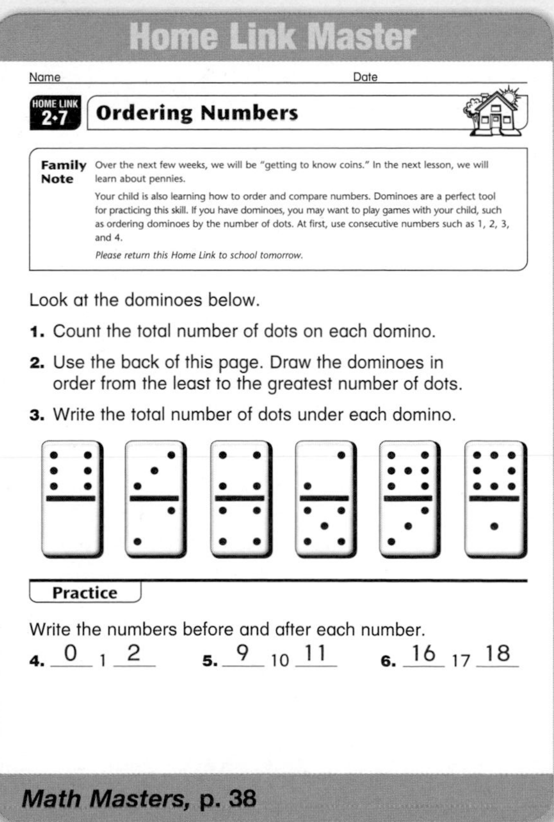

Home Link Master

Name Date

HOME LINK 2•7 **Ordering Numbers**

Family Note Over the next few weeks, we will be "getting to know coins." In the next lesson, we will learn about pennies.
Your child is also learning how to order and compare numbers. Dominoes are a perfect tool for practicing this skill. If you have dominoes, you may want to play games with your child, such as ordering dominoes by the number of dots. At first, use consecutive numbers such as 1, 2, 3, and 4.
Please return this Home Link to school tomorrow.

Look at the dominoes below.

1. Count the total number of dots on each domino.
2. Use the back of this page. Draw the dominoes in order from the least to the greatest number of dots.
3. Write the total number of dots under each domino.

Practice

Write the numbers before and after each number.

4. 0 1 2
5. 9 10 11
6. 16 17 18

Math Masters, p. 38

3 Differentiation Options

READINESS

SMALL-GROU
ACTIVITY

▶ Matching Strings of Equal Lengths

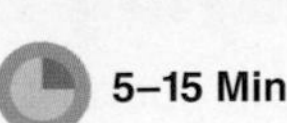

5–15 Min

To explore linear measure, have children compare lengths of string. Show them a pile of strings. Tell them that each string has a matching string of the same length. Ask children to compare the lengths of the strings and match those with the same lengths.

ENRICHMENT

INDEPENDEN
ACTIVITY

▶ Drawing Pattern-Block Shapes

5–15 Min

To explore lengths of sides, have children use their straightedges to draw pattern-block shapes: triangle, square, rhombus, trapezoid, and hexagon. Encourage children to count the number of sides for each shape. Suggest tha children draw dots to show where the sides meet and then connec the dots with their rulers. Have children compare the lengths of the sides of various pattern blocks. Have children trace the longes side of each shape with a red crayon.

2•8 Pennies

Objectives To introduce pennies and cents notation; to provide practice recording numbers of pennies; and to reinforce comparing numbers.

Technology Resources www.everydaymathonline.com

Presentations

eToolkit

Algorithms Practice

EM Facts Workshop Game™

Family Letters

Assessment Management

Common Core State Standards

Curriculum Focal Points

Interactive Teacher's Lesson Guide

1 Teaching the Lesson

Key Concepts and Skills

- Estimate and count the number of objects in a group.
  [Number and Numeration Goal 2]
- Compare quantities and determine which quantity is more.
  [Number and Numeration Goal 7]
- Identify a penny and know its value.
  [Measurement and Reference Frames Goal 2]
- Name the value of a group of pennies using cent notation.
  [Measurement and Reference Frames Goal 2]

Key Activities

Children examine a penny. They play *Penny Grab,* using cent notation to record the results.

Ongoing Assessment: Recognizing Student Achievement
Use *Math Masters,* page 350.
[Operations and Computation Goal 2]

Key Vocabulary

penny ◆ cent

Materials

Home Link 2•7
Math Masters, p. 350
10 pennies per child (to add to tool kit) ◆ Class Data Pad or posterboard ◆ magnifying lenses (at least 1 per 4–5 children)

2 Ongoing Learning & Practice

Playing *Penny Plate*
Math Masters, p. 336 (optional)
per partnership: paper plate, pennies
Children practice finding number combinations for 10.

Math Boxes 2•8
Math Journal 1, p. 17
Children practice and maintain skills through Math Box problems.

Home Link 2•8
Math Masters, p. 39
Children practice and maintain skills through Home Link activities.

3 Differentiation Options

READINESS

Counting Pennies
Number-Grid Poster ◆ pennies
Children count with pennies on the number grid.

ENRICHMENT

Ordering Pennies by Mint Dates
pennies ◆ slate
Children order pennies by the year they were minted.

EXTRA PRACTICE

Playing the *Penny-Dice Game*
per partnership: 20 pennies, 1 die
Children practice numeration skills.

ELL SUPPORT

Building a Math Word Bank
Differentiation Handbook, p. 126
Children add the term *cent* to their Math Word Banks.

Advance Preparation

Use the Class Data Pad or poster board to begin a Story of Money Poster (see page 130). To see the finished poster, see page 683.

***Teacher's Reference Manual,* Grades 1–3** pp. 162–165

Getting Started

Mental Math and Reflexes

Tell "change-to-less" number stories and have children solve them any way they can. Have children share solution strategies after each problem. Then summarize by drawing a "change-to-less" diagram—*but only after children have had a chance to share how they solved the problem. Suggestions:*

●○○ Rupert had 12 pennies when he left for school. He lost 7 pennies. How many pennies does Rupert have left? 5 pennies

To summarize the solution draw a "change-to-less" diagram. *How many pennies did Rupert have when he left for school? 12 That's how many pennies he had to start with.* (Write 12 in the first box.)

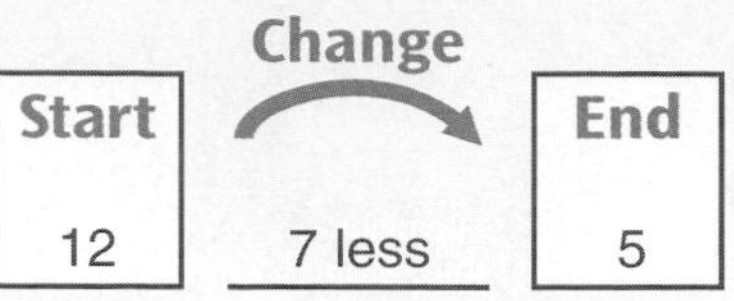

How many pennies did Rupert lose? 7 That's how many fewer pennies Rupert has now. (Write *7 less* under the curved arrow.) *How many pennies does Rupert have left?* 5 (Write 5 in the second box.)

●●○ Maurice's mom baked 20 biscuits. After school, Maurice ate 3 biscuits. How many biscuits were left? 17 biscuits

●●● Tanya bought an 18-inch pencil at the school fair. At the end of the year, she had used about 8 inches of the pencil. About how long was Tanya's pencil then? About 10 inches

Reminder: Diagrams are used only for exposure at this early stage.

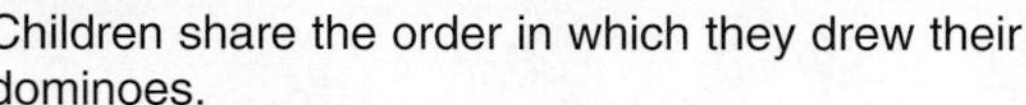

Home Link 2·7 Follow-Up

Children share the order in which they drew their dominoes.

1 Teaching the Lesson

▶ Examining the Penny

Ask children if anyone saves coins in a piggy bank. Clarify the meaning of "piggy bank" for English language learners. Tell children that today they will learn about one coin, the **penny.** Divide the class into small groups. Then ask:

- How many **pennies** do you have in your tool kit? 10 pennies
- How many more pennies do you need so that you would have 20 pennies in all? 10 more pennies

Quickly distribute pennies to each group. Have each child add 10 pennies to his or her tool kit for a total of 20 pennies.

Have children share magnifying lenses for a closer look at both sides of a penny. A picture of Abraham Lincoln is shown on the HEADS side of the penny, and the Lincoln Memorial appears on the TAILS side. Record this information in the Penny column on the Story of Money Poster. (*See margin.*) Discuss the everyday meanings of *heads* and *tails* as well as their meanings in this context.

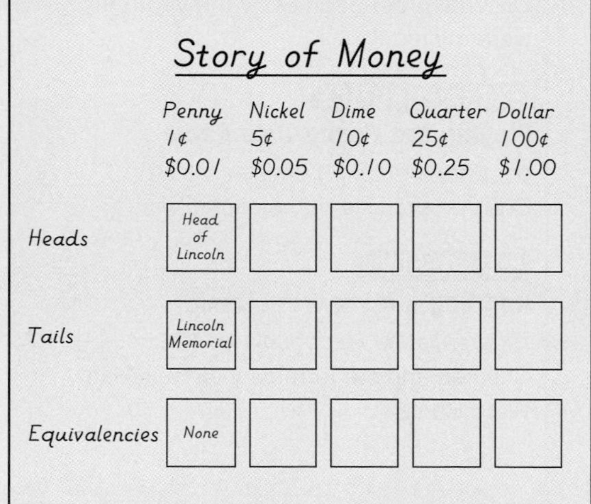

The Story of Money Poster

Spend a few minutes sharing other information about pennies. Two facts of interest:

▷ Pennies are made from copper and zinc.

▷ In the 1940s, pennies were silver-colored.

Adjusting the Activity

If children have access to foreign coins, invite them to bring or describe those with which they are familiar.

AUDITORY ◆ KINESTHETIC ◆ TACTILE ◆ VISUAL

Introducing Cents Notation

WHOLE-CLASS ACTIVITY

Remind the class that a penny is worth one **cent.** Write *one cent* and *1¢* on the board and tell children that the symbol ¢ stands for the word *cent*.

Explain that the word *cent* comes from the Latin word *centesimal,* which means "a hundredth part."

- How many pennies are in 1 dollar? 100 pennies
- Do you know any words that start with the word *cent?* Sample answers: *Centimeter, centipede, century, centigrade*
- Can you think of something that can be bought for a penny? (Today it is difficult to think of anything worth just a penny. Listen to children's suggestions and encourage them to think about how little a penny is worth. You might tell them the cost in pennies of the items they suggest.)
- If each child in our class had a penny, how many cents would our class have in all? Can anyone think of something that could be bought for that amount?

Playing *Penny Grab*

PARTNER ACTIVITY

(*Math Masters,* p. 350)

Partners combine their tool-kit pennies (40 pennies in all). Each partner grabs a handful, estimates how many he or she has, and then counts them. Partners record both numbers of pennies on their record sheets. Then they circle the larger number of pennies.

You may want to demonstrate how to record this information.

Adjusting the Activity

ELL

This game can be played with as few as 20 pennies. To determine who has more pennies, partners can line up their pennies in two rows, one below the other, or partners can put their pennies back into a common pile, one at a time. Whoever runs out of pennies first has the fewer number of pennies.

AUDITORY • KINESTHETIC • TACTILE • VISUAL

Ongoing Assessment: Recognizing Student Achievement

Math Masters Page 350

Use ***Math Masters,* page 350** to assess children's ability to calculate and compare values of sets of pennies. Children are making adequate progress if they can decide who has more pennies.

[Operations and Computation Goal 2]

NOTE The term *penny* is believed to come from one of the following: the Old English *penig*, the German *pfennig*, or the Latin *pannus*, which was a unit of cloth used as a medium of exchange.

Links to the Future

In this lesson, children compare numbers less than 40. By the end of the year, children are expected to compare numbers past 100. Comparing numbers past 1,000 is a Grade 2 Goal.

NOTE Before children begin playing *Penny Grab,* you may wish to provide practice estimating quantities of objects. Show children a clear container filled with between 20 and 100 cubes and have them estimate the number of cubes and discuss their strategies.

Game Master

Name Date

***Penny Grab* Record Sheet**

1. Draw your coins in the chart using Ⓟ.
2. Record your total.
3. Record your partner's total.
4. Circle the greater number of cents in each round.

	Pennies Ⓟ	My Total	My Partner's Total
Round 1		___¢	___¢
Round 2		___¢	___¢
Round 3		___¢	___¢
Round 4		___¢	___¢

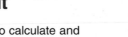

Math Masters, p. 350

2 Ongoing Learning & Practice

▶ Playing *Penny Plate*

(*Math Masters,* p. 336)

Algebraic Thinking This game is played with a plate and a specified number of pennies, appropriate to the proficiency level of the players. (Most partnerships begin with 10 pennies.)

Directions

1. Players take turns. Player A turns the plate upside down, hides some of the pennies under the plate, and places the rest of the pennies on top of the plate.
2. Player B counts the pennies on top of the plate and guesses how many are hidden underneath. If the guess is correct, Player B gets a point.
3. Players trade roles and keep a tally of their points. The player who has more points at the end of 5 rounds wins.

Variation: Players work together to guess how many pennies are under the plate. If their joint guess is correct, they get a team point. The team plays 10 rounds. Their goal is to improve the team score after each round.

Adjusting the Activity

ELL

When playing *Penny Plate* with 10 pennies, children use ten frames (*Math Masters,* page 336). Have them put the pennies from the top of the plate into spaces on the ten frame. Have them count the empty spaces to determine how many pennies are under the plate. Children can then "read" the ten frame by naming the number of spaces covered by pennies, the number of empty spaces, and the total. For example, children might say, "Four and six make ten."

AUDITORY ◆ KINESTHETIC ◆ TACTILE ◆ VISUAL

Math Boxes 2•8

INDEPENDENT ACTIVITY

(*Math Journal 1*, p. 17)

Mixed Practice Math Boxes in this lesson are linked to Math Boxes in Lessons 2-10 and 2-12. The skills in Problems 3 and 4 preview Unit 3 content.

Home Link 2•8

INDEPENDENT ACTIVITY

(*Math Masters*, p. 39)

Home Connection Children begin their investigation of nickels. They trade nickels for the correct number of pennies with someone at home.

3 Differentiation Options

READINESS

SMALL-GROUP ACTIVITY

Counting Pennies

 5–15 Min

To provide experience with counting, have children count pennies by placing them on the number grid. Place the Number-Grid Poster on the floor or a large table. Children grab a handful of pennies from their tool kits and place them one by one on the number grid. Make sure that children place only one penny on each number. Then ask children to find how many pennies in all.

ENRICHMENT

 PARTNER ACTIVITY

Ordering Pennies by Mint Dates

 5–15 Min

To further explore pennies, direct children's attention to the mint date on the face of a penny. Explain that this is the year the penny was made, or minted, by the United States Treasury Department. Have partners work together to put their pennies in order according to the dates they were minted. Children record the years in sequential order on their slates.

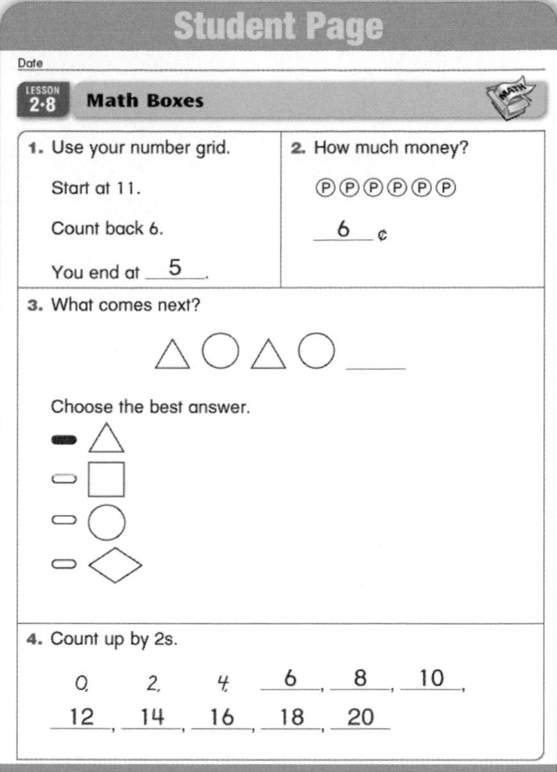

Student Page

Date

LESSON 2•8 **Math Boxes**

1. Use your number grid.
Start at 11.
Count back 6.
You end at 5.

2. How much money?
Ⓟ Ⓟ Ⓟ Ⓟ Ⓟ Ⓟ
6 ¢

3. What comes next?
△ ○ △ ○ ____
Choose the best answer.
● △
○ □
○ ○
○ ◇

4. Count up by 2s.
0, 2, 4, 6, 8, 10,
12, 14, 16, 18, 20

Math Journal 1, p. 17

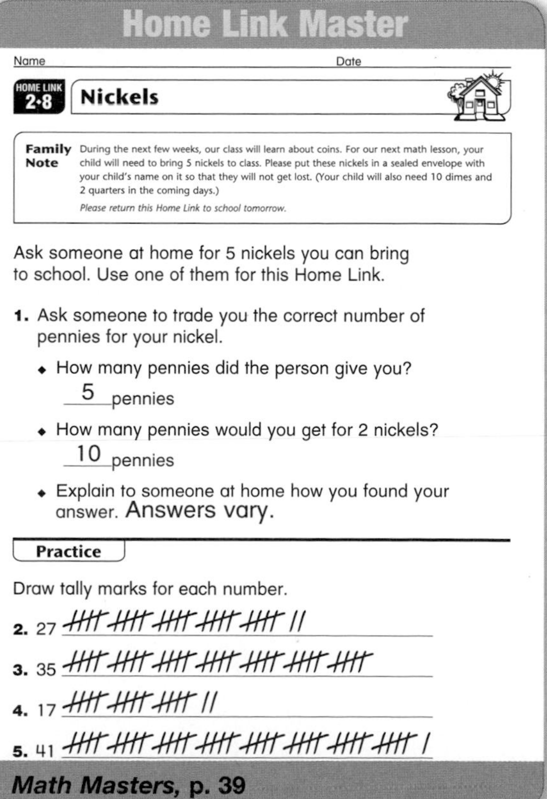

Home Link Master

Name Date

HOME LINK 2•8 **Nickels**

Family Note During the next few weeks, our class will learn about coins. For our next math lesson, your child will need to bring 5 nickels to class. Please put these nickels in a sealed envelope with your child's name on it so that they will not get lost. (Your child will also need 10 dimes and 2 quarters in the coming days.)
Please return this Home Link to school tomorrow.

Ask someone at home for 5 nickels you can bring to school. Use one of them for this Home Link.

1. Ask someone to trade you the correct number of pennies for your nickel.
   - How many pennies did the person give you? 5 pennies
   - How many pennies would you get for 2 nickels? 10 pennies
   - Explain to someone at home how you found your answer. Answers vary.

Practice

Draw tally marks for each number.

2. 27 卌 卌 卌 卌 卌 //
3. 35 卌 卌 卌 卌 卌 卌 卌
4. 17 卌 卌 卌 //
5. 41 卌 卌 卌 卌 卌 卌 卌 卌 /

Math Masters, p. 39

EXTRA PRACTICE

▶ Playing the *Penny-Dice Game*

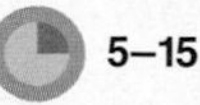

Children compare numbers by playing the *Penny-Dice Game.* For detailed instructions, see Lesson 1-3.

ELL SUPPORT

▶ Building a Math Word Bank

(*Differentiation Handbook,* p. 126)

To provide language support for money, have children use the Word Bank Template found on *Differentiation Handbook,* page 126. Ask children to write the term *cent,* draw a picture representing the term, and write other words that describe it. See the *Differentiation Handbook* for more information.

2•9 Nickels

Objectives To introduce nickels; and to provide practice exchanging pennies for nickels.

www.everydaymathonline.com

ePresentations

eToolkit

Algorithms Practice

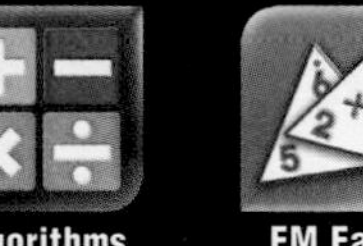
EM Facts Workshop Game™

Family Letters

Assessment Management

Common Core State Standards

Curriculum Focal Points

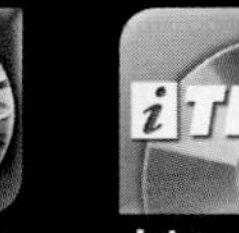

Interactive Teacher's Lesson Guide

1 Teaching the Lesson

Key Concepts and Skills

- Count forward by 1s and 5s from a given number. [Number and Numeration Goal 1]
- Count combinations of pennies and nickels. [Operations and Computation Goal 2]
- Identify a nickel and know its value. [Measurement and Reference Frames Goal 2]
- Exchange pennies for nickels. [Measurement and Reference Frames Goal 2]

Key Activities

Children examine a nickel and discuss its value. They replace up to 14 pennies with an equivalent combination of nickels and pennies.

Ongoing Assessment: Recognizing Student Achievement
Use Mental Math and Reflexes. [Number and Numeration Goal 1]

Key Vocabulary

nickel

Materials

Math Journal 1, p. 18 and inside back cover
Home Link 2•8
per child: 5 nickels ◆ Story of Money Poster ◆ pennies ◆ overhead coins (optional) ◆ per small group: magnifying lens

2 Ongoing Learning & Practice

Counting by 5s
Math Masters, p. 40
Children practice counting by 5s.

Math Boxes 2•9
Math Journal 1, p. 19
Children practice and maintain skills through Math Box problems.

Home Link 2•9
Math Masters, p. 41
Children practice and maintain skills through Home Link activities.

3 Differentiation Options

READINESS

Counting Pennies with Tally Marks
pennies ◆ slate
Children use tally marks to help them count pennies.

ENRICHMENT

Trading Nickels for Pennies
pennies ◆ nickels ◆ slate
Partners make the same amount using different types of coins and compare the number of coins used.

Advance Preparation

For Part 1, display the Story of Money Poster (see Lesson 2•8). Each child will need 5 nickels. Have extra nickels (preferably real ones) on hand for children who did not bring any to school. Children should keep the nickels in their tool kits.

Getting Started

Mental Math and Reflexes ★

Have children use the number grid on the inside back cover of their journals to count up and back by 5s. Start at various multiples of 5; for example, 5, 20, 45, or 60.

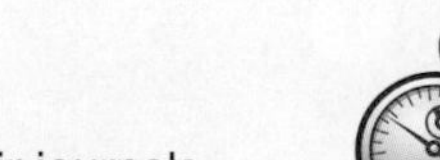

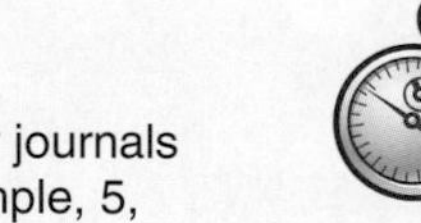

Home Link 2·8 Follow-Up

Briefly go over the answers.

Ongoing Assessment: Recognizing Student Achievement

Mental Math and Reflexes ★

Use **Mental Math and Reflexes** to assess children's ability to count by 5s. Children are making adequate progress if they are able to use their number grids to decide which number comes next in the sequence. Some children may be able to count by 5s without the number grid.

[Number and Numeration Goal 1]

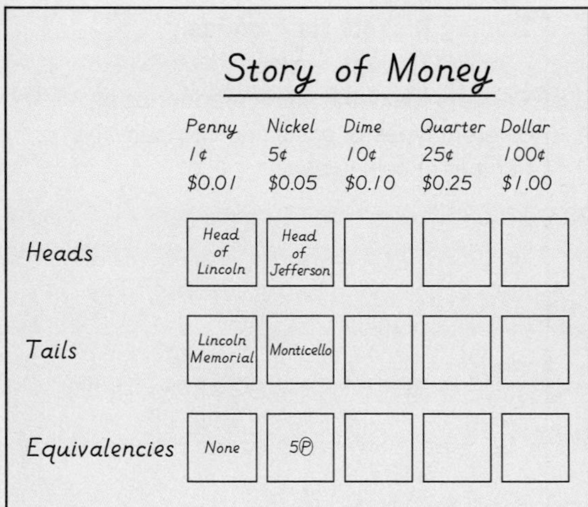

Story of Money

	Penny 1¢ $0.01	Nickel 5¢ $0.05	Dime 10¢ $0.10	Quarter 25¢ $0.25	Dollar 100¢ $1.00
Heads	Head of Lincoln	Head of Jefferson			
Tails	Lincoln Memorial	Monticello			
Equivalencies	None	5Ⓟ			

Add a column for nickels to your Story of Money Poster.

1 Teaching the Lesson

▶ Finding the Value of a Collection of Nickels

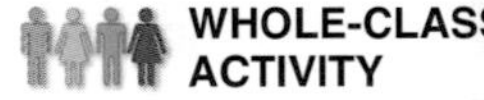

WHOLE-CLASS ACTIVITY

Have each child add 5 nickels to his or her tool kit. Then have children share a magnifying glass to examine both sides of a **nickel**.

Fill in the Nickel column on your Story of Money Poster.

Draw a unit box on the board and write *cents* in it.

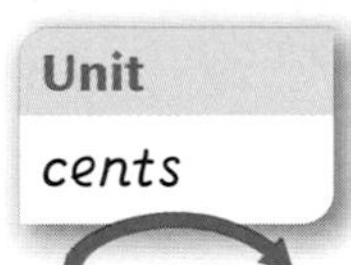

Then pose the following problem: *If every child in our class had one nickel, how much money would our class have in all?*

To solve the problem, have the class count by 5s, with each child saying one of the 5-counts, until all children have had a turn. Write the final amount on the board, using cent notation. Ask children what they might buy for that amount.

Exploring Change

(*Math Journal 1,* p. 18)

1. Draw 8 pennies on the board, using the symbol Ⓟ to represent each penny.

   ▷ Have children take out 8 pennies. Ask them to arrange their pennies into two groups so that there are 5 pennies in one group and 3 pennies in the other group. If possible, model this procedure with overhead coins on the overhead projector.

Adjusting the Activity

Draw tally marks to represent the 8 pennies on the overhead—one group of 5 tally marks and 3 more tally marks to show 8 total. When children exchange the 5 pennies for a nickel in the next step, make sure you place the nickel near the group of 5 tally marks.

AUDITORY ◆ KINESTHETIC ◆ TACTILE ◆ VISUAL

   ▷ Next, have children exchange 5 pennies for 1 nickel. On the board, draw a Ⓝ under the 5 pennies to represent 1 nickel and draw 3 more Ⓟs. Write "8¢" under the coins. (*See margin.*)

   ▷ Explain that 1 nickel and 3 pennies are worth the same amount as 8 pennies. If you went to the store to buy something that cost 8 cents, you could pay for it with either 8 pennies or with 1 nickel and 3 pennies.

   ▷ *Conclusion*: We can count nickels and pennies in the same way we count tally marks. To count 1 nickel and 3 pennies, start with 5 for the nickel and then count by 1s for the pennies—6, 7, 8.

2. Ask children to take out 6 pennies and to show how they would pay for something that costs 6 cents, using fewer coins. 1 nickel and 1 penny

   Count together while pointing to each coin. 5, 6 Write "6¢" on the board.

3. Ask children to take out 10 pennies. Then ask them to show how they would pay for something that costs 10 cents, using fewer coins.

   ▷ As children share their solution strategies, model them on the overhead projector or on the board. Some children may have exchanged only 5 pennies for 1 nickel, ending up with 1 nickel and 5 pennies. This is perfectly acceptable since children are just beginning to do coin exchanges.

   ▷ Whenever children do not end up with the fewest number of coins, you may encourage them to try to exchange those coins for even fewer coins. For 10 pennies, they can arrange their pennies into two groups of 5 pennies each and then exchange the pennies in each group for 1 nickel, ending up with 2 nickels.

   Count together while pointing to each coin. 5, 10 Write "10¢" on the board.

Student Page

Date

LESSON 2•9 **Exploring Pennies and Nickels**

Write the total amount. Then show the amount using fewer coins. Write Ⓟ for penny and Ⓝ for nickel.

(*Hint:* Exchange pennies for nickels.)

1. ⓅⓅⓅⓅⓅⓅⓅ 7 ¢
   Show this amount using fewer coins.
   ⓃⓅⓅ

2. ⓅⓅⓅⓅⓅⓅⓅⓅⓅ 9 ¢
   Show this amount using fewer coins.
   ⓃⓅⓅⓅⓅ

3. ⓅⓅⓅⓅⓅⓅⓅⓅⓅⓅⓅⓅ 12 ¢
   Show this amount using fewer coins.
   ⓃⓃⓅⓅ

Try This

4. ⓃⓅⓅⓅⓅⓅⓅ 11 ¢
   Show this amount using fewer coins.
   ⓃⓃⓅ

***Math Journal 1,* p. 18**

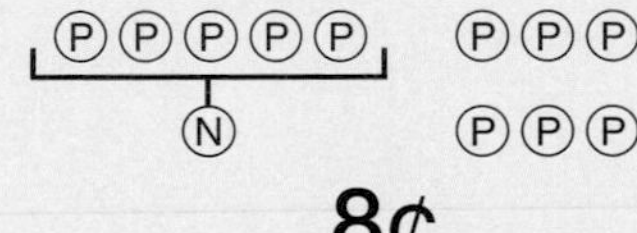

Two ways to show 8¢: 8 pennies; and 1 nickel and 3 pennies

Language Arts Link Ask children why we represent pennies by drawing a circle with the letter *P* inside the circle. The word *penny* begins with the letter *P*. *How could we represent a nickel?* With the letter *N* in a circle

NOTE Remind children that "fewer coins" means making at least one exchange of coins. The total number of coins will be smaller than the previous number, but the value of the coins will be the same.

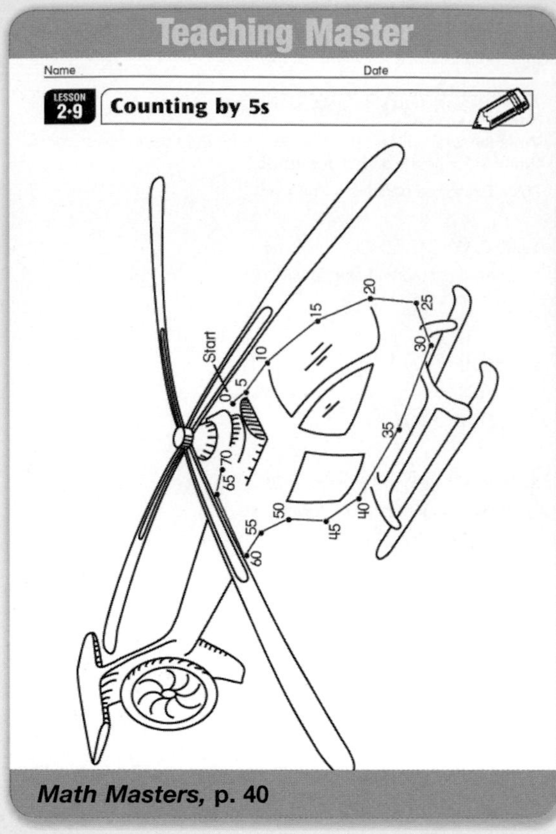

Teaching Master

Name Date

LESSON 2·9 **Counting by 5s**

Math Masters, p. 40

4. Have children work independently or in partnerships to complete journal page 18. They can use coins to help them solve the problems. Circulate and assist as needed. Briefly go over the answers.

NOTE You may wish to discuss why people might want to have nickels rather than pennies in their pockets.

2 Ongoing Learning & Practice

▶ Counting by 5s

INDEPENDENT ACTIVITY

(*Math Masters,* p. 40)

Use *Math Masters,* page 40 to provide more practice counting by 5s.

▶ Math Boxes 2·9

INDEPENDENT ACTIVITY

(*Math Journal 1,* p. 19)

Mixed Practice Math Boxes in this lesson are paired with Math Boxes in Lesson 2-7.

▶ Home Link 2·9

INDEPENDENT ACTIVITY

(*Math Masters,* p. 41)

Home Connection Children practice counting by 5s. They make and count tally marks.

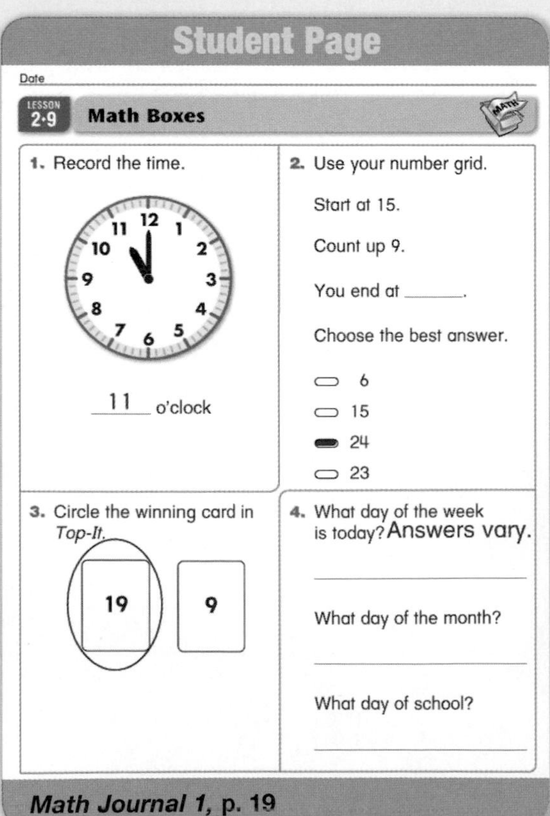

Student Page

Date

LESSON 2·9 **Math Boxes**

1. Record the time.

11 o'clock

2. Use your number grid.

Start at 15.

Count up 9.

You end at ______.

Choose the best answer.

- 6
- 15
- 24 (filled)
- 23

3. Circle the winning card in *Top-It.*

19 (circled) 9

4. What day of the week is today? Answers vary.

What day of the month?

What day of school?

Math Journal 1, p. 19

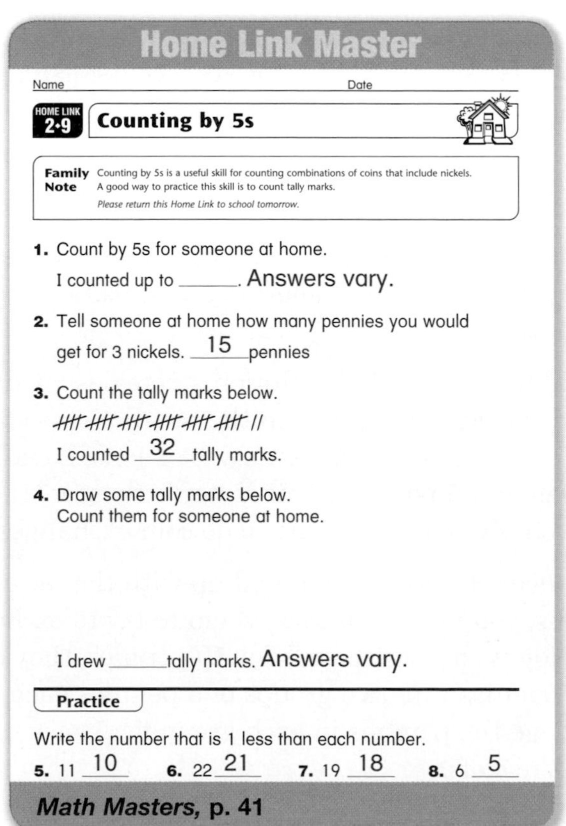

Home Link Master

Name Date

HOME LINK 2·9 **Counting by 5s**

Family Note Counting by 5s is a useful skill for counting combinations of coins that include nickels. A good way to practice this skill is to count tally marks.

Please return this Home Link to school tomorrow.

1. Count by 5s for someone at home.

I counted up to ______. Answers vary.

2. Tell someone at home how many pennies you would get for 3 nickels. 15 pennies

3. Count the tally marks below.

HHH HHH HHH HHH HHH HHH //

I counted 32 tally marks.

4. Draw some tally marks below. Count them for someone at home.

I drew ______ tally marks. Answers vary.

Practice

Write the number that is 1 less than each number.

5. 11 10 6. 22 21 7. 19 18 8. 6 5

Math Masters, p. 41

3 Differentiation Options

READINESS

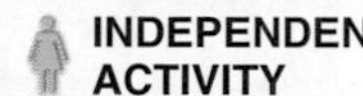

5–15 Min

Counting Pennies with Tally Marks

To explore skip counting by 5s, have children grab a handful of pennies and count the pennies using tally marks. First, they grab the pennies and put them in piles of 5 pennies. Next, they draw tally marks on their slates to show how many pennies they have. Then they count both the piles of pennies and the tally marks by 5s to find the total number of pennies.

ENRICHMENT

PARTNER ACTIVITY

5–15 Min

Trading Nickels for Pennies

To further explore penny-nickel exchanges, have children predict about how many nickels they will get when they exchange a pile of pennies for nickels. Partners pool their pennies. One partner grabs a handful of pennies and spreads them out on the desk. Each partner then guesses how many nickels can be traded for the pennies in the pile. Partners record their guesses on scratch paper or slates. To check their guesses, partners work together to separate the pennies into groups of 5. They replace each group of 5 pennies with 1 nickel and then count the nickels. Partners repeat the activity several times, taking turns grabbing a handful of pennies. The goal is to improve their guesses.

2·10 Counting Pennies and Nickels

Objective To provide practice finding the values of combinations of nickels and pennies.

www.everydaymathonline.com

ePresentations

eToolkit

Algorithms Practice

EM Facts Workshop Game™

Family Letters

Assessment Management

Common Core State Standards

Curriculum Focal Points

Interactive Teacher's Lesson Guide

1 Teaching the Lesson

Key Concepts and Skills

- Count forward by 5s and then on by 1s. [Number and Numeration Goal 1]
- Express the value of groups of nickels and pennies using cent notation. [Operations and Computation Goal 2]
- Identify and know the values of a penny and a nickel. [Measurement and Reference Frames Goal 2]
- Exchange pennies for nickels. [Measurement and Reference Frames Goal 2]

Key Activities

Children explore an efficient way to find the values of various collections of nickels and pennies. They practice this counting skill.

Ongoing Assessment: Recognizing Student Achievement
Use journal page 20.
[Operations and Computation Goal 2]

Materials

Math Journal 1, p. 20
Home Link 2•9
pennies and nickels ◆ slate ◆ overhead coins (optional) ◆ Pattern-Block Template (optional)

2 Ongoing Learning & Practice

Playing *Penny-Nickel Exchange*
per partnership: 20 pennies, 10 nickels, and 1 die (optional: 2 dice)
Children practice exchanging 5 pennies for 1 nickel.

Math Boxes 2·10
Math Journal 1, p. 21
Children practice and maintain skills through Math Box problems.

Home Link 2·10
Math Masters, p. 42
Children practice and maintain skills through Home Link activities.

3 Differentiation Options

READINESS

Identifying Coins Using Touch
pennies ◆ nickels ◆ paper bags
Children identify pennies and nickels by touch.

ENRICHMENT

Making Three-in-a-Row
Math Masters, p. 43
Children make money amounts to get "three-in-a-row."

Advance Preparation

For the optional Readiness activity in Part 3, each partnership will need a paper bag with several pennies and nickels inside. For the optional Enrichment activity in Part 3, copy *Math Masters,* page 43 for each partnership. Fill in each of the nine boxes with an amount less than 30¢. Put $1.00 worth of pennies and nickels in a pile for each child.

Getting Started

Mental Math and Reflexes

Do "stop-and-start" counting with individuals or groups: Count by 5s; stop; continue with a new child or group, counting on from that number by 1s. Stop and repeat the activity with a new starting number. *Suggestions:* Begin with 0, 15, 25, or 30.

Home Link 2·9 Follow-Up

Briefly go over the answers. Find out who made the greatest number of tally marks. Ask that child to draw the tally marks on the board. Then count them in unison.

1 Teaching the Lesson

▸ Counting Nickels and Pennies

WHOLE-CLASS ACTIVITY

Show children a penny and a nickel. Ask how much each coin is worth. Tell them that today they will be finding the value of groups of pennies and nickels.

Ask children to take out 3 nickels and 2 pennies. Give them a few minutes to try to find the total value of the coins. Children then share how they found their answers.

To illustrate one way to count these coins, do the following:

1. Ask 5 children to come to the front of the room. Have 3 children each bring a nickel and 2 children each bring a penny.
2. Move children with nickels to the left end of the line (facing the class) and children with pennies to the right end.
3. Have each child with a nickel hold up 5 fingers. Have each child with a penny hold up 1 finger.
4. Walk behind the children and tap each child lightly on the head as the class counts in unison: 5, 10, 15, 16, 17.
5. Draw Ⓝ Ⓝ Ⓝ Ⓟ Ⓟ on the board. Write 17¢ next to the drawing.

Point out that it doesn't matter which coins we count first, but that it is easier to count the nickels first because then we can count by 5s.

▸ Practicing Coin Counts

WHOLE-CLASS ACTIVITY

(*Math Journal 1,* p. 20)

Put combinations of nickels and pennies on the overhead projector or draw them on the board. Have children use their coins to model the suggested problems on page 142.

NOTE Throughout *Everyday Mathematics,* various versions of nickels are pictured on children's pages. Point out to children the nickel backs shown on *Math Journal,* page 20. Explain that, in addition to the Monticello tails that they are familiar with, there are a few other nickel backs. They will see these different nickel backs throughout the year. Help children understand that all nickels, regardless of the images on them, are worth 5 cents.

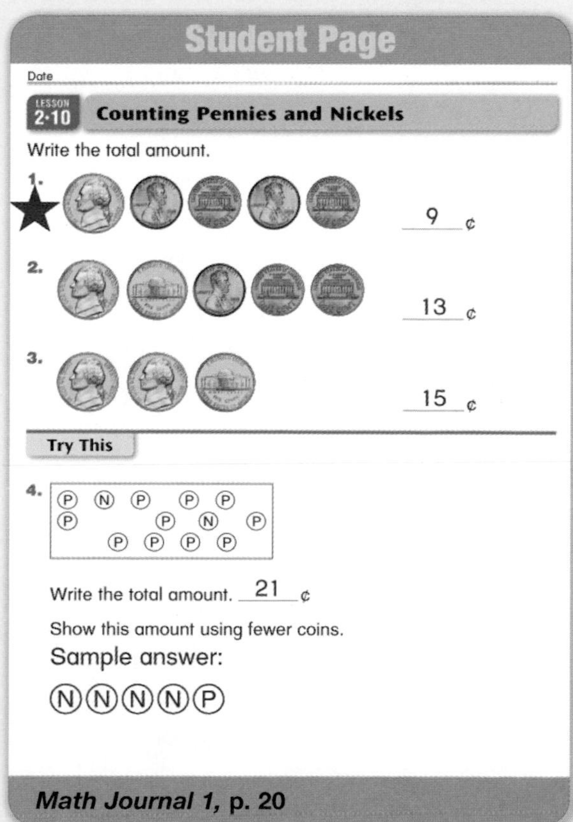

Student Page

Date

LESSON 2·10 **Counting Pennies and Nickels**

Write the total amount.

1. 9 ¢
2. 13 ¢
3. 15 ¢

Try This

4. Ⓟ Ⓝ Ⓟ Ⓟ Ⓟ Ⓟ Ⓟ Ⓝ Ⓟ Ⓟ Ⓟ Ⓟ Ⓟ

Write the total amount. 21 ¢

Show this amount using fewer coins.

Sample answer:

ⓃⓃⓃⓃⓅ

Math Journal 1, p. 20

For the first couple of problems, have children count the coins in unison as they point to their own coins. Thereafter, they can count coins on their own and write their answers on their slates, using cents notation.

Children share answers with the class after each problem and count the coins in unison. *Suggestions:*

Ask: How much is

- 1 nickel and 2 pennies? (Count 5, 6, 7; 7¢)
- 2 nickels and 4 pennies? (Count 5, 10, 11, 12, 13, 14; 14¢)
- 3 nickels and 4 pennies? (Count 5, 10, 15, 16, 17, 18, 19; 19¢)
- 4 nickels? (Count 5, 10, 15, 20; 20¢)
- 4 nickels and 3 pennies? (Count 5, 10, 15, 20, 21, 22, 23; 23¢)

Do more problems if needed. When you believe that children are ready to work without guidance, have them complete journal page 20 independently or with partners. Children may use their coins to help them solve the problems.

Point out that in Problem 4, children are to write the total value of the set of coins and also show the amount using fewer coins. They can use the circles on their Pattern-Block Templates to help them draw coins.

When children are finished, briefly go over the answers.

Adjusting the Activity

Have children replace each nickel with 5 pennies and then count the total number of pennies.

In Problem 4, where nickels and pennies are mixed, suggest that children organize the coins on their slates or on a piece of scratch paper to make counting easier.

AUDITORY ◆ KINESTHETIC ◆ TACTILE ◆ VISUAL

NOTE When children are working on the journal page, encourage them to cross out each coin after they count it. This will help to ensure that children won't count coins twice, especially in Problem 4.

Ongoing Assessment: Recognizing Student Achievement

Journal Page 20

Use **journal page 20** to assess children's ability to count nickels and pennies. Children are making adequate progress if they are able to answer Problem 1 successfully. Some children may be able to accurately answer the remaining problems.

[Operations and Computation Goal 2]

2 Ongoing Learning & Practice

Playing *Penny-Nickel Exchange*

PARTNER ACTIVITY

Directions

1. Partners put 20 pennies and 10 nickels in a pile. This is the bank.
2. Players take turns rolling a die and collecting the number of pennies shown on the die from the bank.
3. Whenever players have at least 5 pennies, they say, "Exchange!" and trade 5 pennies for a nickel from the bank.
4. The game ends when there are no more nickels in the bank. The player who has more nickels wins. If players have the same number of nickels, the player with more pennies wins.

Variation: Have children play with a larger bank and two dice.

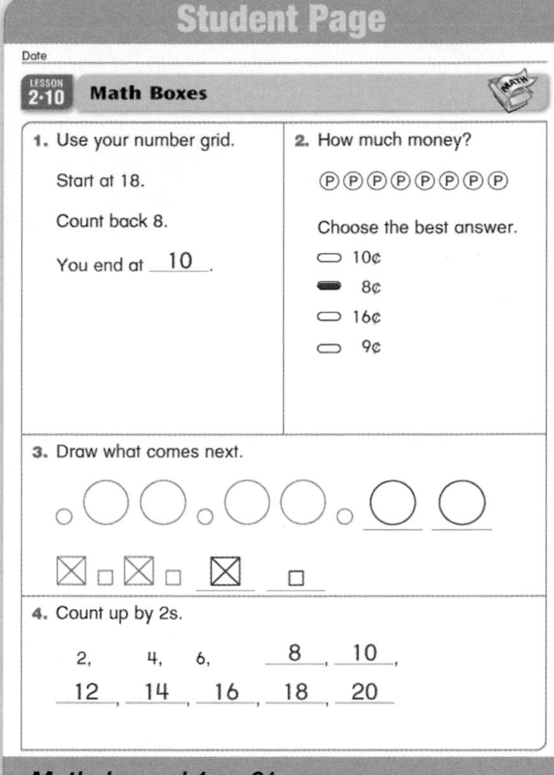

Student Page

Date

LESSON 2·10 **Math Boxes**

1. Use your number grid.
   Start at 18.
   Count back 8.
   You end at 10.

2. How much money?
   Ⓟ Ⓟ Ⓟ Ⓟ Ⓟ Ⓟ Ⓟ Ⓟ
   Choose the best answer.
   - 10¢
   - 8¢ (filled)
   - 16¢
   - 9¢

3. Draw what comes next.

4. Count up by 2s.
   2, 4, 6, 8, 10,
   12, 14, 16, 18, 20

Math Journal 1, p. 21

Math Boxes 2·10

INDEPENDENT ACTIVITY

(*Math Journal 1,* p. 21)

Mixed Practice Math Boxes in this lesson are linked to Math Boxes in Lessons 2-8 and 2-12. The skills in Problems 3 and 4 preview Unit 3 content.

NOTE Remember to reserve time every day to complete the number-line, attendance, calendar, temperature, and weather routines.

Home Link 2·10

INDEPENDENT ACTIVITY

(*Math Masters,* p. 42)

Home Connection Children practice finding total amounts and representing given amounts using different coin combinations.

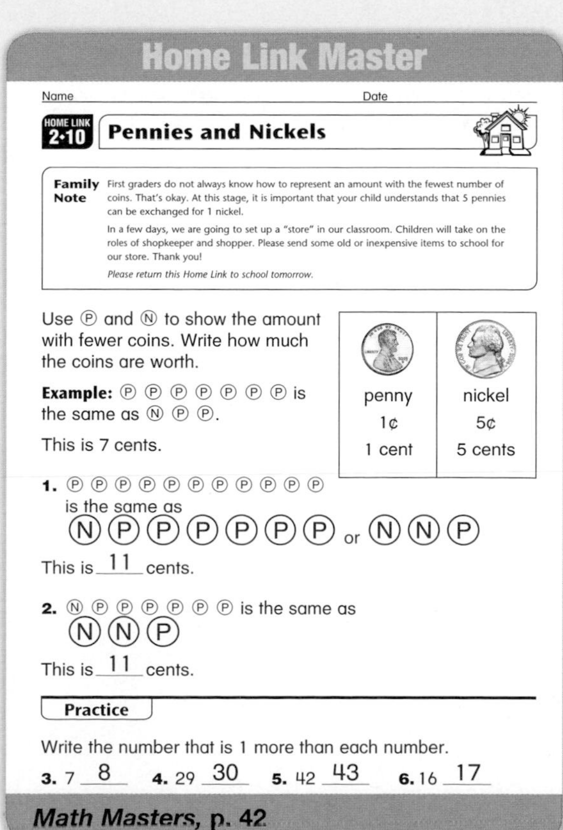

Home Link Master

Name Date

HOME LINK 2·10 **Pennies and Nickels**

Family Note First graders do not always know how to represent an amount with the fewest number of coins. That's okay. At this stage, it is important that your child understands that 5 pennies can be exchanged for 1 nickel.

In a few days, we are going to set up a "store" in our classroom. Children will take on the roles of shopkeeper and shopper. Please send some old or inexpensive items to school for our store. Thank you!

Please return this Home Link to school tomorrow.

Use Ⓟ and Ⓝ to show the amount with fewer coins. Write how much the coins are worth.

penny	nickel
1¢	5¢
1 cent	5 cents

Example: Ⓟ Ⓟ Ⓟ Ⓟ Ⓟ Ⓟ Ⓟ is the same as Ⓝ Ⓟ Ⓟ.
This is 7 cents.

1. Ⓟ Ⓟ Ⓟ Ⓟ Ⓟ Ⓟ Ⓟ Ⓟ Ⓟ Ⓟ Ⓟ is the same as Ⓝ Ⓟ Ⓟ Ⓟ Ⓟ Ⓟ Ⓟ or Ⓝ Ⓝ Ⓟ
   This is 11 cents.

2. Ⓝ Ⓟ Ⓟ Ⓟ Ⓟ Ⓟ Ⓟ is the same as Ⓝ Ⓝ Ⓟ
   This is 11 cents.

Practice

Write the number that is 1 more than each number.

3. 7 8 4. 29 30 5. 42 43 6. 16 17

Math Masters, p. 42

3 Differentiation Options

READINESS

PARTNE ACTIVITY

▶ Identifying Coins Using Touch

5–15 Min

To explore differences between pennies and nickels, have children identify coins by touch. Partners take turns reaching into a paper bag and picking a coin. Without looking in the bag, children use their sense of touch to identify the coin as a penny or a nickel. Then they remove the coin from the bag. If they identified the coin correctly, they keep it; if mistaken, they return the coin to the bag. Partners continue taking turns until all coins are correctly identified.

ENRICHMENT

PARTNE ACTIVITY

▶ Making Three-in-a-Row

15–30 Min

(*Math Masters,* p. 43)

To apply children's understanding of the value of pennies and nickels, have them make coin combinations for given amounts. Partners take turns using coins to make the amounts shown in the boxes on *Math Masters,* page 43. After Partner A makes an amount with his or her coins, Partner B checks the amount. If correct, Partner A crosses off that amount on the Three-in-a-Row page. When one partner gets three in a row, the activity is complete. Three-in-a-row can be made horizontally, vertically, or diagonally.

Planning Ahead

For an optional Enrichment activity that begins in Lesson 2-13, ask children to bring some old items from home to be used in a classroom "store."

Teaching Master

Name Date

LESSON 2·10 Three-in-a-Row

___¢	___¢	___¢
___¢	___¢	___¢
___¢	___¢	___¢

Name Date

LESSON 2·10 Three-in-a-Row

___¢	___¢	___¢
___¢	___¢	___¢
___¢	___¢	___¢

Math Masters, p. 43

2•11 Number Models

Objective To introduce number models for change-to-more situations.

Technology Resources www.everydaymathonline.com

Presentations

eToolkit

Algorithms Practice

EM Facts Workshop Game™

Family Letters

Assessment Management

Common Core State Standards

Curriculum Focal Points

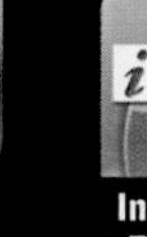
Interactive Teacher's Lesson Guide

1 Teaching the Lesson

Key Concepts and Skills

- Count forward by 1s from a given number. [Number and Numeration Goal 1]
- Solve 1-digit by 1-digit change-to-more stories. [Operations and Computation Goal 1]
- Write number models for 1-digit by 1-digit change-to-more stories using the symbols + and =. [Patterns, Functions, and Algebra Goal 2]

Key Activities

Children are introduced to number models through activities that are a continuation of the Mental Math and Reflexes routine in which children do a listening count. Children learn Penny-Drop Addition. They describe each turn orally and then with a number model.

Key Vocabulary

add ◆ plus ◆ is equal to ◆ number model

Materials

Home Link 2•10
container ◆ pennies ◆ slate

2 Ongoing Learning & Practice

Making a Class Tally Chart
Class Data Pad
Children collect class data about how many teeth they have lost.

Math Boxes 2•11
Math Journal 1, p. 22
Children practice and maintain skills through Math Box problems.

Ongoing Assessment: Recognizing Student Achievement
Use Math Boxes, Problem 2.
[Measurement and Reference Frames Goal 4]

Home Link 2•11
Math Masters, p. 44
Children practice and maintain skills through Home Link activities.

3 Differentiation Options

READINESS
Modeling Number Stories
per partnership: 20 craft sticks
Children use craft sticks to model number stories.

ENRICHMENT
Playing *Nickel-Penny Grab*
Math Masters, p. 347
per partnership: 8 nickels, 20 pennies
Children determine the values of groups of pennies and nickels and compare the values of different groups.

ELL SUPPORT
Building a Math Word Bank
Differentiation Handbook, p. 126
Children add the term *add* to their Math Word Banks.

Advance Preparation

For Penny-Drop Addition in Part 1, use a container that will make a clear, distinct sound when pennies are dropped into it.

***Teacher's Reference Manual,* Grades 1–3** pp. 18, 78, 79, 82, 84–90

Getting Started

Mental Math and Reflexes

Draw a pennies unit box on the board. Drop a selected number of pennies, one at a time, into a container out of children's view. Children count the pennies to themselves. When the last penny has been dropped, children write the total number of pennies on their slates. Then empty the container and repeat this routine until most children get the correct count.

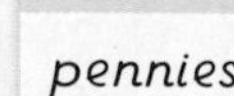

Some children may want to make a tally mark for each penny that is dropped and then count the tallies.

Home Link 2·10 Follow-Up

Briefly go over the answers.

NOTE *Everyday Mathematics* approaches addition and subtraction according to the situations in which the operations are used. Most addition and subtraction situations can be categorized as parts-and-total, change, or comparison situations. Parts-and-total situations are also known as "putting together" or "taking apart" situations. There are two types of change situations: change-to-more and change-to-less. Change-to-more situations are also known as "adding to" situations; change-to-less situations are also known as "taking from" situations. Read more about addition and subtraction situations in the *Teacher's Reference Manual,* pages 84 through 89. With repeated practice and exposure, children will learn to solve all different types of number stories, though they are not expected to categorize number stories in first grade.

1 Teaching the Lesson

▶ Introducing Penny-Drop Addition

1. Begin by doing a "stop-and-start" penny drop.
   - ▷ Drop 5 pennies into a container, one at a time. Ask how many pennies are in the container. 5 pennies
   - ▷ Tell children that you will drop 3 more pennies into the container and that their job is to figure out how many pennies are in the container after you have dropped in the 3 additional pennies.
   - ▷ Drop the 3 pennies. Have children write the total number of pennies on their slates. 8 pennies
   - ▷ If some children did not get the correct total, repeat the routine: Drop 5 pennies. Then, as you drop an additional 3 pennies, have children count in unison: 6, 7, 8.
   - ▷ Summarize what took place with a change-to-more diagram (*See below.*)
   - ▷ Point out that another way to say "3 more" is to say "**add** 3."
   - ▷ Repeat this routine, using different numbers of pennies, until most children get the correct count each time.

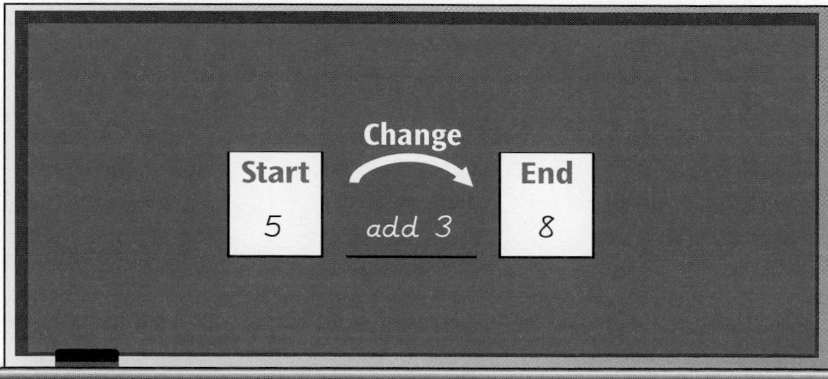

2. Next, introduce a variation of this routine. Tell children what you are going to do before you start dropping the pennies and ask them to predict the total number of pennies that will be in the container. As you describe the problem, write on the board what you are going to do. *For example*:

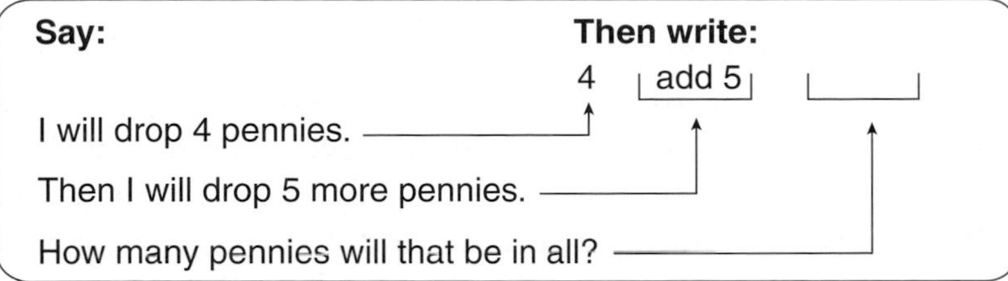

▷ List some of the children's answers on the board. Then do a penny drop to check their answers: Drop 4 pennies; children count. Drop 5 more pennies; children count on. Write the total on the answer blank. 9 pennies

▷ Repeat this routine using other pairs of numbers.

Language Arts Link Discuss the meaning of the word *shorthand.* Ask children if they can think of other examples of people using symbols for words or phrases. Some examples: $ means *dollar,* ¢ means *cent.* In *Everyday Mathematics,* Ⓟ means *penny* and Ⓝ means *nickel.*

Introducing Number Models

WHOLE-CLASS ACTIVITY

Tell the class that in mathematics, we write the symbol + for the word *add*. The + sign is read **plus.** (Write the + sign and the word *plus* above it on the board.) We can write the = sign in front of the answer. The = sign is read **is equal to.** (Write the = sign and the words *is equal to* above it.)

Illustrate the use of these symbols with an example.

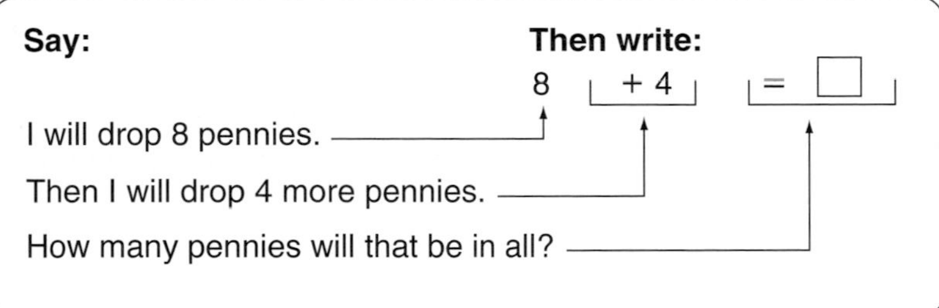

NOTE In Grade 1 of *Everyday Mathematics,* ___ and □ are used interchangeably in number models to represent unknown numbers. In later grades, children will begin to see other symbols used to represent unknown numbers.

▷ After doing the penny drop, write the answer in the answer box: 8 + 4 = [12].

8 + 4 = 12 is called a **number model.**

▷ Do a few more penny drops. You or a volunteer can write the number model on the board, or you may ask children to write number models on their slates.

Student Page

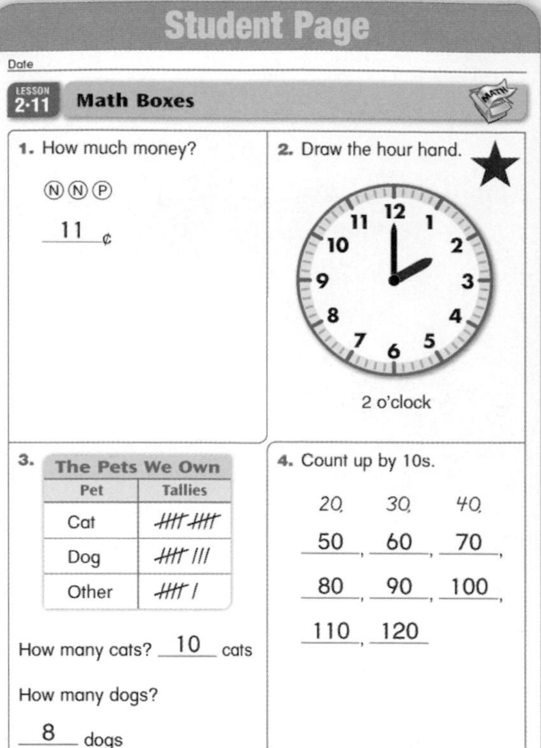
Date

LESSON 2·11 **Math Boxes**

1. How much money?

Ⓝ Ⓝ Ⓟ

11 ¢

2. Draw the hour hand. ★

2 o'clock

3. **The Pets We Own**

Pet	Tallies
Cat	𝍸𝍸
Dog	𝍸 |||
Other	𝍸 |

How many cats? 10 cats

How many dogs?

8 dogs

4. Count up by 10s.

20, 30, 40,
50, 60, 70,
80, 90, 100,
110, 120

Math Journal 1, p. 22

NOTE For practice making a picture graph using this data, go to www.everydaymathonline.com.

Home Link Master

Name Date

HOME LINK 2·11 **Nickels and Pennies**

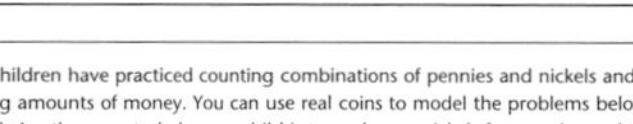
Family Note In class, children have practiced counting combinations of pennies and nickels and then comparing amounts of money. You can use real coins to model the problems below for your child. Another way to help your child is to exchange nickels for pennies and then count the pennies.

We will do a lot of work with money exchanges and with counting money. Do not expect your child to master these skills at this time.

Please return this Home Link to school tomorrow.

1. Sabine grabbed 2 nickels and 7 pennies.
   She had 17 ¢.
   Tony grabbed 3 nickels and 1 penny.
   He had 16 ¢.
   Circle who grabbed more money: **Sabine** or **Tony**
2. Sabine grabbed 2 nickels and 6 pennies.
   She had 16 ¢.
   Tony grabbed 3 nickels and 5 pennies.
   He had 20 ¢.
   Circle who grabbed more money: **Sabine** or **Tony**

Practice

3. How much money? 15 ¢

Math Masters, p. 44

2 Ongoing Learning & Practice

▶ Making a Class Tally Chart

WHOLE-CLASS ACTIVITY

Remind children that they did a tally count of their favorite season in Lesson 1-12. Tell them that they are going to make a class tally chart about how many teeth children have lost. On the Class Data Pad, make a chart like the one below. Allow each child to make a tally mark for the number of teeth that he or she has lost. Once the tally chart is complete, ask children the following questions:

- How many teeth have most children lost?
- How many teeth have the fewest children lost?
- How many children have not lost any teeth?

Number of Teeth Lost

Teeth Lost	Tallies	Total
0	𝍸 |||	8
1	𝍸 |	6
2	𝍸	5
3	||	2
4		0
5 or more	|||	3

▶ Math Boxes 2·11

INDEPENDENT ACTIVITY

(*Math Journal 1,* p. 22)

Mixed Practice Math Boxes in this lesson are paired with Math Boxes in Lesson 2-13. The skills in Problem 4 preview Unit 3 content.

Ongoing Assessment: Recognizing Student Achievement

Math Boxes Problem 2 ★

Use **Math Boxes, Problem 2** to assess children's understanding of telling time to the hour. Children are making adequate progress if they draw the hour hand pointing to the correct number.

[Measurement and Reference Frames Goal 4]

▶ Home Link 2·11

INDEPENDENT ACTIVITY

(*Math Masters,* p. 44)

Home Connection Children find the value of combinations of nickels and pennies and compare the amounts of money.

Reminder: Again ask children to bring old items from home for the School Store if you plan to do the optional Enrichment activity in Lesson 2-13.

3 Differentiation Options

READINESS

PARTNER ACTIVITY

Modeling Number Stories

15–30 Min

To provide experience with addition number stories using a concrete model, have children model and solve number stories using craft sticks. Give each partnership 20 craft sticks. Children listen to number stories told by the teacher and count craft sticks to help them find the answers. *For example:*

> Joseph bought 5 tennis balls at the store. (One child counts 5 craft sticks.) His friend bought 3 tennis balls at the store. (Another child counts 3 more craft sticks.) How many tennis balls do Joseph and his friend have altogether? (Children should group the two sets of craft sticks and determine the total.) 8 tennis balls

Have children retell the stories in their own words.

ENRICHMENT

PARTNER ACTIVITY

Playing *Nickel-Penny Grab*

15–30 Min

(*Math Masters,* p. 347)

To further explore estimating totals with penny-nickel coin combinations, have children grab and count handfuls of coins. Give each partnership 8 nickels and 20 pennies. One partner grabs a handful of coins, and the other partner takes what is left. Children record their amounts on the record sheet. Then they compare the two amounts and circle the larger one on their record sheet. Children can mix the coins and repeat the activity.

ELL SUPPORT

SMALL-GROUP ACTIVITY

Building a Math Word Bank

5–15 Min

(*Differentiation Handbook,* p. 126)

To provide language support for addition, have children use the Word Bank Template found on *Differentiation Handbook,* page 126. Ask children to write the term *add,* draw the symbol and a picture representing the term, and write other words that describe it. See the *Differentiation Handbook* for more information.

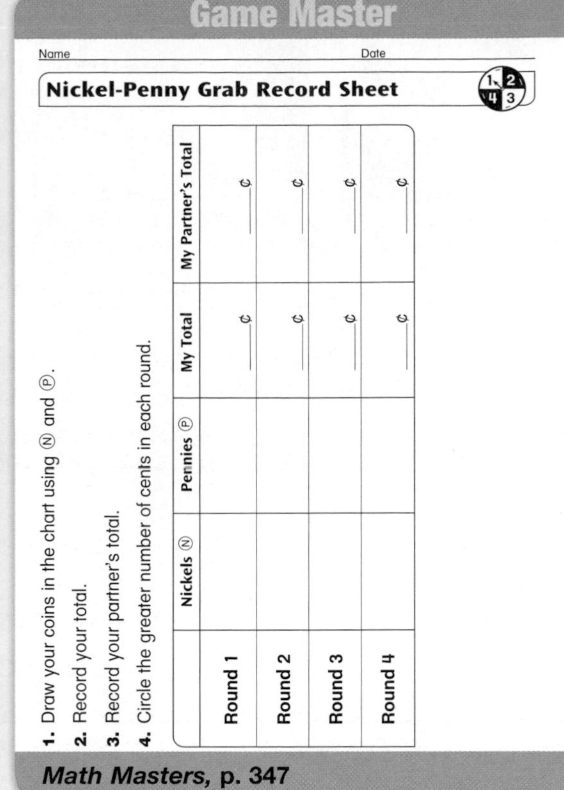

Game Master

Name ____________ Date ____________

Nickel-Penny Grab Record Sheet

1. Draw your coins in the chart using Ⓝ and Ⓟ.
2. Record your total.
3. Record your partner's total.
4. Circle the greater number of cents in each round.

	Nickels Ⓝ	Pennies Ⓟ	My Total	My Partner's Total
Round 1			____ ¢	____ ¢
Round 2			____ ¢	____ ¢
Round 3			____ ¢	____ ¢
Round 4			____ ¢	____ ¢

Math Masters, p. 347

2•12 Subtraction Number Models

Objective To broaden experiences with extending number models to include change-to-less situations.

Technology Resources www.everydaymathonline.com

ePresentations

eToolkit

Algorithms Practice

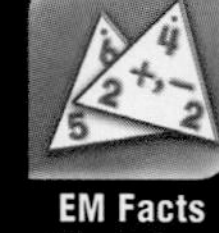
EM Facts Workshop Game™

Family Letters

Assessment Management

Common Core State Standards

Curriculum Focal Points

Interactive Teacher's Lesson Guide

1 Teaching the Lesson

Key Concepts and Skills

- Count backward by 1s from a given number. [Number and Numeration Goal 1]
- Solve 1-digit by 1-digit change-to-less stories. [Operations and Computation Goal 1]
- Write number models for 1-digit by 1-digit change-to-less stories using the symbols – and =. [Patterns, Functions, and Algebra Goal 2]

Key Activities

Cups are placed standing up. Some are knocked over, and children figure out how many are left standing. This routine is represented first with a change-to-less diagram, then with words, and finally with a number model.

Key Vocabulary

subtract ◆ minus

Materials

Home Link 2•11
slate ◆ 12 paper cups ◆ overhead coins (optional)

2 Ongoing Learning & Practice

Playing *High Roller*
Math Masters, p. 344
per partnership: 2 dice
Children practice simple addition facts by counting on.

Ongoing Assessment: Recognizing Student Achievement
Use *Math Masters,* page 344.
[Operations and Computation Goal 1]

Math Boxes 2•12
Math Journal 1, p. 23
Children practice and maintain skills through Math Box problems.

Home Link 2•12
Math Masters, p. 45
Children practice and maintain skills through Home Link activities.

3 Differentiation Options

READINESS

Counting to Zero
20 pennies ◆ Class Number Line (optional)
Children count backward to zero using pennies.

ENRICHMENT

Solving Number Expressions
per group: number cards 0–20 (from the Everything Math Deck, if available)
Children solve simple addition and subtraction expressions.

ELL SUPPORT

Building a Math Word Bank
Differentiation Handbook, p. 126
Children add the term *subtract* to their Math Word Banks.

Advance Preparation

For Part 1, you will need at least 12 paper cups. If overhead nickels and pennies are available, you may find them useful for Mental Math and Reflexes.

Getting Started

Mental Math and Reflexes

Display coin combinations using overhead nickels and pennies, if available. If not, draw Ⓟ and Ⓝ on the board. Children write the total value of each collection on their slates. *Suggestions:*

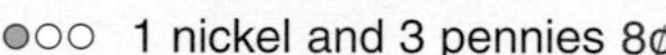

●○○ 1 nickel and 3 pennies 8¢

●●○ 2 nickels and 5 pennies 15¢

●●● 4 nickels and 9 pennies 29¢

Home Link 2•11 Follow-Up

Briefly go over the answers. Have children share their strategies.

1 Teaching the Lesson

▶ Introducing Subtraction Number Models

Explain to children that they will learn about a different kind of number model. This activity is similar to the routine used in Lesson 2-11 to introduce number models for change-to-more situations.

1. Do the following demonstration:

   ▷ Place 9 paper cups standing up in a row.

   How many cups are standing? 9 cups

   ▷ Knock over 4 of the cups.

   How many cups did I knock over? 4 cups

   How many are left standing? 5 cups

   ▷ Summarize what took place with a change-to-less diagram:

Point out that another way to say "4 less" is to say "**subtract** 4."

   ▷ Repeat this routine a few more times. Each time, start with a different number of cups. You might ask volunteers to knock over the cups each time.

How many cups are left standing up?

NOTE Please see the Note in Lesson 2-11 and *Teacher's Reference Manual,* pages 84 through 89 for more information about addition and subtraction situations.

2. Next, introduce a variation of this routine. Tell children what you are going to do and ask them to predict how many cups will be left standing. As you describe the problem, write on the board what you are going to do. *For example:*

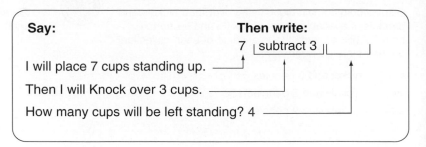

Say:	**Then write:**
	7 subtract 3 ____
I will place 7 cups standing up.	7
Then I will Knock over 3 cups.	subtract 3
How many cups will be left standing? 4	____

▷ List some of the children's answers on the board. Then knock over 3 cups to check their answers. On the answer blank, write the number of cups that are left standing.

3. Tell the class that for the word *subtract*, we can write the symbol –. The – symbol is read **minus.** (Write the – sign and the word *minus* above it on the board.)

Illustrate the use of this symbol with an example.

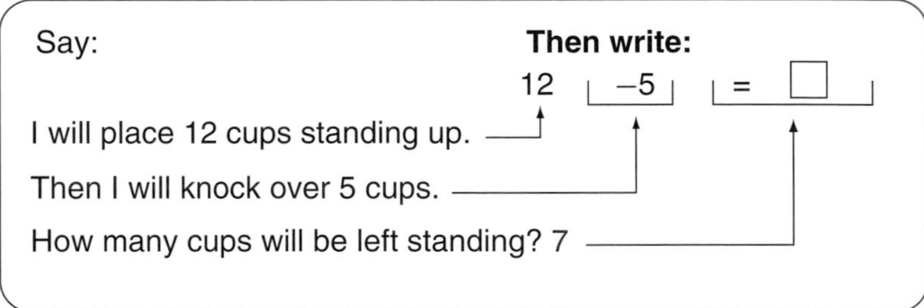

▷ After children have predicted the number of cups that will be left standing, knock 5 cups over to check their answers. In the answer box, write the number of cups that are left standing. A number model to describe this problem is $12 - 5 = 7$.

▷ Do a few more examples, starting with a different number of cups each time. Write a number model on the board each time, or ask children to write number models on their slates.

NOTE Please keep in mind that children are not expected to master writing number models at this time. This is an early exposure to the concept of number models. There will be many future opportunities to reinforce these ideas.

2 Ongoing Learning & Practice

▸ Playing *High Roller*

PARTNER ACTIVITY

(*Math Masters,* p. 344)

This game can be played with 2 players or in small groups. Each group should have a few copies of the *High Roller* recording sheet.

Directions

1. Players take turns. The first player rolls two dice and records the roll in the first two squares. He or she keeps the die with the larger number (the High Roller) and crosses out the smaller number on the recording sheet.
2. The first player rolls the other (smaller) die again and records the roll. He or she counts on from the number rolled on the first die to get the sum of the two dice.
3. The first player records the sum on the line.
4. The second player repeats this process.
5. Players continue to take turns as time allows.

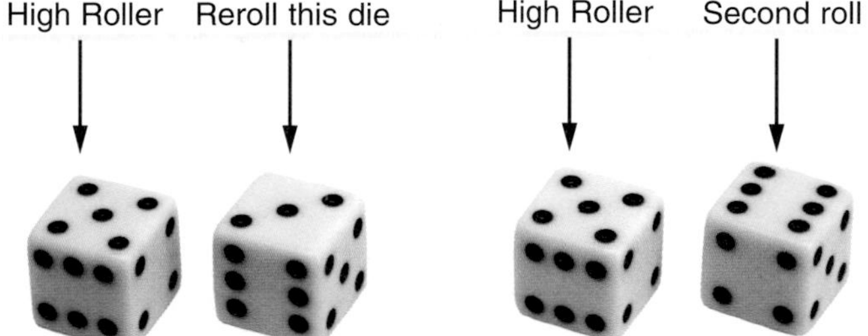

Ongoing Assessment: Recognizing Student Achievement

Math Masters **Page 344**

Use ***Math Masters,* page 344** to assess children's understanding of finding sums of 1-digit numbers. Children are making adequate progress if they correctly count the dots on the dice to find the sum. Some children may be able to find sums without counting the dots.

[Operations and Computation Goal 1]

Game Master

Name Date

***High Roller* Record Sheet**

1. Record your first roll in the first two squares.
2. Cross out the smaller number.
3. Roll the die that shows the smaller number again.
4. Record your second roll in the third square.
5. Record the sum of the two dice on the line.

***Math Masters,* p. 344**

Student Page

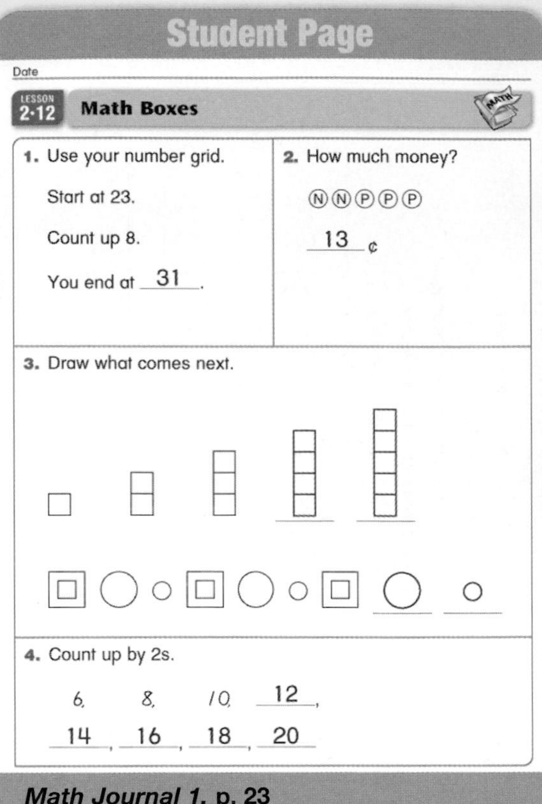
Date

LESSON 2·12 Math Boxes

1. Use your number grid.
Start at 23.
Count up 8.
You end at 31.

2. How much money?
Ⓝ Ⓝ Ⓟ Ⓟ Ⓟ
13 ¢

3. Draw what comes next.

4. Count up by 2s.
6, 8, 10, 12,
14, 16, 18, 20

Math Journal 1, p. 23

▶ Math Boxes 2·12

INDEPENDENT ACTIVITY

(*Math Journal 1,* p. 23)

Mixed Practice Math Boxes in this lesson are linked to Math Boxes in Lessons 2-8 and 2-10. The skills in Problems 3 and 4 preview Unit 3 content.

▶ Home Link 2·12

INDEPENDENT ACTIVITY

(*Math Masters,* p. 45)

Home Connection Children practice telling time to the hour.

Reminder: Once again, ask children to bring old items from home for the School Store if you plan to use the optional Enrichment activity that is introduced in Lesson 2-13.

3 Differentiation Options

READINESS

SMALL-GROUP ACTIVITY

▶ Counting to Zero

5–15 Min

To explore counting backward, have children count the pennies in their tool kits to be sure that they have 20 pennies. Tell them that they are going to count backward as they put the pennies back into their tool kits. Guide children by saying: *I have 20 pennies. I put 1 penny away* (place one penny in the tool kit). *Now I have 19 pennies.* Continue in this way until you reach zero. Use the Class Number Line as a point of reference for counting if necessary. Allow children to repeat the activity independently or with a partner.

Home Link Master

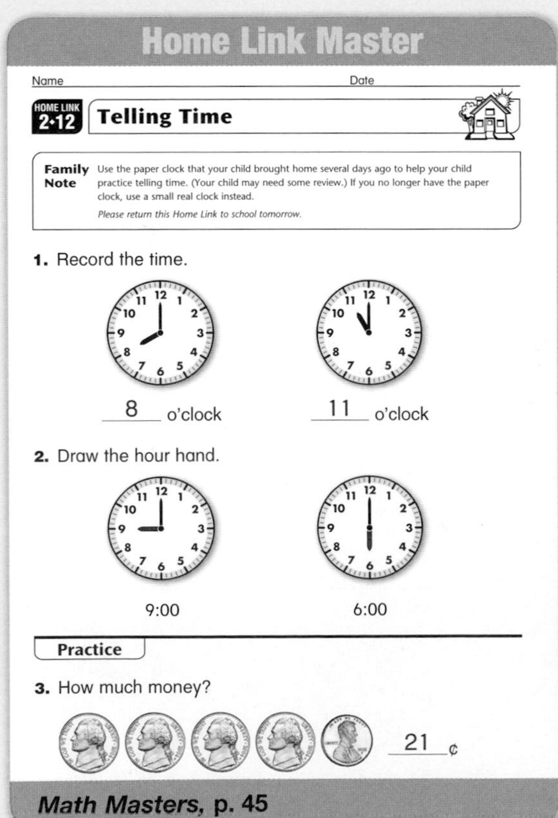
Name Date

HOME LINK 2·12 Telling Time

Family Note Use the paper clock that your child brought home several days ago to help your child practice telling time. (Your child may need some review.) If you no longer have the paper clock, use a small real clock instead.

Please return this Home Link to school tomorrow.

1. Record the time.
8 o'clock
11 o'clock

2. Draw the hour hand.
9:00
6:00

Practice

3. How much money?
21 ¢

Math Masters, p. 45

ENRICHMENT

SMALL-GROUP ACTIVITY

Solving Number Expressions

15–30 Min

To provide further experience with number models, play Who Am I Thinking Of? Give each child a number card. The number on the card is that child's "name." Pick a number and write clues about that number on the board. For example, for the number 5, you might write 1 + 4, 7 − 2, and 0 + 5. Children raise their hands if the clues fit their "name."

ELL SUPPORT

Building a Math Word Bank

5–15 Min

(*Differentiation Handbook,* p. 126)

To provide language support for subtraction, have children use the Word Bank Template found on *Differentiation Handbook,* page 126. Ask children to write the term *subtract,* draw the symbol and a picture representing the term, and write other words that describe it. See the *Differentiation Handbook* for more information.

2•13 Number Stories

Objectives To provide practice making up and solving number stories; to review counting money; and to provide opportunities to find the sum of three 1-digit numbers.

Technology Resources www.everydaymathonline.com

ePresentations

eToolkit

Algorithms Practice

EM Facts Workshop Game™

Family Letters

Assessment Management

Common Core State Standards

Curriculum Focal Points

Interactive Teacher's Lesson Guide

1 Teaching the Lesson

Key Concepts and Skills

- Count forward and backward by 1s from a given number.
  [Number and Numeration Goal 1]
- Solve 1-digit by 1-digit addition and subtraction number stories.
  [Operations and Computation Goal 1]
- Find sums of three 1-digit whole numbers.
  [Operations and Computation Goal 2]
- Show amounts of money using pennies and nickels and make exchanges between them.
  [Measurement and Reference Frames Goal 2]
- Add three numbers in different combinations using the Associative Property of Addition.
  [Patterns, Functions, and Algebra Goal 3]

Key Activities

Children make up and solve number stories about items for school. They practice counting money and solve number stories with three 1-digit numbers.

Ongoing Assessment: Recognizing Student Achievement Use journal page 25.
[Operations and Computation Goal 2]

Ongoing Assessment: Informing Instruction See page 159.

Materials

Math Journal 1, pp. 24, 25, 25A, and 25B
Math Masters, pp. 45A and 45B
Home Link 2•12
pennies and nickels ◆ scissors

2 Ongoing Learning & Practice

Playing *Coin Top-It*
3" by 5" index cards (7 per child) ◆ scissors ◆ Pattern-Block Template (optional)
Children practice finding and comparing the values of coin combinations.

Math Boxes 2•13
Math Journal 1, p. 26
Children practice and maintain skills through Math Box problems.

Home Link 2•13
Math Masters, p. 46
Children practice and maintain skills through Home Link activities.

Minute Math+
Minute Math®+, pp. 16 and 80
Children practice solving number models.

3 Differentiation Options

READINESS
Acting Out Number Models
per group: number and symbol signs
Children act out number stories.

ENRICHMENT
The Classroom Store
per group: class bank, objects from home (optional)
Children simulate running and shopping at a Classroom Store.

EXTRA PRACTICE
Reading About Number Stories
Math Masters, p. 305
Children read *12 Ways To Get To 11* to practice number stories.

Advance Preparation

To make number and symbol signs for the optional Readiness activity in Part 3, use 7 large pieces of construction paper or tagboard. One sign should have a + sign on one side and a − sign on the other side. Another sign should have an = symbol on it. Write each of the numbers 1–10 on one side of the other signs. For the optional Extra Practice activity in Part 3, obtain a copy of ***12 Ways To Get To 11*** by Eve Merriam (Simon and Schuster Children's Publishing, 1996).

***Teacher's Reference Manual,* Grades 1–3** pp. 22, 225–229

Getting Started

Mental Math and Reflexes

Practice "stop-and-start" counting: Count by 10s; stop; continue with a new child or group counting on from that number by 5s; stop; point to a new child or group to count on from there by 1s. This skill will be used in counting combinations of dimes, nickels, and pennies in Unit 3.

Home Link 2·12 Follow-Up

Briefly go over the answers.

1 Teaching the Lesson

Solving Number Stories

(*Math Journal 1,* p. 24)

Tell children that they will practice solving number stories today using whatever methods make sense to them. Have children recall what methods they might use to solve number stories. Sample answers: Using counters or pennies to act out the story; drawing doodles, tallies, or pictures; counting on fingers

Write *cents* in a unit box on the board. Ask children to turn to the School Store Mini-Poster on journal page 24.

Make up a few number stories based on the items on the School Store Mini-Poster and have children solve the number-problem stories, using whatever methods make sense to them.

Give children a few minutes to solve each problem. Then have children share their solution strategies as you record their answers and strategies on the board. Some children may suggest a number model for a problem, but do not expect children to be able to do so at this time.

Use any of the sample problems and solution strategies below or make up your own.

- You have a nickel. You buy 3 pieces of gum. How much money do you have left? 2¢

  Possible strategies:

  1. *A nickel is worth 5 cents, so I drew 5 pennies. Then I crossed out the 3 pennies I used to pay for the gum. I had 2 pennies left.*

     Ⓟ Ⓟ Ⓟ Ⓟ Ⓟ

     $5 - 3 = \square$

     Use pennies to model strategies.

  2. *The gum costs 3¢. I counted up to 5¢: 4¢, 5¢. That's 2 more cents.*

     $3 + 2 = \square$

  Possible number models: $5 - 3 = 2$ or $3 + 2 = 5$.

NOTE This lesson contains a significant amount of content; you may wish to complete it over two days.

Math Journal 1, p. 24

- You have 8 cents. How much more money do you need to buy a crayon? 1¢

  Possible strategy: *I put up 8 fingers. I had to count one more to get to 9. I need one more penny.*

  Possible number models: 8 + 1 = 9 or 9 – 8 = 1.

- How much less does the eraser cost than the scissors? 3¢ less

  Possible strategies:

  1. *I lined up 10 pennies for the cost of the scissors and 7 pennies for the cost of the eraser. I put them in pairs and found that the scissors still had 3 pennies left over.*
  2. *I started with 7¢ and counted up to 10¢—that's 3¢.*

  Possible number models: 10 – 7 = 3 or 7 + 3 = 10.

- You want to buy a pencil and an eraser. How much money do you need? 25¢

  Possible strategy: *I made 18 tallies for the cost of the pencil and 7 tallies for the cost of the eraser. Then I counted the tallies: There were four 5s and five tallies, so I counted 5, 10, 15, 20, 21, 22, 23, 24, 25.*

  Possible number model: 18 + 7 = 25.

- How much more does a pencil cost than a piece of candy? 13¢ more

  Possible strategy: *I used 3 nickels and 3 pennies for the pencil. I used a nickel for the candy. I took a nickel from the pencil pile and a nickel from the candy pile. Then I still had 2 nickels and 3 pennies left for the pencil—that's 13¢.*

  Possible number models: 18 – 5 = 13 or 5 + 13 = 18.

- You have 2 nickels. You want to buy the ball. How much more money do you need? 15¢

  Possible strategy: *I put 2 nickels in one pile—that's how much I have. I know that there are 5 nickels in 25¢, so I put 5 nickels in another pile—that's how much I need. I know the two piles must be the same when I finish. So I need 3 more nickels—that's 15¢.*

  Possible number models: 25 = 10 + 15 or 25 – 10 = 15.

When you think children are ready, have them make up problems for the class to solve.

▶ Solving More Number Stories

(*Math Journal 1*, pp. 24 and 25)

Partners complete *Math Journal 1,* page 25. Encourage them to model problems with coins, pictures, doodles, and tallies—whatever will help. Circulate and assist children who are having difficulty.

Student Page

Date

LESSON 2·13 **Counting Coins**

1. Tell how much money.

   (6 nickels) 30 ¢

   (7 pennies) 7 ¢

   How much money in all? 37 ¢

2. Buy 2 items from the School Store. Draw them below.

   Answers vary for Exercises 2–4.

3. Under each item you drew, show how much it costs. Use Ⓟ for pennies and Ⓝ for nickels.

4. Circle the item that costs more. How much more does it cost? ____¢

Try This

5. Draw 2 items that cost a total of 14¢.

   Sample answer: The crayon and the candy

Math Journal 1, p. 25

Ongoing Assessment: Recognizing Student Achievement

Journal Page 25 Problem 1 ★

Use **Journal page 25, Problem 1** to assess children's ability to count nickels and pennies. Children are making adequate progress if they are able to count the nickels and pennies separately. Some children may be able to count the nickels and pennies together.

[Operations and Computation Goal 2]

Ongoing Assessment: Informing Instruction

Watch for children who use only pennies when showing the costs of items from the School Store. Ask them how many pennies they need to exchange for a nickel. Encourage them to make this exchange so that they are using combinations of coins to show the values.

When most children have completed the problems, briefly go over the answers. Ask children to share how they solved the "Try This" problem on the journal page. Ask children what other combinations of items they could have bought for 14¢. Answers vary.

▸ Adding Three Numbers

WHOLE-CLASS ACTIVITY

Ask children to name some school supplies. Display 7 pencils, 4 pens, and 3 crayons. Gather 14 children in front of the class without counting the children aloud. Distribute one writing tool to each child. Ask other children to name the kind of writing tool each child is holding. Record responses on a tally chart.

Pencil	~~////~~ //
Pen	////
Crayon	///

NOTE The Associative Property of Addition says that when three numbers are added, it does not matter which two are added first. In this lesson, children use this property but should not be expected to use the term.

Invite children to determine how many writing tools their classmates are holding in all. After solving the problem, discuss children's strategies. Then write number models in horizontal format and discuss different ways to find the sum.

Option 1

$4 + 7 + 3 =$

$11 + 3 = 14$

Add 4 and 7 first to make 11; then add 3.

Option 2

$4 + 3 + 7 =$

$7 + 7 = 14$

Add 4 and 3 first to make 7; then double 7.

Option 3

$7 + 3 + 4 =$

$10 + 4 = 14$

Add 7 and 3 first to make 10; then add 4.

Teaching Master

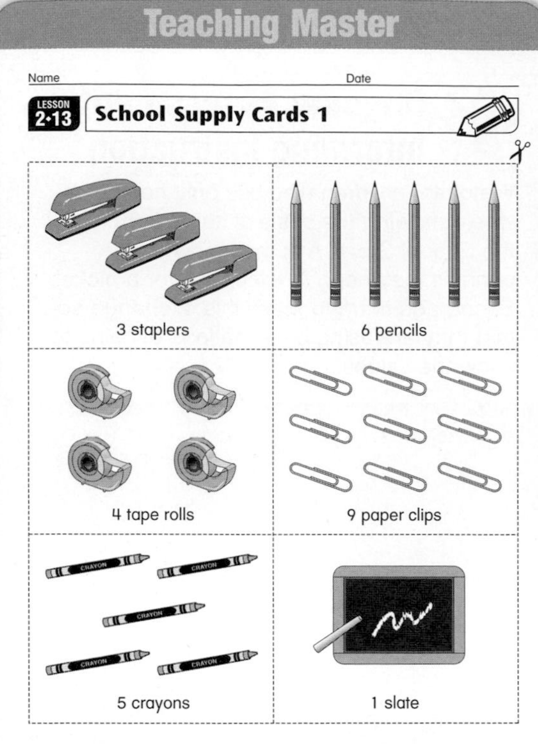
Name Date

LESSON 2·13 School Supply Cards 1

3 staplers	6 pencils
4 tape rolls	9 paper clips
5 crayons	1 slate

Math Masters, **p. 45A**

Ask children the following questions to summarize adding three 1-digit numbers:

- Does the order in which the sums are added make a difference? n
- Which order makes it easiest to find the sum?

Write other combinations of three 1-digit numbers on the board, such as 2 + 8 + 5, 5 + 6 + 6, and 7 + 9 + 4. Ask children to decid which order makes it easiest for them to find the sum. Discuss some number combinations (for example, 7 + 9 + 4) for which there may not be an easy way to add the numbers.

Guide children to understand that three or more numbers can be added in any order. Numbers can also be ordered in a way that makes it easier to find the sum.

▶ Finding Sums of Three Numbers

PARTNE ACTIVITY

(*Math Masters,* pp. 45A and 45B)

Direct children's attention to *Math Masters,* pages 45A and 45B and identify each school supply. Explain that children will cut out the school supply cards and use them to write and solve number sentences.

Have children work in pairs. Children first cut out the cards. Then they mix the cards together and place them face down in a pile. One child picks three cards. The other child writes an addition sentence about the school supplies and finds the sum. Partners then switch roles.

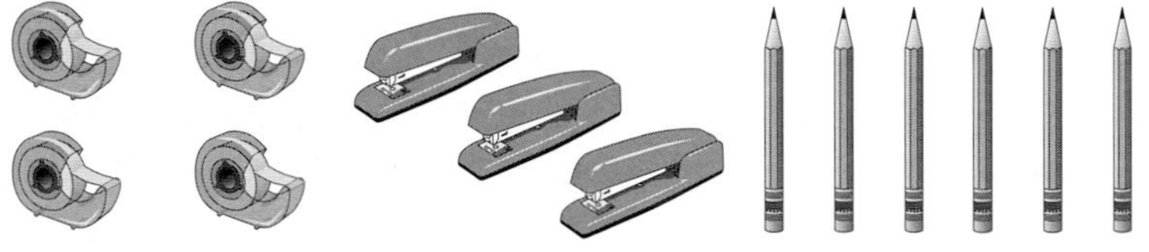

4 + 3 + 6 = 13 school supplies

NOTE A calculator is a good tool to show that the order in which numbers are added does not change the sum. Using the calculator also demonstrates that when adding more than two numbers, it is not necessary to enter their sum and the third number as a new problem.

Teaching Master

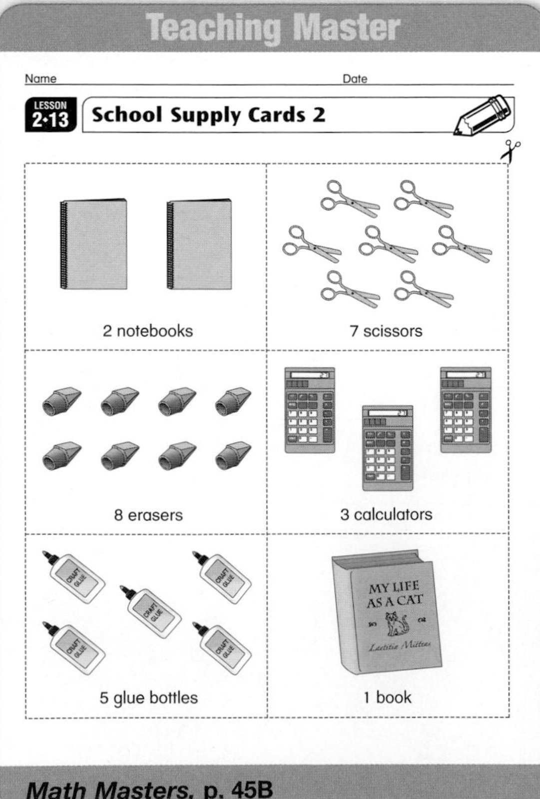
Name Date

LESSON 2·13 School Supply Cards 2

2 notebooks	7 scissors
8 erasers	3 calculators
5 glue bottles	1 book

Math Masters, **p. 45B**

Creating Number Stories

WHOLE-CLASS ACTIVITY

(*Math Journal 1,* pp. 24, 25A, and 25B; *Math Masters,* pp. 45A and 45B)

Explain that children are going to be using the objects from the School Store Mini-Poster (*Math Journal 1,* page 24) and items from their School Supply cards, along with the addition sentences given on journal pages 25A and 25B, to write number stories. Use the first number sentence on journal page 25A as an example:

▷ On the board, write 2 + 3 + 5 = _____. Tell children that you are going to choose objects from the cards to write a number story to go with 2 + 3 + 5 = _____.

▷ Write the following story, or something similar, on the board: *I cleaned my desk. I put away 2 staplers, 3 rolls of tape, and 5 markers. How many items did I put away?* 10 items

▷ Have children solve the number story and write the sum on the board. Tell children that they are to write a number story to go with each number sentence on journal pages 25A and 25B.

Student Page

Date ______

LESSON 2·13 **Creating Number Stories 1**

Write a number story to go with the number sentence. Then solve.

1. 2 + 3 + 5 = 10

Answers vary.

2. 4 + 6 + 8 = 18

Answers vary.

3. 3 + 9 + 1 = 13

Answers vary.

Math Journal 1, p. 25A

2 Ongoing Learning & Practice

Playing *Coin Top-It*

PARTNER ACTIVITY

This game is for 2 players. Each player cuts seven 3" by 5" index cards in half and draws a combination of nickels and pennies on each card. Players can use the circles on their Pattern-Block Templates to draw coins. (Have players label the circles *N* for nickels and *P* for pennies.) Each player should make a card for each amount from 7¢–20¢.

NOTE When making the card decks, children can write the amounts on one side of the cards, using cent notation. When playing with such a deck, the cards should be put in a stack with the coin side face up. When players draw a card, the coin side should remain face up. After they have decided which card shows the larger amount, they turn the cards over to check their answers.

Directions

1. Combine both sets of cards. Mix them and place them facedown in a stack.
2. Each player draws a card and counts the coins shown on the card. The player with the larger amount takes both cards.
3. In case of a tie, each player takes one more card. The player with the larger amount takes all of the cards.
4. The game ends when all of the cards in the stack have been played. The winner is the player with more cards.

Student Page

Date ______

LESSON 2·13 **Creating Number Stories 2**

Write a number story to go with the number sentence. Then solve.

1. 7 + 3 + 4 = 14

Answers vary.

2. 6 + 6 + 3 = 15

Answers vary.

3. 9 + 2 + 4 = 15

Answers vary.

Math Journal 1, p. 25B

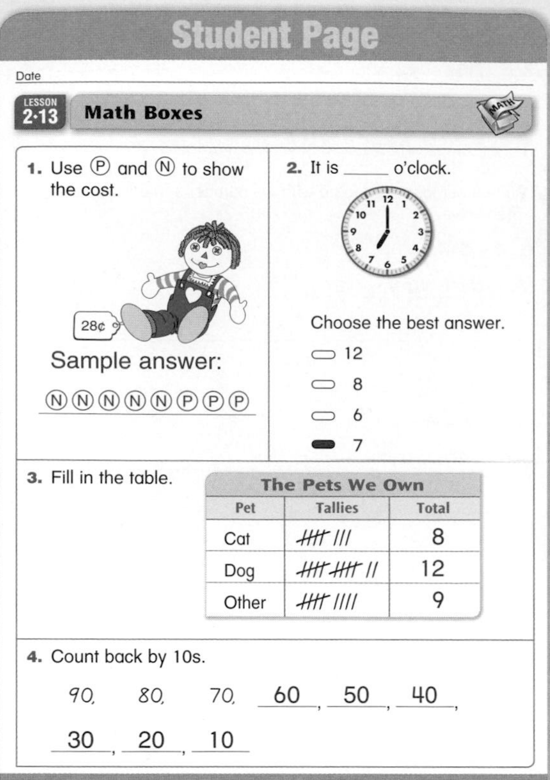

Student Page

Date

LESSON 2·13 **Math Boxes**

1. Use Ⓟ and Ⓝ to show the cost.

28¢

Sample answer:

ⓃⓃⓃⓃⓃⓅⓅⓅ

2. It is _____ o'clock.

Choose the best answer.

○ 12
○ 8
○ 6
● 7

3. Fill in the table.

The Pets We Own

Pet	Tallies	Total
Cat	𝍸 III	8
Dog	𝍸 𝍸 II	12
Other	𝍸 IIII	9

4. Count back by 10s.

90, 80, 70, 60, 50, 40,

30, 20, 10

Math Journal 1, p. 26

NOTE Remember to reserve time every day to complete the number-line, attendance, calendar, temperature, and weather routines.

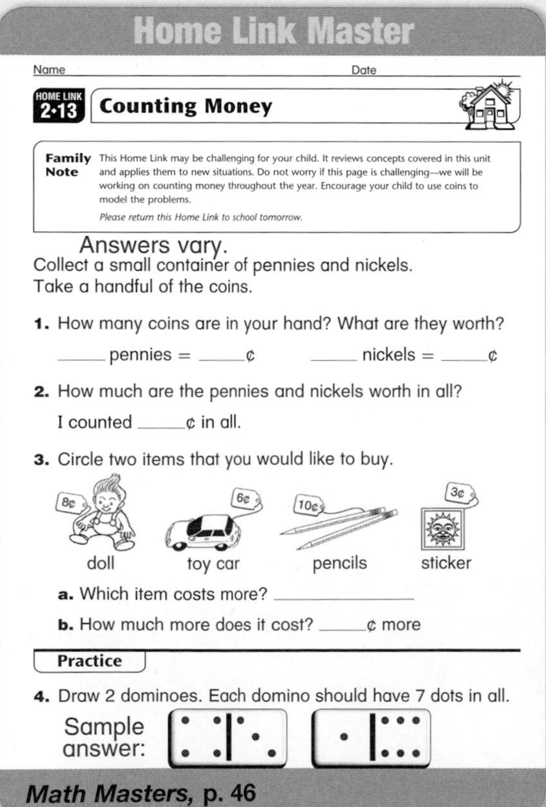

Home Link Master

Name Date

HOME LINK 2·13 **Counting Money**

Family Note This Home Link may be challenging for your child. It reviews concepts covered in this unit and applies them to new situations. Do not worry if this page is challenging—we will be working on counting money throughout the year. Encourage your child to use coins to model the problems.

Please return this Home Link to school tomorrow.

Answers vary.

Collect a small container of pennies and nickels.
Take a handful of the coins.

1. How many coins are in your hand? What are they worth?

_____ pennies = _____¢ _____ nickels = _____¢

2. How much are the pennies and nickels worth in all?

I counted _____¢ in all.

3. Circle two items that you would like to buy.

8¢ doll 6¢ toy car 10¢ pencils 3¢ sticker

a. Which item costs more? _____________

b. How much more does it cost? _____¢ more

Practice

4. Draw 2 dominoes. Each domino should have 7 dots in all.

Sample answer:

Math Masters, p. 46

▶ Math Boxes 2·13

INDEPENDENT ACTIVITY

(*Math Journal 1*, p. 26)

Mixed Practice Math Boxes in this lesson are paired with Math Boxes in Lesson 2-11. The skills in Problem 4 preview Unit 3 content.

▶ Home Link 2·13

INDEPENDENT ACTIVITY

(*Math Masters*, p. 46)

Home Connection Children solve several problems that involve counting combinations of pennies and nickels. Children are encouraged to use real coins to model the problems.

▶ *Minute Math+*

Use *Minute Math+,* pages 16 and 80 to provide more practice solving number stories.

3 Differentiation Options

READINESS

▶ Acting Out Number Models

15–30 Min

To provide experience with addition and subtraction, have children act out number stories with number and operation cards. One child holds up the + or – sign. Another child holds up the = sign and the sum for the number model. The remaining children represent the amounts in the number model.

Tell a number story about children at a party. Use children's names to personalize the stories.

There were 3 children at a party. Two more people came to the party. Ask the +/– child: *Which symbol do you need?* The + symbol The final child should hold up the appropriate number. 5

For a subtraction problem, start with a given number of children at a party. Then have some children "leave" to go home.

ENRICHMENT

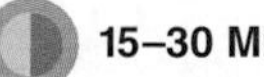

SMALL-GROUP ACTIVITY

The Classroom Store

15–30 Min

To further explore money exchange, run a classroom store using items children have brought from home. Teachers who have done this activity find that children enjoy the hands-on money experience of shopping at the Classroom Store. Run the store for a few minutes a couple of days per week.

NOTE For this activity, make a class bank from which money can be taken for making purchases at the Classroom Store. Children should not use their tool-kit coins because they will need them for future lessons.

Children enjoy being customers and shopkeepers in the classroom store.

EXTRA PRACTICE

SMALL-GROUP ACTIVITY

Reading About Number Stories

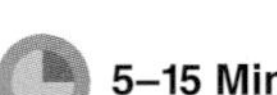

5–15 Min

(*Math Masters,* p. 305)

Literature Link To provide practice with number stories, read ***12 Ways To Get To 11*** by Eve Merriam (Simon and Schuster Children's Publishing, 1996). Have children write a number model on an Exit Slip (*Math Masters,* page 305) and illustrate their number model.

2•14 Progress Check 2

Objective To assess children's progress on mathematical content through the end of Unit 2.

1 Looking Back: Cumulative Assessment

Input children's data from Progress Check 2 into the **Assessment Management Spreadsheets.**

Materials

- Home Link 2•13
- *Math Journal 1,* inside back cover
- *Assessment Handbook,* pp. 60–67, 141–144, 178, and 204–207
- slate; demonstration clock

CONTENT ASSESSED	LESSON(S)	ASSESSMENT ITEMS				
		SELF	ORAL/SLATE	WRITTEN		OPEN RESPONSE
				PART A	PART B	
Count by 1s, 2s, 5s, and 10s. [Number and Numeration Goal 1]	2•1, 2•2, 2•3, 2•13		1		5	
Write whole numbers. [Number and Numeration Goal 3]	2•2, 2•4, 2•6	1				
Solve addition and subtraction problems. [Operations and Computation Goal 1]	2•1, 2•3, 2•4, 2•12		3, 4		4	
Solve number stories. [Operations and Computation Goal 4]	2•11, 2•13	2				
Calculate and compare the values of collections of coins. [Operations and Computation Goal 2]	2•9, 2•10	3, 4		2		✓
Use tally charts to answer questions. [Data and Chance Goal 2]	2•2, 2•4, 2•11, 2•13	6		1		
Know and compare values of pennies and nickels. [Measurement and Reference Frames Goal 2]	2•8–2•10, 2•13					✓
Show and tell time to the nearest hour. [Measurement and Reference Frames Goal 4]	2•7, 2•9–2•11, 2•13	5	2	3		

2 Looking Ahead: Preparing for Unit 3

Math Boxes 2•14

Home Link 2•14: Unit 3 Family Letter

Materials

- *Math Journal 1,* p. 27
- *Math Masters,* pp. 47–50

Getting Started

Home Link 2+13 Follow-Up

Ask children to tell how many nickels and pennies they grabbed. Then have the class calculate how much those sets of coins are worth.

1 Looking Back: Cumulative Assessment

Self Assessment

INDEPENDENT ACTIVITY

(*Assessment Handbook,* p. 141)

Have children complete the Self Assessment. The Self Assessment offers children the opportunity to reflect upon their progress.

Oral and Slate Assessments

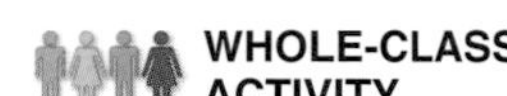

WHOLE-CLASS ACTIVITY

(*Math Journal 1,* inside back cover)

Problems 2 and 4 provide summative information and can be used for grading purposes. Problems 1 and 3 provide formative information that can be useful in planning future instruction.

Oral Assessment

1. Do "stop-and-start" counting. Count by 10s to 40; stop; count by 5s to 60; stop; count by 1s to 75.
2. Tell the time shown on the demonstration clock. Show the following times on the clock: 3 o'clock; 8 o'clock; 11 o'clock; 5 o'clock; 6 o'clock; 1 o'clock.

Slate Assessment

3. Use the number grid on the inside back cover of *Math Journal 1.*
   - Put your finger on 7. Count up 5 spaces. Write where you land. 12
   - Put your finger on 3. Count up 10 spaces. Write where you land. 13
   - Put your finger on 14. Count back 6 spaces. Write where you land. 8
4. Mara had 10 pennies to play *Penny Plate*. She left 4 pennies showing on the table. She put the rest under her plate. How many pennies did Mara put under her plate? 6 pennies

Assessment Master

Name Date

LESSON 2+14 **Self Assessment** Progress Check 2

Put a check in the box that tells how you do each skill.

Skills	I can do this by myself. I can explain how to do this.	I can do this by myself.	I can do this with help.
1. Write 7, 8, 9, and 0.			
2. Solve number stories.			
3. Count pennies.			
4. Count nickels.			
5. Tell time to the hour.			
6. Read a tally chart.			

Assessment Handbook, **p. 141**

Assessment Master

Name Date

LESSON 2+14 **Written Assessment** Progress Check 2

Part A

1. How many children lost 1 tooth?
   7 children

Teeth Lost	Tallies
0	𝍸
1	𝍸 //
2	///

2. How much money does Sarah have?

13 ¢

How much money does Bill have?

10 ¢

Circle the amount that is more.

Assessment Handbook, **p. 142**

Assessment Master

Name Date

LESSON 2·14 **Written Assessment** *continued*

3. Draw the hour hand and the minute hand.

4 o'clock

Part B

4. Add or subtract.

8 + 1 = 9

5 − 1 = 4

4 + 0 = 4

10 − 1 = 9

5. 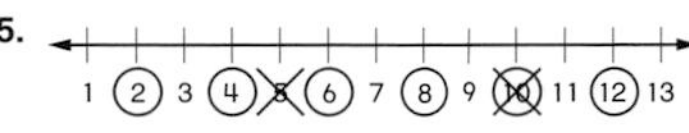

Circle counts by 2s.

Cross out counts by 5s.

Assessment Handbook, p. 143

Assessment Master

Name Date

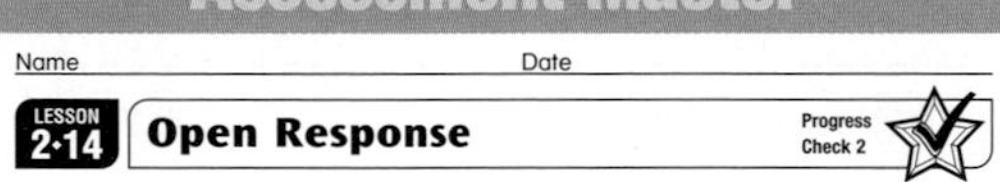

Counting Coins

Bill and Janet have a jar of nickels and pennies.

1. Bill takes 5 coins out of the jar. He has both nickels and pennies. Draw 5 coins that Bill could take out and tell the total value of the coins.

Coins	Value
Sample answer: Ⓝ Ⓝ Ⓝ Ⓟ Ⓟ	17¢

2. Janet takes 5 coins out of the jar. She has both nickels and pennies. She has more money than Bill has. Draw 5 coins that Janet could take out and tell the total value of the coins.

Coins	Value
Sample answer: Ⓝ Ⓝ Ⓝ Ⓝ Ⓟ	21¢

3. Draw 5 coins from the jar that would have the **greatest** total value. Explain how you found your answer.

Coins	Value
Ⓝ Ⓝ Ⓝ Ⓝ Ⓝ	25¢

Assessment Handbook, p. 144

▶ Written Assessment

(*Assessment Handbook,* pp. 142 and 143)

Part A Recognizing Student Achievement

Problems 1–3 provide summative information and may be used fo[r] grading purposes.

Problem(s)	Description
1	Use a tally chart to answer questions.
2	Calculate and compare the value of penny and nickel coin collections.
3	Show time to the hour on an analog clock.

Part B Informing Instruction

Problems 4 and 5 provide formative information that can be usefu[l] in planning future instruction.

Problem(s)	Description
4	Know addition facts.
5	Count forward by 2s and 5s.

Use the checklists on pages 205 and 207 of the *Assessment Handbook* to record results. Then input the data into the **Assessment Management Spreadsheets** to keep an ongoing record of children's progress toward Grade-Level Goals.

▶ Open Response

(*Assessment Handbook,* p. 144)

Counting Coins

The open-response item requires children to apply skills and concepts from Unit 2 to solve a multistep problem. See *Assessment Handbook,* pages 63–67 for rubrics and children's work samples for this problem.

There are two options for completing this open response. For both *Option 1* and *Option 2,* children begin by working independently (or with a partner) to solve a multistep problem. Take this time to circulate throughout the classroom.

Option 1:

Bill has a jar of nickels and pennies. He takes 5 coins out of the *jar.*

- What different combinations of coins could Bill have taken out?
- How many different combinations could Bill have taken out?
- Which combination is worth the most?
- Which combination is worth the least?

Option 2:

Distribute *Assessment Master,* page 144. Read the problem aloud to children. Allow children to solve the problem and record their solutions on the page.

See the *Assessment Handbook* for more information.

After children have had a chance to complete either option, convene the class. Invite individual children to explain their solution strategies. Encourage them to use words and drawings to explain their strategies as you list them on the board. Be sure to discuss both successful and unsuccessful strategies.

NOTE You may wish to give each child a resealable bag containing 15 pennies and 5 nickels. This will allow children to act out the problem if they wish.

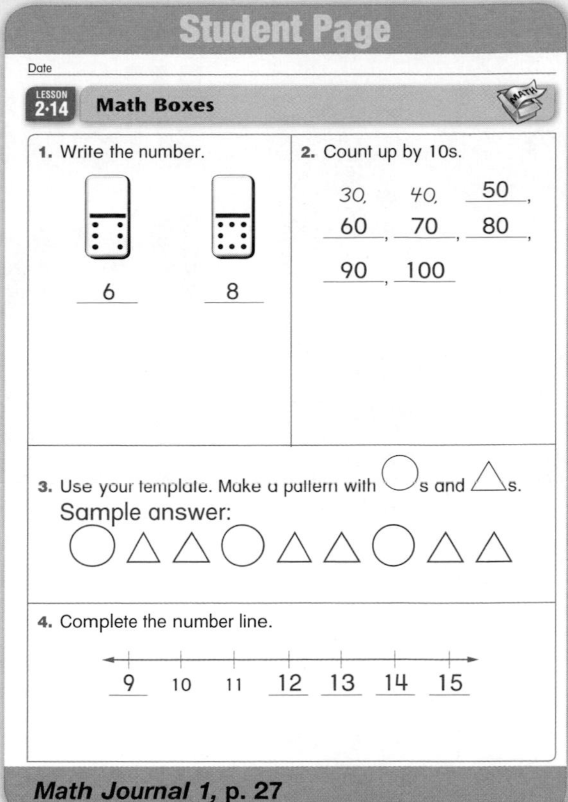
Student Page

Date

LESSON 2•14 **Math Boxes**

1. Write the number.
6 8

2. Count up by 10s.
30, 40, 50, 60, 70, 80, 90, 100

3. Use your template. Make a pattern with ○s and △s.
Sample answer:
○ △ △ ○ △ △ ○ △ △

4. Complete the number line.
9 10 11 12 13 14 15

Math Journal 1, p. 27

2 Looking Ahead: Preparing for Unit 3

Math Boxes 2•14

INDEPENDENT ACTIVITY

(*Math Journal 1,* p. 27)

Mixed Practice This Math Boxes page previews Unit 3 content.

Home Link 2•14: Unit 3 Family Letter

INDEPENDENT ACTIVITY

(*Math Masters,* pp. 47–50)

Home Connection The Unit 3 Family Letter provides families with information and activities related to Unit 3 topics.

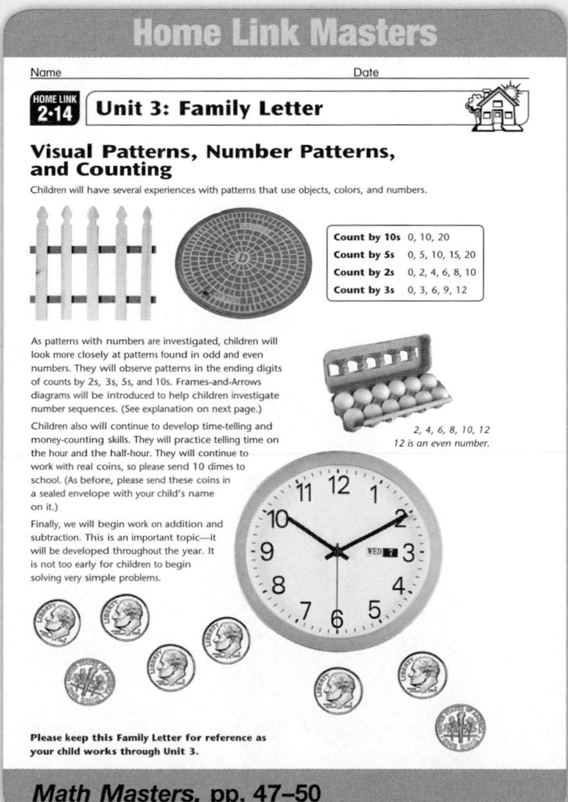
Home Link Masters

Name Date

HOME LINK 2•14 **Unit 3: Family Letter**

Visual Patterns, Number Patterns, and Counting

Children will have several experiences with patterns that use objects, colors, and numbers.

Count by 10s	0, 10, 20
Count by 5s	0, 5, 10, 15, 20
Count by 2s	0, 2, 4, 6, 8, 10
Count by 3s	0, 3, 6, 9, 12

As patterns with numbers are investigated, children will look more closely at patterns found in odd and even numbers. They will observe patterns in the ending digits of counts by 2s, 3s, 5s, and 10s. Frames-and-Arrows diagrams will be introduced to help children investigate number sequences. (See explanation on next page.)

2, 4, 6, 8, 10, 12
12 is an even number.

Children also will continue to develop time-telling and money-counting skills. They will practice telling time on the hour and the half-hour. They will continue to work with real coins, so please send 10 dimes to school. (As before, please send these coins in a sealed envelope with your child's name on it.)

Finally, we will begin work on addition and subtraction. This is an important topic—it will be developed throughout the year. It is not too early for children to begin solving very simple problems.

Please keep this Family Letter for reference as your child works through Unit 3.

Math Masters, pp. 47–50

Unit 3 Organizer

Visual Patterns, Number Patterns, and Counting

Overview

One of the most important topics in mathematics is the study of patterns. Since patterns are predictable, it is usually possible to state a rule that describes each pattern. This rule can then be used to extend the pattern. Much of Unit 3 focuses on number patterns: odd and even numbers; patterns in number lines and number grids; and number sequences. Number patterns will be revisited throughout the year.

This unit continues the steady development of some important first-grade topics: Telling time is extended to times on the half-hour, dimes are added to children's existing collections of coins to be counted, and work is begun on solving simple addition and subtraction problems. Unit 3 has four main areas of focus:

- To explore numeric, visual, and concrete patterns,
- To introduce addition and subtraction on the number line,
- To introduce the Frames-and-Arrows routine, and
- To find the values of collections of dimes, nickels, and pennies.

Linking to the Common Core State Standards

The content of Unit 3 addresses the Common Core State Standards for Mathematics in *Operations and Algebraic Thinking*. The correlation of the Common Core State Standards to the *Everyday Mathematics* Grade 1 lessons begins on page CS1.

Contents

Learning In Perspective

	Lesson Objectives	Links to the Past	Links to the Future
3·1	To guide the exploration and extension of visual patterns.	Children are introduced to non-numeric patterns as well as calendar patterns in Kindergarten. Also in Kindergarten, children create and extend patterns.	In Units 6, 9, and 10, children create, describe, and extend numeric, visual, and concrete patterns.
3·2	To guide exploration of even and odd number patterns.	In Kindergarten, children are introduced to even and odd numbers.	In Unit 6, children use manipulatives to identify and model even and odd numbers.
3·3	To guide exploration of skip-counting patterns on the number grid.	In Unit 2, children count up and back on the number grid. In Kindergarten, they learn to skip count by 1s, 2s, 5s, and 10s on a number grid.	In Units 4–6 and 8–10, children use the number grid to skip count, find numerical patterns, and solve addition and subtraction problems.
3·4	To guide exploration of even and odd numbers; covering shapes with pattern blocks; and creating and continuing repeating patterns.	In Kindergarten, children are introduced to even and odd numbers. They also cover shapes with pattern blocks and create and extend patterns.	In Units 5, 6, and 8–10, children identify and model odd and even numbers, model fractions; and work with patterns.
3·5	To review basic number-line concepts; and to provide practice counting on the number line.	In Unit 1, children count up and back on the number line. They are introduced to the number line in Kindergarten and use the number line to count.	In Units 4–10, children review counting on. They also compare the number line to the scale on a thermometer.
3·6	To introduce addition and subtraction on the number line.	In Unit 1, children count up and back on the number line. In Kindergarten, they use the number line to explore addition and subtraction.	In Units 1–10, children practice addition and subtraction through games and a variety of problem-solving situations.
3·7	To review basic concepts of telling time; and to provide practice telling time to the hour and the half-hour.	In Unit 2, children tell time to the nearest hour. In Kindergarten, children are introduced to the minute hand.	Throughout Grades 1–3, children learn to tell time with increasing precision; by Grade 3 they can tell time to the nearest minute.
3·8	To introduce the Frames-and-Arrows routine.	Children count up by 1s, 2s, 5s, and 10s in Units 1 and 2 and in Kindergarten.	In Units 6 and 9, children work with Frames-and-Arrows problems. In Grades 2 and 3, they extend the routine.
3·9	To introduce Frames-and-Arrows problems in which the "arrow rule" is missing.	Children count up by 1s, 2s, 5s, and 10s in Units 1 and 2 and in Kindergarten.	In Units 6 and 9, children work with Frames-and-Arrows problems. In Grades 2 and 3, they extend the routine.
3·10	To introduce counting up and back on the calculator.	In Unit 2, children use calculators. In Kindergarten, children use calculators to count up.	Children use calculators throughout Grades 1–6. In Units 4–6 and 8–10, they solve simple addition and subtraction problems.
3·11	To introduce the dime; to introduce dollars-and-cents notation; and to provide practice exchanging pennies, nickels, and dimes.	In Unit 2, children are introduced to cent notation and exchanging coins. In Kindergarten, children are introduced to dimes and exchanging coins.	In Units 4–6, 8, and 10, children are introduced to quarters and dollar bills and make exchanges between coins.
3·12	To provide practice finding the values of collections of dimes, nickels, and pennies.	In Unit 2, children find the values of coin combinations including pennies and nickels. Children find the values of coin combinations in Kindergarten.	In Units 4–6, 8, and 10, children calculate combinations of coins, including pennies, nickels, dimes, and quarters.
3·13	To introduce line plots.	In Unit 1, children use tally marks to record data. In Kindergarten, children collect and organize data.	Throughout Grades 1–6, children collect, organize, and analyze data.
3·14	To explore domino-dot patterns; and to provide practice for all of the basic addition facts.	In Unit 2 children work with dominoes. Children work with dominoes in Kindergarten and also solve addition problems.	In Units 4–10, children use dominoes to find patterns and solve addition and subtraction problems.

	Key Concepts and Skills	Grade 1 Goals*
3•1	Count objects by 1s and 2s.	Number and Numeration Goal 2
	Recognize, describe, and create visual patterns.	Patterns, Functions, and Algebra Goal 1
	Identify the pattern rule in a visual pattern.	Patterns, Functions, and Algebra Goal 1
	Use a pattern rule to extend a visual pattern.	Patterns, Functions, and Algebra Goal 1
3•2	Count forward by even and odd numbers.	Number and Numeration Goal 1
	Write numbers to represent quantities.	Number and Numeration Goal 3
	Use manipulatives to identify numbers as odd or even.	Number and Numeration Goal 5
	Identify and describe even and odd number patterns.	Patterns, Functions, and Algebra Goal 1
3•3	Count forward by 2s, 5s, and 10s.	Number and Numeration Goal 1
	Identify the digit in the ones place.	Number and Numeration Goal 3
	Describe and compare number patterns.	Patterns, Functions, and Algebra Goal 1
3•4	Identify even and odd numbers.	Number and Numeration Goal 5
	Use plane shapes for patterning.	Geometry Goal 1
	Create visual patterns.	Patterns, Functions, and Algebra Goal 1
	Sort dominoes.	Patterns, Functions, and Algebra Goal 1
3•5	Count forward by 2s, 3s, 5s, and 10s.	Number and Numeration Goal 1
	Count forward and backward by 1s from a given number.	Number and Numeration Goal 1
	Create skip-counting patterns.	Patterns, Functions, and Algebra Goal 1
3•6	Count forward and backward by 1s from a given number.	Number and Numeration Goal 1
	Model and solve addition and subtraction number stories.	Operations and Computation Goal 1
	Complete number models for addition and subtraction number stories.	Operations and Computation Goal 1
	Use the symbols +, −, and = to complete number models.	Patterns, Functions, and Algebra Goal 2
3•7	Estimate time on an analog clock using only the hour hand.	Measurement and Reference Frames Goal 4
	Show a given time to the hour and half-hour on an analog clock.	Measurement and Reference Frames Goal 4
	Tell and record times shown on an analog clock to the hour and half-hour.	Measurement and Reference Frames Goal 4
	Use language of approximation to describe times on an analog clock.	Measurement and Reference Frames Goal 4
3•8	Count forward and backward 1s, 2s, 3s, 5s, and 10s from a given number.	Number and Numeration Goal 1
	Find the missing numbers in a Frames-and-Arrows problem given the rule.	Patterns, Functions, and Algebra Goal 1
3•9	Count forward and backward by 1s, 2s, 3s, 5s, and 10s from a given number.	Number and Numeration Goal 1
	Find the missing numbers in a Frames-and-Arrows problem given the rule.	Patterns, Functions, and Algebra Goal 1
	Identify rules in Frames-and-Arrows problems.	Patterns, Functions, and Algebra Goal 1
	Create Frames-and-Arrows problems.	Patterns, Functions, and Algebra Goal 1
3•10	Count forward and backward by 1s, 2s, and 5s from a given number.	Number and Numeration Goal 1
	Read numbers and symbols on a calculator.	Number and Numeration Goal 3
	Use the +, −, and = symbols to count forward and backward on a calculator.	Patterns, Functions, and Algebra Goal 2
3•11	Count forward by 1s, 5s, and 10s from a given number.	Number and Numeration Goal 1
	Identify a dime and know its value.	Measurement and Reference Frames Goal 2
	Show equivalent amounts of money.	Measurement and Reference Frames Goal 2
	Exchange pennies for nickels and dimes.	Measurement and Reference Frames Goal 2
3•12	Count forward by 1s, 5s, and 10s from a given number.	Number and Numeration Goal 1
	Find the values of combinations of dimes, nickels, and pennies.	Operations and Computation Goal 2
	Exchange nickels for dimes, and pennies for nickels and dimes.	Measurement and Reference Frames Goal 2
	Show amounts of money with the fewest number of dimes, nickels, and pennies.	Measurement and Reference Frames Goal 2
3•13	Compare whole numbers.	Number and Numeration Goal 7
	Create a tally chart.	Data and Chance Goal 1
	Create a line plot.	Data and Chance Goal 1
	Answer simple questions about a line plot.	Data and Chance Goal 2
3•14	Estimate whether quantities are more than 10, less than 10, or equal to 10.	Number and Numeration Goal 2
	Sort dominoes by even and odd numbers.	Number and Numeration Goal 5
	Order dominoes according to dot patterns.	Number and Numeration Goal 7
	Estimate sums.	Operations and Computation Goal 3
	Find totals using the parts-and-total diagram.	Operations and Computation Goal 4

*See the Appendix for a complete list of Grade 1 Goals.

A Balanced Curriculum

Ongoing Practice

Everyday Mathematics provides numerous opportunities for ongoing practice. These activities are embedded throughout the lessons:

Mental Math and Reflexes activities promote speed and accuracy in mental computation.

Math Boxes offer mixed practice and are paired across lessons as shown in the brackets below. This makes them useful as assessment tools. The last one or two boxes on each page preview the next unit's content.

Mixed practice	[3•1, 3•3], [3•2, 3•4], [3•5, 3•7], [3•6, 3•8], [3•9, 3•11], [3•10, 3•13], [3•12, 3•14]
Mixed practice with multiple choice	3•1, 3•2, 3•5, 3•6, 3•10, 3•11, 3•12
Mixed practice with writing/reasoning opportunity	3•1, 3•2, 3•7, 3•8, 3•10, 3•11, 3•14

Home Links are daily homework assignments that review the content of the lesson and often contain ongoing facts practice.

***Minute Math*+** problems are offered for additional practice in Lessons 3•4, 3•10, 3•11, and 3•12.

EM Facts Workshop Game provides online practice of basic facts and computation.

EXTRA PRACTICE **Extra Practice** activities are included in Lessons 3•1, 3•2, 3•4, 3•5, 3•6, 3•10, and 3•11.

Practice through Games

Games are an essential component of practice in the *Everyday Mathematics* program. Games offer skills practice and promote strategic thinking. See the *Differentiation Handbook* for ways to adapt games to meet children's needs.

Lesson	Game	Skill Practiced
3•1, 3•4	*Before and After*	Counting forward and backward by 1s [NN Goal 1]
3•2, 3•7, 3•10	*Penny-Nickel Exchange*	Exchanging pennies for nickels [MRF Goal 2]
3•5, 3•11	*Coin Top-It*	Calculating and comparing the values of combinations of coins [OC Goal 2]
3•6	*Bunny Hop*	Counting on a number line [NN Goal 1]
3•9	*Ten-Frame Top-It*	Comparing numbers [NN Goal 7]
3•12	*Coin-Dice*	Making coin exchanges [MRF Goal 2]
3•13	*Dime-Nickel-Penny Grab*	Calculating and comparing the values of combinations of coins [OC Goal 2]
3•14	*Domino Top-It*	Finding and comparing sums [NN Goal 7 and OC Goal 2]
3•14	*High Roller*	Comparing quantities and finding sums [NN Goal 7 and OC Goal 2]

[NN] Number and Numeration [OC] Operations and Computation [DC] Data and Chance
[MRF] Measurement and Reference Frames [GEO] Geometry [PFA] Patterns, Functions, and Algebra

Problem Solving 

Good problem solvers use a variety of strategies, including the following:

- Draw a picture.
- Act out the problem.
- Make a table, chart, or list.
- Look for a pattern.
- Try a simpler version of the problem.
- Make a guess and try it out.

The table below lists some of the opportunities in this unit for children to practice these strategies.

Lessons that teach *through* problem solving, not just *about* problem solving

Lesson	Activity
3•2	Explore even and odd numbers.
3•4	Explore even and odd number patterns with dominoes.
3•4	Cover shapes with pattern blocks.
3•5	Count hops on the number line.
3•6	Add and subtract on the number line.
3•8	Solve Frames-and-Arrows problems.
3•9	Solve Frames-and-Arrows problems.
3•14	Use parts-and-total diagrams to solve problems.

See Chapter 18: Problem Solving in the *Teacher's Reference Manual* for more information.

The Language of Mathematics

Everyday Mathematics provides lesson-specific suggestions to help all children acquire, process, and express mathematical ideas. Throughout Unit 3, there are lesson-specific language development notes that address the needs of English language learners, indicated by ELL.

ELL SUPPORT Activities to support English language learners are in Part 3 of Lessons 3•2, 3•3, 3•7, 3•11, and 3•13.

The *English Learners Handbook* and the *Differentiation Handbook* have suggestions for promoting language development and acquisition of mathematics vocabulary. See Unit 3 in each handbook.

Unit 3 Vocabulary

arrow
arrow rule
column
decimal point
dime
dollars-and-cents notation
even number
frame
Frames-and-Arrows diagram
half-past (the hour)
line plot
negative number
number line
odd number
pattern
program
row

Literacy Connection

Lesson 3•1 *Pattern Bugs,* by Trudy Harris, Millbrook Press, 2001

Lesson 3•2 *Missing Mittens,* by Stuart J. Murphy, HarperCollins Publishers, 2001

Lesson 3•3 *Each Orange Had 8 Slices: A Counting Book,* by Paul Giganti Jr., Greenwillow Books, 1999

Lesson 3•5 *Two Ways to Count to Ten,* by Ruby Dee, Henry Holt & Company, 1988

For more literacy connections, see the *Home Connection Handbook,* Grades 1–3.

Cross-Curricular Links 

Music – Lesson 3•1

Social Studies – Lesson 3•11

Language Arts – Lesson 3•11

Literature – Lessons 3•1, 3•2, 3•5

Balanced Assessment

Daily Assessments

- **Recognizing Student Achievement** – A daily assessment that is included in every lesson to evaluate children's progress toward the Grade 1 Grade-Level Goals.
- **Informing Instruction** – Notes that appear throughout the unit to help anticipate children's common errors and suggest appropriate problem-solving strategies.

Lesson	Recognizing Student Achievement	Informing Instruction
3•1	Create and extend patterns. [PFA Goal 1]	
3•2	Distinguish between even and odd numbers. [NN Goal 5]	
3•3	Compare numbers. [NN Goal 7]	
3•4	Count spaces on a number grid. [OC Goal 2]	Use pattern blocks to create patterns.
3•5	Skip count. [NN Goal 1]	Count hops on a number line.
3•6	Write number models. [PFA Goal 2]	
3•7	Use a tally chart to answer questions. [DC Goal 2]	Display times on tool-kit clocks.
3•8	Count up and back from a given number. [NN Goal 1]	Use the rule box in a Frames-and-Arrows problem.
3•9	Solve Frames-and-Arrows problems. [PFA Goal 1]	State the Frames-and-Arrow rule.
3•10	Count by 5s and then by 1s. [NN Goal 1]	Remember to clear calculators.
3•11	Make coin exchanges. [MRF Goal 2]	Know the values of coins.
3•12	Solve parts-and-total number stories. [OC Goal 4]	Find the value of coin combinations.
3•13	Make sums of 10. [OC Goal 1]	
3•14	Find dice sums. [OC Goal 1]	

[NN] Number and Numeration [OC] Operations and Computation [DC] Data and Chance
[MRF] Measurement and Reference Frames [GEO] Geometry [PFA] Patterns, Functions, and Algebra

Portfolio Opportunities

The following lessons provide opportunities to gather samples of children's mathematical writings, drawings, and creations to add balance to the assessment process: Lessons 3•1, 3•2, 3•7, 3•8, 3•10, 3•11, 3•14, and 3•15.

See pages 16 and 17 in the *Assessment Handbook* for more information about portfolios and how to use them.

Unit Assessment

Progress Check 3 – A cumulative assessment of concepts and skills taught in Unit 3 and in previous units, providing information for evaluating children's progress and planning for future instruction. These assessments include oral/slate, written, and open-response activities, as shown below in the sample Progress Check lesson opener.

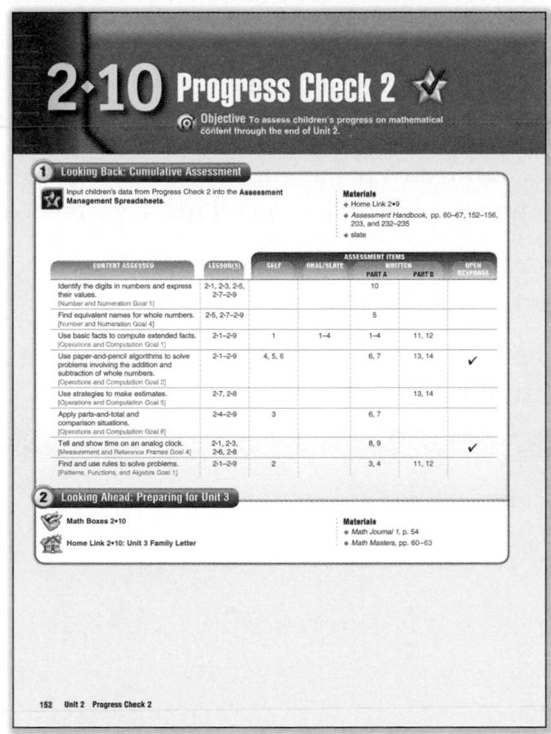

2·10 Progress Check 2

Objective To assess children's progress on mathematical content through the end of Unit 2.

1 Looking Back: Cumulative Assessment

Input children's data from Progress Check 2 into the **Assessment Management Spreadsheets**.

Materials
- Home Link 2•9
- *Assessment Handbook*, pp. 60–67, 152–156, 203, and 232–235
- slate

Content Assessed	Lesson(s)	Assessment Items: Self	Oral/Slate	Written: Part A	Written: Part B	Open Response
Identify the digits in numbers and express their values. [Number and Numeration Goal 1]	2·1, 2·3, 2·5, 2·7–2·9			10		
Find equivalent names for whole numbers. [Number and Numeration Goal 4]	2·5, 2·7–2·9			5		
Use basic facts to compute extended facts. [Operations and Computation Goal 1]	2·1–2·9	1	1–4	1–4	11, 12	
Use paper-and-pencil algorithms to solve problems involving the addition and subtraction of whole numbers. [Operations and Computation Goal 2]	2·1–2·9	4, 5, 6		6, 7	13, 14	✓
Use strategies to make estimates. [Operations and Computation Goal 5]	2·7, 2·8				13, 14	
Apply parts-and-total and comparison situations. [Operations and Computation Goal 6]	2·4–2·9	3		6, 7		
Tell and show time on an analog clock. [Measurement and Reference Frames Goal 4]	2·1, 2·3, 2·6, 2·8			8, 9		✓
Find and use rules to solve problems. [Patterns, Functions, and Algebra Goal 1]	2·1–2·9	2		3, 4	11, 12	

2 Looking Ahead: Preparing for Unit 3

Math Boxes 2•10

Home Link 2•10: Unit 3 Family Letter

Materials
- *Math Journal 1*, p. 54
- *Math Masters*, pp. 60–63

152 Unit 2 Progress Check 2

Core Assessment Resources

Assessment Handbook

- **Unit 3 Assessment Overview,** pages pages 68–75
- **Unit 3 Assessment Masters,** pages 145–148
- **Unit 3 Individual Profiles of Progress,** pages 208, 209, and 248
- **Unit 3 Class Checklists,** pages 210, 211, and 249
- **Math Logs,** pages 254–256
- **Exit Slip,** page 251
- **Other Student Assessment Forms,** pages 252, 253, 257, and 258

Assessment Management Spreadsheets

The Assessment Management Spreadsheets consist of the Digital Class Checklists and Individual Profile of Progress Checklists. Use them to monitor, record, and report children's progress.

Addressing All Needs

Differentiated Instruction

Adjusting the Activity – suggests adaptations that target advanced learners, English language learners, or learners who need additional instructional support.

ELL SUPPORT / **ELL** – provides lesson-specific suggestions to help English language learners understand and process the mathematical content.

READINESS – accesses children's prior knowledge or previews content that prepares children to engage in the lesson's Part 1 activities.

EXTRA PRACTICE – provides additional opportunities to apply the mathematical content of the lesson.

ENRICHMENT – enables children to apply or further explore the mathematical content of the lesson.

Lesson	Adjusting the Activity	ELL Support/ ELL	Readiness	Extra Practice	Enrichment
3•1	•	•	•	•	•
3•2	•	•	•	•	•
3•3	•	•	•		•
3•4		•	•	•	
3•5		•	•	•	•
3•6	•	•	•	•	•
3•7		•	•		•
3•8	•	•	•		•
3•9	•		•		•
3•10	•			•	•
3•11	•	•	•	•	
3•12	•	•	•		•
3•13		•	•		•
3•14	•		•		•

Additional Resources

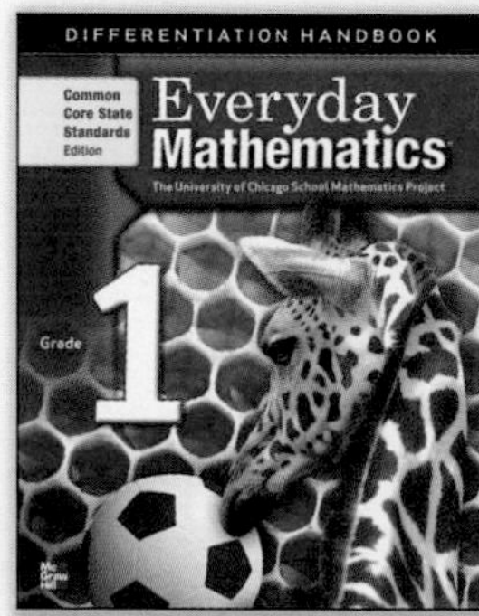

Differentiation Handbook
Provides ideas and strategies for differentiating instruction.
Pages 64–70

English Learners Handbook
Contains lesson-specific comprehension strategies.
Pages 27–40

Multilingual Handbook
Previews concepts and vocabulary. It is written in six languages.
Pages 53–80

Planning Tips

Multiage Classroom

Companion Lessons from Grades K and 2 can help you meet instructional needs of a multiage classroom. The full Scope and Sequence can be found in the Appendix.

Grade K	1•9, 1•10, 2•5	2•5	5•15	1•2, 2•5	4•1	4•1	6•13, 8•2, 8•3, 8•11	4•5, 8•13	4•5, 8•13	5•5	6•7, 6•8	6•1, 6•2, 6•7, 6•8	6•5	3•5, 7•6
Grade 1	**3•1**	**3•2**	**3•3**	**3•4**	**3•5**	**3•6**	**3•7**	**3•8**	**3•9**	**3•10**	**3•11**	**3•12**	**3•13**	**3•14**
Grade 2	7•5, 9•6, 10•7	1•10, 7•1, 7•4	1•8, 1•10, 7•3	7•1, 7•5, 10•7	7•1		1•3, 3•3, 12•2	2•10, 3•6	2•10, 3•6	1•10	3•7, 3•8, 10•1–10•6	3•7–3•8, 10•1–10•6	3•5, 6•3, 7•6	2•2–2•5, 4•2

Pacing for Success

Pacing depends on a number of factors, such as children's individual needs and how long your school has been using *Everyday Mathematics*. At the beginning of Unit 3, you may want to use tools available at www.everydaymathonline.com to help you set your pace.

Home Support

Unit 3 Family Letter (English/Spanish) provides families with an overview, Do-Anytime Activities, Building Skills through Games, a list of vocabulary, and answers to the daily homework (Home Links). Family Letters in English, Spanish, and seven other languages are also available online.

Home Links are the daily homework assignments. They consist of active projects and ongoing review problems.

▶ Home Support Resources

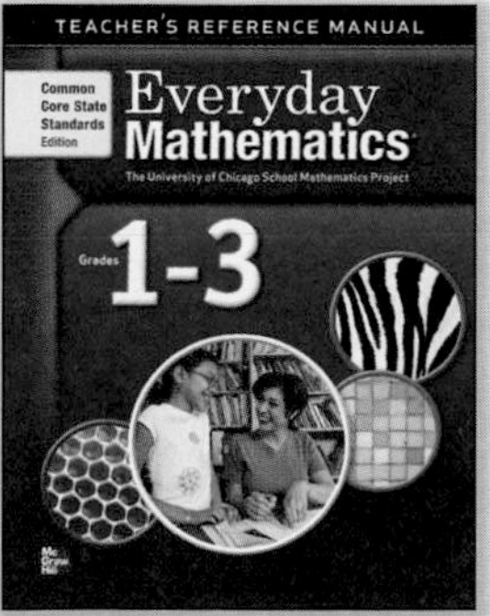

Home Connection Handbook
Offers ideas and reproducible masters for communicating with families. See Table of Contents for unit information.

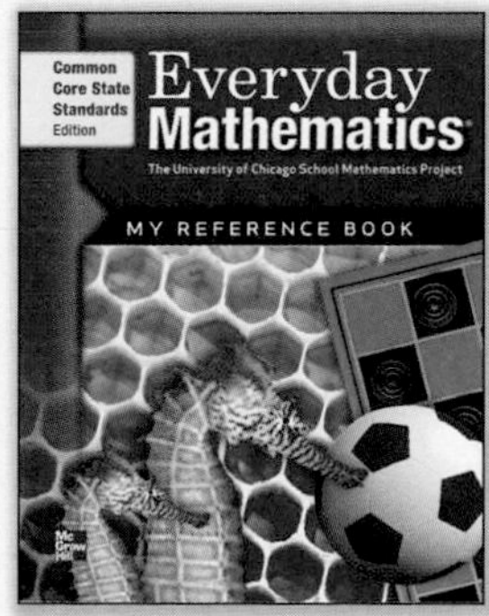

My Reference Book
Beginning in Unit 6, *My Reference Book* provides a resource for children and parents.

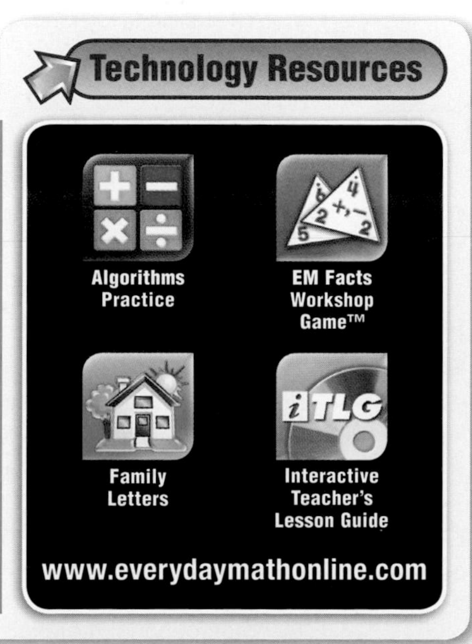

Unit 3 Organizer

Materials

Technology Resources www.everydaymathonline.com

ePresentations

eToolkit

Algorithms Practice

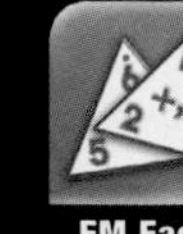
EM Facts Workshop Game™

Family Letters

Assessment Management

Common Core State Standards

Curriculum Focal Points

Interactive Teacher's Lesson Guide

Lesson	Masters	Manipulative Kit	Other Items
3•1	Teaching Aid Master, p. 305 Home Link Master, p. 51 Teaching Master, p. 52	Class Number Line; 16 craft sticks; per group: number cards 1–10	masking tape or magnets*; stick-on notes*; *Pattern Bugs;* Number-Grid Poster; Pattern-Block Template
3•2	Home Link Master, p. 53; Teaching Master, p. 54; Teaching Aid Master, p. 305; *Differentiation Handbook,* p. 126	per group: 1 die or 2 dice*; slate; Class Number Line	Class Data Pad; pennies and nickels; *Missing Mittens*
3•3	Transparency of *Math Masters,* p. 311* Home Link Master, p. 55 Teaching Master, p. 56 *Differentiation Handbook,* p. 127	slate	colored marking pens*; "Stop" sign or red paper circle; laminated number grid*; colored pencils
3•4	Teaching Masters, pp. 57–62 and 64 Home Link Master, p. 63	1 set of double-9 dominoes; slate; pattern blocks; number cards 1–10	Pattern-Block Template
3•5	Transparency of *Math Masters,* p. 65* Home Link Master, p. 66 Teaching Master, p. 67 Teaching Aid Master, p. 305	Class Number Line*; die; tool-kit coins	pennies or overhead pennies*; money cards from Lesson 2•13; on-the-floor number line; scissors; glue or tape; *Two Ways to Count to Ten: A Liberian Folktale*
3•6	Teaching Aid Master, p. 305 Transparency of *Math Masters,* p. 68* Teaching Master, p. 68; Home Link Master, p. 69; Game Master, p. 341	Class Number Line*; per group: 1 die; slate	20 pennies per group
3•7	Home Link Masters, pp. 70 and 71 Transparency of *Math Masters,* p. 65*	per group: 1 die or 2 dice*; slate; Class Number Line*; per group: tool-kit clocks	demonstration clock with hour hand only; demonstration clock with hour and minute hands; 20 pennies and 10 nickels per group; mouse puppet*; index cards*
3•8	Teaching Aid Master, p. 312 Transparencies of *Math Masters,* pp. 65* and 312; Home Link Masters, pp. 73 and 74; Teaching Masters, pp. 72 and 75	Class Number Line*	
3•9	Home Link 3•8; Transparency of *Math Masters,* p. 312*; Home Link Master, p. 77; Teaching Masters, pp. 76, 78, 79; Teaching Aid Masters, pp. 311, 336A, and 336B		
3•10	Home Link Master, p. 80 Teaching Master, p. 68 Teaching Aid Master, p. 305	per partnership: 3 dice	overhead calculator*; calculator*; overhead nickels and pennies*; per group: 20 pennies and 10 nickels
3•11	Home Link Masters, pp. 81 and 82 *Differentiation Handbook,* p. 126	tool-kit coins; slate	counters*; per child: 10 dimes; per small group: 1 magnifying lens; Story of Money Poster; overhead coins*; money cards from Lesson 2•13; calculator*
3•12	Home Link Master, p. 83 Teaching Master, p. 84	tool-kit coins; per group: 2 dice; slate	overhead coins*
3•13	Home Link Master, p. 85; Game Master, p. 342; *Differentiation Handbook,* p. 126	tool-kit coins; slate; number cards 1–20; craft sticks	stick-on notes; Class Data Pad; calculator*
3•14	Home Link Master, p. 86; Game Master, p. 344; Teaching Master, pp. 58–60	per group: 2 dice; number cards 1–18, double-9 dominoes; slate	resealable plastic bag; paper plate and counters*
3•15	Assessment Masters, pp. 145–148 Home Link Masters, pp. 87–90	slate	

*Denotes optional materials

Mathematical Background

The discussion below highlights the major content ideas presented in Unit 3 and helps establish instructional priorities.

Patterns All Around (Lessons 3◆1 and 3◆4)

The main thrust of these lessons is to help children become aware that there are shapes or combinations of shapes and colors that can be arranged in regular ways according to patterns.

You may wish to read Section 17.1 in the *Teacher's Reference Manual* for additional information about patterns.

The lessons focus on simple patterns so that children can see how predictable patterns are. These patterns should be merely a starting point to sensitize children to more complex patterns in their everyday world. For example, patterns around the classroom or school include grilles on light fixtures, panes in windows, wire or slats in fences, the array of milk cartons in a box or crate, floor or ceiling tiles, and patterns in magazine or newspaper pictures and advertisements. Encourage children to look for and bring examples of patterns to school.

Visual patterns can be very helpful in building both aesthetic sensibilities and intuition about geometry.

Use Project 1, Geometric Gift Wrap and Greeting Cards, to provide opportunities for children to use geometric shapes to create designs for gift wrap and greeting cards.

Odd and Even Number Patterns (Lessons 3◆2 and 3◆4)

An understanding of odd and even numbers can lead children to generalizations of mathematical importance. For example, when an odd number of things is paired or shared between two people, there will always be one thing left over. From this understanding, children may begin to observe relationships such as the following:

- The sum of two even numbers is always an even number—the pieces remain paired.
- The sum of two odd numbers is also always an even number—the two leftover pieces can be paired.
- The sum of an even number and an odd number is always an odd number—the leftover piece cannot be paired.

Kevin: Odd numbers are neat. They always have a dot in the middle.

Father: What?

Kevin: See (pointing to the middle dot on the 5 side of the domino), always something in the middle. But with even numbers (pointing to the 4 side of the domino), there is just a space in the middle.

Odd numbers of people or things are often seen as a nuisance because they spoil equal sharing or make it impossible to get the same number of players on two teams. But consider Kevin's insight on the previous page, as reported by his father. Mathematicians would recognize this observation to be a nice, solid "theorem." As children work with data, they will find that this property of odd numbers makes identifying a "middle value" easier. Not many children can express such pattern-based properties, even if they see and feel them. But children often know things long before they can express them verbally or write them on paper.

Number-Grid Patterns

(Lesson 3◆3)

Much use is made of number grids because these grids are so effective in showing patterns in our number system. For example, by coloring the results of various counts on the number grid, patterns become apparent.

In future lessons, number grids will also be quite useful for illustrating place-value concepts and for solving addition and subtraction problems.

Refer to Section 9.7.2 of the *Teacher's Reference Manual* for more information about number grids.

Number Lines

(Lessons 3◆5 and 3◆6)

Number lines were introduced in *Kindergarten Everyday Mathematics.* Lesson 3-5 focuses on number-line concepts that children have seen and worked with, but may not have talked about in specific terms:

- The marks on any number line are equally spaced, but the spacing need not be the same on all number lines.
- Number lines can be vertical, horizontal, diagonal, or oriented any other direction.
- Number lines can begin and end with any numbers—they need not begin with zero.

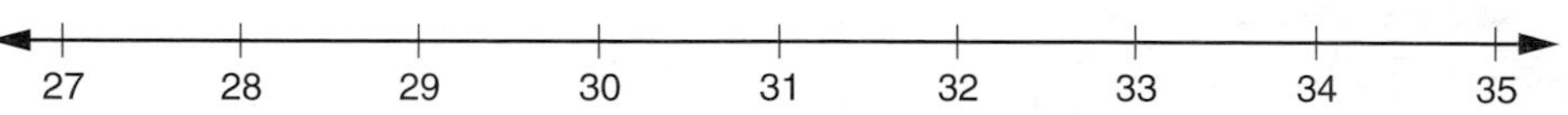

- The arrow at each end of a number line indicates that a number line can go on forever in either direction. Therefore, the line may show both positive and negative numbers.

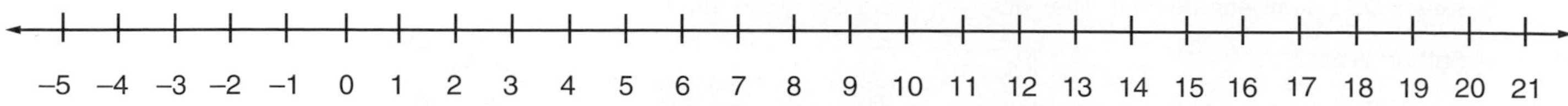

Number lines are particularly important in this unit as a visual device that can be used for solving simple addition and subtraction problems. In Lesson 3-5, children practice counting up and back by 1s, starting at any number. In Lesson 3-6, these "hops" on the number line are related to addition and subtraction. For example, to solve the problem $3 + 5 =$ ____, start at 3 on the number line and count up 5 hops. You end on 8, which is the answer to the problem.

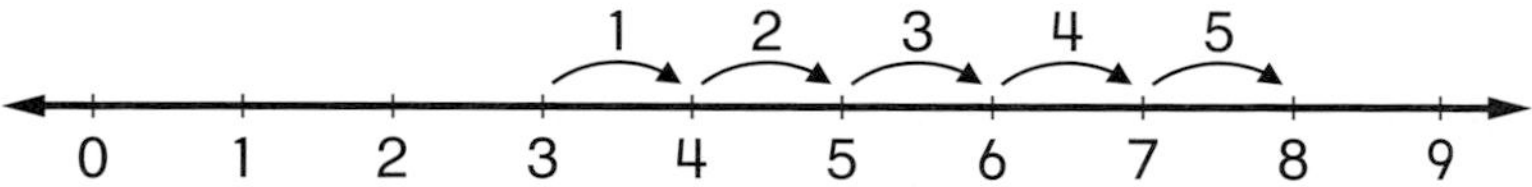

Note

The *Everyday Mathematics* authors prefer number grids with a few negative numbers before zero and a few numbers after 100. The grids in children's math journals include numbers from −9 to 110.

Number lines do have limitations. As numbers become larger, number lines become cumbersome when stretched along a wall of the classroom, and it is nearly impossible to print long number lines in children's books without breaking them into chunks. On the other hand, number grids fit nicely on a page or on a classroom poster. Number grids may be used in the same way as number lines: Children can count up and back from any number on the grid, thus using it as an aid for addition and subtraction. Later, children will learn to add and subtract 2-digit numbers on the number grid without having to count by 1s. For example, to add 37 to a number, they can simply count down 3 rows and then count to the right 7 spaces. This procedure leads to an addition algorithm in which the tens are added first and then the ones.

−9	−8	−7	−6	−5	−4	−3	−2	−1	0
1	2	3	4	5	6	7	8	9	10
11	12	13	14	15	16	17	18	19	20
21	22	23	24	25	26	27	28	29	30
31	32	33	34	35	36	37	38	39	40
41	42	43	44	45	46	47	48	49	50
51	52	53	54	55	56	57	58	59	60
61	62	63	64	65	66	67	68	69	70
71	72	73	74	75	76	77	78	79	80
81	82	83	84	85	86	87	88	89	90
91	92	93	94	95	96	97	98	99	100
101	102	103	104	105	106	107	108	109	110

Section 9.7.2 in the *Teacher's Reference Manual* can provide you with more information about number lines.

Time and Money

(Lessons 3•7, 3•11, and 3•12)

These lessons continue where Lessons 2-5 through 2-10 left off. The purpose of introducing time and money incrementally is to give children time to practice what has been introduced before adding new elements.

Lesson 3-7 extends telling time to the nearest half-hour. Continue to practice estimating time using the hour-hand-only clock.

Lesson 3-11 adds dimes to children's tool-kit coin collections. As in Unit 2, the material first focuses on coin exchanges as a prerequisite for counting collections of dimes, nickels, and pennies. It is most efficient to count the coins with the greatest value (dimes) first, and then the nickels, and finally the pennies. This should not be too difficult because children have already practiced start-and-stop counts by 10s, 5s, and 1s.

Dollars-and-cents notation is introduced in Lesson 3-11 as a first exposure to decimals. Children should have no difficulty with amounts that are 1 dollar or more. Expect many children to make errors with amounts that are less than 1 dollar, especially with amounts that are less than 10 cents. Children may write *$0.5* or *$0.50* for 5 cents. Don't worry; they will get it right with repeated exposures.

Chapters 14 and 15, located in the *Teacher's Reference Manual*, offer additional information about time and money concepts.

Frames and Arrows (Lessons 3◆8 and 3◆9)

The Frames-and-Arrows diagram is one of several formats used for showing regular sequences of numbers. It allows for many variations and experiences in problem solving. Frames-and-Arrows diagrams consist of three basic elements:

- **Frames** in which numbers are written or can be written.
- **Arrows** that link the frames. These arrows represent a consistent pattern or rule for progressing from one frame to the next.
- A **rule box** that identifies the pattern or rule for the arrows.

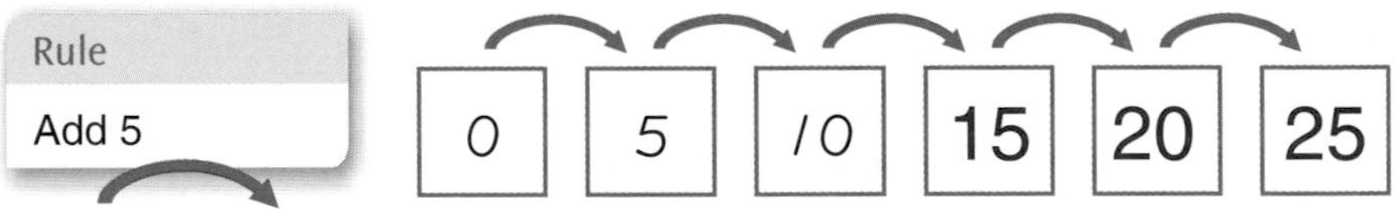

In a given problem, some or all of the frames may be blank, or the rule may not be shown. Children use the information provided to find the missing parts. In Lesson 3-8, the rule is given and children apply the rule to find the numbers that belong in the blank frames. In Lesson 3-9, the numbers in the frames are given, and children find the rule that dictates the sequence of numbers. Problems in which the first frame is blank are avoided at this level, because these kinds of problems involve applying the rule in the opposite direction.

You may wish to refer to Section 1.3.2 in the *Teacher's Reference Manual* to learn more about Frames-and-Arrows problems.

Counting with the Calculator (Lesson 3◆10)

To help children learn to count with calculators, they are taught that the calculator must be programmed. There are three elements that must be entered first: the starting number, an indication of whether the calculator is to count up [+] or down [−] from the starting number, and the number the calculator is to count by.

Calculator counts will be used as an aid in solving number-sequence problems and to observe place-value digit patterns.

See Section 3.1.1, Managing Tools—located in the *Teacher's Reference Manual*—for additional information about calculators.

Data Day (Lesson 3•13)

This lesson builds on children's experiences with collecting, organizing, displaying, and analyzing data. In Units 1 and 2, children collected and recorded various kinds of data on tally charts. In this lesson, they collect data about the class members' siblings and display the data using a line plot. A line plot is similar to a tally chart, but it looks like a bar graph. As such, it is a useful interim step between a tally chart and a bar graph.

Read Section 12.2 in the *Teacher's Reference Manual* for more information about data collection, organization, and analysis.

Problem Solving (Lessons 3•11–3•13)

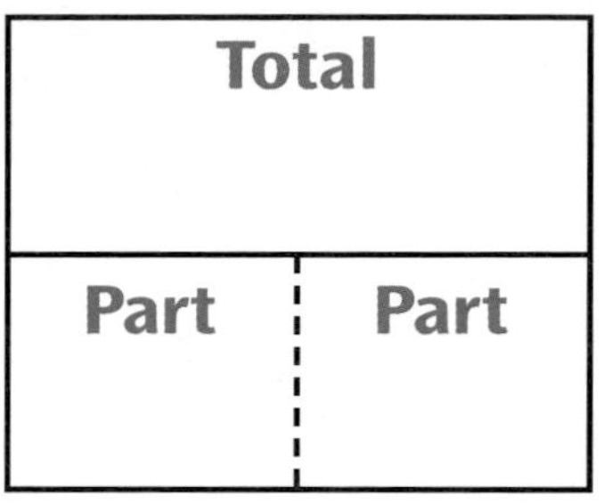

The Mental Math and Reflexes problems in these lessons consist of parts-and-total number stories. As with the change-to-more and change-to-less problems in Unit 2, displaying a parts-and-total diagram can summarize each problem situation. It is important that this not be done until after children have had a chance to share their solution strategies. Use the diagrams as a way to summarize the discussions.

See Chapter 2 of the *Teacher's Reference Manual* to learn more about the importance of problem solving in mathematics.

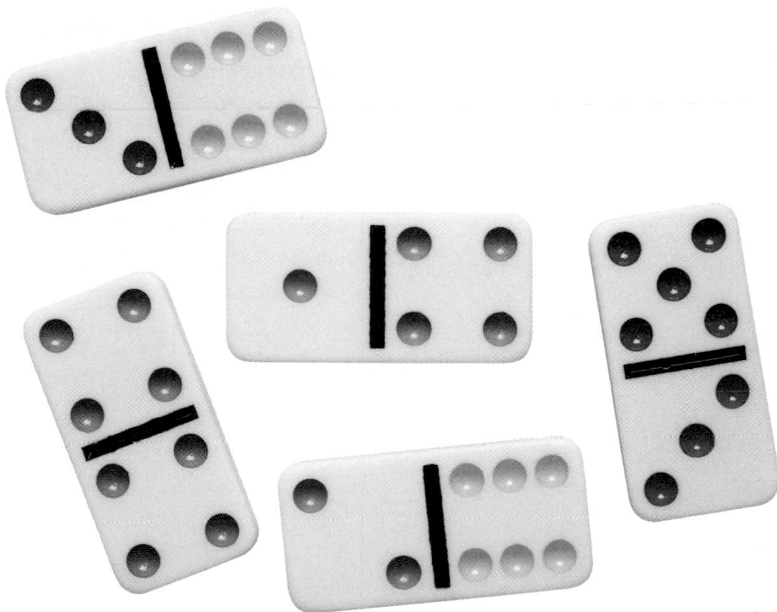

Domino-Dot Patterns and Domino Combinations (Lesson 3•14)

Domino combinations are used in preparation for the study of fact families, which will be introduced in Lesson 6-3. Here, the focus is on addition facts. Children observe that three numbers can be associated with any domino: the number of dots on each half of the domino and the total number of dots. When viewed in this way, dominoes are examples of parts-and-total situations. Some children may observe this relationship, but it need not be discussed unless someone brings it up.

3·1 Visual Patterns

Objective To guide the exploration and extension of visual patterns.

www.everydaymathonline.com

ePresentations

eToolkit

Algorithms Practice

EM Facts Workshop Game™

Family Letters

Assessment Management

Common Core State Standards

Curriculum Focal Points

Interactive Teacher's Lesson Guide

1 Teaching the Lesson

Key Concepts and Skills

- Count objects by 1s and 2s.
  [Number and Numeration Goal 2]
- Recognize, describe, and create visual patterns.
  [Patterns, Functions, and Algebra Goal 1]
- Identify the pattern rule in a visual pattern.
  [Patterns, Functions, and Algebra Goal 1]
- Use a pattern rule to extend a visual pattern.
  [Patterns, Functions, and Algebra Goal 1]

Key Activities

Children explore, create, and extend patterns using craft sticks. They also look for patterns in the classroom.

Ongoing Assessment: Recognizing Student Achievement
Use an Exit Slip (*Math Masters,* page 305).
[Patterns, Functions, and Algebra Goal 1]

Key Vocabulary

pattern

Materials

Math Journal 1, p. 28
Math Masters, p. 305
Number-Grid Poster ◆ Class Number Line ◆ per partnership: 16 craft sticks, masking tape or magnets (optional), stick-on notes (optional) ◆ Pattern-Block Template

2 Ongoing Learning & Practice

Playing *Before and After*

per partnership: 4 each of number cards 1–10 (from the Everything Math Deck, if available)
Children practice identifying the numbers that are 1 less and 1 more than a given number.

Math Boxes 3·1

Math Journal 1, p. 29
Children practice and maintain skills through Math Box problems.

Home Link 3·1

Math Masters, p. 51
Children practice and maintain skills through Home Link activities.

3 Differentiation Options

READINESS

Exploring Color Patterns

Math Masters, p. 52
Children color visual patterns and create their own two-colored patterns.

ENRICHMENT

Finding AB and ABC Patterns

Math Journal 1, p. 28
Children examine different types of patterns.

EXTRA PRACTICE

Reading About Patterns

Math Masters, p. 305
Children read *Pattern Bugs* to practice patterning skills.

Advance Preparation

For the optional Extra Practice activity in Part 3, obtain a copy of ***Pattern Bugs*** by Trudy Harris (Millbrook Press, 2001).

***Teacher's Reference Manual,* Grades 1–3** pp. 11, 12, 203, 204

Getting Started

Mental Math and Reflexes

Count by 2s in unison as you point to the Class Number Line.

- ▷ Start at 0 and count up by 2s to 40. 0, 2, 4, ..., 40
- ▷ Count back by 2s, starting at 30. 30, 28, 26, ..., 0 Stop at 0 and ask children if they can figure out what will happen if you continue to count back by 2s. You will name negative numbers. Children might notice that the numbers that come before 0 on the number line are in the opposite order from those that come after 0. Children should not be expected to understand negative numbers at this time; however, some children may enjoy discussing them.

Children count up and back by 2s in unison as you point to the Number-Grid Poster.

- ▷ Start at 0 and count up by 2s to 40. 0, 2, 4, ..., 40
- ▷ Count back by 2s, starting at 30. 30, 28, 26, ..., 0

How is counting by 2s on the number grid the same as counting by 2s on the number line? You land on the same numbers. *How is it different?* Instead of going from left to right in a straight line, you go from left to right in each row and then go to the beginning of the next row. Children may notice that you land in the same columns in each row. Acknowledge that this is correct, but do not emphasize it at this time.

Teaching the Lesson

Introducing Visual Patterns

WHOLE-CLASS ACTIVITY

Interactive whiteboard-ready ePresentations are available at www.everydaymathonline.com to help you teach the lesson.

Explain to children that they will look for patterns in the classroom and create their own patterns with a partner.

Display a simple craft-stick pattern on the overhead (or by attaching the sticks with masking tape or magnets to the board). *For example:*

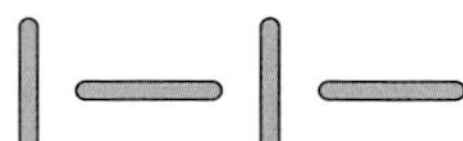

Record the pattern on the board with vertical and horizontal marks: | — | —.

Ask children to figure out what comes next. | Then add a vertical mark to the pattern on the board.

Repeat this routine using another pattern. *For example:*
| | — | | —

Tell children that these are examples of **patterns.** Write the word *patterns* on the board. Have them describe a pattern. It's something that happens over and over and allows you to predict what will come next.

Invite children to suggest other craft-stick patterns. Display these patterns on the overhead or on the board. Ask the class to describe each pattern and tell what comes next. Encourage children to describe the patterns using words and gestures.

Links to the Future

This lesson is the beginning of children's work with visual patterns. In first grade, children should become comfortable extending both visual and numerical patterns. Describing rules for patterns and using them to solve problems is a Grade 2 Goal.

NOTE Many *Everyday Mathematics* teachers and children enjoy making a Patterns Museum by displaying patterns children find in their everyday world. The exhibits may include patterns in the classroom, patterns from Home Link 3-1, and patterns from Lesson 3-4.

NOTE Keep a supply of extra craft sticks on hand in case children devise elaborate patterns that require more craft sticks.

▶ Finding Patterns in the Classroom

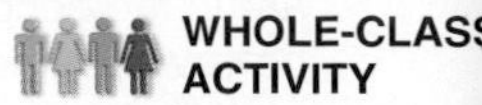

Algebraic Thinking Ask children to point out and describe any patterns they observe in the classroom. Sample answers: Floor tiles, light fixtures, clothing Explain that patterns are a part of our world. Some patterns are simple; others are complex. Patterns are everywhere.

▶ Creating Craft-Stick Patterns

Algebraic Thinking Partners use 16 craft sticks and take turns doing the following: One child starts a pattern; the other child continues the pattern for 2 cycles and then describes it. For one of the patterns, have partners take turns continuing the pattern until they run out of sticks.

This represents 2 cycles.

Remind children of partner etiquette: "Guide, Check, Praise." This will help to keep these pattern activities from becoming competitive and prevent less successful attempts from being criticized.

Ongoing Assessment: Recognizing Student Achievement

Exit Slip

Portfolio Ideas

On an **Exit Slip** (*Math Masters,* page 305), have each child draw at least two cycles of a pattern he or she made. Use the Exit Slip to assess children's ability to create and extend patterns. Children are making adequate progress if they draw two cycles of a repeating pattern. Some children may be able to draw more than two cycles.

[Patterns, Functions and Algebra Goal 1]

Music Link Explain that there are many patterns in music. Play a song. Encourage children to listen to the rhythm and identify patterns that they hear. Invite children to use classroom objects or instruments to make their own musical patterns.

Extending Patterns

PARTNER ACTIVITY

(*Math Journal 1,* p. 28)

Algebraic Thinking Children extend patterns and then create their own patterns for their partners to extend.

Adjusting the Activity

ELL

Cover all but the first row of shapes with stick-on notes. Children color-code the triangles in this row so that triangles oriented the same way are the same color. The colors provide additional visual cues for children as they continue the pattern. Proceed in the same manner with each row, first visually isolating the row with stick-on notes, then color-coding the shapes in the row, and finally continuing the patterns.

AUDITORY ◆ KINESTHETIC ◆ TACTILE ◆ VISUAL

Encourage children to discuss the patterns they created. Invite a few children to draw their patterns on the board.

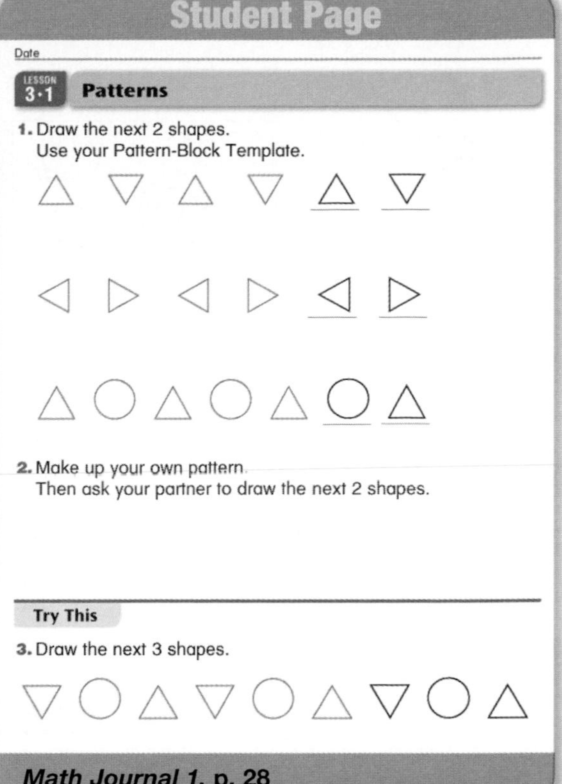

Student Page

Date

LESSON 3·1 **Patterns**

1. Draw the next 2 shapes.
   Use your Pattern-Block Template.

2. Make up your own pattern.
   Then ask your partner to draw the next 2 shapes.

Try This

3. Draw the next 3 shapes.

Math Journal 1, p. 28

2 Ongoing Learning & Practice

Playing *Before and After*

PARTNER ACTIVITY

This game is for 2 players. Each partnership needs a deck of cards consisting of four of each card numbered 1–10.

Directions

1. Shuffle the cards.
2. Deal 6 cards to each player.
3. Put 2 cards number-side up on the table.
4. Put the rest of the cards number-side down in a pile.
5. Take turns. When it is your turn:
   - Look for any number in your hand that comes just *before* or just *after* one of the faceup numbers. Put it on top of the number. Play as many cards as you can.
   - Take as many cards as you need from the deck so that you have 6 cards again.
   - If you can't play any cards when it is your turn, take 2 cards from the deck. Place them number-side up on top of the 2 cards on the table. Try to play cards from your hand again. If you still can't play, your turn is over.
6. The game is over when:
   - All cards have been taken from the deck.
   - No one can play any more cards.
7. The player holding fewer cards wins.

Adjusting the Activity

ELL

Have children play with the 0–6 cards only. Or, have each child start with only 3 cards instead of 6.

AUDITORY ◆ KINESTHETIC ◆ TACTILE ◆ VISUAL

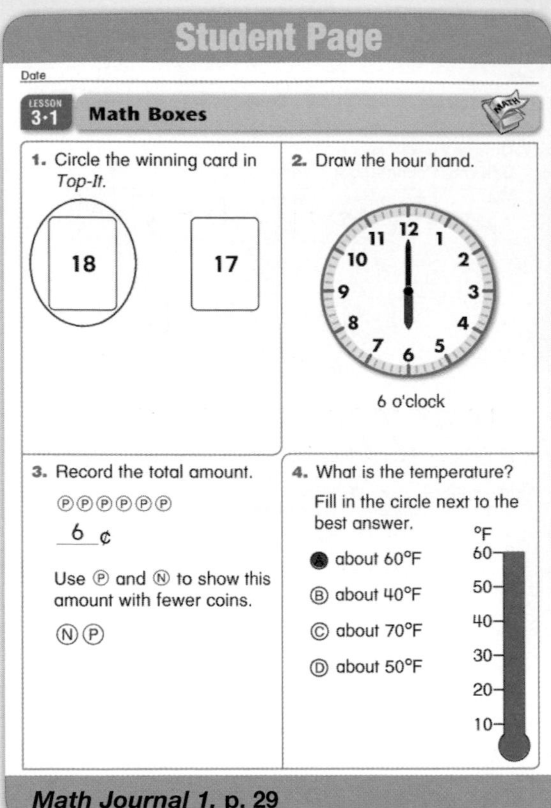
Student Page

Date

LESSON 3·1 **Math Boxes**

1. Circle the winning card in *Top-It.*

18 17

2. Draw the hour hand.

6 o'clock

3. Record the total amount.

ⓅⓅⓅⓅⓅⓅ

6 ¢

Use Ⓟ and Ⓝ to show this amount with fewer coins.

ⓃⓅ

4. What is the temperature?

Fill in the circle next to the best answer.

● about 60°F

Ⓑ about 40°F

Ⓒ about 70°F

Ⓓ about 50°F

Math Journal 1, p. 29

▶ Math Boxes 3·1

INDEPENDENT ACTIVITY

(*Math Journal 1,* p. 29)

Mixed Practice Math Boxes in this lesson are paired with Math Boxes in Lesson 3-3. The skills in Problem 4 preview Unit 4 content.

This is the first time that children are asked to respond to a Writing/Reasoning prompt.

Writing/Reasoning Have children draw, write, or verbalize an answer to the following question: *How do you know which is the winning number in* Top-It? A reasonable answer should include a pictorial representation of the two numbers or reference to a number line. Sample answer Because if you count when you say 1, 2, 3, 4, 5, 6, 7, 8; the seven is before the eight.

▶ Home Link 3·1

INDEPENDENT ACTIVITY

(*Math Masters,* p. 51)

Home Connection Children draw patterns they find in their homes and in their community. They are encouraged to look for articles of clothing that have patterns and to wear them to school the next day.

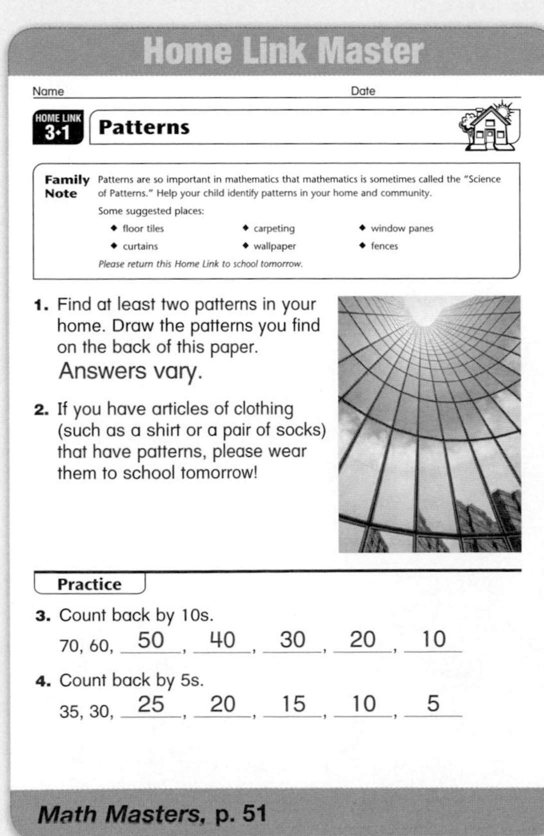
Home Link Master

Name Date

HOME LINK 3·1 **Patterns**

Family Note Patterns are so important in mathematics that mathematics is sometimes called the "Science of Patterns." Help your child identify patterns in your home and community.

Some suggested places:
- floor tiles
- curtains
- carpeting
- wallpaper
- window panes
- fences

Please return this Home Link to school tomorrow.

1. Find at least two patterns in your home. Draw the patterns you find on the back of this paper. Answers vary.
2. If you have articles of clothing (such as a shirt or a pair of socks) that have patterns, please wear them to school tomorrow!

Practice

3. Count back by 10s.
70, 60, 50, 40, 30, 20, 10
4. Count back by 5s.
35, 30, 25, 20, 15, 10, 5

Math Masters, p. 51

3 Differentiation Options

READINESS

SMALL-GROUP ACTIVITY

▶ Exploring Color Patterns

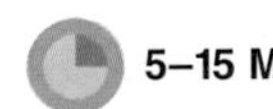
5–15 Min

(*Math Masters,* p. 52)

Algebraic Thinking To explore visual patterns, have children shade shapes to complete and continue patterns on *Math Masters* page 52. Begin by having children underline the word *red* with their red crayon every time it appears on the page. Have children underline the other color words on the page with the corresponding color. Once they have finished underlining words, they should color the shapes with the indicated color. For Problem 2, children determine how to continue the color pattern. For Problem 3, children create their own two-color patterns. When children have finished the page, have them describe what they have done. Do not expect children to use the word *pattern* at this time. Sample answer: I colored the first square red, the next one blue, and the next one red. I did this over and over.

ENRICHMENT

SMALL-GROUP ACTIVITY

Finding AB and ABC Patterns

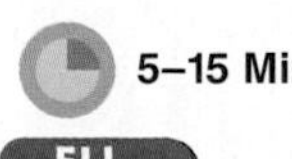
5–15 Min

ELL

(*Math Journal 1,* p. 28)

Algebraic Thinking To further explore patterning, write *ABABAB* and *ABCABCABC* on the board. Explain to children that patterns are sometimes named with letters of the alphabet. Point out that they have been working with AB and ABC patterns. To support English language learners, write *AB pattern* along with an example on the board. Explain that this pattern has the name AB. Do the same for ABC pattern. Ask children to identify patterns on journal page 28 that are AB or ABC patterns. The patterns in Problem 1 are AB patterns and the pattern in Problem 3 is an ABC pattern.

EXTRA PRACTICE

SMALL-GROUP ACTIVITY

Reading About Patterns

5–15 Min

Literature Link To provide practice with patterns, read ***Pattern Bugs*** by Trudy Harris (The Millbrook Press, 2001). Using the patterns in the book as a model, have children write a word pattern on an Exit Slip (*Math Masters,* page 305).

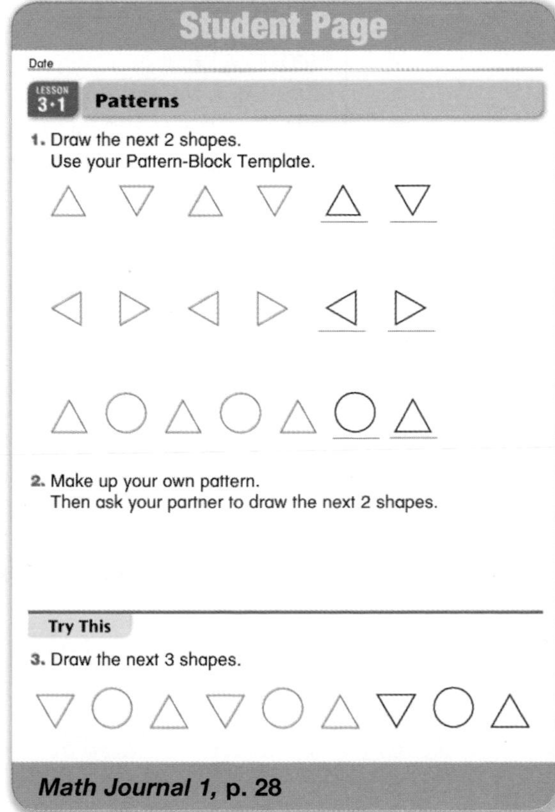

Student Page

Date

LESSON 3·1 Patterns

1. Draw the next 2 shapes.
Use your Pattern-Block Template.

△ ▽ △ ▽ △ ▽

◁ ▷ ◁ ▷ ◁ ▷

△ ○ △ ○ △ ○ △

2. Make up your own pattern.
Then ask your partner to draw the next 2 shapes.

Try This

3. Draw the next 3 shapes.

▽ ○ △ ▽ ○ △ ▽ ○ △

Math Journal 1, p. 28

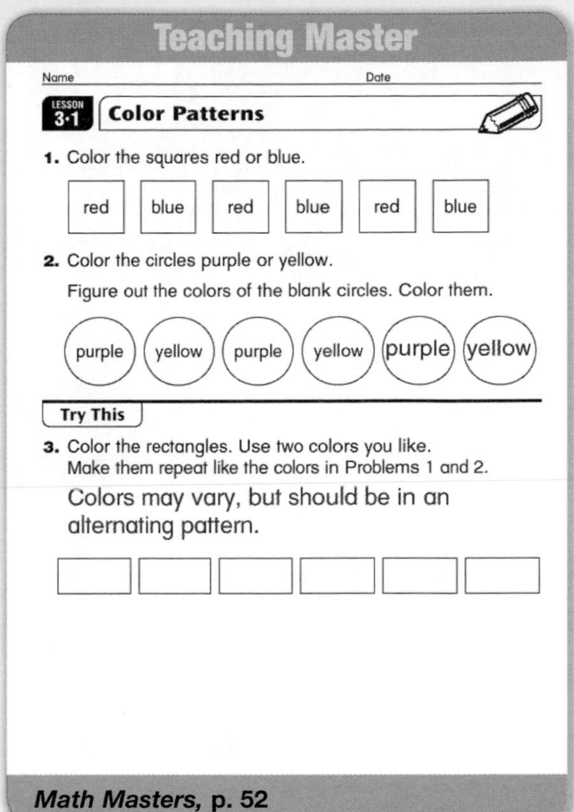

Teaching Master

Name Date

LESSON 3·1 Color Patterns

1. Color the squares red or blue.

red blue red blue red blue

2. Color the circles purple or yellow.
Figure out the colors of the blank circles. Color them.

purple yellow purple yellow purple yellow

Try This

3. Color the rectangles. Use two colors you like.
Make them repeat like the colors in Problems 1 and 2.

Colors may vary, but should be in an alternating pattern.

Math Masters, p. 52

3•2 Even and Odd Number Patterns

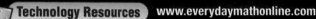

Objective To guide exploration of even and odd number patterns.

Technology Resources www.everydaymathonline.com

ePresentations

eToolkit

Algorithms Practice

EM Facts Workshop Game™

Family Letters

Assessment Management

Common Core State Standards

Curriculum Focal Points

Interactive Teacher's Lesson Guide

1 Teaching the Lesson

Key Concepts and Skills

- Count forward by even and odd numbers. [Number and Numeration Goal 1]
- Write numbers to represent quantities. [Number and Numeration Goal 3]
- Use manipulatives to identify numbers as odd or even. [Number and Numeration Goal 5]
- Identify and describe even and odd number patterns. [Patterns, Functions, and Algebra Goal 1]

Key Activities

Children are introduced to even and odd numbers by pairing members of groups of various sizes. They use the pairing procedure to determine whether a randomly chosen number of pennies is odd or even. Children also explore even and odd number patterns and practice identifying even and odd numbers.

Ongoing Assessment: Recognizing Student Achievement
Use journal page 30.
[Number and Numeration Goal 5]

Key Vocabulary

even number ◆ odd number

Materials

Math Journal 1, p. 30 and inside back cover
Home Link 3•1
Class Data Pad ◆ Class Number Line ◆ slate ◆ per partnership: 40 pennies

2 Ongoing Learning & Practice

Playing *Penny-Nickel Exchange*
per partnership: 20 pennies and 10 nickels, die (using a second die is optional)
Children practice money skills.

Math Boxes 3•2
Math Journal 1, p. 31
Children practice and maintain skills through Math Box problems.

Home Link 3•2
Math Masters, p. 53
Children practice and maintain skills through Home Link activities.

3 Differentiation Options

READINESS

Dividing Groups in Half
Children divide different groups of classmates in half to explore odd and even numbers.

ENRICHMENT

Finding Even and Odd Numbers in Skip Counts
Math Masters, p. 54
Children find even and odd numbers in skip counts.

EXTRA PRACTICE

Reading About Even and Odd Numbers
Math Masters, p. 305
Children read *Missing Mittens* to practice with even and odd numbers.

ELL SUPPORT

Building a Math Word Bank
Differentiation Handbook, p. 126
Children add the terms *even* and *odd* to their Math Word Banks.

Advance Preparation

For the optional Extra Practice activity in Part 3, obtain a copy of ***Missing Mittens*** by Stuart Murphy (HarperCollins Publisher, 2001).

***Teacher's Reference Manual,* Grades 1–3** p. 204

Getting Started

Mental Math and Reflexes

Children skip count using the number grid on the inside back cover of their journals.

●○○ Count up by 2s from 0 to 30, by 5s from 0 to 50, and by 10s from 0 to 100.

●●○ Count up by 2s from 26 to 60, by 5s from 25 to 100, and by 10s from 30 to 150.

●●● Count back by 2s from 20 to 0, by 5s from 100 to 50, and by 10s from 200 to 10.

Home Link 3·1 Follow-Up

Children display and tell about the patterns on their Home Links and on their clothing.

1 Teaching the Lesson

▸ Introducing Even and Odd Numbers

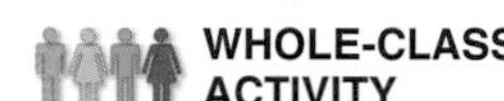

For this demonstration, children are called to the front of the room, one at a time.

Draw a table on the Class Data Pad with columns labeled *All in Pairs* and *Not All in Pairs*. Ask two children to come to the front of the room. Two children make a pair, so write the number 2 in the *All in Pairs* column. (Leave a blank line above the 2, to be filled in later.)

All in Pairs	Not All in Pairs
2	3
4	5
6	7
8	9
10	11

Invite another child to the front of the room. Ask whether there is another child standing with whom this child can be paired. No, this child is temporarily the "odd person out." Write 3 in the *Not All in Pairs* column.

Call another child to the front of the room. This child can be paired with the third child, so now each child has a partner.
Write 4 in the *All in Pairs* column.

Continue calling children one at a time, until there are 10 children (5 pairs). With each new child, record the total number of children in the appropriate column of the table. (You may want to remind children of the first-grade chant: *2, 4, 6, 8, first graders are really great!*)

- In which column would you write 11? *Not All in Pairs* column

Discuss the following with children:

▷ Whenever each child standing can be paired with another child the total number standing is called an **even number.** (Add the word *Even* to the table beside the words *All in Pairs.*) Discuss the everyday meaning of *even* as well as its meaning in this context.

▷ When one child cannot be paired with another child, the total number standing is called an **odd number.** (Add the word *Odd* to the table beside the words *Not All in Pairs.*)

Links to the Future

In this lesson, children use concrete materials to identify and model even and odd numbers. Recognizing even and odd numbers without the use of concrete materials is a Grade 2 Goal.

▶ Exploring Even and Odd Number Patterns

Algebraic Thinking Divide the class into partnerships and have partners pool their pennies. Each partnership should have 40 pennies. One partner grabs a fistful of pennies; the other partner takes the rest. Children count their pennies and write their total on their slates. Then each child arranges his or her pennies in pairs and decide whether the number of pennies is an even number or an odd number. They report their results for you to record in the table.

Adjusting the Activity

For smaller numbers, have each partnership use 20 pennies.

AUDITORY ◆ KINESTHETIC ◆ TACTILE ◆ VISUAL

When all children have reported their results, bring the class together to explore the patterns in the table. Discuss the following concepts:

▷ Even numbers end in 0, 2, 4, 6, or 8. Odd numbers end in 1, 3, 5, 7, or 9. (Circle the ones digits in the numbers in the table.)

▷ Even numbers are counts by 2s, starting with 0.

▷ If you know an even number, then you know that its two neighbors—the number that comes before it and the number that comes after it—are odd numbers.

For example: 8 is an even number, so 7 and 9—its neighbors—are both odd numbers. Try to elicit recognition of this pattern by referring to the Class Number Line.

▷ If you know an odd number, then you know that its two neighbors are even numbers.

For example: 9 is an odd number, so 8 and 10—its neighbors—are both even numbers. Again, refer to the Class Number Line.

Ask children the following questions:

- Do you think that 1 is an even number or an odd number? Why? It is an odd number because it comes before 2, which is an even number.
- What about 0? 0 is an even number because it comes before 1, which is an odd number. (Write 0 and 1 in the first line of the table.)

NOTE The pairing definition for even numbers does not apply to the number zero, since 0 objects cannot be paired. In later grades, children will learn that a number is even if, when it is divided by 2, the remainder is 0. Using this definition, 0 is an even number, since 0 ÷ 2 has a remainder of 0.

Adjusting the Activity

Write some large numbers on the board and ask whether they are even numbers or odd numbers. How can children tell? By looking at the ones digit for each number

AUDITORY ♦ KINESTHETIC ♦ TACTILE ♦ VISUAL

NOTE You may want to draw a "circle of digits" for even and odd numbers on the board.

0 → 2 → 4 → 6 → 8 → 0

1 → 3 → 5 → 7 → 9 → 1

All in Pairs—Even	Not All in Pairs—Odd
0	1
2	3
4	5
6	7
8	9
10	11

As you point to the digits, lead the class in a choral recitation of the even or odd numbers into the forties or beyond.

Identifying Even and Odd Numbers

INDEPENDENT ACTIVITY

(*Math Journal 1,* p. 30)

Children count each group and determine whether the number is even or odd.

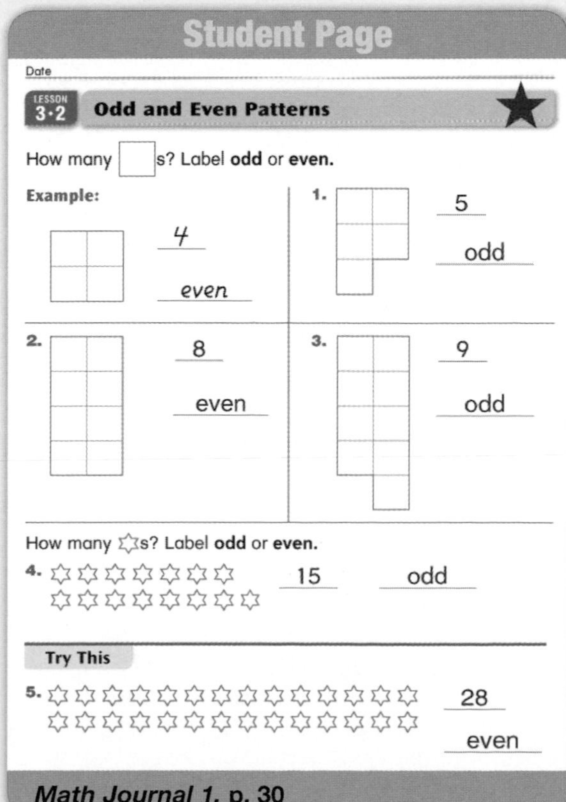
Student Page

Date

LESSON 3·2 **Odd and Even Patterns**

How many ☐s? Label **odd** or **even.**

Example: 4 even

1. 5 odd

2. 8 even

3. 9 odd

How many ☆s? Label **odd** or **even.**

4. 15 odd

Try This

5. 28 even

Math Journal 1, p. 30

Ongoing Assessment: Recognizing Student Achievement

Journal Page 30 

Use **journal page 30** to assess children's ability to distinguish between even and odd numbers. Children are making adequate progress if they are able to correctly count the boxes and the stars. Some children will have success distinguishing between even and odd numbers even at this early stage.

[Number and Numeration Goal 5]

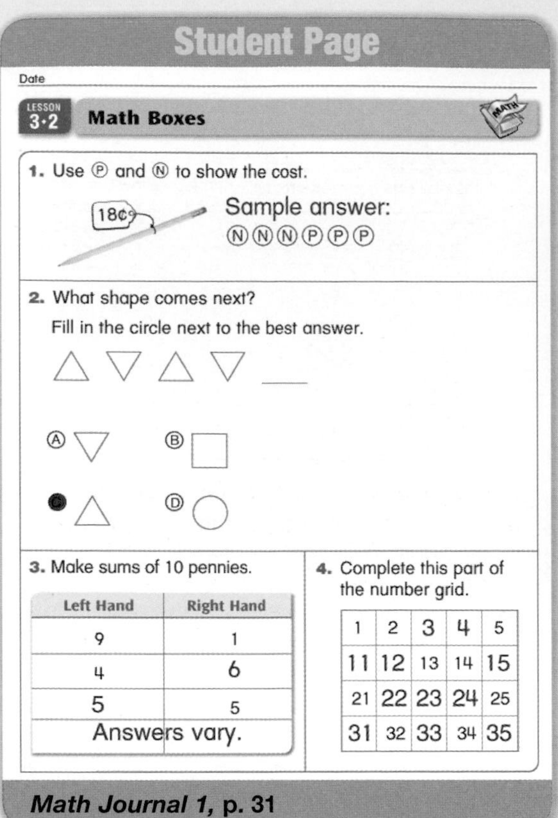
Student Page

Date

LESSON 3·2 **Math Boxes**

1. Use Ⓟ and Ⓝ to show the cost.

18¢

Sample answer: ⓃⓃⓃⓅⓅⓅ

2. What shape comes next? Fill in the circle next to the best answer.

△ ▽ △ ▽ ___

Ⓐ ▽ Ⓑ □

● △ Ⓓ ○

3. Make sums of 10 pennies.

Left Hand	Right Hand
9	1
4	6
5	5
Answers vary.	

4. Complete this part of the number grid.

1	2	3	4	5
11	12	13	14	15
21	22	23	24	25
31	32	33	34	35

Math Journal 1, p. 31

NOTE Remember to reserve time every day to complete the number-line, attendance, calendar, temperature, and weather routines. You may wish to include reviewing even and odd numbers as part of your daily routines.

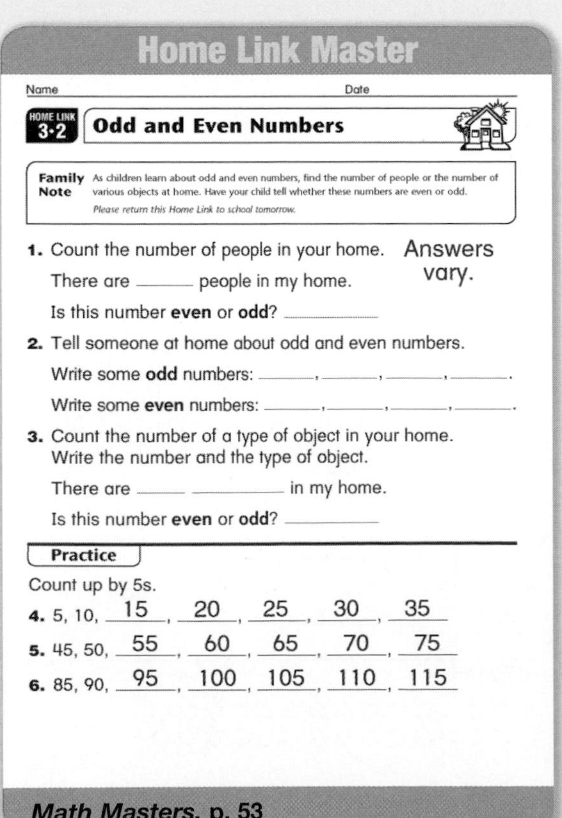
Home Link Master

Name Date

HOME LINK 3·2 **Odd and Even Numbers**

Family Note As children learn about odd and even numbers, find the number of people or the number of various objects at home. Have your child tell whether these numbers are even or odd.

Please return this Home Link to school tomorrow.

1. Count the number of people in your home. Answers vary.
There are ______ people in my home.
Is this number **even** or **odd**? ______

2. Tell someone at home about odd and even numbers.
Write some **odd** numbers: ____, ____, ____, ____.
Write some **even** numbers: ____, ____, ____, ____.

3. Count the number of a type of object in your home. Write the number and the type of object.
There are ______ ______ in my home.
Is this number **even** or **odd**? ______

Practice

Count up by 5s.

4. 5, 10, 15, 20, 25, 30, 35
5. 45, 50, 55, 60, 65, 70, 75
6. 85, 90, 95, 100, 105, 110, 115

Math Masters, p. 53

2 Ongoing Learning & Practice

▶ Playing *Penny-Nickel Exchange*

PARTNER ACTIVITY

Children practice money skills by playing *Penny-Nickel Exchange.* For detailed instructions, see Lesson 2-10.

▶ Math Boxes 3·2

INDEPENDENT ACTIVITY

(*Math Journal 1,* p. 31)

Mixed Practice Math Boxes in this lesson are paired with Math Boxes in Lesson 3-4. The skills in Problem 4 preview Unit 4 content.

Writing/Reasoning Have children draw, write, or verbalize an answer to the following question: *How do you know which coins show the cost?* A reasonable answer should identify the value of coins or reference counting by 5s and 1s.

▶ Home Link 3·2

INDEPENDENT ACTIVITY

(*Math Masters,* p. 53)

Home Connection Children count the number of people in their homes. They record this number and tell if it is odd or even. After telling someone about odd and even numbers, they record some examples.

3 Differentiation Options

READINESS

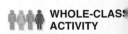

WHOLE-CLASS ACTIVITY

▶ Dividing Groups in Half

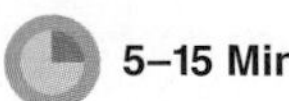
5–15 Min

To explore the concept of even and odd using a concrete model, have children act out even and odd numbers. Call an even number of children to the front of the class. Ask how you can divide the group into two equal groups. You will probably find that children have little trouble doing this with equal sharing—that is, one child goes to one group, the next child to the other group, and so on. Count both groups to be sure that they have the same number of children. Try to divide an odd-numbered group in half. Ask why it is not possible to do so. You would have to split the last child in half.

ENRICHMENT

INDEPENDENT ACTIVITY

Finding Even and Odd Numbers in Skip Counts

15–30 Min

(*Math Masters,* p. 54)

Algebraic Thinking To further explore even and odd numbers in skip counts, have children complete *Math Masters,* page 54. Have children look at the different skip-counting patterns marked with shapes. Encourage them to generalize rules about the even and odd numbers generated when skip counting by different numbers. Ask: *If you count by an even number, do you always land on even numbers?* Yes *If you count by an odd number, do you always land on odd numbers?* No; you alternate between even and odd numbers.

EXTRA PRACTICE

SMALL-GROUP ACTIVITY

Reading About Even and Odd Numbers

5–15 Min

Literature Link To provide practice with even and odd numbers, read ***Missing Mittens*** by Stuart J. Murphy (HarperCollins Publishers, 2001). On an Exit Slip (*Math Masters,* page 305), have children draw a number of mittens greater than 8 and tell whether the number is even or odd.

ELL SUPPORT

SMALL-GROUP ACTIVITY

Building a Math Word Bank

5–15 Min

(*Differentiation Handbook,* p. 126)

To provide language support for even and odd numbers, have children use the Word Bank Template found on *Differentiation Handbook,* page 126. Ask children to write the terms *odd* and *even,* draw pictures representing the terms, and write other words that describe them. See the *Differentiation Handbook* for more information.

Teaching Master

Name Date

LESSON 3·2 **Patterns on the Number Grid**

1. Color the even numbers yellow. Color the odd numbers orange. Even numbers should be shaded yellow and odd numbers should be shaded orange.

									0
1	2	3	4	5	6	7	8	9	10
11	12	13	14	15	16	17	18	19	20
21	22	23	24	25	26	27	28	29	30
31	32	33	34	35	36	37	38	39	40
41	42	43	44	45	46	47	48	49	50

2. Start at 0 and count up by 2s.
   Circle these numbers on the grid.
   Are these numbers even, odd, or both? even
3. Start at 0 and count up by 5s.
   Put a triangle around these numbers on the grid.
   Are these numbers even, odd, or both? both
4. Start at 0 and count up by 10s.
   Put an X on these numbers on the grid.
   Are these numbers even, odd, or both? even

Math Masters, p. 54

3•3 Number-Grid Patterns

Objective To guide exploration of skip-counting patterns on the number grid.

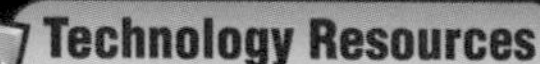

www.everydaymathonline.com

ePresentations

eToolkit

Algorithms Practice

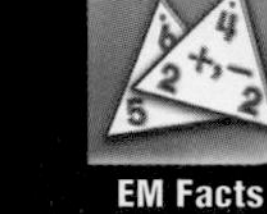
EM Facts Workshop Game™

Family Letters

Assessment Management

Common Core State Standards

Curriculum Focal Points

Interactive Teacher's Lesson Guide

1 Teaching the Lesson

Key Concepts and Skills

- Count forward by 2s, 5s, and 10s. [Number and Numeration Goal 1]
- Identify the digit in the ones place. [Number and Numeration Goal 3]
- Describe and compare number patterns. [Patterns, Functions, and Algebra Goal 1]

Key Activities

Children explore the patterns in counts by 2s, 5s, and 10s on the number grid and in the ones digits of 2-digit numbers.

Key Vocabulary

column ◆ row

Materials

Math Journal 1, p. 32 and inside back cover
Home Link 3•2
slate ◆ transparency of *Math Masters,* p. 311 or a laminated number grid (optional) ◆ colored marking pens (optional)

2 Ongoing Learning & Practice

Discussing Weather and Probability

Children use probability language to discuss weather.

Math Boxes 3•3

Math Journal 1, p. 33
Children practice and maintain skills through Math Box problems.

Ongoing Assessment: Recognizing Student Achievement

Use Math Boxes, Problem 1.
[Number and Numeration Goal 7]

Home Link 3•3

Math Masters, p. 55
Children practice and maintain skills through Home Link activities.

3 Differentiation Options

Counting with Stops

"Stop" sign or red paper circle
Children do interrupted skip counting.

ENRICHMENT

Exploring the 3s Pattern

Math Masters, p. 56
colored pencils
Children explore the pattern in counts by 3s on the number grid.

ELL SUPPORT

Building a Math Word Bank

Differentiation Handbook, p. 127
Children add the terms *row, column,* and *diagonal* to their Math Word Banks.

Advance Preparation

For Part 1, use an overhead transparency of a number grid or make a large, laminated number grid and use marking pens that are easily erasable. You may wish to find the book ***Each Orange Had 8 Slices*** by Paul Giganti (Greenwillow Books, 1999) as it relates to lesson content.

***Teacher's Reference Manual,* Grades 1–3** pp. 117, 118

Getting Started

Mental Math and Reflexes

Children solve problems like the ones below using the number line on the inside back cover of their journals. They record answers on their slates.

Count the hops from

●○○	4 to 10. 6	6 to 11. 5	8 to 13. 5
●●○	9 to 18. 9	5 to 17. 12	4 to 12. 8
●●●	12 to 18. 6	16 to 20. 4	21 to 30. 9

NOTE Circulate as children count on their number lines. Watch for children who include the starting number in their counts—their answers will be 1 more than the correct answer.

Home Link 3·2 Follow-Up

Tally how many children have odd or even numbers of people living at home.

Have children share some of the even and odd numbers they recorded. Write their numbers in two columns on the board—labeled *Even* and *Odd*—as instructed by children. Review the first-grade chant: *2, 4, 6, 8, first graders are really great!* Remind children of the ones digits for even numbers—and perhaps amend the chant to include 0. What are the largest even and odd numbers children wrote?

1 Teaching the Lesson

Exploring Skip-Counting Patterns on a Number Grid

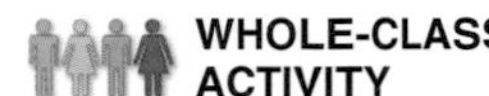

WHOLE-CLASS ACTIVITY

Algebraic Thinking Explain to children that they will be finding patterns on the number grid by marking skip counts with colored dots.

Use either an overhead transparency of a number grid or a laminated number grid. Children count by 5s, one child at a time, in turn. Mark the 5s count (multiples of 5) on the number grid with colored dots. Once a pattern begins to emerge, ask: *How can you find the numbers in the 5s count without actually counting?* The numbers in the 5s count are found in the 5s and 10s columns.

NOTE Do not expect children to use the word *multiples* at this time.

Adjusting the Activity

It may be helpful for some children to find the 5s counts by counting 5 "hops" to arrive at each new number.

AUDITORY ◆ KINESTHETIC ◆ TACTILE ◆ VISUAL

Make a list of the first few 5s counts and circle their ones digits. Ask children to describe the pattern in the ones digits. The numbers 5 and 0 alternate. *How many numbers does it take for the pattern to be repeated?* 2

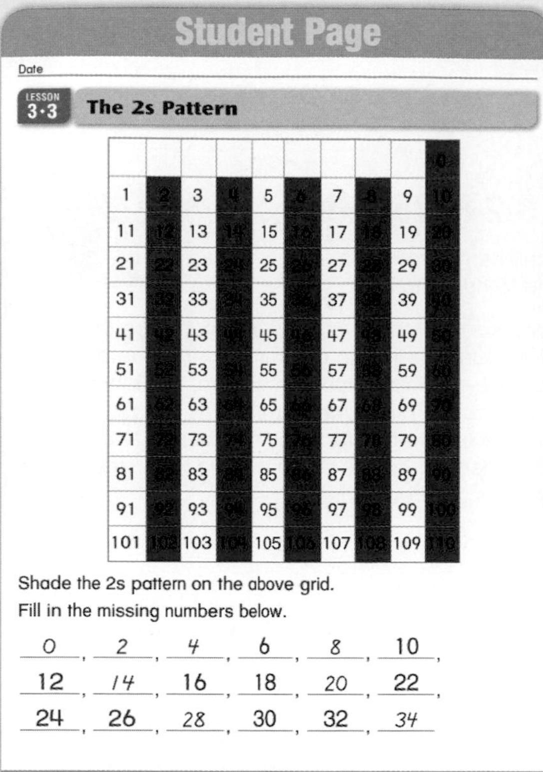
Student Page

Date

LESSON 3·3 **The 2s Pattern**

									0
1	2	3	4	5	6	7	8	9	10
11	12	13	14	15	16	17	18	19	20
21	22	23	24	25	26	27	28	29	30
31	32	33	34	35	36	37	38	39	40
41	42	43	44	45	46	47	48	49	50
51	52	53	54	55	56	57	58	59	60
61	62	63	64	65	66	67	68	69	70
71	72	73	74	75	76	77	78	79	80
81	82	83	84	85	86	87	88	89	90
91	92	93	94	95	96	97	98	99	100
101	102	103	104	105	106	107	108	109	110

Shade the 2s pattern on the above grid.
Fill in the missing numbers below.

0, 2, 4, 6, 8, 10,
12, 14, 16, 18, 20, 22,
24, 26, 28, 30, 32, 34

Math Journal 1, p. 32

Use different-colored dots to repeat this routine with 10s counts. (If you don't have different-colored markers, use different marks, such as dots, checks, and stars, for each set of counts.) Children should observe the following:

▷ The 10s are found only in the 10s **column.**

▷ All 10s end in 0.

Ask which numbers have been marked more than once. The 10s; this shows that all 10s are in counts by both 5s and 10s.

▶ Exploring the 2s Pattern

SMALL-GROUP ACTIVITY

(*Math Journal 1,* p. 32)

Algebraic Thinking Children work in small groups. Ask all group members to do the following:

1. Make light marks for the counts by 2s on the number grid on page 32 in your journal.
2. Check with other children in your group to see if everyone agrees. Then shade the 2s pattern on your own grid.
3. List the numbers you have shaded at the bottom of the page.
4. Study the number patterns on your grid and talk about what you discovered with your group.

Bring the class together and have volunteers tell about the patterns that their groups discovered.

Possible patterns include the following:

▷ The 2s are found in the 2s, 4s, 6s, 8s, and 10s columns.

▷ The 2s are all even numbers.

▷ The 2s end in the digits 0, 2, 4, 6, and 8.

▷ The 2s pattern in the ones digit repeats every five numbers.

▷ The pattern repeats in every **row.**

2 Ongoing Learning & Practice

▶ Discussing Weather and Probability

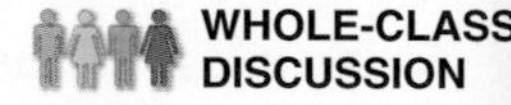
WHOLE-CLASS DISCUSSION

To offer children experience using probability language, ask questions about temperature and weather. Examples include:

- Look outside. Do you think it is *likely* to snow today?
- Is it *possible* or *impossible* that the temperature tomorrow will be warm enough to wear shorts?
- Will you need to bring a raincoat tomorrow? Are you *certain* or *uncertain*?

Math Boxes 3•3

INDEPENDENT ACTIVITY

(*Math Journal 1,* p. 33)

Mixed Practice Math Boxes in this lesson are paired with Math Boxes in Lesson 3-1. The skills in Problem 4 preview Unit 4 skills.

Ongoing Assessment: Recognizing Student Achievement

Math Boxes Problem 1

Use **Math Boxes, Problem 1** to assess children's understanding of comparing numbers. Children are making adequate progress if they circle the greater number.

[Number and Numeration Goal 7]

Home Link 3•3

(*Math Masters,* p. 55)

Home Connection Children use the number line to find the distance between two numbers. They count the number of hops from one number to another.

Differentiation Options

READINESS

SMALL-GROUP ACTIVITY

Counting with Stops

5–15 Min

To review skip counting, have children do interrupted skip counting. Begin by saying a number to a small group of children. Ask them to continue counting on from that number. After they have said a few numbers, hold up the "stop" sign to indicate that children should stop counting. Begin counting again from a higher number. For example: 11, 12, 13, 14, *Stop! Now begin at 19.* 19, 20, 21, ... Repeat the activity, counting by 2s, 5s, and 10s.

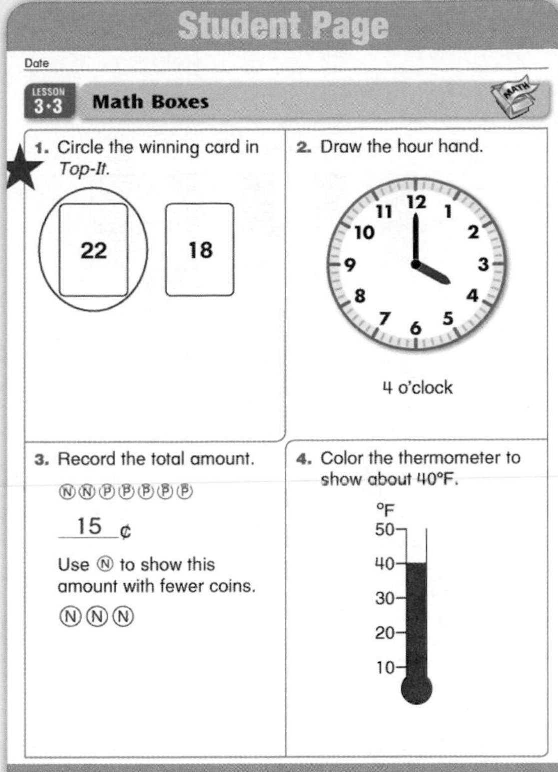

Student Page

Date

LESSON 3•3 Math Boxes

1. Circle the winning card in *Top-It.*

22 18

2. Draw the hour hand.

4 o'clock

3. Record the total amount.

Ⓝ Ⓝ Ⓟ Ⓟ Ⓟ Ⓟ Ⓟ

15 ¢

Use Ⓝ to show this amount with fewer coins.

Ⓝ Ⓝ Ⓝ

4. Color the thermometer to show about 40°F.

°F 50 40 30 20 10

Math Journal 1, p. 33

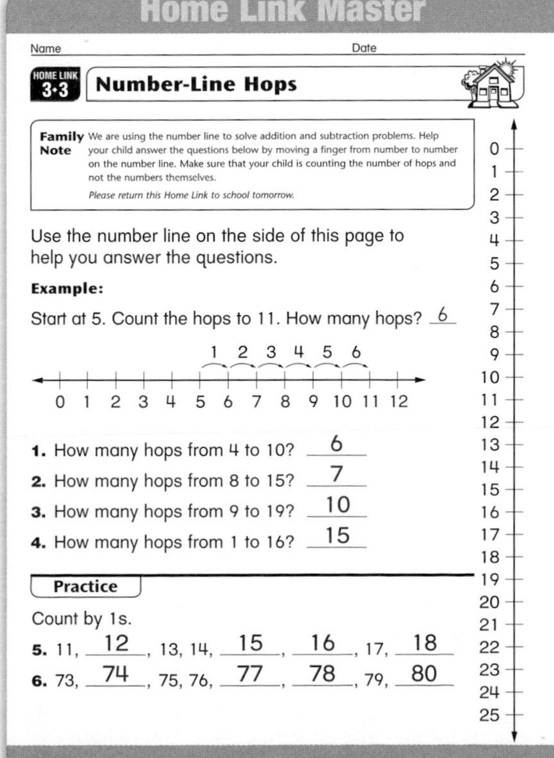

Home Link Master

Name Date

HOME LINK 3•3 Number-Line Hops

Family Note We are using the number line to solve addition and subtraction problems. Help your child answer the questions below by moving a finger from number to number on the number line. Make sure that your child is counting the number of hops and not the numbers themselves.

Please return this Home Link to school tomorrow.

Use the number line on the side of this page to help you answer the questions.

Example:

Start at 5. Count the hops to 11. How many hops? 6

1. How many hops from 4 to 10? 6
2. How many hops from 8 to 15? 7
3. How many hops from 9 to 19? 10
4. How many hops from 1 to 16? 15

Practice

Count by 1s.

5. 11, 12, 13, 14, 15, 16, 17, 18
6. 73, 74, 75, 76, 77, 78, 79, 80

Math Masters, p. 55

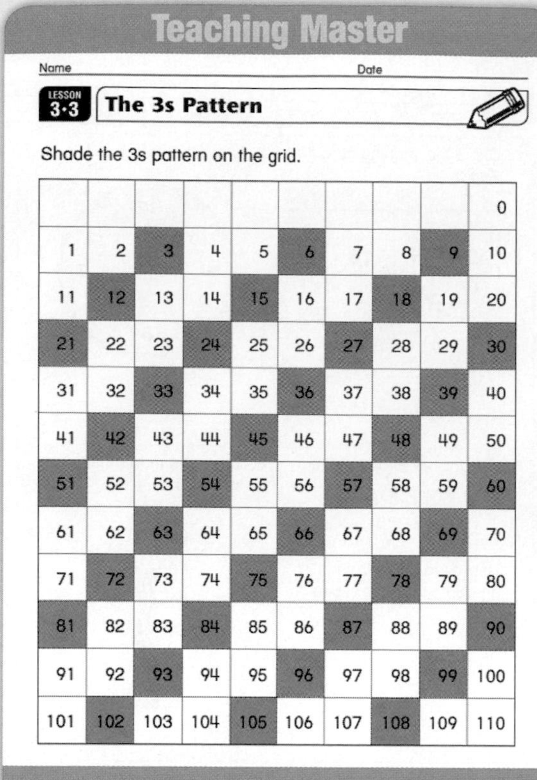
Teaching Master

Name Date

LESSON 3·3 **The 3s Pattern**

Shade the 3s pattern on the grid.

									0
1	2	3	4	5	6	7	8	9	10
11	12	13	14	15	16	17	18	19	20
21	22	23	24	25	26	27	28	29	30
31	32	33	34	35	36	37	38	39	40
41	42	43	44	45	46	47	48	49	50
51	52	53	54	55	56	57	58	59	60
61	62	63	64	65	66	67	68	69	70
71	72	73	74	75	76	77	78	79	80
81	82	83	84	85	86	87	88	89	90
91	92	93	94	95	96	97	98	99	100
101	102	103	104	105	106	107	108	109	110

Math Masters, **p. 56**

ENRICHMENT

SMALL-GROUP ACTIVITY

▶ Exploring the 3s Pattern

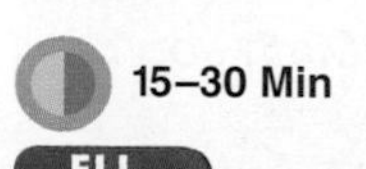
15–30 Min

ELL

(*Math Masters,* p. 56)

Algebraic Thinking To further explore number-grid patterns, have children count by 3s and shade the pattern. Ask each child to begin by making light marks for the counts by 3s in the number grid on *Math Masters,* page 56. Then ask children to shade the 3s pattern. Have children study the shaded patterns and discuss what they discovered with their groups. Prompt children to describe the number pattern in the *diagonal* that starts with 9 in the second row and goes down and to the left. Note that this diagonal shows counts by 9s. To support English language learners, write *diagonal* on the board. Ask children to identify some additional diagonals on the number grid.

ELL SUPPORT

SMALL-GROUP ACTIVITY

▶ Building a Math Word Bank

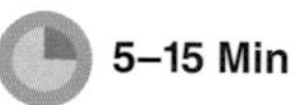
5–15 Min

(*Differentiation Handbook,* p. 127)

To provide language support for navigating the number grid, use the Word Bank template found on *Differentiation Handbook,* page 127. Ask children to write the terms *row*, *column*, and *diagonal,* draw pictures representing the terms, and write other words that describe them. See the *Differentiation Handbook* for more information. Make a classroom poster to provide further support. (See below for a suggestion.)

ROW C D
O I
L A
U G
M O
N N
A
L

3•4 Exploring Number Patterns, Shapes, and Patterns

Explorations

Objectives To guide exploration of even and odd numbers; covering shapes with pattern blocks; and creating and continuing repeating patterns.

Technology Resources www.everydaymathonline.com

ePresentations

eToolkit

Algorithms Practice

EM Facts Workshop Game™

Family Letters

Assessment Management

Common Core State Standards

NCTM
Curriculum Focal Points

Interactive Teacher's Lesson Guide

1 Teaching the Lesson

Key Concepts and Skills

- Identify even and odd numbers. [Number and Numeration Goal 5]
- Use plane shapes for patterning. [Geometry Goal 1]
- Create visual patterns. [Patterns, Functions, and Algebra Goal 1]
- Sort dominoes. [Patterns, Functions, and Algebra Goal 1]

Key Activities

Exploration A: Children sort dominoes according to whether the numbers of dots on the two sides are both even, both odd, or even and odd.

Exploration B: Children cover shapes with pattern blocks in various ways.

Exploration C: Children create and continue repeating patterns using pattern blocks.

Ongoing Assessment: Recognizing Student Achievement Use Mental Math and Reflexes. [Operations and Computation Goal 2]

Ongoing Assessment: Informing Instruction See page 202.

Materials

Math Journal 1, inside back cover
Home Link 3•3
slate

Exploration A: Per group:
Math Masters, pp. 57, 58, 59, and 60
1 set of double-9 dominoes

Exploration B: Per group:
Math Masters, pp. 61 and 62
pattern blocks ◆ Pattern-Block Template

Exploration C: Per group:
pattern blocks

2 Ongoing Learning & Practice

Playing *Before and After*
per partnership: 4 each of number cards 1–10 (from the Everything Math Deck, if available)

Math Boxes 3•4
Math Journal 1, p. 34

Home Link 3•4
Math Masters, p. 63

3 Differentiation Options

READINESS

Exploring Domino-Dot Patterns
Math Masters, p. 64

EXTRA PRACTICE

Minute Math+
Minute Math®+, pp. 55 and 56

Advance Preparation

Explorations A, B, and C are best done in small groups. Spend most of your time on Exploration A, described on *Math Masters,* page 57. You can place copies of this master at appropriate workstations if another adult is helping children. Children record their work on *Math Masters,* pages 58–60.

Getting Started

Mental Math and Reflexes 

Children use the number grid on the inside back cover of their journals to solve problems like the ones below. They record their answers on their slates.

●○○ Start at 12. Count the number of spaces to 20. 8

●●○ Count the number of spaces from 36 to 50. 14

●●● Count the spaces from 45 to 71. 26

Be aware of children who include the starting numbers in their counts. Their answers will be 1 more than the correct answers.

- How is counting on the number grid similar to counting on the number line? You count 1 space or hop each time you move to the next number.
- How is it different? On the number grid, when you come to the end of a row, you go to the beginning of the next row.

Home Link 3·3 Follow-Up

Briefly go over the answers.

Ongoing Assessment: Recognizing Student Achievement

Mental Math and Reflexes ★

Use **Mental Math and Reflexes** to assess children's ability to count spaces on a number grid. Children are making adequate progress if they are able to use the number grid to count the hops between two numbers with a difference of 10 or less. Some children may be able to give correct answers for numbers with a greater difference.

[Operations and Computation Goal 2]

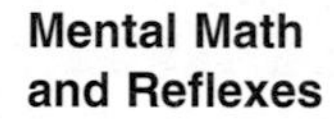

1 Teaching the Lesson

Plan to spend most of your time with the group that is working on Exploration A. You may also need to help other children get started on the other Explorations.

▶ Exploration A: Sorting Dominoes by Odd and Even Numbers of Dots

SMALL-GROUP ACTIVITY

(*Math Masters,* pp. 57–60)

Children work in groups of 4. Each workstation should have a copy of *Math Masters,* page 57 and a set of 55 dominoes, up to and including double-9s. Give one child a copy of *Math Masters,* page 58; one child a copy of *Math Masters,* page 59; and each of the two remaining children copies of *Math Masters,* page 60. Have children write their names on their papers.

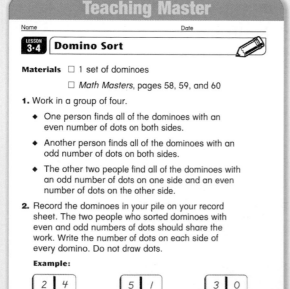

Teaching Master

Name Date

LESSON 3·4 **Domino Sort**

Materials □ 1 set of dominoes

□ *Math Masters,* pages 58, 59, and 60

1. Work in a group of four.
   - One person finds all of the dominoes with an even number of dots on both sides.
   - Another person finds all of the dominoes with an odd number of dots on both sides.
   - The other two people find all of the dominoes with an odd number of dots on one side and an even number of dots on the other side.
2. Record the dominoes in your pile on your record sheet. The two people who sorted dominoes with even and odd numbers of dots should share the work. Write the number of dots on each side of every domino. Do not draw dots.

Example:

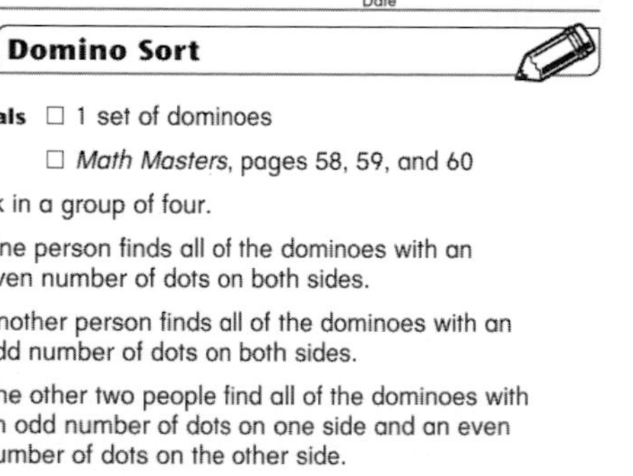

3. Count the dominoes in each pile.

Math Masters, p. 57

Assign tasks to each member of the group as follows:

- ▷ One child finds all of the dominoes that have an even number of dots on both sides.
- ▷ One child finds all of the dominoes that have an odd number of dots on both sides.
- ▷ The other two children find all of the dominoes that have an even number of dots on one side and an odd number of dots on the other side.

NOTE Lead children to the conclusion that dominoes that have an odd number of dots on one side can be recognized by a dot in the middle.

- ▷ Children record the dominoes they sorted by writing numbers for the numbers of dots, rather than by drawing the dots.

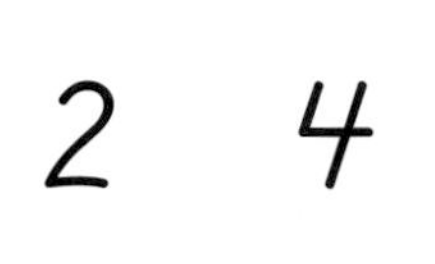

Children record the *number* of dots on the dominoes they have sorted.

- ▷ The two children who were assigned to sort dominoes with an even number on one side and an odd number on the other side share the recording task. Each child should record about half the dominoes on his or her recording sheet. **The answer blank under each domino will be filled during Lesson 3-14, so save the children's work.**
- ▷ Children in each group count how many of each kind of domino there are in each of the three groups. You may wish to have children use tallies to count the dominoes. There are 15 dominoes with even numbers on both sides, 15 dominoes with odd numbers on both sides, and 25 dominoes with both even numbers and odd numbers.

Exploration B: Covering Shapes with Pattern Blocks

SMALL-GROUP ACTIVITY

PROBLEM SOLVING

(*Math Masters,* pp. 61 and 62)

For this activity, do the following:

1. Using pattern blocks, each child works independently to cover the shapes on *Math Masters,* pages 61 and 62.
2. Children trace the blocks or use Pattern-Block Templates and crayons to record each configuration they make.
3. Children then use pattern blocks to make their own shapes and record those configurations.
4. After they finish, children compare their work.

NOTE As children complete Exploration B, reinforce the idea that they are composing a larger shape from several smaller ones.

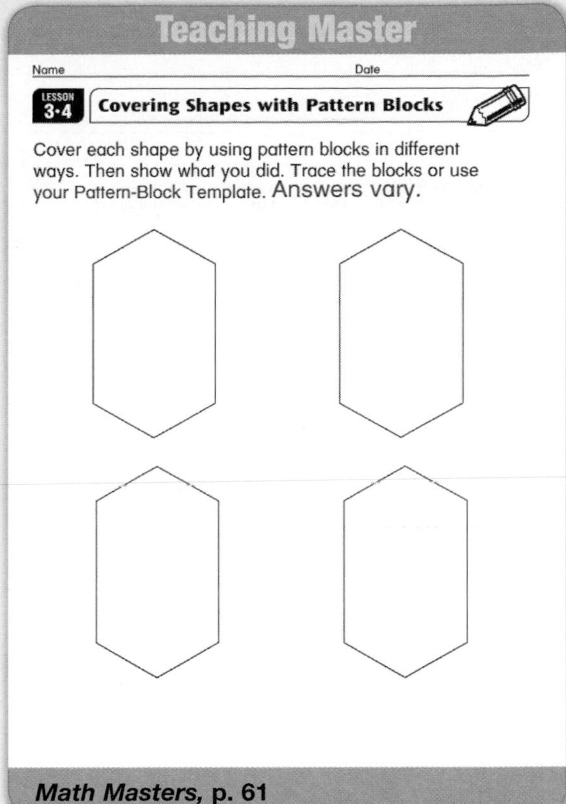

Teaching Master

Name Date

LESSON 3·4 **Covering Shapes with Pattern Blocks**

Cover each shape by using pattern blocks in different ways. Then show what you did. Trace the blocks or use your Pattern-Block Template. Answers vary.

Math Masters, p. 61

NOTE Collect *Math Masters,* pages 58–60 from children. These masters will be used in an optional Enrichment activity in Lesson 3-14.

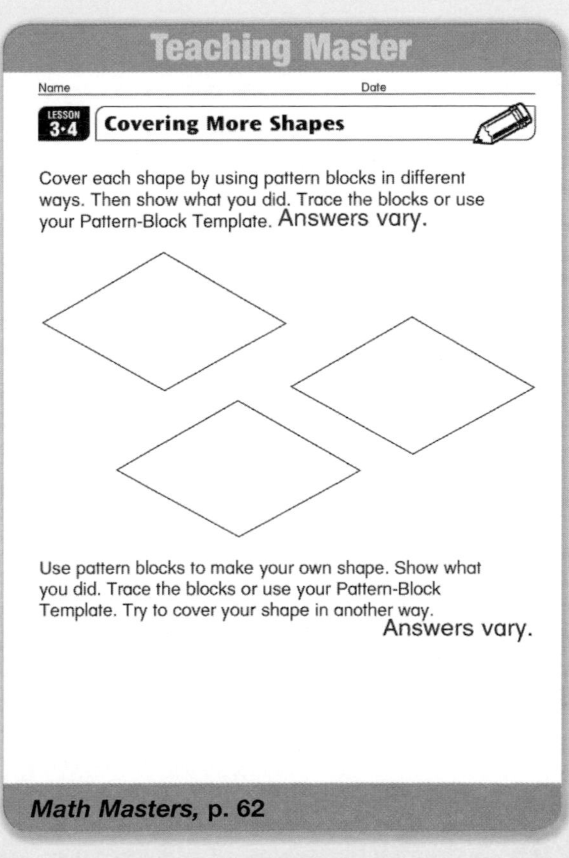

Teaching Master

Name Date

LESSON 3·4 **Covering More Shapes**

Cover each shape by using pattern blocks in different ways. Then show what you did. Trace the blocks or use your Pattern-Block Template. Answers vary.

Use pattern blocks to make your own shape. Show what you did. Trace the blocks or use your Pattern-Block Template. Try to cover your shape in another way. Answers vary.

Math Masters, p. 62

Student Page

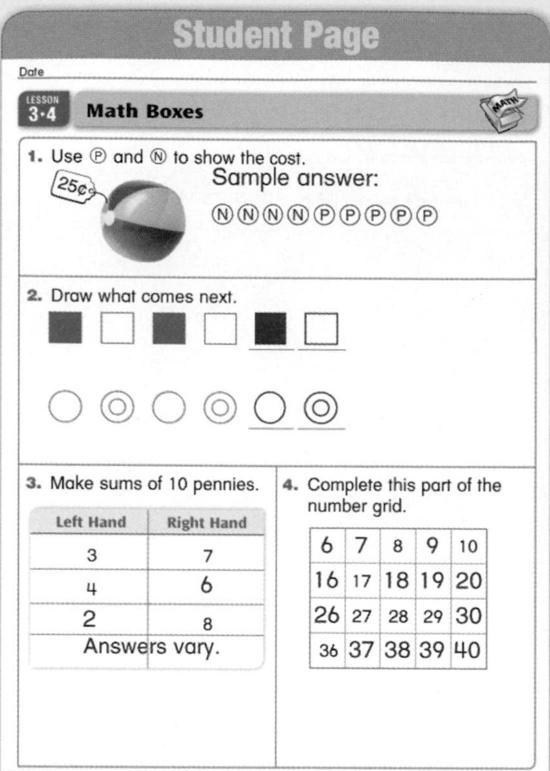

Math Journal 1, p. 34

Links to the Future

This exploration leads to lessons in future units in which children will cover shapes with only one type of pattern block. This work will, in turn, lead to an introduction of fraction concepts.

▶ Exploration C: Exploring Patterns with Pattern Blocks

SMALL-GROUP ACTIVITY

ELL

Algebraic Thinking One child creates a pattern with pattern blocks. Other children in the group take turns continuing the pattern.

Ongoing Assessment: Informing Instruction

Watch for children who use pattern blocks to create pictures. Remind them that during this Exploration, they are to create patterns. Help them begin a pattern for their group members to continue.

Encourage children to demonstrate or explain how they used their pattern blocks to create their designs by using words such as *slide, flip,* or *turn.* Have children also use positional words such as *above, below, to the right of,* and so on. To support English language learners, write *slide, flip,* and *turn* on the board. Model the meaning of these words using blocks on the overhead projector.

2 Ongoing Learning & Practice

▶ Playing *Before and After*

PARTNER ACTIVITY

Children play *Before and After* to practice finding numbers that are one more and one less than a given number. For detailed instructions, see Lesson 3-1.

▶ Math Boxes 3•4

INDEPENDENT ACTIVITY

(*Math Journal 1,* p. 34)

Mixed Practice Math Boxes in this lesson are paired with Math Boxes in Lesson 3-2. The skills in Problem 4 preview Unit 4 content.

Home Link 3·4

INDEPENDENT ACTIVITY

(*Math Masters,* p. 63)

Home Connection Children tell whether their addresses and the addresses across the street from their homes are represented by odd or even numbers. They use tally marks to show an even number and an odd number.

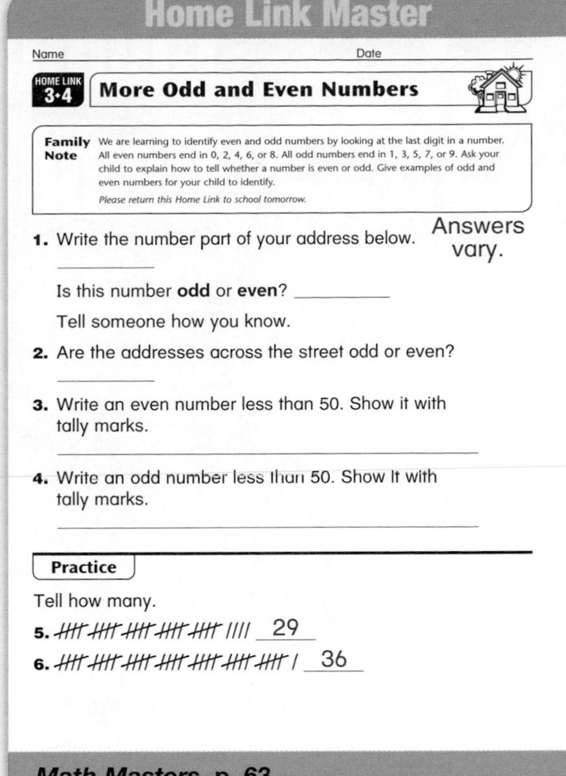

Home Link Master

Name Date

HOME LINK 3·4 **More Odd and Even Numbers**

Family Note We are learning to identify even and odd numbers by looking at the last digit in a number. All even numbers end in 0, 2, 4, 6, or 8. All odd numbers end in 1, 3, 5, 7, or 9. Ask your child to explain how to tell whether a number is even or odd. Give examples of odd and even numbers for your child to identify.

Please return this Home Link to school tomorrow.

1. Write the number part of your address below. Answers vary.
   ______
   Is this number **odd** or **even**? ______
   Tell someone how you know.
2. Are the addresses across the street odd or even?
   ______
3. Write an even number less than 50. Show it with tally marks.
   ______
4. Write an odd number less than 50. Show it with tally marks.
   ______

Practice

Tell how many.

5. ~~||||~~ ~~||||~~ ~~||||~~ ~~||||~~ ~~||||~~ |||| 29
6. ~~||||~~ ~~||||~~ ~~||||~~ ~~||||~~ ~~||||~~ ~~||||~~ ~~||||~~ | 36

Math Masters, p. 63

3 Differentiation Options

READINESS

SMALL-GROUP ACTIVITY

5–15 Min

Exploring Domino-Dot Patterns

(*Math Masters,* p. 64)

To explore even and odd numbers using a visual model, have children look for patterns in the dots on *Math Masters*, page 64. When children have finished the page, have them discuss any patterns they see in the sets of dots that are even and the sets of dots that are odd. The odd number patterns always have a dot in the middle. The even number patterns never have a dot in the middle.

NOTE The dot patterns on *Math Masters,* page 64 match the dot patterns on domino halves.

EXTRA PRACTICE

SMALL-GROUP ACTIVITY

5–15 Min

Minute Math+

Use *Minute Math+,* pages 55 and 56, to provide practice identifying and forming shapes.

Planning Ahead

For the optional Readiness activity in Lesson 3-5, you will need a large, on-the-floor number line. See page 208 in Lesson 3-5 for more details on preparing the number line.

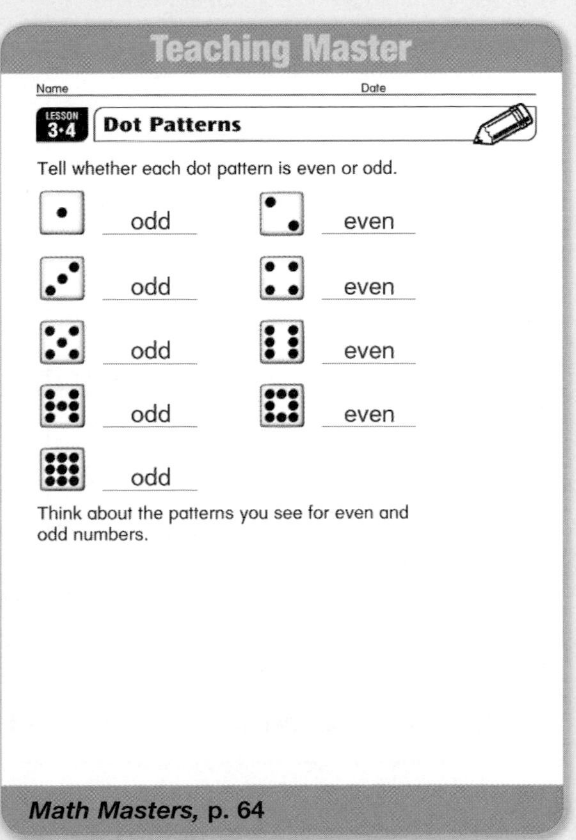

Teaching Master

Name Date

LESSON 3·4 **Dot Patterns**

Tell whether each dot pattern is even or odd.

•	odd	••	even
•••	odd	••••	even
•••••	odd	••••••	even
•••••••	odd	••••••••	even
•••••••••	odd		

Think about the patterns you see for even and odd numbers.

Math Masters, p. 64

3•5 Counting on the Number Line

Objectives To review basic number-line concepts; and to provide practice counting on the number line.

Technology Resources www.everydaymathonline.com

ePresentations

eToolkit

Algorithms Practice

EM Facts Workshop Game™

Family Letters

Assessment Management

Common Core State Standards

Curriculum Focal Points

Interactive Teacher's Lesson Guide

1 Teaching the Lesson

Key Concepts and Skills

- Count forward by 2s, 3s, 5s, and 10s. [Number and Numeration Goal 1]
- Count forward and backward by 1s from a given number. [Number and Numeration Goal 1]
- Create skip-counting patterns. [Patterns, Functions, and Algebra Goal 1]

Key Activities

Children learn about features of a number line. They skip count up and back by 2s, 5s, 10s, and 3s on the number line. They use the number line to do choral counts. Children also practice counting up and back by 1s on the number line, from 0 and from other numbers.

Ongoing Assessment: Recognizing Student Achievement Use journal page 35. [Number and Numeration Goal 1]

Ongoing Assessment: Informing Instruction See page 207.

Key Vocabulary

number line ♦ negative number

Materials

Math Journal 1, p. 35 and inside back cover
Home Link 3•4
Class Number Line or transparency of *Math Masters,* p. 65 (optional) ♦ pennies or overhead pennies (optional)

2 Ongoing Learning & Practice

Playing *Coin Top-It*

per partnership: money cards from Lesson 2-13, tool-kit coins
Children practice comparing money amounts.

Math Boxes 3•5

Math Journal 1, p. 36
Children practice and maintain skills through Math Box problems.

Home Link 3•5

Math Masters, p. 66
Children practice and maintain skills through Home Link activities.

3 Differentiation Options

READINESS

Hopping Along the On-the-Floor Number Line

large number line on-the-floor ♦ die
Children hop on a large on-the-floor number line.

ENRICHMENT

Completing a Negative Number Line

Math Masters, p. 67
glue or tape ♦ scissors
Children complete a number line with negative numbers.

EXTRA PRACTICE

Reading About Skip Counting

Math Masters, p. 305
Children read *Two Ways to Count to Ten* to practice skip counting.

Advance Preparation

See the optional Readiness activity in Part 3 for instructions on making a large number line.

For the optional Extra Practice activity in Part 3, obtain a copy of ***Two Ways to Count to Ten*** by Ruby Dee (Henry Holt and Co., 1990).

***Teacher's Reference Manual,* Grades 1–3** pp. 64, 65

Getting Started

Mental Math and Reflexes

Set a group of pennies on the overhead. Turn on the overhead for about 3 seconds; turn it off. Ask children to estimate how many nickels could be exchanged for the pennies they saw on the overhead.

●○○ Show 8 pennies. About how many nickels could be exchanged for the pennies?

●●○ Show 15 pennies. About how many nickels could be exchanged for the pennies?

●●● Show 24 pennies. About how many nickels could be exchanged for the pennies?

Home Link 3·4 Follow-Up

List the addresses of several children. Ask: *How can you tell whether these large numbers are even or odd?* If the ones digit is 0, 2, 4, 6, or 8; then the number is even. If the ones digit is 1, 3, 5, 7, or 9; then the number is odd.

Children tell whether each of the addresses on the board is even or odd. Depending on where children live, there may be a pattern in the house or building numbers. Ask: *Are all the numbers on one side of the street even numbers? Are all the numbers on the opposite side odd number?*

1 Teaching the Lesson

Reviewing Basic Number-Line Concepts

Sketch a variety of **number lines** on the board and discuss some of their features. *For example:*

▷ Number lines can go in any direction—left or right, up or down, or slanted.

▷ The arrows at the beginning and end of a number line show that the number line goes on forever in both directions.

▷ A number line can start with any number.

▷ A number line can extend to the left of, or below, zero.

▷ Numbers on the below-zero part of the number line are called **negative numbers** and are written with a "–" symbol before the number. Remind children of below-zero temperatures on thermometers. To support English language learners, write the term *negative numbers* on the board, write some negative numbers, and discuss some examples of how negative numbers are used.

NOTE When we draw a number line, we are really drawing only a part of it, since a line extends indefinitely.

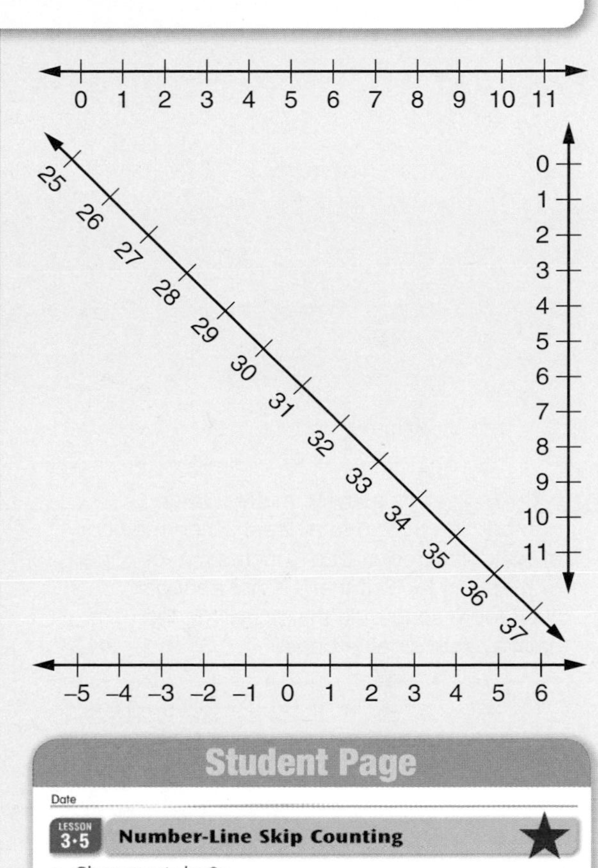

Reviewing Skip Counting on Number Lines

(*Math Journal 1,* p. 35)

Use the Class Number Line or a transparency of *Math Masters,* page 65 to demonstrate how to show counts by 2s with arcs.

Student Page

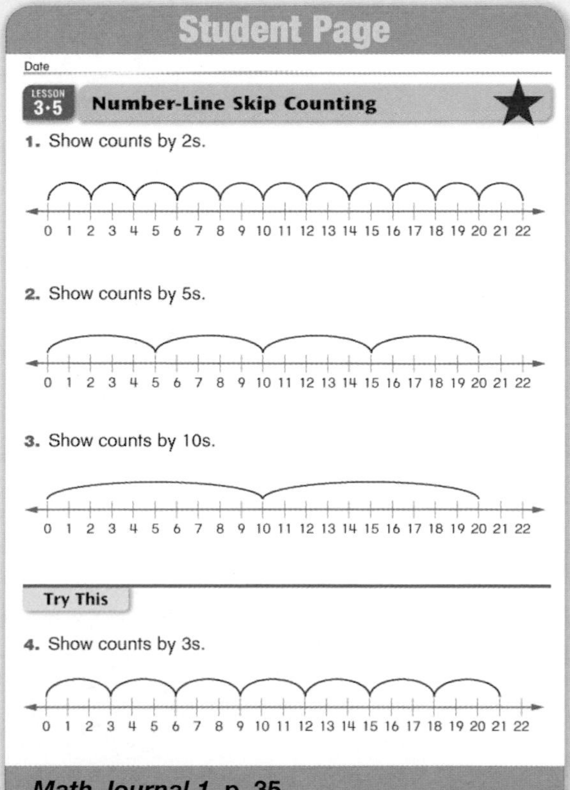

Date
LESSON 3·5 Number-Line Skip Counting
1. Show counts by 2s.
0 1 2 3 4 5 6 7 8 9 10 11 12 13 14 15 16 17 18 19 20 21 22
2. Show counts by 5s.
0 1 2 3 4 5 6 7 8 9 10 11 12 13 14 15 16 17 18 19 20 21 22
3. Show counts by 10s.
0 1 2 3 4 5 6 7 8 9 10 11 12 13 14 15 16 17 18 19 20 21 22
Try This
4. Show counts by 3s.
0 1 2 3 4 5 6 7 8 9 10 11 12 13 14 15 16 17 18 19 20 21 22

Math Journal 1, p. 35

Children follow along, showing counts by 2s on the first number line on the journal page. On their own, they show counts by 5s, 10s, and 3s on the other number lines.

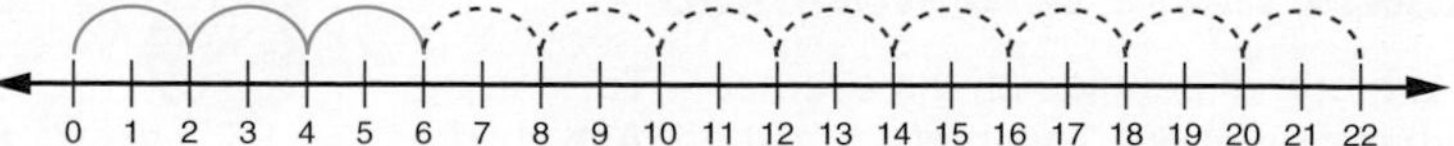

When children have completed the number-line counts, they count up and back by 2s, 5s, 10s, and 3s in unison. They follow along on their number lines, using their fingers to hop from one number to the next.

Ongoing Assessment: Recognizing Student Achievement

Journal Page 35

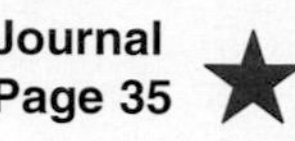

Use **journal page 35** to assess children's ability to skip count. Children are making adequate progress if they are able to correctly answer Problems 1, 2, and 3. Some children may be able to correctly answer Problem 4.

[Number and Numeration Goal 1]

▶ Counting Hops Up and Back on the Number Line

WHOLE-CLASS ACTIVITY

NOTE For this activity, make a large number line from 0 to at least 20 on the floor of your classroom. Use 4-inch strips of paper or masking tape. If there is not enough classroom space, do this activity in the hallway with small groups.

Children count hops on the number line on the inside back cover of their journals. Use the Class Number Line or a transparency of *Math Masters,* page 65 to review the answers.

Suggestions:

- Start at 0. Count up 5 hops. Where do you end up? At 5 Count up 3 more hops. Where do you end up? At 8
- Start at 0. Count up 3 hops. Where do you end up? At 3 Count up 7 more hops. Where do you end up? At 10
- Start at 3. Count up 7 hops. Where do you end up? At 10
- Start at 0. Count up 9 hops. Then count back 2 hops. Where do you end up? At 7
- Start at 0. Count up 12 hops. Then count back 7 hops. Where do you end up? At 5
- Start at 12. Count back 7 hops. Where do you end up? At 5
- Start at 6. Count up to 10. How many hops are there from 6 to 10? 4 hops

Some children may notice that counting up 3 hops, starting at 0, and then counting 7 more hops gives the same result as counting up 7 hops, starting at 3.

Similarly, counting up 12 hops, starting at 0, and then counting back 7 hops gives the same result as counting back 7 hops, starting at 12.

Ongoing Assessment: Informing Instruction

Watch for children who include the starting number in their counts. Show children that they should put their finger on the starting number and then count "1" as they hop to the next number.

Tell children that next they will learn to use the number line to help them solve addition and subtraction problems.

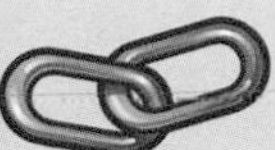

Links to the Future

The purpose of this routine is to prepare children for addition and subtraction on the number line, which will be addressed in the next lesson.

2 Ongoing Learning & Practice

Playing *Coin Top-It*

PARTNER ACTIVITY

Children practice comparing money amounts by playing *Coin Top-It*. For detailed instructions, see Lesson 2-13.

Math Boxes 3•5

INDEPENDENT ACTIVITY

(*Math Journal 1*, p. 36)

Mixed Practice Math Boxes in this lesson are paired with Math Boxes in Lesson 3-7. The skills in Problem 4 preview Unit 4 content.

Home Link 3•5

INDEPENDENT ACTIVITY

(*Math Masters*, p. 66)

Home Connection Children tell someone what they know about number lines. They show how to count by 10s, 5s, 3s, and 2s on a number line, beginning at zero. They record their counts and talk about counting patterns.

Student Page

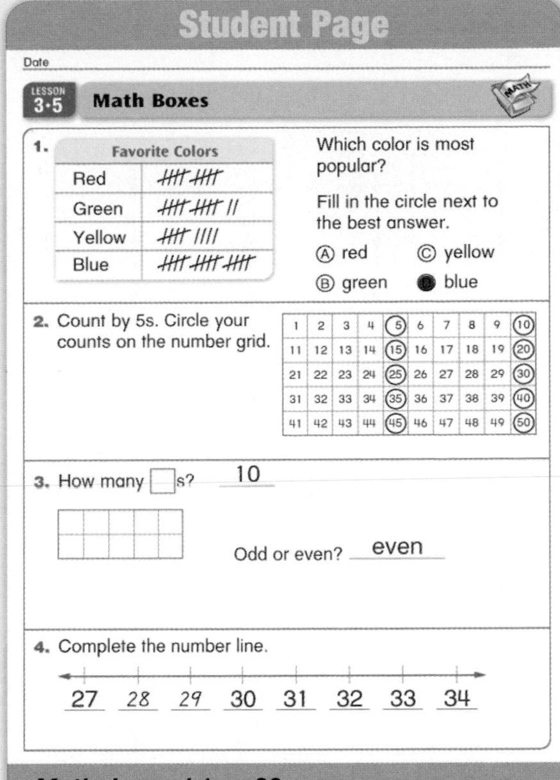

Date

LESSON 3•5 **Math Boxes**

1.

Favorite Colors	
Red	HHT HHT
Green	HHT HHT II
Yellow	HHT IIII
Blue	HHT HHT HHT

Which color is most popular?

Fill in the circle next to the best answer.

Ⓐ red Ⓑ green Ⓒ yellow ● blue

2. Count by 5s. Circle your counts on the number grid.

1	2	3	4	(5)	6	7	8	9	(10)
11	12	13	14	(15)	16	17	18	19	(20)
21	22	23	24	(25)	26	27	28	29	(30)
31	32	33	34	(35)	36	37	38	39	(40)
41	42	43	44	(45)	46	47	48	49	(50)

3. How many □s? 10

Odd or even? even

4. Complete the number line.

27 28 29 30 31 32 33 34

Math Journal 1, p. 36

Home Link Master

Name Date

LESSON 3•5 **Number Lines and Counting Patterns**

Family Note Listen as your child tells you about number lines and counts. Be sure he or she records the numbers counted. Provide several objects, such as pennies, for your child to use to count by 10s, 5s, 2s, and 3s.

Please return this Home Link to school tomorrow.

Tell someone at home what you know about number lines and counting patterns.

Count by 10s, 5s, 2s, and 3s. Begin at 0 each time.

1. **Count by 10s.** 0, 10, 20
2. **Count by 5s.** 0, 5, 10, 15, 20
3. **Count by 2s.** 0, 2, 4, 6, 8
4. **Count by 3s.** 0, 3, 6, 9, 12
5. Circle all of the odd numbers on the number line.

0 (1) 2 (3) 4 (5) 6 (7) 8 (9) 10 (11) 12 (13) 14 (15) 16 (17) 18 (19) 20

Practice

What time is it?

6. 12 o'clock

7. 9 o'clock

Math Masters, p. 66

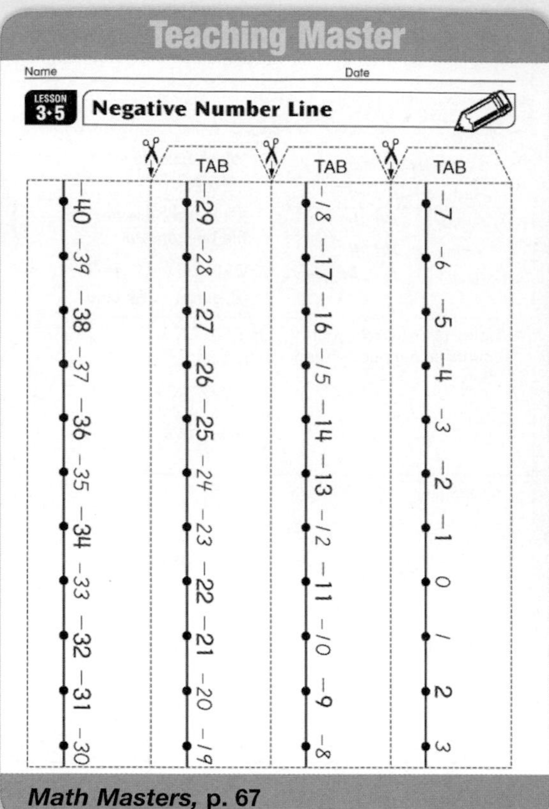

Math Masters, p. 67

3 Differentiation Options

READINESS

SMALL-GROU ACTIVITY

▶ Hopping Along the On-the-Floor Number Line

5–15 Min

To explore navigating along a number line, have children count hops on a number line. Make a large number line from 0 to at least 20 on the floor of your classroom. Have two children stand o either side of the number line. Determine whether it would be better to hop forward or backward. Roll a die to determine the number of hops the children will make. After they have practiced their hops, have children predict where they might land before they make their hops.

ENRICHMENT

SMALL-GROU ACTIVITY

▶ Completing a Negative Number Line

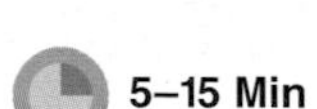
5–15 Min

(*Math Masters*, p. 67)

To further explore number lines, children complete a number line that extends below zero. Ask children to fill in the missing negative numbers on *Math Masters*, page 67, cut the strips apart, put them in order, and glue or tape them together at the tabs. Make sure that 0 is on the right and the negative number line extends to the left. Have children describe the patterns they see. For example, "The negative numbers look like they go in the othe direction."

EXTRA PRACTICE

SMALL-GROU ACTIVITY

▶ Reading About Skip Counting

5–15 Min

Literature Link To provide practice with skip counting, rea ***Two Ways to Count to Ten*** by Ruby Dee (Henry Holt and Company, 1990). On an Exit Slip (*Math Masters,* page 305), have children write 3 ways to count to ten.

Planning Ahead

Keep your large, on-the-floor number line intact. You will be using it again in Lessons 3-6 and 3-8.

3•6 Adding and Subtracting on the Number Line

Objective To introduce addition and subtraction on the number line.

Technology Resources www.everydaymathonline.com

Presentations

eToolkit
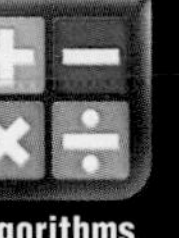
Algorithms Practice

EM Facts Workshop Game™

Family Letters

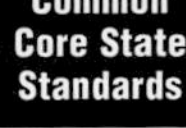
Assessment Management

Common Core State Standards

Curriculum Focal Points

Interactive Teacher's Lesson Guide

1 Teaching the Lesson

Key Concepts and Skills

- Count forward and backward by 1s from a given number. [Number and Numeration Goal 1]
- Model and solve addition and subtraction number stories. [Operations and Computation Goal 1]
- Complete number models for addition and subtraction number stories. [Operations and Computation Goal 1]
- Use the symbols +, −, and = to complete number models. [Patterns, Functions, and Algebra Goal 2]

Key Activities

Children use the number line to solve simple addition and subtraction problems.

Ongoing Assessment: Recognizing Student Achievement
Use an Exit Slip (*Math Masters,* page 305).
[Patterns, Functions, and Algebra Goal 2]

Materials

Math Journal 1, p. 37 and inside back cover
Home Link 3•5
Math Masters, pp. 68 and 305
Class Number Line or transparency of *Math Masters,* p. 68 (optional) ◆ slate

2 Ongoing Learning & Practice

Identifying True and False Number Models
Math Journal 1, inside back cover
Children learn the meanings of *true* and *false* and identify number models that are true and false.

Math Boxes 3•6
Math Journal 1, p. 38
Children practice and maintain skills through Math Box problems.

Home Link 3•6
Math Masters, p. 69
Children practice and maintain skills through Home Link activities.

3 Differentiation Options

READINESS

Reading and Writing Number Models
slate
Children practice reading and writing addition and subtraction number models.

ENRICHMENT

Making Up and Solving Penny Stories
per partnership: 20 pennies
Children work with a partner to model number stories with pennies.

EXTRA PRACTICE

Playing *Bunny Hop*
Math Masters, p. 341
per partnership: 1 die
Children play *Bunny Hop* to practice counting on a number line.

Advance Preparation

***Teacher's Reference Manual,* Grades 1–3** p. 84

Getting Started

Mental Math and Reflexes

Tell "change-to-more" and "change-to-less" number stories. Have children solve them any way they can: by using counters, by drawing pictures, by making doodles, by counting on their fingers, and so on.

Have children share solution strategies after each problem. Summarize each solution by drawing the appropriate "change" diagram on the board. (Use the change-to-more and change-to-less diagrams introduced in Mental Math and Reflexes in Lessons 2-7 and 2-8.) *Do this only after children have had a chance to share what they did to solve the problem.* Ask children to suggest a number model for each story.

●○○ Malcolm's plant was about 4 inches tall the first time he measured it. Since then, it has grown about 6 inches. About how tall is Malcom's plant now? About 10 inches tall; Sample number model: $4 + 6 = 10$

●●○ Bruno is 8 years old. He learned to ride a two-wheel bicycle 3 years ago. How old was Bruno then? 5 years old; Sample number model: $8 - 3 = 5$

●●● Sue had an 18-piece puzzle. She dropped it and lost some pieces. She has 10 pieces left. How many pieces did Sue lose? 8 pieces; Sample number model: $18 - 8 = 10$

Home Link 3·5 Follow-Up

Go over the answers. Discuss the odd/even number patterns in each sequence of numbers.

NOTE Be sure to do the Mental Math and Reflexes problems with your class. They are an important part of the problem-solving strand in *Everyday Mathematics* and will help children as they problem solve in future lessons.

1 Teaching the Lesson

▶ Introducing Addition on the Number Line

Pose the following number story:

Cynthia had 8 model cars. She got 3 more model cars for her birthday. How many model cars does Cynthia have now? 11 model cars

After children have solved the problem in the story, demonstrate how to use the number line to find the answer. You might say:

Cynthia had 8 model cars, so I'll start at 8. She got 3 more model cars, so I'll count up 3 hops. I've landed on 11. That's how many model cars Cynthia has now.

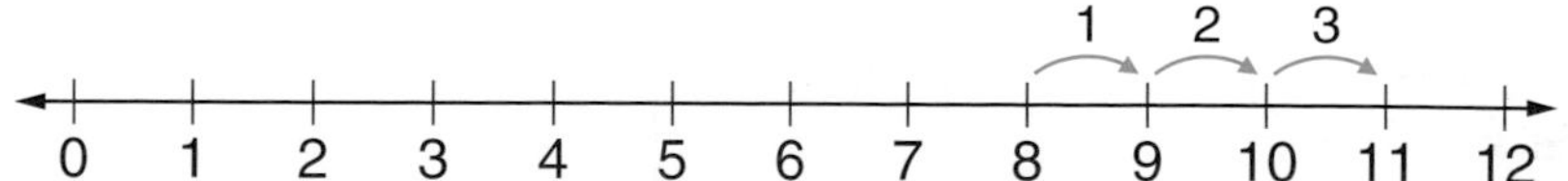

Then write a number model for the problem on the board: $8 + 3 = 11$.

Use the following routine to practice adding on the number line:

1. Write an addition problem on the board: $5 + 7 = \square$.
2. Have children use the number line on the inside back cover of their journals to find the answer.
3. Have children write the answer on their slates.
4. Ask a child to show the class how to find the answer using the Class Number Line.
5. Complete the addition problem: $5 + 7 = \boxed{12}$.

Suggestions:

▷ 6 + 4 = □ Start at 6. Count up 4 hops. End up on 10. Complete: 6 + 4 = [10].

▷ 2 + 9 = □ Start at 2. Count up 9 hops. End up on 11. Complete: 2 + 9 = [11].

▷ 15 + 0 = □ Start at 15. Count up 0 hops. End up on 15. Complete: 15 + 0 = [15].

Introducing Subtraction on the Number Line

Pose the following number story:

Ali bought a dozen eggs at the store. On his way home, he dropped the carton. Five eggs broke. How many eggs did not break? 7 eggs

To support English language learners, discuss the meaning of *dozen.*

After children have solved the number story, ask if someone can show how to use the number line to find the answer. Start at 12 on the number line. Count back 5 hops. You end on 7. That's how many eggs did not break.

Then write a number model for the problem on the board: 12 – 5 = 7.

Follow the same routine you used for addition to practice subtracting on the number line. *Suggestions:*

▷ 9 – 4 = □ Start at 9. Count back 4 hops. End up on 5. Complete: 9 – 4 = [5].

▷ 13 – 6 = □ Start at 13. Count back 6 hops. End up on 7. Complete: 13 – 6 = [7].

▷ 12 – 1 = □ Start at 12. Count back 1 hop. End up on 11. Complete: 12 – 1 = [11].

Ongoing Assessment: Recognizing Student Achievement

Exit Slip

Portfolio Ideas

Have children write a number model for one of the above subtraction problems on an **Exit Slip** (*Math Masters,* page 305). Use the Exit Slip to assess children's ability to write number models. Children are making adequate progress if they are able to include the correct subtrahend and minuend in the problem. Some children may be able to write the entire number model correctly.

[Patterns, Functions, and Algebra Goal 2]

Finally, do a couple of mixed problems before children solve problems in their journals.

▷ 8 + 8 = □ Start at 8. Count up 8 hops. End up on 16. Complete: 8 + 8 = [16].

▷ 15 – 9 = □ Start at 15. Count back 9 hops. End up on 6. Complete: 15 – 9 = [6].

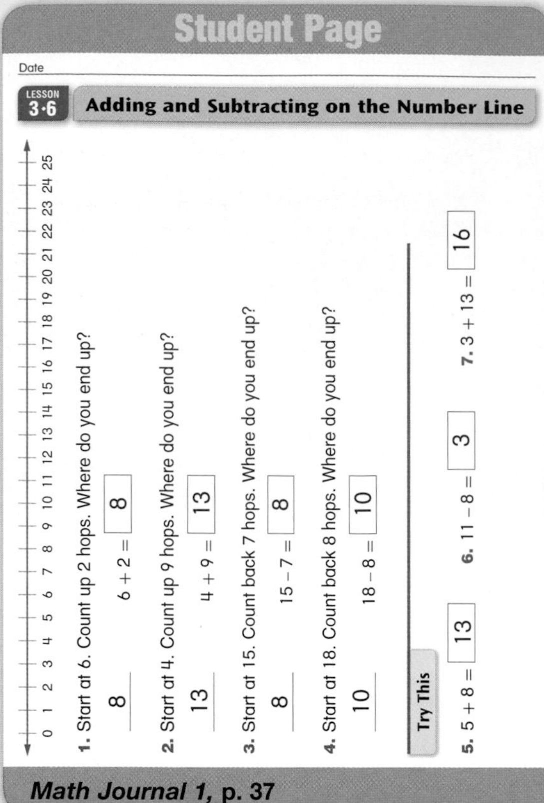

▶ Adding and Subtracting on the Number Line

INDEPENDENT ACTIVITY

(*Math Journal 1,* p. 37)

Children complete the page individually or with a partner while you circulate and assist as needed. Be sure to reserve time to discuss the answers.

Adjusting the Activity

Provide children with a copy of *Math Masters,* page 68 so that they can draw the hops on the number line to illustrate their thinking for each problem. You may want to laminate the page so that children can reuse it.

AUDITORY ◆ KINESTHETIC ◆ TACTILE ◆ VISUAL

2 Ongoing Learning & Practice

▶ Identifying True and False Number Models

WHOLE-CLASS ACTIVITY

(*Math Journal 1,* inside back cover)

Ask children what it means if something is *true.* It is correct or accurate. Explain that the opposite of true is *false.* Make statements, such as those listed below, that children will easily be able to identify as true or false. After you say each statement, have children stand if the statement is true or remain seated if the statement is false.

- Fish can swim. true
- The sky is green. false
- I have three feet. false

Explain that sometimes people disagree about whether something is true or false. For example, the statement *Apples are the best fruit* may be true for some and false for others. Explain, however, that number models are not debatable; they are either true or false.

Write number models, such as those listed below, on the board. Have children show "thumbs up" if the number model is true and "thumbs down" if the number model is false. Encourage children to use the number lines on the inside back covers of their journals to help them.

▷ $5 = 5$ true

▷ $7 + 1 = 9$ false

▷ $5 = 3 + 2$ true

▷ $5 - 2 = 2$ false

▷ $2 + 2 = 1 + 3$ true

After all children have responded, have children explain why they chose true or false. Write *true* or *false* next to each number model.

Math Boxes 3·6

INDEPENDENT ACTIVITY

(*Math Journal 1,* p. 38)

Mixed Practice Math Boxes in this lesson are paired with Math Boxes in Lesson 3-8. The skills in Problem 4 preview Unit 4 skills.

Home Link 3·6

INDEPENDENT ACTIVITY

(*Math Masters,* p. 69)

Home Connection Children use the number line to solve simple addition and subtraction problems. They start at a given number, count up or back a given number of hops, and then tell where they end up.

3 Differentiation Options

READINESS

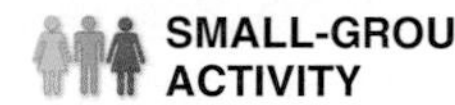

SMALL-GROUP ACTIVITY

Reading and Writing Number Models

5–15 Min

To provide experience using the symbols +, −, and = to write number models, dictate number models. For example, say: $3 + 6 = 9$. Children record the number sentence on their slates. The focus is not on solving number sentences, but on writing symbols to match words. Consider recording the sentences and number models on the board so that children can check their work.

ENRICHMENT

PARTNER ACTIVITY

Making Up and Solving Penny Stories

5–15 Min

To provide concrete experience with solving number stories, have children tell number stories and model them with pennies. For example, the first partner tells a penny story, "Lucy had 7 pennies. She lost 3 pennies. How many pennies does Lucy have left?" The second partner models the story using pennies. Have children write number models for their stories. For the example, possible number models are $7 - 3 = 4$ or $7 = 3 + 4$.

EXTRA PRACTICE

PARTNER ACTIVITY

Playing *Bunny Hop*

5–15 Min

(*Math Masters,* p. 341)

Children practice counting on the number line by playing *Bunny Hop*. For detailed instructions, see Lesson 1–5.

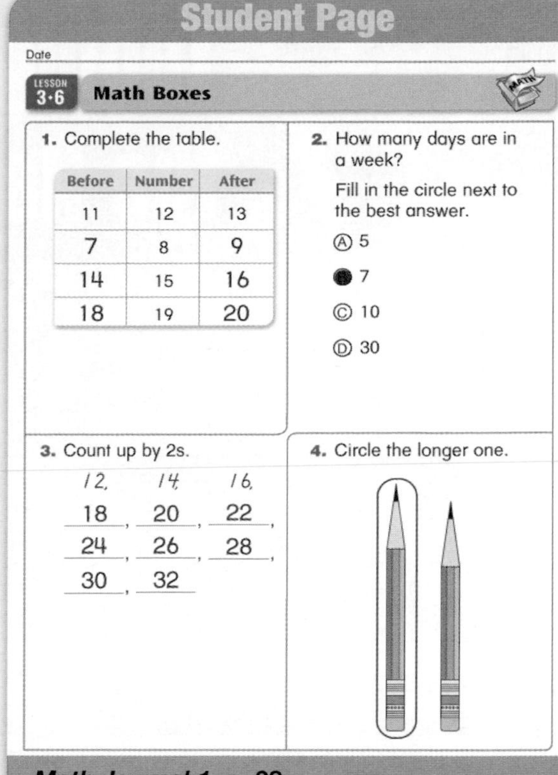

Student Page

Date

LESSON 3·6 **Math Boxes**

1. Complete the table.

Before	Number	After
11	12	13
7	8	9
14	15	16
18	19	20

2. How many days are in a week?

Fill in the circle next to the best answer.

Ⓐ 5
● 7
Ⓒ 10
Ⓓ 30

3. Count up by 2s.

12, 14, 16,
18, 20, 22,
24, 26, 28,
30, 32

4. Circle the longer one.

Math Journal 1, p. 38

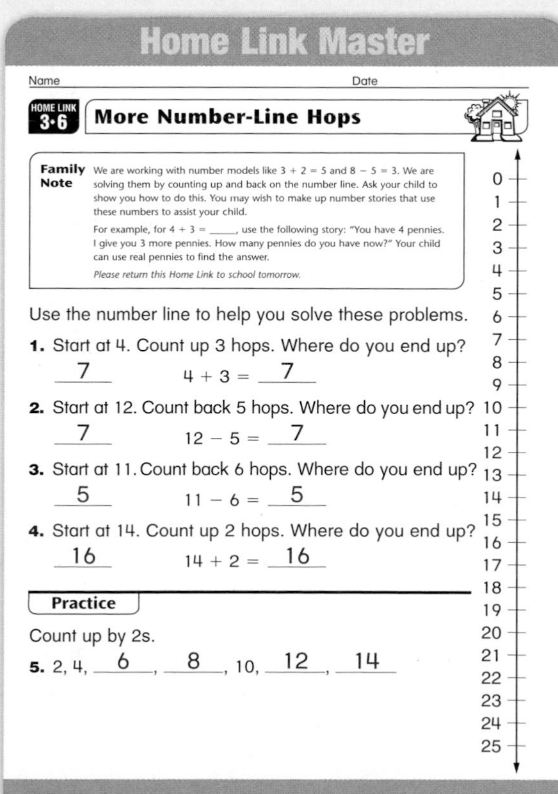

Home Link Master

Name Date

HOME LINK 3·6 **More Number-Line Hops**

Family Note We are working with number models like 3 + 2 = 5 and 8 − 5 = 3. We are solving them by counting up and back on the number line. Ask your child to show you how to do this. You may wish to make up number stories that use these numbers to assist your child.

For example, for 4 + 3 = ____, use the following story: "You have 4 pennies. I give you 3 more pennies. How many pennies do you have now?" Your child can use real pennies to find the answer.

Please return this Home Link to school tomorrow.

Use the number line to help you solve these problems.

1. Start at 4. Count up 3 hops. Where do you end up?
7   4 + 3 = 7
2. Start at 12. Count back 5 hops. Where do you end up?
7   12 − 5 = 7
3. Start at 11. Count back 6 hops. Where do you end up?
5   11 − 6 = 5
4. Start at 14. Count up 2 hops. Where do you end up?
16   14 + 2 = 16

Practice

Count up by 2s.

5. 2, 4, 6, 8, 10, 12, 14

Math Masters, p. 69

3•7 Telling Time to the Half-Hour

Objectives To review basic concepts of telling time; and to provide practice telling time to the hour and the half-hour.

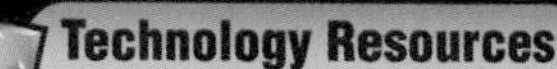
Technology Resources www.everydaymathonline.com

ePresentations

eToolkit

Algorithms Practice

EM Facts Workshop Game™

Family Letters

Assessment Management

Common Core State Standards

Curriculum Focal Points

Interactive Teacher's Lesson Guide

1 Teaching the Lesson

Key Concepts and Skills

- Estimate time on an analog clock using only the hour hand.
  [Measurement and Reference Frames Goal 4]
- Show a given time to the hour and half-hour on an analog clock.
  [Measurement and Reference Frames Goal 4]
- Tell and record times shown on an analog clock to the hour and half-hour.
  [Measurement and Reference Frames Goal 4]
- Use language of approximation to describe times on an analog clock.
  [Measurement and Reference Frames Goal 4]

Key Activities

Children review what they have learned about telling time on an analog clock. They are introduced to and practice telling time to the half-hour.

Ongoing Assessment: Informing Instruction See page 216.

Key Vocabulary

half-past (the hour)

Materials

Math Journal 1, p. 39 and inside back cover
Home Link 3•6
slate ◆ demonstration clock with hour and minute hands ◆ demonstration clock with hour hand only ◆ tool-kit clock ◆ Class Number Line or transparency of *Math Masters,* p. 65 (optional)

2 Ongoing Learning & Practice

Playing *Penny-Nickel Exchange*
per partnership: 20 pennies and 10 nickels, die (using a second die is optional)
Children practice money skills.

Math Boxes 3•7
Math Journal 1, p. 40
Children practice and maintain skills through Math Box problems.

Ongoing Assessment: Recognizing Student Achievement
Use Math Boxes, Problem 1.
[Data and Chance Goal 2]

Home Link 3•7
Math Masters, pp. 70 and 71
Children practice and maintain skills through Home Link activities.

3 Differentiation Options

READINESS

***Hickory Dickory Dock* with Clocks**
per group: tool-kit clocks, mouse puppet (optional), demonstration clock (optional)
Children say a familiar rhyme to practice telling time to the hour.

ENRICHMENT

Ordering Clocks by Displayed Times
per partnership: 8 tool-kit clocks, index cards (optional)
Children order clocks by the times they display.

ELL SUPPORT

Describing Time
Children discuss the term *half-past* in reference to time.

Advance Preparation

***Teacher's Reference Manual,* Grades 1–3** p. 173

Getting Started

Mental Math and Reflexes

Use the following routine to add and subtract on the number grid:

1. Write an addition or subtraction problem on the board.
2. Children use the number grid on the inside back cover of their journals to find the answer.
3. Children write the answers on their slates.

●○○ 12 + 7 = ____ 19

●●○ 41 + 10 = ____ 51

●●○ 56 + 14 = ____ 42

Home Link 3·6 Follow-Up

Go over the answers. Ask several children to demonstrate how to solve the problems on the Class Number Line or on a transparency of *Math Masters,* page 65.

1 Teaching the Lesson

Revisiting Telling Time on an Analog Clock

WHOLE-CLASS ACTIVITY

Review which hand is the hour hand and which hand is the minute hand. Ask children in what direction the minute hand points when it is 3 o'clock. Straight up

1. Use your demonstration clock as you discuss the following questions:
    - In which direction do the hands move? Review the term *clockwise.*
    - How long does it take for the minute hand to go all the way around the clock face? 1 hour, or 60 minutes
    - How long does it take for the hour hand to go all the way around the clock face? 12 hours
    - When the minute hand points straight up, what does the hour hand point to? The number on the clock face that tells the hour
2. Practice telling time to the hour.
    - ▷ Show a time to the hour on the demonstration clock and ask children to say the time.
    - ▷ Name a time on the hour and ask children to show it on their tool-kit clocks.
3. Practice estimating the time, using an hour-hand-only clock.
    - ▷ Move the hour hand so that it points to the 5. *About what time is it?* About 5 o'clock
    - ▷ Move the hour hand so that it points halfway between the 6 and the 7. *About what time is it?* Between 6 o'clock and 7 o'clock

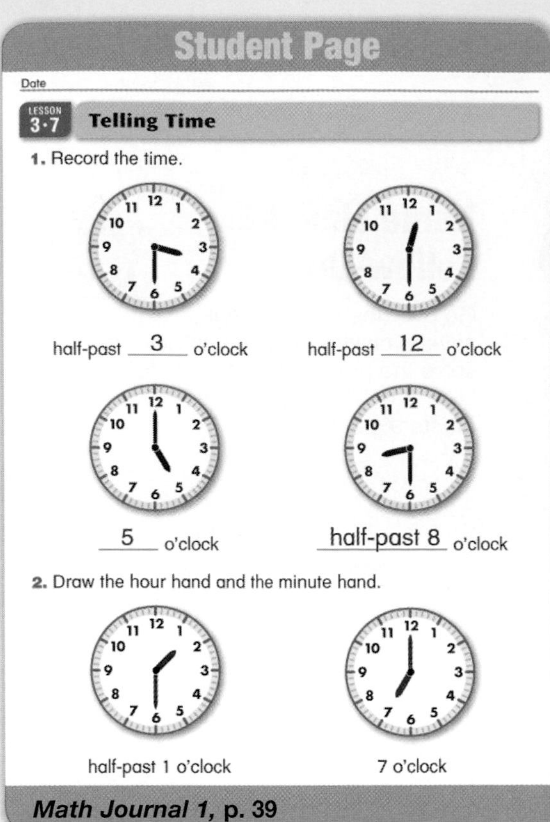

Student Page
Date
LESSON 3·7 Telling Time
1. Record the time.
half-past 3 o'clock
half-past 12 o'clock
5 o'clock
half-past 8 o'clock
2. Draw the hour hand and the minute hand.
half-past 1 o'clock
7 o'clock
Math Journal 1, p. 39

NOTE Be consistent in saying *about* when stating a time. Remind children that time is an estimate: Clocks may be set differently; we don't know exactly where the hand is pointing; and by the time we say or write a time, it is already a little later!

Repeat this routine a few more times. Move the hour hand to various positions and ask children to tell about what time it is. Remind them to use phrases like *about* ____, *almost* ____, *just before* ____, *a little after* ____, and *between* ____ *and* ____.

If some children can tell time using the terms *half-hour*, *quarter-past, quarter-to*, and so on, explain that those are ways of saying the "between" times.

▶ Introducing Telling Time to the Half-Hour

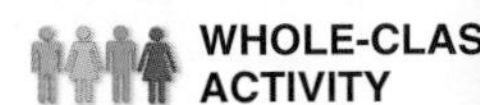

(*Math Journal 1*, p. 39)

Set your demonstration clock to 4 o'clock. Ask: *If I move the minute hand halfway around the clock, which direction will it be pointing?* Straight down

Ask children to watch the hour hand as you move the minute hand so that it is pointing straight down. Mention that the hour hand now points halfway between the 4 and the 5, so the time shown is between 4 o'clock and 5 o'clock. It is half an hour after 4 o'clock. We say that it is "**half-past** 4 o'clock," "half-past 4," or "four-thirty."

Use the following routine to practice telling time to the half-hour:

1. Show a time on the demonstration clock with the minute hand pointing straight down.
2. Have children show the same time on their tool-kit clocks.
3. Have children tell about what time is shown on the clock.

As a variation, give different times to the half-hour and ask children to show those times on their clocks. Mix in a few times on the hour.

NOTE Some children may benefit from a visual aid showing half of the clock face shaded as a representation of a half-hour.

Ongoing Assessment: Informing Instruction

Watch for children who are having trouble displaying times on their tool-kit clocks. Ask children what hour they are trying to display and have them set the hour hand. Then ask them if they are trying to show an *o'clock* (or *on-the-hour*) time or a *half-past* time. Help them position the minute hand accordingly.

When you feel that children have had sufficient practice, have them complete the journal page independently or with a partner. When children have completed the page, have them discuss how time to the hour looks different from time to the half-hour.

2 Ongoing Learning & Practice

▶ Playing *Penny-Nickel Exchange*

Children practice money skills by playing *Penny-Nickel Exchange.* For instructions, see Lesson 2-10.

▶ Math Boxes 3•7

(*Math Journal 1,* p. 40)

Mixed Practice Math Boxes in this lesson are paired with Math Boxes in Lesson 3-5. The skills in Problem 4 preview Unit 4 content.

Writing/Reasoning Have children draw, write, or verbalize an answer to the following: *How do you know if a number is even or odd?* A reasonable answer should include a reference to pairs or to skip counting by 2s.

ten is even because there is a half
to ten and all even nubers have a half

One child's work in response to the Writing/Reasoning prompt.

Ongoing Assessment: Recognizing Student Achievement

Math Boxes Problem 1

Use **Math Boxes, Problem 1** to assess children's ability to read a tally chart. Children are making adequate progress if they are able to answer the second question in Problem 1 correctly. Some children may be able to answer both questions correctly.

[Data and Chance Goal 2]

▶ Home Link 3•7

(*Math Masters,* pp. 70 and 71)

Home Connection Children practice telling time to the nearest hour and half-hour. Family members are asked to talk with children about the times of two daily events.

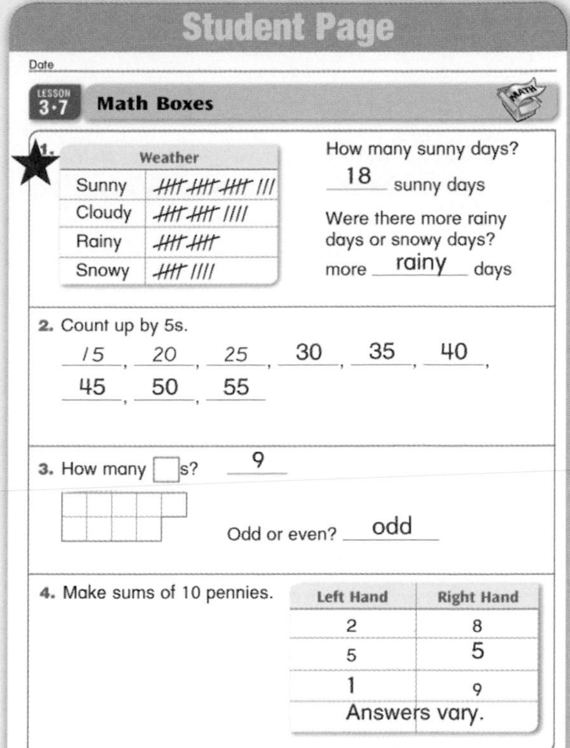

Student Page

Date

LESSON 3•7 **Math Boxes**

1. ★

Weather	
Sunny	~~HHHH~~ ~~HHHH~~ ~~HHHH~~ III
Cloudy	~~HHHH~~ ~~HHHH~~ IIII
Rainy	~~HHHH~~ ~~HHHH~~
Snowy	~~HHHH~~ IIII

How many sunny days? 18 sunny days

Were there more rainy days or snowy days? more rainy days

2. Count up by 5s.

15, 20, 25, 30, 35, 40, 45, 50, 55

3. How many □s? 9

Odd or even? odd

4. Make sums of 10 pennies.

Left Hand	Right Hand
2	8
5	5
1	9
Answers vary.	

Math Journal 1, p. 40

NOTE Use the activities in this lesson often during the next few weeks. Encourage children to set their tool-kit clocks to estimate the time of an activity during the day, such as recess, lunch, or music. Occasionally set the hour-hand-only display clock to match the hour hand on the classroom clock and call on children to estimate the time. Keep in mind that mastery of telling-time skills happens rapidly for some children and slowly for others.

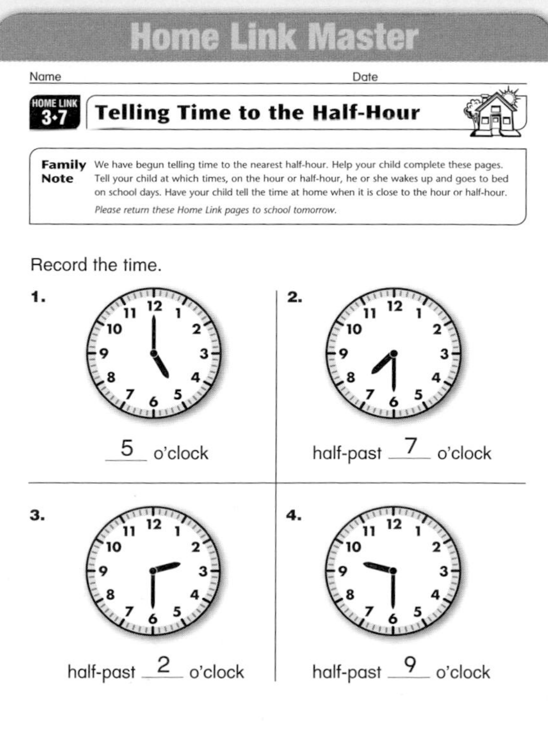

Home Link Master

Name Date

HOME LINK 3•7 **Telling Time to the Half-Hour**

Family Note We have begun telling time to the nearest half-hour. Help your child complete these pages. Tell your child at which times, on the hour or half-hour, he or she wakes up and goes to bed on school days. Have your child tell the time at home when it is close to the hour or half-hour.

Please return these Home Link pages to school tomorrow.

Record the time.

1. 5 o'clock

2. half-past 7 o'clock

3. half-past 2 o'clock

4. half-past 9 o'clock

Math Masters, p. 70

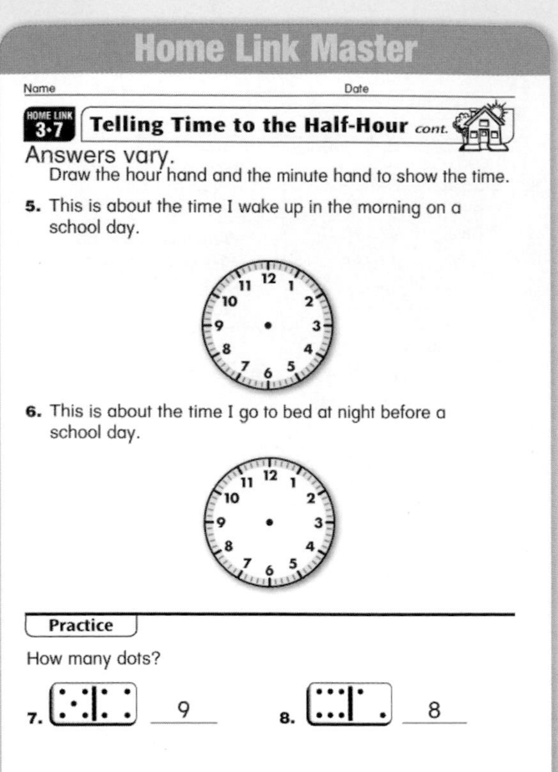

Home Link Master

Name Date

HOME LINK 3·7 **Telling Time to the Half-Hour** *cont.*

Answers vary.

Draw the hour hand and the minute hand to show the time.

5. This is about the time I wake up in the morning on a school day.

6. This is about the time I go to bed at night before a school day.

Practice

How many dots?

7. 9

8. 8

***Math Masters,* p. 71**

Hickory Dickory Dock

Hickory dickory dock,
The mouse ran up the clock;
The clock struck _____,
The mouse ran down;
Hickory dickory dock.

Repeat this verse with different times on the hour.

NOTE Remember to reserve time every day to complete the number-line, attendance, calendar, temperature, and weather routines.

3 Differentiation Options

READINESS

SMALL-GROUP ACTIVITY

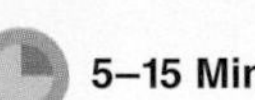

5–15 Min

▶ *Hickory Dickory Dock* with Clocks

To provide experience telling time to the hour, lead children in saying the familiar nursery rhyme, *Hickory Dickory Dock*. After each verse, have children show the time on their tool-kit clocks. You may want to use your demonstration clock and a mouse puppet to act out the rhyme as you say it.

ENRICHMENT

PARTNER ACTIVITY

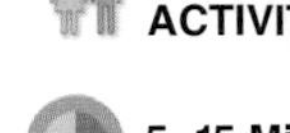

5–15 Min

▶ Ordering Clocks by Displayed Times

To further explore telling time, have children order clocks showing a variety of times. Give each partnership eight tool-kit clocks. For each clock, partners decide on a time and set the clock. When they have finished setting all eight clocks, they arrange them in order from earliest to latest. When clocks are set to half-past the hour, make sure the hour hand is set appropriately. Consider having children make index-card labels for the time shown on each clock.

ELL SUPPORT

SMALL-GROUP ACTIVITY

5–15 Min

▶ Describing Time

To provide language support for telling time, discuss with children why we use the words *half-past* to describe time when the minute hand points straight down. Emphasize how the minute hand has gone halfway around the clock and that the hour hand is half-way between two numbers on the clock. Consider putting two labels on your classroom clock—one above that says *o'clock* and one that says *half-past*. To build meaning for the term *half-past,* color the right half of a clock and show that the turn from 12 to 6 on the clock is half of a full turn.

3•8 Introduction to the Frames-and-Arrows Routine

Objective To introduce the Frames-and-Arrows routine.

Technology Resources www.everydaymathonline.com

ePresentations

eToolkit

Algorithms Practice

EM Facts Workshop Game™

Family Letters

Assessment Management

Common Core State Standards

Curriculum Focal Points

Interactive Teacher's Lesson Guide

1 Teaching the Lesson

Key Concepts and Skills

- Count forward and backward by 1s, 2s, 3s, 5s, and 10s from a given number. [Number and Numeration Goal 1]
- Find the missing numbers in a Frames-and-Arrows problem given the rule. [Patterns, Functions, and Algebra Goal 1]

Key Activities

Children are introduced to the Frames-and-Arrows routine. They complete Frames-and-Arrows diagrams in which the arrow rule and the first number are given.

Ongoing Assessment: Recognizing Student Achievement Use Mental Math and Reflexes. [Number and Numeration Goal 1]

Ongoing Assessment: Informing Instruction See page 221.

Key Vocabulary

Frames-and-Arrows diagram ◆ frame ◆ arrow ◆ arrow rule

Materials

Math Journal 1, p. 41 and inside back cover
Home Link 3•7
transparencies of *Math Masters,* pp. 65 and 308; transparency of *Math Masters,* p. 312 (optional) ◆ Class Number Line (optional)

2 Ongoing Learning & Practice

Practicing Telling Time

Math Masters, p. 72
Children practice telling time to the hour and half-hour.

Math Boxes 3•8

Math Journal 1, p. 42
Children practice and maintain skills through Math Box problems.

Home Link 3•8

Math Masters, pp. 73 and 74
Children practice and maintain skills through Home Link activities.

3 Differentiation Options

READINESS

Counting Patterns on the Number Line

Math Masters, p. 75
Children do number-line counts.

ENRICHMENT

Creating and Solving Frames-and-Arrows Problems

Math Masters, p. 312
Children create their own Frames-and-Arrows diagrams.

Advance Preparation

***Teacher's Reference Manual,* Grades 1–3** pp. 204–209

Getting Started

Mental Math and Reflexes ★

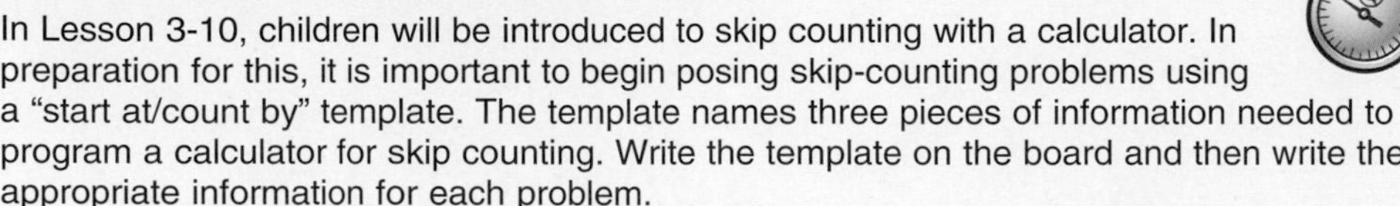

In Lesson 3-10, children will be introduced to skip counting with a calculator. In preparation for this, it is important to begin posing skip-counting problems using a "start at/count by" template. The template names three pieces of information needed to program a calculator for skip counting. Write the template on the board and then write the appropriate information for each problem.

Pose problems like the ones below. Children count in unison as they follow along on the number grid on the inside back cover of their journals.

Start at:	8	40	5
Count:	up	back	up
By:	2s	5s	3s

Home Link 3·7 Follow-Up

Briefly go over the answers.
You might ask children to report the times they usually wake up and go to bed on school days and then tally the results on the board.

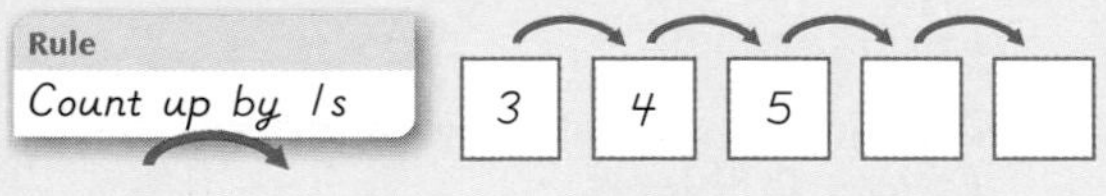

Ongoing Assessment: Recognizing Student Achievement

Mental Math and Reflexes ★

Use **Mental Math and Reflexes** to assess children's ability to count up and back from a given number. Children are making adequate progress if they are able to use a number grid to count up by 2s and back by 5s. Some children may be able to do so without a number grid.

[Number and Numeration Goal 1]

1 Teaching the Lesson

▶ Introducing the Frames-and-Arrows Routine

WHOLE-CLASS DISCUSSION

ELL

Algebraic Thinking Use a transparency of *Math Masters,* page 312 or draw a Frames-and-Arrows diagram on the board. (*See margin.*)

Discuss the following features of the diagram:

The diagram is called a **Frames-and-Arrows diagram.** Frames-and-Arrows diagrams consist of **frames,** or shapes, connected by **arrows** that show the path from one frame to the next. Each arrow represents a rule—**the arrow rule**—that determines which number goes in the next frame. Note that *frame* has everyday meanings, such as *picture frame* or *glass frame,* but also has a mathematical meaning. Likewise, the word *rule* has an everyday usage, such as classroom rules, and a mathematical usage. Discuss these differences to support English language learners.

Teaching Aid Master

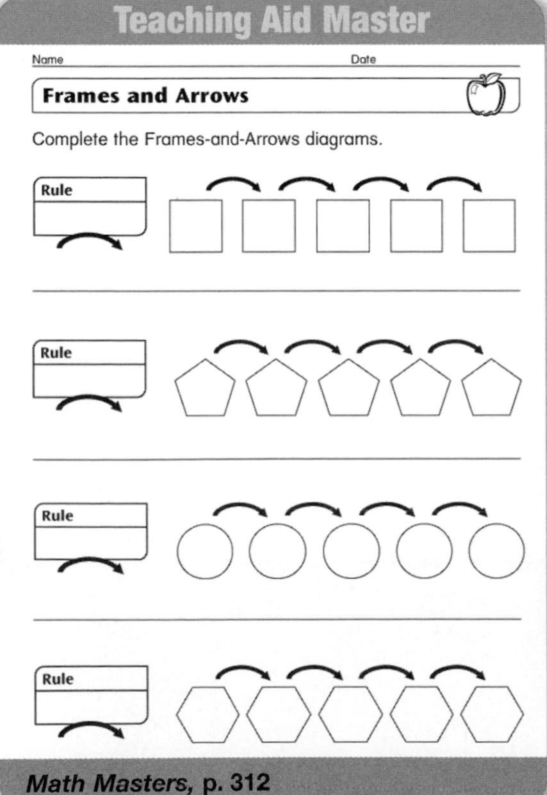
Name Date

Frames and Arrows

Complete the Frames-and-Arrows diagrams.

Rule

Rule

Rule

Rule

Math Masters, p. 312

In this particular diagram, the arrow rule is "Count up by 1s." Some of the frames have numbers in them; other frames are empty. To solve a Frames-and-Arrows problem, use the arrow rule to fill in the empty frames.

With the children's help, fill in the missing numbers in the empty frames. Explain that counting up by 1s is like adding 1 to each number to get the next number. Filling a blank frame in a Frames-and-Arrows diagram is like finding the unknown in a number model.

For example: $3 + 1 = \boxed{4}$, $4 + 1 = \boxed{5}$, $5 + 1 = \boxed{6}$, and so on. Another way to state the arrow rule for this diagram is "Add 1" or "+ 1."

Display the following Frames-and-Arrows diagram and ask children to help you fill in the missing numbers:

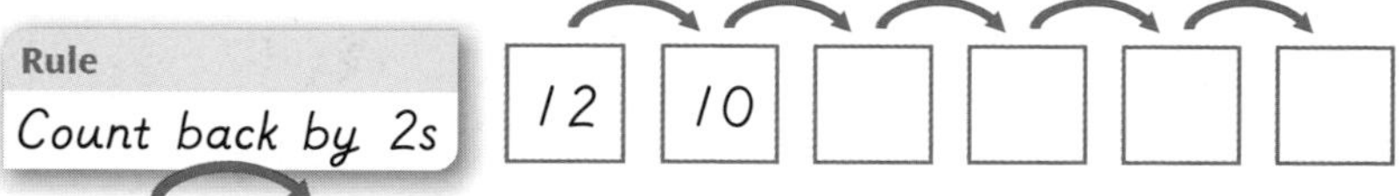

Mention that counting back by 2s is like subtracting 2 from each number to get the next number. Therefore, filling a blank frame is like finding the unknown in a number model.

For example: $12 - 2 = \boxed{10}$, $10 - 2 = \boxed{8}$, $8 - 2 = \boxed{6}$, and so on. Another way to state the arrow rule is "Subtract 2" or "– 2."

Repeat this routine with other problems. Keep the rules simple, and always provide the starting numbers. Children should use their number lines if necessary.

Ongoing Assessment: Informing Instruction

Watch for children who confuse the direction of the arrow in the rule box with the direction in which to count. The arrow in the rule box does not change direction. Remind children to pay close attention to the words, symbol, and number inside the rule box to help them decide which way to count.

Suggestions:

Rule	First Frames	Missing Frames
Count up by 1s	15, 16	17, 18,19
Count up by 2s	8, 10	12, 14, 16
Count back by 1s	15,14	13, 12, 11
Add 10	10, 20	30, 40, 50
Subtract 2	13, 11	9, 7, 5
* Count back by 5s	25, 20	15, 10, 5
* Subtract 3	18, 15	12, 9, 6

* Denotes a "Try This" problem

Adjusting the Activity

ELL

Use hops on the Class Number Line or on the number-line transparency of *Math Masters,* page 308, to count back by 2s as children follow on the number line on the inside back cover of their journals.

AUDITORY • KINESTHETIC • TACTILE • VISUAL

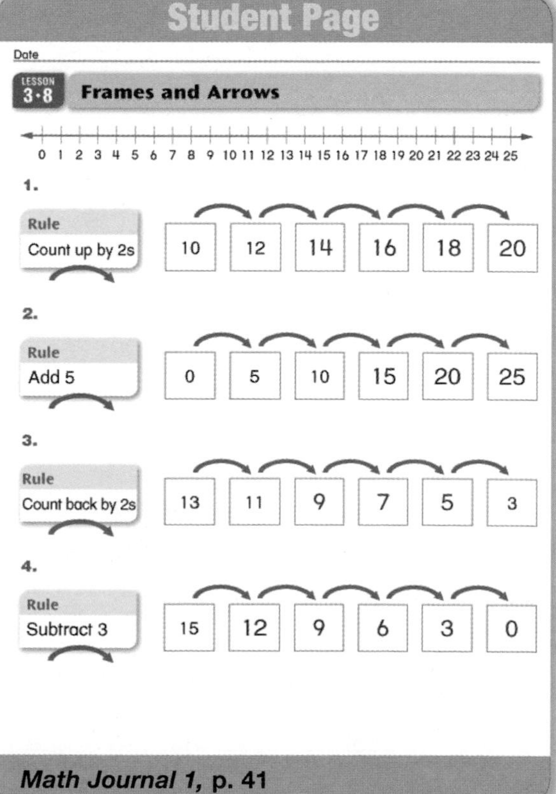

Student Page
Date
LESSON 3·8
Frames and Arrows
0 1 2 3 4 5 6 7 8 9 10 11 12 13 14 15 16 17 18 19 20 21 22 23 24 25
1.
Rule
Count up by 2s
10 12 14 16 18 20
2.
Rule
Add 5
0 5 10 15 20 25
3.
Rule
Count back by 2s
13 11 9 7 5 3
4.
Rule
Subtract 3
15 12 9 6 3 0

Math Journal 1, p. 41

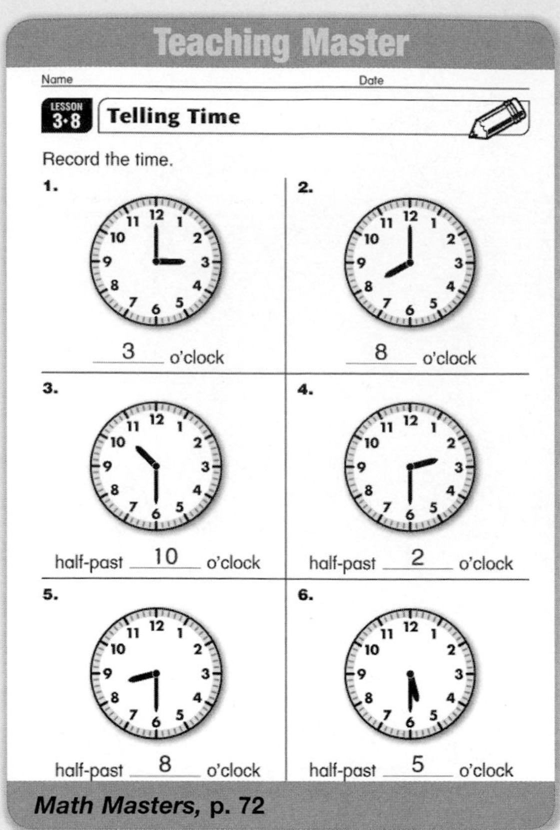

Teaching Master

Name Date

LESSON 3·8 **Telling Time**

Record the time.

1. 3 o'clock
2. 8 o'clock
3. half-past 10 o'clock
4. half-past 2 o'clock
5. half-past 8 o'clock
6. half-past 5 o'clock

Math Masters, p. 72

Ask children to make up Frames-and-Arrows problems for the class to solve.

NOTE This lesson focuses on the simplest kind of Frames-and-Arrows diagram, in which the rule is known and the first number is given.

Have children complete one or two problems in which they find the rule, given all of the numbers. *For example:*

▶ Solving Frames-and-Arrows Problems

(*Math Journal 1,* p. 41)

Algebraic Thinking Partners work together to solve the problems. Encourage children to help each other and check each other's work. They should use the number line to help them with the more difficult problems.

NOTE Remember to reserve time every day to complete the number-line, attendance, calendar, temperature, and weather routines.

2 Ongoing Learning & Practice

▶ Practicing Telling Time

(*Math Masters,* p. 72)

Use *Math Masters,* page 72 to provide more practice telling time to the hour and half-hour.

▶ Math Boxes 3·8

(*Math Journal 1,* p. 42)

Mixed Practice Math Boxes in this lesson are paired with Math Boxes in Lesson 3-6. The skills in Problem 4 preview Unit 4 content.

Writing/Reasoning Have children draw, write, or verbalize an answer to the following question: *Why is it important to use a calendar?* A reasonable answer should describe keeping track of time.

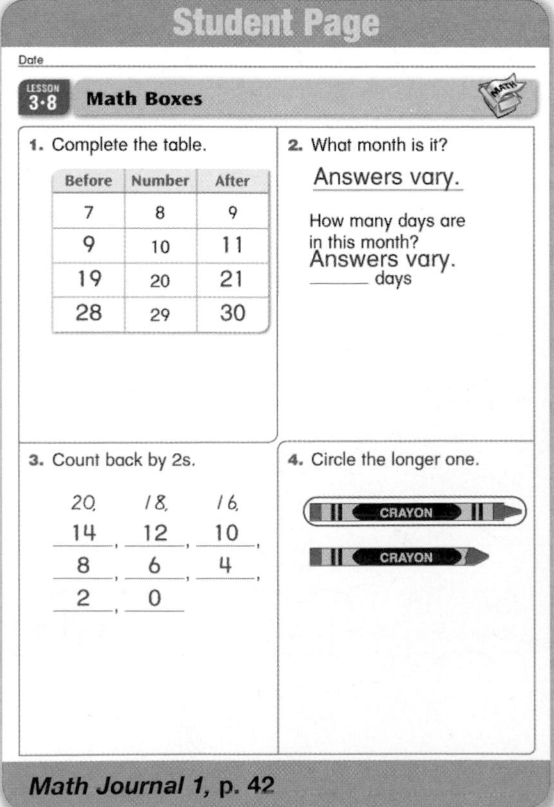

Student Page

Date

LESSON 3·8 **Math Boxes**

1. Complete the table.

Before	Number	After
7	8	9
9	10	11
19	20	21
28	29	30

2. What month is it?
Answers vary.

How many days are in this month?
Answers vary. days

3. Count back by 2s.
20, 18, 16, 14, 12, 10, 8, 6, 4, 2, 0

4. Circle the longer one.
CRAYON
CRAYON

Math Journal 1, p. 42

Home Link 3·8

(*Math Masters,* pp. 73 and 74)

INDEPENDENT ACTIVITY

Home Connection Children complete Frames-and-Arrows diagrams. An extended Family Note on the Home Link explains these diagrams.

3 Differentiation Options

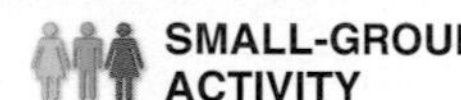

READINESS

SMALL-GROUP ACTIVITY

Counting Patterns on the Number Line

5–15 Min

(*Math Masters,* p. 75)

Algebraic Thinking To provide children with a visual model for how the Frames-and-Arrows sequences are related to counting on a number line, have children complete *Math Masters,* page 75. When children have finished the page, consider having them draw arrows to connect the circled numbers across the top of each number line with the "rule" (counting pattern) written above. Have children describe the counting patterns. For example, "When I count by 2s, I say 0, 2, 4, 6, 8, ..."

NOTE After children complete the page, you may wish to have them write the number word for each of the numbers they circled in Problem 1 at the bottom of the page.

ENRICHMENT

INDEPENDENT ACTIVITY

Creating and Solving Frames-and-Arrows Problems

5–15 Min

PROBLEM SOLVING

(*Math Masters,* p. 312)

Algebraic Thinking To apply children's understanding of Frames-and-Arrows problems, have children write their own Frames-and-Arrows problems in the diagrams on *Math Masters*, page 312. Encourage children to use creative rules and higher numbers to make the problems more challenging.

Planning Ahead

Before you begin Lesson 3-11, each child should bring 10 dimes to school.

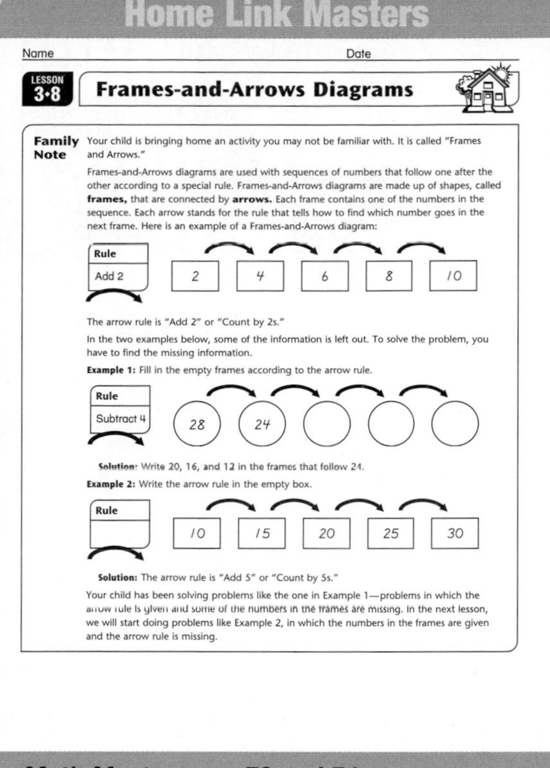

Home Link Masters

Name Date

LESSON 3·8 **Frames-and-Arrows Diagrams**

Family Note Your child is bringing home an activity you may not be familiar with. It is called "Frames and Arrows."

Frames-and-Arrows diagrams are used with sequences of numbers that follow one after the other according to a special rule. Frames-and-Arrows diagrams are made up of shapes, called **frames,** that are connected by **arrows.** Each frame contains one of the numbers in the sequence. Each arrow stands for the rule that tells how to find which number goes in the next frame. Here is an example of a Frames-and-Arrows diagram:

Rule: Add 2

2 → 4 → 6 → 8 → 10

The arrow rule is "Add 2" or "Count by 2s."

In the two examples below, some of the information is left out. To solve the problem, you have to find the missing information.

Example 1: Fill in the empty frames according to the arrow rule.

Rule: Subtract 4

28 → 24 → ☐ → ☐ → ☐

Solution: Write 20, 16, and 12 in the frames that follow 24.

Example 2: Write the arrow rule in the empty box.

Rule: ☐

10 → 15 → 20 → 25 → 30

Solution: The arrow rule is "Add 5" or "Count by 5s."

Your child has been solving problems like the one in Example 1—problems in which the arrow rule is given and some of the numbers in the frames are missing. In the next lesson, we will start doing problems like Example 2, in which the numbers in the frames are given and the arrow rule is missing.

Math Masters, pp. 73 and 74

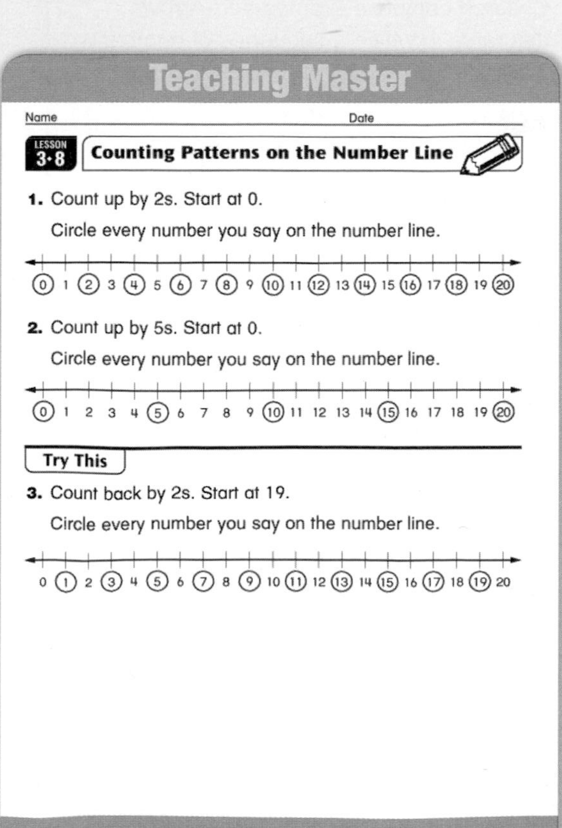

Teaching Master

Name Date

LESSON 3·8 **Counting Patterns on the Number Line**

1. Count up by 2s. Start at 0.

Circle every number you say on the number line.

(0) 1 (2) 3 (4) 5 (6) 7 (8) 9 (10) 11 (12) 13 (14) 15 (16) 17 (18) 19 (20)

2. Count up by 5s. Start at 0.

Circle every number you say on the number line.

(0) 1 2 3 4 (5) 6 7 8 9 (10) 11 12 13 14 (15) 16 17 18 19 (20)

Try This

3. Count back by 2s. Start at 19.

Circle every number you say on the number line.

0 (1) 2 (3) 4 (5) 6 (7) 8 (9) 10 (11) 12 (13) 14 (15) 16 (17) 18 (19) 20

Math Masters, p. 75

3•9 More Frames-and-Arrows Problems

Objective To introduce Frames-and-Arrows problems in which the "arrow rule" is missing.

Technology Resources www.everydaymathonline.com

ePresentations

eToolkit

Algorithms Practice

EM Facts Workshop Game™

Family Letters

Assessment Management

Common Core State Standards

Curriculum Focal Points

Interactive Teacher's Lesson Guide

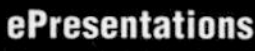

1 Teaching the Lesson

Key Concepts and Skills

- Count forward and backward by 1s, 2s, 3s, 5s, and 10s from a given number. [Number and Numeration Goal 1]
- Find the missing numbers in a Frames-and-Arrows problem given the rule. [Patterns, Functions, and Algebra Goal 1]
- Identify rules in Frames-and-Arrows problems. [Patterns, Functions, and Algebra Goal 1]
- Create Frames-and-Arrows problems. [Patterns, Functions, and Algebra Goal 1]

Key Activities

Children complete Frames-and-Arrows diagrams in which a sequence of numbers is given and they are to find the rule.

Ongoing Assessment: Informing Instruction See page 225.

Ongoing Assessment: Recognizing Student Achievement Use journal page 43. [Patterns, Functions, and Algebra Goal 1]

Materials

Math Journal 1, p. 43 and inside back cover
Home Link 3•8
Math Masters, pp. 336A and 336B
transparency of *Math Masters,* p. 312 (optional)

2 Ongoing Learning & Practice

Practicing Adding on the Number Grid
Math Masters, p. 76
Children practice adding on a number grid.

Math Boxes 3•9
Math Journal 1, p. 44
Children practice and maintain skills through Math Box problems.

Home Link 3•9
Math Masters, p. 77
Children practice and maintain skills through Home Link activities.

3 Differentiation Options

READINESS

Finding Patterns on the Number Line
Math Masters, p. 78; p. 312 (optional)
Children find patterns as they count on a number line.

ENRICHMENT

Making Frames-and-Arrows Diagrams from Skip-Counting Patterns
Math Masters, p. 79
Children skip count on a number grid and apply those numbers to Frames-and-Arrows.

Getting Started

Mental Math and Reflexes

Play *Ten-Frame Top-It.* See Lesson 2-3 for detailed instructions. Depending on children's comfort level with ten frames, you may wish to have children write the addition facts for their cards. For example, if a player's ten-frame card shows 7, the player would write 7 + 3 = 10 or 3 + 7 = 10.

Home Link 3·8 Follow-Up

Briefly go over the answers.

1 Teaching the Lesson

Finding the Arrow Rule

WHOLE-CLASS ACTIVITY

(*Math Masters,* p. 312)

Algebraic Thinking On the board, write a set of numbers that represents a simple skip count, such as 5, 10, 15, and 20. Ask children to be detectives and determine how many hops it takes to move from one number to the next. 5 Tell children that today they will be solving mystery problems like this one.

Begin by doing a few problems like those in Lesson 3-8, in which the rule and the first few numbers are given. You can use the suggestions given in the margin. (Write the problems on the board, or use a transparency of *Math Masters,* page 312.)

When you feel that children are ready, pose the following problem:

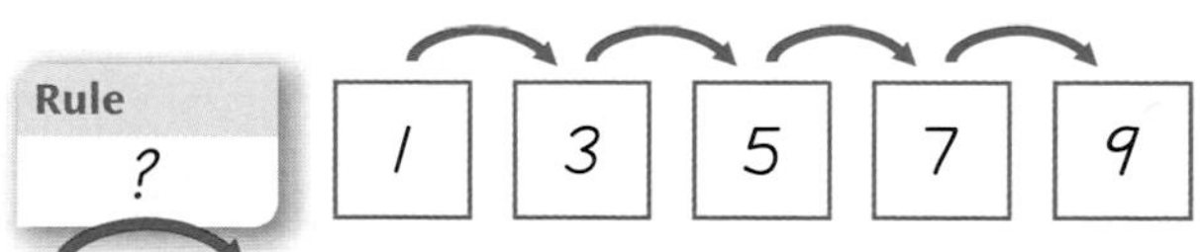

Ask children to guess the rule. Answers include "Count up by 2s," "Add 2," "2 more," and "+ 2." Encourage children to suggest various ways to state the rule.

Continue with other problems in which the rule is missing. (See the second set of suggestions in the margin.) Children should use the number grid on the inside back cover of their journals if they need help figuring out the rule or pattern.

Ongoing Assessment: Informing Instruction

Watch for children who have difficulty stating the rule. Encourage them to determine how many hops there are between two numbers by using the number grid. Record the number of hops in the rule box. Then help them determine if they are hopping up or back. Show them how to record this information with a + or − sign in the rule box.

Suggestions:

Rules	First Frames	Missing Frames
Count up by 2s	7, 9	11, 13, 15
Count back by 2s	12, 10	8, 6, 4
Add 3	4, 7	10, 13, 16
− 10	60, 50	40, 30, 20

NOTE Once children have determined that the numbers in the frames increase from left to right (indicating that you should add), you may wish to explain that finding the arrow rule is like finding the unknown number that makes these number models true.

$1 + \square = 3$

$3 + \square = 5$

$5 + \square = 7$

$7 + \square = 9$

Suggestions:

Frames	Missing Rules
2, 4, 6, 8, 10	Count up by 2s, or add 2
15, 14, 13, 12, 11	Count back by 1s, or subtract 1
3, 6, 9, 12, 15	Count up by 3s, or add 3
15, 13, 11, 9, 7	Count back by 2s, or subtract 2
20, 30, 40, 50, 60	Count up by 10s, or add 10

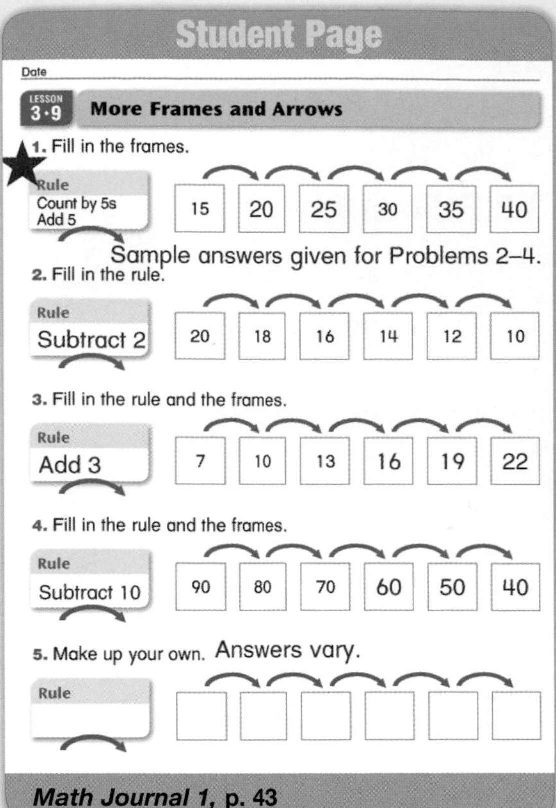
Student Page

Date

LESSON 3·9 **More Frames and Arrows**

1. Fill in the frames.

Rule: Count by 5s / Add 5 — 15, 20, 25, 30, 35, 40

Sample answers given for Problems 2–4.

2. Fill in the rule.

Rule: Subtract 2 — 20, 18, 16, 14, 12, 10

3. Fill in the rule and the frames.

Rule: Add 3 — 7, 10, 13, 16, 19, 22

4. Fill in the rule and the frames.

Rule: Subtract 10 — 90, 80, 70, 60, 50, 40

5. Make up your own. Answers vary.

Rule

Math Journal 1, p. 43

NOTE *Math Journal 1,* page 43, will be used again for the optional Enrichment activity in Lesson 3-10.

▶ Making up Frames-and-Arrows Problems

WHOLE-CLASS ACTIVITY

(*Math Masters,* p. 312)

Algebraic Thinking Ask children to make up their own Frames-and-Arrows problems. Since the simplest problems are those in which the rule and the first number are given, begin with these. Then encourage children to suggest more difficult problems.

Adjusting the Activity

Suggest that children make up problems in which the first frame is empty. This requires counting back to fill in the first frame.

AUDITORY ◆ KINESTHETIC ◆ TACTILE ◆ VISUAL

▶ Solving Frames-and-Arrows Problems

PARTNER ACTIVITY

(*Math Journal 1,* p. 43)

Algebraic Thinking Partners work together to solve the problems. Encourage children to help each other and to check each other's work. They should use a number grid to help them with the more difficult problems.

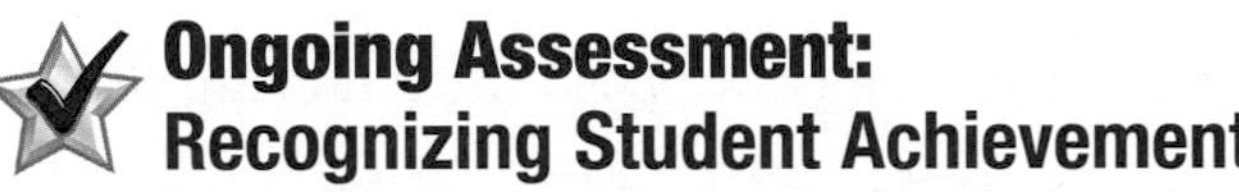

Ongoing Assessment: Recognizing Student Achievement

Journal Page 43 Problem 1

Use **journal page 43,** Problem 1 to assess children's understanding of Frames and Arrows. Children are making adequate progress if they are able to correctly answer Problem 1. Some children may be able to correctly answer more problems.

[Patterns, Functions and Algebra Goal 1]

2 Ongoing Learning & Practice

Practicing Adding on the Number Grid

INDEPENDENT ACTIVITY

(*Math Masters,* p. 76)

Use *Math Masters,* page 76 to provide additional practice adding on the number grid.

Math Boxes 3•9

INDEPENDENT ACTIVITY

(*Math Journal 1,* p. 44)

Mixed Practice Math Boxes in this lesson are paired with Math Boxes in Lesson 3-11. The skills in Problem 4 preview Unit 4 content.

Home Link 3•9

INDEPENDENT ACTIVITY

(*Math Masters,* p. 77)

Home Connection Children find the missing rules in Frames-and-Arrows problems.

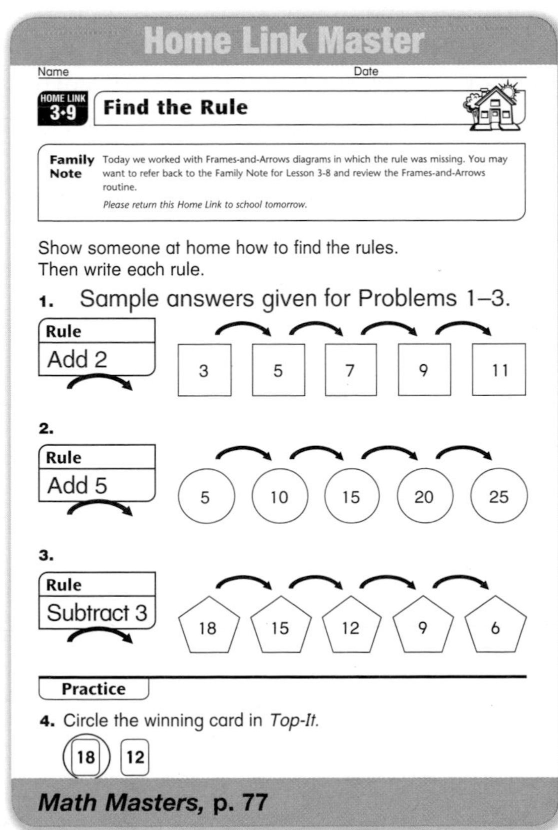

Home Link Master

Name Date

HOME LINK 3•9 **Find the Rule**

Family Note Today we worked with Frames-and-Arrows diagrams in which the rule was missing. You may want to refer back to the Family Note for Lesson 3-8 and review the Frames-and-Arrows routine.

Please return this Home Link to school tomorrow.

Show someone at home how to find the rules.
Then write each rule.

1. Sample answers given for Problems 1–3.

Rule: Add 2

3, 5, 7, 9, 11

2. Rule: Add 5

5, 10, 15, 20, 25

3. Rule: Subtract 3

18, 15, 12, 9, 6

Practice

4. Circle the winning card in *Top-It.*

(18) 12

Math Masters, p. 77

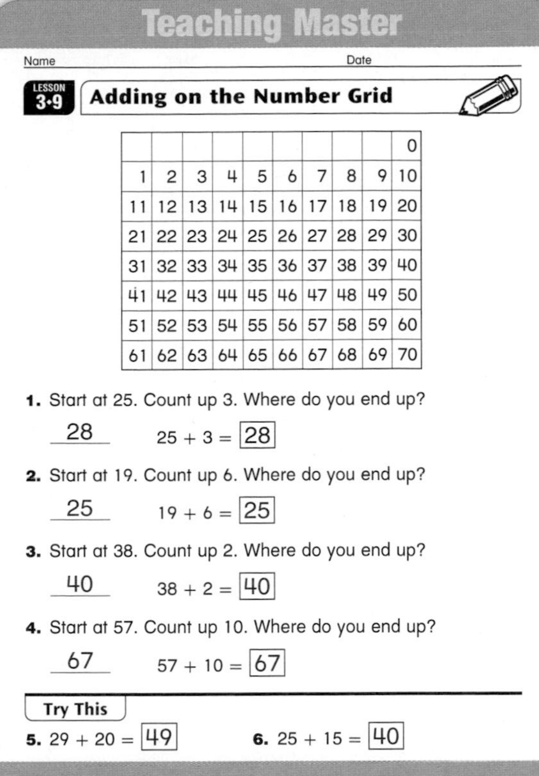

Teaching Master

Name Date

LESSON 3•9 **Adding on the Number Grid**

									0
1	2	3	4	5	6	7	8	9	10
11	12	13	14	15	16	17	18	19	20
21	22	23	24	25	26	27	28	29	30
31	32	33	34	35	36	37	38	39	40
41	42	43	44	45	46	47	48	49	50
51	52	53	54	55	56	57	58	59	60
61	62	63	64	65	66	67	68	69	70

1. Start at 25. Count up 3. Where do you end up?
28 $25 + 3 = 28$

2. Start at 19. Count up 6. Where do you end up?
25 $19 + 6 = 25$

3. Start at 38. Count up 2. Where do you end up?
40 $38 + 2 = 40$

4. Start at 57. Count up 10. Where do you end up?
67 $57 + 10 = 67$

Try This

5. $29 + 20 = 49$
6. $25 + 15 = 40$

Math Masters, p. 76

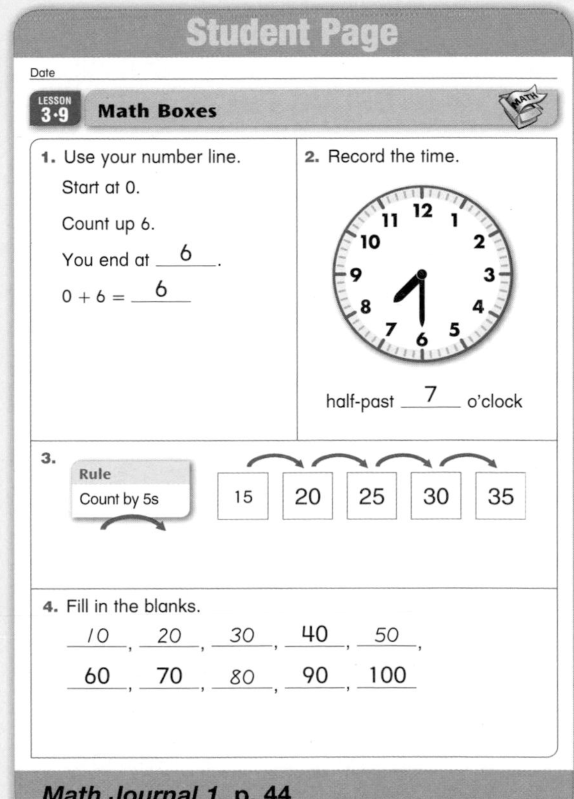

Student Page

Date

LESSON 3•9 **Math Boxes**

1. Use your number line.
Start at 0.
Count up 6.
You end at 6.
$0 + 6 = 6$

2. Record the time.
half-past 7 o'clock

3. Rule: Count by 5s
15, 20, 25, 30, 35

4. Fill in the blanks.
10, 20, 30, 40, 50,
60, 70, 80, 90, 100

Math Journal 1, p. 44

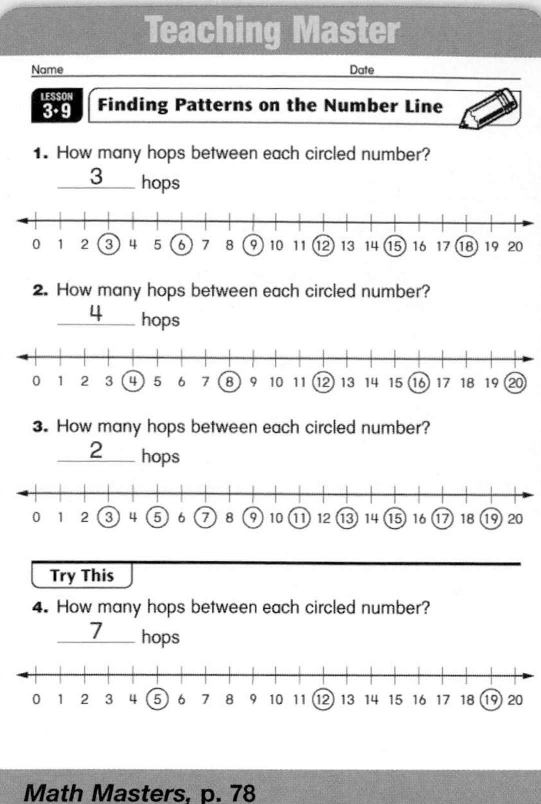

Teaching Master

Name Date

LESSON 3·9 **Finding Patterns on the Number Line**

1. How many hops between each circled number?
 3 hops

0 1 2 (3) 4 5 (6) 7 8 (9) 10 11 (12) 13 14 (15) 16 17 (18) 19 20

2. How many hops between each circled number?
 4 hops

0 1 2 3 (4) 5 6 7 (8) 9 10 11 (12) 13 14 15 (16) 17 18 19 (20)

3. How many hops between each circled number?
 2 hops

0 1 2 (3) 4 (5) 6 (7) 8 (9) 10 (11) 12 (13) 14 (15) 16 (17) 18 (19) 20

Try This

4. How many hops between each circled number?
 7 hops

0 1 2 3 4 (5) 6 7 8 9 10 11 (12) 13 14 15 16 17 18 (19) 20

Math Masters, p. 78

Teaching Master

Name Date

LESSON 3·9 **Number Grids and Frames and Arrows**

1. Fill in the number grid. Answers vary.
 Count by ____s. Color your number pattern on the grid.

Make your number pattern into a Frames-and-Arrows diagram.

Rule

2. Fill in the number grid.
 Count by ____s. Color your number pattern on the grid.

Make your number pattern into a Frames-and-Arrows diagram.

Rule

Math Masters, p. 79

3 Differentiation Options

READINESS

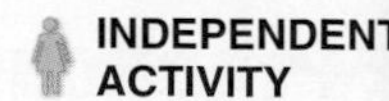

INDEPENDENT ACTIVITY

5–15 Min

▶ Finding Patterns on the Number Line

(*Math Masters,* p. 78)

Algebraic Thinking To provide children with a visual model for how to find the rule in Frames-and-Arrows sequences, have children count on a number line. Children complete *Math Masters,* page 78. When children have finished the page, share ideas on how to solve the problems and discuss which problem was the most difficult. Consider having children state rules for each problem. The rules could be to either add or subtract, depending on which direction children choose to move. Consider recording the problems as Frames-and-Arrows diagrams on *Math Masters,* page 312. Have children read the number of hops for each number line. For example, "There were three hops between the numbers on this number line."

ENRICHMENT

INDEPENDENT ACTIVITY

5–15 Min

▶ Making Frames-and-Arrows Diagrams from Skip-Counting Patterns

(*Math Masters,* p. 79)

Algebraic Thinking To further explore Frames-and-Arrows diagrams, have children complete Frames-and-Arrows diagrams for patterns on the number grid. Have children fill in each number-grid section on *Math Masters,* page 79 with a series of consecutive numbers. Invite them to shade a skip-counting pattern on the number-grid section. Challenge them to transfer their skip counting pattern into a Frames-and-Arrows diagram. Encourage children to repeat the process with a different section of the number grid.

3•10 Counting with a Calculator

Objective To introduce counting up and back on the calculator.

Technology Resources www.everydaymathonline.com

ePresentations

eToolkit

Algorithms Practice

EM Facts Workshop Game™

Family Letters

Assessment Management

Common Core State Standards

Curriculum Focal Points

Interactive Teacher's Lesson Guide

1 Teaching the Lesson

Key Concepts and Skills

- Count forward and backward by 1s, 2s, and 5s from a given number. [Number and Numeration Goal 1]
- Read numbers and symbols on a calculator. [Number and Numeration Goal 3]
- Use the +, −, and = symbols to count forward and backward on a calculator. [Patterns, Functions, and Algebra Goal 2]

Key Activities

Children learn to count up and back using a calculator.

Ongoing Assessment: Recognizing Student Achievement Use Mental Math and Reflexes. [Number and Numeration Goal 1]

Ongoing Assessment: Informing Instruction See page 232.

Key Vocabulary

program

Materials

Home Link 3•9
calculator ◆ overhead nickels and pennies (optional) ◆ overhead calculator (optional)

2 Ongoing Learning & Practice

Playing *Penny-Nickel Exchange*
per partnership: 20 pennies and 10 nickels, die (using a second die is optional)
Children practice skip counting with money.

Finding Sums of Three Numbers
Math Masters, p. 305
per partnership: 3 dice
Children practice adding three 1-digit numbers.

Math Boxes 3•10
Math Journal 1, p. 45
Children practice and maintain skills through Math Box problems.

Home Link 3•10
Math Masters, p. 80
Children practice and maintain skills through Home Link activities.

Minute Math+
Minute Math®+, pp. 10 and 46
Children practice addition and subtraction concepts.

3 Differentiation Options

ENRICHMENT

Checking Frames-and-Arrows Problems with a Calculator
Math Journal 1, p. 43
calculator
Children use their calculators to check solutions to Frames-and-Arrows problems.

EXTRA PRACTICE

Skip Counting
Math Masters, p. 68
Children practice skip counting by counting up and back on number lines.

Advance Preparation

Two calculator programs are included in this lesson. Before you begin this lesson, decide which program you should teach based on the calculators available at your school. You should only present one program.

***Teacher's Reference Manual,* Grades 1–3** pp. 114, 115

Getting Started

Mental Math and Reflexes

Do "stop-and-start" counts by 5s, and then by 1s. Count by 5s beginning with 0. Stop at 25. Then continue counting by 1s to 29.

Put a collection of pennies and nickels on the overhead (or draw them on the board). Count them in unison, first counting the nickels by 5s and then counting the pennies by 1s. Repeat as time allows.

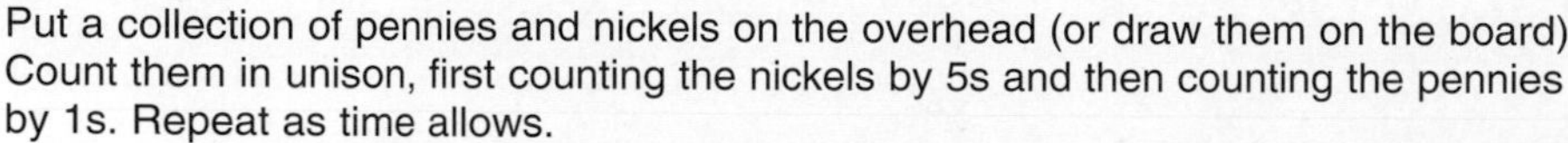

Home Link 3·9 Follow-Up

Children share strategies for figuring out the missing rules.

Ongoing Assessment: Recognizing Student Achievement

Mental Math and Reflexes ★

Use **Mental Math and Reflexes** to assess children's ability to count by 5s and then by 1s. Children are making adequate progress if they are able to count on by 1s after they have stopped counting by 5s. Some children will be able to make the counting transition more easily than others.

[Number and Numeration Goal 1]

1 Teaching the Lesson

▶ Counting Up and Back with a Calculator

WHOLE-CLASS ACTIVITY

Tell children that they are going to learn how to use a calculator to count.

Review some of the basic rules for using calculators:

▷ Do not drop or throw calculators.

▷ It is easier to use a calculator when it is on a firm, flat surface.

▷ Press the middle of a key to make sure that only one key is pressed at a time. Discuss the various meanings of the word *key* and the meaning in this context.

▷ Use only your finger to press a key.

Write the following information on the board:

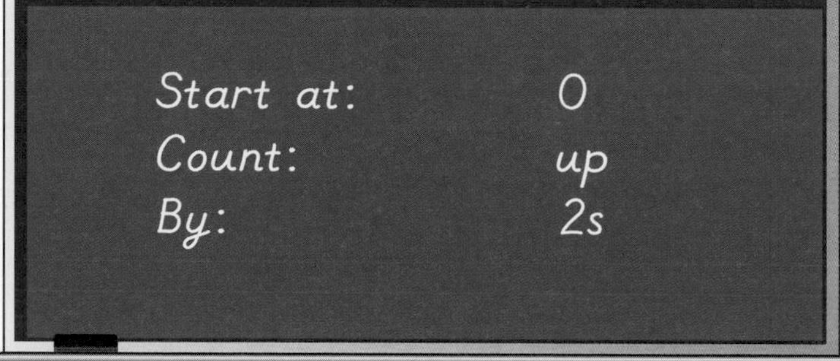

NOTE Most basic four-function calculators provide for counting up and back. Read the instruction manual for the calculator that your class is using for a description of the counting (constant) function.

Before you use the calculator to count, you must **program** it, or get it ready to count. Discuss the various meanings of the word *program* and the meaning in this context. Describe how to program the calculator to count up by 2s, as children follow along on their calculators. You may find it helpful to use an overhead calculator. Use the program that follows if your class is using the TI–108.

1. Press ON/C. This clears your calculator.
2. Press 0. This is the *starting number.*
3. Press the + key. This tells the calculator to count *up*.
4. Press 2. This tells the calculator to *count by 2s.*

Now the calculator is ready to start counting by 2s. Direct the class to do the following:

- Without clearing your calculator, press the = key. Which number is in the calculator display? 2
- Without clearing your calculator, press the = key again. Which number is in the display now? 4
- Continue to press the = key. (Each time, the class calls out the number in the display.)

Repeat the procedure, this time counting up by 5s, starting at 0. Write the following information on the board:

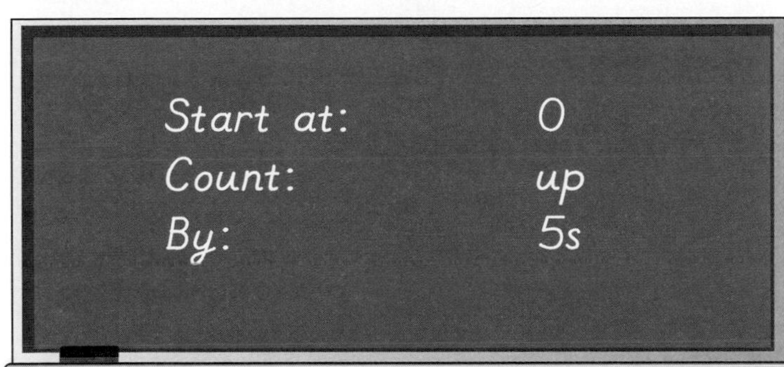

Have a volunteer describe how to program the calculator to count by 5s, as the class follows along.

Next, write the information for counting back by 1s, starting at 12, on the board:

Start at: 12
Count: back
By: 1s

NOTE Different calculators may have different programs for counting. If your class is using the Casio SL-450L, use the program that follows.

1. Press the AC key to clear the calculator.
2. Press the count up number, in this case 2.
3. Press + + to tell the calculator to count up.
4. Press the start number, in this case 0.
5. Press the = key to run the program.

You may enter a new starting number and the = key, and the calculator will continue to count by 2s.

To count back, press − −.

NOTE Some people find it helpful to use the nonwriting hand for calculator keying while keeping the writing hand available for recording. In a playful, challenging way, see if children can do the counts using their nonwriting hands.

Adjusting the Activity

Describe what happens when you press the [=] *key again after 0 has been displayed.* You get –1 Do this several times. *What are these numbers called?* Negative numbers

AUDITORY ◆ KINESTHETIC ◆ TACTILE ◆ VISUAL

Describe how to program a calculator to count back. Use the steps taught on page 231, but press [−] instead of [+].

Ask: *How is programming the calculator to count up different from programming it to count back?* To count up, press the [+] key; to count back, press the [−] key.

Do a few more counts back from a given number on the calculator.

▶ Counting Up, Starting from Any Number

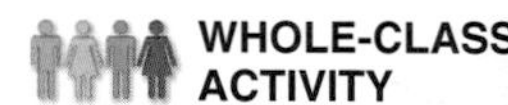

Ask someone to supply the information for counting up by 2s, starting at 5. Write it on the board, as follows:

Start at: 5
Count: up
By: 2s

Give children a couple of minutes to program their calculators to do this count. Children should press the [=] key a few times to check that they have programmed their calculators correctly. Have a volunteer describe what he or she did as the class follows along. Ask: *How is programming the calculator to count up from 5 different from programming it to count up from 0?* 5 is used as your start number rather than 0.

Do a few more counts up, starting with numbers other than 0.

Ongoing Assessment: Informing Instruction

Watch for children who do not clear their calculators before starting a new count.

2 Ongoing Learning & Practice

▶ Playing *Penny-Nickel Exchange*

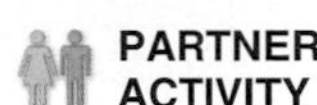

Children practice skip counting with money by playing *Penny-Nickel Exchange.* For detailed instructions, see Lesson 2-10.

▶ Finding Sums of Three Numbers

(*Math Masters,* p. 305)

Provide pairs of children with 3 dice. Children take turns rolling the dice, writing addition number sentences representing the dots shown, and finding the sums.

6 + 6 + 5 = 17

For one roll, have children draw the faces of the 3 dice and write the number model on an Exit Slip (*Math Masters,* page 305). Ask: *Would the sum be the same if you added the numbers in a different order?* Sample answer: Yes, it does not matter which order you add the numbers; you will still get the same sum.

▶ Math Boxes 3·10

INDEPENDENT ACTIVITY

(*Math Journal 1,* p. 45)

Mixed Practice Math Boxes in this lesson are paired with Math Boxes in Lesson 3-13. The skills in Problem 4 preview Unit 4 content.

Writing/Reasoning Have children draw, write, or verbalize an answer to the following question: *How do you find a missing number to make a sum of 10?* A reasonable answer should describe an addition strategy such as using 10 pennies or counting on a number line.

▶ Home Link 3·10

(*Math Masters,* p. 80)

Home Connection Children determine dime exchanges. They are asked to bring 10 dimes to school to add to their tool-kit coin collections.

▶ *Minute Math+*

Use *Minute Math+,* pages 10 and 46, to provide more practice with easy addition and subtraction concepts.

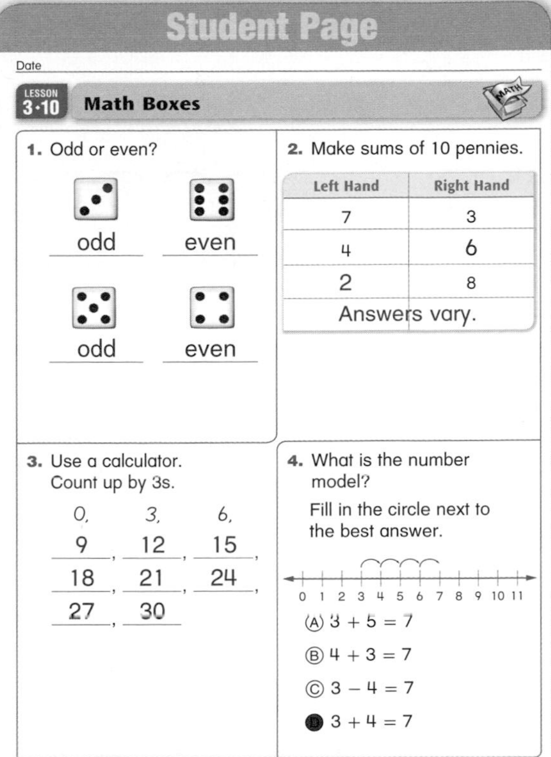

Student Page

Date

LESSON 3·10 **Math Boxes**

1. Odd or even?

odd · even · odd · even

2. Make sums of 10 pennies.

Left Hand	Right Hand
7	3
4	6
2	8
Answers vary.	

3. Use a calculator. Count up by 3s.

0, 3, 6, 9, 12, 15, 18, 21, 24, 27, 30

4. What is the number model?

Fill in the circle next to the best answer.

0 1 2 3 4 5 6 7 8 9 10 11

Ⓐ 3 + 5 = 7
Ⓑ 4 + 3 = 7
Ⓒ 3 − 4 = 7
● 3 + 4 = 7

Math Journal 1, p. 45

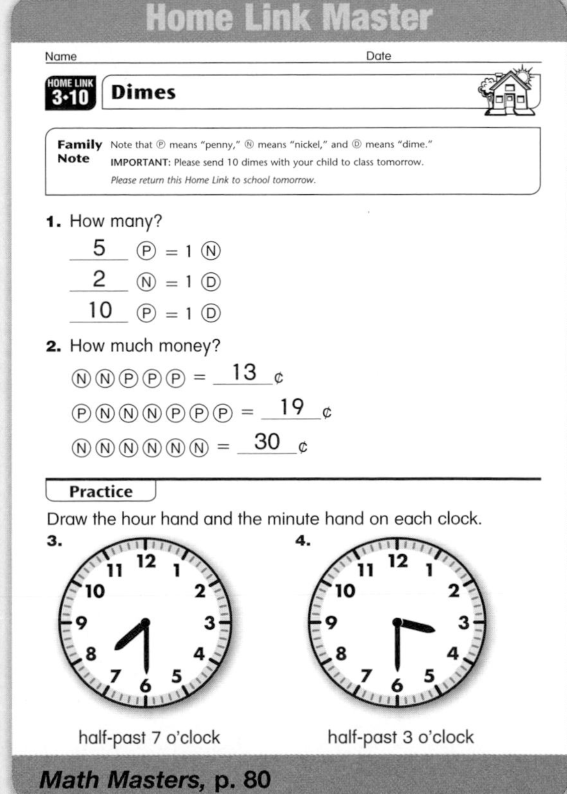

Home Link Master

Name Date

HOME LINK 3·10 **Dimes**

Family Note Note that Ⓟ means "penny," Ⓝ means "nickel," and Ⓓ means "dime."
IMPORTANT: Please send 10 dimes with your child to class tomorrow.
Please return this Home Link to school tomorrow.

1. How many?

5 Ⓟ = 1 Ⓝ
2 Ⓝ = 1 Ⓓ
10 Ⓟ = 1 Ⓓ

2. How much money?

ⓃⓃⓅⓅⓅ = 13 ¢
ⓅⓃⓃⓃⓅⓅⓅ = 19 ¢
ⓃⓃⓃⓃⓃⓃ = 30 ¢

Practice

Draw the hour hand and the minute hand on each clock.

3. half-past 7 o'clock

4. half-past 3 o'clock

Math Masters, p. 80

Student Page

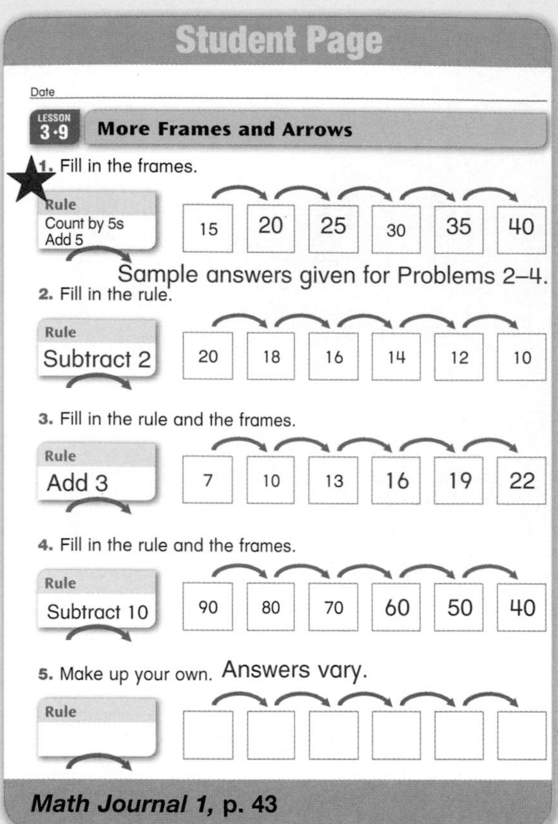
Date

LESSON 3·9 More Frames and Arrows

1. Fill in the frames.

Rule						
Count by 5s Add 5	15	20	25	30	35	40

Sample answers given for Problems 2–4.

2. Fill in the rule.

Rule						
Subtract 2	20	18	16	14	12	10

3. Fill in the rule and the frames.

Rule						
Add 3	7	10	13	16	19	22

4. Fill in the rule and the frames.

Rule						
Subtract 10	90	80	70	60	50	40

5. Make up your own. Answers vary.

Rule						

Math Journal 1, p. 43

NOTE Remember to allow time for the Mental Math and Reflexes routine every day. The skills addressed will help to develop children's problem-solving skills.

Teaching Master

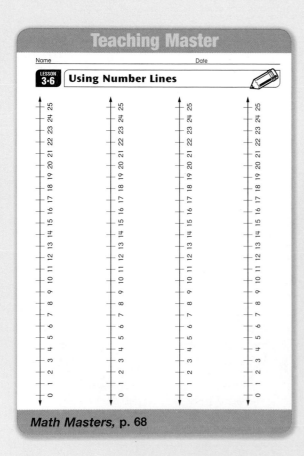

Name Date

LESSON 3·6 Using Number Lines

0 1 2 3 4 5 6 7 8 9 10 11 12 13 14 15 16 17 18 19 20 21 22 23 24 25

0 1 2 3 4 5 6 7 8 9 10 11 12 13 14 15 16 17 18 19 20 21 22 23 24 25

0 1 2 3 4 5 6 7 8 9 10 11 12 13 14 15 16 17 18 19 20 21 22 23 24 25

0 1 2 3 4 5 6 7 8 9 10 11 12 13 14 15 16 17 18 19 20 21 22 23 24 25

Math Masters, p. 68

3 Differentiation Options

ENRICHMENT

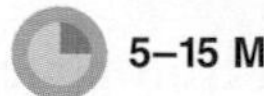
INDEPENDENT ACTIVITY

5–15 Min

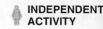

▶ Checking Frames-and-Arrows Problems with a Calculator

(*Math Journal 1,* p. 43)

Algebraic Thinking To further explore calculators, children use their calculators to check the Frames-and-Arrows problems on journal page 43. The first frame tells children which number to start with; the rule tells whether to enter [+] or [−] and which number to enter and count by.

EXTRA PRACTICE

INDEPENDENT ACTIVITY

5–15 Min

▶ Skip Counting

(*Math Masters,* p. 68)

Have children count up and back on number lines to practice skip counting. For each number line, give oral directions to children telling them what to count by and whether to count up or back.

3•11 Dimes

Objectives To introduce the dime; to introduce dollars-and-cents notation; and to provide practice exchanging pennies, nickels, and dimes.

Technology Resources www.everydaymathonline.com

ePresentations

eToolkit

Algorithms Practice

EM Facts Workshop Game™

Family Letters

Assessment Management

Common Core State Standards

Curriculum Focal Points

Interactive Teacher's Lesson Guide

1 Teaching the Lesson

Key Concepts and Skills

- Count forward by 1s, 5s, and 10s from a given number.
  [Number and Numeration Goal 1]
- Identify a dime and know its value.
  [Measurement and Reference Frames Goal 2]
- Show equivalent amounts of money.
  [Measurement and Reference Frames Goal 2]
- Exchange pennies for nickels and dimes.
  [Measurement and Reference Frames Goal 2]

Key Activities

Children explore dimes. They figure out how much money the class would have if each child had a dime. They write the total using dollars-and-cents notation. They exchange tool-kit pennies for nickels and dimes.

Ongoing Assessment: Informing Instruction See page 236.

Ongoing Assessment: Recognizing Student Achievement Use journal page 46.
[Measurement and Reference Frames Goal 2]

Key Vocabulary

dime ◆ dollars-and-cents notation ◆ decimal point

Materials

Math Journal 1, p. 46
Home Link 3•10
slate ◆ counters (optional) ◆ 10 dimes per child ◆ Story of Money Poster ◆ tool-kit coins ◆ overhead coins (optional) ◆ calculator (optional)

2 Ongoing Learning & Practice

Playing *Coin Top-It*
per partnership: tool-kit coins, money cards from Lesson 2-13
Children practice counting and comparing money amounts.

Math Boxes 3•11
Math Journal 1, p. 47
Children practice and maintain skills through Math Box problems.

Home Link 3•11
Math Masters, pp. 81 and 82
Children practice and maintain skills through Home Link activities.

3 Differentiation Options

READINESS
Doing Stop-and-Start Counting
Children do stop-and-start counting by 10s, 5s, and 1s using their fingers and hands.

EXTRA PRACTICE
Minute Math+
Minute Math®+, pp. 65–67
Children practice making money exchanges and finding coin equivalencies.

ELL SUPPORT
Building a Math Word Bank
Differentiation Handbook, p. 126
Children add the terms *dime,* Ⓓ, *10¢*, and *$0.10* to their Math Word Banks.

Advance Preparation

For Part 1, display the Story of Money Poster. (See Lesson 2•8.) Each child will need 10 dimes to add to their tool kits. Have extras available for children who did not bring any to school.

***Teacher's Reference Manual,* Grades 1–3** pp. 18, 84–90, 163–165

Getting Started

Mental Math and Reflexes

Today's Mental Math and Reflexes activity may take longer than usual. Take the time necessary to complete it. It is an important part of the problem-solving strand in *Everyday Mathematics*.

Tell parts-and-total number stories. Have children solve them any way they can (using counters, pictures, and so on) and write the answers on their slates. Have children share solution strategies after each problem. Summarize each solution by drawing a parts-and-total diagram on the board, *but only after children have had a chance to share what they did to solve the problem.*

Total	
13	
Part	Part
8	5

Suggestions:

●○○ Brooke walked 8 blocks to meet Andrea on her way to school. Then Brooke walked another 5 blocks to school. How many blocks did Brooke walk in all? 13 blocks

●●○ Lupe read 10 books in April. She read 10 more books in May. How many books did Lupe read altogether? 20 books

●●● Rich needs 12 balloons for his class party. He already has 4 balloons. How many more balloons does Rich need for the class party? 8 balloons

Children can use counters to model the problems or you may ask children to write number models for the problems.

Home Link 3·10 Follow-Up

Briefly go over the answers.

NOTE *Everyday Mathematics* approaches addition and subtraction according to the situations in which the operations are used. Most addition and subtraction situations can be categorized as parts-and-total, change, or comparison situations. Parts-and-total situations are also known as "putting together" or "taking apart" situations. There are two types of change situations: change-to-more and change-to-less. Change-to-more situations are also known as "adding to" situations; change-to-less situations are also known as "taking from" situations. Read more about addition and subtraction situations in the *Teacher's Reference Manual,* pages 84 through 89. With repeated practice and exposure, children will learn to solve all different types of number stories, though they are not expected to categorize number stories in first grade.

Story of Money

	Penny 1¢ \$0.01	Nickel 5¢ \$0.05	Dime 10¢ \$0.10		
Heads	Head of Lincoln	Head of Jefferson	Head of Roosevelt		
Tails	Lincoln Memorial	Monticello	Torch with Olive and Oak Branches		
Equivalencies	None	5 Ⓟ	10 Ⓟ 2 Ⓝ		

1 Teaching the Lesson

▶ Introducing Dollars-and-Cents Notation

Tell children that a **dime** is worth 10 cents. Ask them how many nickels they would get in exchange for 1 dime. 2 nickels For 2 dimes? 4 nickels

Fill in the Dime column on your Story of Money Poster. (*See margin.*)

NOTE *Cents* is an interesting word because it has several homonyms, for example, *scents* and *sense.* Clarify the meaning of *cents* in this context.

Language Arts Link Explain that the word *dime* comes from the Latin word *decima,* which means *tenth.* Ask children if they know other words that have the same root. Sample answers: *decade, decimeter, decibel, and decimal.*

Ongoing Assessment: Informing Instruction

Watch for children who think that larger coins have greater values. It may be helpful to point out the different sizes of coins and reinforce the idea that even though the dime is the smallest coin in size, it is worth more than a penny and a nickel.

NOTE A dime is a metal sandwich—the coating is a combination of nickel and copper; the middle is copper. Franklin Roosevelt, who is pictured on the HEADS side, was president from 1933 until he died in 1945.

Links to the Future

In this lesson, the examples are limited to amounts that are 1 dollar or more. In the next lesson, dollars-and-cents notation for amounts that are less than 1 dollar will be introduced. Do not expect children to be proficient with dollars-and-cents notation. This is their first exposure to recording amounts using this notation. Reading and writing amounts using dollars-and-cents notation is a Grade 2 Goal.

Pose the following problem: *If every child in our class had one dime, how much money would our class have in all?*

To solve the problem, have the class count by 10s (10 cents, 20 cents, 30 cents, ...), with each child saying one of the 10-counts, until all children have had a turn. You might point to the numbers on the number grid (as high as it goes) as you do this count. Children have not yet had much experience with counts over 100, so some children may falter as the count gets higher.

Start the count again. This time, when children get to 100 cents, tell them to say "1 dollar," since there are 100 cents in 1 dollar. As they continue, instead of saying "110 cents," they say "1 dollar and 10 cents," and so on.

Record both final counts on the board: 250 cents = 2 dollars and 50 cents (or whichever amount applies to your class). Then write the final amount using **dollars-and-cents notation:** $2.50. Discuss how to interpret this notation:

▷ The symbol "$" stands for the word *dollar.*

▷ The dot (or period) after the 2 is called a **decimal point.**

▷ The number before the decimal point shows the number of dollars; the numbers after the decimal point show the number of cents.

Ask children to suggest things that cost about that much money.

NOTE You may wish to demonstrate how to enter this amount in a calculator. Tell children: *Clear the calculator. Then press 2 (.) 50.*

Write several amounts greater than one dollar in dollars-and-cents notation on the board. Have children read the amounts and enter them into their calculators. Remind them to clear their calculators before they enter each new amount.

Exchanging Pennies and Nickels for Dimes

WHOLE-CLASS ACTIVITY

(*Math Journal 1,* p. 46)

Do the following activity with children:

1. Draw 3 nickels on the board using Ⓝ to represent each nickel.
2. Have children take out 3 nickels from their tool-kits and arrange them into two groups: 2 nickels in one group and 1 nickel in the other. (Model this with overhead coins, if available.)

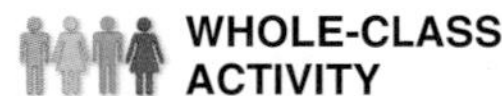

Social Studies Link Discuss with children the monetary systems found in other countries. Encourage class members who are familiar with coins from other countries to share their experiences. (For information on foreign currency, consult a world almanac or the business section of a Sunday newspaper.)

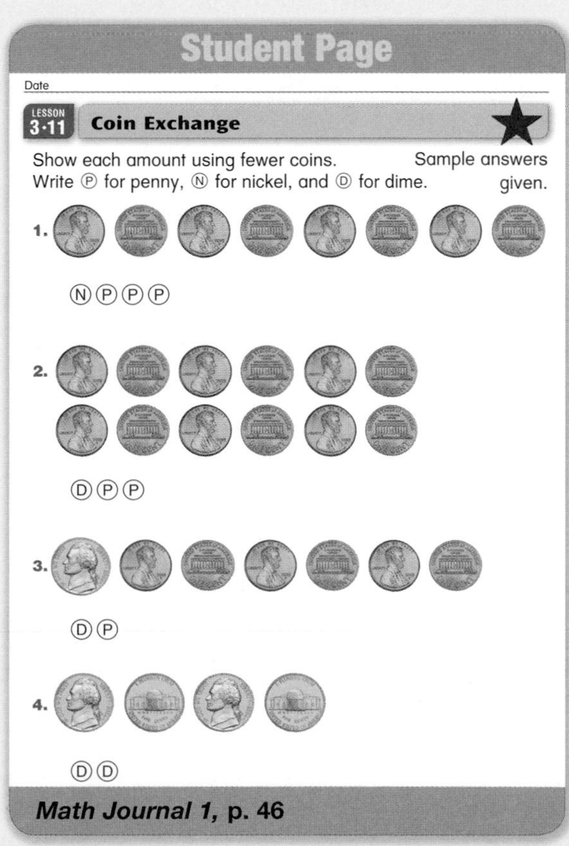
Student Page

Date

LESSON 3·11 Coin Exchange

Show each amount using fewer coins. Write Ⓟ for penny, Ⓝ for nickel, and Ⓓ for dime. Sample answers given.

1. ⓃⓅⓅⓅ

2. ⒹⓅⓅ

3. ⒹⓅ

4. ⒹⒹ

Math Journal 1, p. 46

3. Next, have children exchange 2 of the nickels for 1 dime.

4. On the board, draw a Ⓓ under the two nickels to represent 1 dime and draw 1 Ⓝ next to it. Explain that 1 dime and 1 nickel are worth the same amount as 3 nickels, or 15 cents. Point to the dime and the nickel as you count together: 10 cents, 15 cents.

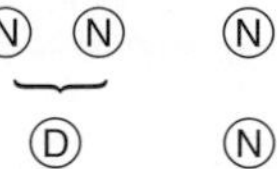

5. Next, draw 18 pennies on the board using Ⓟ to represent each penny.

6. Have children take out 18 pennies. Ask them to show how they would pay for something that costs 18 cents using fewer coins. 1 dime, 1 nickel, 3 pennies

7. If children show an exchange that does not consist of the fewest number of coins, ask them whether they can exchange any more pennies for nickels or any more nickels for dimes.

8. Draw a diagram like the one shown below to summarize the exchange, and point to the coins as you count together: *10 cents, 15 cents, 16 cents, 17 cents, 18 cents.*

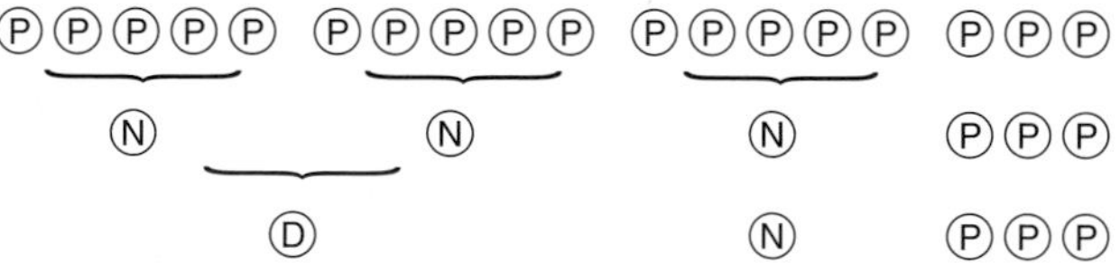

Do a few more examples with the class, as needed. Children then work independently or in partnerships to complete the journal page.

Ongoing Assessment: Recognizing Student Achievement

Journal Page 46

Use **journal page 46** to assess children's ability to make exchanges between coins. Children are making adequate progress if they make at least 1 exchange for each problem. Some children will be able to show each amount with the fewest possible number of coins.

[Measurement and Reference Frames Goal 2]

Adjusting the Activity

ELL

Have children model the problems and make exchanges using their tool-kit coins. Encourage them to keep their coins grouped according to value, as you did in your examples.

AUDITORY • KINESTHETIC • TACTILE • VISUAL

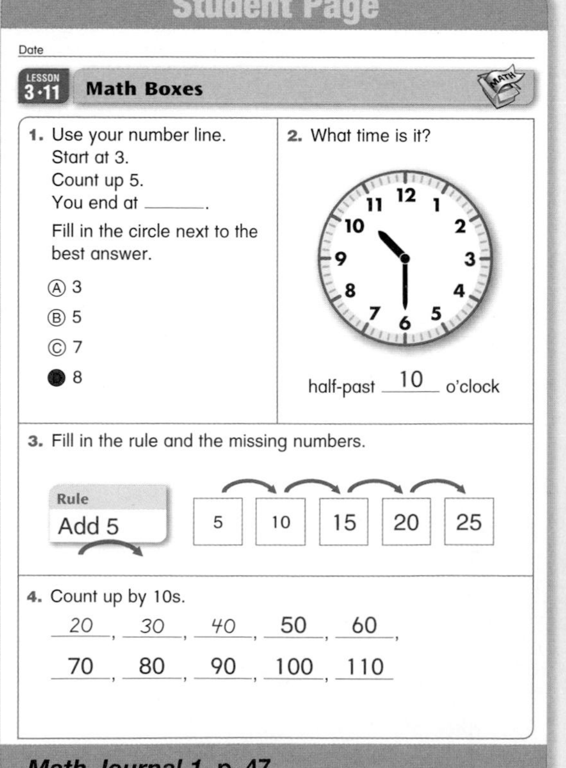

Student Page

Date

LESSON 3·11 **Math Boxes**

1. Use your number line.
Start at 3.
Count up 5.
You end at ____.
Fill in the circle next to the best answer.
Ⓐ 3
Ⓑ 5
Ⓒ 7
● 8

2. What time is it?
half-past 10 o'clock

3. Fill in the rule and the missing numbers.
Rule: Add 5
5, 10, 15, 20, 25

4. Count up by 10s.
20, 30, 40, 50, 60,
70, 80, 90, 100, 110

Math Journal 1, p. 47

2 Ongoing Learning & Practice

▸ Playing *Coin Top-It*

PARTNER ACTIVITY

Children practice counting and comparing money amounts by playing *Coin Top-It.* For instructions, see Lesson 2-13. Adjust the level of difficulty by adding cards with harder coin combinations to the deck, including those with dimes.

▸ Math Boxes 3•11

INDEPENDENT ACTIVITY

(*Math Journal 1,* p. 47)

Mixed Practice Math Boxes in this lesson are paired with Math Boxes in Lesson 3-9. The Skills in Problem 4 preview Unit 4 content.

Writing/Reasoning Have children draw, write, or verbalize an answer to the following: *How do you find the missing numbers in a Frames-and-Arrows problem?* A reasonable answer should include a reference to skip counting by 5s. Sample answer: I got my number grid out. And I know that 5, 10 is the beginning of counting by 5s.

▸ Home Link 3•11

INDEPENDENT ACTIVITY

(*Math Masters,* pp. 81 and 82)

Home Connection Children practice exchanging pennies for nickels and dimes and finding the fewest number of coins for a given amount.

3 Differentiation Options

READINESS

▸ Doing Stop-and-Start Counting

SMALL-GROUP ACTIVITY

5–15 Min

ELL

To provide experience with counting by 10s, then 5s, and finally 1s, have children use fingers as a concrete model of counts. Tell them that they will be doing *high tens, high fives,* and *high ones*. To support English language learners, model the meaning of *high five*. A *high ten* is a *high five* that uses two hands. Have children sit in a circle. Ask children to be ready to give you a *high ten* as you come to them. As you give *high tens,* count by 10s: *10, 20, 30, 40.* Continue around the circle again giving *high 5s* while counting by 5s: *45, 50, 55, 60.* Finally, continue around the circle again giving *high ones* while counting by 1s to arrive at a final sum: *61, 62, 63, 64.*

Home Link Master

Name ______ Date ______

HOME LINK 3•11 **Coin Exchanges**

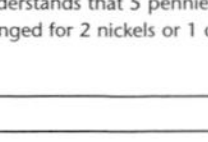

Family Note First graders do not always know how to represent a given amount of money with the fewest number of coins. At this stage, it is important that your child understands that 5 pennies can be exchanged for 1 nickel and that 10 pennies can be exchanged for 2 nickels or 1 dime.

Please return this Home Link to school tomorrow.

1 cent 1¢ Ⓟ	5 cents 5¢ Ⓝ	10 cents 10¢ Ⓓ

1. Tell or show someone at home how many dimes you get for 4 nickels. ⒹⒹ

Show each amount below using the fewest coins. Use Ⓟ, Ⓝ, and Ⓓ.

(*Hint:* Exchange pennies for nickels and nickels for dimes.) Then write how much the coins are worth.

Example: ⓅⓅⓅⓅⓅⓅ is the same as ⓃⓅ.

This is 6 cents.

2. ⓅⓅⓅⓅⓅⓅⓅⓅⓅⓅ is the same as Ⓓ.

This is 10 cents.

Math Masters, p. 81

Home Link Master

Name ______ Date ______

HOME LINK 3•11 **Coin Exchanges** *continued*

3. ⓅⓅⓅⓅⓅⓅⓅⓅⓅⓅⓅⓅ is the same as ⒹⓅⓅ.

This is 12 cents.

4. ⓃⓅⓅⓅⓅⓅⓅⓅⓅⓅ is the same as ⒹⓅⓅⓅⓅ.

This is 14 cents.

5. ⓃⓃⓃⓅⓅⓅⓅⓅⓅⓅⓅⓅⓅ is the same as ⒹⒹⓃ.

This is 25 cents.

6. ⓃⓅⓃⓅⓃⓅⓅⓅ is the same as ⒹⒹ.

This is 20 cents.

Practice

Fill in the missing numbers.

7. 10, 20, 30, 40, 50, 60, 70, 80

Math Masters, p. 82

EXTRA PRACTICE

▶ *Minute Math+*

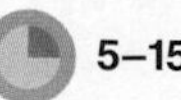

Use *Minute Math+,* pages 65–67, to provide practice making exchanges and finding coin equivalences.

ELL SUPPORT

SMALL-GROUP ACTIVITY

▶ Building a Math Word Bank

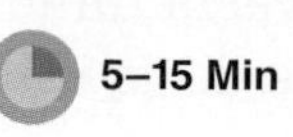

(*Differentiation Handbook,* p. 126)

To provide language support for coins, have children use the Word Bank Template found on *Differentiation Handbook,* page 126. Ask children to write the terms *dime,* Ⓓ, *10¢,* and *$0.10;* draw pictures representing the terms; and write other words that describe them. If you have a coin stamp, have children stamp their pages with the dime stamp. See the *Differentiation Handbook* for more information.

3·12 Counting Dimes, Nickels, and Pennies

Objective To provide practice finding the values of collections of dimes, nickels, and pennies.

Technology Resources www.everydaymathonline.com

Presentations

eToolkit

Algorithms Practice

EM Facts Workshop Game™

Family Letters

Assessment Management

Common Core State Standards

Curriculum Focal Points

Interactive Teacher's Lesson Guide

1 Teaching the Lesson

Key Concepts and Skills

- Count forward by 1s, 5s, and 10s from a given number. [Number and Numeration Goal 1]
- Find the values of combinations of dimes, nickels, and pennies. [Operations and Computation Goal 2]
- Exchange nickels for dimes, and pennies for nickels and dimes. [Measurement and Reference Frames Goal 2]
- Show amounts of money with the fewest number of dimes, nickels, and pennies. [Measurement and Reference Frames Goal 2]

Key Activities

Children count collections of dimes, nickels, and pennies.

Ongoing Assessment: Recognizing Student Achievement Use Mental Math and Reflexes. [Operations and Computation Goal 4]

Ongoing Assessment: Informing Instruction See page 243.

Materials

Math Journal 1, p. 48
Home Link 3·11
tool-kit coins ◆ overhead coins (optional) ◆ slate

2 Ongoing Learning & Practice

Playing *Coin-Dice*
per partnership: tool-kit coins, 2 dice
Children practice making money exchanges.

Math Boxes 3·12
Math Journal 1, p. 49
Children practice and maintain skills through Math Box problems.

Home Link 3·12
Math Masters, p. 83
Children practice and maintain skills through Home Link activities.

Minute Math+
Minute Math®+, pp. 69 and 70
Children practice counting money.

3 Differentiation Options

READINESS

Counting Collections of the Same Kind of Coin
tool-kit coins ◆ slate
Children find the values of coin groups of the same type.

ENRICHMENT

Exchanging Coins
Math Masters, p. 84
Children show amounts of money using the fewest coins.

Getting Started

Mental Math and Reflexes ★

Tell parts-and-total number stories. Children solve them any way they can and write the answers on their slates. Have children share solution strategies after each problem. Summarize each solution by drawing a parts-and-total diagram on the board, *but only after children have had a chance to share what they did to solve the problem.* If children are doing well, challenge them to write number models for the problems.

●○○ Megan's cat had 4 female kittens and 4 male kittens. How many kittens did Megan's cat have in all? 8 kittens; 4 + 4 = 8

●●○ Jake and Theresa were playing *Penny Grab* with 14 pennies. Jake grabbed some pennies. Theresa was left with 6 pennies. How many pennies did Jake grab? 8 pennies; 14 – 8 = 6 or 6 + 8 = 14

●●● Kareem had some toy cars. His sister took 7 of his toy cars. Kareem has 4 cars left. How many toy cars did Kareem have before his sister took some of them? 11 toy cars; 11 – 7 = 4 or 7 + 4 = 11

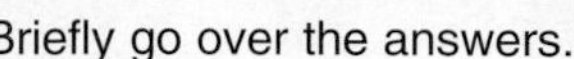

Home Link 3·11 Follow-Up

Briefly go over the answers.

Ongoing Assessment: Recognizing Student Achievement

Mental Math and Reflexes ★

Use **Mental Math and Reflexes** to assess children's ability to solve parts-and-total number stories. Children are making adequate progress if they are able to answer the first problem correctly. Some children may be able to answer all three problems correctly.

[Operations and Computation Goal 4]

1 Teaching the Lesson

▶ Counting Combinations of Dimes, Nickels, and Pennies

To review counting nickels and pennies:

1. Have four children come up to the front of the room, each bringing a nickel.
2. Have three children join them, each bringing a penny.
3. Have the seven children form a line, with the "nickels" at the left end of the line (facing the rest of the class), followed by the "pennies." The "nickels" hold up 5 fingers each and the "pennies" hold up 1 finger each.
4. Walk behind the children and, starting with the "nickels," tap each one on the head as the class counts together. 5, 10, 15, 20, 21, 22, 23
5. Draw Ⓝ Ⓝ Ⓝ Ⓝ Ⓟ Ⓟ Ⓟ on the board. Write 23¢ next to th coin drawings. Then write the same amount using dollars-and cents notation: \$0.23. The 0 before the decimal point shows that there are 0 dollars. \$0.23 is read *23 cents.*

Adjusting the Activity

Do this routine using dimes and pennies and then do an example using dimes and nickels before doing the routine with all three kinds of coins.

AUDITORY ◆ KINESTHETIC ◆ TACTILE ◆ VISUAL

To introduce counting dimes, nickels, and pennies:

1. Have three children come up to the front of the room, each bringing a dime.
2. Have two children come up, each bringing a nickel.
3. Have four children come up, each bringing a penny.
4. Have the nine children form a line, with the "dimes" at the left end of the line followed by the "nickels," and then the "pennies." The "dimes" hold up 10 fingers each, the "nickels" 5 fingers each, and the "pennies" 1 finger each.
5. Walk behind the children and tap each one on the head as the class counts together. 10, 20, 30, 35, 40, 41, 42, 43, 44
6. Draw Ⓓ Ⓓ Ⓓ Ⓝ Ⓝ Ⓟ Ⓟ Ⓟ Ⓟ on the board. Write 44¢ next to the coin drawings. Ask: *How would you write 44¢ in dollars-and-cents notation?* $0.44

More Counting Combinations of Dimes, Nickels, and Pennies

(*Math Journal 1,* p. 48)

Use overhead pennies, nickels, and dimes, if they are available, or draw the coins on the board. Children count their own coins and write the total value of each combination on their slates. Write the answers on the board. Children then count the coins in unison.

Suggestions:

- What is the value of 4 dimes and 3 pennies? 43¢ (Count: *10 cents, 20 cents, 30 cents, 40 cents, 41 cents, 42 cents, 43 cents*)
- What is the value of 2 dimes and 2 nickels? 30¢ (Count: *10 cents, 20 cents, 25 cents, 30 cents*)
- What is the value of 3 dimes, 1 nickel, and 2 pennies? 37¢ (Count: *10 cents, 20 cents, 30 cents, 35 cents, 36 cents, 37 cents*)
- What is the value of 2 dimes, 3 nickels, and 7 pennies? 42¢ (Count: *10 cents, 20 cents, 25 cents, 30 cents, 35 cents, 36 cents, 37 cents, 38 cents, 39 cents, 40 cents, 41 cents, 42 cents*)

Do more problems like these, as needed. Children then work independently or in partnerships to complete the journal page. They should use coins to model the problems.

Briefly go over the answers.

Ongoing Assessment: Informing Instruction

Watch for children who have difficulty finding the total value of penny, nickel, and dime combinations. Encourage children to sort the coins into separate piles before beginning to determine the total value. When children begin counting, they should start by counting the coins with the highest value.

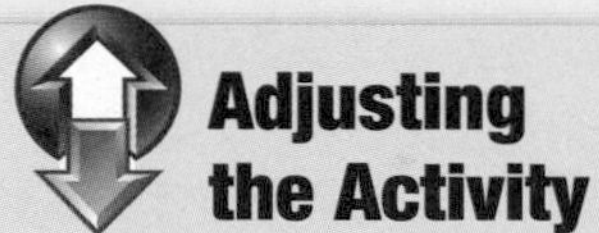

Adjusting the Activity

ELL

Have children write the amount that each coin is worth above or below the coin and/or show the value of each coin by drawing tally marks.

AUDITORY ◆ KINESTHETIC ◆ TACTILE ◆ VISUAL

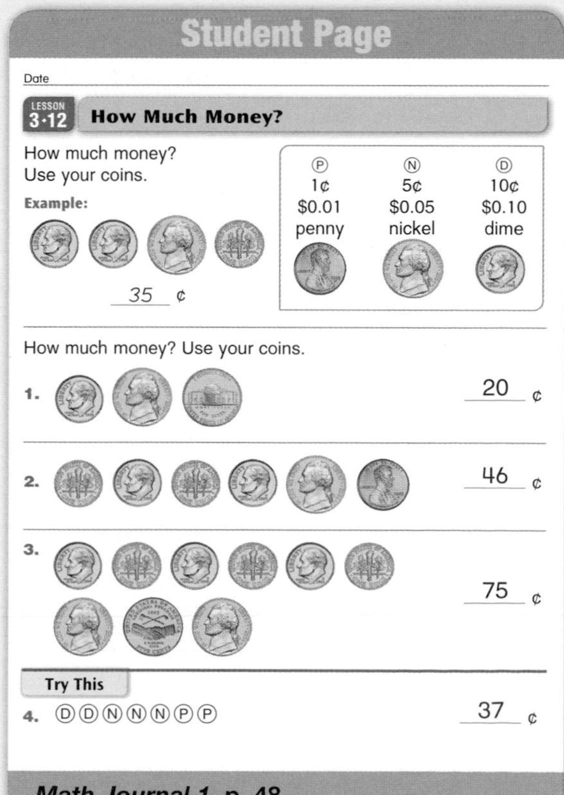

Student Page

Date

LESSON 3·12 How Much Money?

How much money?
Use your coins.

Example:

35 ¢

Ⓟ	Ⓝ	Ⓓ
1¢	5¢	10¢
$0.01	$0.05	$0.10
penny	nickel	dime

How much money? Use your coins.

1. 20 ¢
2. 46 ¢
3. 75 ¢

Try This

4. ⒹⒹⓃⓃⓃⓅⓅ 37 ¢

Math Journal 1, p. 48

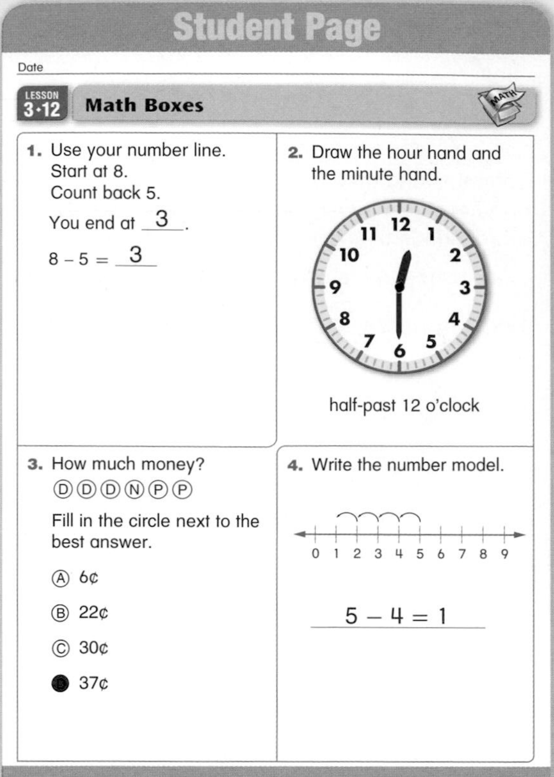

Student Page

Date

LESSON 3·12 **Math Boxes**

1. Use your number line. Start at 8. Count back 5.
You end at 3.
8 − 5 = 3

2. Draw the hour hand and the minute hand.
half-past 12 o'clock

3. How much money?
ⒹⒹⒹⓃⓅⓅ
Fill in the circle next to the best answer.
Ⓐ 6¢
Ⓑ 22¢
Ⓒ 30¢
● 37¢

4. Write the number model.
0 1 2 3 4 5 6 7 8 9
5 − 4 = 1

Math Journal 1, p. 49

REMINDER Remember to reserve time every day to complete the number-line, attendance, calendar, temperature, and weather routines.

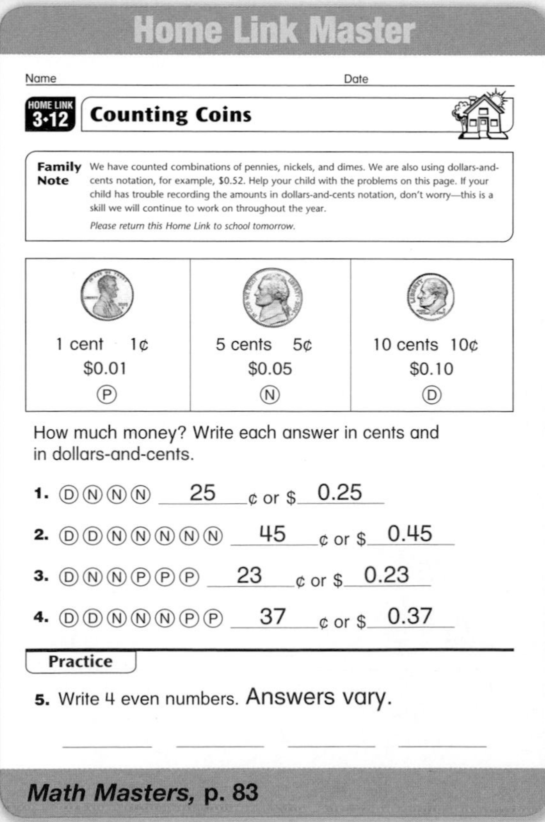

Home Link Master

Name Date

HOME LINK 3·12 **Counting Coins**

Family Note We have counted combinations of pennies, nickels, and dimes. We are also using dollars-and-cents notation, for example, $0.52. Help your child with the problems on this page. If your child has trouble recording the amounts in dollars-and-cents notation, don't worry—this is a skill we will continue to work on throughout the year.

Please return this Home Link to school tomorrow.

1 cent 1¢ $0.01 Ⓟ	5 cents 5¢ $0.05 Ⓝ	10 cents 10¢ $0.10 Ⓓ

How much money? Write each answer in cents and in dollars-and-cents.

1. ⒹⓃⓃⓃ 25 ¢ or $ 0.25
2. ⒹⒹⓃⓃⓃⓃⓃ 45 ¢ or $ 0.45
3. ⒹⓃⓃⓅⓅⓅ 23 ¢ or $ 0.23
4. ⒹⒹⓃⓃⓃⓅⓅ 37 ¢ or $ 0.37

Practice

5. Write 4 even numbers. Answers vary.

Math Masters, p. 83

2 Ongoing Learning & Practice

▶ Playing *Coin-Dice*

Directions

1. Partners pool their tool-kit coins.
2. Partners take turns rolling two dice and picking up as many pennies as the total number on the two dice.
3. Each player makes exchanges at the end of his or her turn—5 pennies for 1 nickel, 2 nickels for 1 dime, or 10 pennies for 1 dime.
4. To pick up the last coins, the total number on the two dice must match the total value of the remaining coins.

Play a variation of *Coin-Dice* where children only use pennies and nickels.

▶ Math Boxes 3·12

(*Math Journal 1,* p. 49)

Mixed Practice Math Boxes in this lesson are paired with Math Boxes in Lesson 3-14. The skills in Problem 4 preview Unit 4 content.

▶ Home Link 3·12

(*Math Masters,* p. 83)

Home Connection Children calculate the values of various combinations of pennies, nickels, and dimes and record their answers using dollars-and-cents notation.

▶ *Minute Math+*

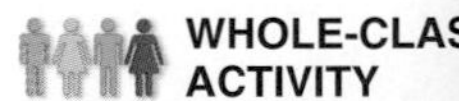

Use *Minute Math+*, pages 69 and 70, to provide more practice counting money.

3 Differentiation Options

READINESS

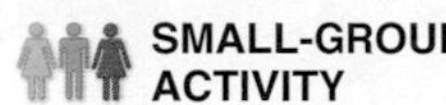

SMALL-GROUP ACTIVITY

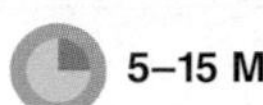

5–15 Min

Counting Collections of the Same Kind of Coin

To provide experience with coin values, have children count collections of the same kind of coin. Children record the total value. They might begin by counting a collection of pennies and then recording the total value in cents notation on their slates.

Continue to practice using different collections. *Suggestions:*

- What is the value of 12 pennies? 12¢
- What is the value of 3 nickels? 15¢
- What is the value of 4 dimes? 40¢

ENRICHMENT

INDEPENDENT ACTIVITY

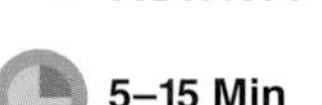

5–15 Min

Exchanging Coins

(*Math Masters,* p. 84)

To further explore counting coins, children make exchanges for collections of coins on *Math Masters,* page 84. Remind children that in order to show an amount with the fewest number of coins, they must make all possible exchanges. Encourage children to describe their coin combinations by telling the names of the coins and their value.

Planning Ahead

In Lesson 3-14, children need the dominoes from *Math Journal 1,* Activity Sheets 4 and 5. Children's dominoes may be stored in resealable plastic bags with their identification numbers on them. It is worthwhile to provide each child with his or her own set of dominoes since dominoes are valuable tools for memorizing basic addition facts.

Teaching Master

Name ______ Date ______

LESSON 3·12 **Coin Exchange**

Use (D), (N), and (P) to show each amount using the fewest possible coins.

1. (P) (P) (N) (P) (P) (P) (D)	2. (D) (N) (P) (N) (N) (P) (D)(D)(N)(P)(P)	3. (P) (D) (N) (P) (N) (P) (N) (D) (D)(D)(D)(N) (P)(P)(P)
4. (N) (N) (N) (N) (N) (N) (N) (P) (N) (D)(D)(D)(D)(P)	5. (N) (N) (N) (N) (D) (D) (P) (P) (P) (P) (D) (D) (D)(D)(P)(P)(P)(P)	6. (P) (P) (P) (P) (P) (P) (P) (P) (P) (P) (N) (D)(N)

Try This

7. Show the amount using the fewest possible coins. Use (D), (N), and (P).

(D)(D)(N)(N)(N)(N)(N)(N)(N)(P)(P)(P)(P)

(D)(D)(D)(D)(D)(N)(P)(P)(P)(P)

Math Masters, p. 84

3•13 Data Day

Objective To introduce line plots.

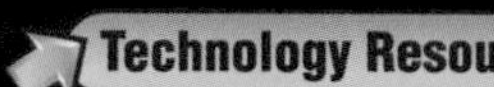

Technology Resources www.everydaymathonline.com

ePresentations

eToolkit

Algorithms Practice

EM Facts Workshop Game™

Family Letters

Assessment Management

Common Core State Standards

Curriculum Focal Points

Interactive Teacher's Lesson Guide

1 Teaching the Lesson

Key Concepts and Skills

- Compare whole numbers. [Number and Numeration Goal 7]
- Create a tally chart. [Data and Chance Goal 1]
- Create a line plot. [Data and Chance Goal 1]
- Answer simple questions about a line plot. [Data and Chance Goal 2]

Key Activities

Children tally how many siblings they have. They record their answers on stick-on notes and use the notes to make a line plot. Children answer questions about the data set.

Key Vocabulary

line plot

Materials

Home Link 3•12
slate ◆ stick-on notes ◆ Class Data Pad ◆ calculator (optional)

2 Ongoing Learning & Practice

Playing *Dime-Nickel-Penny Grab*
Math Masters, p. 342
tool-kit coins
Children practice counting and comparing collections of coins.

Math Boxes 3•13
Math Journal 1, p. 50
Children practice and maintain skills through Math Box problems.

Ongoing Assessment: Recognizing Student Achievement
Use Math Boxes, Problem 2.
[Operation and Computation Goal 1]

Home Link 3•13
Math Masters, p. 85
Children practice and maintain skills through Home Link activities.

3 Differentiation Options

READINESS

Making Tallies with Craft Sticks
per group: craft sticks, number cards 1–20 (from the Everything Math Deck, if available)
Children use craft sticks to model tally marks.

ENRICHMENT

Transferring Information to a Line Plot
per group: Class Data Pad, stick-on notes
Children display previously-collected data in a line plot.

ELL SUPPORT

Building a Math Word Bank
Differentiation Handbook, p. 126
Children add the term *line plot* to their Math Word Banks.

Advance Preparation

***Teacher's Reference Manual,* Grades 1–3** pp. 119–125

Getting Started

Mental Math and Reflexes

Tell change-to-more, change-to-less, and parts-and-total number stories. Children solve the problems any way they can and write the answers on their slates. They share solution strategies after each problem. Summarize each solution by drawing an appropriate diagram on the board, *but only after children have shared what they did to solve the problem.*

Do not force a number story into a particular mold. Do not say there is a "best" diagram for a problem.

●○○ Gabriela bought 13 muffins. She and her sister ate 5 of them. How many muffins did the girls have left? 8 muffins

●●○ Melinda has 14 stamps in her album. Her friend gives her 7 more stamps. How many stamps does Melinda have now? 21 stamps

●●● There are 26 children in Eduardo's gym class. 12 of the children are girls. How many of the children are boys? 14 of the children are boys.

Home Link 3·12 Follow-Up

As you go over the answers, record them on the board in both cents notation and dollars-and-cents notation. To extend the activity, have children find the fewest number of coins to represent each total.

1 Teaching the Lesson

Making a Line Plot

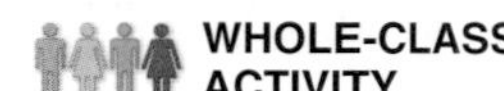

Give each child a stick-on note.

Each child writes the number of siblings he or she has on the note. Make a tally chart on the Class Data Pad. Ask children, one at a time, how many siblings they have, and tally the responses. Children then count the tally marks to determine the number of siblings that the greatest number of children have.

Number of Siblings	Tallies
0	
1	
2	
3	
4	
5 or more	

Explain that another way to show the results of the survey is to make a **line plot.**

1. Draw a horizontal line on the board and label it as shown on page 248.
2. Have children come up to the board, one at a time, and attach their stick-on notes to the board in columns above their number of siblings. Help them make vertical columns with no overlap between the notes.

NOTE Line plots are used extensively to organize and display data. A line plot shows data by using checks, Xs, or stick-on notes. Think of a line plot as a rough sketch of a bar graph.

NOTE After children have completed the line plot, have them use their data to help them make predictions about all of the first graders in the school. *For example:*

▷ How many siblings the greatest number of first graders have

▷ The number of first graders who have 5 or more siblings

Children may use their calculators to help them do this activity.

Ask questions about the line plot, such as the following:

- Can you tell how many siblings the greatest number of children in our class have without counting? How?
- How many children in our class have 0 siblings? 1 sibling? 2 siblings? 3 siblings? 4 siblings? 5 or more siblings?
- How many more children in our class have 0 siblings than have 1 sibling (or any combination of two numbers)?
- How many fewer children in our class have 3 siblings than have 4 siblings (or any combination of two numbers)?
- How can you tell how many children in our class are included in the line plot? Sample answer: Count all of the stick-on notes.

NOTE You may wish to use the data from the line plot to create a class picture graph with children. Have children draw pictures of their siblings on stick-on notes. When the picture graph is complete, ask children questions that require them to draw conclusions from the graph.

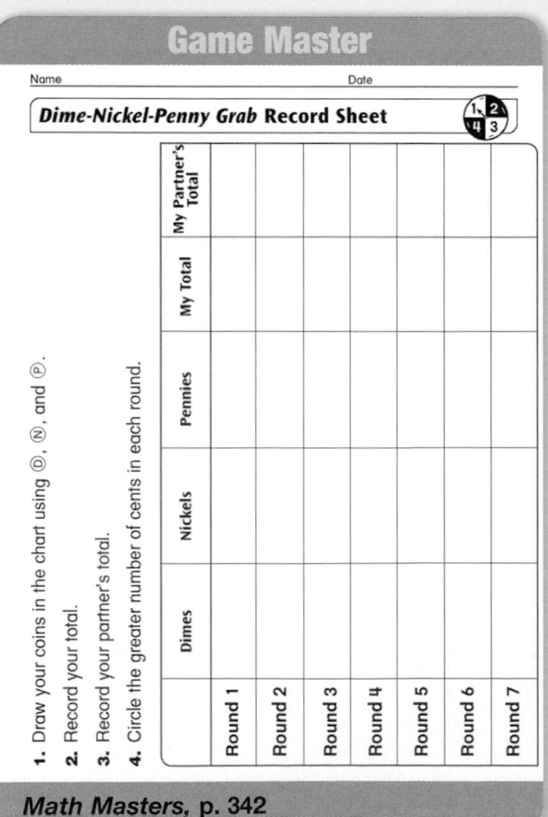

Game Master

Name Date

Dime-Nickel-Penny Grab **Record Sheet**

1. Draw your coins in the chart using Ⓓ, Ⓝ, and Ⓟ.
2. Record your total.
3. Record your partner's total.
4. Circle the greater number of cents in each round.

	Dimes	Nickels	Pennies	My Total	My Partner's Total
Round 1					
Round 2					
Round 3					
Round 4					
Round 5					
Round 6					
Round 7					

Math Masters, p. 342

2 Ongoing Learning & Practice

▶ Playing *Dime-Nickel-Penny Grab*

(*Math Masters,* p. 342)

Directions

Partners play with 10 dimes, 8 nickels, and 20 pennies.

1. Players mix the coins together and place them in a pile.
2. One player grabs a handful of coins.
3. The other player takes the coins that are left.
4. Players fill in the record sheet and circle the larger total value.
5. The player with the larger total value wins the round.

Math Boxes 3·13

INDEPENDENT ACTIVITY

(*Math Journal 1*, p. 50)

Mixed Practice Math Boxes in this lesson are paired with Math Boxes in Lesson 3-10. The skills in Problem 4 preview Unit 4 content.

Ongoing Assessment: Recognizing Student Achievement

Math Boxes Problem 2 ★

Use **Math Boxes, Problem 2** to assess children's ability to make sums of 10. Children are making adequate progress if they are able to fill in the blank boxes in the second and third rows. Some children may be able to fill in the boxes in the fourth row.

[Operations and Computation Goal 1]

Home Link 3·13

(*Math Masters*, p. 85)

Home Connection Children discuss a data set with someone at home.

3 Differentiation Options

READINESS

SMALL-GROUP ACTIVITY

Making Tallies with Craft Sticks

5–15 Min

To provide experience making tally marks, have children use craft sticks to show tallies for number cards. Children spread the number cards and craft sticks on the table. Each child should choose a number card and take the appropriate number of craft sticks. Then children should arrange their craft sticks to look like tallies for the number on their card. For example, if a child chooses the number 7, he or she would take seven craft sticks and stand four of them tall, cross them with the fifth craft stick, and stand the remaining two tall. Allow children to repeat this activity with different number cards.

Student Page

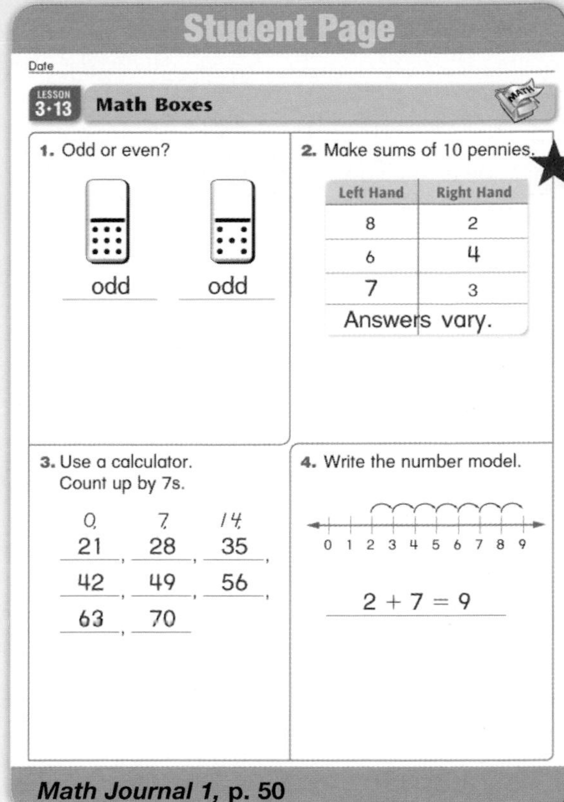

Date

LESSON 3·13 Math Boxes

1. Odd or even?

odd odd

2. Make sums of 10 pennies. ★

Left Hand	Right Hand
8	2
6	4
7	3
Answers vary.	

3. Use a calculator. Count up by 7s.

0, 7, 14, 21, 28, 35, 42, 49, 56, 63, 70

4. Write the number model.

2 + 7 = 9

Math Journal 1, p. 50

Home Link Master

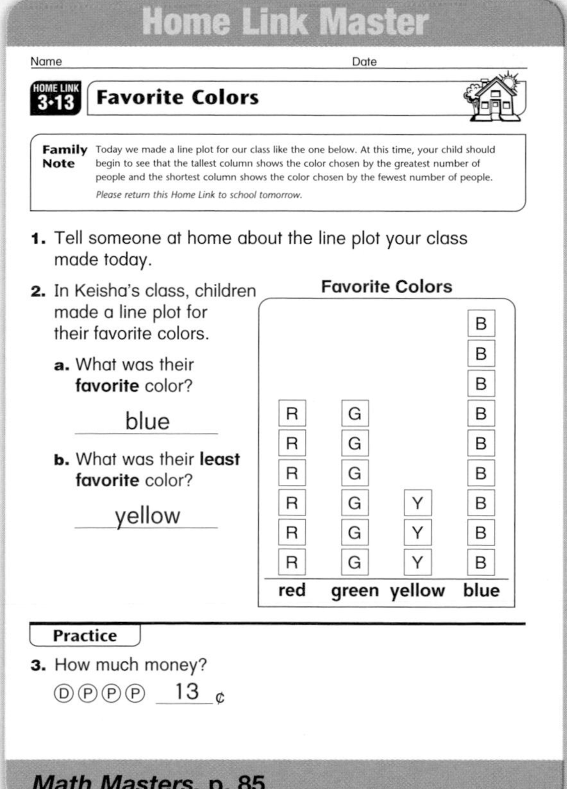

Name Date

HOME LINK 3·13 Favorite Colors

Family Note Today we made a line plot for our class like the one below. At this time, your child should begin to see that the tallest column shows the color chosen by the greatest number of people and the shortest column shows the color chosen by the fewest number of people.

Please return this Home Link to school tomorrow.

1. Tell someone at home about the line plot your class made today.

2. In Keisha's class, children made a line plot for their favorite colors.

a. What was their **favorite** color? blue

b. What was their **least favorite** color? yellow

Practice

3. How much money?

Ⓓ Ⓟ Ⓟ Ⓟ 13 ¢

Math Masters, p. 85

ENRICHMENT

▶ Transferring Information to a Line Plot

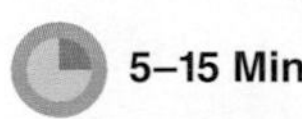

To further explore line plots, have children create a line plot and answer questions about previously-collected data. Display the tall chart of children's favorite seasons or number of lost teeth. Children work together to create a line plot using the information in the chart.

Then state one piece of information from the line plot. Have children pose a question that could be answered with that piece of information. *For example:*

- 7 children; Question: How many children lost two teeth?
- Winter; Question: Which season did most children in the class like best?

ELL SUPPORT

▶ Building a Math Word Bank

(*Differentiation Handbook,* p. 126)

To provide language support for data concepts, have children use the Word Bank Template found on *Differentiation Handbook,* page 126. Ask children to write the term *line plot,* draw a picture representing the term, and write other words that describe it.

Discuss what they know by looking at the line plot. See the *Differentiation Handbook* for more information. Consider giving children an example like the following:

Number of
Brothers and Sisters

```
    x
x   x x
-------
0 1 2 3
```

3•14 Domino Addition

Objectives To explore domino-dot patterns; and to provide practice for all of the basic addition facts.

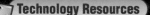

Technology Resources www.everydaymathonline.com

ePresentations

eToolkit

Algorithms Practice

EM Facts Workshop Game™

Family Letters

Assessment Management

Common Core State Standards

Curriculum Focal Points

Interactive Teacher's Lesson Guide

1 Teaching the Lesson

Key Concepts and Skills

- Estimate whether quantities are more than 10, less than 10, or equal to 10.
  [Number and Numeration Goal 2]
- Sort dominoes by even and odd numbers.
  [Number and Numeration Goal 5]
- Order dominoes according to dot patterns.
  [Number and Numeration Goal 7]
- Estimate sums.
  [Operations and Computation Goal 3]
- Find totals using the parts-and-total diagram.
  [Operations and Computation Goal 4]

Key Activities

Children look for patterns in even-and-odd number representations on dominoes. They use parts-and-total diagrams to find the total numbers of dots on dominoes. They play *Domino Top-It* to practice finding sums of dots.

Materials

Math Journal 1, p. 51
Home Link 3•13
double-9 dominoes (*Math Journal 1,* Activity Sheets 4 and 5) ◆ resealable plastic bag ◆ slate ◆ paper plate and counters (optional)

2 Ongoing Learning & Practice

Playing *High Roller*
Math Masters, p. 344
per partnership: 2 dice
Children practice addition facts.

Ongoing Assessment: Recognizing Student Achievement
Use *Math Masters,* page 344.
[Operations and Computation Goal 1]

Math Boxes 3•14
Math Journal 1, p. 52
Children practice and maintain skills through Math Box problems.

Home Link 3•14
Math Masters, p. 86
Children practice and maintain skills through Home Link activities.

3 Differentiation Options

READINESS

Matching Numbers and Dots
per partnership: number cards 1–18 (from the Everything Math Deck, if available), double-9 dominoes
Children match dots on dominoes with numbers.

ENRICHMENT

Exploring Sums of Even and Odd Numbers
Math Masters, pp. 58–60
Children find the sums of the dots on the dominoes they sorted in Exploration A in Lesson 3•4. Then they look for even/odd patterns.

Advance Preparation

For Part 1, children will need a set of dominoes from *Math Journal 1,* Activity Sheets 4 and 5. For the optional Enrichment activity in Part 3, children will need *Math Masters,* pages 58–60 that they completed in Lesson 3•4.

Getting Started

Mental Math and Reflexes

Lead children in the special first-grade chant: *2, 4, 6, 8, first graders are really great!* Ask children to name the first five even numbers. Record them on the board. Do the same for the first five odd numbers.

Remind children that a number is even if it ends in 0, 2, 4, 6, or 8; and that it is odd if it ends in 1, 3, 5, 7, or 9.

Dictate some numbers. Children write them on their slates. Then they write *E* if the number is even and *O* if it is odd.

Home Link 3·13 Follow-Up

Ask children to describe how they figured out the answers to the questions.

NOTE Children's dominoes may be stored in resealable plastic bags with children's identification numbers on them.

1 Teaching the Lesson

▶ Exploring Dot Patterns on Halves of Dominoes

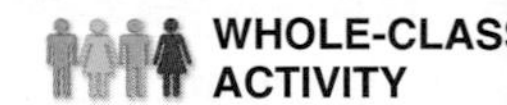

Tell children that today they will be exploring dot patterns on dominoes.

Ask children to use their cutout dominoes to do the following:

1. Find all the dominoes that have at least one blank half (a side with no dots). There should be 10 of these dominoes.
2. Line up these 10 dominoes in order from 0 dots to 9 dots on one side.

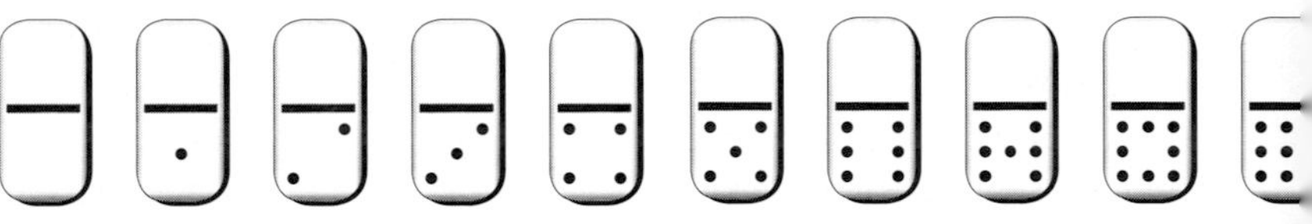

3. Separate these dominoes into two groups: dominoes with even numbers of dots and dominoes with odd numbers of dots.
4. Try to find a common pattern for all of the dominoes in each group.

Children share the patterns they found. If no one brings it up, point out that dominoes with an odd number of dots have a dot in the middle and that dominoes with an even number of dots have no dot in the middle.

Introducing Number Combinations on Entire Dominoes

WHOLE-CLASS ACTIVITY

Draw a 3|5 domino on the board. Point out that this domino shows two numbers: one number on each half of the domino. Then point out that there is a third number that corresponds to this domino. Ask: *What is the total number of dots on both halves of this domino?* 8

Draw a parts-and-total diagram with 3 and 5 as the parts and 8 as the whole, or total. Point out that this domino has a part with 3 dots and a part with 5 dots—and that the whole domino has 8 dots.

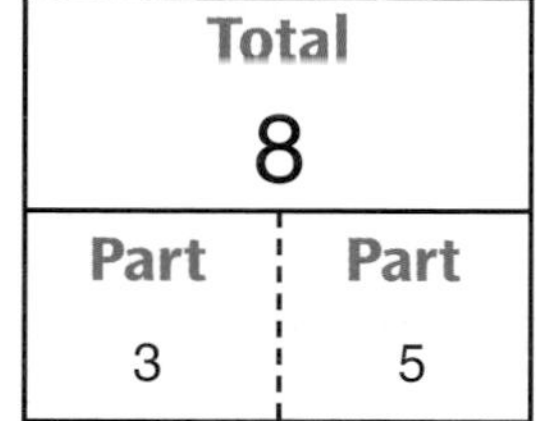

Ask several children to each choose a domino, hold it up, and name the three numbers associated with that domino. Draw a parts-and-total diagram for each of these dominoes. Keep doing this until most children have grasped the concept.

Playing *Domino Top-It*

PARTNER ACTIVITY

Domino Top-It is similar to *Top-It*. At first, limit the game to two players and have players use the sets of cutout dominoes from *Math Journal 1*, Activity Sheets 4 and 5.

NOTE The double-9 set of dominoes contains all of the basic addition facts. Encourage children to play the game often as a way of building recognition of and quick responses to these basic facts.

Directions

1. A player places all of the dominoes facedown on the table.
2. Each player turns over a domino and finds the total number of dots.
3. The player with the larger total takes both dominoes. In case of a tie, each player turns over another facedown domino, and the player with the larger total takes all of the faceup dominoes.
4. Play continues until all of the dominoes have been played. The player with more dominoes wins.

Paper plates divided into sections may help children count the total number of domino dots.

Adjusting the Activity

Limit the set of dominoes to those on Activity Sheet 4. You can also give each child a paper plate divided into three sections (two quarter-sections and one half-section). Children place counters in the smaller sections to match the number of dots on the two sides of the domino. Then they move the counters into the larger section and count the total.

AUDITORY ◆ KINESTHETIC ◆ TACTILE ◆ VISUAL

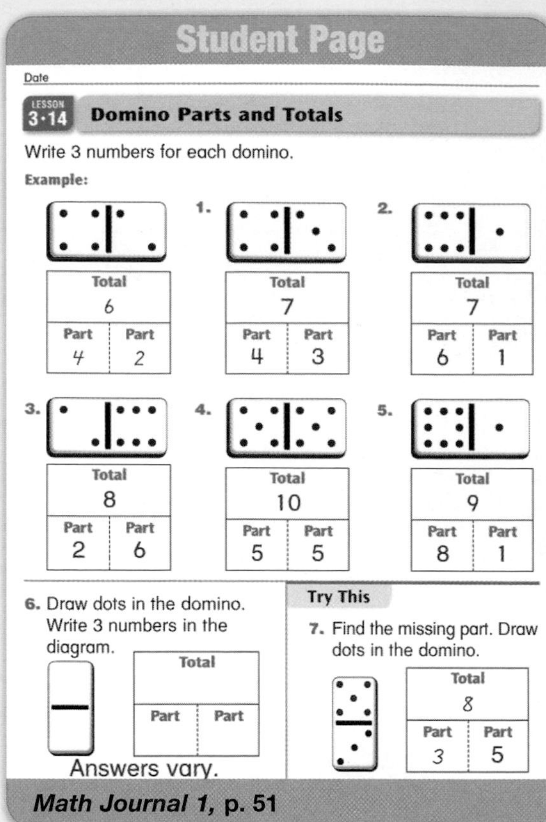

Student Page
Date
LESSON 3·14
Domino Parts and Totals
Write 3 numbers for each domino.
Example:
Total 6
Part 4 Part 2
1. Total 7 Part 4 Part 3
2. Total 7 Part 6 Part 1
3. Total 8 Part 2 Part 6
4. Total 10 Part 5 Part 5
5. Total 9 Part 8 Part 1
6. Draw dots in the domino. Write 3 numbers in the diagram.
Total
Part Part
Answers vary.
Try This
7. Find the missing part. Draw dots in the domino.
Total 8
Part 3 Part 5
Math Journal 1, p. 51

NOTE Problem 7 on journal page 51 suggests the use of dominoes to model subtraction facts.

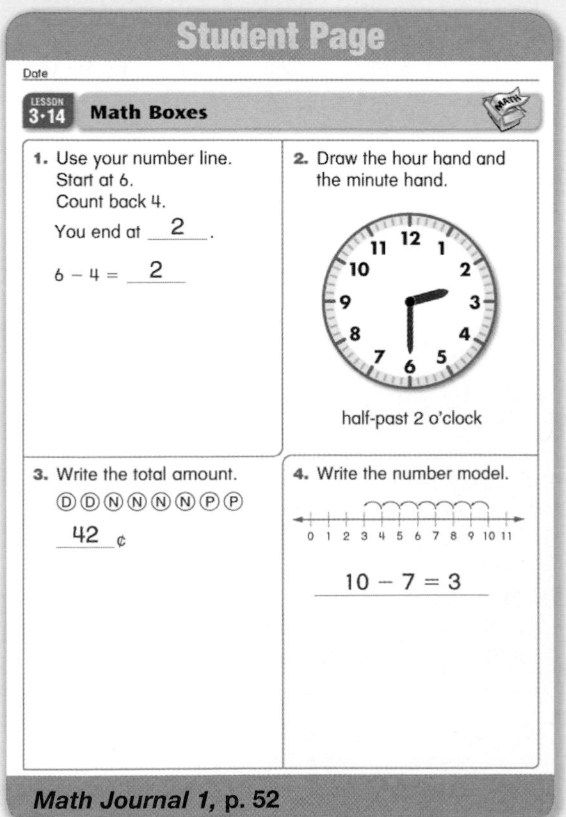

Student Page
Date
LESSON 3·14
Math Boxes
1. Use your number line. Start at 6. Count back 4.
You end at 2.
6 − 4 = 2
2. Draw the hour hand and the minute hand.
half-past 2 o'clock
3. Write the total amount.
Ⓓ Ⓓ Ⓝ Ⓝ Ⓝ Ⓝ Ⓟ Ⓟ
42 ¢
4. Write the number model.
0 1 2 3 4 5 6 7 8 9 10 11
10 − 7 = 3
Math Journal 1, p. 52

▶ Finding the Total Numbers of Dots on Dominoes

(*Math Journal 1,* p. 51)

Children can estimate sums using dominoes. Draw a 5|5 domino on the overhead projector and have children find the total number of dots. Then turn off the projector and draw another domino. Tell children you want them to estimate the sum of the dots.

▷ If their estimate is more than 10, they show a thumbs-up.

▷ If their estimate is less than 10, they show a thumbs-down.

▷ If their estimate is 10, they hold out a clenched fist.

Turn on the overhead for about 3 seconds—not long enough to allow counting—and have children quickly show their estimates. Repeat with other dominoes. Then ask children to share how they decided whether the sum was more than, less than, or equal to 10.

On the journal page, children use parts-and-total diagrams to find the total numbers of dots on dominoes.

2 Ongoing Learning & Practice

▶ Playing *High Roller*

(*Math Masters,* p. 344)

Children practice addition facts by playing *High Roller.* For directions, see Lesson 2-12.

Ongoing Assessment: Recognizing Student Achievement

***Math Masters,* Page 344**

Use ***Math Masters,* page 344** to assess children's ability to find dice sums. Children are making adequate progress if they find the correct sums. You should see progress since children last played this game in Lesson 2-12.

[Operations and Computation Goal 1]

▶ Math Boxes 3·14

INDEPENDENT ACTIVITY

(*Math Journal 1,* p. 52)

Mixed Practice Math Boxes in this lesson are paired with Math Boxes in Lesson 3-12. The skills in Problem 4 preview Unit 4 content.

Writing/Reasoning Have children draw, write, or verbalize an answer to the following question: *Why do you use a number line?* A reasonable answer may mention hopping up and back to solve problems.

Home Link 3·14

INDEPENDENT ACTIVITY

(*Math Masters,* p. 86)

Home Connection Children teach their families how to play *Domino Top-It.* Make copies of *Math Journal 1,* Activity Sheets 4 and 5 for children to take home. They can use real dominoes if they have them at home.

3 Differentiation Options

READINESS

SMALL-GROUP ACTIVITY

Matching Numbers and Dots

5–15 Min

To explore solving parts-and-total problems using a concrete model, have children match domino dots with number cards. Place the number cards in numerical order on the table. Ask each child to choose a domino, count the total number of dots on it, and place it under the number card that shows the domino's sum. After all the dominoes have been matched to a number card, have the group check their work.

ENRICHMENT

SMALL-GROUP ACTIVITY

Exploring Sums of Even and Odd Numbers

5–15 Min

(*Math Masters,* pp. 58–60)

To further explore even and odd numbers, have children find the sums for the domino parts and determine whether these sums are odd or even. Children work in the same groups as in Exploration A in Lesson 3-4. Distribute *Math Masters,* pages 58–60 that you collected during that lesson. Children record the total number of dots on each of the dominoes.

Bring the class together to discuss the following questions:

- If each side of a domino has an even number of dots, is the total number of dots even or odd? even
- If each side of a domino has an odd number of dots, is the total number of dots even or odd? even
- If a domino has an odd number of dots on one side and an even number of dots on the other side, is the total number of dots even or odd? odd

Home Link Master

Name Date

HOME LINK 3·14 **Domino Top-It**

Family Note Today your child examined dot patterns on dominoes and played with dominoes. The relationship between the numbers of dots on each domino part is useful for learning basic facts.

Domino Top-It is a great game for helping your child practice basic addition facts.

Show someone at home how to play *Domino Top-It.* Use a set of real dominoes, if you have one. Or use the paper dominoes your teacher gave you.

Directions

1. If you have real dominoes, turn them facedown on the table. If you are using paper dominoes, put them facedown in a stack.
2. Each player takes a domino and turns it over. If you are using paper dominoes, take one from the top of the stack.
3. The player with the larger total number of dots takes both dominoes. First estimate; then count.
4. In case of a tie, each player turns over another domino. The player with the larger total takes all of the dominoes that are faceup.
5. The game is over when all of the dominoes have been played. The player who has more dominoes wins.

Practice

6. Write 4 odd numbers.
Answers vary.

Math Masters, p. 86

3•15 Progress Check 3

Objective To assess children's progress on mathematical content through the end of Unit 3.

1 Looking Back: Cumulative Assessment

Input children's data from Progress Check 3 into the **Assessment Management Spreadsheets**.

Materials

- Home Link 3•14
- *Assessment Handbook,* pp. 68–75, 145–148, 179, and 208–211
- slate

CONTENT ASSESSED	LESSON(S)	ASSESSMENT ITEMS				
		SELF	ORAL/SLATE	WRITTEN PART A	WRITTEN PART B	OPEN RESPONSE
Count forward by 2s and 5s to 100; count backward by 1s from any number less than 100. [Number and Numeration Goal 1]	3•1–3•13	6		2, 3	7	
Count collections of objects. [Number and Numeration Goal 2]	3•1, 3•14					✓
Know sums of 10; solve problems involving addition and subtraction facts. [Operations and Computation Goal 1]	3•2–3•4, 3•6, 3•7, 3•9–3•14	2	2	1		
Know the value of a penny, a nickel, and a dime; calculate the value of a combination of coins. [Measurement and Reference Frames Goal 2]	3•1–3•5, 3•7, 3•10–3•14	4	3	4, 5		
Show and tell time on an analog clock to the nearest half-hour. [Measurement and Reference Frames Goal 4]	3•7–3•9, 3•11, 3•12, 3•14	5			8, 9	
Continue simple, non-numeric patterns; use patterns to solve problems; solve problems involving simple functions represented in Frames-and-Arrows. [Patterns, Functions, and Algebra Goal 1]	3•1, 3•2, 3•4, 3•5, 3•8–3•10	1, 3	1, 4	2, 3, 6	7	✓

2 Looking Ahead: Preparing for Unit 4

Math Boxes 3•15

Home Link 3•15: Unit 4 Family Letter

Materials

- *Math Journal 1,* p. 53
- *Math Masters,* pp. 87–90

Getting Started

Home Link 3·14 Follow-Up

Ask if there are any questions about *Domino Top-It.*

1 Looking Back: Cumulative Assessment

Self Assessment

INDEPENDENT ACTIVITY

(Self Assessment, *Assessment Handbook,* p. 145)

Have children complete the Self Assessment. The Self Assessment offers children an opportunity to reflect upon their progress.

Oral and Slate Assessments

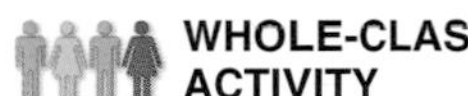
WHOLE-CLASS ACTIVITY

Problems 1 and 2 provide summative information and can be used for grading purposes. Problems 3 and 4 provide formative information that can be useful in planning future instruction.

Oral Assessment

1. Draw the following patterns on the board. Ask children to describe how to continue each pattern.

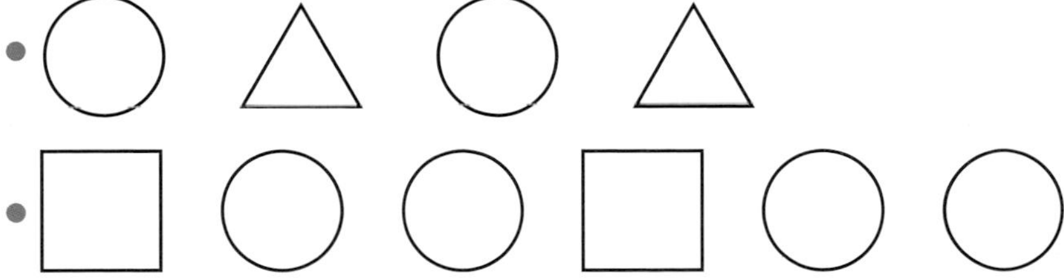

2. Ask children to use the number grid on the inside back cover of *Math Journal 1* to do the following:
   - Count the hops from 7 up to 15. 8
   - Count the hops from 20 back to 10. 10
   - Count the hops from 0 up to 6. 6
   - Count the hops from 9 up to 13. 4

Slate Assessment

3. Draw the following coin combinations on the board. Ask children to write each value on their slates using cent notation.
   - Ⓟ Ⓟ Ⓟ Ⓟ Ⓟ 5¢
   - Ⓝ Ⓝ Ⓟ Ⓟ 12¢
   - Ⓓ Ⓝ Ⓟ 16¢
   - Ⓓ Ⓝ Ⓝ Ⓓ Ⓓ Ⓟ Ⓟ Ⓟ Ⓟ 44¢

Assessment Master

Name Date

LESSON 3·15 **Self Assessment** Progress Check 3

Put a check in the box that tells how you do each skill.

Skills	I can do this by myself. I can explain how to do this.	I can do this by myself.	I can do this with help.
1. Do Frames-and-Arrows problems.			
2. Find sums of 10.			
3. Continue patterns.			
4. Count money.			
5. Tell time to the half-hour.			
6. Skip count.			

Assessment Handbook, **p. 145**

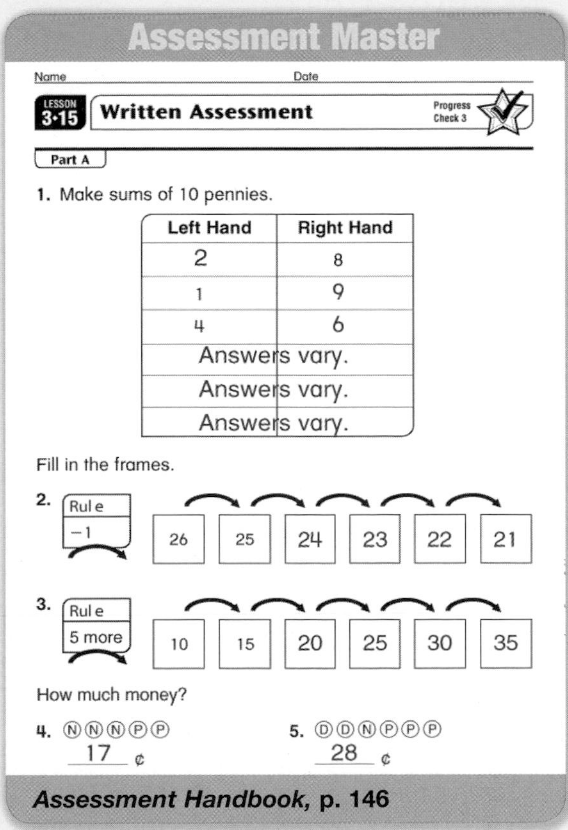
Assessment Master

Name Date

LESSON 3·15 **Written Assessment** Progress Check 3

Part A

1. Make sums of 10 pennies.

Left Hand	Right Hand
2	8
1	9
4	6
Answers vary.	
Answers vary.	
Answers vary.	

Fill in the frames.

2. Rule: −1 — 26, 25, 24, 23, 22, 21

3. Rule: 5 more — 10, 15, 20, 25, 30, 35

How much money?

4. Ⓝ Ⓝ Ⓝ Ⓟ Ⓟ 17 ¢

5. Ⓓ Ⓓ Ⓝ Ⓟ Ⓟ Ⓟ 28 ¢

Assessment Handbook, **p. 146**

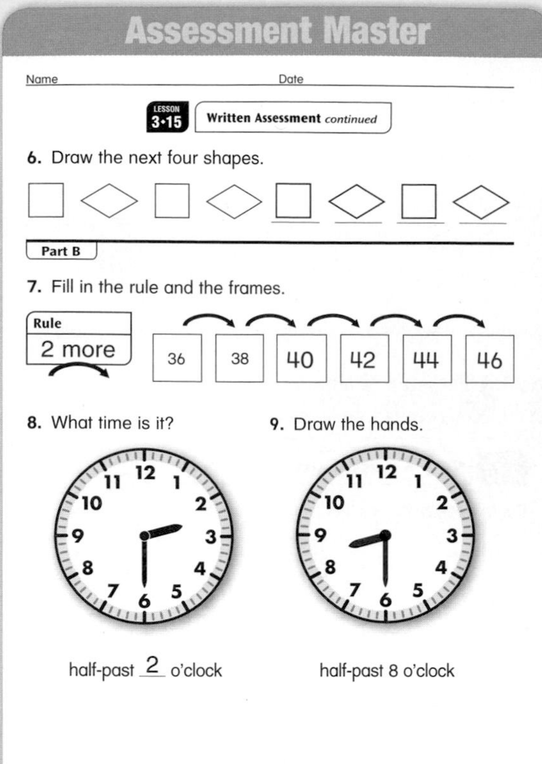

Assessment Master

Name ____________ Date ____________

LESSON 3·15 **Written Assessment** *continued*

6. Draw the next four shapes.

7. Fill in the rule and the frames.

Rule: 2 more

36	38	40	42	44	46

8. What time is it?

half-past 2 o'clock

9. Draw the hands.

half-past 8 o'clock

Assessment Handbook, p. 147

Use the checklists on pages 209 and 211 of the *Assessment Handbook* to record results. Then input the data into the **Assessment Management Spreadsheets** to keep an ongoing record of children's progress toward Grade-Level Goals.

Assessment Master

Name ____________ Date ____________

LESSON 3·15 **Open Response** Progress Check 3

The Bike Shop

Olivia walked past the Bike Shop on Monday.
She saw some tricycles in the window.
She counted 18 wheels.

1. How many tricycles did Olivia see in the window?
6 tricycles

Draw or write to explain how you know.

2. On Tuesday, she counted 21 wheels.
On Wednesday, she counted 24 wheels.
On Thursday, she counted 27 wheels.
How many wheels do you think she counted on Friday?
30 wheels

Draw or write to explain how you know.

Assessment Handbook, p. 148

4. Draw the following frames-and-arrows problems on the board. Ask children to write the rules.
Sample Answers:

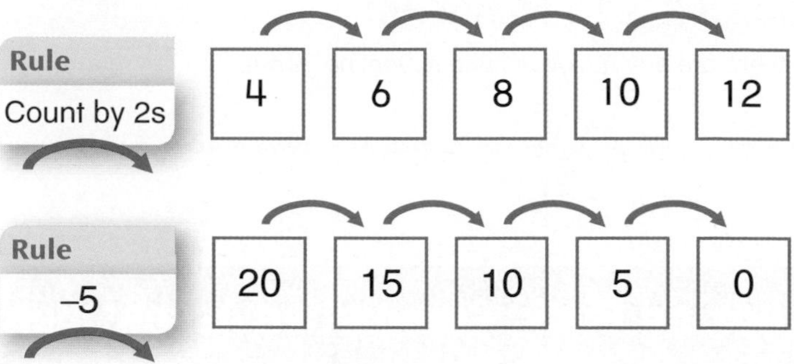

▶ Written Assessment

(*Assessment Handbook,* pp. 146 and 147)

Part A Recognizing Student Achievement

Problems 1–6 provide summative information and may be used for grading purposes.

Problem(s)	Description
1	Know sums of 10.
2, 3	Count forward by 5s; count backward by 1s; solve problems involving simple functions represented in Frames-and-Arrows problems.
4, 5	Know the value of a penny, nickel, and dime; calculate the value of a combination of coins.
6	Continue non-numeric patterns.

Part B Informing Instruction

Problems 7–9 provide formative information that can be useful in planning future instruction.

Problem(s)	Description
7	Count forward by 2s to 100; solve problems involving simple functions represented in Frames-and-Arrows problems.
8, 9	Show and tell time on an analog clock to the nearest half-hour.

▶ Open Response

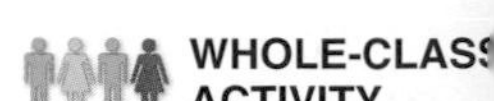

(*Assessment Handbook,* p. 148)

The Bike Shop

The open-response requires children to apply skills and concepts from Unit 3 to solve a multistep problem. See *Assessment Handbook,* pages 71–75 for rubrics and children's work samples for this problem.

There are two options for completing this open response. For both Option 1 and Option 2, children begin by working independently (or with a partner) to solve a multistep problem. Take this time to circulate throughout the classroom.

Option 1:

Olivia went to the Bike Shop. She saw some tricycles in the window. She counted 18 wheels. How many tricycles did Olivia see in the window?

On Tuesday, she counted 21 wheels. On Wednesday, she counted 24 wheels. On Thursday, she counted 27 wheels. How many wheels do you think she counted on Friday?

Option 2:

Distribute *Assessment Master,* page 148. Read the problem aloud to children. Allow them to solve the problem and record their solutions on the page.

After children have had a chance to complete either option, invite individual children to explain their solution strategies. Encourage them to use words and drawings to explain their strategies as you list them on the board. Be sure to discuss both successful and unsuccessful strategies.

See the *Assessment Handbook,* (page 148) for more information.

2 Looking Ahead: Preparing for Unit 4

Math Boxes 3•15

INDEPENDENT ACTIVITY

(*Math Journal 1,* p. 53)

Mixed Practice This Math Boxes page previews Unit 4 content.

Home Link 3•15: Unit 4 Family Letter

INDEPENDENT ACTIVITY

(*Math Masters,* pp. 87–90)

Home Connection The Unit 4 Family Letter provides families with information and activities related to Unit 4 activities.

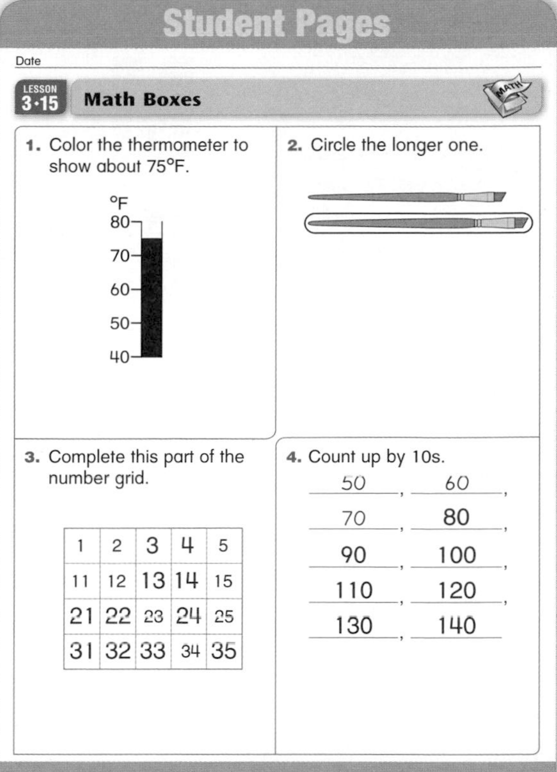

Student Pages

Date

LESSON 3•15 **Math Boxes**

1. Color the thermometer to show about 75°F.

°F
80
70
60
50
40

2. Circle the longer one.

3. Complete this part of the number grid.

1	2	3	4	5
11	12	13	14	15
21	22	23	24	25
31	32	33	34	35

4. Count up by 10s.

50, 60,
70, 80,
90, 100,
110, 120,
130, 140

Math Journal 1, p. 53

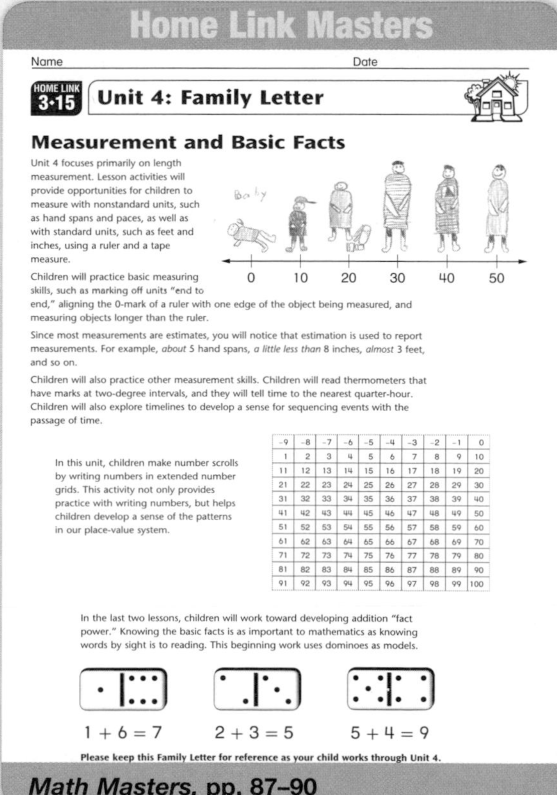

Home Link Masters

Name Date

HOME LINK 3•15 **Unit 4: Family Letter**

Measurement and Basic Facts

Unit 4 focuses primarily on length measurement. Lesson activities will provide opportunities for children to measure with nonstandard units, such as hand spans and paces, as well as with standard units, such as feet and inches, using a ruler and a tape measure.

Children will practice basic measuring skills, such as marking off units "end to end," aligning the 0-mark of a ruler with one edge of the object being measured, and measuring objects longer than the ruler.

Since most measurements are estimates, you will notice that estimation is used to report measurements. For example, *about* 5 hand spans, *a little less than* 8 inches, *almost* 3 feet, and so on.

Children will also practice other measurement skills. Children will read thermometers that have marks at two-degree intervals, and they will tell time to the nearest quarter-hour. Children will also explore timelines to develop a sense for sequencing events with the passage of time.

In this unit, children make number scrolls by writing numbers in extended number grids. This activity not only provides practice with writing numbers, but helps children develop a sense of the patterns in our place-value system.

-9	-8	-7	-6	-5	-4	-3	-2	-1	0
1	2	3	4	5	6	7	8	9	10
11	12	13	14	15	16	17	18	19	20
21	22	23	24	25	26	27	28	29	30
31	32	33	34	35	36	37	38	39	40
41	42	43	44	45	46	47	48	49	50
51	52	53	54	55	56	57	58	59	60
61	62	63	64	65	66	67	68	69	70
71	72	73	74	75	76	77	78	79	80
81	82	83	84	85	86	87	88	89	90
91	92	93	94	95	96	97	98	99	100

In the last two lessons, children will work toward developing addition "fact power." Knowing the basic facts is as important to mathematics as knowing words by sight is to reading. This beginning work uses dominoes as models.

$1 + 6 = 7$ $2 + 3 = 5$ $5 + 4 = 9$

Please keep this Family Letter for reference as your child works through Unit 4.

Math Masters, pp. 87–90

Unit 4 Organizer

Measurement and Basic Facts

Overview

In this unit, children work with linear measures and review and extend their use of thermometers and clocks. They measure in nonstandard units, such as digits and hand spans, as well as in the U.S. customary units of inches and feet. They use rulers and tape measures to practice measuring classroom objects and themselves. Children also begin the important work of achieving "automaticity" (automatic recall) of basic addition facts. Unit 4 has three main areas of focus:

- To measure and compare lengths using nonstandard and standard units,
- To review telling time on the hour, half-hour, and quarter-hour, and
- To introduce and practice addition facts.

CCSS Linking to the Common Core State Standards

The content of Unit 4 addresses the Common Core State Standards for Mathematics in *Operations and Algebraic Thinking* and *Measurement and Data*. The correlation of the Common Core State Standards to the *Everyday Mathematics* Grade 1 lessons begins on page CS1.

Contents

Unit 4 Organizer

Learning In Perspective

	Lesson Objectives	Links to the Past	Links to the Future
4•1	To introduce the Math Message routine; to review thermometers; and to introduce reading temperatures to the nearest two degrees.	In Units 1 and 2, children record the daily temperature and learn how thermometers work. Children work with temperatures in Kindergarten.	In Grades 1 and 2, children complete daily Math Message routines and solve problems involving temperature change.
4•2	To provide practice measuring and comparing lengths using nonstandard units.	In Unit 2, children compare the lengths of objects. In Kindergarten, children compare and measure lengths.	In Grades 1 and 2, children measure and compare length, using standard and nonstandard units, to the nearest inch and centimeter.
4•3	To provide practice measuring with a nonstandard unit and with the standard foot; and to facilitate understanding of the need for standard units.	In Unit 2, children compare the lengths of objects. In Kindergarten, children compare and measure lengths.	In Grades 1 and 2, children measure and compare length, using standard and nonstandard units, to the nearest inch and centimeter.
4•4	To introduce the inch as a standard unit of length; and to provide practice measuring to the nearest inch.	In Unit 2, children compare the lengths of objects. In Kindergarten, children compare and measure lengths.	In Grades 1 and 2, children measure and compare length, using standard and nonstandard units, to the nearest inch and centimeter.
4•5	To provide practice estimating and measuring the lengths of objects in inches.	In Unit 2, children compare the lengths of objects. In Kindergarten, children estimate and measure lengths.	In Grades 1 and 2, children estimate and measure length, using standard and nonstandard units, to the nearest inch and centimeter.
4•6	To provide practice using a tape measure to measure curved and flat objects in inches.	In Unit 2, children compare the lengths of objects. In Kindergarten, children measure lengths.	In Grades 1 and 2, children measure lengths, using standard and nonstandard units, to the nearest inch and centimeter.
4•7	To measure children's heights; to provide experiences making a bar graph; to guide the exploration of 2-dimensional shapes; and to develop familiarity with base-10 blocks.	In Units 1–3, children explore tally marks, line plots, and base-10 blocks. Earlier in Grade 1 and in Kindergarten, children explore shapes, and collect and organize data.	Throughout Grades 1–3, children measure lengths; collect, organize, and analyze data; use base-10 blocks; and explore 2-dimensional shapes.
4•8	To review telling time on the hour and half-hour; and to introduce telling time on the quarter-hour.	In Units 2 and 3, children tell time to the nearest hour and half-hour. In Kindergarten, children begin telling time to the nearest hour.	Throughout Grades 1–3, children learn to tell time with greater precision. By Grade 3, they are able to tell time to the nearest minute.
4•9	To facilitate the investigation of timelines.	In Units 1–3, children use the class number line as a timeline of the school year. In Kindergarten, children begin sequencing events in a day.	In Units 5–10, children add important events to the class timeline. In Grade 2, they further explore timelines.
4•10	To introduce scrolls; and to provide opportunities to make a number scroll for numbers to 100 and beyond.	In Units 2 and 3, children use the number grid to count on and skip count. Children are introduced to number scrolls in Kindergarten.	Children continue to work with number scrolls throughout Grades 1 and 2.
4•11	To introduce addition facts, fact power, turn-around facts, and doubles facts; and to practice adding and subtracting 10.	In Unit 3, children use the number line and dominoes to solve addition and subtraction problems. In Kindergarten, children solve addition problems.	In Units 5–10, children develop fact power for simple addition and subtraction facts and practice addition through games and problem-solving situations.
4•12	To provide practice with addition facts; and to introduce and provide practice with the making-ten addition strategy.	In Unit 3, children use the number line and dominoes to solve addition and subtraction problems. In Kindergarten, children solve addition problems.	In Units 5–10, children develop fact power for simple addition and subtraction facts and practice addition through games and problem-solving situations.

	Key Concepts and Skills	Grade 1 Goals*
4·1	Count forward by 2s from a multiple of 10.	Number and Numeration Goal 1
	Read temperature to the nearest 10° on a thermometer.	Measurement and Reference Frames Goal 3
	Read temperature to the nearest 2° on a thermometer.	Measurement and Reference Frames Goal 3
4·2	Count forward by 1s.	Number and Numeration Goal 1
	Compare heights.	Measurement and Reference Frames Goal 1
	Measure lengths in nonstandard units and compare lengths.	Measurement and Reference Frames Goal 1
	Choose and label measurement units.	Measurement and Reference Frames Goal 1
4·3	Use language of approximation when measuring.	Measurement and Reference Frames Goal 1
	Measure length with nonstandard units.	Measurement and Reference Frames Goal 1
	Measure length to the nearest foot.	Measurement and Reference Frames Goal 1
4·4	Count forward by 1s.	Number and Numeration Goal 1
	Use language of approximation when measuring.	Measurement and Reference Frames Goal 1
	Measure length to the nearest inch.	Measurement and Reference Frames Goal 1
	Compare standard units of measure and lengths of objects.	Measurement and Reference Frames Goal 1
4·5	Use reference objects to estimate length.	Measurement and Reference Frames Goal 1
	Measure length to the nearest inch.	Measurement and Reference Frames Goal 1
	Measure and draw line segments to the nearest inch.	Measurement and Reference Frames Goal 1
4·6	Count forward by 1s.	Number and Numeration Goal 1
	Measure length to the nearest inch.	Measurement and Reference Frames Goal 1
	Identify inch and centimeter scales.	Measurement and Reference Frames Goal 1
4·7	Count and record the number of flats, longs, and cubes.	Number and Numeration Goal 3
	Create a line plot and a bar graph to organize data.	Data and Chance Goal 1
	Answer questions about data collected using a bar graph; find typical value in a data set.	Data and Chance Goal 2
	Estimate and measure height to the nearest inch.	Measurement and Reference Frames Goal 1
	Create plane shapes and designs on a geoboard.	Geometry Goal 1
4·8	Count forward by 5s.	Number and Numeration Goal 1
	Show time on an analog clock to the nearest half-hour and quarter-hour.	Measurement and Reference Frames Goal 4
	Tell and record times on an analog clock to the nearest half-hour and quarter-hour.	Measurement and Reference Frames Goal 4
	Use language of approximation to describe times on an analog clock.	Measurement and Reference Frames Goal 4
4·9	Order events on a timeline.	Number and Numeration Goal 7
	Create a simple timeline.	Measurement and Reference Frames Goal 4
4·10	Count forward by 1s.	Number and Numeration Goal 1
	Order numbers through 100 or more.	Number and Numeration Goal 7
	Identify and use patterns on a number grid.	Patterns, Functions, and Algebra Goal 1
4·11	Find sums for addition facts; find sums for dice rolls.	Operations and Computation Goal 1
	Solve facts with +10 and −10.	Operations and Computation 1
	Identify and discuss patterns for easy facts.	Patterns, Functions, and Algebra Goal 1
	Identify pairs of turn-around addition facts.	Patterns, Functions, and Algebra Goal 3
4·12	Compare sums.	Number and Numeration Goal 7
	Recite easy addition facts; use ten frames and counters to solve addition facts; solve +8 and +9 addition facts by making ten.	Operations and Computation Goal 1
	Use numeric patterns to find +8 and +9 shortcuts.	Patterns, Functions, and Algebra Goal 1

*See the Appendix for a complete list of Grade 1 Goals.

A Balanced Curriculum

Ongoing Practice

Everyday Mathematics provides numerous opportunities for ongoing practice. These activities are embedded throughout the lessons:

Mental Math and Reflexes activities promote speed and accuracy in mental computation.

Math Boxes offer mixed practice and are paired across lessons as shown in the brackets below. This makes them useful as assessment tools. The last one or two boxes on each page preview the next unit's content.

Mixed practice	[4•1, 4•3], [4•2, 4•4], [4•5, 4•7], [4•6, 4•8], [4•9, 4•11], [4•10, 4•12]
Mixed practice with multiple choice	4•2, 4•3, 4•6, 4•7, 4•9, 4•12
Mixed practice with writing/reasoning opportunity	4•3, 4•4, 4•5, 4•8, 4•11, 4•12

Home Links are daily homework assignments that review the content of the lesson and often contain ongoing facts practice.

Minute Math+ problems are offered for additional practice in Lessons 4•2, 4•7, 4•9, and 4•11.

EM Facts Workshop Game provides online practice of basic facts and computation.

EXTRA PRACTICE **Extra Practice** activities are included in Lessons 4•2, 4•7, 4•9, and 4•11.

Practice through Games

Games are an essential component of practice in the *Everyday Mathematics* program. Games offer skills practice and promote strategic thinking. See the *Differentiation Handbook* for ways to adapt games to meet children's needs.

Lesson	Game	Skill Practiced
4•1, 4•5	*Domino Top-It*	Finding and comparing sums [NN Goal 7 and OC Goal 2]
4•3	*Coin-Dice*	Making coin exchanges [MRF Goal 2]
4•4, 4•10	*Time Match*	Telling time on an analog clock [MRF Goal 4]
4•8	*Dime-Nickel-Penny Grab*	Calculating and comparing the values of combinations of coins [OC Goal 2]
4•11	*High Roller*	Comparing quantities and finding sums [NN Goal 7 and OC Goal 2]
4•12	*Shaker Addition Top-It*	Finding and comparing sums [NN Goal 7 and OC Goal 2]
4•12	*Penny Plate*	Finding sums of 10 [OC Goal 1]

[NN] Number and Numeration
[MRF] Measurement and Reference Frames
[OC] Operations and Computation
[GEO] Geometry
[DC] Data and Chance
[PFA] Patterns, Functions, and Algebra

Problem Solving 

Good problem solvers use a variety of strategies, including the following:

- Draw a picture.
- Act out the problem.
- Make a table, chart, or list.
- Look for a pattern.
- Try a simpler version of the problem.
- Make a guess and try it out.

The table below lists some of the opportunities in this unit for children to practice these strategies.

Lessons that teach *through* problem solving, not just *about* problem solving

Lesson	Activity
4•2	Decide which nonstandard units to use to measure lengths.
4•3	Find things that are taller than, shorter than, and about the same height as they are.
4•3	Determine the need for standard units.
4•5	Estimate the length of an object.
4•10	Make a number scroll.

See Chapter 18: Problem Solving in the *Teacher's Reference Manual* for more information.

The Language of Mathematics

Everyday Mathematics provides lesson-specific suggestions to help all children acquire, process, and express mathematical ideas. Throughout Unit 4, there are lesson-specific language development notes that address the needs of English language learners, indicated by **ELL**.

ELL SUPPORT Activities to support English language learners are in Part 3 of Lessons 4•1, 4•3, 4•4, 4•8, and 4•11.

The *English Learners Handbook* and the *Differentiation Handbook* have suggestions for promoting language development and acquisition of mathematics vocabulary. See Unit 4 in each handbook.

Unit 4 Vocabulary

addition facts
arm span
bar graph
cubit
degree
digit
doubles fact
estimate
fact power
Fahrenheit
feet
foot
half-past (the hour)
hand
hand span
in.
inch
length
Math Message
measure
quarter-after
quarter-before
quarter-past (the hour)
quarter-to (the hour)
scroll
standard foot
sum
tape measure
temperature
thermometer
timeline
turn-around fact
typical
unit
yard

Literacy Connection

Lesson 4•3 *How Big Is a Foot?,* by Rolf Myller, Random House Children's Books, 1991

Lesson 4•5 *Jack and the Beanstalk* (any version)

For more literacy connections, see the *Home Connection Handbook,* Grades 1–3.

Cross-Curricular Links 

Science and Literature
Lesson 4•5 Children explore measurement by reading *Jack and the Beanstalk* and planting bean plants.

Literature
Lesson 4•3 Children read *How Big Is a Foot?* and discuss the importance of standard measurement units.

Social Studies
Lesson 4•9 Children study timelines of historical events.

Balanced Assessment

 Daily Assessments

- **Recognizing Student Achievement** – A daily assessment that is included in every lesson to evaluate children's progress toward the Grade 1 Grade-Level Goals.
- **Informing Instruction** – Notes that appear throughout the unit to help anticipate children's common errors and suggest appropriate problem-solving strategies.

Lesson	Recognizing Student Achievement	Informing Instruction
4•1	Skip count by 2s. [NN Goal 1]	
4•2	List the complements of 6 and 7. [OC Goal 1]	Measure length from the beginning of an object. Find complements of numbers.
4•3	Solve Frames-and-Arrows problems. [PFA Goal 1]	Measure length.
4•4	Measure in feet. [MRF Goal 1]	Align the measuring tool.
4•5	Find domino sums and compare quantities. [NN Goal 7]	Measure with a 6-inch ruler.
4•6	Solve parts-and-total number stories. [OC Goal 4]	
4•7	Solve easy dice sums. [OC Goal 1]	
4•8	Tell time. [MRF Goal 4]	
4•9	Measure to the nearest inch. [MRF Goal 1]	
4•10	Answer probability questions. [DC Goal 3]	Fill in a 100-number grid.
4•11	Tell time to the quarter-hour. [MRF Goal 4]	Find sums.
4•12	Write addition facts. [OC Goal 1]	

[NN] Number and Numeration
[MRF] Measurement and Reference Frames
[OC] Operations and Computation
[GEO] Geometry
[DC] Data and Chance
[PFA] Patterns, Functions, and Algebra

Portfolio Opportunities 

The following lessons provide opportunities to gather samples of children's mathematical writings, drawings, and creations to add balance to the assessment process: Lessons 4•3, 4•4, 4•5, 4•8, 4•9, 4•11, 4•12, and 4•13.

See pages 16 and 17 in the *Assessment Handbook* for more information about portfolios and how to use them.

Unit Assessment

Progress Check 4 – A cumulative assessment of concepts and skills taught in Unit 4 and in previous units, providing information for evaluating children's progress and planning for future instruction. These assessments include oral/slate, written, and open-response activities, as shown below in the sample Progress Check lesson opener.

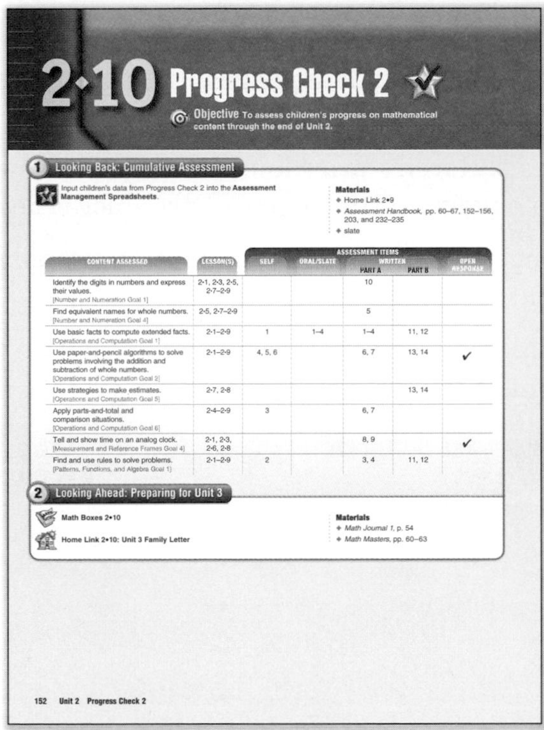

2•10 Progress Check 2

Objective To assess children's progress on mathematical content through the end of Unit 2.

1 Looking Back: Cumulative Assessment

Input children's data from Progress Check 2 into the **Assessment Management Spreadsheets**.

Materials
- Home Link 2•9
- *Assessment Handbook*, pp. 60–67, 152–156, 203, and 232–235
- slate

Content Assessed	Lesson(s)	Assessment Items: Self	Oral/Slate	Written: Part A	Written: Part B	Open Response
Identify the digits in numbers and express their values. [Number and Numeration Goal 1]	2•1, 2•3, 2•5, 2•7–2•9			10		
Find equivalent names for whole numbers. [Number and Numeration Goal 4]	2•5, 2•7–2•9			5		
Use basic facts to compute extended facts. [Operations and Computation Goal 1]	2•1–2•9	1	1–4	1–4	11, 12	
Use paper-and-pencil algorithms to solve problems involving the addition and subtraction of whole numbers. [Operations and Computation Goal 2]	2•1–2•9	4, 5, 6		6, 7	13, 14	✓
Use strategies to make estimates. [Operations and Computation Goal 5]	2•7, 2•8				13, 14	
Apply parts-and-total and comparison situations. [Operations and Computation Goal 6]	2•4–2•9	3		6, 7		
Tell and show time on an analog clock. [Measurement and Reference Frames Goal 4]	2•1, 2•3, 2•6, 2•8			8, 9		✓
Find and use rules to solve problems. [Patterns, Functions, and Algebra Goal 1]	2•1–2•9	2		3, 4	11, 12	

2 Looking Ahead: Preparing for Unit 3

Math Boxes 2•10

Home Link 2•10: Unit 3 Family Letter

Materials
- *Math Journal 1*, p. 54
- *Math Masters*, pp. 60–63

152 Unit 2 Progress Check 2

Core Assessment Resources

Assessment Handbook

- **Unit 4 Assessment Overview,** pages 76–83
- **Unit 4 Assessment Masters,** pages 149–152
- **Unit 4 Individual Profiles of Progress,** pages 212, 213, and 248
- **Unit 4 Class Checklists,** pages 214, 215, and 249
- **Math Logs,** pages 254–256
- **Exit Slip,** page 251
- **Other Student Assessment Forms,** pages 252, 253, 257, and 258

Assessment Management Spreadsheets

The Assessment Management Spreadsheets consist of the Digital Class Checklists and Individual Profile of Progress Checklists. Use them to monitor, record, and report children's progress.

Addressing All Needs

Differentiated Instruction

Adjusting the Activity – suggests adaptations that target advanced learners, English language learners, or learners who need additional instructional support.

ELL SUPPORT / **ELL** – provides lesson-specific suggestions to help English language learners understand and process the mathematical content.

READINESS – accesses children's prior knowledge or previews content that prepares children to engage in the lesson's Part 1 activities.

EXTRA PRACTICE – provides additional opportunities to apply the mathematical content of the lesson.

ENRICHMENT – enables children to apply or further explore the mathematical content of the lesson.

Lesson	Adjusting the Activity	ELL Support/ ELL	Readiness	Extra Practice	Enrichment
4•1	•	•	•		•
4•2	•	•	•	•	
4•3	•	•	•		•
4•4	•	•	•		•
4•5	•	•	•		•
4•6			•		•
4•7		•		•	•
4•8	•	•	•		•
4•9			•	•	•
4•10	•		•		•
4•11		•	•	•	
4•12	•		•		•

Additional Resources

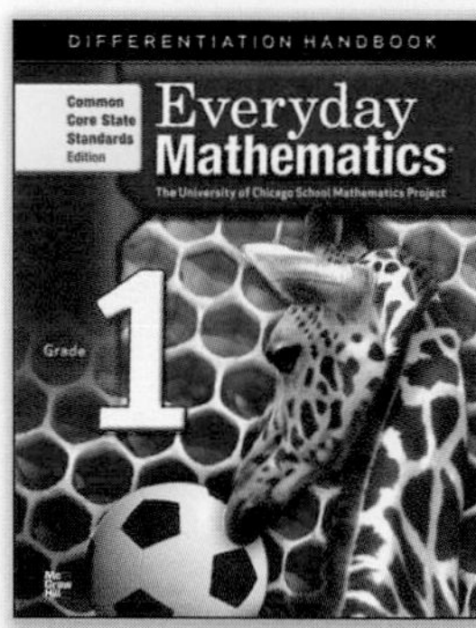

Differentiation Handbook
Provides ideas and strategies for differentiating instruction.
Pages 71–77

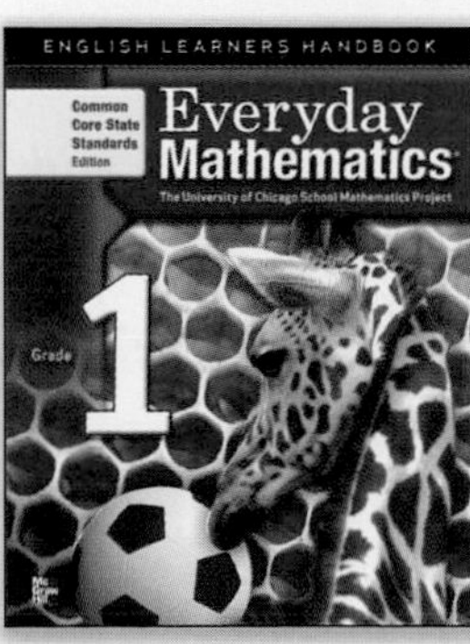

English Learners Handbook
Contains lesson-specific comprehension strategies.
Pages 41–52

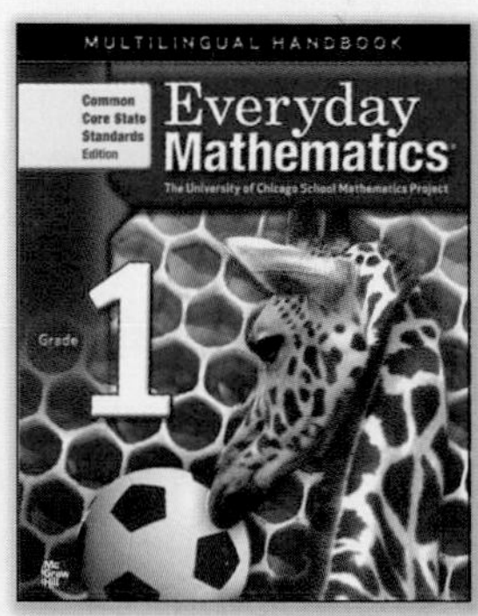

Multilingual Handbook
Previews concepts and vocabulary. It is written in six languages.
Pages 81–104

Planning Tips

Multiage Classroom

Companion Lessons from Grades K and 2 can help you meet instructional needs of a multiage classroom. The full Scope and Sequence can be found in the Appendix.

Grade K	Routine 7	1•13, 5•6, 5•7	5•6, 5•7, 5•11	5•12	5•12	5•12	4•10, 6•5, 7•8	8•2, 8•3, 8•11	6•4	7•10	7•6, 7•12	7•6, 7•12
Grade 1	**4•1**	**4•2**	**4•3**	**4•4**	**4•5**	**4•6**	**4•7**	**4•8**	**4•9**	**4•10**	**4•11**	**4•12**
Grade 2	1•1, 1•12, 4•4	9•2	9•1, 9•2	9•1, 9•2	9•1–9•4	9•1–9•5	1•12, 3•4, 3•5	1•3, 3•3, 12•2	12•3	1•8	2•2–2•5, 2•7	1•4, 2•2–2•5

Pacing for Success

Pacing depends on a number of factors, such as children's individual needs and how long your school has been using *Everyday Mathematics*. At the beginning of Unit 4, you may want to use tools available at www.everydaymathonline.com to help you set your pace.

Home Support

Unit 4 Family Letter (English/Spanish) provides families with an overview, Do-Anytime Activities, Building Skills through Games, a list of vocabulary, and answers to the daily homework (Home Links). Family Letters in English, Spanish, and seven other languages are also available online.

Home Links are the daily homework assignments. They consist of active projects and ongoing review problems.

▸ Home Support Resources

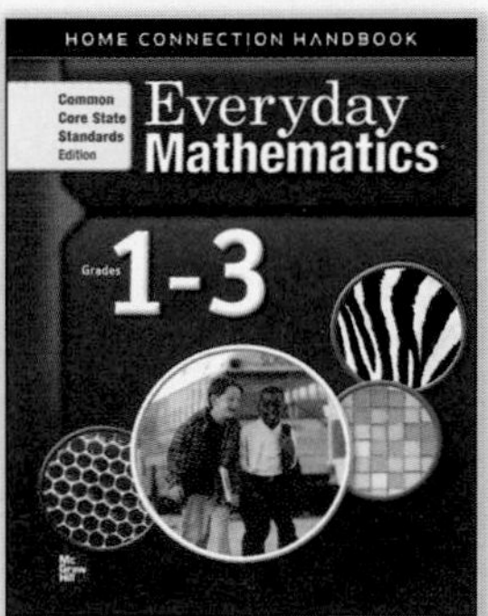

Home Connection Handbook
Offers ideas and reproducible masters for communicating with families. See Table of Contents for unit information.

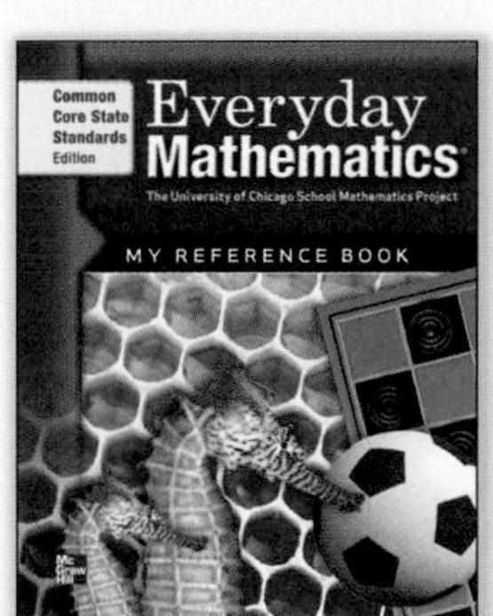

My Reference Book
Beginning in Unit 6, *My Reference Book* provides a resource for children and parents.

Technology Resources

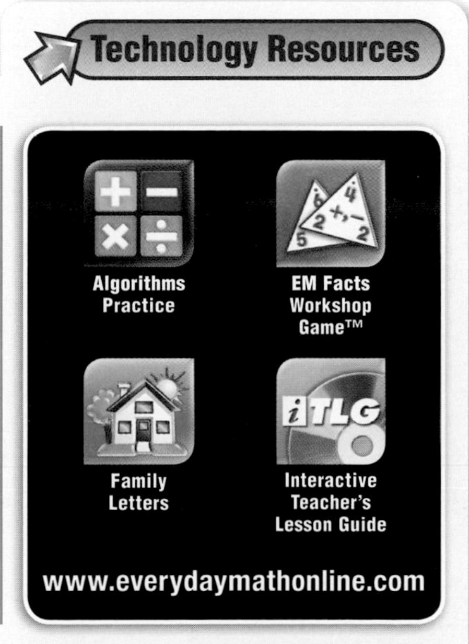

Materials

Technology Resources www.everydaymathonline.com

ePresentations

eToolkit

Algorithms Practice

EM Facts Workshop Game™

Family Letters

Assessment Management

Common Core State Standards

Curriculum Focal Points

Interactive Teacher's Lesson Guide

Lesson	Masters	Manipulative Kit	Other Items
4•1	Home Link Masters, pp. 91 and 92 Teaching Masters, pp. 93 and 94 *Differentiation Handbook,* p. 126	Class Number Line; dominoes	outdoor thermometer; Class Thermometer Posters; daily newspaper or weather Web site
4•2	Teaching Aid Masters, pp. 336A and 336B Home Link Master, p. 96 Teaching Master, p. 95	slate*	items of various lengths; pennies; 4" by 6" note cards; 1-inch stacking cubes*
4•3	Teaching Master, p. 97 Home Link Master, p. 98 *Differentiation Handbook,* p. 126	per partnership: tool-kit coins; 2 dice; number cards	$8\frac{1}{2}$" by 11" or larger construction paper; scissors; *How Big Is a Foot?*
4•4	Teaching Aid Masters, pp. 305 and 313 Teaching Master, p. 97 Home Link Master, p. 99 Game Masters, pp. 354 and 355 *Differentiation Handbook,* p. 126	clock-face stamp*	1-inch stacking cubes; scissors; objects shorter than a foot; overhead ruler*; 3" by 5" note cards*; 10" and 11" paper strips; objects between 1 and 2 feet long
4•5	Teaching Aid Masters, pp. 305, 313*, and 314 Transparency of *Math Masters,* p. 314* Home Link Master, p. 100	6-inch ruler; dominoes	pennies or overhead coins; *Jack and the Beanstalk;* plastic foam cup or half-pint milk carton; soil; bean (or sunflower) seeds; dowel rod or stick at least 14" long; ties or string for supporting plant; 1" by 8" strips of paper*
4•6	Home Link Master, p. 101	tool-kit tape measure	string; classroom objects
4•7	Teaching Aid Master, p. 315 or 316 Teaching Masters, pp. 95, 102, and 104 Home Link Master, p. 103	tape measure; 6-inch ruler; base-10 blocks; geoboards; rubber bands (colored, if possible)	stick-on notes; Class Data Pad; a book; pennies
4•8	Home Link Master, p. 106 Teaching Masters, pp. 105 and 107 Game Masters, pp. 342 and 355	tool-kit clock; tool-kit coins	demonstration clock with hour and minute hands; clock labels
4•9	Home Link Master, p. 108	tool-kit clock; slate	demonstration clock with hour and minute hands; 24-hour timeline; scissors; glue; construction paper; age-appropriate storybooks
4•10	Teaching Masters, pp. 109, 110, and 111* Home Link Master, p. 112 Game Masters, pp. 354–356	tool-kit coins*; number cards 0–9; slate	overhead coins; examples of scrolls; Chinese or other arts scrolls; paper-towel roll; scissors; tape or glue; large chart paper or tagboard; 2" by 1" stick-on notes
4•11	Teaching Aid Master, p. 336 Home Link Master, p. 113 Game Master, p. 344 Teaching Aid Master, p. 317 *Differentiation Handbook,* p. 126	per partnership: dice; slate; counters*	calculator
4•12	Teaching Aid Master, p. 336 Game Master, p. 353 Home Link Master, p. 114	base-10 cubes; per group: 2 six-sided dice, 2 polyhedral dice, marked 0–9*; slate	per group: 20 pennies or counters, 1 paper plate, 3" by 5" note cards, calculator
4•13	Assessment Masters, pp. 149–152 Home Link Masters, pp. 115–118	slate	pennies

*Denotes optional materials

Mathematical Background

The discussion below highlights the major content ideas presented in Unit 4 and helps establish instructional priorities.

Math Message (Lesson 4◆1)

Beginning with Lesson 4-1, a Math Message is included as a part of each lesson. Some Math Messages review previous topics; others are tasks for children to complete in preparation for one or more activities. Many teachers use the Math Message as a routine to help start the day. Children should complete the Math Message before the lesson.

Decide how you will display the Math Message and how you will expect children to respond to the message.

Read about Math Messages in Section 1.2.5 of the *Teacher's Reference Manual.*

Measurement and Reference Frames

Although reference frames (such as clocks, calendars, timelines, and thermometers) often make use of measures, numbers in reference frames mean different things and are used differently from measures. For example, ordinary arithmetic is seldom meaningful when applied to numbers from reference frames: 30°F is not "twice as warm" as 15°F; 3:00 P.M. plus 2:00 P.M. is not 5:00 P.M.

Note

You may need to read each day's Math Message to the class, depending upon the reading abilities of children in your class.

Knowledge about the reference frame itself is needed to make sense of the numbers in it. For example, the year 2007 on the standard United States calendar does not mean 2007 on the Jewish calendar, the Muslim calendar, or the Chinese calendar.

Measurements are never negative, but there are many negative numbers in reference frames.

For more information about measurement and reference frames, see Chapters 14 and 15 in the *Teacher's Reference Manual.*

Reading a Thermometer (Lesson 4◆1)

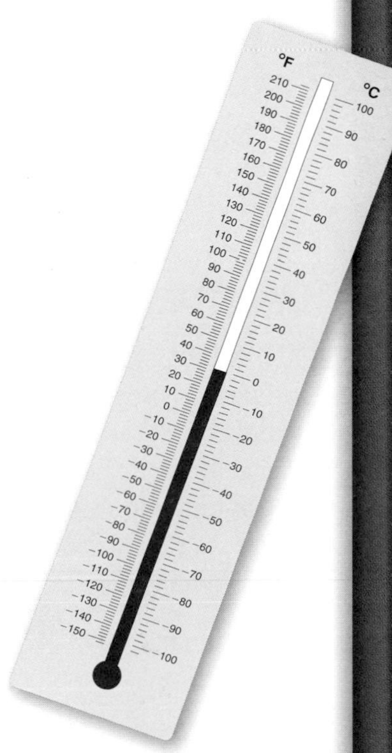

Most people think of temperatures as measures, but temperatures are actually numbers used in different number-line reference systems. There is an arbitrary zero (where a saturated salt solution freezes in the Fahrenheit system and where pure water freezes in the Celsius system), and temperatures are measured above and below that zero. Also, the value of one *degree* is different in different systems. There are 180 degrees from freezing to boiling water in the Fahrenheit system and 100 degrees from freezing to boiling water in the Celsius system.

In this lesson, children begin reading temperatures to the nearest two degrees. Encourage children to report temperatures using phrases like *between _ and _ degrees Fahrenheit* or *almost _ degrees Fahrenheit.*

Read more about measuring temperature in Section 15.1, located in the *Teacher's Reference Manual.*

Nonstandard Linear Measures

(Lesson 4◆2)

Children measure the lengths of classroom objects using nonstandard units, such as hands, paces, and arm spans. Children learn that basic measuring techniques require placing the units end to end without gaps, and labeling the resulting measure with whichever unit was used.

Measurements are approximations, so a measurement is taken to the nearer unit. This is because the object being measured never corresponds exactly to marked intervals and because the tools we use to measure things are imprecise. Thus, the development of estimation vocabulary like *about, almost, a little more,* and *a little less* is encouraged.

Personal "Foot" and Standard Foot

(Lesson 4◆3)

Children use tracings of their feet to measure the lengths of objects. Then they compare the measurements and find that they get different numbers of feet for measurements of the same objects. A standard U.S. customary foot unit is then used to measure the same objects to get the same measures, thus emphasizing the need for standard units.

Read Section 14.1 in the *Teacher's Reference Manual* to learn more about personal measures.

The Inch (Lesson 4◆4)

The inch is introduced as a standard unit for measuring objects smaller than a foot and for measuring objects whose lengths are "between feet." Children use inch rulers with the half-inches marked to help them measure to the nearest inch.

Measuring Tools and Standards for Measures (Lessons 4◆5 and 4◆6)

Measuring tools provide ways to attach numbers to many common and uncommon things. Much of modern industry and technology depends on using precise and accurate measures that are standardized throughout the world.

In these two lessons, children estimate the total length of an object to begin to develop a sense of the length of a foot and of an inch. They also estimate to measure to the nearest foot or inch.

For more information about measuring tools, please read Section 14.10, located in the *Teacher's Reference Manual.*

Project Note

Use Project 2, Amaryllis Plant, to provide opportunities for children to observe plant growth over time and to collect and graph data.

Explorations (Lesson 4◆7)

In this lesson, you should direct the measuring and recording of children's heights. (This activity will also be done later in the school year so that children can find out how much they have grown.) The data from this activity are used to make a bar graph to find a "typical" height for a first grader.

Another activity provides for children's exploration of base-10 blocks. Time spent getting familiar with the blocks is important, since the blocks will be used for developing place-value concepts and for early work with computational algorithms.

You can read more about Explorations in the Management Guide Section 1.2.1 of the *Teacher's Reference Manual.*

Telling Time and Timelines (Lessons 4◆8 and 4◆9)

This lesson refines children's time-telling skills. Notice that times continue to be reported with phrases that suggest approximation: *about, between, almost.* Also, note that digital notation will be introduced in Unit 6 and children will learn about the division of an hour into 60 minutes.

Timelines showing when events took place are intended to help children begin to develop a sense of longer periods of time. Children make timelines for a 24-hour day, for the first half of the school year, and for a week in their lives.

See Section 15.2.3 in the *Teacher's Reference Manual* for additional information about timelines.

Number Scrolls (Lesson 4◆10)

Many teachers have found the activity of filling in blank number grids to be a fruitful exercise both for number-writing practice and for increased intuition about how our base-ten place-value system works. This activity can be continued in small doses over several days or many weeks, depending on the interest of children in extending their scrolls.

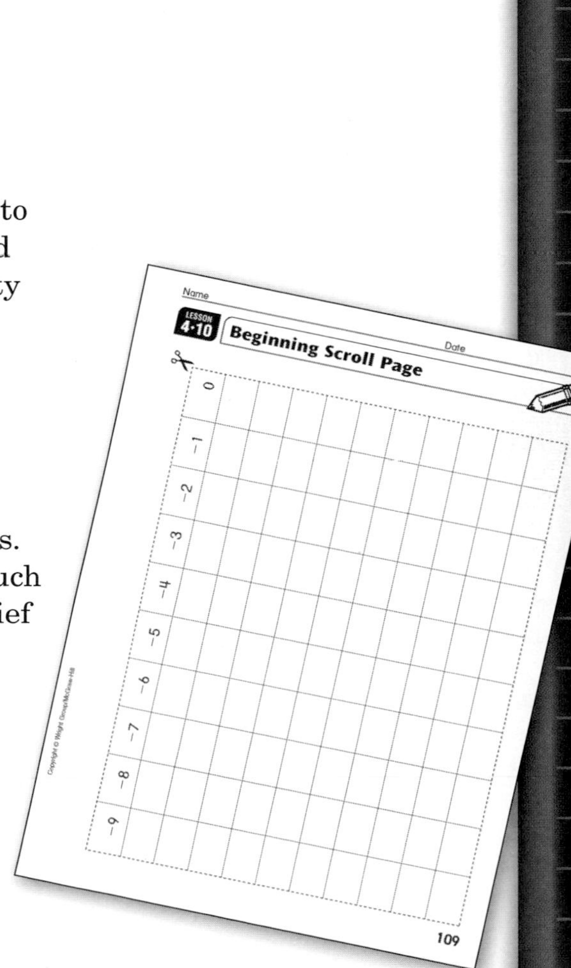

Name

Date

LESSON 4·10 Beginning Scroll Page

0
−1
−2
−3
−4
−5
−6
−7
−8
−9

109

Fact Power (Lessons 4◆11 and 4◆12)

This lesson begins children's work toward automatic recall of basic facts. *Everyday Mathematics* provides practice and drill in several formats, such as games, choral responses, and paper-and-pencil work, in relatively brief sessions throughout the year.

Lessons designed to build instant recall of the basic facts appear throughout the *Everyday Mathematics* program. The regular class routine includes games to practice basic facts at each grade level. This lesson introduces *Shaker Addition Top-It.* In addition to playing mathematics games, the choral-response routine provides for frequent practice of basic facts.

Read Section 16.3.2 in the *Teacher's Reference Manual* for more information about basic facts and fact power.

4•1 Math Message and Reading a Thermometer

Objectives To introduce the Math Message routine; to review thermometers; and to introduce reading temperatures to the nearest two degrees.

www.everydaymathonline.com

ePresentations

eToolkit

Algorithms Practice

EM Facts Workshop Game™

Family Letters

Assessment Management

Common Core State Standards

Curriculum Focal Points

Interactive Teacher's Lesson Guide

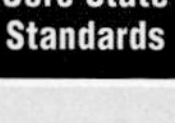
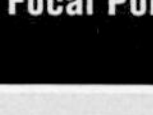

1 Teaching the Lesson

Key Concepts and Skills

- Count forward by 2s from a multiple of 10. [Number and Numeration Goal 1]
- Read temperature to the nearest 10° on a thermometer. [Measurement and Reference Frames Goal 3]
- Read temperature to the nearest 2° on a thermometer. [Measurement and Reference Frames Goal 3]

Key Activities

Children are introduced to the Math Message. Children review the features of a thermometer and how it works. They learn how to read a thermometer that has marks for every two degrees.

Ongoing Assessment: Recognizing Student Achievement
Use Mental Math and Reflexes.
[Number and Numeration Goal 1]

Key Vocabulary

Math Message ◆ thermometer ◆ temperature ◆ degree ◆ Fahrenheit

Materials

Math Journal 1, p. 54
outdoor thermometer ◆ Class Number Line ◆ Class Thermometer Poster (°F) ◆ Class Thermometer Poster (°F/°C)

2 Ongoing Learning & Practice

Playing *Domino Top-It*
dominoes
Children practice finding sums and comparing quantities.

Math Boxes 4•1
Math Journal 1, p. 55
Children practice and maintain skills through Math Box problems.

Home Link 4•1
Math Masters, pp. 91 and 92
Children practice and maintain skills through Home Link activities.

3 Differentiation Options

READINESS

Reading Numbers in Thermometers
Math Masters, p. 93
Class Number Line
Children fill in missing numbers on thermometers and count by 2s.

ENRICHMENT

Recording Warmer and Cooler Temperatures
Math Masters, p. 94
daily newspaper or weather Web site
Children record temperatures of places that are warmer and cooler than where they live.

ELL SUPPORT

Building a Math Word Bank
Differentiation Handbook, p. 126
Children add the term *temperature* to their Math Word Banks.

Advance Preparation

***Teacher's Reference Manual,* Grades 1–3** pp. 12, 171

Getting Started

Mental Math and Reflexes 

First, count up and back by 2s, starting at multiples of 10. Then start at even numbers that are not multiples of 10.

Math Message

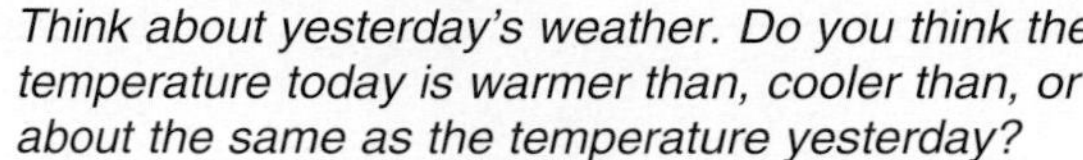

Think about yesterday's weather. Do you think the temperature today is warmer than, cooler than, or about the same as the temperature yesterday?

Ongoing Assessment: Recognizing Student Achievement

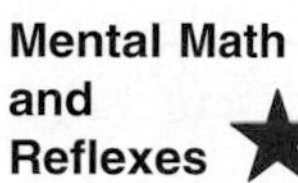

Mental Math and Reflexes

Use **Mental Math and Reflexes** to assess children's ability to skip count by 2s. Children are making adequate progress if they are able to count by 2s from a multiple of 10. Some children may be able to count by 2s from any even number.

[Number and Numeration Goal 1]

1 Teaching the Lesson

Interactive whiteboard-ready ePresentations are available at www.everydaymathonline.com to help you teach the lesson.

Introducing the Math Message Routine

WHOLE-CLASS DISCUSSION

Explain the routine you will use for your daily **Math Message.**

1. Tell children that the Math Message will give them a task to complete each day.
2. Show the specific place in the classroom where the Math Message will appear.
3. Tell children when to complete the task, discuss how their answers might be recorded, and tell them where to hand in their work.

When you begin to use the Math Message routine, read the message aloud, and have the class work on it together. As children learn to read independently, the Math Message routine should become more independent. Use rebuses or pictures as you write the Math Messages. At times, you might need an oral explanation of a written message.

We think today is cooler than yesterday.
Yesterday it was about 60°F.
Children's Predictions
48°F
56°F

NOTE You might mention that another measurement unit of temperature is °C (degrees Celsius). Show children the Class Thermometer Poster (°F/°C). Fahrenheit and Celsius are different scales for measuring temperatures. A temperature scale is a number line made by choosing a cold point and a hot point and then marking a number of equal spaces between them.

ELL When you use *Everyday Mathematics* posters with English language learners, display either the English version only or the English and Spanish versions simultaneously.

▶ Math Message Follow-Up

Have children tell if they think today's temperature is warmer than, cooler than, or about the same as yesterday's temperature by showing "thumbs-up," "thumbs-down," or fists. Come to a class consensus and write the class's decision on the board. Next, ask children what the temperature was yesterday and record this information. Then have children predict what the temperature is today, keeping in mind what is written on the board. Record children's predictions. Complete the temperature routine and discuss the accuracy of their predictions.

▶ Reviewing Thermometers and How to Read Them

Ask questions like the following to review how thermometers work.

- What is a **thermometer** used for? Measuring temperature
- What is **temperature?** A measurement of how cold or hot something is
- How does a thermometer measure temperature? The colored liquid in the glass tube goes up when the temperature of the air, a person, or an object gets warmer, and it goes down when the temperature gets colder.
- How is temperature reported? Temperature is reported as the number of **degrees** indicated by a thermometer. The number next to the mark that is closest to the top of the colored liquid names the number of degrees.
- What does °F at the top of the thermometer mean? °F means degrees **Fahrenheit.** The "°" symbol means *degrees,* and the *F* means *Fahrenheit.* It names the measurement unit of temperature.
- How is the Class Thermometer Poster (°F) like the Class Number Line? Sample answer: They both have evenly spaced marks that represent numbers.
- How is the Class Thermometer Poster (°F) different from the Class Number Line? Sample answers: Numbers on the thermometer are marked only at the 10s. There are no arrows at either end of the thermometer as there are on the number line.

Adjusting the Activity

Review reading temperatures to the nearest 10 degrees before children read temperatures to the nearest 2 degrees. Set the red ribbon on the Class Thermometer Poster (°F) to show temperatures that are multiples of 10 and then show temperatures between multiples of 10. Make the readings more difficult as appropriate. Remind children to use phrases such as *between* ___ *and* ___ *degrees Fahrenheit* and *almost* ___ *degrees Fahrenheit.*

AUDITORY • KINESTHETIC • TACTILE • VISUAL

▶ Reading Temperatures to the Nearest Two Degrees

(*Math Journal 1,* p. 54)

Show children the Class Thermometer Poster (°F/°C).

1. Ask how the Fahrenheit thermometer shown on this side is different from the previous one. This thermometer has marks between the 10s.
2. Ask children what they think the shorter marks stand for. Numbers that are not written that name temperatures between multiples of 10 (You might relate these marks to marks between the numbered marks on other measuring tools children may have seen, such as rulers and bath scales.)
3. Explain how to find the numbers represented by these marks. Point to the numbers 40 and 50 on the thermometer.
   - ▷ Point out that there are 10 spaces from 40 to 50 on the thermometer, just as there are 10 spaces from 40 to 50 on the Class Number Line. Each mark stands for 1 degree.
   - ▷ Count with children from 40 to 50 on the thermometer. Ask them to recall the numbers they recited for the longer marks. Ask children what the numbers at the longer marks have in common. They are even numbers.

NOTE Beginning with journal page 54, children will only be working with sections of thermometers. To aid in this transition, a complete thermometer has been added to this journal page.

4. Have children practice reading temperatures that are multiples of two. Set the red ribbon on the Class Thermometer Poster (°F/°C) to a temperature. Have the class count in unison the number of degrees, starting with the largest multiple of 10 and then counting up by 2s. Repeat as time allows.
5. Children complete the journal page on their own or with a partner. For Problems 1–6, remind children to label their answers °F since the numbers stand for "degrees Fahrenheit." Circulate and assist as children color the thermometers in Problems 7–9 on the journal page to show temperatures.

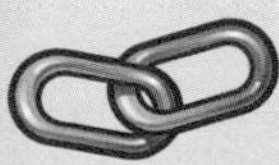

Links to the Future

This is the first time children are formally asked to read a thermometer to the nearest two degrees. At this time, most children should be able to read temperatures to the nearest 10 degrees, using language such as *a little more than* and *about halfway between.* Children will continue to practice reading temperatures to the nearest two degrees throughout the year, but it is not a Grade 1 Goal. Reading temperature on a thermometer is a Grade 2 Goal.

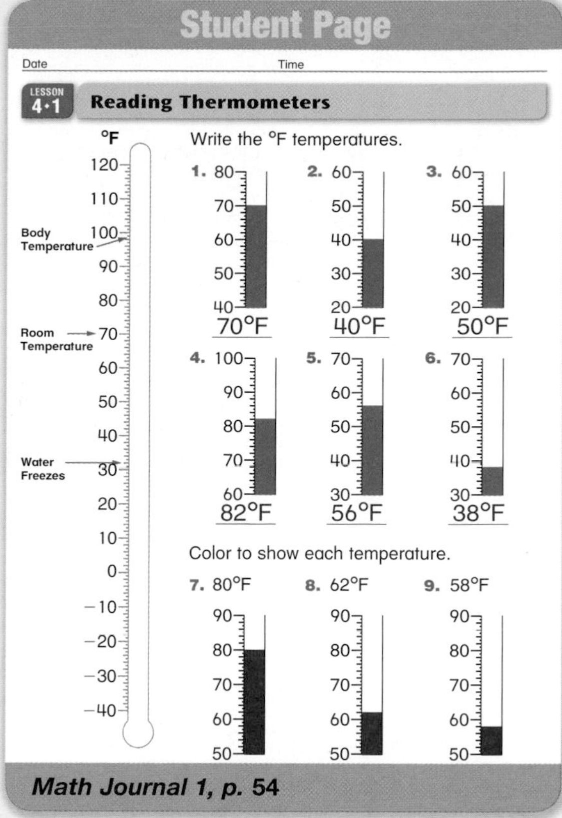

Student Page

Date Time

LESSON 4•1 **Reading Thermometers**

Write the °F temperatures.

1. 70°F
2. 40°F
3. 50°F
4. 82°F
5. 56°F
6. 38°F

Color to show each temperature.

7. 80°F
8. 62°F
9. 58°F

Math Journal 1, p. 54

NOTE You may want to lightly color the different zones on the Class Thermometer Poster (°F/°C) to match those on the Class Thermometer Poster (°F). Uncover the marks between 10s on the Fahrenheit scale of the outdoor thermometer. Keep the Celsius scale covered with masking tape. (The outdoor thermometer should resemble the thermometer pictured on journal page 54.)

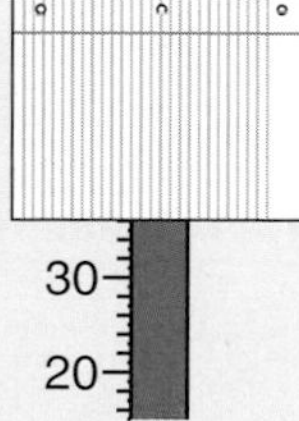

A sheet of paper can make it easier to read temperatures.

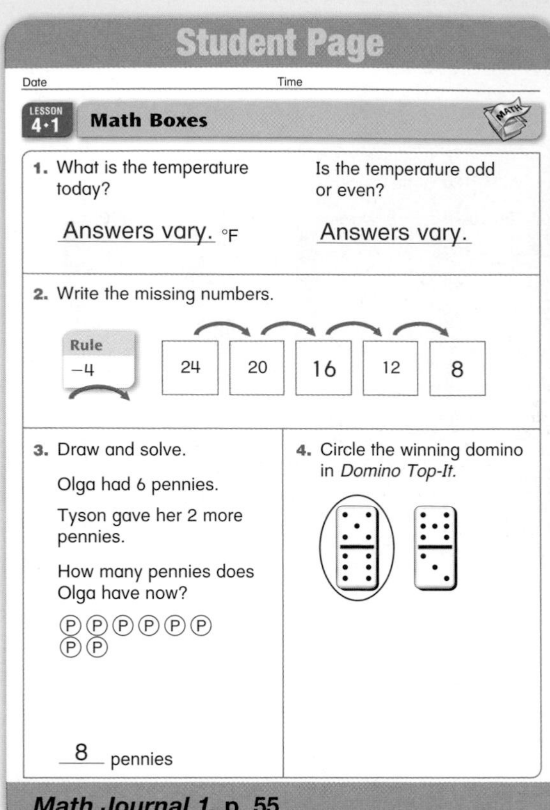

Student Page

Date Time

LESSON 4•1 **Math Boxes**

1. What is the temperature today?

Answers vary. °F

Is the temperature odd or even?

Answers vary.

2. Write the missing numbers.

Rule: −4

24, 20, 16, 12, 8

3. Draw and solve.

Olga had 6 pennies.

Tyson gave her 2 more pennies.

How many pennies does Olga have now?

Ⓟ Ⓟ Ⓟ Ⓟ Ⓟ Ⓟ Ⓟ Ⓟ

8 pennies

4. Circle the winning domino in *Domino Top-It.*

Math Journal 1, p. 55

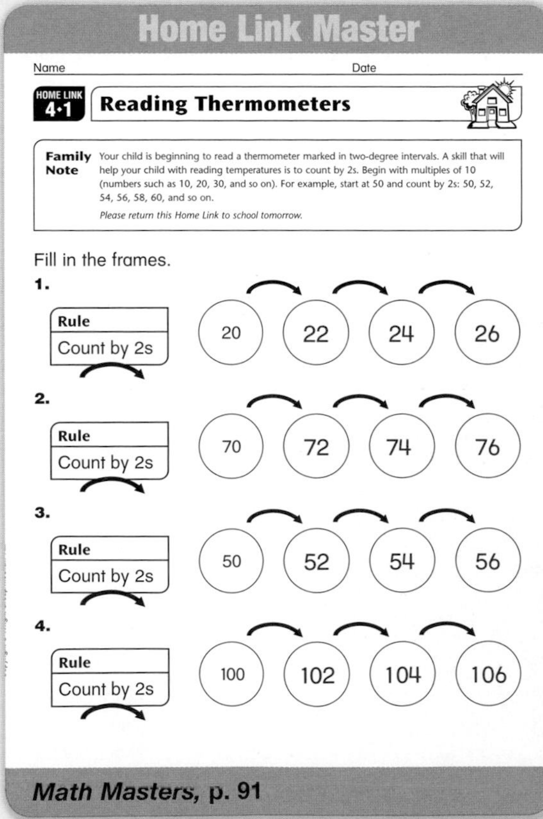

Home Link Master

Name Date

HOME LINK 4•1 **Reading Thermometers**

Family Note Your child is beginning to read a thermometer marked in two-degree intervals. A skill that will help your child with reading temperatures is to count by 2s. Begin with multiples of 10 (numbers such as 10, 20, 30, and so on). For example, start at 50 and count by 2s: 50, 52, 54, 56, 58, 60, and so on.

Please return this Home Link to school tomorrow.

Fill in the frames.

1. Rule: Count by 2s — 20, 22, 24, 26

2. Rule: Count by 2s — 70, 72, 74, 76

3. Rule: Count by 2s — 50, 52, 54, 56

4. Rule: Count by 2s — 100, 102, 104, 106

Math Masters, p. 91

Adjusting the Activity

Have children use a piece of paper to align the top of the liquid with the number on the scale. Position the paper from the top of the thermometer so that both the liquid column and the number scale are visible below the paper.

AUDITORY ◆ KINESTHETIC ◆ TACTILE ◆ VISUAL

After children finish the journal page, ask volunteers to take turns setting the Class Thermometer Poster to the temperatures in Problems 7–9 (°F/°C). Ask children to explain how they knew where to position the red ribbon.

2 Ongoing Learning & Practice

▶ Playing *Domino Top-It*

This is a variation of the *Top-It* game first introduced in Lesson 1-6. This game is for two or three players.

Directions

1. Children place the dominoes facedown on the table.
2. Each child chooses a domino and compares the total number of dots to the total number on his or her partner's domino.
3. The child with the larger total takes both dominoes. Ties are settled by another draw.
4. The game ends when time is up or when all of the dominoes have been drawn.

▶ Math Boxes 4•1

(*Math Journal 1,* p. 55)

Mixed Practice Math Boxes in this lesson are paired with Math Boxes in Lesson 4-3. The skills in Problem 4 preview Unit 5 content.

▶ Home Link 4•1

INDEPENDENT ACTIVITY

(*Math Masters,* pp. 91 and 92)

Home Connection Children complete Frames-and-Arrow diagrams to practice counting by 2s. They also read temperatures.

3 Differentiation Options

READINESS

SMALL-GROUP ACTIVITY

5–15 Min

Reading Numbers in Thermometers

(*Math Masters,* p. 93)

To provide experience reading the intervals on a thermometer scale, have children fill in the missing numbers on different thermometer sections. Begin with a choral counting warm-up. Direct children's attention to the Class Number Line and do a choral count by 2s from 0 to 30. Discuss similarities and differences between the Class Number Line and the thermometers on *Math Masters,* page 93. Remind children that number lines can go in any direction. Ask them to fill in the numbers on the first two thermometers and circle the counts by 2s. Then have children fill in the missing numbers on the third thermometer.

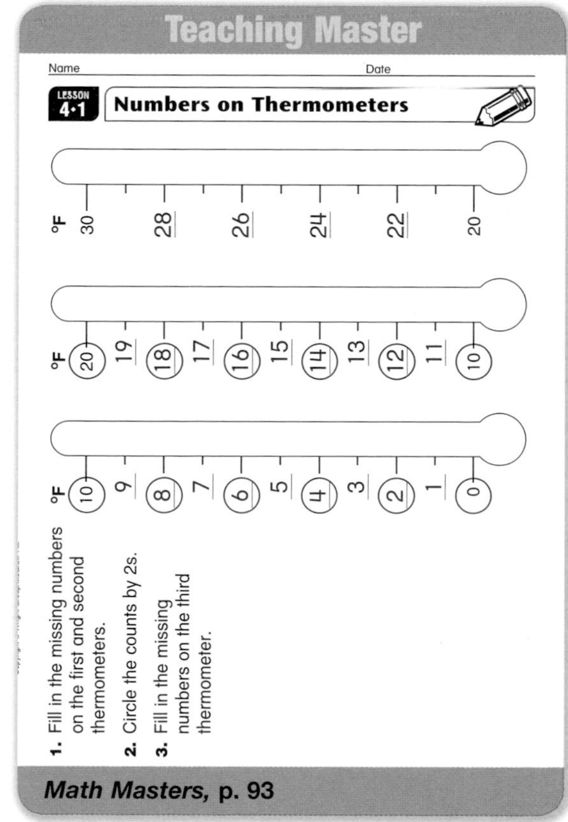

Teaching Master
Name
Date
LESSON 4·1
Numbers on Thermometers
°F 30 28 26 24 22 20
°F 20 19 18 17 16 15 14 13 12 11 10
°F 10 9 8 7 6 5 4 3 2 1 0
1. Fill in the missing numbers on the first and second thermometers.
2. Circle the counts by 2s.
3. Fill in the missing numbers on the third thermometer.

Math Masters, p. 93

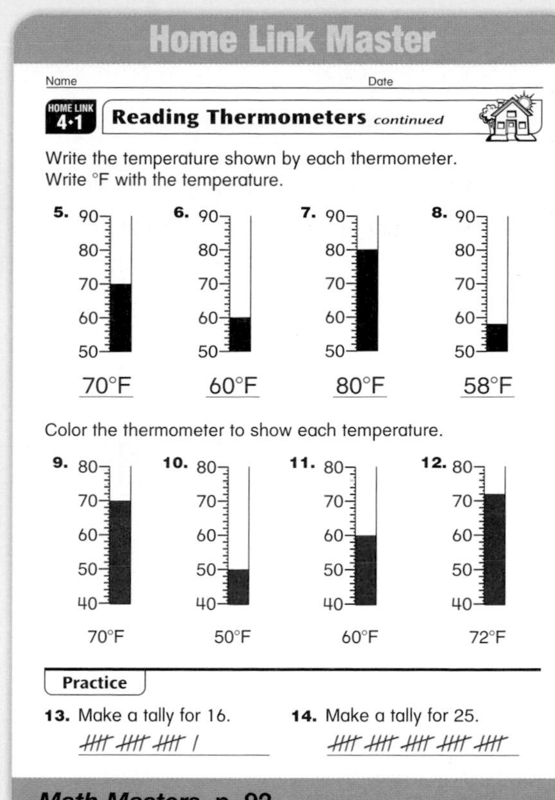

Home Link Master
Name
Date
HOME LINK 4·1
Reading Thermometers continued
Write the temperature shown by each thermometer.
Write °F with the temperature.
5. 70°F
6. 60°F
7. 80°F
8. 58°F
Color the thermometer to show each temperature.
9. 70°F
10. 50°F
11. 60°F
12. 72°F
Practice
13. Make a tally for 16.
14. Make a tally for 25.

Math Masters, p. 92

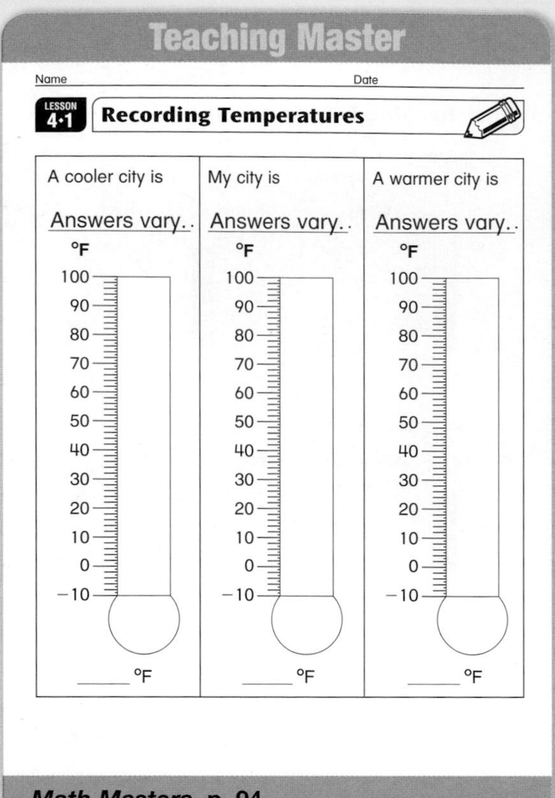

Teaching Master

Name Date

LESSON 4·1 **Recording Temperatures**

A cooler city is	My city is	A warmer city is
Answers vary.	Answers vary.	Answers vary.
____ °F	____ °F	____ °F

Math Masters, p. 94

ENRICHMENT

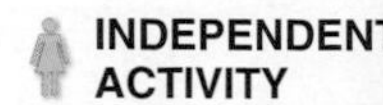

15–30 Min

▶ Recording Warmer and Cooler Temperatures

(*Math Masters,* p. 94)

To apply children's understanding of weather and temperature concepts, have them use a weather map to compare the temperatures and weather in different cities. Have children record today's predicted high temperature for their city on the middle thermometer on *Math Masters,* page 94. They then find a city with a cooler predicted temperature and a city with a warmer predicted temperature. Children record these temperatures and compare the temperatures in the three cities. Challenge children to locate the warmer and cooler places on a map.

ELL SUPPORT

▶ Building a Math Word Bank

(*Differentiation Handbook,* p. 126)

To provide language support for weather concepts, have children use the Word Bank Template found on *Differentiation Handbook,* page 126. Ask children to write the term *temperature,* draw a picture representing the term, and write other words that describe it. See the *Differentiation Handbook* for more information.

4•2 Nonstandard Linear Measures

Objective To provide practice measuring and comparing lengths using nonstandard units.

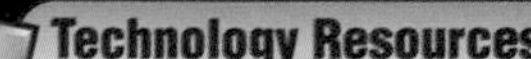

www.everydaymathonline.com

ePresentations

eToolkit

Algorithms Practice

EM Facts Workshop Game™

Family Letters

Assessment Management

Common Core State Standards

Curriculum Focal Points

Interactive Teacher's Lesson Guide

1 Teaching the Lesson

Key Concepts and Skills

- Count forward by 1s.
  [Number and Numeration Goal 1]
- Compare heights.
  [Measurement and Reference Frames Goal 1]
- Measure lengths in nonstandard units and compare lengths.
  [Measurement and Reference Frames Goal 1]
- Choose and label measurement units.
  [Measurement and Reference Frames Goal 1]

Key Activities

Children learn how to use parts of their bodies to measure lengths of objects. They compare lengths of two objects indirectly by using a third object. Children also compare their heights to the heights of objects in the classroom.

Ongoing Assessment: Informing Instruction See page 283.

Key Vocabulary

unit ◆ measure ◆ length ◆ digit ◆ hand ◆ hand span ◆ yard ◆ cubit ◆ arm span

Materials

Math Journal 1, pp. 56, 57, and inside back cover
Home Link 4•1
Ten-Frame Cards (*Math Masters,* pp. 336A and 336B)
items of various lengths ◆ slate (optional)

2 Ongoing Learning & Practice

Using 6 and 7 Pennies in Two-Fisted Penny Addition
Math Masters, p. 95
pennies
Children find and record complements of 6 and 7.

Ongoing Assessment: Recognizing Student Achievement
Use *Math Masters,* page 95.
[Operations and Computation Goal 1]

Ongoing Assessment: Informing Instruction See page 284.

Practicing Subtraction on a Number Grid
Math Journal 1, p. 58
Children practice subtraction using a number grid.

Math Boxes 4•2
Math Journal 1, p. 59
Children practice and maintain skills through Math Box problems.

Home Link 4•2
Math Masters, p. 96
Children practice and maintain skills through Home Link activities.

3 Differentiation Options

READINESS

Comparing Objects by Length
4" by 6" note cards ◆ small objects of various lengths ◆ 1-inch stacking cubes (optional)
Children compare the lengths of various objects.

EXTRA PRACTICE

Minute Math+
Minute Math®+, pp. 61 and 62
Children practice selecting measuring tools.

Advance Preparation

Select and label at least 8 classroom items of various lengths for children to measure in Part 1. For the optional Readiness activity in Part 3, gather 8 small objects of various lengths and use 3 note cards to make the following labels: *shorter than, longer than,* and *about the same as.*

***Teacher's Reference Manual,* Grades 1–3** pp. 155–158

Getting Started

Mental Math and Reflexes

Play *Ten-Frame Top-It.* See Lesson 2-3 for detailed instructions. Depending on children's comfort level with ten frames, you may wish to have them play the variation given on *Teacher's Lesson Guide,* page 107.

Math Message

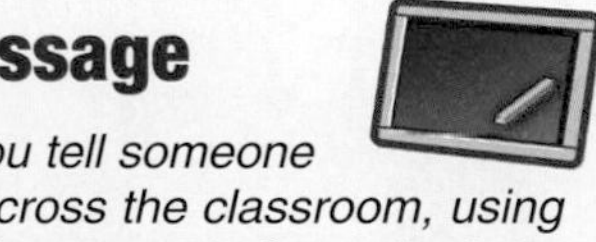

How would you tell someone how far it is across the classroom, using only your body or a part of your body to describe the distance?

Home Link 4·1 Follow-Up

Review answers to the Frames-and-Arrows and temperature problems. Ask children to share strategies for solving the Frames-and-Arrows problems.

1 Teaching the Lesson

▶ Math Message Follow-Up

Ask children how they would describe the distance and which bod parts they would use as **units.** For example, they might use arm lengths, foot lengths, steps, or hops. The **measure** of the distance is the number of times a particular body part is used to mark the distance. Remind children that these body parts must be marked off "end to end," without leaving spaces, to get an accurate measurement.

▶ Measuring Things with Fingers, Hands, Feet, and Arms

(*Math Journal 1,* p. 56)

Using journal page 56 as a reference, explain that for centuries, people used their bodies and parts of their bodies as units to tell about how long something was from end to end—**length**—or about how far one place was from another.

Children take turns coming to the front of the class and measurin the various items you selected. The rest of the children make tallies on their slates, or orally count in unison, to help keep track of about how many units are marked off. They record the measurements on their journal page. Remind children to line up the units end to end without leaving gaps.

Discuss the use of smaller units such as **digits** (finger widths), **hands,** or **hand spans** (outstretched fingers) to measure small items (such as a pencil or a book) and larger units such as feet, paces, historical **yards, cubits** (forearms), or **arm spans** (fathoms) to measure larger items (such as a bulletin board, a rug, a desk, or a table).

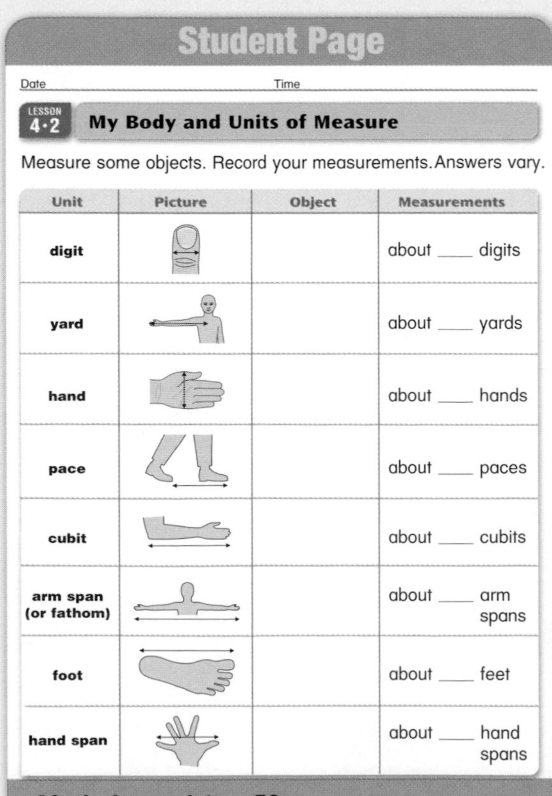

Student Page

Date Time

LESSON 4·2 My Body and Units of Measure

Measure some objects. Record your measurements. Answers vary.

Unit	Picture	Object	Measurements
digit			about ___ digits
yard			about ___ yards
hand			about ___ hands
pace			about ___ paces
cubit			about ___ cubits
arm span (or fathom)			about ___ arm spans
foot			about ___ feet
hand span			about ___ hand spans

Math Journal 1, p. 56

Ongoing Assessment: Informing Instruction

Watch for children who do not start measuring at the beginning of an object. Remind them that they need to align the edge of their body part with the beginning of the object being measured.

Children work in partnerships to measure objects in the room. Have several partnerships measure the same object using different units. For example, one pair measures a desk in digits, while another measures the desk in hand spans. Follow up with a brief discussion comparing the measurements. Discuss why there are such differences in the measurements.

- ▷ Different partnerships used different units.
- ▷ Even if the same units (such as digits, hands, or arm spans) were used, the units are nonstandard because people have different-sized bodies and body parts.
- ▷ There may have been gaps between units or accidental overlapping of units when measuring.

It is important that you and children use the unit labels, as well as estimation words such as *about* or *nearly.* For example, *about* 5 Ling digits; *nearly* 2 Diana hands; *a little shorter than* 3 Josh arm spans; and *about* 6 Paulo feet.

Comparing Lengths of Objects

WHOLE-CLASS DISCUSSION

Introduce children to the concept of comparing lengths of two objects indirectly by using a third object. Select a new pencil, a new crayon, and a small paper clip (or you may wish to use three different-sized items from the previous activity). Hold up the pencil and the crayon and ask children to tell which is longer. The pencil is longer than the crayon. Next, hold up the crayon and the paper clip and have children tell which is longer. The crayon is longer than the paper clip. Then hide all three objects. Ask the following questions:

- Which is longer, the pencil or the paper clip? The pencil
- How do you know without looking at the objects? Sample answer: The pencil is longer than the crayon and crayon is longer than the paper clip, so the pencil must be longer than the paper clip.

After the class has discussed this indirect comparison, hold the pencil and paper clip side by side to verify that the pencil is longer than the paper clip.

Student Page

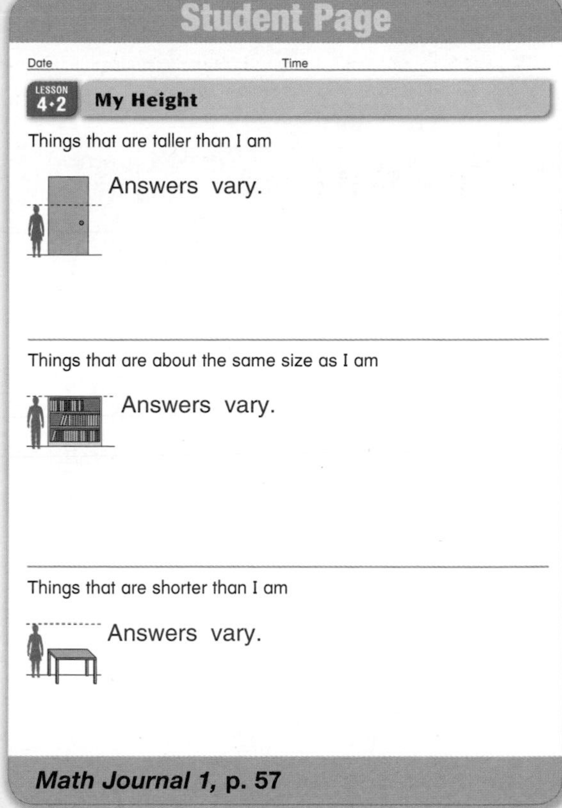

Date
Time
LESSON 4·2
My Height
Things that are taller than I am
Answers vary.
Things that are about the same size as I am
Answers vary.
Things that are shorter than I am
Answers vary.

Math Journal 1, p. 57

NOTE Since most measurements are estimates, encourage children to report measurements using words such as *about, almost, a little more than,* and *a little less than.*

NOTE In this lesson, children use the Transitive Property of Equality as they compare lengths of objects indirectly. Children need to understand this concept, but they should not be expected to use the term.

Student Page

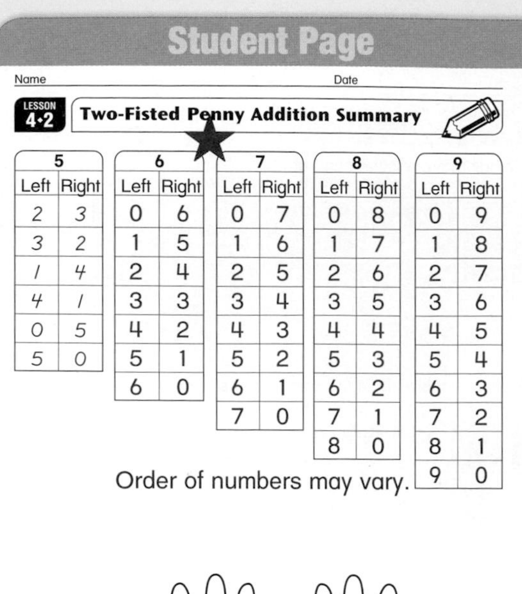

Name Date

LESSON 4·2 **Two-Fisted Penny Addition Summary**

5	
Left	Right
2	3
3	2
1	4
4	1
0	5
5	0

6	
Left	Right
0	6
1	5
2	4
3	3
4	2
5	1
6	0

7	
Left	Right
0	7
1	6
2	5
3	4
4	3
5	2
6	1
7	0

8	
Left	Right
0	8
1	7
2	6
3	5
4	4
5	3
6	2
7	1
8	0

9	
Left	Right
0	9
1	8
2	7
3	6
4	5
5	4
6	3
7	2
8	1
9	0

Order of numbers may vary.

Math Masters, p. 95

Adjusting the Activity

ELL

Have children directly compare the lengths and heights of objects to their own heights side by side, from a common base. Or cut pieces of string the same lengths as children's heights for comparing lengths and heights of objects not resting on the floor.

AUDITORY ◆ KINESTHETIC ◆ TACTILE ◆ VISUAL

Student Page

Date

LESSON 4·2 **Subtracting on a Number Grid**

-9	-8	-7	-6	-5	-4	-3	-2	-1	0
1	2	3	4	5	6	7	8	9	10
11	12	13	14	15	16	17	18	19	20
21	22	23	24	25	26	27	28	29	30
31	32	33	34	35	36	37	38	39	40
41	42	43	44	45	46	47	48	49	50
51	52	53	54	55	56	57	58	59	60
61	62	63	64	65	66	67	68	69	70

1. Start at 38. Count back 4. Where do you end up? 34
   38 – 4 = 34
2. Start at 59. Count back 9. Where do you end up? 50
   59 – 9 = 50
3. Start at 62. Count back 11. Where do you end up? 51
   62 – 11 = 51
4. Start at 70. Count back 17. Where do you end up? 53
   70 – 17 = 53

Try This

Subtract.

5. 43 – 20 = 23
6. 35 – 15 = 20

Math Journal 1, p. 58

▶ Comparing Individual Heights to Objects in the Classroom

PARTNER ACTIVITY

PROBLEM SOLVING

(*Math Journal 1,* p. 57)

Children find things that are taller (longer) than, shorter than, and about the same height as they are. They record the names or pictures on journal page 57 for discussion.

Ask children to identify some of the objects that are taller than, the same size as, and shorter than they are. Compare children's heights, using references to those objects. For example, Santos and Ian are taller than the red bookshelf. Essence and Wendy are shorter than the red bookshelf. Therefore, Santos and Ian are taller than Essence and Wendy.

2 Ongoing Learning & Practice

▶ Using 6 and 7 Pennies in Two-Fisted Penny Addition

INDEPENDENT ACTIVITY

(*Math Masters,* p. 95)

Children begin a systematic record of complements of numbers from 5 to 18 as a means of developing readiness for learning the basic addition and subtraction facts and the commutative propert of addition. Have children find and record all of the complements of 6 and 7. Children will find the complements of different numbers in future lessons.

Ongoing Assessment: Recognizing Student Achievement

Math Masters Page 95

Use ***Math Masters,* page 95** to assess children's ability to find complements of numbers in preparation for learning addition and subtraction facts. Children are making adequate progress if they are able to list some of the complements of 6 and 7. Some children may be able to list all of the complements of 6 and 7.

[Operations and Computation Goal 1]

Ongoing Assessment: Informing Instruction

Watch for children who write the same complements multiple times and do not realize they can write turn-around complements instead. Show children that just like they can flip-flop the hands that are holding the coins—from left hand to right hand and from right hand to left hand—they can also flip-flop the numbers on the record sheet.

Practicing Subtraction on a Number Grid

INDEPENDENT ACTIVITY

(*Math Journal 1*, p. 58)

Use journal page 58 to provide more practice with subtraction on the number grid.

Math Boxes 4·2

INDEPENDENT ACTIVITY

(*Math Journal 1*, p. 59)

Mixed Practice Math Boxes in this lesson are paired with Math Boxes in Lesson 4-4.

Home Link 4·2

INDEPENDENT ACTIVITY

(*Math Masters*, p. 96)

Home Connection Children measure their beds using hand spans. Children will discover that there are many different measurements.

3 Differentiation Options

READINESS

SMALL-GROUP ACTIVITY

Comparing Objects by Length

5–15 Min

To explore linear measurements using a concrete model, have children compare the lengths of objects. Lay out the labeled index cards in order of indicated size. Display a group of objects. Ask a volunteer to pick one object to compare. Ask another child to select a different object and place it next to the card with the appropriate label. Have children verbalize as they compare. For example: "The pencil is longer than the eraser." Children can compare the objects side by side from a common base or edge, or they can measure each object with a cube stack and use the stack to check the relative lengths.

SMALL-GROUP ACTIVITY

EXTRA PRACTICE

Minute Math+

5–15 Min

Use *Minute Math+*, pages 61 and 62 to provide practice selecting measuring tools.

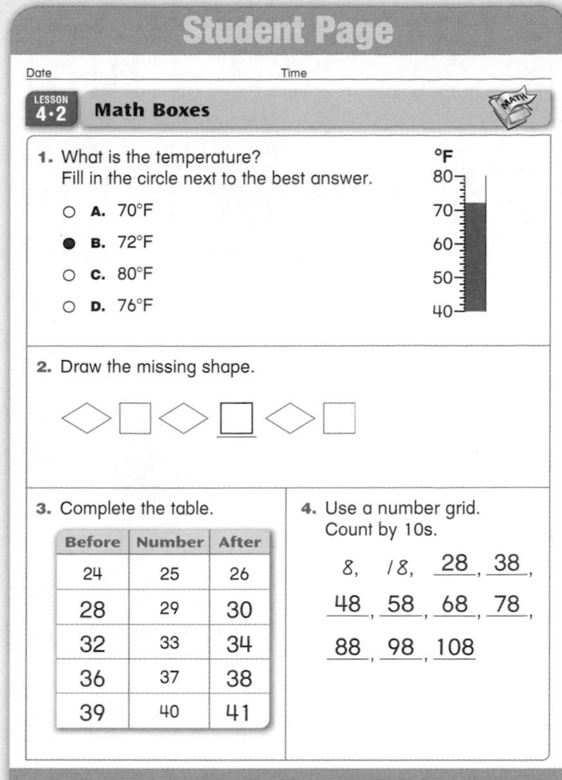

Student Page

Date Time

LESSON 4·2 **Math Boxes**

1. What is the temperature? Fill in the circle next to the best answer.
   - A. 70°F
   - B. 72°F
   - C. 80°F
   - D. 76°F

2. Draw the missing shape.

3. Complete the table.

Before	Number	After
24	25	26
28	29	30
32	33	34
36	37	38
39	40	41

4. Use a number grid. Count by 10s.

8, 18, 28, 38, 48, 58, 68, 78, 88, 98, 108

Math Journal 1, p. 59

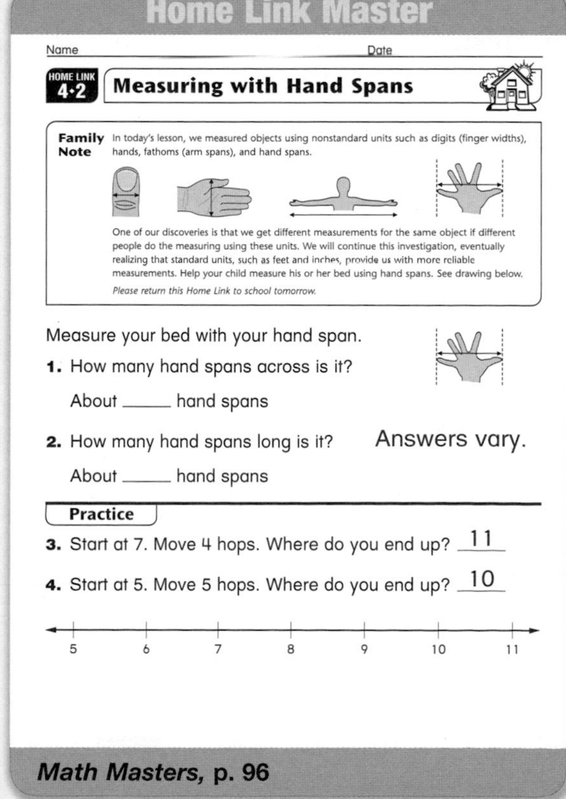

Home Link Master

Name Date

HOME LINK 4·2 **Measuring with Hand Spans**

Family Note In today's lesson, we measured objects using nonstandard units such as digits (finger widths), hands, fathoms (arm spans), and hand spans.

One of our discoveries is that we get different measurements for the same object if different people do the measuring using these units. We will continue this investigation, eventually realizing that standard units, such as feet and inches, provide us with more reliable measurements. Help your child measure his or her bed using hand spans. See drawing below.

Please return this Home Link to school tomorrow.

Measure your bed with your hand span.

1. How many hand spans across is it?
   About _____ hand spans
2. How many hand spans long is it? Answers vary.
   About _____ hand spans

Practice

3. Start at 7. Move 4 hops. Where do you end up? 11
4. Start at 5. Move 5 hops. Where do you end up? 10

Math Masters, p. 96

4•3 Personal "Foot" and Standard Foot

Objectives To provide practice measuring with a nonstandard unit and with the standard foot; and to facilitate understanding of the need for standard units.

www.everydaymathonline.com

ePresentations

eToolkit

Algorithms Practice

EM Facts Workshop Game™

Family Letters

Assessment Management

Common Core State Standards

Curriculum Focal Points

Interactive Teacher's Lesson Guide

1 Teaching the Lesson

Key Concepts and Skills

- Use language of approximation when measuring.
  [Measurement and Reference Frames Goal 1]
- Measure length with nonstandard units.
  [Measurement and Reference Frames Goal 1]
- Measure length to the nearest foot.
  [Measurement and Reference Frames Goal 1]

Key Activities

Children measure objects with their personal feet and with a standard foot.

Ongoing Assessment: Informing Instruction See page 288.

Key Vocabulary

foot ◆ feet ◆ standard foot

Materials

Math Journal 1, p. 60
Home Link 4•2
Math Masters, p. 97 (2 per child)
$8\frac{1}{2}$" by 11" or larger construction paper ◆ scissors

2 Ongoing Learning & Practice

Playing *Coin-Dice*
per partnership: tool-kit coins, 2 dice
Children practice making coin exchanges.

Math Boxes 4•3
Math Journal 1, p. 61
Children practice and maintain skills through Math Box problems.

Ongoing Assessment: Recognizing Student Achievement
Use Math Boxes, Problem 2.
[Patterns, Functions, and Algebra Goal 1]

Home Link 4•3
Math Masters, pp. 97 and 98
Children practice and maintain skills through Home Link activities.

3 Differentiation Options

READINESS

Investigating Length
per partnership: number cards (from the Everything Math Deck, if available)
Children measure the length of flat surfaces with nonstandard units.

ENRICHMENT

Solving Problems with *How Big Is a Foot?*
Children apply their understanding of standard measurement.

ELL SUPPORT

Building a Math Word Bank
Differentiation Handbook, p. 126
Children add the term *foot* to their Math Word Banks.

Advance Preparation

For Part 1, cut 1-foot strips of construction paper in case children need additional feet for measuring.

For the optional Enrichment activity in Part 3, obtain a copy of ***How Big Is a Foot?*** by Rolf Myller (Random House Children's Books, 1991).

***Teacher's Reference Manual,* Grades 1–3** pp. 157, 158

Getting Started

Mental Math and Reflexes

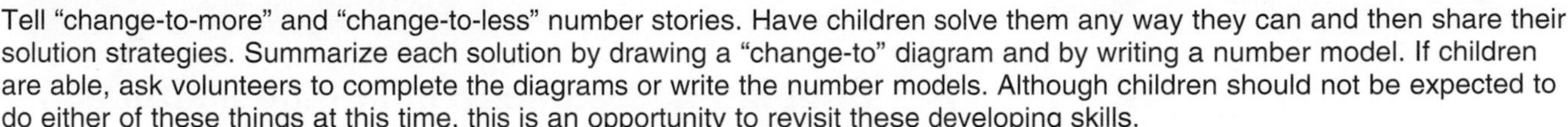

Tell "change-to-more" and "change-to-less" number stories. Have children solve them any way they can and then share their solution strategies. Summarize each solution by drawing a "change-to" diagram and by writing a number model. If children are able, ask volunteers to complete the diagrams or write the number models. Although children should not be expected to do either of these things at this time, this is an opportunity to revisit these developing skills.

●○○ Brielle woke up to find that it was about 28°F. By lunchtime, it had warmed up about 5 degrees. What was the temperature at lunchtime? About 33°F

●●○ The warmest temperature Thursday night was about 52°F. By morning, the temperature had cooled down about 12°F. What was the temperature Friday morning? About 40°F

●●● Ming saw that it was raining. He noticed that it was about 35°F. An hour later, the rain turned into snow and the temperature had dropped to about 25°F. How much colder was it? About 10°F colder Why do you think the rain turned to snow? The temperature fell below 32°F, the temperature at which water freezes.

Math Message

An adult and a child measured the same thing with their feet. Why might they get different answers?

Home Link 4•2 Follow-Up

Volunteers share how they measured their beds. *Why do you think different children might get different hand-span measures?* Their beds may be different sizes, and their hands are probably different sizes.

1 Teaching the Lesson

Math Message Follow-Up

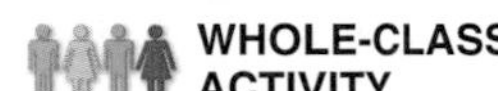

WHOLE-CLASS ACTIVITY

Invite children to share their answers to the Math Message problem. Ask them why they think their answers are different. Their feet are different lengths. Then do the following:

1. Measure heel to toe the number of teacher feet it takes to measure a marked distance across the floor. Have children count the steps. Point out that you are leaving no gaps between your feet. Record the total number of teacher feet.
2. Next, have a child follow the same procedure to measure the same distance. Make sure that the child leaves no gaps. Record the total in child feet. Use the child's name to describe the unit, such as *Jane feet.*
3. Discuss who got the larger total number of units. Informally develop the idea that it takes more small units than large units to measure something.

Measuring with Construction-Paper Cutouts of Children's Feet

PARTNER ACTIVITY

(*Math Journal 1,* p. 60)

Pass out construction paper, one piece per child. Partners trace each other's foot onto the paper, either with or without shoes. Then each partner cuts out the foot and writes his or her name on it.

Student Page

Date ______ Time ______

LESSON 4•3 **My Foot and the Standard Foot**

Measure two objects with the cutout of your foot. Draw pictures of the objects or write their names.

1. I measured Answers vary.

   It is about ______ ______ (your name) feet.

2. I measured

   It is about ______ ______ (your name) feet.

Measure the same two objects with the foot-long foot. Sometimes it is called the *standard foot.*

3. I measured

   It is about ______ feet.

4. I measured

   It is about ______ feet.

***Math Journal 1,* p. 60**

NOTE If time is short, rather than have children trace and cut out their feet, have them take off their shoes and use the shoes as their personal "feet" for measuring.

Children develop their measuring skills.

NOTE Overlapping and leaving gaps between units may cause differences in measurements for the same items.

Teaching Master

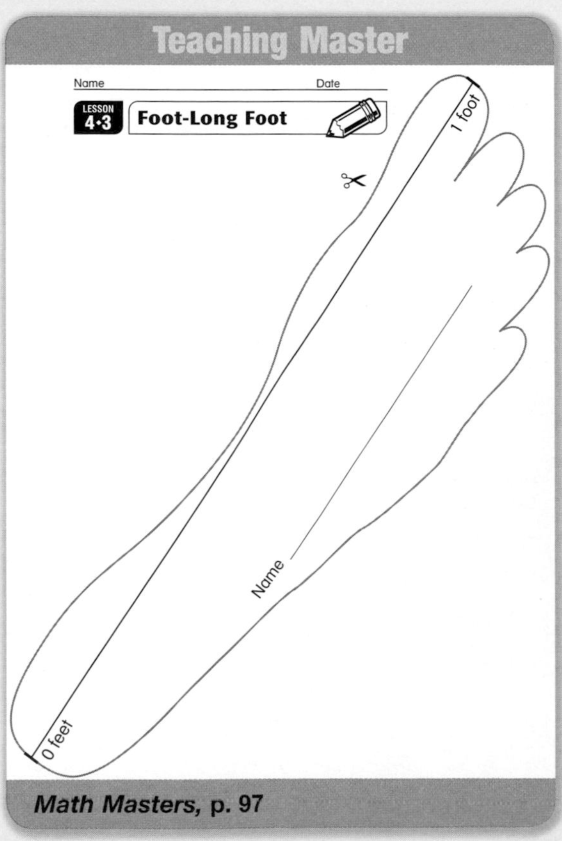

Name Date

LESSON 4·3 **Foot-Long Foot**

1 foot

Name

0 feet

Math Masters, p. 97

Partners use their foot cutouts to measure tables, the board, a desk, and so on. Then each partner names or draws two objects on journal page 60 and records about how many "[my name] feet" long each object is.

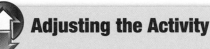

Ongoing Assessment: Informing Instruction

Watch for children who are ...

- overlapping units.
- leaving gaps between units.
- not naming the measurement to the nearest unit.
- alternating their foot with a partner's when they should be measuring only with their personal foot.

Bring the group together and compare children's personal foot-length measurements. Children with different-sized foot tracings will get different foot measurements for the same item. Ask children what they might do to solve the problem.

Adjusting the Activity

Children cut out four or five feet from construction paper. Each child can then practice lining up the feet—without gaps and without overlapping—to measure objects. When each child is ready, have him or her work on measuring with two feet and then finally with only one foot.

AUDITORY ◆ KINESTHETIC ◆ TACTILE ◆ VISUAL

▶ Measuring with a Standard Foot-Long Foot

PARTNEF ACTIVITY

(*Math Journal 1,* p. 60 and *Math Masters,* p. 97)

Children cut out one foot-long **foot** from copies of *Math Masters,* page 97.

Partners remeasure the same two objects that they measured wit their personal "foot." Partners measure the objects independently but collaborate to agree on a number that is close; for example, "a little more than 2 feet." Objects will usually be longer or shorter than a whole number of **feet.**

Children record their two measurements, using a **standard foot,** in Problems 3 and 4 on journal page 60. As with all measurements, encourage children to use the language of approximation: *about* —— *feet, a little less than* —— *feet,* or *about halfway between* —— *and* —— *feet.*

Discuss why children were able to find a number to agree on whe they were using the foot-long foot. They were measuring with a tool that was the same length.

Have children fold and save their foot-long feet for use in Lesson 4-

2 Ongoing Learning & Practice

Playing *Coin-Dice*

PARTNER ACTIVITY

Children practice making coin exchanges by playing *Coin-Dice*. For detailed instructions, see Lesson 3-12.

Math Boxes 4•3

INDEPENDENT ACTIVITY

(*Math Journal 1,* p. 61)

Mixed Practice Math Boxes in this lesson are paired with Math Boxes in Lesson 4-1. The skills in Problem 4 preview Unit 5 content.

Ongoing Assessment: Recognizing Student Achievement

Math Boxes Problem 2 

Use **Math Boxes, Problem 2** to assess children's ability to solve Frames-and-Arrows problems. Children are making adequate progress if they can solve this problem correctly.

[Patterns, Functions, and Algebra Goal 1]

Writing/Reasoning Have children discuss, draw, or write an answer to the following question: *How does drawing help you solve a number story?* A reasonable answer should explain the importance of a picture in determining the problem situation and its solution.

Home Link 4•3

INDEPENDENT ACTIVITY

(*Math Masters,* p. 98)

Home Connection In addition to the Home Link, children take home a copy of The Foot-Long Foot *Math Masters,* page 97. Using different-colored crayons, they trace each family member's foot onto the foot-long foot and then compare the foot lengths of their family members.

NOTE You may wish to ask children to order the foot lengths of their family members from smallest to largest.

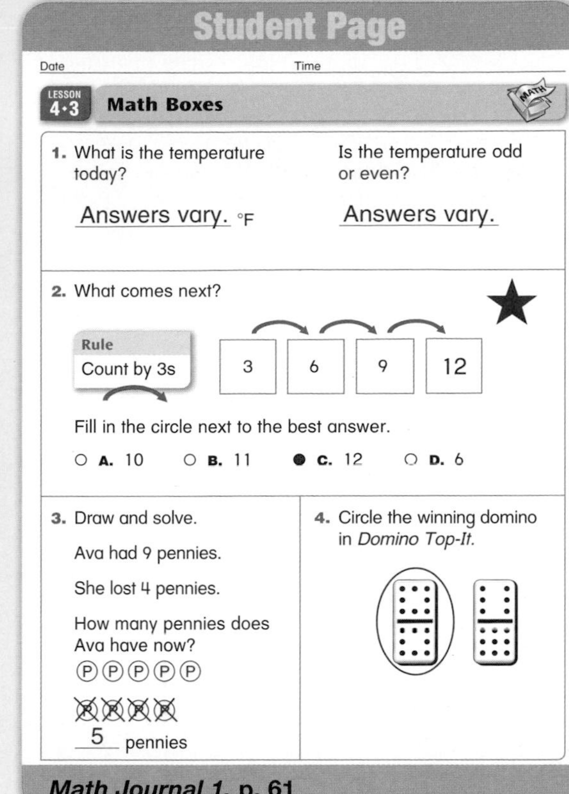

Student Page

Date Time

LESSON 4•3 **Math Boxes**

1. What is the temperature today?
Answers vary. °F

Is the temperature odd or even?
Answers vary.

2. What comes next? ★

Rule: Count by 3s

3 → 6 → 9 → 12

Fill in the circle next to the best answer.

○ A. 10 ○ B. 11 ● C. 12 ○ D. 6

3. Draw and solve.
Ava had 9 pennies.
She lost 4 pennies.
How many pennies does Ava have now?
Ⓟ Ⓟ Ⓟ Ⓟ Ⓟ
Ⓟ Ⓟ Ⓟ Ⓟ
5 pennies

4. Circle the winning domino in *Domino Top-It.*

Math Journal 1, p. 61

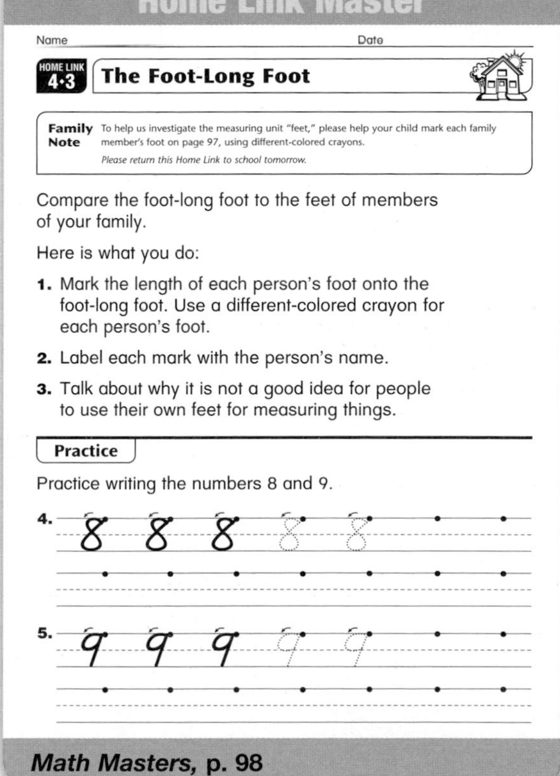

Home Link Master

Name Date

HOME LINK 4•3 **The Foot-Long Foot**

Family Note To help us investigate the measuring unit "feet," please help your child mark each family member's foot on page 97, using different-colored crayons.
Please return this Home Link to school tomorrow.

Compare the foot-long foot to the feet of members of your family.

Here is what you do:

1. Mark the length of each person's foot onto the foot-long foot. Use a different-colored crayon for each person's foot.
2. Label each mark with the person's name.
3. Talk about why it is not a good idea for people to use their own feet for measuring things.

Practice

Practice writing the numbers 8 and 9.

4. 8 8 8 8 8

5. 9 9 9 9 9

Math Masters, p. 98

3 Differentiation Options

READINESS

SMALL-GROUP ACTIVITY

5–15 Min

▶ Investigating Length

To explore approximating length with nonstandard units, have children measure objects by laying cards end to end with no overlap and no gaps. Ask children to measure their desks in the same way. Children compare their answers and their strategies with each other. As time permits, have children work with a partner to measure other flat surfaces in the room. Consider having children record what surfaces they measured and the length of each surface.

ENRICHMENT

SMALL-GROUP DISCUSSION

15–30 Min

▶ Solving Problems with *How Big Is a Foot?*

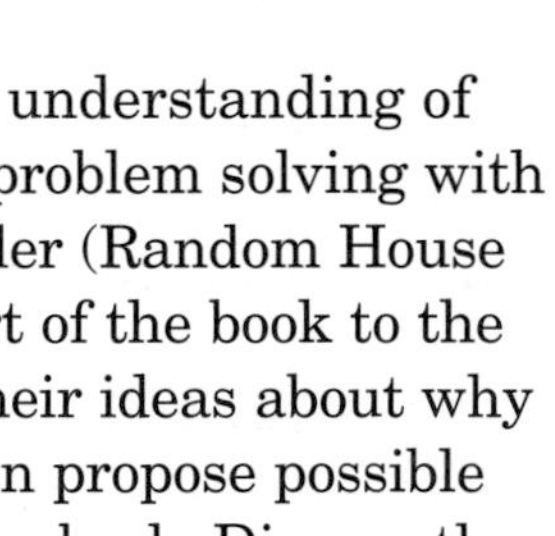

Literature Link To apply children's understanding of standard measurement, engage in problem solving with the book ***How Big Is a Foot?*** by Rolf Myller (Random House Children's Books, 1991). Read the first part of the book to the group. Pause and have volunteers share their ideas about why the bed did not fit the queen. Have children propose possible solutions to the problem. Finish reading the book. Discuss the importance of standard measurement units.

ELL SUPPORT

SMALL-GROUP ACTIVITY

5–15 Min

▶ Building a Math Word Bank

(*Differentiation Handbook,* p. 126)

To provide language support for measurement, have children use the Word Bank Template found on *Differentiation Handbook,* page 126. Ask children to write the term *foot,* draw a picture representing the term, and write other words that describe it. See the *Differentiation Handbook* for more information.

4•4 The Inch

Objectives To introduce the inch as a standard unit of length; and to provide practice measuring to the nearest inch.

Technology Resources www.everydaymathonline.com

 ePresentations
 eToolkit
 Algorithms Practice
 EM Facts Workshop Game™
 Family Letters
 Assessment Management
 Common Core State Standards
 Curriculum Focal Points
 Interactive Teacher's Lesson Guide

1 Teaching the Lesson

Key Concepts and Skills

- Count forward by 1s.
  [Number and Numeration Goal 1]
- Use language of approximation when measuring.
  [Measurement and Reference Frames Goal 1]
- Measure length to the nearest inch.
  [Measurement and Reference Frames Goal 1]
- Compare standard units of measure and lengths of objects.
  [Measurement and Reference Frames Goal 1]

Key Activities

Children measure using 1-inch long objects and then measure to the nearest inch with a 1-foot ruler. They order and compare lengths of objects.

Ongoing Assessment: Recognizing Student Achievement Use the Math Message. [Measurement and Reference Frames Goal 1]

Ongoing Assessment: Informing Instruction See page 293.

Key Vocabulary

inch ◆ in.

Materials

Math Journal 1, p. 62
Home Link 4•3
Math Masters, p. 305
Math Masters, p. 313 (2 per child)
Foot-Long Foot (*Math Masters,* p. 97) ◆ 1-inch stacking cubes ◆ scissors ◆ several objects shorter than a foot ◆ overhead ruler (optional)

2 Ongoing Learning & Practice

Playing *Time Match*
per partnership: 16 of 24 *Time Match* Cards (*Math Masters,* pp. 354 and 355), 3" by 5" note cards (optional), clock-face stamp (optional)
Children practice telling time on analog clocks.

Math Boxes 4•4
Math Journal 1, p. 63
Children practice and maintain skills through Math Box problems.

Home Link 4•4
Math Masters, p. 99
Children practice and maintain skills through Home Link activities.

3 Differentiation Options

READINESS

Comparing Lengths
Foot-Long Foot (*Math Masters,* p. 97)
per partnership: 10" and 11" paper strips, 1-inch stacking cubes
Children use cubes to measure different objects.

ENRICHMENT

Measuring Objects Longer than One Foot
Foot-Long Foot (*Math Masters,* p. 97)
objects between 1 and 2 feet long ◆ 12-inch ruler from Part 1
Children measure objects between 1 and 2 feet.

ELL SUPPORT

Building a Math Word Bank
Differentiation Handbook, p. 126
Children add *inch* to their Math Word Banks.

Advance Preparation

For Part 1, gather 1-inch cubes (or other 1-inch long objects) for each partnership. In Part 2, save the decks of 24 cards from *Time Match* for reuse in Lesson 4•10. For the optional Readiness activity in Part 3, half of the children will need 10" strips. The other half will need 11" strips.

 ***Teacher's Reference Manual,* Grades 1–3** pp. 166, 167

Getting Started

Mental Math and Reflexes

Have children show thumbs up for even numbers and thumbs down for odd numbers.

●○○ 2, 5, 9, 10 2 and 10 are even; 5 and 9 are odd.

●●○ 14, 18, 23, 31 14 and 18 are even; 23 and 31 are odd.

●●● 67, 76, 102, 111 76 and 102 are even; 67 and 111 are odd.

Math Message 

Estimate about how many feet it is from your seat to the meeting area.

Call children to the meeting area in groups of 3 or 4. Ask them to use the foot-long foot to measure and record in feet how far it is from their seat to the meeting area.

Home Link 4•3 Follow-Up

Did anyone find a person with a foot-long foot? Should people use their own feet as a unit of measure? Why or why not? No; it might give a good estimate, but each person might get a different measurement.

Teaching Aid Master

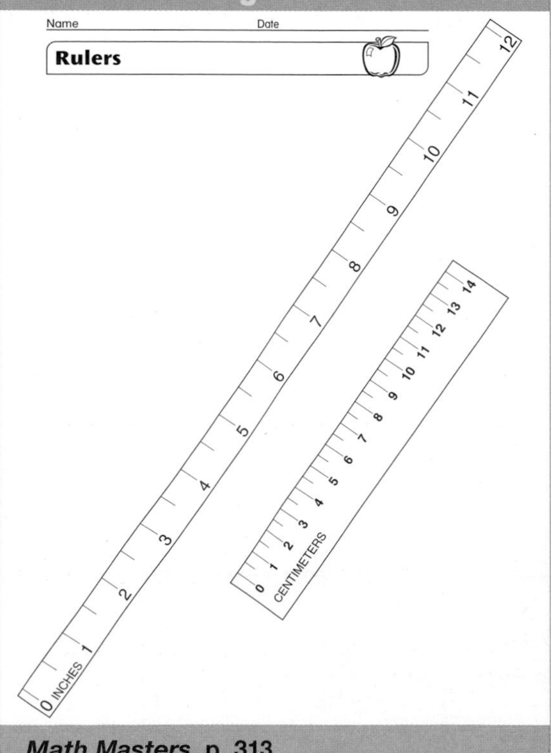

Math Masters, p. 313

1 Teaching the Lesson

▶ Math Message Follow-Up

Discuss children's measurements. Ask if anyone had a part of a foot "left over" as he or she reached the meeting area, and, if so, how did he or she record that part of a foot in the total distance. Half of a foot, part of a foot, less than 1 whole foot

Ask children if they know of rulers other than the foot-long foot that they can use to measure smaller distances. If no one suggests inches (or centimeters), discuss the need for a unit of measure smaller than a foot.

Ongoing Assessment: Recognizing Student Achievement

Math Message 

Use the **Math Message** to assess children's ability to measure in feet. Children are making adequate progress if they use the foot-long foot correctly, not overlapping or leaving gaps between units. Some children may get exact measurements.

[Measurement and Reference Frames Goal 1]

▶ Introducing the Inch As a Standard Unit of Length

(*Math Masters,* p. 313)

1. Review the process of measuring objects that are longer than one foot by marking and counting with one foot-long foot cutout or by laying several cutouts end to end.

2. Next, distribute at least eight 1-inch stacking cubes (or other 1-inch objects) to each partnership. (As an alternative, children can use the distance across their index and middle fingers to approximate 1 inch.) Tell children that the **inch** is a standard unit of length that is shorter than the foot. Each edge of the cube (or other object) is 1 inch long.

3. Partners measure several objects, such as a pencil or a book, by laying a row of cubes next to the object and counting them. The edge of the first cube should align with one end of the object. Observe partners' actions and interactions. After a few minutes, bring the class together to share results.

4. Children cut out the 12-inch ruler on *Math Masters,* page 313. Children match a 1-inch cube against a 1-inch space on the ruler. They then compare the ruler to their foot-long foot and count the number of inches in a foot.

Adjusting the Activity

Ask if anyone knows what the smaller marks on the cutout ruler indicate. half-inches Note that the half-inch marks are positioned halfway between the inch marks.

AUDITORY • KINESTHETIC • TACTILE • VISUAL

Measuring in Inches with the Cutout Ruler

(*Math Journal 1,* p. 62)

Display an object shorter than a foot. Show children how to use the cutout ruler to measure the object, as follows:

1. Place the object on or alongside the ruler, with one end at the 0-mark. Explain that this is like lining up objects side by side to compare their lengths.

2. Find the inch mark nearest to the other end of the object by using the mark halfway between whole inches to help you decide. (Children may need several demonstrations at this stage of using a measuring tool.)

Ongoing Assessment: Informing Instruction

Watch for children who do not align one end of the object with the 0-mark.

Adjusting the Activity

Draw a large "ruler" on the board or use a transparent ruler on an overhead projector to demonstrate how the ruler should be used. Show children how to line up an object at the 0-mark and how to find a measurement to the nearest inch.

AUDITORY • KINESTHETIC • TACTILE • VISUAL

Student Page

Date ______ Time ______

LESSON 4·4 **Inches**

Pick 4 short objects to measure. Draw or name them. Then measure the objects with your ruler. Answers vary.

1.

About ______ inches long

2.

About ______ inches long

3.

About ______ inches long

4.

About ______ inches long

Math Journal 1, p. 62

Adjusting the Activity

Have children use crayons to mark the inch marks on their rulers to help them distinguish between the inch and $\frac{1}{2}$-inch marks.

AUDITORY ◆ KINESTHETIC ◆ TACTILE ◆ VISUAL

NOTE Some children may give a measurement to the nearest $\frac{1}{2}$ inch if the end of an object is close to that mark. In second grade, children will measure to the nearest $\frac{1}{2}$ inch using the $\frac{1}{4}$-inch marks on a ruler.

Partners pick four short objects not already measured. They draw or name each object on journal page 62. Then they use their rulers to measure the actual objects to the nearest inch and record their measurements.

Put a unit box (labeled **inches** or **in.**) on the board. To support English language learners, discuss the difference between the abbreviation *in.* and the word *in.* Circulate and help children to line up one end of the object to be measured with the 0-mark on the ruler and then to read the nearest inch at the other end of the object. Explain that inches give more precise measurements than feet, although objects rarely end at an inch mark.

Bring the class together to share results. Make the following points:

- Standard measures, such as feet and inches, enable different people measuring the same thing to get about the same measurements.
- Measure by starting at the 0-mark (or end mark if there is no zero).
- Many times things are not an exact number of inches or feet in length. Therefore, descriptions such as *between* ____ *and* ____ *inches* (or *feet*), *just past* ____ *inches* (or *feet*), *about* ____ *inches* (or *feet*), or *almost* ____ *inches* (or *feet*) are good phrases to use.
- 12 inches equals 1 foot.

Links to the Future

This is children's first exposure to measuring with inches. Do not expect all children to master this skill while in first grade. Measuring to the nearest inch is a Grade 2 Goal.

Reinforce ordering lengths of objects and comparing lengths of two objects indirectly using a third object by writing the following sentence on the board:

If ____ *is longer than* ____,
and ____ *is longer than* ____,
then ____ *is longer than* ____.

For example, if the pencil is longer than the crayon, and the crayon is longer than the eraser, then the pencil is longer than the eraser. Use three of the four objects children measured to complete *Math Journal 1,* page 62 and have them take turns completing this sentence orally. Have children work in pairs to complete the sentence on an Exit Slip (*Math Masters,* page 305) using other objects.

2 Ongoing Learning & Practice

▶ Playing *Time Match*

PARTNER ACTIVITY

(*Math Masters,* pp. 354 and 355)

Children practice telling time on analog clocks. This game can be played by 2 or 3 players using a prepared deck of 16 cards.

Directions

1. One player shuffles the cards and places all 16 cards clock-side down in a 4 × 4 array.
2. Players take turns turning over 2 cards at a time. If the cards match, the player keeps them. If the cards don't match, they are returned clock-side down in the same positions.
3. When all of the cards have been collected, the player with the most matches wins.

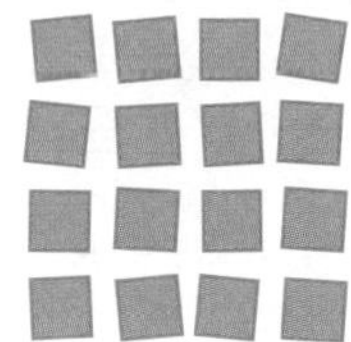

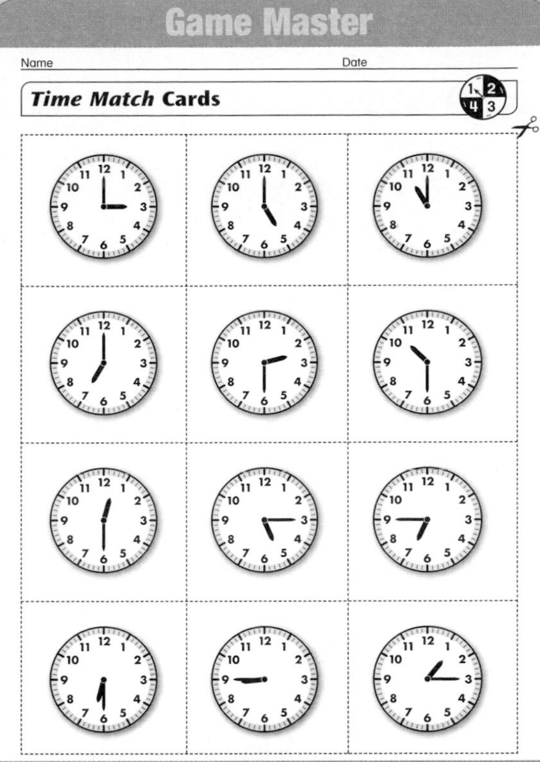

Game Master

Name Date

Time Match Cards

Math Masters, p. 354

NOTE Prepare the deck of 16 cards by removing the 4 clock-face cards and the 4 word cards that reference quarter-hours. To create your own deck of cards, cut eight 3" by 5" index cards in half. On 8 of the cards, stamp a clock face. Fill in appropriate times on the clock faces and write the same times in words on the other 8 cards.

Game Master

Name Date

Time Match Cards *continued*

3 o'clock	5 o'clock	11 o'clock
7 o'clock	Half-past 2 o'clock	Half-past 10 o'clock
Half-past 12 o'clock	Quarter-past 5 o'clock	Quarter-before 7 o'clock
Half-past 6 o'clock	Quarter-to 9 o'clock	Quarter-after 1 o'clock

Math Masters, p. 355

▶ Math Boxes 4•4

INDEPENDENT ACTIVITY

(*Math Journal 1,* p. 63)

Mixed Practice Math Boxes in this lesson are paired with Math Boxes in Lesson 4-2. The skills in Problem 4 preview Unit 5 content.

Writing/Reasoning Have children discuss, draw, or write an answer to the following question: *Why is it important to use a thermometer?* A reasonable answer should connect reading the thermometer to making everyday decisions as to what to wear or what to do.

▶ Home Link 4•4

INDEPENDENT ACTIVITY

(*Math Masters,* p. 99)

Home Connection Children use a ruler to measure and record lengths. In addition to the Home Link, you might wish to send home copies of the ruler (*Math Masters,* page 313) for children who may not have rulers at home.

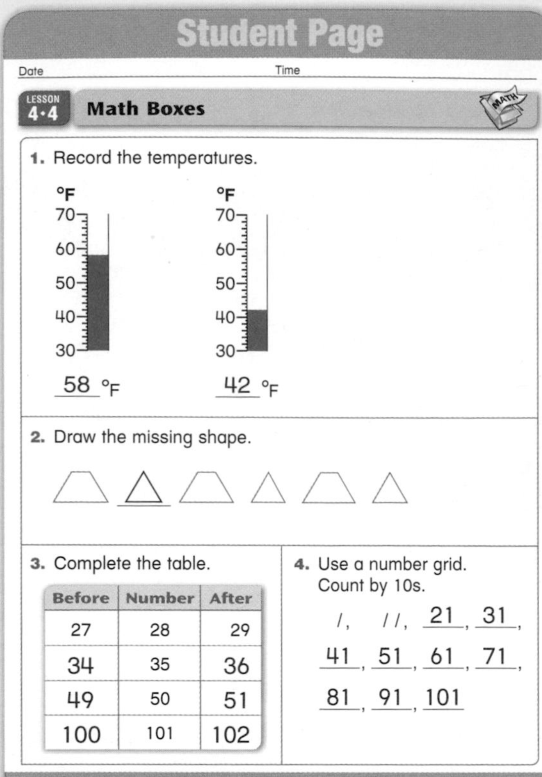

Student Page

Date Time

LESSON 4·4 **Math Boxes**

1. Record the temperatures.

°F 70 60 50 40 30 — 58 °F

°F 70 60 50 40 30 — 42 °F

2. Draw the missing shape.

3. Complete the table.

Before	Number	After
27	28	29
34	35	36
49	50	51
100	101	102

4. Use a number grid. Count by 10s.

/, //, 21, 31, 41, 51, 61, 71, 81, 91, 101

Math Journal 1, p. 63

NOTE Remember to reserve time every day to complete the number-line, attendance, calendar, temperature, and weather routines.

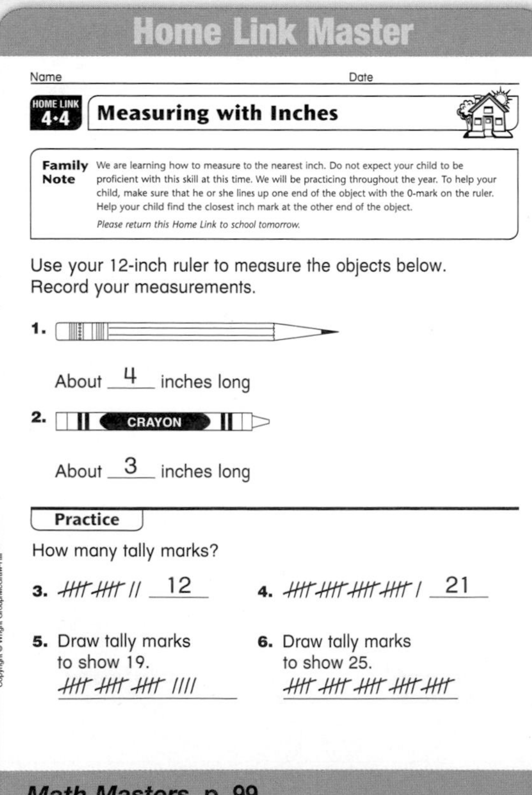

Home Link Master

Name Date

HOME LINK 4·4 **Measuring with Inches**

Family Note We are learning how to measure to the nearest inch. Do not expect your child to be proficient with this skill at this time. We will be practicing throughout the year. To help your child, make sure that he or she lines up one end of the object with the 0-mark on the ruler. Help your child find the closest inch mark at the other end of the object.

Please return this Home Link to school tomorrow.

Use your 12-inch ruler to measure the objects below. Record your measurements.

1. About 4 inches long

2. CRAYON About 3 inches long

Practice

How many tally marks?

3. 𝍸𝍸 // 12

4. 𝍸𝍸𝍸𝍸 / 21

5. Draw tally marks to show 19. 𝍸𝍸𝍸 ////

6. Draw tally marks to show 25. 𝍸𝍸𝍸𝍸𝍸

Math Masters, p. 99

3 Differentiation Options

READINESS

SMALL-GROUP ACTIVITY

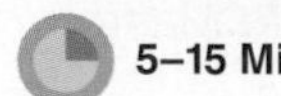

5–15 Min

▶ Comparing Lengths

To provide experience with estimating and comparing lengths, have children determine which of two strips is longer. Give one half of the group 10-inch strips and give the other half 11-inch strips. Do not allow children to directly compare strips. Have children measure their strips with the foot-long foot from Lesson 4-3. Ask children how they can tell which set of strips is longer without directly comparing the strips.

Have children set aside their strips and use 1-inch stacking cubes to make a stack as tall as their foot-long foot. They should compare their strips to their cube stack. Ask them if they can now tell which set of strips is longer. Ask why it was easier to compare the lengths using the cube stacks. With the cube stacks, you can tell that one set of strips is 10 cubes long and the other set of strips is 11 cubes long. Encourage children to use their cube stacks to measure objects in the room to the nearest "cube."

ENRICHMENT

SMALL-GROUP ACTIVITY

5–15 Min

▶ Measuring Objects Longer than One Foot

To apply children's understanding of linear measurement to the nearest inch, have children measure objects that are longer than one foot but shorter than two feet. Ask children how they might use their foot-long foot and their 12-inch ruler to measure these objects. Have a volunteer demonstrate how to do this by measuring to the nearest inch. Have children work together to measure the selected objects to the nearest inch or half-inch, as appropriate. Children can record the objects and their lengths. Some children may want to measure objects longer than two feet.

ELL SUPPORT

SMALL-GROUP ACTIVITY

5–15 Min

▶ Building a Math Word Bank

(*Differentiation Handbook*, p. 126)

To provide language support for measurement, have children use the Word Bank Template found on *Differentiation Handbook*, page 126. Ask children to write the term *inch*, draw a picture to represent the term, and write other words that describe it. See the *Differentiation Handbook* for more information.

Planning Ahead

Label children's tape measures with their identification numbers for distribution in Lesson 4-6.

4•5 The 6-Inch Ruler

Objective To provide practice estimating and measuring the lengths of objects in inches.

Technology Resources www.everydaymathonline.com

ePresentations

eToolkit

Algorithms Practice

EM Facts Workshop Game™

Family Letters

Assessment Management

Common Core State Standards

Curriculum Focal Points

Interactive Teacher's Lesson Guide

1 Teaching the Lesson

Key Concepts and Skills

- Use reference objects to estimate length.
  [Measurement and Reference Frames Goal 1]
- Measure length to the nearest inch.
  [Measurement and Reference Frames Goal 1]
- Measure and draw line segments to the nearest inch.
  [Measurement and Reference Frames Goal 1]

Key Activities

Children discuss the markings on a 6-inch ruler. They use the ruler to measure objects longer than 6 inches. They measure and draw line segments of specified lengths.

Ongoing Assessment: Informing Instruction See page 299.

Key Vocabulary

estimate

Materials

Math Journal 1, p. 64
Home Link 4•4
Math Masters, p. 314
transparency of *Math Masters,* p. 314 (optional) ◆ pennies or overhead coins ◆ 6-inch ruler

2 Ongoing Learning & Practice

Playing *Domino Top-It*
dominoes
Children practice finding sums and comparing quantities.

Ongoing Assessment: Recognizing Student Achievement
Use an Exit Slip (*Math Masters,* page 305).
[Number and Numeration Goal 7]

Math Boxes 4•5
Math Journal 1, p. 65
Children practice and maintain skills through Math Box problems.

Home Link 4•5
Math Masters, p. 100; p. 313 (optional)
Children practice and maintain skills through Home Link activities.

3 Differentiation Options

READINESS

Writing Names with a Straightedge
ruler
Children use a 6-inch ruler as a straightedge to write their names.

ENRICHMENT

Starting the *Jack and the Beanstalk* Activity
Jack and the Beanstalk
per partnership: plastic foam cup or half-pint milk carton, soil, bean (or sunflower) seeds, dowel or stick at least 14" long, ties or string for supporting plant; 1" by 8" strips of paper (optional)
Children plant bean (or sunflower) seeds and measure the growth of the plants.

Advance Preparation

For the optional Enrichment activity in Part 3, obtain a copy of ***Jack and the Beanstalk***.

***Teacher's Reference Manual,* Grades 1–3** p. 166

Getting Started

Mental Math and Reflexes

Set a group of pennies on the overhead. Turn on the overhead for about 3 seconds; turn it off. Ask children to estimate how many dimes could be exchanged for the pennies they saw on the overhead.

●○○ Show 10 pennies. *About how many dimes could be exchanged for the pennies?*

●●○ Show 15 pennies. *About how many dimes could be exchanged for the pennies?*

●●● Show 20 pennies. *About how many dimes could be exchanged for the pennies?*

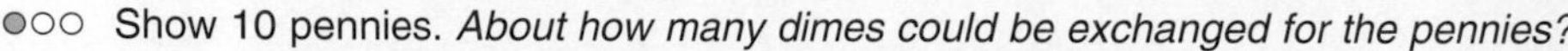

Math Message

Look at the marks on your 6-inch ruler. Think about what the marks might mean.

Home Link 4·4 Follow-Up

Have children give the length of each object and describe how they measured the objects.

NOTE The metric system of measurement will be introduced in Unit 6.

Teaching Aid Master

Name ______ Date ______

6-Inch Rulers

0 1 2 3 4 5 6
inches

0 1 2 3 4 5 6
inches

0 1 2 3 4 5 6
inches

0 1 2 3 4 5 6
inches

Math Masters, p. 314

1 Teaching the Lesson

▶ Math Message Follow-Up

WHOLE-CLASS DISCUSSION

ELL

(*Math Masters,* p. 314)

Have children identify the inch-scale on the 6-inch ruler. To support English language learners, discuss the multiple meanings of the word *scale*; for example, the Fahrenheit scale and the scale children use to weigh themselves. Ask if anyone knows what the other scale shows. centimeters Explain that inches and feet are units in what is called the U.S. Customary System and that centimeters are units in the metric system.

On the ruler or a transparency of the ruler, point out the subdivisions of the inch scale. Focus on the half-inch mark. In measuring to the nearest inch, the half-inch mark helps the person decide what the nearest inch is. You might ask if anyone knows what the other marks are. Quarter-inch, eighth-inch, sixteenth-inch

Adjusting the Activity

ELL

On the transparency of *Math Masters,* page 314, color over each inch mark with a colored transparency marker. Count up from zero—1 inch, 2 inches, and so on. You might lay an object next to the transparency ruler and review how to measure the length of the object. Review on the overhead how to estimate the length to the nearest inch.

AUDITORY ◆ KINESTHETIC ◆ TACTILE ◆ VISUAL

▶ Estimating the Length of an Object

Children have been measuring objects to the nearest unit by comparing the objects to the lengths of their bodies, other objects, and rulers.

Explain that now they will **estimate** the length of an object before actually measuring it. Tell children that sometimes guesses are called *estimates*.

Discuss how reference objects can be used to help make an estimate. For example, children might use a square pattern block or the combined width of their index finger and middle finger as a reference for an inch. Then, to estimate the total length of an object in inches, they can think: "About how many blocks (or combined finger widths) long is this object?" or "The (object) is between ____ and ____ combined finger widths (or blocks) long."

With the class, estimate the length in inches of a few objects. Expect the estimates to be very rough since children are in the early stages of developing measurement sense.

▶ Measuring Objects with the 6-Inch Ruler

(*Math Journal 1,* p. 64)

Ask children to suggest ways to measure something longer than the 6-inch ruler. Select something to measure, such as the side of a wall calendar. Demonstrate the following:

1. Put the 0-end of the ruler at one edge of the object.
2. Use something like the point of a pencil to mark the point along the object to show where the 6-inch end of the ruler falls. Then shift the 0-end of the ruler ahead to this mark. (Or put the 0-end of a second ruler at the 6-inch end of the first ruler.)
3. Decide on the measure to the nearest inch; for example, by counting on from 6 (6, 7, 8, 9, ...) or by adding (6 + additional inches = ____ inches).

Partners select two objects to measure. They draw or name the objects on the top part of journal page 64, estimate the lengths, and then measure and record the lengths.

Ongoing Assessment: Informing Instruction

Watch for children ...

- who do not count on from 6 when the object is longer than 6 inches.
- who use the wrong scale on the ruler.

NOTE You may wish to have children order the line segments they measured in Problems 2–5 on *Math Journal 1,* page 64 from longest to shortest. Problems: 5, 3, 2, 4

Student Page

Date ______ Time ______

LESSON 4·5 **Measuring in Inches**

1. Choose two objects to measure. Estimate each object's length. Measure the objects to the nearest inch.

Object (Name it or draw it.)	My Estimate	My Measurement
Answers vary.	about ____ inches	about ____ inches
	about ____ inches	about ____ inches

Measure each line segment.

2. ______________________

about 5 inches

3. ______________________

about 6 inches

4. ____________

about 3 inches

5. ____________________________

about 7 inches

Draw a line segment about

6. 4 inches long. ________________

7. 2 inches long. ________

Math Journal 1, p. 64

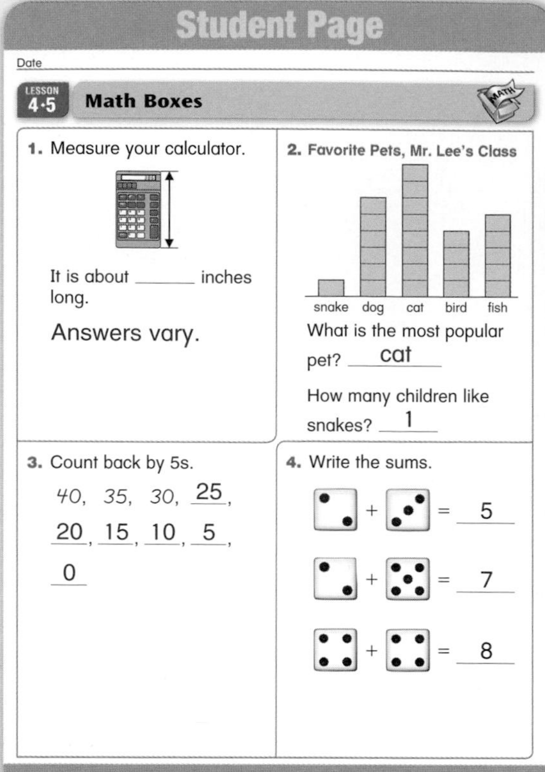

Adjusting the Activity

Encourage children to draw line segments involving half-inches or quarter-inches, such as $5\frac{1}{2}$ inches and $3\frac{1}{4}$ inches.

AUDITORY ◆ KINESTHETIC ◆ TACTILE ◆ VISUAL

▶ Measuring and Drawing Line Segments

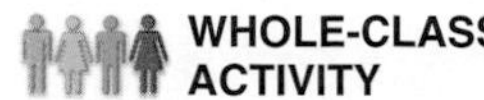

(*Math Journal 1,* p. 64)

Demonstrate on the board or on an overhead projector how to draw a line segment of a specified length. For example, to draw a line segment 4 inches long:

1. Make a dot for the beginning of the line segment.
2. Place the 0-mark of the ruler at the dot, with the inch marks on the ruler going in the direction the line will be drawn.
3. Make a second dot at the 4-inch mark on the ruler.
4. Use the ruler's edge to draw a line to connect the dots.

Partners use their rulers to measure line segments and to draw line segments to lengths specified on journal page 64.

2 Ongoing Learning & Practice

▶ Playing *Domino Top-It*

Children practice addition skills and compare quantities by playing *Domino Top-It*. For detailed instructions, see Lesson 4-1.

Ongoing Assessment: Recognizing Student Achievement

Exit Slip

Use an **Exit Slip** (*Math Masters,* page 305) to assess children's ability to find domino sums and to compare quantities. On an Exit Slip, have children draw the dominoes from one round of *Domino Top-It.* Have them write under the domino the total number of dots for each domino. Then have them circle the greater number. Children are making adequate progress if they are able to correctly identify the total number of dots, as well as identify the greater sum.

[Number and Numeration Goal 7]

▶ Math Boxes 4·5

(*Math Journal 1,* p. 65)

Mixed Practice Math Boxes in this lesson are paired with Math Boxes in Lesson 4-7.

Writing/Reasoning Have children draw, write, or verbalize an answer to the following question: *How do you know which pet is most popular?* A reasonable answer should include the number of pets shown in the line plot. Sample answer: I know the cat has more blocks than the other animals.

Home Link 4·5

INDEPENDENT ACTIVITY

(*Math Masters,* p. 100)

Home Connection Children measure the lengths of objects to the nearest inch. You might wish to send home additional copies of *Math Masters,* page 313 with children who may not have rulers at home.

3 Differentiation Options

READINESS

PARTNER ACTIVITY

Writing Names with a Straightedge

5–15 Min

To provide experience drawing straight lines, have children use their rulers as straightedges. Review how to use a ruler to draw a straight line. Then ask children to write their first names using only straight lines. Suggest that they use just capital letters. Children can share their names with a partner and discuss the shapes of the letters in their names.

ENRICHMENT

SMALL-GROUP ACTIVITY

Starting the *Jack and the Beanstalk* Activity

15–30 Min

Science and Literature Links To further explore measurement, read and discuss the story of ***Jack and the Beanstalk*** to the group. Individual children or partners fill their planters with soil and plant their seeds. Tell children to push their dowels into the soil and mark where the dowel meets the soil. Go on to explain that the marked dowels become a record of the plant's growth. Children can measure and record the growth using a ruler. Naturally, watering will be required.

Consider tracking the growth of plants in the classroom from now until the end of the school year or for a specified length of time. You can record the height by using 1" by 8" paper strips. Children place a strip of paper next to the plant and cut it off to indicate the height of the plant. These strips can then be glued to a bar graph.

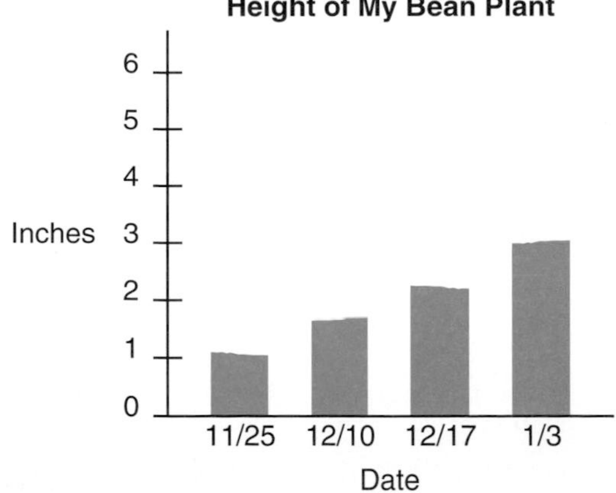

Home Link Master

Name Date

HOME LINK 4·5 **Measuring with a Ruler**

Family Note This activity is the same as the activity on the previous Home Link, except that this time your child will choose objects to measure.

Have your child measure objects to the nearest inch. Make sure your child lines up one end of the object being measured with the 0-mark on the ruler.

Please return this Home Link to school tomorrow.

Use your 12-inch ruler to measure 2 small objects to the nearest inch. Draw a picture of each object. Record your measurements. Answers vary.

1.

About ____ inches long

2.

About ____ inches long

Practice

3. How much money?

ⓃⓃⓃⓅⓅⓅⓅⓅⓅ 21 ¢

***Math Masters,* p. 100**

The dowels are used to support the vines and to keep them growing fairly straight. Children mark the growth point on the dowel each day or two as the seeds begin to sprout and grow. The soil mark is the "zero" point.

4•6 Measuring with a Tape Measure

Objective To provide practice using a tape measure to measure curved and flat objects in inches.

www.everydaymathonline.com

ePresentations

eToolkit

Algorithms Practice

EM Facts Workshop Game™

Family Letters

Assessment Management

Common Core State Standards

Curriculum Focal Points

Interactive Teacher's Lesson Guide

1 Teaching the Lesson

Key Concepts and Skills

- Count forward by 1s. [Number and Numeration Goal 1]
- Measure length to the nearest inch. [Measurement and Reference Frames Goal 1]
- Identify inch and centimeter scales. [Measurement and Reference Frames Goal 1]

Key Activities

Children are introduced to a tape measure and how to use it to measure curved objects. They practice using a tape measure to measure around and across objects. Children also measure parts of their bodies.

Ongoing Assessment: Recognizing Student Achievement Use Mental Math and Reflexes. [Operations and Computation Goal 4]

Key Vocabulary

tape measure

Materials

Math Journal 1, p. 66
Home Link 4•5
tool-kit tape measure

2 Ongoing Learning & Practice

Discussing Weather and Probability
Children predict weather using probability language.

Practicing Finding Totals
Math Journal 1, p. 67
Children practice finding totals using parts-and-total diagrams.

Math Boxes 4•6
Math Journal 1, p. 68
Children practice and maintain skills through Math Box problems.

Home Link 4•6
Math Masters, p. 101
Children practice and maintain skills through Home Link activities.

3 Differentiation Options

READINESS

Measuring with String
per partnership: string, classroom objects
Children use strings of varying lengths to measure around classroom objects.

ENRICHMENT

Measuring Tool Match-Up
Children list classroom objects and match them with an appropriate tool used to measure the object.

Advance Preparation

For Part 1, prepare tape measures for distribution. For the optional Readiness activity in Part 3, select eight classroom objects for children to measure such as crayon boxes or tissue boxes. Cut eight pieces of string to match the girth of objects.

Getting Started

Mental Math and Reflexes 

Tell "parts-and-total" number stories. Have children solve them any way they can and share their solution strategies. Summarize each solution by drawing a "parts-and-total" diagram and by writing a number model.

●○○ Kisho baked almond cookies. He baked 4 cookies on one tray and 6 cookies on another tray. How many cookies did Kisho bake in all? 10 cookies; 4 + 6 = 10

●●○ Jim had 8 rocks in his collection. His grandmother brought him some rocks from her trip to Africa. Now Jim has 12 rocks. How many rocks did his grandmother bring him from Africa? 4 rocks; 8 + 4 = 12

●●● Josephine invited 16 friends to her party. 10 friends can come. The rest cannot come. How many friends cannot come to Josephine's party? 6 friends can't come; 16 − 6 = 10 or 16 − 10 = 6

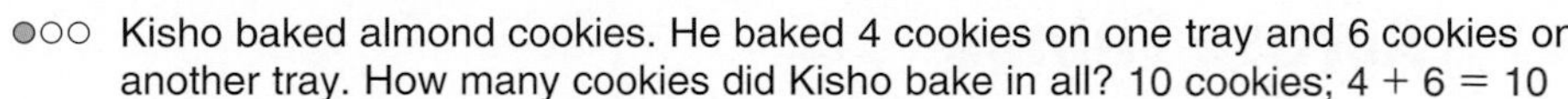

Math Message

How could you measure the distance around your wrist?

Home Link 4·5 Follow-Up

Have children share their measurements. Discuss using a ruler to measure objects longer than the ruler.

Ongoing Assessment: Recognizing Student Achievement

Mental Math and Reflexes ★

Use **Mental Math and Reflexes** to assess children's ability to solve "parts-and-total" number stories. Children are making adequate progress if they are able to answer the first problem correctly and share their solution strategy. Some children may be able to answer all three problems correctly.

[Operations and Computation Goal 4]

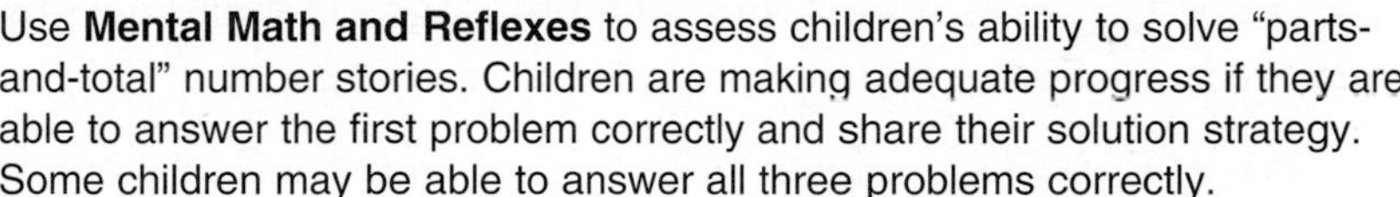

1 Teaching the Lesson

Math Message Follow-Up

 WHOLE-CLASS DISCUSSION

Discuss solutions for the Math Message problem. Possible methods include using a string and then measuring the string with a ruler, using a paper ruler, or using a tape measure.

Introducing Tape Measures

 WHOLE-CLASS ACTIVITY

Show children a **tape measure.** Encourage them to share their experiences with or knowledge of tape measures. Explain how a tailor uses a tape measure to measure a person's body in order to sew clothes for that person. Tell children that they will be learning to use a tape measure to measure objects.

Distribute tape measures. Teach (or review) the 2-inch (5-centimeter), no-zap rule. Have children look at both sides of the tape measure. Review the two kinds of units for measuring length that also appear on the 6-inch ruler: inches and centimeters. The inch side will be used in this lesson.

NOTE If children are using retractable tape measures, teaching and enforcing the "2-inch, no-zap rule" (do not "zap" the tape measure until less than 2 inches are showing) will extend the life of these tools.

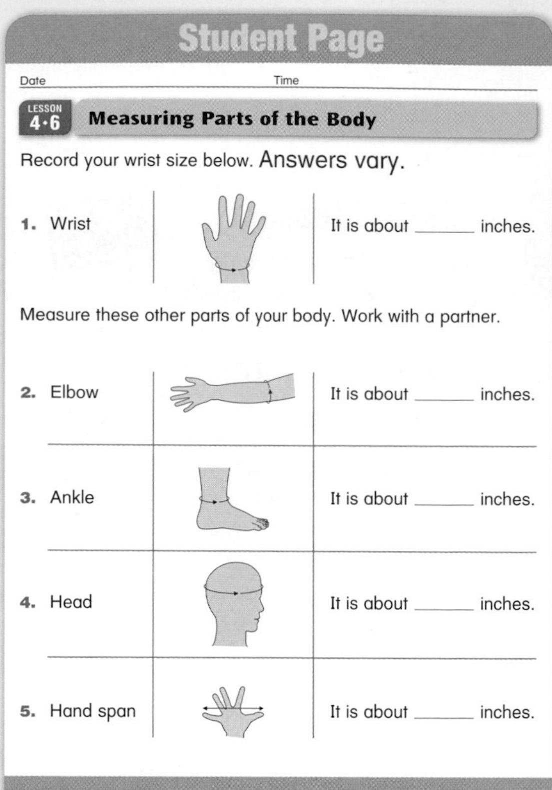

Student Page

Date Time

LESSON 4·6 **Measuring Parts of the Body**

Record your wrist size below. Answers vary.

1. Wrist		It is about ______ inches.

Measure these other parts of your body. Work with a partner.

2. Elbow		It is about ______ inches.
3. Ankle		It is about ______ inches.
4. Head		It is about ______ inches.
5. Hand span		It is about ______ inches.

Math Journal 1, p. 66

Have children measure a "flat" item to the nearest inch using their tape measures, such as the width of their desks, their math journals, or crayon boxes. Record some results on the board and get general agreement on the measurements.

▶ Measuring Around and Across Things

PARTNER ACTIVITY

(*Math Journal 1,* p. 66)

Discuss and demonstrate how tape measures can be used to measure *around* and *across* objects that are not "flat."

Ask partners to measure in inches around each other's wrists. Show children how to wrap the tape around and read the number nearest the edge of the metal end without overlapping. Children record their measurements at the top of journal page 66. On the board, record some of the measurements so children can compare results.

Talk about the advantages and disadvantages of tape measures compared to rulers, yardsticks, and meter sticks.

▷ **Advantages:** Tape measures are easy to store. They bend, so they can be used to measure around things.

▷ **Disadvantages:** The ends of tape measures might be more difficult to line up with the ends of an object. Two people may be needed to stretch and read the tape measure when measuring longer distances.

Finally, partners measure each other's elbows, ankles, heads, and hand spans and record the measurements in inches on journal page 66.

Links to the Future

Do not expect that children will be proficient with tape measures. Although some children may be doing well, it is likely that most children will need more practice. Measuring to the nearest inch is a Grade 2 Goal.

2 Ongoing Learning & Practice

▶ Discussing Weather and Probability

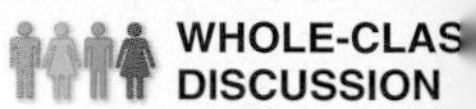
WHOLE-CLAS[S] DISCUSSION

To provide more experience using probability language such as *certain, likely, unlikely, possible,* and *impossible,* ask questions about the temperature and weather. *For example:*

- Based on what you know about today's weather, do you think i[t] is likely or unlikely that the temperature is higher than 100°[F]

- Is it possible, impossible, or certain that the temperature will reach 32 °F tomorrow? Explain.
- Are you certain that it will snow next week? How do you know?

Practicing Finding Totals

INDEPENDENT ACTIVITY

(*Math Journal 1,* p. 67)

Algebraic Thinking Use journal page 67 to practice finding totals and missing parts using parts-and-total diagrams.

Math Boxes 4•6

INDEPENDENT ACTIVITY

(*Math Journal 1,* p. 68)

Mixed Practice Math Boxes in this lesson are paired with Math Boxes in Lesson 4-8. The skills in Problem 4 preview Unit 5 content.

Home Link 4•6

INDEPENDENT ACTIVITY

(*Math Masters,* p. 101)

Home Connection Children name and draw three measuring tools they find in their homes, such as rulers, tape measures, scales, and measuring cups.

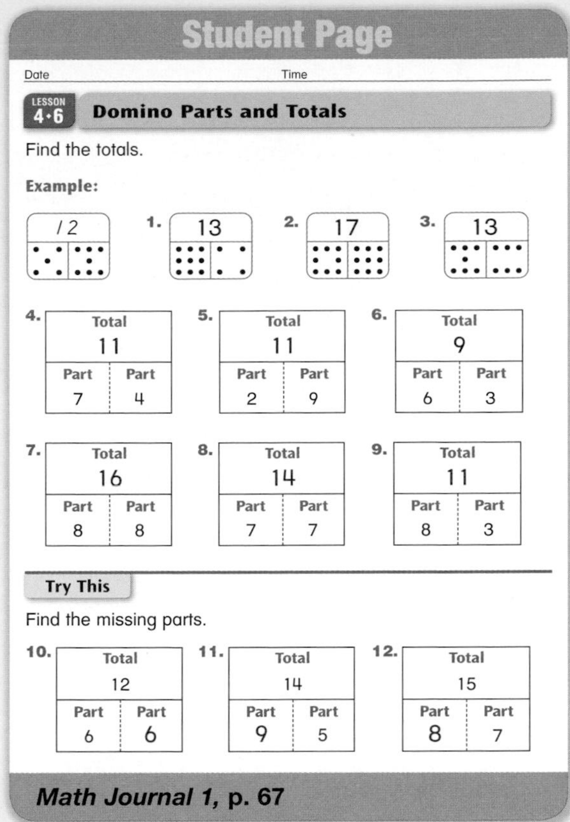

Student Page

Date Time

LESSON 4•6 **Domino Parts and Totals**

Find the totals.

Example: 12

1. 13
2. 17
3. 13

4. Total 11; Part 7, Part 4
5. Total 11; Part 2, Part 9
6. Total 9; Part 6, Part 3
7. Total 16; Part 8, Part 8
8. Total 14; Part 7, Part 7
9. Total 11; Part 8, Part 3

Try This

Find the missing parts.

10. Total 12; Part 6, Part 6
11. Total 14; Part 9, Part 5
12. Total 15; Part 8, Part 7

Math Journal 1, p. 67

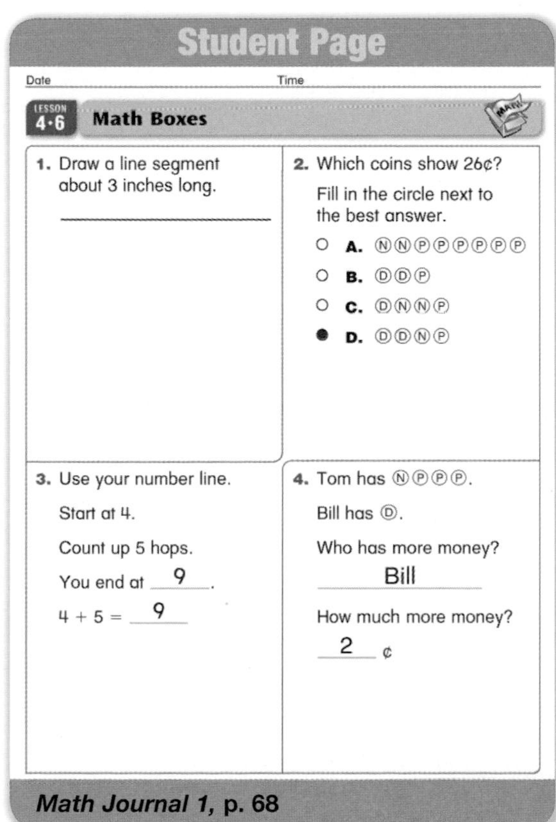

Student Page

Date Time

LESSON 4•6 **Math Boxes**

1. Draw a line segment about 3 inches long.

2. Which coins show 26¢? Fill in the circle next to the best answer.
   - ○ A. ⓃⓃⓅⓅⓅⓅⓅⓅ
   - ○ B. ⒹⒹⓅ
   - ○ C. ⒹⓃⓃⓅ
   - ● D. ⒹⒹⓃⓅ

3. Use your number line. Start at 4. Count up 5 hops. You end at 9. 4 + 5 = 9

4. Tom has ⓃⓅⓅⓅ. Bill has Ⓓ. Who has more money? Bill. How much more money? 2 ¢

Math Journal 1, p. 68

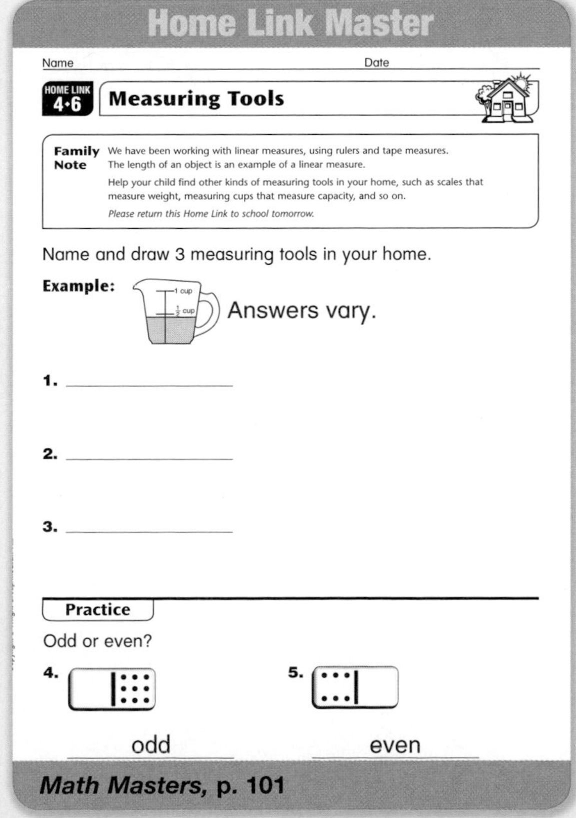

Home Link Master

Name Date

HOME LINK 4•6 **Measuring Tools**

Family Note We have been working with linear measures, using rulers and tape measures. The length of an object is an example of a linear measure.

Help your child find other kinds of measuring tools in your home, such as scales that measure weight, measuring cups that measure capacity, and so on.

Please return this Home Link to school tomorrow.

Name and draw 3 measuring tools in your home.

Example: Answers vary.

1. ________
2. ________
3. ________

Practice

Odd or even?

4. odd
5. even

Math Masters, p. 101

3 Differentiation Options

READINESS

PARTNER ACTIVITY

5–15 Min

▶ Measuring with String

To provide experience measuring nonlinear distances, have children work with a partner to measure around eight classroom objects using string. Show children the selected objects and ask how they could find the distance around one of them. Show children eight pieces of string that have been cut to varying lengths. Explain that each string fits around one of the objects. Tell children to wrap the string around each object in order to determine which string matches the distance around each object. Children should touch both ends of the string together without overlapping or leaving gaps. Have children briefly discuss and compare their matches. If time permits, have children measure the length of each piece of string.

ENRICHMENT

SMALL-GROUP ACTIVITY

5–15 Min

▶ Measuring Tool Match-Up

To apply children's understanding of measuring tools, have them list various tools used for measuring. Have children draw a line down the middle of a full sheet of paper. Ask them to list names of different measuring tools on one side of the paper. On the other side, have them record the names of objects in the classroom that they would like to measure. Then have children draw a line from each object to be measured to a tool that they could use to measure it.

4•7 Exploring Data, Shapes, and Base-10 Blocks

Explorations

Objectives To measure children's heights; to provide experiences making a bar graph; to guide the exploration of 2-dimensional shapes; and to develop familiarity with base-10 blocks.

Technology Resources www.everydaymathonline.com

ePresentations

eToolkit

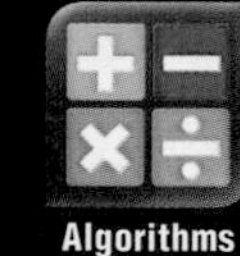
Algorithms Practice

EM Facts Workshop Game™

Family Letters

Assessment Management

Common Core State Standards

Curriculum Focal Points

Interactive Teacher's Lesson Guide

1 Teaching the Lesson

Key Concepts and Skills

- Count and record the number of flats, longs, and cubes. [Number and Numeration Goal 3]
- Create a line plot and a bar graph to organize data. [Data and Chance Goal 1]
- Answer questions about data collected using a bar graph; find typical value in a data set. [Data and Chance Goal 2]
- Estimate and measure height to the nearest inch. [Measurement and Reference Frames Goal 1]
- Create plane shapes and designs on a geoboard. [Geometry Goal 1]

Key Activities

Exploration A: Children measure their heights and help make a line plot as the measurements are taken. They use the data in the line plot to create a bar graph.

Exploration B: Children make shapes and designs on a geoboard and record them on dot paper.

Exploration C: Children build structures with base-10 blocks and record how many of each type of block they use.

Key Vocabulary

typical ◆ bar graph

Materials

Home Link 4•6

Exploration A: Per group:
Math Journal 1, p. 69
tape measure ◆ a book ◆ Class Data Pad ◆ stick-on notes

Exploration B: Per group:
Math Masters, p. 315 or 316
geoboards ◆ rubber bands (colored, if possible)

Exploration C: Per group:
Math Masters, p. 102
base-10 blocks

2 Ongoing Learning & Practice

Using 8 and 9 Pennies in Two-Fisted Penny Addition
Math Masters, p. 95
pennies

Math Boxes 4•7
Math Journal 1, p. 70

Ongoing Assessment: Recognizing Student Achievement
Use Math Boxes, Problem 4.
[Operations and Computation Goal 1]

Home Link 4•7
Math Masters, p. 103

3 Differentiation Options

ENRICHMENT

Estimating Length on a Geoboard
Math Masters, p. 104
per partnership: geoboard, rubber bands, 6-inch ruler

EXTRA PRACTICE

Minute Math+
Minute Math®+, pp. 18, 53, and 58

Advance Preparation

For Exploration B, make copies of the geoboard dot paper that matches your geoboards by using *Math Masters,* page 315 or 316. For Exploration C, make copies of *Math Masters,* page 102. Cut them in half.

***Teacher's Reference Manual,* Grades 1–3** pp. 119–125, 151, 152

Getting Started

Mental Math and Reflexes

Tell the following number stories. Have children solve them any way they can, sharing their solution strategies. Encourage children having difficulty to draw pictures or doodles, count on the number line or number grid, or use cubes or coins to model the problems.

You may want to ask children what information in the last two problems is not needed to solve the problems.

●○○ Ricardo bought 12 red apples. At the end of the week, 10 apples had been eaten. How many apples were left? 2 apples

●●○ Antonia and Kris went to the zoo. They saw 6 monkeys, 7 parakeets, and 4 parrots. How many birds did they see? 11 birds

●●● Miranda made 2 pizzas for 5 of her friends. Miranda put 21 slices of pepperoni on the first pizza and 16 slices of pepperoni on the second pizza. How many more slices of pepperoni were on the first pizza than on the second? 5 slices of pepperoni

Math Message

Estimate about how many feet tall most of the first graders in our class are.

Home Link 4·6 Follow-Up

Ask volunteers to describe and discuss the use of the measuring tools they found at home.

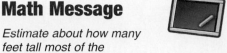

1 Teaching the Lesson

▶ Math Message Follow-Up

Have children share their estimates. Use a tape measure or yardstick to show the estimates. Mention that another name for the height of most first graders in the class is the **typical** height of a first grader in the class. To support English language learners, discuss the meaning of typical and review its pronunciation.

Ask children how they would check their estimates. Here are a few possibilities:

Measure the heights of all first graders. Then:

- ▷ choose the most frequent height.
- ▷ choose a number to which many heights seem to be close.
- ▷ choose one of the heights from the middle if the heights are lined up in order.
- ▷ measure just one child. (In this case, talk briefly about how one would choose whom to measure.)

You may want to extend the discussion by having children estimate how many inches tall a *typical* first grader is.

Exploration A: Measuring Children's Heights and Making a Line Plot

SMALL-GROUP ACTIVITY

(*Math Journal 1,* p. 69)

Attach a tape measure, showing inches, to the wall. Have a volunteer stand straight, with head level, against the tape measure. Demonstrate how to measure the child's height. Show children how to use a book held against the wall on top of the head to get an accurate measurement. Explain that the measurement is read at the bottom of the book.

Have children record today's date on the journal page. Work with children to measure the height of each child in each group. When the group agrees on the height of a child, the child records his or her height in the first section of the journal page and on a stick-on note.

Draw a horizontal line on the Class Data Pad. Number the line from 38 to 52 or use other numbers that are appropriate for your class and label the line *Inches Tall.* Make a line plot by having children attach their stick-on notes above their heights.

NOTE Children will measure their heights again in Unit 9. Save the stick-on notes so the data can be used in Lesson 9-5.

Exploration B: Exploring Shapes on the Geoboard

SMALL-GROUP ACTIVITY

(*Math Masters,* p. 315 or 316)

Children make different shapes and designs on the geoboard using (colored) rubber bands. They then copy their favorite designs onto geoboard dot paper.

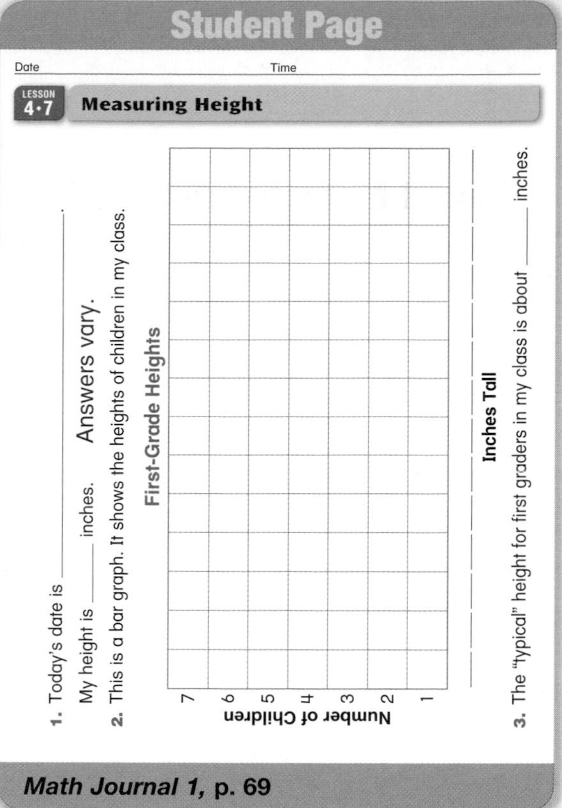
Student Page

Date ______ Time ______

LESSON 4·7 **Measuring Height**

1. Today's date is ______

My height is ______ inches. Answers vary.

2. This is a bar graph. It shows the heights of children in my class.

First-Grade Heights

Number of Children: 7, 6, 5, 4, 3, 2, 1

Inches Tall

3. The "typical" height for first graders in my class is about ______ inches.

***Math Journal 1,* p. 69**

NOTE For practice constructing object graphs, go to www.everydaymathonline.com.

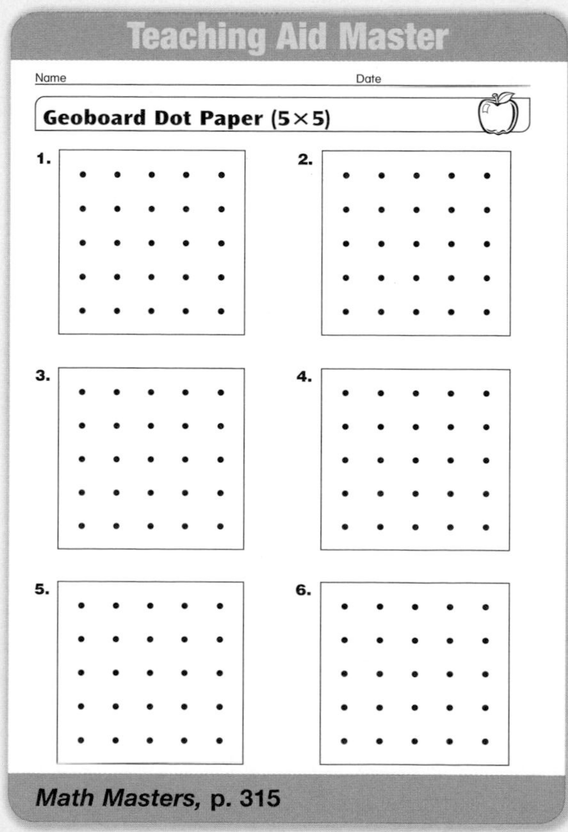
Teaching Aid Master

Name ______ Date ______

Geoboard Dot Paper (5×5)

1.

2.

3.

4.

5.

6.

***Math Masters,* p. 315**

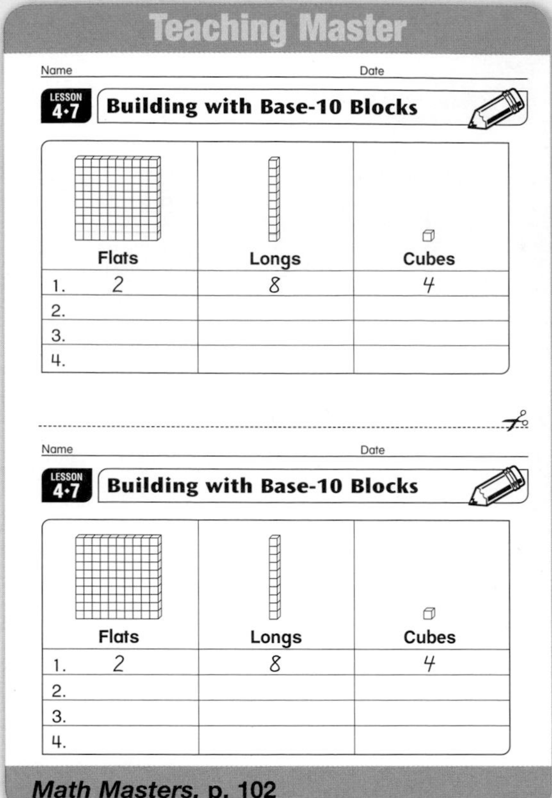
Teaching Master

Name Date

LESSON 4·7 Building with Base-10 Blocks

	Flats	Longs	Cubes
1.	2	8	4
2.			
3.			
4.			

Name Date

LESSON 4·7 Building with Base-10 Blocks

	Flats	Longs	Cubes
1.	2	8	4
2.			
3.			
4.			

Math Masters, p. 102

▶ Exploration C: Building Structures with Base-10 Blocks

SMALL-GROUP ACTIVITY

(*Math Masters,* p. 102)

Children build structures with base-10 blocks to become familiar with the names, shapes, and sizes of these manipulatives.

Children record how many flats, longs, and cubes they use for each structure.

NOTE Provide enough base-10 blocks for each child to have 25 cubes (ones), 12 longs (tens), and 2 flats (hundreds).

▶ Making a Bar Graph and Finding a "Typical" Height

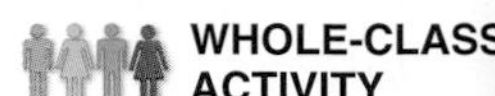
WHOLE-CLASS ACTIVITY

(*Math Journal 1,* p. 69)

After all children have been measured, make a **bar graph** using the class line plot of heights.

Review the title of the graph and the labels of the axes.

Point out that "inches" is the unit that goes with all of the numbers on the bottom axis. Have children fill in the numbers of inches from the line plot.

Together with children, count the number of stick-on notes for each height. Then have children color that number of squares above each height on the graph.

Ask children questions about the data, such as the following:

- How many children are 42 inches tall?
- How many children in our class have their heights recorded in this bar graph?
- How many more children are 48 inches tall than 47 inches tall (or any combination of two heights)?
- How many fewer children are 42 inches tall than 43 inches tall (or any combination of two heights)?

As you ask questions like those listed above, encourage children to ask their own questions that can be answered using the graph. Ask questions such as the following to guide them:

- What question can you ask that can be answered using this graph?
- What other questions can you ask that compare the data in one column with the data in another column?

After children have asked questions about the graph, discuss how the tallest bar on the graph shows a "typical" height for the class. Have children record that height in their journals. Then children can use their data to predict the typical height of all first graders in their school or neighborhood.

NOTE The horizontal axis is a reference line for listing the different heights. The vertical axis is a reference line for the number of children who are a certain height.

NOTE *Everyday Mathematics* does not draw a distinction between histograms and bar graphs. For a discussion on how some people contrast them, see Section 12.2.3: Organizing and Displaying Data in the *Teacher's Reference Manual.*

NOTE To find a typical height in another way, first list the heights in order and then find the height in the middle of the list. This description of a data set is called the *median.* Another way to describe a set of data is to find the most frequent value in the set of data. This is called the *mode.*

Consider using a graphing software to demonstrate how technology can be used to generate the graph.

2 Ongoing Learning & Practice

Using 8 and 9 Pennies in Two-Fisted Penny Addition

(*Math Masters,* p. 95)

This activity is a continuation of the systematic record of complements of the numbers 5 to 18 begun in Lesson 4-2. Encourage children to find and record all of the complements of 8 and 9.

Math Boxes 4·7

(*Math Journal 1,* p. 70)

Mixed Practice Math Boxes in this lesson are paired with Math Boxes in Lesson 4-5. The skills in Problem 4 preview Unit 5 content.

Ongoing Assessment: Recognizing Student Achievement

Math Boxes Problem 4

Use **Math Boxes, Problem 4** to assess children's ability to solve easy dice sums. Children are making adequate progress if they are able to count the dots to find the sums.

[Operations and Computation Goal 1]

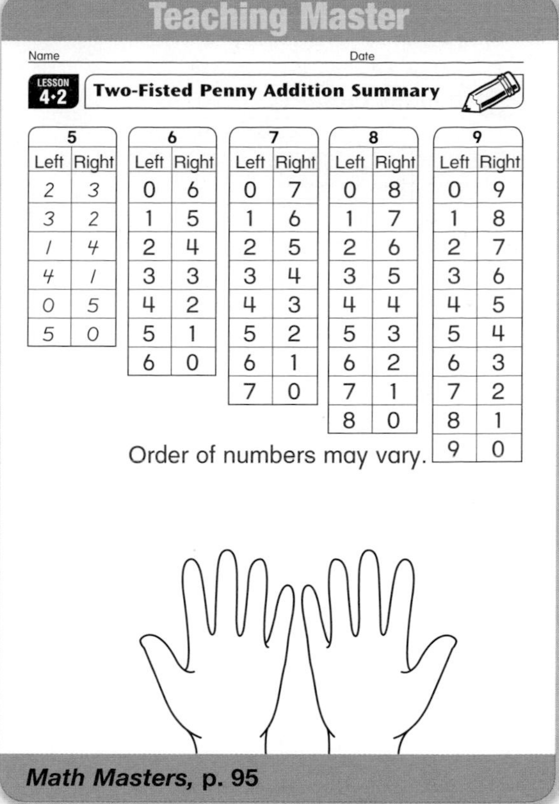

Teaching Master

Name Date

LESSON 4·2 **Two-Fisted Penny Addition Summary**

5 Left	5 Right	6 Left	6 Right	7 Left	7 Right	8 Left	8 Right	9 Left	9 Right
2	3	0	6	0	7	0	8	0	9
3	2	1	5	1	6	1	7	1	8
1	4	2	4	2	5	2	6	2	7
4	1	3	3	3	4	3	5	3	6
0	5	4	2	4	3	4	4	4	5
5	0	5	1	5	2	5	3	5	4
		6	0	6	1	6	2	6	3
				7	0	7	1	7	2
						8	0	8	1
								9	0

Order of numbers may vary.

Math Masters, p. 95

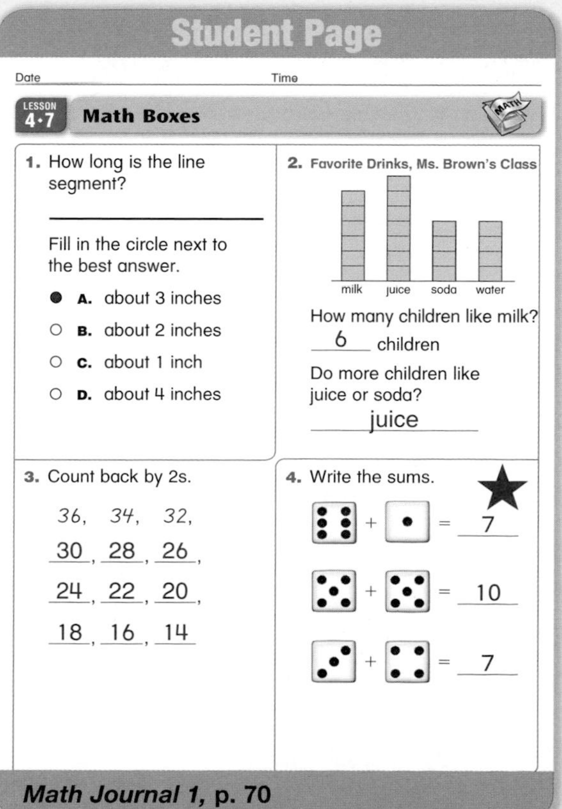

Student Page

Date Time

LESSON 4·7 **Math Boxes**

1. How long is the line segment?

Fill in the circle next to the best answer.

- ● **A.** about 3 inches
- ○ **B.** about 2 inches
- ○ **C.** about 1 inch
- ○ **D.** about 4 inches

2. Favorite Drinks, Ms. Brown's Class

How many children like milk?
6 children

Do more children like juice or soda?
juice

3. Count back by 2s.

36, 34, 32,
30, 28, 26,
24, 22, 20,
18, 16, 14

4. Write the sums.

⚅ + ⚀ = 7
⚄ + ⚄ = 10
⚂ + ⚃ = 7

Math Journal 1, p. 70

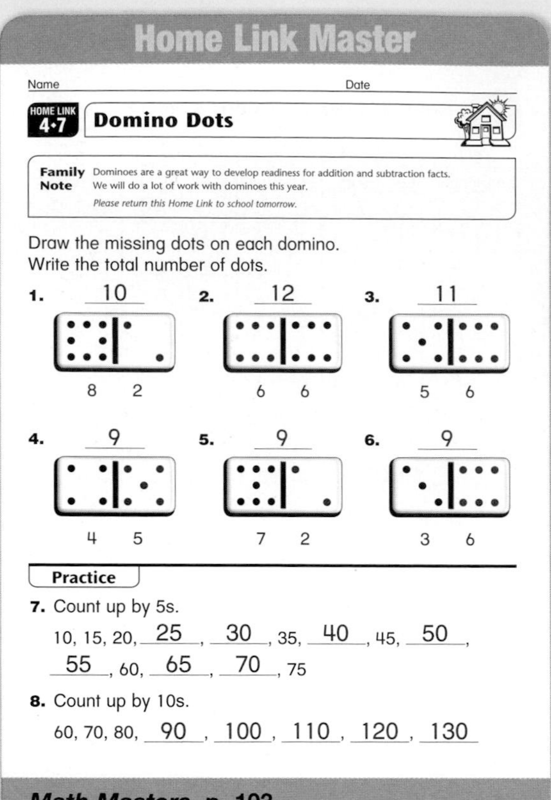

Home Link Master

Name Date

HOME LINK 4·7 **Domino Dots**

Family Note Dominoes are a great way to develop readiness for addition and subtraction facts. We will do a lot of work with dominoes this year.

Please return this Home Link to school tomorrow.

Draw the missing dots on each domino.
Write the total number of dots.

1. 10 (8, 2)
2. 12 (6, 6)
3. 11 (5, 6)
4. 9 (4, 5)
5. 9 (7, 2)
6. 9 (3, 6)

Practice

7. Count up by 5s.
10, 15, 20, 25, 30, 35, 40, 45, 50, 55, 60, 65, 70, 75
8. Count up by 10s.
60, 70, 80, 90, 100, 110, 120, 130

Math Masters, p. 103

Home Link 4·7

(*Math Masters,* p. 103)

Home Connection Children draw domino dot patterns and record the total number of dots on dominoes.

3 Differentiation Options

ENRICHMENT

PARTNER ACTIVITY

5–15 Min

Estimating Length on a Geoboard

(*Math Masters,* p. 104)

To apply children's estimation skills with linear measurement, have them make shapes on the geoboard by estimating their lengths. Have one partner try to make the shapes described on *Math Masters,* page 104. Then have the other child measure the lengths to see how close the estimates were. Allow children to change roles. Have them explain which lengths were easiest to estimate and why.

EXTRA PRACTICE

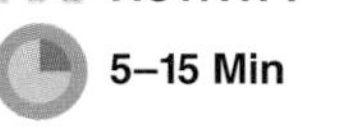

Use *Minute Math+,* pages 18, 53, and 58, to provide practice describing and identifying shapes.

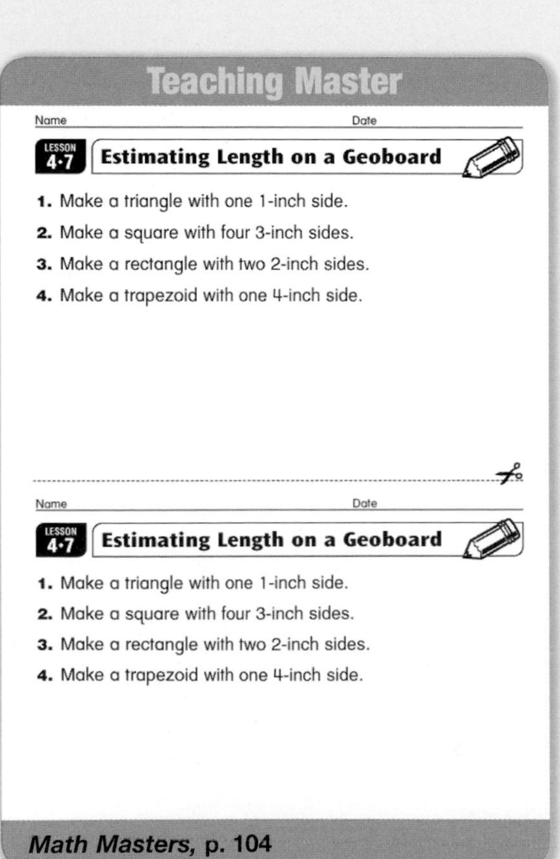

Teaching Master

Name Date

LESSON 4·7 **Estimating Length on a Geoboard**

1. Make a triangle with one 1-inch side.
2. Make a square with four 3-inch sides.
3. Make a rectangle with two 2-inch sides.
4. Make a trapezoid with one 4-inch side.

Name Date

LESSON 4·7 **Estimating Length on a Geoboard**

1. Make a triangle with one 1-inch side.
2. Make a square with four 3-inch sides.
3. Make a rectangle with two 2-inch sides.
4. Make a trapezoid with one 4-inch side.

Math Masters, p. 104

4•8 Telling Time on the Quarter-Hour

Objectives To review telling time on the hour and half-hour; and to introduce telling time on the quarter-hour.

Technology Resources www.everydaymathonline.com

ePresentations

eToolkit

Algorithms Practice

EM Facts Workshop Game™

Family Letters

Assessment Management

Common Core State Standards

Curriculum Focal Points

Interactive Teacher's Lesson Guide

1 Teaching the Lesson

Key Concepts and Skills

- Count forward by 5s.
  [Number and Numeration Goal 1]
- Show time on an analog clock to the nearest half-hour and quarter-hour.
  [Measurement and Reference Frames Goal 4]
- Tell and record times on an analog clock to the nearest half-hour and quarter-hour.
  [Measurement and Reference Frames Goal 4]
- Use language of approximation to describe times on an analog clock.
  [Measurement and Reference Frames Goal 4]

Key Activities

Children review the movements of the hour and minute hands and telling time on the hour and half-hour. They learn to tell time on the quarter-hour.

Ongoing Assessment: Recognizing Student Achievement
Use journal page 71.
[Measurement and Reference Frames Goal 4]

Key Vocabulary

half-past (the hour) ◆ quarter-after, quarter-past (the hour) ◆ quarter-before, quarter-to (the hour)

Materials

Math Journal 1, p. 71
Home Link 4•7
demonstration clock with hour and minute hands ◆ tool-kit clock

2 Ongoing Learning & Practice

Playing *Dime-Nickel-Penny Grab*
Math Masters, p. 342
tool-kit coins
Children practice comparing money amounts.

Using 10, 11, and 12 Pennies in Two-Fisted Penny Addition
Math Masters, p. 105
Children build readiness for basic addition facts by finding and recording all of the complements of 10, 11, and 12.

Math Boxes 4•8
Math Journal 1, p. 72
Children practice and maintain skills through Math Box problems.

Home Link 4•8
Math Masters, p. 106
Children practice and maintain skills through Home Link activities.

3 Differentiation Options

READINESS

Making Hour and Half-Hour Times on a Clock
8 of 24 *Time Match* Cards for hour and half-hour times (*Math Masters,* p. 355) ◆ tool-kit clocks
Children practice making times to the hour and half-hour on their tool-kit clocks.

ENRICHMENT

Exploring Time
Math Masters, p. 107
Children draw pictures of things they can do in various amounts of time.

ELL SUPPORT

Discussing Terms Related to Telling Time
clock labels
Children discuss and visually represent various terms related to telling time.

Advance Preparation

***Teacher's Reference Manual,* Grades 1–3** p. 173

Getting Started

Mental Math and Reflexes

Do stop-and-start counting by 10s, by 5s, and then by 1s.

●○○ Count by 10s beginning with 0. Stop at 40. Count by 5s to 75. Then continue counting by 1s to 90.

●●○ Count by 10s beginning with 40. Stop at 60. Count by 5s to 100. Then continue counting by 1s to 130.

●●● Count by 10s beginning with 100. Stop at 150. Count by 5s to 180. Then continue counting by 1s to 200.

Math Message

Draw a picture of a circular pizza. Divide the pizza into 2 pieces that are the same size. Then divide it into 4 pieces that are the same size.

Home Link 4·7 Follow-Up

Briefly review children's strategies for solving the domino problems.

1 Teaching the Lesson

▶ Math Message Follow-Up

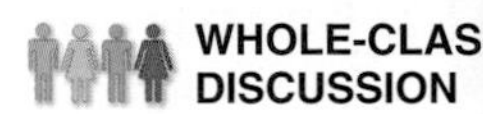

WHOLE-CLASS DISCUSSION

Have several children share how they divided the pizza into four equal pieces. Ask if anyone knows what one of the four pieces is called. Quarter or fourth

Tell children that just as a pizza can be divided into four equal pieces, so can a clock face. Explain that dividing a clock face into four equal parts makes it easier to tell times between o'clock and half-hour times.

▶ Reviewing Hour and Half-Hour Times

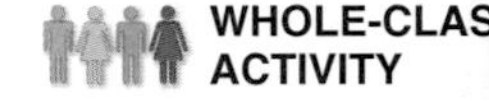

WHOLE-CLASS ACTIVITY

Use the demonstration clock to show several times on the hour. Ask children to name each time. Repeat the procedure for times on the half-hour.

Point out that for exact-hour times, it is easy to tell the time with just the hour hand. For the times halfway between hours (the **half-pasts**) and for the other "between" times, we can make a reasonable estimate with just the hour hand, but the minute hand helps us to be more exact.

▶ Telling Time to the Quarter-Hour

WHOLE-CLASS ACTIVITY

ELL

1. Show 10 o'clock on the demonstration clock. Move the minute hand 15 minutes so that it points to the right.

- What happened to the hour hand? It moved part of the way to 11.
- About what time does the clock show? The time is between 10 o'clock and 11 o'clock.

2. Establish that it takes one-quarter of an hour for the minute hand to move from pointing up to pointing to the right. Remind children of dividing the pizza into four equal parts and relate it to the clock face being divided into four equal parts; each part is a quarter of an hour. We say that the time shown is "about **quarter-after** 10 o'clock," or "about **quarter-past** 10 o'clock."

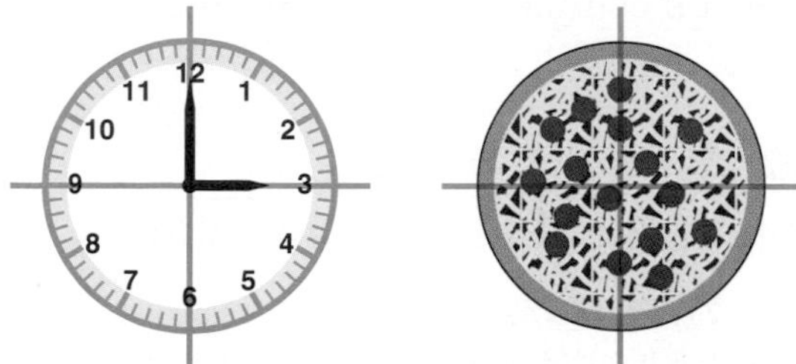

Children can think of a quarter of an hour as a quarter of a pizza.

3. Move the minute hand so that it points down.
   - What happened to the hour hand? It moved closer to 11; it is about halfway between 10 o'clock and 11 o'clock.
   - What time does the clock show now? About half-past 10
4. Move the minute hand so that it is pointing to the left.
   - What happened to the hour hand? It moved even closer to 11.
   - About what time does the clock show now? The time is still between 10 o'clock and 11 o'clock, but closer to 11 than to 10.

To support English language learners, discuss and visually represent the meanings of *quarter-after, quarter-past, quarter-before,* and *quarter-to.*

5. Move the minute hand so that it is pointing up. Then move it back so that it is pointing left. Establish that it takes one-quarter of an hour for the minute hand to move from pointing to the left to pointing up.
   - What time is it now? About a **quarter-before** 11 o'clock, or about a **quarter-to** 11 o'clock.

Adjusting the Activity

Ask children how many minutes are in a half-hour and in a quarter-hour. 30 minutes; 15 minutes

AUDITORY • KINESTHETIC • TACTILE • VISUAL

NOTE In this unit, time is still being named and written using words. Digital notation and language will be introduced in Unit 6.

Remember to use *about* when stating the time. Continue reminding children that telling time is always an estimate.

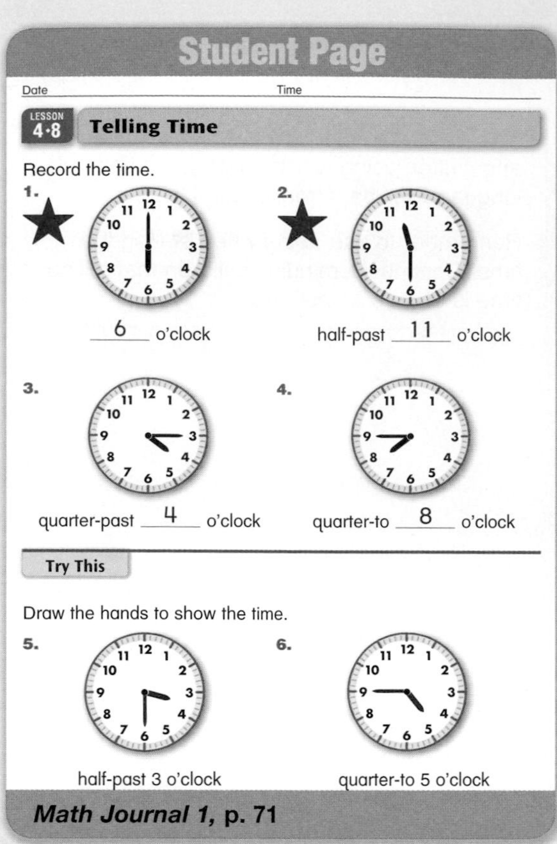
Student Page

Date Time

LESSON 4·8 **Telling Time**

Record the time.

1. ★ 6 o'clock
2. ★ half-past 11 o'clock
3. quarter-past 4 o'clock
4. quarter-to 8 o'clock

Try This

Draw the hands to show the time.

5. half-past 3 o'clock
6. quarter-to 5 o'clock

Math Journal 1, p. 71

▶ Practicing Telling Time to the Quarter-Hour and Half-Hour

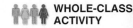

WHOLE-CLASS ACTIVITY

(*Math Journal 1,* p. 71)

1. Show times on the demonstration clock: 4 o'clock, quarter-past 4, half-past 4, quarter-to 5, and so on. Have children say the times.
2. Name a variety of hour, half-hour, and quarter-hour times. Have children show them on their tool-kit clocks. Use words to write the times on the board so that children recognize them.
3. Have children complete the journal page.

Ongoing Assessment: Recognizing Student Achievement

Journal page 71 Problems 1 and 2 ★

Use **journal page 71, Problems 1 and 2** to assess children's ability to tell time. Children are making adequate progress if they are able to answer Problems 1 and 2 correctly. [Measurement and Reference Frames Goal 4]

Teaching Master

Name Date

LESSON 4·8 **Two-Fisted Penny Addition Summary**

10		11		12		13		14	
Left	Right	Left	Right	Left	Right	Left	Right	Left	Right
0	10	0	11	0	12	0	13	0	14
1	9	1	10	1	11	1	12	1	13
2	8	2	9	2	10	2	11	2	12
3	7	3	8	3	9	3	10	3	11
4	6	4	7	4	8	4	9	4	10
5	5	5	6	5	7	5	8	5	9
6	4	6	5	6	6	6	7	6	8
7	3	7	4	7	5	7	6	7	7
8	2	8	3	8	4	8	5	8	6
9	1	9	2	9	3	9	4	9	5
10	0	10	1	10	2	10	3	10	4
		11	0	11	1	11	2	11	3
				12	0	12	1	12	2
						13	0	13	1
								14	0

Order of numbers may vary.

Math Masters, p. 105

2 Ongoing Learning & Practice

▶ Playing *Dime-Nickel-Penny Grab*

(*Math Masters,* p. 342)

Children practice comparing money amounts by playing *Dime-Nickel-Penny Grab*. For detailed instructions, see Lesson 3-13.

▶ Using 10, 11, and 12 Pennies in Two-Fisted Penny Addition

INDEPENDENT ACTIVITY

(*Math Masters,* p. 105)

This activity is a continuation of the systematic record of complements of the numbers 5 to 18. Encourage children to find and record all of the complements of 10, 11, and 12.

Math Boxes 4·8

INDEPENDENT ACTIVITY

(*Math Journal 1,* p. 72)

Mixed Practice Math Boxes in this lesson are paired with Math Boxes in Lesson 4-6. The skills in Problem 4 preview Unit 5 content.

Writing/Reasoning Have children discuss, draw, or write an answer to the following question: *How do you draw a line segment?* A reasonable answer should mention starting at the 0 mark and moving the pencil along the ruler to the given length.

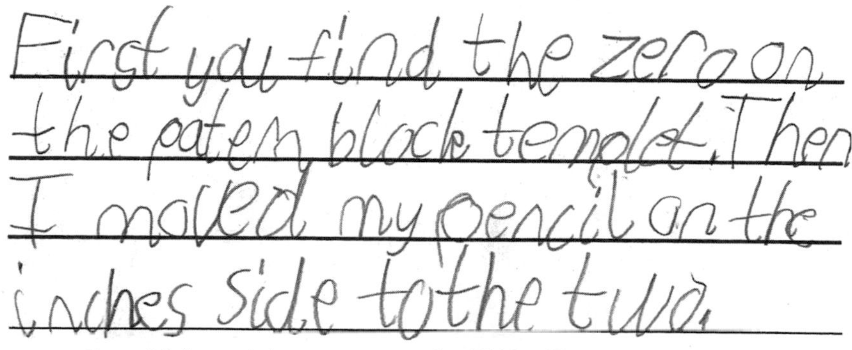

One child's work in response to the Writing/Reasoning prompt

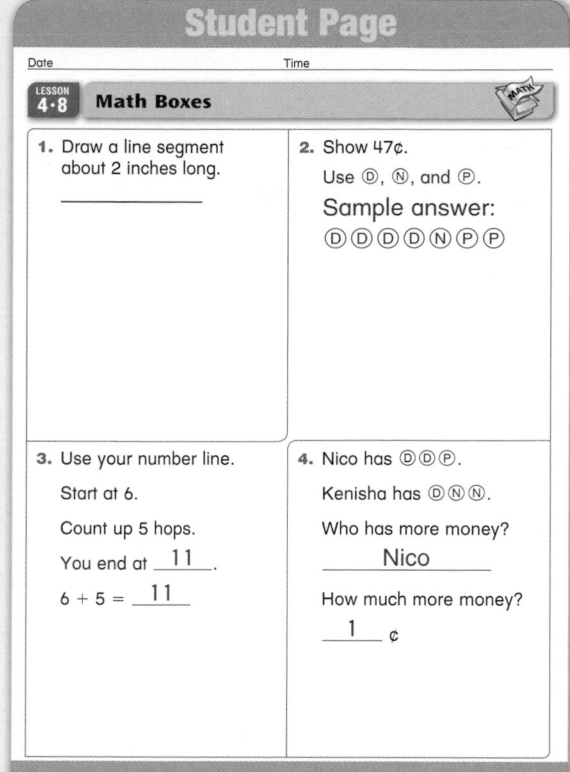

Student Page

Date Time

LESSON 4·8 **Math Boxes**

1. Draw a line segment about 2 inches long.

2. Show 47¢. Use Ⓓ, Ⓝ, and Ⓟ. Sample answer: ⒹⒹⒹⒹⓃⓅⓅ

3. Use your number line. Start at 6. Count up 5 hops. You end at 11. 6 + 5 = 11

4. Nico has ⒹⒹⓅ. Kenisha has ⒹⓃⓃ. Who has more money? Nico How much more money? 1 ¢

Math Journal 1, p. 72

NOTE Remember to reserve time every day to complete the number-line, attendance, calendar, temperature, and weather routines.

Home Link 4·8

INDEPENDENT ACTIVITY

(*Math Masters,* p. 106)

Home Connection Children record the times shown on clock faces.

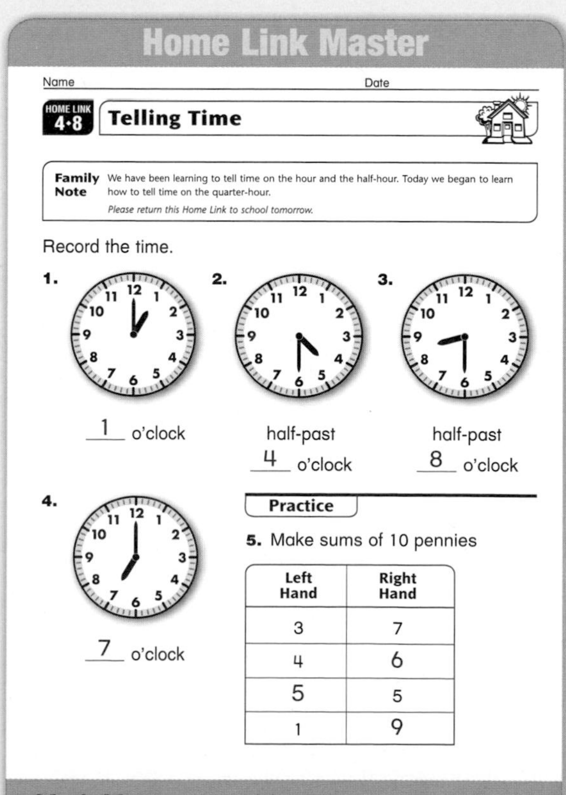

Home Link Master

Name Date

HOME LINK 4·8 **Telling Time**

Family Note We have been learning to tell time on the hour and the half-hour. Today we began to learn how to tell time on the quarter-hour.
Please return this Home Link to school tomorrow.

Record the time.

1. 1 o'clock

2. half-past 4 o'clock

3. half-past 8 o'clock

4. 7 o'clock

Practice

5. Make sums of 10 pennies

Left Hand	Right Hand
3	7
4	6
5	5
1	9

Math Masters, p. 106

3 Differentiation Options

READINESS

SMALL-GROUP ACTIVITY

Making Hour and Half-Hour Times on a Clock

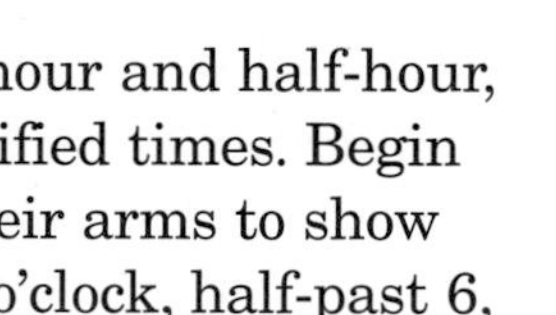

5–15 Min

To provide experience showing times to the hour and half-hour, have children set their tool-kit clocks to specified times. Begin with a brief warm-up. Ask children to use their arms to show where the hands are when it is 12 o'clock, 6 o'clock, half-past 6, and half-past 12. Each time, ask them where the minute hand points and where the hour hand points.

Use only the hour and half-hour word cards from *Time Match* in Lesson 4-4. Place the word cards facedown on the table. Allow each child to turn over a word card and set the appropriate time on his or her tool-kit clock. Repeat the activity several times.

ENRICHMENT

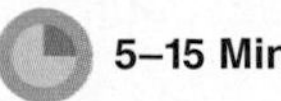

INDEPENDENT ACTIVITY

5–15 Min

▶ Exploring Time

(*Math Masters,* p. 107)

To apply children's understanding of time, have them draw pictures of what they can do in each amount of time on *Math Masters,* page 107.

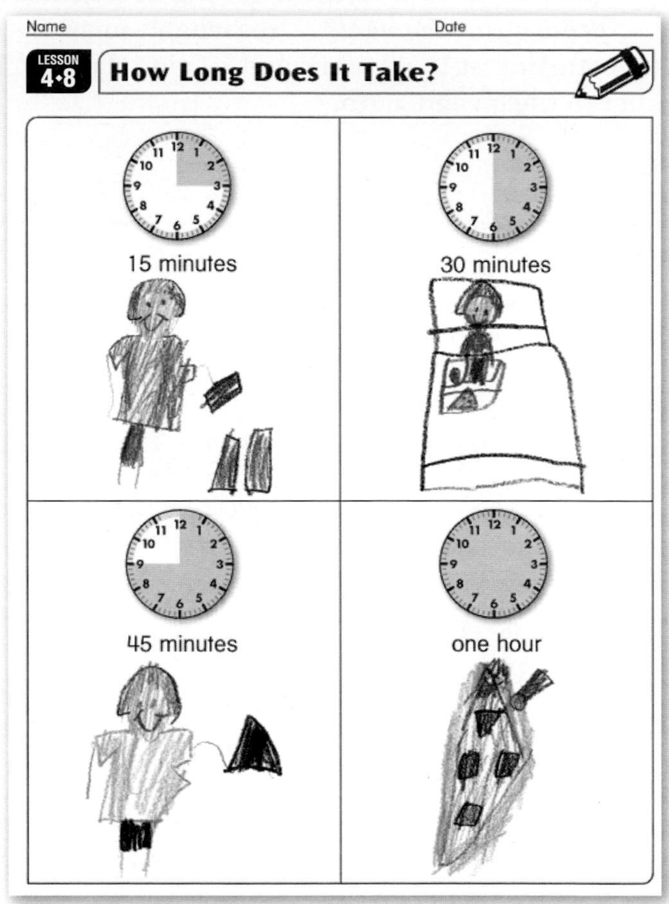

A sample of one child's work for *Math Masters,* page 107

ELL SUPPORT

SMALL-GROUP ACTIVITY

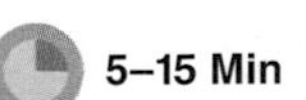

5–15 Min

▶ Discussing Terms Related to Telling Time

To provide language support for telling time, label your classroom clock with words on strips of paper: over the 12, *o'clock;* next to the three, *quarter-past* or *quarter-after;* under the six, *half-past;* and next to the nine, *quarter-to* or *quarter-before.* Talk with children about the meanings of the labels.

Planning Ahead

For Lesson 4-10, have each child bring in a paper-towel roll.

4•9 Timelines

Objective To facilitate the investigation of timelines.

Technology Resources www.everydaymathonline.com

ePresentations

eToolkit

Algorithms Practice

EM Facts Workshop Game™

Family Letters

Assessment Management

Common Core State Standards

Curriculum Focal Points

Interactive Teacher's Lesson Guide

1 Teaching the Lesson

Key Concepts and Skills

- Order events on a timeline. [Number and Numeration Goal 7]
- Create a simple timeline. [Measurement and Reference Frames Goal 4]

Key Activities

Children are introduced to timelines by making a 24-hour timeline. They draw pictures for a timeline of the first half of the school year.

Key Vocabulary

timeline

Materials

Math Journal 1, p. 73
Home Link 4•8
slate ◆ tool-kit clock ◆ demonstration clock with hour and minute hands ◆ 24-hour timeline ◆ Class Number Line (optional)

2 Ongoing Learning & Practice

Practicing Telling Time

Math Journal 1, p. 74
Children practice telling time to the quarter- and half-hour.

Math Boxes 4•9

Math Journal 1, p. 75
Children practice and maintain skills through Math Box problems.

Ongoing Assessment: Recognizing Student Achievement
Use Math Boxes, Problem 1.
[Measurement and Reference Frames Goal 1]

Home Link 4•9

Math Masters, p. 108
Children practice and maintain skills through Home Link activities.

3 Differentiation Options

READINESS

Sequencing Before-School Activities

scissors ◆ glue ◆ construction paper
Children sequence the routines or activities they do to get ready for school.

ENRICHMENT

Making a Storybook Timeline

age-appropriate storybooks
Children make timelines for storybooks.

EXTRA PRACTICE

Minute Math+

Minute Math®+, p. 20
Children sequence dates, days of the week, and months.

Advance Preparation

For Part 1, draw a 24-hour timeline on the board. See the example on page 320.

***Teacher's Reference Manual,* Grades 1–3** p. 176

Getting Started

Mental Math and Reflexes

Pose problems like the following and have children write their answers on their slates. If needed, children can draw pictures or doodles, count on the number line or number grid, or use pennies or counters to help them solve the number stories.

●○○ Jeanine picked 6 red flowers and 3 yellow flowers. How many flowers did Jeanine pick altogether? 9 flowers

●●○ Ahmad had 7 video games. His brother broke 2 of the games. How many working video games does Ahmad have left? 5 working games

●●● Lorenzo has 10 baseball cards today. Yesterday, he was given 4 cards for his birthday. How many baseball cards did Lorenzo have before his birthday? 6 baseball cards

Math Message

Show quarter-past 6 o'clock on your tool-kit clock.

Home Link 4·8 Follow-Up

Briefly go over the times shown on the clocks. Discuss with children how the placement of the hour hand helped them to determine the time.

1 Teaching the Lesson

▶ Math Message Follow-Up

WHOLE-CLASS ACTIVITY

Have children describe the placement of the hands on their clocks.

Show times to the quarter-hour on the demonstration clock and have children name the times. Or, name times to the quarter-hour and have children display times on their clocks.

▶ Introducing Timelines

WHOLE-CLASS ACTIVITY

Explain how people use timelines to help them keep track of when important events happen. Tell children that a **timeline** is like a number line on which the numbers indicate time periods such as years, hours, months, or days.

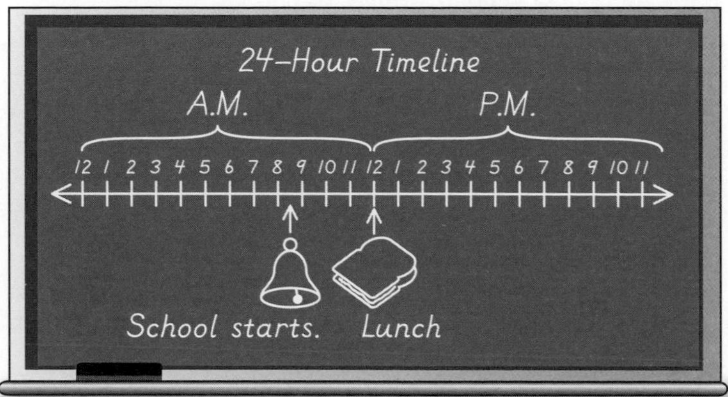

Show the 24-hour timeline. Ask the class how many hours are in a day. 24 hours Talk about events that usually occur at various times during the day, such as getting up for school, beginning the school day, and eating dinner. Write the names of the events on the timeline. Have children suggest a picture to represent each activity.

You may want to review A.M. and P.M. (introduced in Lesson 2-6), the number of days in a week, and the number of days in a month.

Making a Timeline

WHOLE-CLASS ACTIVITY

(*Math Journal 1,* p. 73)

Help children recall important school-related events that have taken place since the beginning of the school year.

Direct children's attention to journal page 73 and the arrow at the right side of the timeline. Ask: *What do you think the arrow means?* It means that the timeline continues past December 1.

Children draw a picture on the journal page to represent an event for each month. Suggest that they draw arrows to a point on the timeline to show whether the event happens at the beginning, middle, or end of the month.

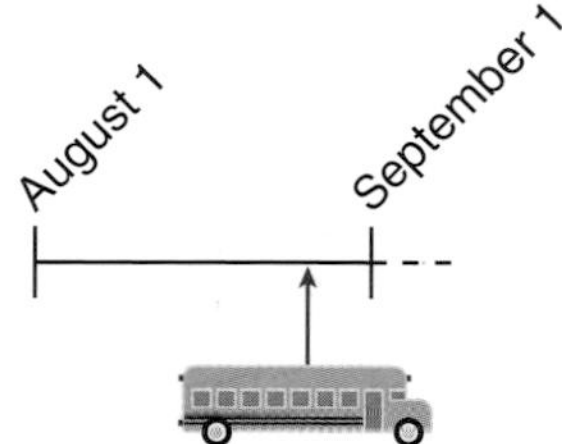

Children may draw a bus to show that school starts at the end of August.

Social Studies Link Show children a variety of timelines about the history of their city, inventions, technology, or another topic of interest to them. Encourage children to discuss the similarities and differences in the timelines. Children might enjoy making a timeline about the history of their school.

NOTE Do not forget to refer children to the Class Number Line if you have been using it as a timeline to record special events.

2 Ongoing Learning & Practice

Practicing Telling Time

INDEPENDENT ACTIVITY

(*Math Journal 1,* p. 74)

Use journal page 74 to provide practice telling time to the quarter-hour.

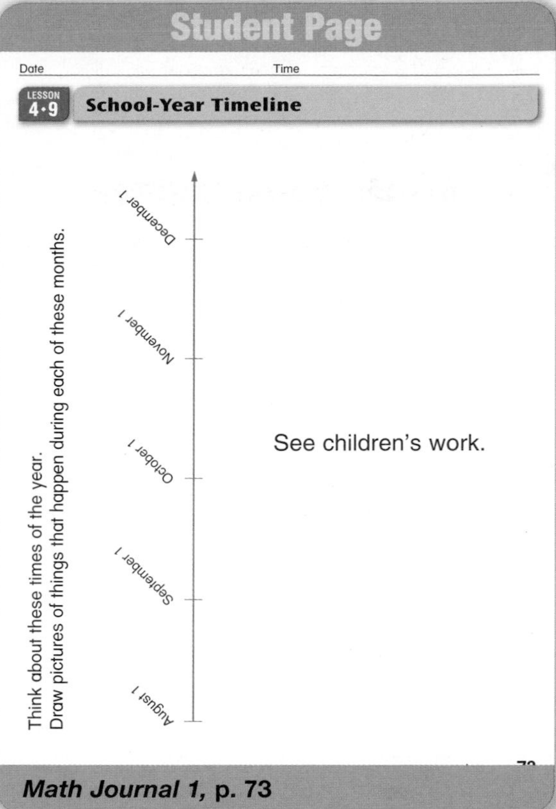

Math Journal 1, p. 73

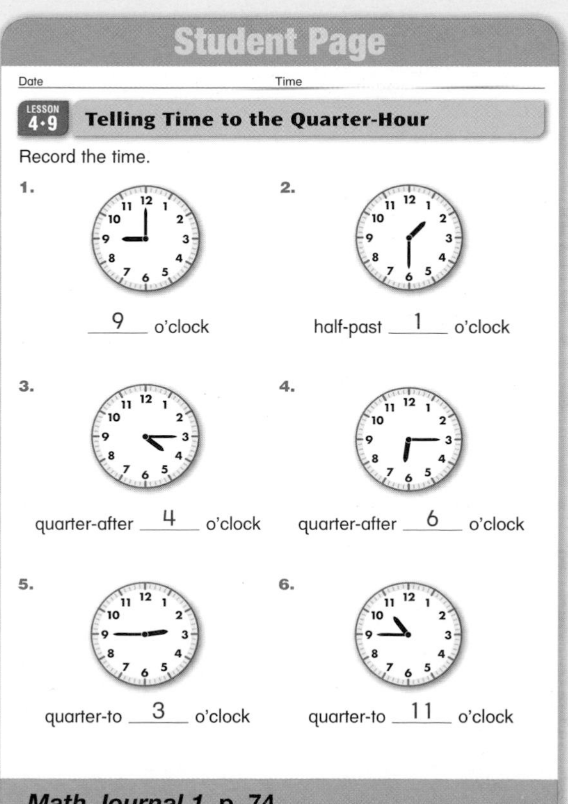

Math Journal 1, p. 74

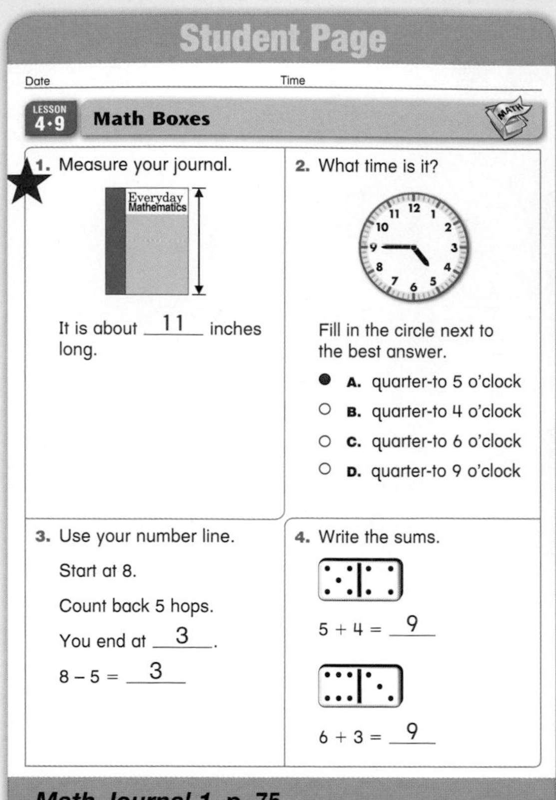
Student Page

Date Time

LESSON 4·9 **Math Boxes**

1. Measure your journal.

It is about 11 inches long.

2. What time is it?

Fill in the circle next to the best answer.

- ● A. quarter-to 5 o'clock
- ○ B. quarter-to 4 o'clock
- ○ C. quarter-to 6 o'clock
- ○ D. quarter-to 9 o'clock

3. Use your number line.

Start at 8.

Count back 5 hops.

You end at 3.

8 − 5 = 3

4. Write the sums.

5 + 4 = 9

6 + 3 = 9

Math Journal 1, p. 75

▶ Math Boxes 4·9

INDEPENDENT ACTIVITY

(*Math Journal 1,* p. 75)

Mixed Practice Math Boxes in this lesson are paired with Math Boxes in Lesson 4-11. The skills in Problem 4 preview Unit 5 content.

Ongoing Assessment: Recognizing Student Achievement

Math Boxes Problem 1

Use **Math Boxes, Problem 1** to assess children's ability to measure to the nearest inch. Children are making adequate progress if they are able to measure within 1 inch of the exact measurement. Some children may be able to measure accurately to the nearest inch.

[Measurement and Reference Frames Goal 1]

▶ Home Link 4·9

INDEPENDENT ACTIVITY

(*Math Masters,* p. 108)

Home Connection Children make a timeline of family events for a week. Consider giving children two days to complete this Home Link.

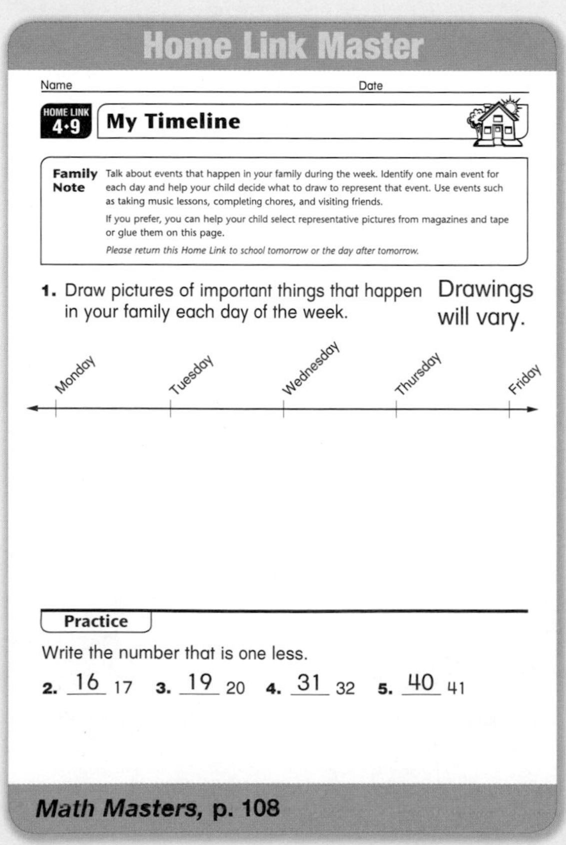
Home Link Master

Name Date

HOME LINK 4·9 **My Timeline**

Family Note Talk about events that happen in your family during the week. Identify one main event for each day and help your child decide what to draw to represent that event. Use events such as taking music lessons, completing chores, and visiting friends.

If you prefer, you can help your child select representative pictures from magazines and tape or glue them on this page.

Please return this Home Link to school tomorrow or the day after tomorrow.

1. Draw pictures of important things that happen in your family each day of the week. Drawings will vary.

Monday Tuesday Wednesday Thursday Friday

Practice

Write the number that is one less.

2. 16 17 3. 19 20 4. 31 32 5. 40 41

Math Masters, p. 108

3 Differentiation Options

READINESS

INDEPENDENT ACTIVITY

▶ Sequencing Before-School Activities

5–15 Min

Portfolio Ideas

To provide experience sequencing events, have children sequence a set of before-school activities. Children fold a piece of paper into fourths. In each box, they draw an activity they do to get ready for school. Children cut apart the four boxes; sequence the activities in the order in which they are done each morning; and then glue them, in that order, onto construction paper. Have children label each activity using sequencing language: *before, after, first, second, third,* and so on.

ENRICHMENT

INDEPENDENT ACTIVITY

Making a Storybook Timeline

30+ Min

Portfolio Ideas

To further explore timelines, each child begins by choosing a favorite picture book or fairy tale and identifying the main events in that story. Have each child decide on a time frame for the timeline. Label the timeline with appropriate time units and intervals. Have each child describe each scene illustrated from the story. Encourage the use of language such as *before, after,* and *first.*

EXTRA PRACTICE

SMALL-GROUP ACTIVITY

Minute Math+

5–15 Min

Use *Minute Math+*, page 20, to provide opportunities to sequence dates, days of the week, and months.

4•10 Number Scrolls

Objectives To introduce scrolls; and to provide opportunities to make a number scroll for numbers to 100 and beyond.

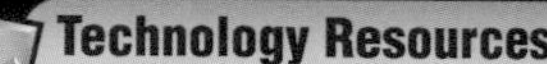

www.everydaymathonline.com

ePresentations

eToolkit

Algorithms Practice

EM Facts Workshop Game™

Family Letters

Assessment Management

Common Core State Standards

Curriculum Focal Points

Interactive Teacher's Lesson Guide

1 Teaching the Lesson

Key Concepts and Skills

- Count forward by 1s. [Number and Numeration Goal 1]
- Order numbers through 100 or more. [Number and Numeration Goal 7]
- Identify and use patterns on a number grid. [Patterns, Functions, and Algebra Goal 1]

Key Activities

Children fill 100-number grids, continuing with additional grids for numbers beyond 100, and then make number scrolls.

Ongoing Assessment: Informing Instruction See page 326.

Key Vocabulary

scroll

Materials

Home Link 4•9
Math Masters, pp. 109, 110, and 111 (optional)
overhead coins ◆ slate ◆ examples of scrolls, such as a pull-down screen, shade, or wall map, or Chinese or other art scrolls ◆ paper-towel roll ◆ scissors ◆ tape or glue ◆ calculator (optional) ◆ tool-kit coins (optional)

2 Ongoing Learning & Practice

Playing *Time Match* with Quarter-Hours

Math Masters, p. 356
Time Match Cards (*Math Masters,* pp. 354 and 355)
Children practice telling time on analog clocks.

Math Boxes 4•10

Math Journal 1, p. 76
Children practice and maintain skills through Math Box problems.

Ongoing Assessment: Recognizing Student Achievement
Use Math Boxes, Problem 1.
[Data and Chance Goal 3]

Home Link 4•10

Math Masters, p. 112
Children practice and maintain skills through Home Link activities.

3 Differentiation Options

READINESS

Naming Numbers Before and After 2-Digit Numbers

per partnership: number cards 0–9 (from the Everything Math Deck, if available)
Children name the numbers that are 1 less and 1 more than a given 2-digit number.

ENRICHMENT

Constructing a Number-Grid Poster

2" by 1" stick-on notes ◆ large chart paper or tagboard
Children make a Number-Grid Poster with numbered stick-on notes.

Advance Preparation

For Part 1, obtain a paper-towel roll for each child. For Part 2, add *Time Match* Cards from *Math Masters,* page 356 to each deck of cards used in Lesson 4•4. For the optional Enrichment activity in Part 3, number 2" by 1" stick-on notes from 1–100. Mix up the numbers and place them facedown around the classroom.

***Teacher's Reference Manual,* Grades 1–3** pp. 70–76, 177–182

Getting Started

Mental Math and Reflexes

Write or show coin combinations on the overhead projector. Children record totals on their slates. If necessary, children can use tool-kit coins to help them figure out the totals.

Extend the activity by asking how much two dimes and four nickels are worth altogether. 40¢ (Do not show the coin combinations. Keep the exercise oral.)

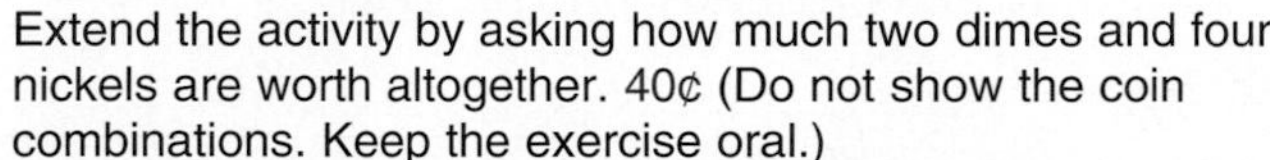

Math Message

What is the largest 3-digit number you know?

Home Link 4·9 Follow-Up

Have children explain how the timelines made at home differ from those made in class.

1 Teaching the Lesson

Math Message Follow-Up

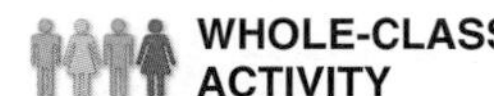

WHOLE-CLASS ACTIVITY

Write some of the children's 3-digit numbers on the board. Ask a volunteer to circle the largest number on the board and put a box around the smallest number. Tell them that they will be learning even larger numbers than the ones they know now.

Introducing Scrolls

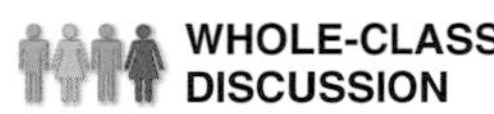

WHOLE-CLASS DISCUSSION

Discuss how the number grid extends in both directions like a number line. Tell children that they will record numbers past 100 on the number grid by creating a number **scroll**. Explain that a scroll is a roll of paper or another material, usually with writing or pictures on it. Examples of scrolls include a list of names, a pull-down screen, a shade, a wall map, TV or movie credits moving vertically up the screen, the Torah and the Koran (scriptures of the Jewish and Islamic religions, respectively), and some artwork.

Show children samples of scrolls you have gathered.

NOTE Many teachers have found making scrolls to be a worthwhile exercise, as it strengthens children's number sense and their grasp of the order of numbers. They have continued doing the activity several weeks or longer, depending on children's interest. Scrolls do not fit with the general theme of this unit, but they do need to be started early in the year.

Teaching Master

LESSON 4·10 **Beginning Scroll Page**

-9	-8	-7	-6	-5	-4	-3	-2	-1	0
1	2	3	4	5	6	7	8	9	10
11	12	13	14	15	16	17	18	19	20
21	22	23	24	25	26	27	28	29	30
31	32	33	34	35	36	37	38	39	40
41	42	43	44	45	46	47	48	49	50
51	52	53	54	55	56	57	58	59	60
61	62	63	64	65	66	67	68	69	70
71	72	73	74	75	76	77	78	79	80
81	82	83	84	85	86	87	88	89	90
91	92	93	94	95	96	97	98	99	100

109

Math Masters, p. 109

Teaching Master

Name Date

LESSON 4·10 **Continuing Scroll Page**

Paste/tape here.

Math Masters, p. 110

▶ Filling in a 100-Number Grid

PARTNER ACTIVITY

(*Math Masters,* pp. 109 and 110)

Algebraic Thinking Children fill in the 100-number grid on *Math Masters,* page 109. As they discover patterns and shortcuts, let them share these discoveries with classmates. If children cannot decide which number to write next, encourage them to work with their partners, using patterns already on the grid.

Adjusting the Activity

Enter a few selected numbers on the number-grid page before children begin working. They can then self-check as they work through the page. If children reach a number that does not agree with the number that comes next, they can then trace the numbers back to find the error.

AUDITORY ◆ KINESTHETIC ◆ TACTILE ◆ VISUAL

Remind children that they can also use calculators to help fill the number grid by adding 1 to the previous number on the scroll to find the next number.

Check the rows and completed grids before children begin a new grid page. Use the Continuing Scroll Page (*Math Masters,* page 110) for writing numbers beyond 100. All children should eventually complete several pages.

Ongoing Assessment: Informing Instruction

Watch for children who make mistakes such as recording the wrong number or skipping a space on the number grid. Help children find grid patterns to use as a means of self-checking.

After most children have written numbers to 200 or 300, you may wish to put the scrolls away for a while. For the remainder of the year, have children work on their scrolls during independent class time. A Math Message might be: *Fill in a row (or more) on your number scrolls.*

NOTE Encourage the use of pencils and frequent checking (with partners or you) to enable quick correction of errors and to avoid disappointment, excess work, and spoiled pages. Find creative ways to correct mistakes. For example, instead of having children rewrite a complete sheet if a row is left out, let them cut an extra grid apart and insert a blank row or rows. Supply extra copies of *Math Masters,* pages 109 and 110. It is important that the number-scrolls task be user friendly. Assure children that they can set their own pace and that their enjoyment and learning are more important than the number of pages on their scroll.

▶ Constructing a Number Scroll

(*Math Masters,* pp. 109 and 110)

After all children have completed and checked both the Beginning Scroll Page and the first Continuing Scroll Page, teach them how to glue or tape their grids together. (This activity is repeated as children complete each new Continuing Scroll Page.) Show the class how to roll the connected sheets into a scroll. The scrolls may be rolled onto a paper-towel roll.

NOTE One method teachers have recommended for storing scrolls while children are still working uses empty paper-towel rolls. Each day when children finish working on their scrolls, they roll up the scrolls and tuck them inside the tube. This protects the scrolls from damage. Children do not tape their scrolls onto the roll until they are completed.

Optional: Have children keep their pages together as a book rather than as a scroll.

Adjusting the Activity

Have children fill in the next page of the scroll by writing numbers in the grid boxes to form the first letter of their names. See the margin for an example. To help children decide which numbers to fill in, have them shade the area they want to complete, using a colored pencil before they begin.

Children may enjoy filling in a grid starting at 0 and counting backward with negative numbers. *Math Masters,* page 111 shows a grid with negative numbers in the last row, ending with 0.

AUDITORY ◆ KINESTHETIC ◆ TACTILE ◆ VISUAL

Tell children that they will continue to work on their number scrolls throughout the year. Discuss what times are appropriate to work on scrolls and where Continuing Scroll Pages will be kept.

		303	304	305	306				
		313				317			
		323				327			
		333				337			
		343				347			
		353	354	355	356				
		363				367			
		373					378		
		383						389	
		393							400

Robert filled in numbers in the grid boxes to look like the first letter of his name.

2 Ongoing Learning & Practice

▶ Playing *Time Match* with Quarter-Hours

PARTNER ACTIVITY

(*Math Masters,* p. 356)

This game is an extension of the game introduced in Lesson 4-4. Each partnership will use the 12 cards from *Math Masters,* page 356 and 4 cards from Lesson 4-4. The game is played with the same rules. See page 295.

NOTE In order to make a 4 × 4 array, which is a manageable size for most children, you need to add 4 more cards from Lesson 4-4 to the deck. You can add additional cards if children are ready to play with a larger array.

Game Master

Name Date

Time Match Cards *continued*

Quarter-past 9 o'clock	Quarter-before 3 o'clock	Quarter-to 11 o'clock
Quarter-to 4 o'clock	Quarter-after 4 o'clock	Quarter-after 1 o'clock

Math Masters, p. 356

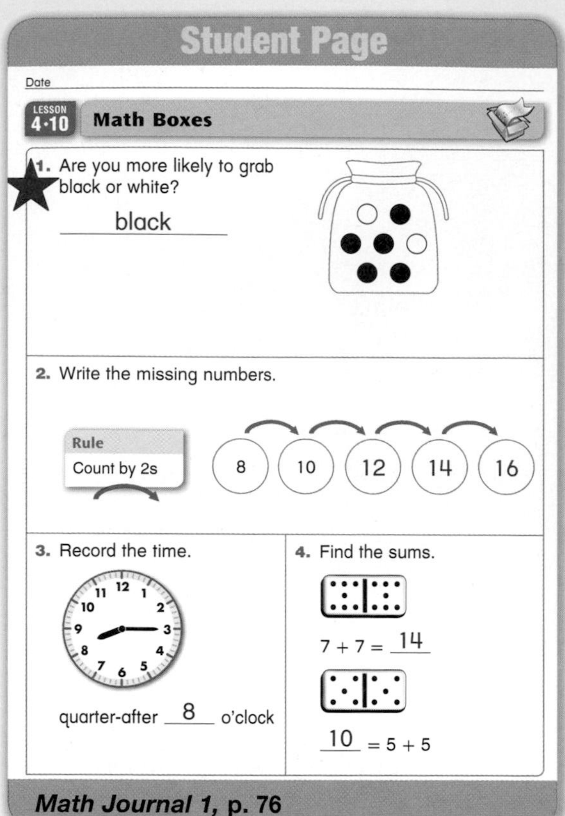

Student Page

Date

LESSON 4·10 **Math Boxes**

1. Are you more likely to grab black or white?
black

2. Write the missing numbers.
Rule: Count by 2s
8, 10, 12, 14, 16

3. Record the time.
quarter-after 8 o'clock

4. Find the sums.
7 + 7 = 14
10 = 5 + 5

Math Journal 1, **p. 76**

▶ Math Boxes 4·10

INDEPENDENT ACTIVITY

(*Math Journal 1,* p. 76)

Mixed Practice Math Boxes in this lesson are paired with Math Boxes in Lesson 4-12. The skills in Problem 4 preview Unit 5 content.

Ongoing Assessment: Recognizing Student Achievement

Math Boxes Problem 1

Use **Math Boxes, Problem 1** to assess children's ability to answer probability questions. Children are making adequate progress if they are able to answer the question correctly.

[Data and Chance Goal 3]

▶ Home Link 4·10

INDEPENDENT ACTIVITY

(*Math Masters,* p. 112)

Home Connection Children tell their families about number grids and number scrolls. They ask family members if they know of other kinds of scrolls. Children fill in a number grid from 100 to 130.

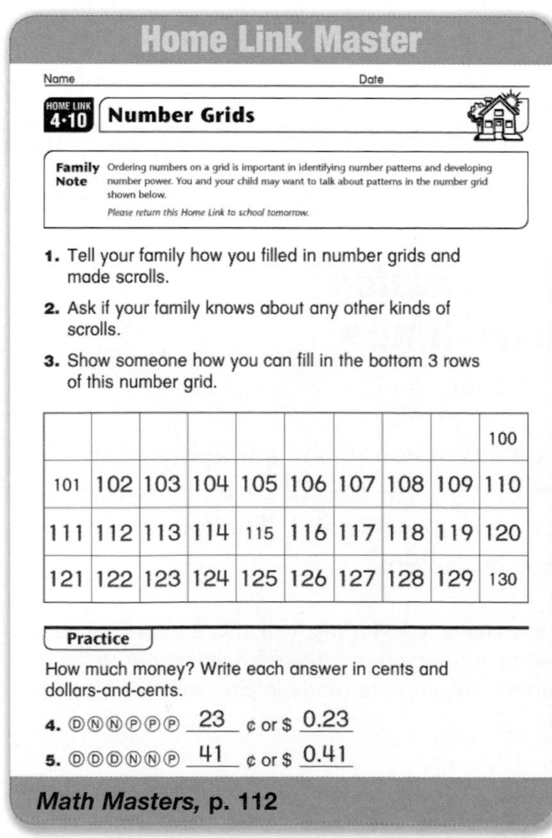

Home Link Master

Name Date

HOME LINK 4·10 **Number Grids**

Family Note Ordering numbers on a grid is important in identifying number patterns and developing number power. You and your child may want to talk about patterns in the number grid shown below.

Please return this Home Link to school tomorrow.

1. Tell your family how you filled in number grids and made scrolls.
2. Ask if your family knows about any other kinds of scrolls.
3. Show someone how you can fill in the bottom 3 rows of this number grid.

									100
101	102	103	104	105	106	107	108	109	110
111	112	113	114	115	116	117	118	119	120
121	122	123	124	125	126	127	128	129	130

Practice

How much money? Write each answer in cents and dollars-and-cents.

4. Ⓓ Ⓝ Ⓝ Ⓟ Ⓟ Ⓟ 23 ¢ or $ 0.23
5. Ⓓ Ⓓ Ⓓ Ⓝ Ⓝ Ⓟ 41 ¢ or $ 0.41

Math Masters, **p. 112**

3 Differentiation Options

READINESS

Naming Numbers Before and After 2-Digit Numbers

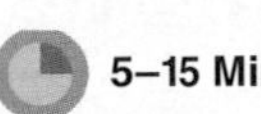

To review ordering numbers, have children name the numbers that come just before and just after a given 2-digit number. One partner turns over 2 number cards to create a 2-digit number. The other partner names the numbers that are 1 less and 1 more than that number. Then partners reverse roles and repeat the activity as time allows. Encourage children to use the number grid to check each other's answers.

ENRICHMENT

Constructing a Number-Grid Poster

To further explore number-grid patterns, children gather a set number of stick-on notes from around the classroom. (See Advance Preparation.) Then invite children with specific numbers to place their numbers on the grid. For example, invite children who have the numbers 1–10 or who have a 2 in their number to place their numbers on the grid in the correct location. Remind children to use patterns on the grid to find the correct spot for each note. Have children check each other's work. After the number grid is complete, remove the stick-on notes, mix up the numbers, and repeat the activity.

NOTE Draw a 10-by-10 blank number grid with cells large enough to hold 2" by 1" stick-on notes.

4•11 Introducing Fact Power

Objectives To introduce addition facts, fact power, turn-around facts, and doubles facts; and to practice adding and subtracting 10.

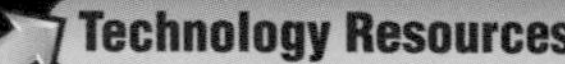

www.everydaymathonline.com

ePresentations

eToolkit

Algorithms Practice

EM Facts Workshop Game™

Family Letters

Assessment Management

Common Core State Standards

Curriculum Focal Points

Interactive Teacher's Lesson Guide

1 Teaching the Lesson

Key Concepts and Skills

- Find sums for addition facts; find sums for dice rolls.
  [Operations and Computation Goal 1]
- Solve facts with +10 and –10.
  [Operations and Computation 1]
- Identify and discuss patterns for easy facts.
  [Patterns, Functions, and Algebra Goal 1]
- Identify pairs of turn-around addition facts.
  [Patterns, Functions, and Algebra Goal 3]

Key Activities

Children find addition-fact sums using pictures of dominoes. They discuss their strategies and the importance of "fact power." Children investigate turn-around facts. They do a turn-around facts activity and look for patterns in their recording tables. Children explore facts with +10 and –10 and suggest strategies for solving them.

Ongoing Assessment: Informing Instruction See page 332A.

Key Vocabulary

addition facts ◆ sum ◆ fact power ◆ turn-around fact ◆ doubles fact

Materials

Math Journal 1, p. 77
Math Masters, p. 336
Home Link 4•10
calculator ◆ slate ◆ counters (optional) ◆ dice

2 Ongoing Learning & Practice

Playing *High Roller*
Math Masters, p. 344
per partnership: 2 dice
Children practice addition facts.

Math Boxes 4•11
Math Journal 1, p. 78
Children practice and maintain skills through Math Box problems.

Ongoing Assessment: Recognizing Student Achievement
Use Math Boxes, Problem 2.
[Measurement and Reference Frames Goal 4]

Home Link 4•11
Math Masters, p. 113
Children practice and maintain skills through Home Link activities.

***Minute Math*+**
Minute Math®+, p. 7
Children practice skip counting.

3 Differentiation Options

READINESS

Hopping to the Roll
on-the-floor number line ◆ dice
Children explore the Commutative Property of Addition by hopping on the floor number line.

EXTRA PRACTICE

Solving Easy Addition Facts
Math Masters, p. 317
Children practice solving easy addition facts.

ELL SUPPORT

Building a Math Word Bank
Differentiation Handbook, p. 126
Children add *sum* to their Math Word Banks.

ELL SUPPORT

Using Gestures for Turn-Around Facts
Children learn gestures for turn-around facts.

Advance Preparation

Fill in *Math Masters,* page 317 with +0 and +1 addition facts before copying it for the optional Extra Practice activity in Part 3.

***Teacher's Reference Manual,* Grades 1–3** pp. 195–198

Getting Started

Mental Math and Reflexes

▷ Children count up and back by 10s using the number grid. Ask: *What pattern do you see in the numbers on the grid?* Each time you move down a row, the number in the tens place is one more. Each time you move up a row, the number in the tens place is one less.

▷ Children count up and back by 10s using a calculator and saying the numbers aloud as they count. On the board, write the following calculator program (change the program for addition counts as time allows):

Start at:	0	25	38	81	92	157
Count:	Up	Up	Up	Up	Back	Back
By:	10s	10s	10s	10s	10s	10s

Math Message

Draw a domino. Write the 3 numbers that go with the domino.

Home Link 4•10 Follow-Up

Children share information about scrolls discussed at home.

1 Teaching the Lesson

NOTE This lesson contains a significant amount of content; you may wish to complete it over two days.

Math Message Follow-Up

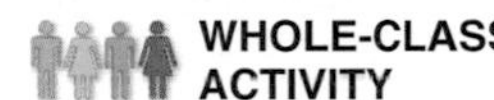

WHOLE-CLASS ACTIVITY

Draw a blank domino on the board. Ask a volunteer to suggest what to draw in the domino.

- Which three numbers go with the domino?
- What number model represents the domino?

If no one suggests one, write a possible number model on the board and explain what each number represents. For example, for the 3|5 domino, you might write $3 + 5 = 8$.

Tell children that they will use dominoes today to practice adding.

Introducing Addition Facts

WHOLE-CLASS DISCUSSION

ELL

Show examples of **addition facts,** each with two 1-digit numbers and a **sum.** To support English language learners, discuss the meaning of *sum* and how it differs from *some*.

Explain that addition facts are all sums of two 1-digit numbers. Tell children that knowing these facts will help them solve other addition problems. Have them write examples of addition facts on their slates.

Next, on the board, write some addition facts without the sums. Have children recite answers together. When they can recite addition-fact sums as easily as reading 1-digit numbers, they will have developed **fact power** for these facts.

A goal of *Everyday Mathematics* is for children, over time, to develop fact power.

▶ Discussing Fact Power

Addition fact power is the instant recall of sums of 1-digit numbers without stopping to figure them out. Discuss fact power. To support English language learners, discuss the everyday meaning of *power,* as well as its meaning in this context. Include the following points:

▷ Having fact power is like being a good reader. Reading is easier and more enjoyable if you recognize many words automatically. The same is true of number facts. Solving problems is easier if you automatically know the sum of two numbers from 0 to 9.

▷ Just as you sound out or decode unfamiliar words, you can figure out facts you don't know, but the goal is not to have to do that.

▷ Some facts lead to other facts. There are not that many different facts to learn or memorize. You will learn some easy "shortcuts" in later lessons.

▷ Playing number games and practicing will help you develop addition fact power.

▶ Introducing Turn-Around Facts

List several addition facts on the board written in a variety of formats. Be sure to include 3 or 4 pairs of turn-around facts.

▷ Write the addends to the left of the equal symbol.

▷ Write the addends to the right of the equal symbol.

▷ Write the addends in vertical form.

Highlight a pair of turn-around facts in your list, such as $3 + 4 = 7$ and $4 + 3 = 7$, or $4 + 2 = 6$ and $2 + 4 = 6$.

- What do these facts have in common? The same numbers are being added. They have the same sum.
- How are they different? The numbers being added are not written in the same order.

Explain that facts in which the same two numbers are added, but not in the same order, are called **turn-around facts.**

Because pairs of turn-around facts have the same answer, children need to learn only one of the facts. If one fact is known, then children also know its turn-around fact.

Ask children to identify other pairs of turn-around facts in the list on the board.

Turn-Around Facts Activity

PARTNER ACTIVITY

(*Math Journal 1,* p. 77)

Each child needs the Turn-Around Facts Record on journal page 77. Partners will need 2 dice.

1. Children take turns rolling the dice. One child rolls the dice and finds the total number of dots on the two dice.
2. Both children write the sum in the appropriate box on their Turn-Around Facts Record and then find the box for their turn-around fact, if there is one, and write the sum in that box. Turns are over when children find sums of dots that have already been recorded.
3. The activity is over when all of the boxes contain sums.

Discussing Patterns in the Turn-Around Facts Record

WHOLE-CLASS DISCUSSION

(*Math Journal 1,* p. 77)

When children finish filling in the Turn-Around Facts Record, discuss patterns in the table.

Review the meanings of *row, column,* and *diagonal:* Rows go across; columns go up and down; diagonals slant up or down from right to left or from left to right.

- Which facts do not have turn-around facts? $1 + 1 = 2$, $2 + 2 = 4$, $3 + 3 = 6$, $4 + 4 = 8$, $5 + 5 = 10$, and $6 + 6 = 12$

Tell the class that these facts are called **doubles facts.** In a doubles fact, both numbers that are being added are the same. Elicit from the class that doubles facts are found on the diagonal of the table that goes from the upper left-hand corner of the table to the lower right-hand corner.

- Are the sums of doubles facts even or odd numbers? Even numbers

Help children notice one other doubles fact pattern: When the sums are listed in order, they can be counted by 2s.

Discuss other patterns.

- What is the pattern of sums in each row? Each sum is 1 more than the sum before it. Each column? Each sum is 1 more than the sum above it.
- How would you describe the pattern of the sums of 7? They are on the diagonal that goes from the upper right-hand corner to the lower left-hand corner. This pattern also occurs in other sums that are the same. They are all on diagonals from right to left as you go down from row to row.

Review the idea of fact power. Have children share ways to practice addition facts, such as by playing math games, completing Math Boxes and Home Links, and using flash cards and computer programs.

Student Page

Date

LESSON 4·11 **Turn-Around Facts Record**

1 + 1 = 2	1 + 2 = 3	1 + 3 = 4	1 + 4 = 5	1 + 5 = 6	1 + 6 = 7
2 + 1 = 3	2 + 2 = 4	2 + 3 = 5	2 + 4 = 6	2 + 5 = 7	2 + 6 = 8
3 + 1 = 4	3 + 2 = 5	3 + 3 = 6	3 + 4 = 7	3 + 5 = 8	3 + 6 = 9
4 + 1 = 5	4 + 2 = 6	4 + 3 = 7	4 + 4 = 8	4 + 5 = 9	4 + 6 = 10
5 + 1 = 6	5 + 2 = 7	5 + 3 = 8	5 + 4 = 9	5 + 5 = 10	5 + 6 = 11
6 + 1 = 7	6 + 2 = 8	6 + 3 = 9	6 + 4 = 10	6 + 5 = 11	6 + 6 = 12

Math Journal 1, **p. 77**

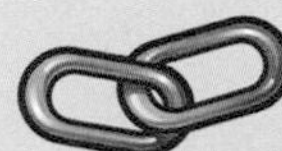

Links to the Future

This is the first time children are introduced to turn-around facts. Children use the turn-around fact rule to solve basic addition facts. Using and explaining the Commutative Property of Addition is a Grade 2 Goal.

NOTE Remember to reserve time every day to complete the number-line, attendance, calendar, temperature, and weather routines.

Ongoing Assessment: Informing Instruction

Watch for children who need to use counters, fingers, dominoes, and number lines to calculate addition fact sums. These children need more time to practice these facts in order to recite them automatically.

NOTE Be sure to add each of the strategies introduced in this lesson (turn-around facts, doubles facts, +10 facts, and −10 facts) to your Fact Strategy Wall.

▶ Facts with Ten

(*Math Masters,* p. 336)

Write the numbers 11 through 19 in a row on the board. Start with the number 11. Have children count out 11 counters. Ask children to fill their ten frames with 11 counters. Once children notice that there is only room on the ten frame for 10 of the counters, explain that while there is only room for 10 counters on the ten frame, they can begin a third row (and subsequently a fourth row) under the ten frame for the last counter. Ask: *How many counters fit in the ten frame?* 10 Ask: *How many counters did not fit in the ten frame?* 1 Under the 11 on the board, write 10 + 1 = 11.

Have children remove the 10 counters on the ten frame. Write 11 − 10 = ☐ under 10 + 1 = 11. Ask: *How many counters are left?* 1 Write 1 in the answer box.

Repeat the above procedure for the remaining numbers. You may wish to have children work independently to complete some of the numbers. Have children look at the row of addition facts written below the numbers. Ask: *What do all of these addition facts have in common?* Sample answer: They all have "+ 10." Ask children if they can think of a strategy for remembering the + 10 facts. Sample answers: Replace the 0 in 10 with the number you are adding, or add a one in the tens place of the number you are adding.

Ask: *What do all of the subtraction facts have in common?* Sample answer: They all have "– 10." Ask children if they can think of a strategy for remembering the – 10 facts. Sample answer: Take away the first digit; the second digit is the answer.

Game Master

Name ______ Date ______

High Roller Record Sheet

1. Record your first roll in the first two squares.
2. Cross out the smaller number.
3. Roll the die that shows the smaller number again.
4. Record your second roll in the third square.
5. Record the sum of the two dice on the line.

Math Masters, p. 344

2 Ongoing Learning & Practice

▶ Playing *High Roller*

(*Math Masters,* p. 344)

Children practice addition facts by playing *High Roller.* For detailed instructions, see Lesson 2-12.

NOTE To extend the activity, have children add all three numbers rolled. Have them choose the easiest order to add the numbers. For example, if they roll a 4, 5, and 1, they might first add 4 + 1 = 5, followed by 5 + 5 = 10. Have children note that the order in which they add the numbers does not change the sum. This activity demonstrates the *Associative Property of Addition.*

Math Boxes 4•11

INDEPENDENT ACTIVITY

(*Math Journal 1,* p. 78)

Mixed Practice Math Boxes in this lesson are paired with Math Boxes in Lesson 4-9. The skills in Problem 4 preview Unit 5 content.

Ongoing Assessment: Recognizing Student Achievement

Math Boxes Problem 2 ★

Use **Math Boxes, Problem 2** to assess children's ability to tell time to the quarter-hour. Children are making adequate progress if they are able to tell the time correctly.

[Measurement and Reference Frames Goal 4]

Writing/Reasoning Have children draw, write, or verbalize an answer to the following question: *Why is it important to use a ruler?* A reasonable answer should include a reference to getting a standard measurement—the same number of units every time.

Home Link 4•11

INDEPENDENT ACTIVITY

(*Math Masters,* p. 113)

Home Connection Children find sums for addition facts pictured with dice. This activity works with turn-around facts.

Minute Math+

SMALL-GROUP ACTIVITY

Use *Minute Math+,* page 7, to provide more practice with skip counting.

3 Differentiation Options

READINESS

Hopping to the Roll

SMALL-GROUP ACTIVITY

5–15 Min

To explore the Commutative Property of Addition, have children solve the addition problems on the number line by switching the positions of the addends. Gather children around the on-the-floor number line.

NOTE Children need to understand the concept of the Commutative Property of Addition, but do not need to memorize the term.

Student Page

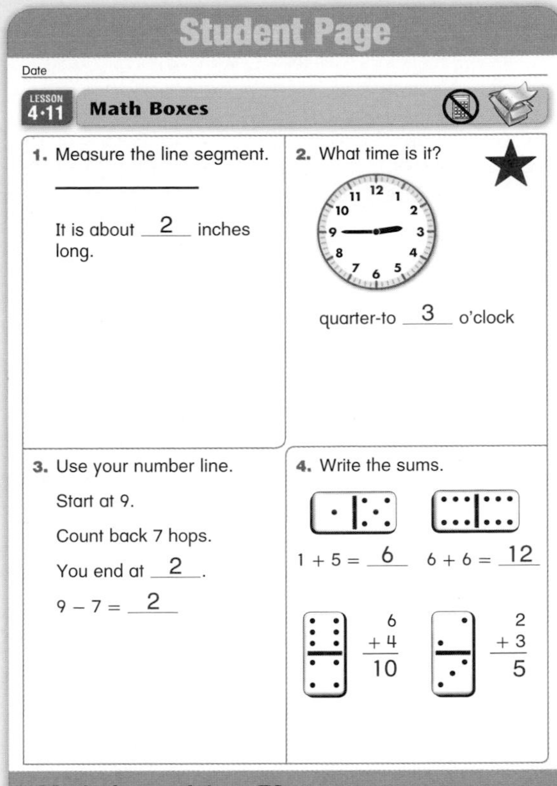

Date

LESSON 4•11 Math Boxes

1. Measure the line segment.

It is about 2 inches long.

2. What time is it? ★

quarter-to 3 o'clock

3. Use your number line.

Start at 9.

Count back 7 hops.

You end at 2.

9 − 7 = 2

4. Write the sums.

1 + 5 = 6 6 + 6 = 12

6 + 4 = 10 2 + 3 = 5

Math Journal 1, p. 78

NOTE Remember to reserve time every day to complete the number-line, attendance, calendar, temperature, and weather routines.

Home Link Master

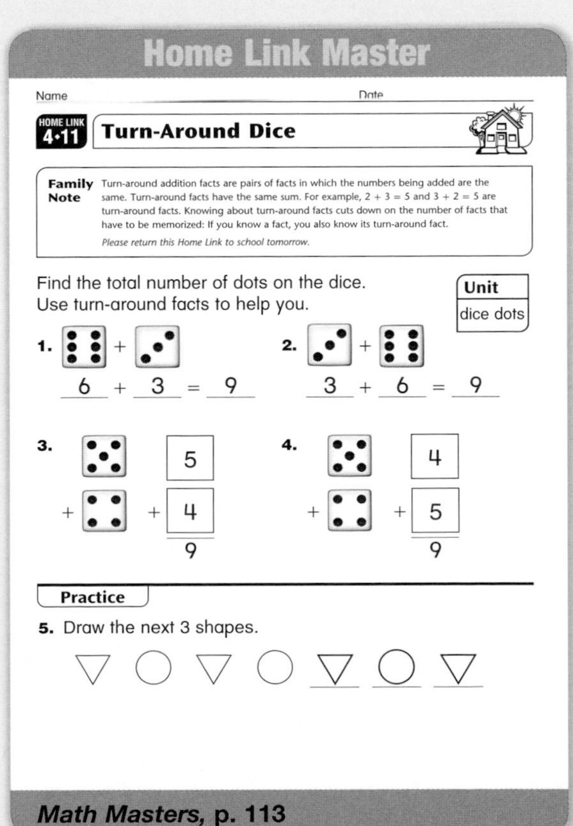

Name Date

HOME LINK 4•11 Turn-Around Dice

Family Note Turn-around addition facts are pairs of facts in which the numbers being added are the same. Turn-around facts have the same sum. For example, 2 + 3 = 5 and 3 + 2 = 5 are turn-around facts. Knowing about turn-around facts cuts down on the number of facts that have to be memorized: If you know a fact, you also know its turn-around fact.

Please return this Home Link to school tomorrow.

Find the total number of dots on the dice. Use turn-around facts to help you.

Unit: dice dots

1. 6 + 3 = 9

2. 3 + 6 = 9

3. 5 + 4 = 9

4. 4 + 5 = 9

Practice

5. Draw the next 3 shapes.

Math Masters, p. 113

1. Appoint one child to be the "Roller." Position two other children, the "Hoppers," at zero on the number line.
2. Have the Roller roll the pair of dice. The Roller then tells the Hoppers how far to hop based on the dice roll. For example, if one die shows a 3 and the other die shows a 4, the Roller tells the first Hopper to take 3 hops and the second Hopper to take 4 hops. The Roller then tells the first Hopper to take 4 more hops and the second Hopper to take 3 more hops.
3. Ask: *Where did the Hoppers land?* On the 7
4. Have children change roles and repeat the activity.
5. After you have done this activity a few times, allow children watching to predict where the second Hopper will land and to explain their thinking. Sample answer: The second Hopper wil land on the same number as the first because they are hoppin the same number of times, just in the opposite order.

EXTRA PRACTICE

▶ Solving Easy Addition Facts

5–15 Min

(*Math Masters,* p. 317)

Children find sums of easy addition facts on *Math Masters,* page 317 to help develop fact power.

ELL SUPPORT

▶ Building a Math Word Bank

5–15 Min

(*Differentiation Handbook,* p. 126)

To provide language support for addition, use the Word Bank template found on *Differentiation Handbook,* page 126. Ask children to write the term *sum,* draw a picture to represent the term, and write other words that describe it. See the *Differentiation Handbook* for more information.

ELL SUPPORT

▶ Using Gestures for Turn-Around Facts

5–15 Min

To provide language support for "turn-around" facts, teach childre a gesture that demonstrates the idea of the numbers switching order. This gesture could be used to remind children when the turn-around rule is being applied.

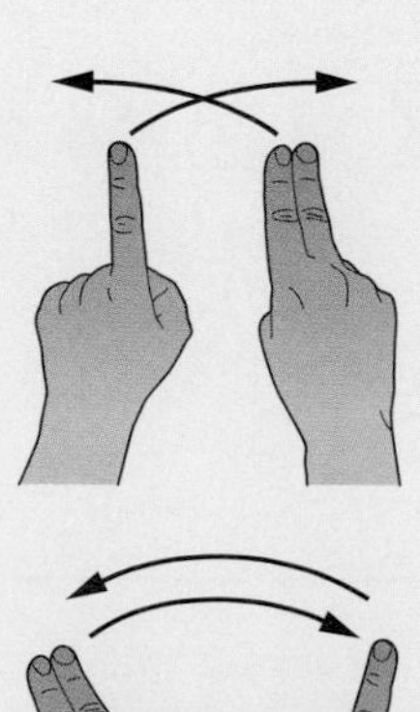

4•12 Good Fact Habits and Making Ten

Objectives To provide practice with addition facts; and to introduce and provide practice with the making-ten addition strategy.

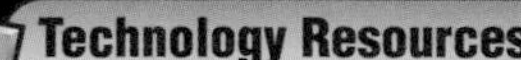

Technology Resources www.everydaymathonline.com

ePresentations

eToolkit

Algorithms Practice

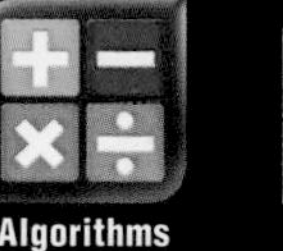
EM Facts Workshop Game™

Family Letters

Assessment Management

Common Core State Standards

Curriculum Focal Points

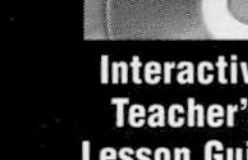
Interactive Teacher's Lesson Guide

1 Teaching the Lesson

Key Concepts and Skills

- Compare sums.
  [Number and Numeration Goal 7]
- Recite easy addition facts; use ten frames and counters to solve addition facts; solve +8 and +9 addition facts by making ten.
  [Operations and Computation Goal 1]
- Use numeric patterns to find +8 and +9 shortcuts.
  [Patterns, Functions, and Algebra Goal 1]

Key Activities

Children practice addition facts through the use of choral (group) responses. They are introduced to the making-ten addition strategy. Children practice making ten to solve +8 and +9 addition problems and discover a shortcut for these facts. They play *Shaker Addition Top-It.*

Ongoing Assessment: Recognizing Student Achievement Use the Math Message.
[Operations and Computation Goal 1]

Materials

Home Link 4•11
Math Masters, pp. 336 and 353
Math Journal 1, p. 78A
base-10 cubes ◆ per group: two 6-sided dice, 2 polyhedral dice marked 0–9 (optional), 20 pennies or counters

2 Ongoing Learning & Practice

Playing *Penny Plate*
per partnership: paper plate, pennies
Children practice finding sums of 10.

Labeling True and False Number Models
Math Journal 1, p. 78B
Children label number models as true or false. They write true and false number models.

Math Boxes 4•12
Math Journal 1, p. 79
Children practice and maintain skills through Math Box problems.

Home Link 4•12
Math Masters, p. 114
Children practice and maintain skills through Home Link activities.

3 Differentiation Options

READINESS

Fact Power Cards
3" by 5" note cards
Children make fact power cards to practice easy addition facts.

ENRICHMENT

Adding Dice Rolls to 20
per partnership: die, calculator, slate
Children find cumulative totals by adding dice rolls to 20.

Advance Preparation

***Teacher's Reference Manual,* Grades 1–3** pp. 196–199

Getting Started

Mental Math and Reflexes

Set the following quantities of base-10 cubes on the overhead, one set at a time.

▷ 3 cubes
▷ 8 cubes
▷ 15 cubes

Turn on the overhead for about 3 seconds; turn it off. Ask children to estimate whether they saw more or less than 10 cubes. Count the cubes with the class to check the accuracy of their estimates.

Math Message 

Write 3 addition facts.

Home Link 4·11 Follow-Up

Discuss solution strategies as needed.

NOTE This lesson contains a significant amount of content; you may wish to complete it over two days.

1 Teaching the Lesson

▶ Math Message Follow-Up

Have children share their addition facts. Then draw several pictures of dominoes. Have children write at least one addition fac for each domino.

Ongoing Assessment: Recognizing Student Achievement

Use the **Math Message** to assess children's ability to write addition facts. Children are making adequate progress if they are able to write at least one easy addition fact. Some children may be able to write additional facts or more complicated ones.

[Operations and Computation Goal 1]

▶ Reinforcing Fact Reflexes as "Habits" with Choral Responses

NOTE The number zero is called the *Additive Identity* because the sum of zero and any number is that number.

Tell children that one way to develop "fact power" is to recite addition facts and sums chorally. You may be able to remind the class of how choral readings helped them memorize a poem. Establish a lively rhythm, with responses given clearly and simultaneously. Keep group-response activities brief. Facts to stress now are those with 0, 1, and 2, as well as doubles facts:

▷ $0 + 0 = 0, 0 + 1 = 1, 0 + 2 = 2$ (and so on)
▷ $1 + 1 = 2, 1 + 2 = 3, 1 + 3 = 4$ (and so on)
▷ $2 + 2 = 4, 2 + 3 = 5, 2 + 4 = 6$ (and so on)
▷ $3 + 3 = 6, 4 + 4 = 8, 5 + 5 = 10$ (and so on)

NOTE A doubles fact such as $4 + 4$ shows an example of repeated addition. At later grades, repeated addition and rectangular arrays will be used as a basis to teach multiplication. For more information about these topics, see *My Reference Book,* pages 36–38.

NOTE Choral readings have proven to be beneficial, not only for beginning readers, but also for primary-grade mathematics learners. Group responses allow each child to participate at his or her own level without being put on the spot.

Introducing Making Ten

(*Math Masters,* p. 336)

Have children work in pairs with 2 ten frames and 2 different sets of counters per pair. Write 8 + 4 = ____ on the board. Have one partner show 8 on a ten frame using counters and the other partner show 4 on another ten frame using counters. Ask the child with 4 counters to use some of the counters to fill the partner's ten frame. Ask: *How many of your counters were used to fill your partner's ten frame?* 2 Ask: *How many counters do you have left on your ten frame?* 2 Have the child put the remaining counters below the partner's ten frame. Write 8 + 2 + 2 = ____ on the board beneath the first number model. Ask: *How many counters are IN the ten frame now?* 10 Ask: *How many counters are BELOW the ten frame?* 2 Write 10 + 2 = ____ on the board beneath the first two number models. Ask: *What number does the ten frame show now?* 12 Write 12 on the last line.

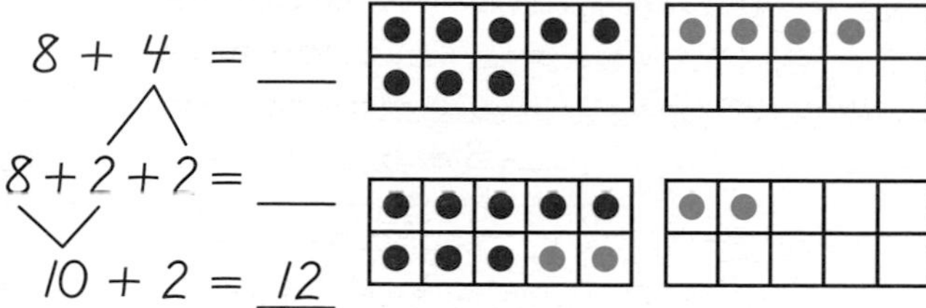

Repeat this activity for several +8 and +9 facts; be sure to allow 8 and 9 to be both the first and second addend. Help children understand that they are taking enough from the number added to 8 or 9 to "make ten" and then adding the remainder to 10 to solve. This strategy is most effective for adding 8 and 9, but is often used by children for +7 facts as well.

NOTE While *Everyday Mathematics* calls this addition fact strategy Making Ten, it is also known by other names, including "Up-Over-10" and "Going Through 10."

NOTE Be sure to add the Making-Ten Strategy to your Fact Strategy Wall.

Student Page

Date ____________

LESSON 4·12 **Practice Making 10**

1. 4 + 9 = ____

4 + 9 = 13

Find the sums.

2. 11 = 8 + 3

3. 9 + 6 = 15

4. $\begin{array}{r} 8 \\ +9 \\ \hline 17 \end{array}$

5. $\begin{array}{r} 8 \\ +7 \\ \hline 15 \end{array}$

6. Explain how you found the answer to Problem 5.

Answers vary.

Math Journal 1, p. 78A

▶ Practicing Making Ten

INDEPENDENT ACTIVITY

(*Math Masters,* p. 336; *Math Journal 1,* p. 78A)

Have pairs use their ten frames and counters to work through the steps to solve Problem 1 on journal page 78A, as shown in the box at the top of the page. Then have children complete Problems 2–6 independently. Discuss children's responses to Problem 6. This is a good opportunity for them to practice writing explanations of their mathematical thinking using words or pictures, a skill that many children find difficult.

NOTE Take care not to force a particular strategy for a problem. Your most efficient strategy for solving a particular problem may not be the most efficient strategy for every child. Demonstrating a variety of strategies and allowing children to share and discuss their own strategies with the class will in time allow children to internalize the strategies that are most efficient for them.

▶ Making-Ten Shortcut

Write the following three facts in order across the board: 3 + 10 = ____, 3 + 9 = ____, 3 + 8 = ____. Ask children to use their ten frames and counters to find the sums. Write the sums on the board. Ask: *What pattern do you see in the sums from the first fact to the third fact?* Sample answer: It goes down by 1 and then by 1 again. Repeat the task by adding 4 to 8, 9, and 10, and then adding 5 to 8, 9, and 10. Leave all of the facts on the board in columns. Discuss how children could use these facts to help find a shortcut for solving the +9 and the +8 facts. For example, help children describe the +9 shortcut in a way that they can understand. Sample answer: Add 10 instead of 9 and then count back 1. *How would this shortcut change for a +8 fact?* Sample answer: Add 10 instead of 8 and then count back 2.

NOTE Recall from long-term memory is the most efficient strategy for solving addition and subtraction facts. While we are ultimately aiming at quick recall for all children, it is important not to rush. Teaching a variety of strategies helps children learn to think mathematically and builds understanding, flexibility, and confidence. While the ultimate goal is for children to have quick recall of addition and subtraction facts, the authors of *Everyday Mathematics* caution teachers that this does not mean that children should be drilled on their facts at this early stage. Premature drill for speed can be counterproductive and can give children the impression that in mathematics, memorization is more important than thinking.

Introducing *Shaker Addition Top-It*

SMALL-GROUP ACTIVITY

(*Math Masters,* p. 353)

This game may be played by 2 to 5 players. Use two 6-sided dice to provide review and practice with facts containing numbers 1–6 or use two polyhedral dice, marked 0–9, to provide review and practice for all basic addition facts. Begin the game with about 20 pennies or other counters for each small group.

Directions

1. For each round, players take turns shaking and rolling the dice, adding the numbers using any method (except a calculator), and stating the sum.
2. Saying the wrong sum disqualifies a player for that round. This encourages children to check every sum, not just their own. A disqualified player may still check others' responses.
3. The player with the highest sum for each round takes a penny or a counter from the pile. If there are ties, the tied players each take a penny or a counter.
4. The player with the most pennies or counters at the end of a given time wins.

Variation: Have children practice finding sums of three addends using the Associative Property of Addition while playing *Shaker Addition Top-It.* Have children use three dice instead of two.

NOTE *Math Masters,* page 353 provides spaces in which children can record the facts they answer as they play the game.

Adjusting the Activity

Children sit in a circle. One after another, they roll a die. The group works together to find the cumulative total after each roll until the total passes a goal set before play began.

AUDITORY ◆ KINESTHETIC ◆ TACTILE ◆ VISUAL

NOTE Expect that many children may still need to add numbers using counters or counting on their fingers. The basic addition facts will be continually practiced throughout the year. Fluency with addition facts through 10 + 10 is a Grade 1 Goal.

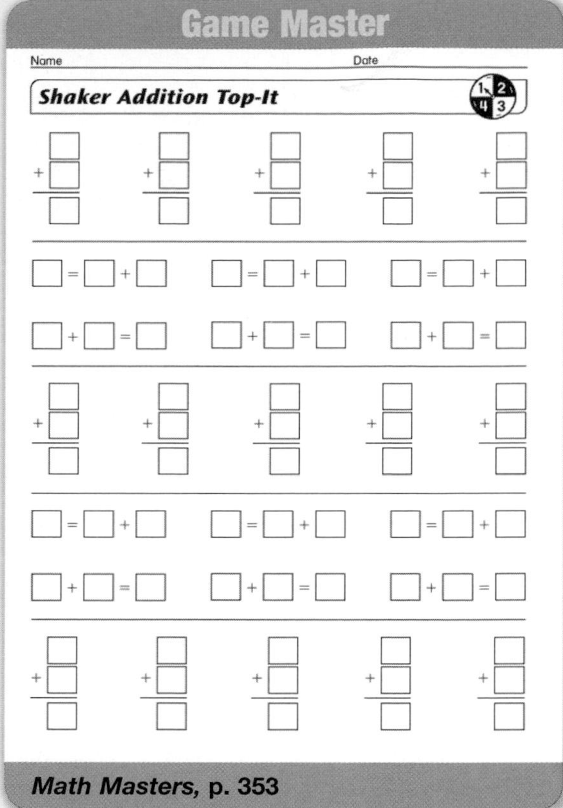

Game Master
Name
Date
Shaker Addition Top-It
Math Masters, p. 353

Using polyhedral dice will provide practice for all addition facts.

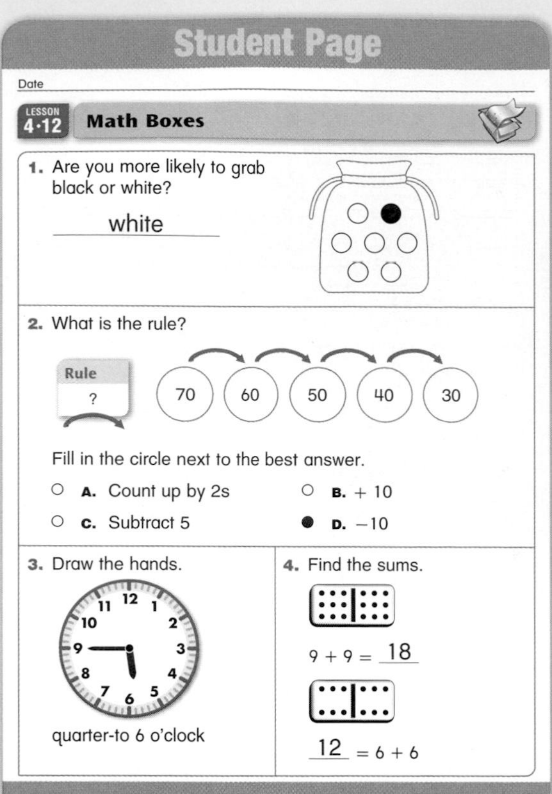
Student Page

Date

LESSON 4·12 **Math Boxes**

1. Are you more likely to grab black or white?
white

2. What is the rule?
Rule ?
70 60 50 40 30
Fill in the circle next to the best answer.
○ A. Count up by 2s
○ B. + 10
○ C. Subtract 5
● D. −10

3. Draw the hands.
quarter-to 6 o'clock

4. Find the sums.
9 + 9 = 18
12 = 6 + 6

Math Journal 1, p. 79

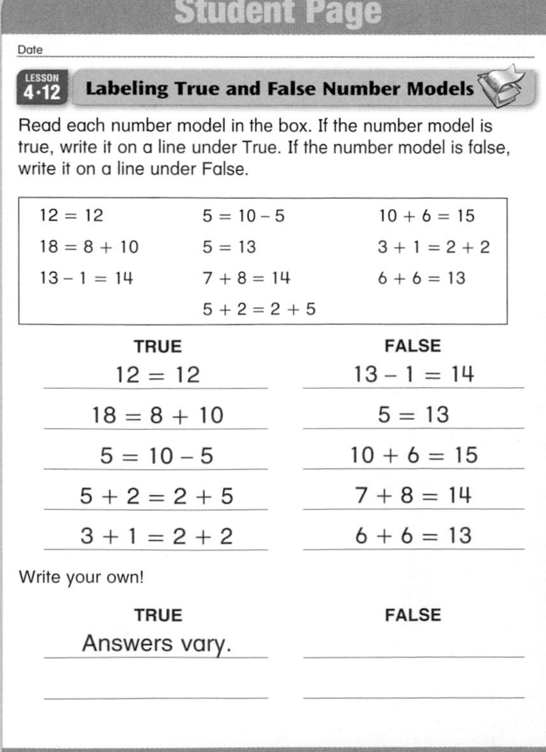
Student Page

Date

LESSON 4·12 **Labeling True and False Number Models**

Read each number model in the box. If the number model is true, write it on a line under True. If the number model is false, write it on a line under False.

12 = 12	5 = 10 − 5	10 + 6 = 15
18 = 8 + 10	5 = 13	3 + 1 = 2 + 2
13 − 1 = 14	7 + 8 = 14	6 + 6 = 13
	5 + 2 = 2 + 5	

TRUE	FALSE
12 = 12	13 − 1 = 14
18 = 8 + 10	5 = 13
5 = 10 − 5	10 + 6 = 15
5 + 2 = 2 + 5	7 + 8 = 14
3 + 1 = 2 + 2	6 + 6 = 13

Write your own!

TRUE	FALSE
Answers vary.	

Math Journal 1, p. 78B

2 Ongoing Learning & Practice

▶ Playing *Penny Plate*

Children practice finding sums of 10 by playing *Penny Plate.* For detailed instructions, see Lesson 2-8.

▶ Labeling True and False Number Models

(*Math Journal 1,* p. 78B)

Children label number models as true or false using addition and subtraction fact strategies. They write their own true and false number models.

▶ Math Boxes 4·12

(*Math Journal 1,* p. 79)

Mixed Practice Math Boxes in this lesson are paired with Math Boxes in Lesson 4-10. The skills in Problem 4 preview Unit 5 content.

Writing/Reasoning Have children draw, write, or verbalize an answer to the following question*: How do you know which color you are more likely to grab?* A reasonable answer should include a comparison of the number of black and white chips in the bag.

NOTE Do not expect children to use probability language yet.

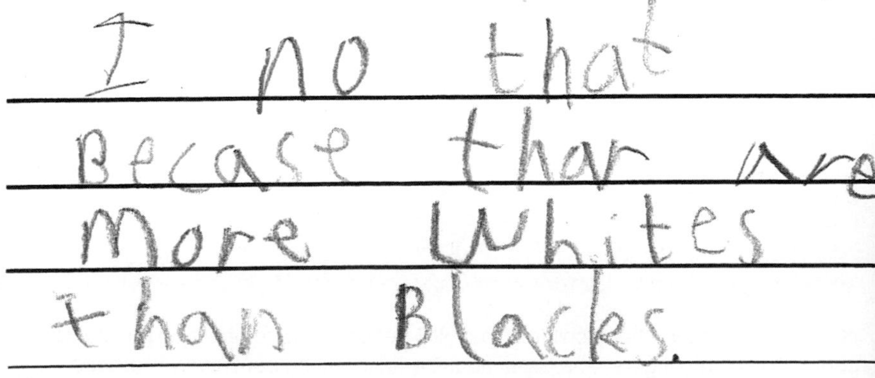

One child's work in response to the Writing/Reasoning prompt

Home Link 4·12

INDEPENDENT ACTIVITY

(*Math Masters,* p. 114)

Home Connection Children complete addition facts and color spaces according to directions to reveal the picture.

3 Differentiation Options

READINESS

Fact Power Cards

SMALL-GROUP ACTIVITY

5–15 Min

To provide experience with easy addition facts, have children write facts on index cards. Explain to children that "easy" facts include + 0, + 1, sums of 10, and doubles. Hand out index cards to each child. Have children write an addition fact on one side of the card and the addition-fact sum on the other. Children flip over one card at a time and solve the fact on the card.

ENRICHMENT

PARTNER ACTIVITY

Adding Dice Rolls to 20

15–30 Min

To further explore cumulative totals, have children add dice rolls to 20. Each partnership needs one die, a calculator, and slate to keep tallies.

1. One child rolls the die. If the first roll is not a 6, the child rolls again and adds the two numbers together. The second child checks the total with a calculator.
2. The same child continues rolling until a 6 is rolled, adding each roll to the previous sum. The second child checks each new total with the calculator. If the first child reaches a total of 10 or more before rolling a 6, he or she should make 1 tally.
3. If the first child reaches a total of 20 or more before rolling a 6, he or she should make another tally.
4. After rolling a 6 or reaching 20, partners switch roles.
5. Play continues until one partner has 10 tallies.

Variation: If the child accumulating a total gives the wrong total, his or her turn ends.

Home Link Master

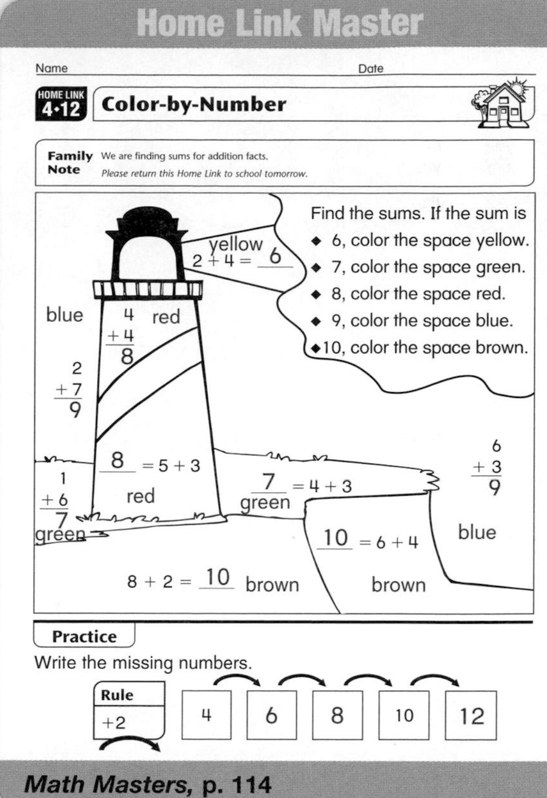

Name Date

HOME LINK 4·12 **Color-by-Number**

Family Note We are finding sums for addition facts.
Please return this Home Link to school tomorrow.

Find the sums. If the sum is
- 6, color the space yellow.
- 7, color the space green.
- 8, color the space red.
- 9, color the space blue.
- 10, color the space brown.

Practice

Write the missing numbers.

Rule +2	4	6	8	10	12

Math Masters, p. 114

4•13 Progress Check 4

Objective To assess children's progress on mathematical content through the end of Unit 4.

1 Looking Back: Cumulative Assessment

Input children's data from Progress Check 4 into the **Assessment Management Spreadsheets**.

Materials
- Home Link 4•12
- *Assessment Handbook,* pp. 76–83, 149–152, 180, and 212–215
- pennies; slate

CONTENT ASSESSED	LESSON(S)	ASSESSMENT ITEMS: SELF	ORAL/SLATE	WRITTEN PART A	WRITTEN PART B	OPEN RESPONSE
Count forward and backward by 2s from any number less than 100. [Number and Numeration Goal 1]	4•1, 4•2, 4•4, 4•7, 4•10, 4•12			5		
Order whole numbers through 100s. [Number and Numeration Goal 7]	4•1–4•5, 4•10	2	4	2		
Know addition facts. [Operations and Computation Goal 1]	4•1, 4•11, 4•12	1	3	1, 6	10	
Solve number stories; demonstrate parts-and-total situations. [Operations and Computation Goal 4]	4•1, 4•6, 4•7, 4•9	3	3	1		✓
Estimate and compare lengths of objects. [Measurement and Reference Frames Goal 1]	4•2–4•7	6	1		7	
Make exchanges between coins. [Measurement and Reference Frames Goal 2]	4•3, 4•5	4		4		
Show and tell time on an analog clock to the nearest quarter-hour. [Measurement and Reference Frames Goal 4]	4•8–4•12	5	2		8, 9	
Continue simple non-numeric patterns. [Patterns, Functions, and Algebra Goal 1]	4•2, 4•4			3		
Solve problems involving simple functions represented in Frames and Arrows. [Patterns, Functions, and Algebra Goal 1]	4•1, 4•10, 4•12			5		

2 Looking Ahead: Preparing for Unit 5

Math Boxes 4•13

Home Link 4•13: Unit 5 Family Letter

Materials
- *Math Journal 1,* p. 80
- *Math Masters,* pp. 115–118

Getting Started

Math Message

Complete the Self Assessment (Assessment Handbook, *page* 149).

Home Link 4·12 Follow-Up

Briefly go over the answers to the addition problems.

1 Looking Back: Cumulative Assessment

Math Message Follow-Up

INDEPENDENT ACTIVITY

(Self Assessment, *Assessment Handbook,* p. 149)

The Self Assessment offers children the opportunity to reflect upon their progress.

Oral and Slate Assessments

WHOLE-CLASS ACTIVITY

Problems 3 and 4 provide summative information and can be used for grading purposes. Problems 1 and 2 provide formative information that can be useful in planning future instruction.

Oral Assessment

1. Draw a 6-inch line on the board as a point of reference. Then show children objects of various lengths. Ask them to estimate if the object is shorter, longer, or about the same length as the 6-inch line.
2. Ask children to show the following times using their tool-kit clocks.
   - 3:15
   - 7:45
   - 1:45
   - 8:15

Slate Assessment

3. Show or draw the following dominoes. Ask children to write the three numbers that go with each domino.

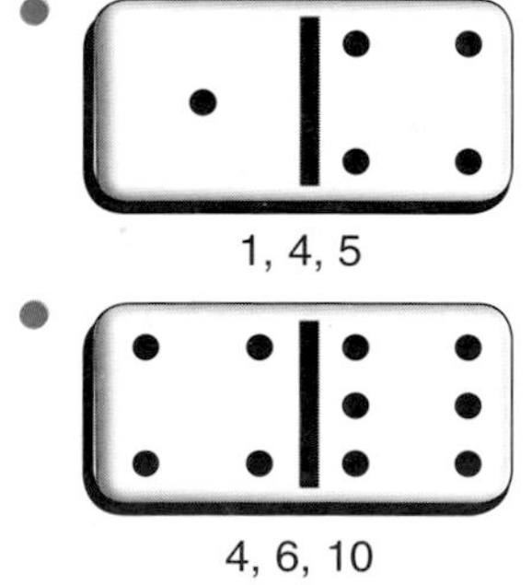

- 1, 4, 5
- 4, 6, 10

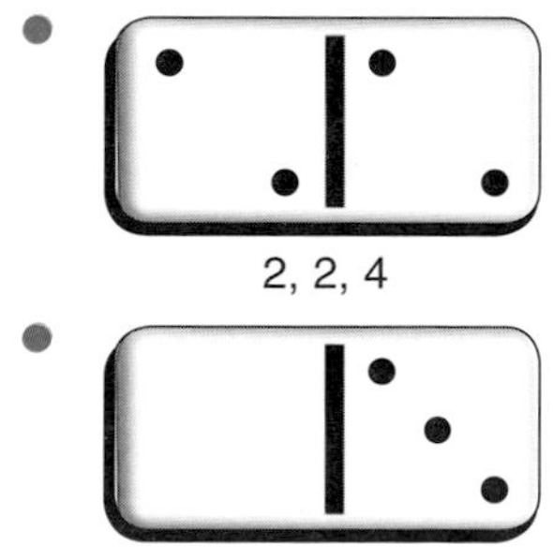

- 2, 2, 4
- 0, 3, 3

4. Write the number that comes after each number:
   - 14 15
   - 25 26
   - 40 41
   - 59 60
   - 71 72

   Write the number that comes before each number:
   - 13 12
   - 20 19
   - 55 54
   - 80 79
   - 99 98

Assessment Master

Name Date

LESSON 4·13 **Self Assessment** Progress Check 4

Put a check in the box that tells how you do each skill.

Skills	I can do this by myself. I can explain how to do this.	I can do this by myself.	I can do this with help.
1. Solve addition facts.			
2. Use the number grid.			
3. Solve change-to-more and change-to-less problems.			
4. Make amounts of money with the fewest coins.			
5. Tell time to the quarter-hour.			
6. Tell which is longer and which is shorter.			

Assessment Handbook, p. 149

Assessment Master

Name Date

LESSON 4·13 **Written Assessment** Progress Check 4

Part A

1. Fill in the missing numbers.

Total	
8	
Part	Part
7	1

2. Fill in the missing numbers in the number grid.

61	62	63	64	65	66	67	68	69	70
71	72	73	74	75	76	77	78	79	80

3. Draw the missing shape.

4. How much money has Wes saved?

Ⓝ Ⓝ Ⓟ Ⓟ Ⓟ Ⓟ Ⓟ Ⓟ 16 ¢

Show the same amount using fewer coins. Use Ⓟ, Ⓝ, and Ⓓ.

Sample answer: Ⓓ Ⓝ Ⓟ

Assessment Handbook, p. 150

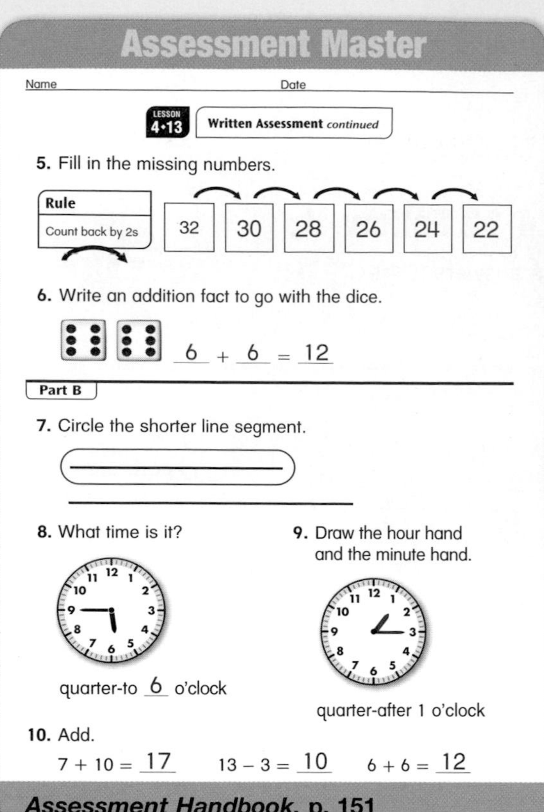

Assessment Master

Name ________ Date ________

LESSON 4·13 Written Assessment *continued*

5. Fill in the missing numbers.

Rule: Count back by 2s

32 | 30 | 28 | 26 | 24 | 22

6. Write an addition fact to go with the dice.

6 + 6 = 12

Part B

7. Circle the shorter line segment.

8. What time is it?

quarter-to 6 o'clock

9. Draw the hour hand and the minute hand.

quarter-after 1 o'clock

10. Add.

7 + 10 = 17 13 − 3 = 10 6 + 6 = 12

Assessment Handbook, p. 151

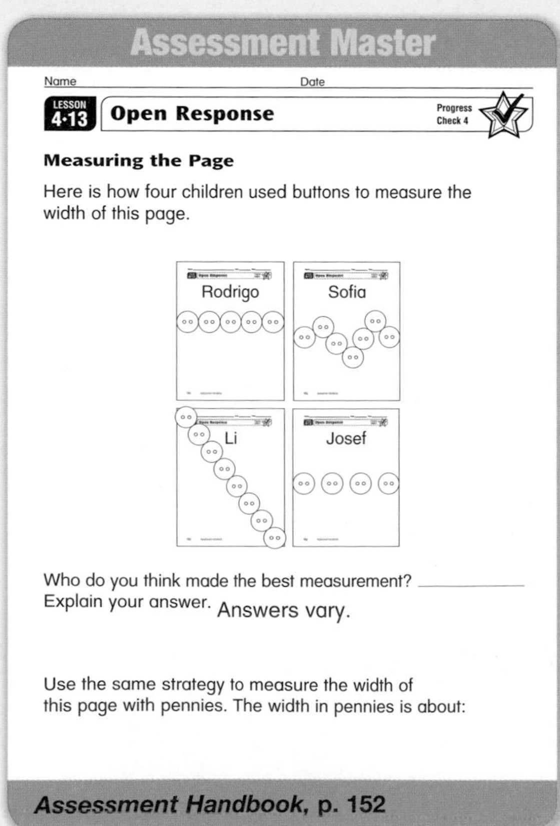

Assessment Master

Name ________ Date ________

LESSON 4·13 Open Response Progress Check 4

Measuring the Page

Here is how four children used buttons to measure the width of this page.

Rodrigo Sofia Li Josef

Who do you think made the best measurement? ________
Explain your answer. Answers vary.

Use the same strategy to measure the width of this page with pennies. The width in pennies is about:

Assessment Handbook, p. 152

▶ Written Assessment

(*Assessment Handbook,* pp. 150 and 151)

Part A Recognizing Student Achievement

Problems 1–6 provide summative information and may be used for grading purposes.

Problem(s)	Description
1	Know addition facts; demonstrate parts-and-total situations.
2	Order whole numbers through 100s.
3	Continue simple non-numeric patterns.
4	Make exchanges between coins.
5	Solve problems involving simple functions represented in Frames and Arrows.
5	Count back by 2s.
6	Know addition facts.

Part B Informing Instruction

Problems 7–9 provide formative information that can be useful in planning future instruction.

Problem(s)	Description
7	Compare lengths of objects.
8, 9	Show and tell time on an analog clock to the nearest quarter-hour.
10	Know addition facts.

Use the checklists on pages 213 and 215 of the *Assessment Handbook* to record results. Then input the data into the **Assessment Management Spreadsheets** to keep an ongoing record of children's progress toward Grade-Level Goals.

▶ Open Response

(*Assessment Handbook,* p. 152)

Measuring the Page

The open-response item requires children to apply skills and concepts from Unit 4 to solve a multistep problem. See *Assessment Handbook,* pages 79–83 for rubrics and children's work samples for this problem.

There are two options for completing this open response. For both Option 1 and Option 2, children begin by working independently (or with a partner) to solve a multistep problem.

Take this time to circulate throughout the classroom.

Option 1:

Four children used buttons to measure the width of this page. Look at the page to see how they did it.

- Who do you think made the best measurement? How do you know?
- Measure your paper using pennies. How many pennies wide is your page?

Children use *Assessment Master,* page 152 to record their work.

Option 2:

Distribute *Assessment Master,* page 152. Read the problem aloud to children. Allow children to solve the problem and record their solution strategies on the page.

NOTE Each child needs pennies to complete the pages.

After children have had a chance to complete either option, invite individual children to explain their solution strategies. Encourage them to use words and drawings to explain their strategies as you write them on the board. Be sure to discuss both successful and unsuccessful strategies.

2 Looking Ahead: Preparing for Unit 5

Math Boxes 4·13

INDEPENDENT ACTIVITY

(*Math Journal 1,* p. 80)

Mixed Practice This Math Boxes page previews Unit 5 content.

Home Link 4·13: Unit 5 Family Letter

INDEPENDENT ACTIVITY

(*Math Masters,* pp. 115–118)

Home Connection The Unit 5 Family Letter provides families with information and activities related to Unit 5 topics.

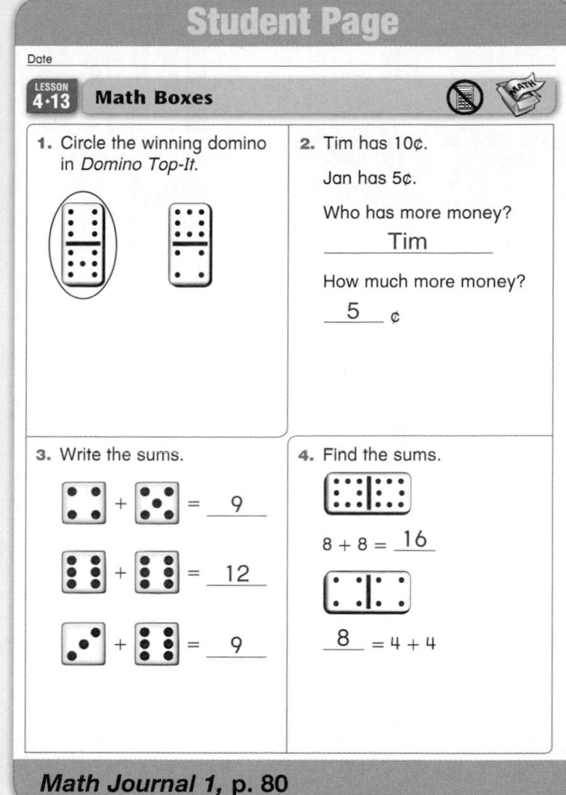

Student Page

Date

LESSON 4·13 **Math Boxes**

1. Circle the winning domino in *Domino Top-It.*
2. Tim has 10¢. Jan has 5¢. Who has more money? Tim. How much more money? 5 ¢
3. Write the sums. (4 + 5 =) 9; (6 + 6 =) 12; (3 + 6 =) 9
4. Find the sums. 8 + 8 = 16; 8 = 4 + 4

Math Journal 1, p. 80

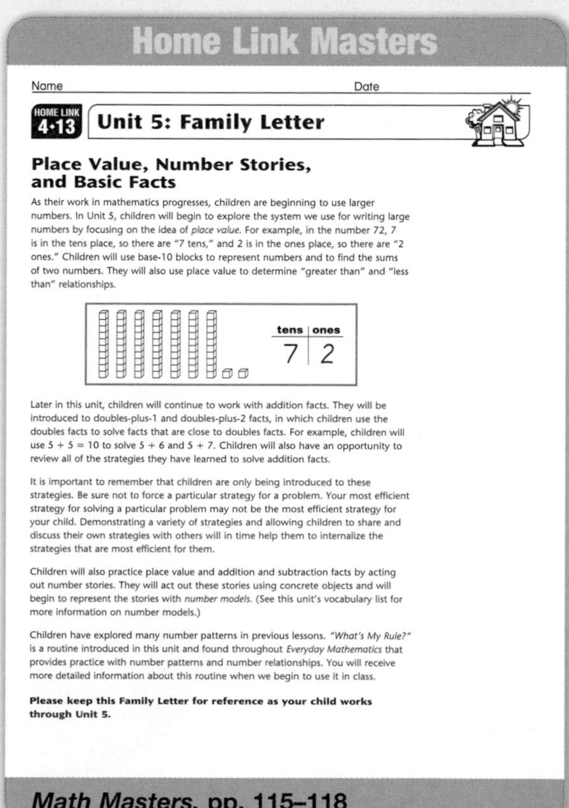

Home Link Masters

Name Date

HOME LINK 4·13 **Unit 5: Family Letter**

Place Value, Number Stories, and Basic Facts

As their work in mathematics progresses, children are beginning to use larger numbers. In Unit 5, children will begin to explore the system we use for writing large numbers by focusing on the idea of *place value.* For example, in the number 72, 7 is in the tens place, so there are "7 tens," and 2 is in the ones place, so there are "2 ones." Children will use base-10 blocks to represent numbers and to find the sums of two numbers. They will also use place value to determine "greater than" and "less than" relationships.

tens	ones
7	2

Later in this unit, children will continue to work with addition facts. They will be introduced to doubles-plus-1 and doubles-plus-2 facts, in which children use the doubles facts to solve facts that are close to doubles facts. For example, children will use 5 + 5 = 10 to solve 5 + 6 and 5 + 7. Children will also have an opportunity to review all of the strategies they have learned to solve addition facts.

It is important to remember that children are only being introduced to these strategies. Be sure not to force a particular strategy for a problem. Your most efficient strategy for solving a particular problem may not be the most efficient strategy for your child. Demonstrating a variety of strategies and allowing children to share and discuss their own strategies with others will in time help them to internalize the strategies that are most efficient for them.

Children will also practice place value and addition and subtraction facts by acting out number stories. They will act out these stories using concrete objects and will begin to represent the stories with *number models.* (See this unit's vocabulary list for more information on number models.)

Children have explored many number patterns in previous lessons. *"What's My Rule?"* is a routine introduced in this unit and found throughout *Everyday Mathematics* that provides practice with number patterns and number relationships. You will receive more detailed information about this routine when we begin to use it in class.

Please keep this Family Letter for reference as your child works through Unit 5.

Math Masters, pp. 115–118

Unit 5 Organizer

Place Value, Number Stories, and Basic Facts

Overview

Most of Unit 5 is devoted to extending children's understanding of, and proficiency with, addition and subtraction. Children make up and solve number stories, helping to foster links between verbal representations and concrete, pictorial, and number-model representations. Unit 5 has four main areas of focus:

- To investigate place-value concepts for tens and ones,
- To explore addition of 2-digit numbers,
- To make up and solve a variety of number stories, and
- To introduce the "What's My Rule?" routine.

CCSS Linking to the Common Core State Standards

The content of Unit 5 addresses the Common Core State Standards for Mathematics in *Operations and Algebraic Thinking* and *Number and Operations in Base Ten.* The correlation of the Common Core State Standards to the *Everyday Mathematics* Grade 1 lessons begins on page CS1.

Contents

Unit 5 Organizer

Learning In Perspective

	Lesson Objectives	Links to the Past	Links to the Future
5•1	To provide experiences with place-value concepts for tens and ones.	Children explore base-10 blocks in Units 1 and 4. In Kindergarten, children explore place value using manipulatives.	Throughout Grades 1–3, children read, write, and model whole numbers. They also identify places in such numbers and values of the digits in those places.
5•2	To provide experiences investigating place-value digit patterns.	Children explore base-10 blocks in Units 1 and 4. In Kindergarten, children explore place value using manipulatives.	Throughout Grades 1–3, children read, write, and model whole numbers. They also identify places in such numbers and values of the digits in those places.
5•3	To introduce the relation symbols < and >.	In Units 1–4, children compare numbers and quantities. Children begin ordering and comparing numbers in Kindergarten.	In Units 8–10, children compare numbers and quantities using relation symbols.
5•4	To develop the concept of area by counting units; to provide experience weighing objects with a pan balance; and to provide practice with rational counting.	In Units 1–3, children cover shapes with pattern blocks and count objects. In Kindergarten, children cover shapes with pattern blocks, use a pan balance, and count objects.	In Units 6, 8, and 9, children compare weights and count objects. In Grades 2 and 3, they count unit squares to find area. They also measure and estimate weight.
5•5	To introduce addition of 2-digit numbers.	In Units 3 and 4, children explore addition and subtraction using manipulatives. Children work with single-digit addition in Kindergarten.	Children solve 2-digit addition and subtraction problems using manipulatives in Units 8 and 10. In Grades 2 and 3, they use algorithms.
5•6	To provide practice with *more than* and *less than* number stories; and to provide experiences with writing number models for number stories.	In Units 1 and 2 and in Kindergarten, children tell and solve number stories. They are also introduced to situation diagrams.	In Units 8–10, children solve change-to-less and change-to-more number stories using situation diagrams.
5•7	To introduce number stories that involve finding differences.	In Units 1 and 2 and in Kindergarten, children tell and solve number stories. They are also introduced to situation diagrams.	In Units 8–10, children solve change-to-less and change-to-more number stories using situation diagrams.
5•8	To provide practice making up and solving a variety of number stories involving relations, addition, and subtraction.	In Units 1 and 2 and in Kindergarten, children tell and solve number stories. They are also introduced to situation diagrams.	In Units 8–10, children solve change-to-less and change-to-more number stories using situation diagrams.
5•9	To provide experience with sums generated by rolling pairs of dice.	In Units 3 and 4, children begin to explore addition and subtraction using manipulatives. In Kindergarten, children count dots on dice.	Children develop fact power for simple addition and subtraction facts in Units 6–10.
5•10	To provide opportunities for children to explore and practice doubles-plus-1 and doubles-plus-2 facts, as well as review strategies for solving other addition facts.	In Units 3 and 4, children explore addition and subtraction using manipulatives. Children explore single-digit addition in Kindergarten.	Children develop fact power for simple addition and subtraction facts in Units 6–10.
5•11	To review various addition fact strategies; and to provide practice with addition facts with sums to 20.	In Units 3 and 4, children explore addition and subtraction using manipulatives. Children explore single-digit addition in Kindergarten.	Children develop fact power for simple addition and subtraction facts in Units 6–10.
5•12	To introduce the "What's My Rule?" routine.	In Kindergarten, children are introduced to "What's My Rule?"	Children solve "What's My Rule?" problems in Units 6, 8, and 9. In Grades 2 and 3, "What's My Rule?" is extended.
5•13	To provide experiences with finding the output for given rules and input numbers.	In Kindergarten, children are introduced to "What's My Rule?"	Children solve "What's My Rule?" problems in Units 6, 8, and 9. In Grades 2 and 3, "What's My Rule?" is extended.

	Key Concepts and Skills	Grade 1 Goals*
5•1	Count objects by 1s.	Number and Numeration Goal 2
	Use base-10 blocks to model whole numbers less than 100.	Number and Numeration Goal 3
	Name whole numbers less than 100 modeled by base-10 blocks.	Number and Numeration Goal 3
	Exchange base-10 cubes and longs to show different representations of the same number.	Number and Numeration Goal 3
5•2	Count forward by 1s and 10s on a calculator.	Number and Numeration Goal 1
	Use base-10 blocks to model whole numbers; name whole numbers modeled by base-10 blocks.	Number and Numeration Goal 3
	Exchange base-10 cubes, longs, and flats to show different representations of the same number.	Number and Numeration Goal 3
	Recognize patterns on a number grid.	Patterns, Functions, and Algebra Goal 1
5•3	Compare whole numbers using <, >, and =.	Number and Numeration Goal 7
	Calculate and compare money amounts using <, >, and =.	Patterns, Functions, and Algebra Goal 2
5•4	Count objects by 1s.	Number and Numeration Goal 2
	Estimate and count objects.	Number and Numeration Goal 2
	Compare weights of pairs of objects.	Measurement and Reference Frames Goal 1
	Exchange pennies for nickels and dimes.	Measurement and Reference Frames Goal 2
5•5	Use base-10 blocks to model 2- and 3-digit whole numbers.	Number and Numeration Goal 3
	Exchange base-10 longs and cubes to show different representations of the same number.	Number and Numeration Goal 3
	Use base-10 blocks to find sums of 2- and 3-digit numbers.	Operations and Computation Goal 2
	Model parts-and-total diagrams for addition number stories.	Operations and Computation Goal 4
5•6	Compare pairs of 2-digit numbers based on meanings of the tens and ones digits.	Number and Numeration Goal 7
	Use base-10 blocks to model and solve addition problems.	Operations and Computation Goal 2
	Write number models using < and >.	Patterns, Functions, and Algebra Goal 2
5•7	Count collections of objects by 1s.	Number and Numeration Goal 2
	Use number grids, base-10 blocks, and other strategies to add and subtract.	Operations and Computation Goal 2
	Compare groups of objects.	Number and Numeration Goal 7
	Write number models to match solution strategies.	Patterns, Functions, and Algebra Goal 2
5•8	Order 1- and 2-digit whole numbers.	Number and Numeration Goal 7
	Use number grids, base-10 blocks, and other strategies to add and subtract.	Operations and Computation Goal 2
	Solve number stories.	Operations and Computation Goal 4
	Generate and record number models to match solution strategies.	Patterns, Functions, and Algebra Goal 2
5•9	Count up from the larger number to solve addition problems.	Operations and Computation Goal 1
	Create and use a tally chart to represent data.	Data and Chance Goal 1
	Draw conclusions about the probability of dice rolls.	Data and Chance Goal 3
5•10	Develop and practice strategies for addition that use doubles facts.	Operations and Computation Goal 1
	Use a variety of addition fact strategies for solving multi-addend addition problems.	Operations and Computation Goals 1 and 2
5•11	Recite addition facts; use strategies to solve addition facts; find sums of addition facts with and without a calculator.	Operations and Computation Goal 1
	Discuss patterns in addition facts.	Patterns, Functions, and Algebra Goal 1
	Identify and explain turn-around facts.	Patterns, Functions, and Algebra Goal 3
5•12	Count forward and backward from a given number.	Number and Numeration Goal 1
	Use addition and subtraction to solve "What's My Rule?" problems.	Operations and Computation Goal 2
	Find and describe rules in "What's My Rule?" problems.	Patterns, Functions, and Algebra Goal 1
5•13	Count forward and backward from a given number.	Number and Numeration Goal 1
	Use addition and subtraction to solve "What's My Rule?" problems.	Operations and Computation Goal 2
	Continue patterns in "What's My Rule?" problems.	Patterns, Functions, and Algebra Goal 1
	Find the rule in "What's My Rule?" problems.	Patterns, Functions, and Algebra Goal 1

*See the Appendix for a complete list of Grade 1 Goals.

A Balanced Curriculum

Ongoing Practice

Everyday Mathematics provides numerous opportunities for ongoing practice. These activities are embedded throughout the lessons:

Mental Math and Reflexes activities promote speed and accuracy in mental computation.

Math Boxes offer mixed practice and are paired across lessons as shown in the brackets below. This makes them useful as assessment tools. The last one or two boxes on each page preview the next unit's content.

Mixed practice	[5•1, 5•3], [5•2, 5•4], [5•5, 5•7], [5•6, 5•8], [5•9, 5•11, 5•13], [5•10, 5•12]
Mixed practice with multiple choice	5•3, 5•4, 5•7, 5•8, 5•12, 5•13
Mixed practice with writing/reasoning opportunity	5•1, 5•2, 5•5, 5•8, 5•9, 5•12

Home Links are daily homework assignments that review the content of the lesson and often contain ongoing facts practice.

Minute Math+ problems are offered for additional practice in Lessons 5•2, 5•4, and 5•13.

EM Facts Workshop Game provides online practice of basic facts and computation.

EXTRA PRACTICE **Extra Practice** activities are included in Lessons 5•1, 5•2, 5•3, 5•4, 5•9, 5•10, 5•11, and 5•13.

Practice through Games

Games are an essential component of practice in the *Everyday Mathematics* program. Games offer skills practice and promote strategic thinking. See the *Differentiation Handbook* for ways to adapt games to meet children's needs.

Lesson	Game	Skill Practiced
5•1, 5•4	*Digit Game*	Place value and comparing numbers [NN Goals 3 and 7]
5•3	*Top-It*	Comparing numbers [NN Goal 7]
5•3, 5•9	*Base-10 Exchange*	Place value [NN Goal 3]
5•5; 5•5; 5•10	*Animal Weight Top-It; Shaker Addition Top-It; Domino Top-It*	Finding and comparing sums [NN Goal 7 and OC Goal 2]
5•7	*Difference Game*	Subtraction [OC Goal 2]
5•11	*Penny Plate*	Finding sums of 10 [OC Goal 1]
5•11, 5•12, 5•13	*Beat the Calculator*	Addition facts [OC Goal 2]
5•13	*Penny-Nickel-Dime Exchange*	Making coin exchanges [MRF Goal 2]

[NN] Number and Numeration
[MRF] Measurement and Reference Frames
[OC] Operations and Computation
[GEO] Geometry
[DC] Data and Chance
[PFA] Patterns, Functions, and Algebra

Problem Solving 

Good problem solvers use a variety of strategies, including the following:

- Draw a picture.
- Act out the problem.
- Make a table, chart, or list.
- Look for a pattern.
- Try a simpler version of the problem.
- Make a guess and try it out.

The table below lists some of the opportunities in this unit for children to practice these strategies.

Lesson	Activity
5•2	Find digit patterns in calculator counts by 1s and 10s.
5•5	Solve number stories.
5•5	Use base-10 blocks to find sums.
5•7	Solve comparison number stories.
5•8	Make up and solve number stories involving addition and subtraction.
5•9	Find which sum occurs most often when two dice are thrown.
5•12, 5•13	Solve "What's My Rule?" problems.

Lessons that teach *through* problem solving, not just *about* problem solving

See Chapter 18: Problem Solving in the *Teacher's Reference Manual* for more information.

The Language of Mathematics

Everyday Mathematics provides lesson-specific suggestions to help all children acquire, process, and express mathematical ideas. Throughout Unit 5, there are lesson-specific language development notes that address the needs of English language learners, indicated by ELL.

ELL SUPPORT Activities to support English language learners are in Part 3 of Lessons 5•3, 5•7, and 5•12.

The *English Learners Handbook* and the *Differentiation Handbook* have suggestions for promoting language development and acquisition of mathematics vocabulary. See Unit 5 in each handbook.

Unit 5 Vocabulary

area
base-10 blocks
cubes
difference
digit
doubles-plus-1 fact
doubles-plus-2 fact
flat
function machine
hundreds
is less than
is more than
longs
multiple of 10
ones place
pan balance
rule
tens place

Literacy Connection

Lesson 5•1 *The Warlord's Beads,* by Virginia Walton Pilegard, Pelican Publishing Company, 2001

Lesson 5•1 *Let's Count,* by Tana Hoban, Greenwillow Books, 1999

Lesson 5•3 *Just Enough Carrots,* by Stuart J. Murphy, HarperCollins Publishers, 1997

Lesson 5•9 *Probably Pistachio,* by Stuart J. Murphy, HarperTrophy, 2001

For more literacy connections, see the *Home Connection Handbook,* Grades 1–3.

Cross-Curricular Links 

Literature – Lessons 5•1, 5•3, 5•9
Language Arts – Lessons 5•2, 5•6
Science – Lesson 5•5

Balanced Assessment

Daily Assessments

- **Recognizing Student Achievement** – A daily assessment that is included in every lesson to evaluate children's progress toward the Grade 1 Grade-Level Goals.
- **Informing Instruction** – Notes that appear throughout the unit to help anticipate children's common errors and suggest appropriate problem-solving strategies.

Lesson	Recognizing Student Achievement	Informing Instruction
5•1	Name numbers represented by base-10 blocks. [NN Goal 3]	Understand tens and ones.
5•2	Find complements of the numbers 13 and 14. [OC Goal 1]	
5•3	Solve Frames-and-Arrows problems. [PFA Goal 1]	Use the < and > symbols.
5•4	Find equivalent names for numbers. [NN Goal 6]	Count pennies.
5•5	Compare lengths. [MRF Goal 1]	Work with base-10 blocks.
5•6	Compare numbers through hundreds using < and >. [PFA Goal 2]	Use the < and > symbols.
5•7	Solve comparison problems using pennies. [NN Goal 7]	
5•8	Identify digits in 2-digit numbers. [NN Goal 3]	
5•9	Show time to the quarter-hour on a clock. [MRF Goal 4]	Add dots on dice.
5•10	Solve simple number stories. [OC Goal 4]	
5•11	Write turn-around facts. [PFA Goal 3]	
5•12	Record temperature to the nearest 10 degrees. [MRF Goal 3]	Solve "What's My Rule?" problems.
5•13	Compare values of coin combinations. [OC Goal 2]	

[NN] Number and Numeration
[MRF] Measurement and Reference Frames
[OC] Operations and Computation
[GEO] Geometry
[DC] Data and Chance
[PFA] Patterns, Functions, and Algebra

Portfolio Opportunities

The following lessons provide opportunities to gather samples of children's mathematical writings, drawings, and creations to add balance to the assessment process: Lessons 5•1, 5•2, 5•5, 5•7, 5•8, 5•9, 5•12, and 5•14.

See pages 16 and 17 in the *Assessment Handbook* for more information about portfolios and how to use them.

Unit Assessment

Progress Check 5 – A cumulative assessment of concepts and skills taught in Unit 5 and in previous units, providing information for evaluating children's progress and planning for future instruction. These assessments include oral/slate, written, and open-response activities, as shown below in the sample Progress Check lesson opener.

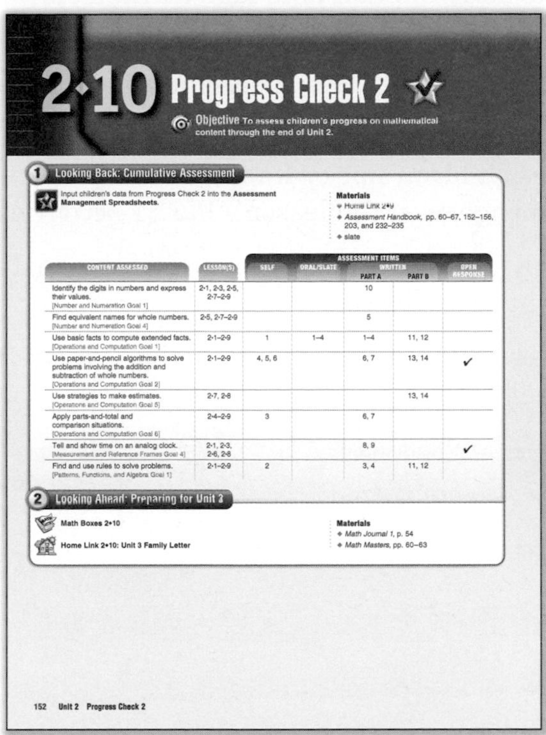

2·10 Progress Check 2

Objective To assess children's progress on mathematical content through the end of Unit 2.

1 Looking Back: Cumulative Assessment

Input children's data from Progress Check 2 into the **Assessment Management Spreadsheets.**

Materials
- Home Link 2•9
- *Assessment Handbook,* pp. 60–67, 152–156, 203, and 232–235
- slate

CONTENT ASSESSED	LESSON(S)	ASSESSMENT ITEMS: SELF	ORAL/SLATE	WRITTEN: PART A	WRITTEN: PART B	OPEN RESPONSE
Identify the digits in numbers and express their values. [Number and Numeration Goal 1]	2·1, 2·3, 2·5, 2·7–2·9			10		
Find equivalent names for whole numbers. [Number and Numeration Goal 4]	2·5, 2·7–2·9			5		
Use basic facts to compute extended facts. [Operations and Computation Goal 1]	2·1–2·9	1	1–4	1–4	11, 12	
Use paper-and-pencil algorithms to solve problems involving the addition and subtraction of whole numbers. [Operations and Computation Goal 2]	2·1–2·9	4, 5, 6		6, 7	13, 14	✓
Use strategies to make estimates. [Operations and Computation Goal 5]	2·7, 2·8				13, 14	
Apply parts-and-total and comparison situations. [Operations and Computation Goal 6]	2·4–2·9	3		6, 7		
Tell and show time on an analog clock. [Measurement and Reference Frames Goal 4]	2·1, 2·3, 2·6, 2·8			8, 9		✓
Find and use rules to solve problems. [Patterns, Functions, and Algebra Goal 1]	2·1–2·9	2		3, 4	11, 12	

2 Looking Ahead: Preparing for Unit 3

Math Boxes 2•10

Home Link 2•10: Unit 3 Family Letter

Materials
- *Math Journal 1,* p. 54
- *Math Masters,* pp. 60–63

152 Unit 2 Progress Check 2

Core Assessment Resources

Assessment Handbook

- **Unit 5 Assessment Overview,** pages pages 84–91
- **Unit 5 Assessment Masters,** pages 153–156
- **Unit 5 Individual Profiles of Progress,** pages 216, 217, and 248
- **Unit 5 Class Checklists,** pages 218, 219, and 249
- **Mid-Year Assessment,** pages 92, 93, and 187–190
- **Math Logs,** pages 254–256
- **Exit Slip,** page 251
- **Other Student Assessment Forms,** pages 252, 253, 257, and 258

Assessment Management Spreadsheets

The Assessment Management Spreadsheets consist of the Digital Class Checklists and Individual Profile of Progress Checklists. Use them to monitor, record, and report children's progress.

Addressing All Needs

Differentiated Instruction

Adjusting the Activity – suggests adaptations that target advanced learners, English language learners, or learners who need additional instructional support.

ELL SUPPORT / **ELL** – provides lesson-specific suggestions to help English language learners understand and process the mathematical content.

READINESS – accesses children's prior knowledge or previews content that prepares children to engage in the lesson's Part 1 activities.

EXTRA PRACTICE – provides additional opportunities to apply the mathematical content of the lesson.

ENRICHMENT – enables children to apply or further explore the mathematical content of the lesson.

Lesson	Adjusting the Activity	ELL Support/ ELL	Readiness	Extra Practice	Enrichment
5•1	•	•	•	•	•
5•2	•	•	•	•	
5•3	•	•	•	•	•
5•4	•			•	•
5•5	•	•	•		•
5•6	•		•		•
5•7	•	•	•		•
5•8			•		•
5•9				•	•
5•10	•		•	•	
5•11	•		•	•	
5•12	•	•	•		•
5•13	•			•	•

Additional Resources

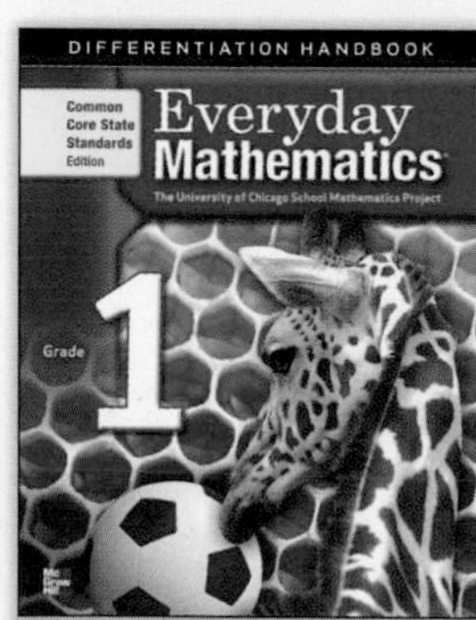

Differentiation Handbook
Provides ideas and strategies for differentiating instruction.
Pages 78–84

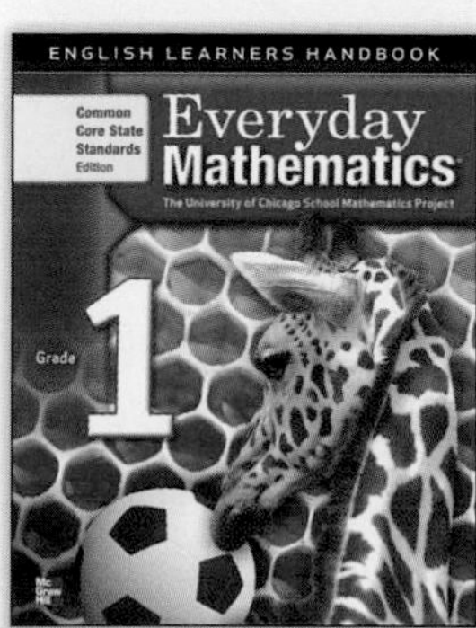

English Learners Handbook
Contains lesson-specific comprehension strategies.
Pages 53–65

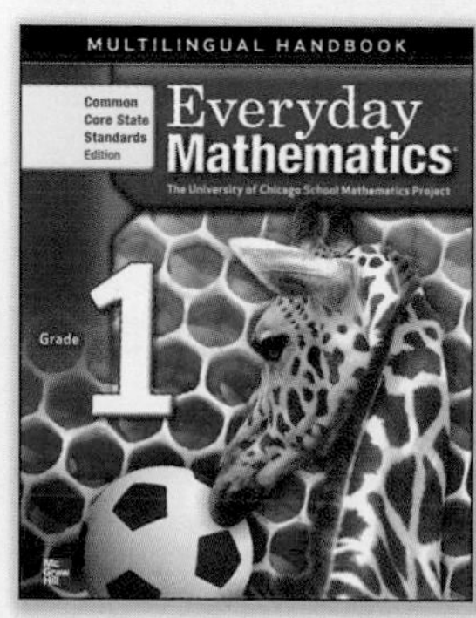

Multilingual Handbook
Previews concepts and vocabulary. It is written in six languages.
Pages 105–130

Planning Tips

Multiage Classroom

Companion Lessons from Grades K and 2 can help you meet instructional needs of a multiage classroom. The full Scope and Sequence can be found in the Appendix.

Grade K	7•8, 8•1	4•7, 7•8	1•11, 1•13, 6•9	1•12, 3•4, 4•3	3•4, 3•12, 8•15	2•14, 4•15	2•14, 4•15, 6•9	2•14, 4•15	7•6, 7•13	4•4, 4•11	4•4, 4•11	8•10	8•10
Grade 1	**5•1**	**5•2**	**5•3**	**5•4**	**5•5**	**5•6**	**5•7**	**5•8**	**5•9**	**5•10**	**5•11**	**5•12**	**5•13**
Grade 2	3•1, 10•8–10•10	10•3, 10•8–10•10	1•11	7•5, 9•6, 10•7	4•8, 4•9, 11•1	1•11	6•2	2•1, 4•1, 6•4	7•7, 12•7	2•2, 2•4	2•2, 2•3	2•11, 3•6	2•10, 2•11

Pacing for Success

Pacing depends on a number of factors, such as children's individual needs and how long your school has been using *Everyday Mathematics*. At the beginning of Unit 5, you may want to use tools available at www.everydaymathonline.com to help you set your pace.

Home Support

Unit 5 Family Letter (English/Spanish) provides families with an overview, Do-Anytime Activities, Building Skills through Games, a list of vocabulary, and answers to the daily homework (Home Links). Family Letters in English, Spanish, and seven other languages are also available online.

Home Links are the daily homework assignments. They consist of active projects and ongoing review problems.

Home Support Resources

Home Connection Handbook
Offers ideas and reproducible masters for communicating with families. See Table of Contents for unit information.

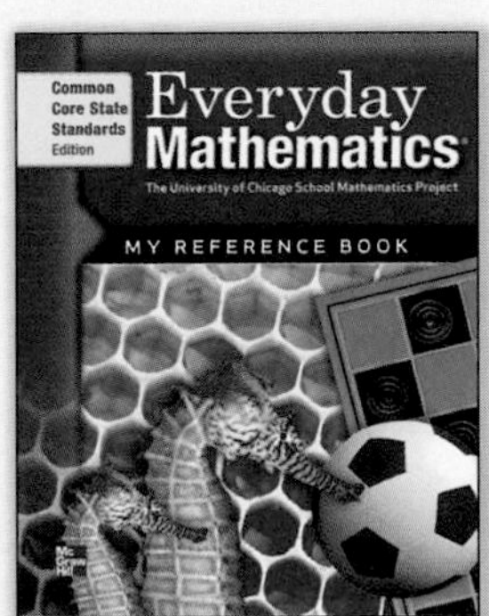

My Reference Book
Beginning in Unit 6, *My Reference Book* provides a resource for children and parents.

Technology Resources

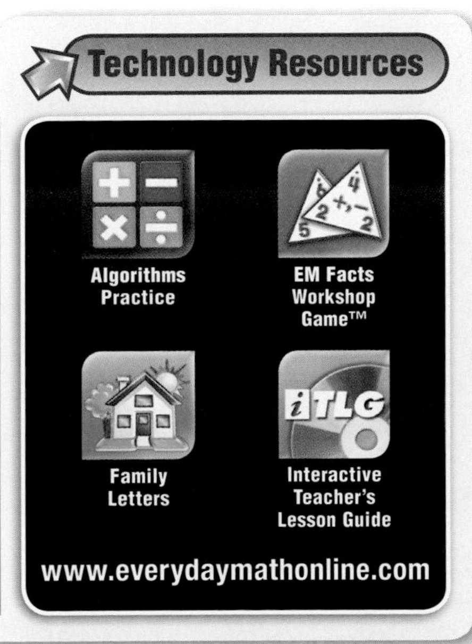

Unit 5 Organizer

Materials

Technology Resources www.everydaymathonline.com

ePresentations

eToolkit

Algorithms Practice

EM Facts Workshop Game™

Family Letters

Assessment Management

Common Core State Standards

Curriculum Focal Points

Interactive Teacher's Lesson Guide

Lesson	Masters	Manipulative Kit	Other Items
5•1	Teaching Masters, pp. 119* and 121 Teaching Aid Master, p. 305 Transparency of *Math Masters,* p. 318* Home Link Master, p. 120	per child: base-10 blocks (12 longs and 25 cubes); 4 each of number cards 0–9; slate	overhead coins*; *The Warlord's Beads*
5•2	Teaching Aid Masters, pp. 318 and 319 Transparency of *Math Masters,* p. 319* Home Link Master, p. 122 Teaching Master, p. 105	base-10 blocks (flats, longs, and cubes); tool-kit pennies; slate	grid paper; calculator
5•3	Teaching Aid Masters, pp. 305 and 318–321 Game Master, p. 339 Home Link Master, p. 123 Teaching Master, p. 124 *Differentiation Handbook,* p. 127	slate; number cards; 1 die; base-10 blocks (cubes and longs)	*Just Enough Carrots*
5•4	Teaching Aid Master, p. 318 Teaching Masters, pp. 125–129 and 131 Home Link Master, p. 130	base-10 blocks (cubes and longs); slate; pan balance; tool-kit coins and about 50 extra pennies; 4 each of number cards 0–9	objects to use as units; sets of objects
5•5	Teaching Masters, pp. 132–137 and 139 Home Link Master, p. 138 Game Master, p. 353	slate; base-10 blocks (cubes and longs); two 6-sided dice or two polyhedral dice marked 0–9	domino for overhead projector*; per group: 20 pennies or counters; paper plates
5•6	Animal Cards (*Math Masters,* pp. 132–137) Home Link Master, p. 141 Teaching Masters, pp. 140 and 142	slate; base-10 blocks (cubes and longs)	Class Number Line or Number-Grid Poster*; small paper cups; pan balance
5•7	Teaching Aid Master, p. 305 Home Link Master, p. 143 Teaching Master, p. 144 *Differentiation Handbook,* p. 126	slate; tool-kit pennies; per partnership: 4 each of number cards 1–10	overhead coins*; 2 clear counters
5•8	Animal Cards (*Math Masters,* pp. 132–137) Home Link Master, p. 146 Teaching Master, p. 145	slate; counters	
5•9	Teaching Aid Master*, p. 318 Home Link Master, p. 147 Game Master, p. 339 Teaching Master, p. 148 Teaching Aid Master, p. 305	slate; base-10 blocks (cubes and longs); per partnership: pair of dice	Number-Grid Poster; *Probably Pistachio*
5•10	Home Link Master, p. 149	dominoes; per group: 3 or 4 dice; pattern blocks; counters of two colors or types	clear plastic bag; paper bag*; on-the-floor number line
5•11	Home Link Master, p. 150 Teaching Master, p. 151 Teaching Aid Masters, pp. 317 and 336*	base-10 blocks (cubes); tool-kit pennies; counters*	per partnership: 1 paper plate; calculator
5•12	Home Link Masters, pp. 153–155 Teaching Master, p. 152 Teaching Aid Master, p. 323 *Differentiation Handbook,* p. 126	craft sticks; slate; counters*	paper bag; calculator
5•13	Home Link Master, p. 156 Teaching Aid Master, p. 323	per partnership: 2 dice, additional tool-kit coins*, 2 polyhedral dice*	per partnership: 20 pennies, 10 nickels, and 10 dimes, calculator, overhead calculator*
5•14	Assessment Masters, pp. 153–156 Home Link Masters, pp. 157–160	slate	

*Denotes optional materials

Mathematical Background

The discussion below highlights the major content ideas presented in Unit 5 and helps establish instructional priorities.

Place Value

(Lessons 5◆1, 5◆2, and 5◆5)

Most of us take our numeration system for granted, yet it is one of the most amazing of human inventions. Our numeration system makes it possible to represent any whole number or decimal, however large or small, by using one or more of the digits 0 through 9 and, sometimes, a decimal point. This is possible because the value of any digit in a numeral is determined by its position in the numeral.

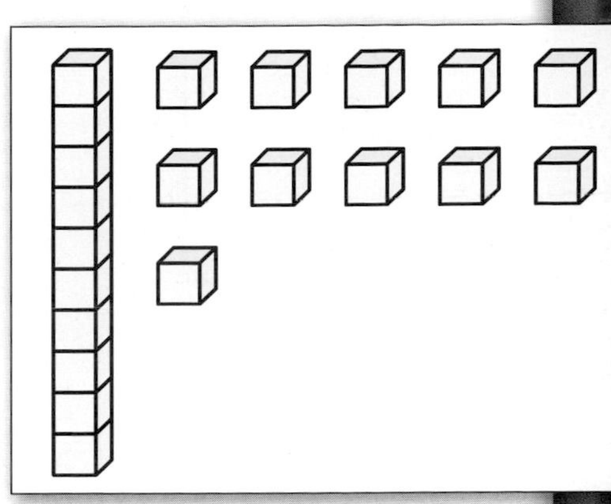

What number am I?

An understanding of place value is essential because it forms the basis for computational algorithms with whole numbers and decimals. In Lessons 5-1 and 5-2, children begin to explore the idea of place value—using only tens and ones at this stage—by representing numbers with base-10 blocks. Base-10 blocks are then used in Lesson 5-5 to find the sums of 1- and 2-digit numbers. Some of these addition problems require exchanges of cubes (ones blocks) for longs (tens blocks) in order to compose a new ten and end up with a numeral that follows the properties of our numeration system.

For additional information about place value, please see Section 9.2.1 in the *Teacher's Reference Manual.*

Project Note

Use Project 3, Pumpkin Math, to provide opportunities for children to estimate weight and girth, compare objects, and count the number of objects in a large collection.

Greater Than and Less Than Relationships between Two Numbers

(Lessons 5◆3 and 5◆6)

Lesson 5-3 introduces the $<$ and $>$ symbols. These symbols are used in Lesson 5-6 in number models for number stories in which two quantities are compared. You may invent your own ways to help children recall the symbols' meanings until children can remember them without prompts.

See Section 9.6 in the *Teacher's Reference Manual* for more information about numeric relations.

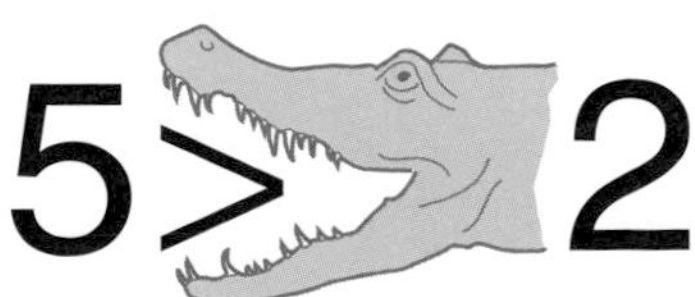

Number Stories (Lessons 5◆5–5◆8)

Math Journal 1, Activity Sheets 7 and 8 feature pictures of animals that can be cut apart and used as a deck of animal cards. The animal cards include information that you and children can use to make up a variety of number stories, both realistic and fanciful. The numbers on the cards vary in size and complexity, so success is possible at many different levels.

These same animal pictures are available on *Math Masters,* pages 132–137, so that they may be displayed for demonstration or arranged in many different ways to meet the needs of the current activity.

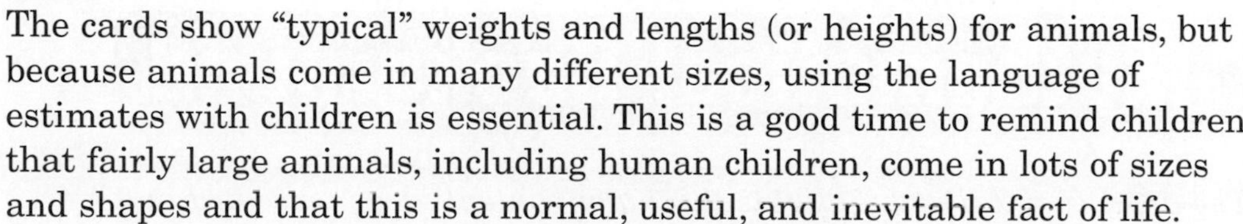

The cards show “typical” weights and lengths (or heights) for animals, but because animals come in many different sizes, using the language of estimates with children is essential. This is a good time to remind children that fairly large animals, including human children, come in lots of sizes and shapes and that this is a normal, useful, and inevitable fact of life.

Children were introduced to change-to-more and change-to-less number stories in Unit 2 and to parts-and-total number stories in Unit 3. In Lesson 5-7, they begin to solve comparison number stories, which involve finding the difference between two quantities. Then, in Lesson 5-8, they make up and solve all three types of number stories.

Most adults are quite surprised at the ingenuity and thoughtfulness of children in devising and sharing their many strategies for solving number stories. For example, some children will subtract when you expect addition, or add when you expect subtraction. As children grapple with addition and subtraction of larger, double-digit numbers, teachers may highlight particular strategies that children might find useful, such as Making Ten. However, teachers should encourage children as they develop their own strategies and allow them to share and use a variety of methods.

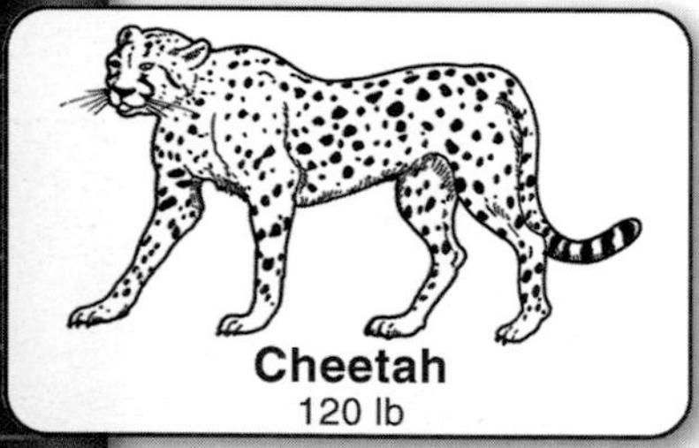

For more information about number stories, please read Section 18.4.1 in the *Teacher's Reference Manual.*

Number Models (Lesson 5•8)

Until now you have been asked to write number models as one of several representations of number stories, but children have not been required to do so themselves. In this lesson children begin to write number models as “shorthand” for illustrating number stories.

As you give examples and talk about children's stories, try to vary the phrases and language used in order to help children forge links among the words, situations, and symbols. (For example, use *About how many does that equal? About how many is that all together? About how many does that leave? Approximately how much bigger is that?* and *Estimate how far from this to that.*) Please insist that children keep track of the units that go with their solutions and with their number models. For oral discussion, insist that the units be given. (For example, *15 what? Years, tons, pounds?*) It is often cumbersome to write the unit words next to every number in a number model, so this is a good place to use a unit box as a reminder of what the numbers mean.

Research shows that children have only a partial understanding of the role of the = symbol in number models. They have no difficulty with number models like $3 + 8 = 11$ and $15 - 7 = 8$. But many children, even those in higher grades, reject number models such as $5 = 5$ (they may say there is no problem), $4 = 2 + 2$ (they may say that the answer is on the wrong side), or $4 + 3 = 5 + 2$ (they may say there are two problems but no answers). The origin of these conceptual errors seems very clear: Children in school generally see only number models with a single number on the right of the = symbol. To prevent such misconceptions, get into the

Project Note

Use Project 6, Celebrate the Hundredth Day, to provide opportunities for children to explore the number 100.

habit of writing 12 = 5 + 7 just as often as 5 + 7 = 12 and of consistently asking children to say "means the same as" or "looks different, but is really the same" wherever the = symbol appears.

See Section 10.1 in the *Teacher's Reference Manual* for more information about number models.

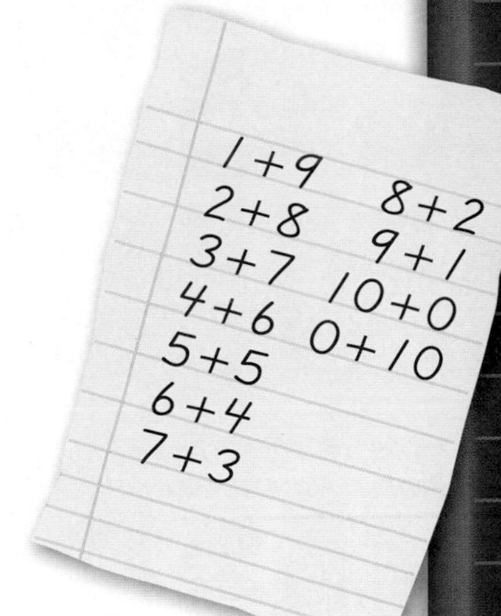

Addition Facts (Lessons 5•9–5•11)

The *Everyday Mathematics* goal is that most children will know the addition facts by the end of first grade. The +0 and +1 facts should be easy to learn. Children also often have an easier time with doubles than with some of the other facts. Two-Fisted Penny Addition with 10 pennies, which was introduced in Unit 2, has prepared them for the facts with sums of 10. In this unit, children will add new strategies to the Fact Strategy Wall in the classroom.

You can read more about operations and facts in Sections 16.3.2, 16.3.3, and 16.3.4 of the *Teacher's Reference Manual.*

Functions and "What's My Rule?" (Lessons 5•12 and 5•13)

The "What's My Rule?" routine provides a format for thinking about rule-based relationships between pairs of numbers and also provides practice with number patterns and number facts.

A function machine is simply a diagram or metaphor to indicate how the input and output numbers in "What's My Rule?" tables are produced. The machines are thought of as being "programmed" to take in numbers, change the numbers according to a rule, and then send out new numbers. Thus, there are three parts to a function machine and a "What's My Rule?" table: input (the number that goes in), output (the number that comes out), and rule (what is done to an input number to change it to the output number). "What's My Rule?" may vary by having partial information about inputs, outputs, or rules.

One option for teaching "What's My Rule?" problems is to set up a class-size function machine so children may act out the problems. The function machine can be as simple or as elaborate as you wish. Some teachers have children sit under a desk or a table to receive the "in" numbers on slips of paper or on a slate, change those numbers according to the rule, and then return the output number on another slip of paper or slate. Other teachers have made a large box into a function machine, with slots labeled "in" and "out." A child sits inside the box, receives "in" numbers, changes them according to the rule, and returns the result through the "out" slot.

For more information about function machines and "What's My Rule?", see Section 1.3.7 in the *Teacher's Reference Manual.*

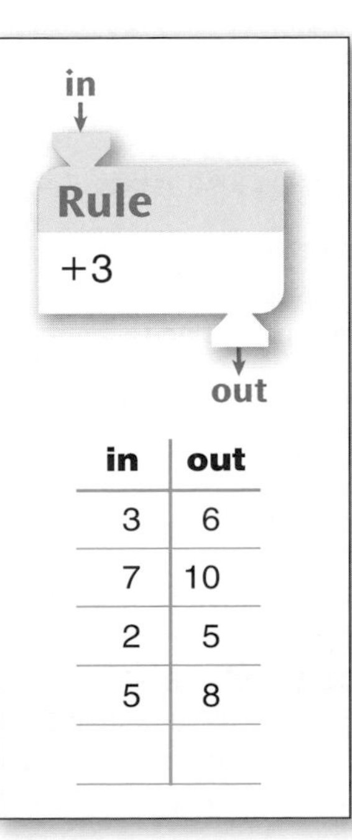

in	out
3	6
7	10
2	5
5	8

"What's My Rule?" table

5•1 Place Value: Tens and Ones

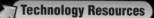

Objective To provide experiences with place-value concepts for tens and ones.

www.everydaymathonline.com

ePresentations

eToolkit

Algorithms Practice

EM Facts Workshop Game™

Family Letters

Assessment Management

Common Core State Standards

Curriculum Focal Points

Interactive Teacher's Lesson Guide

1 Teaching the Lesson

Key Concepts and Skills

- Count objects by 1s.
  [Number and Numeration Goal 2]
- Use base-10 blocks to model whole numbers less than 100. Name whole numbers less than 100 modeled by base-10 blocks. Exchange base-10 cubes and longs to show different representations of the same number.
  [Number and Numeration Goal 3]

Key Activities

Children name numbers less than 100 represented by base-10 blocks. They exchange cubes for longs in order to represent numbers by using the fewest number of base-10 blocks.

Ongoing Assessment: Recognizing Student Achievement Use an Exit Slip (*Math Masters,* page 305).
[Number and Numeration Goal 3]

Ongoing Assessment: Informing Instruction See page 360.

Key Vocabulary

base-10 blocks ◆ longs ◆ cubes ◆ tens place ◆ ones place

Materials

Math Journal 1, pp. 81 and 82
Math Masters, p. 119 (optional); p. 305
transparency of *Math Masters,* p. 318 (optional) ◆ base-10 blocks (12 longs and 25 cubes) ◆ overhead coins (optional)

2 Ongoing Learning & Practice

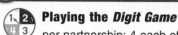

Playing the *Digit Game*
per partnership: 4 each of number cards 0–9 (from the Everything Math Deck, if available)
Children practice comparing numbers.

Math Boxes 5•1
Math Journal 1, p. 83
Children practice and maintain skills through Math Box problems.

Home Link 5•1
Math Masters, p. 120
Children practice and maintain skills through Home Link activities.

3 Differentiation Options

READINESS
Reading and Writing Numbers to 99
slate
Children practice reading and writing 1- and 2-digit numbers.

ENRICHMENT
Guessing My 2-Digit Number
Math Masters, p. 121
Children determine an unknown number by using clues that describe its digits.

EXTRA PRACTICE
Reading About Place Value
Math Masters, p. 305
Children read *The Warlord's Beads* to practice place-value concepts.

Advance Preparation

You may wish to find the book ***Let's Count*** by Tana Hoban (Greenwillow Books, 1999) as it relates to lesson content. For the optional Extra Practice activity in Part 3, obtain a copy of ***The Warlord's Beads*** by Virginia Walton Pilegard (Pelican Publishing Company, 2001).

***Teacher's Reference Manual,* Grades 1–3** pp. 56, 57, 69, 70

Getting Started

Mental Math and Reflexes

Explain that children can estimate the costs of items by knowing the costs of similar items and that they can use estimation to help them determine if they have enough money to pay for certain items.

Draw the items and the price tags on the overhead projector, and show the prices using coins if you wish. Have children estimate the cost of the items in question.

●○○ A small ball of clay costs 25¢, and a large ball of clay costs 75¢. What would you estimate to be the cost of a medium ball of clay?

●●○ A small soda costs 70¢ and a large soda costs $1.00. What would you estimate to be the cost of a medium soda?

●●● A small box of crayons costs 50¢ and a medium box of crayons costs $1.00. What would you estimate to be the cost of a large box of crayons?

Math Message

Line up cubes next to a long. How many cubes equal the length of a long?

1 Teaching the Lesson

▶ Math Message Follow-Up

WHOLE-CLASS DISCUSSION

Check that children lined up 10 cubes next to a long. Discuss the fact that 10 cubes is the same as 1 long, but that it is easier to display 1 long than to count 10 individual cubes.

▶ Naming Numbers with Base-10 Blocks

WHOLE-CLASS ACTIVITY

ELL

(*Math Journal 1,* p. 81)

Use the following routine:

1. Place 3 longs and 4 cubes on your Tens-and-Ones Mat transparency. Or, draw a mat on the board and use vertical lines | and dots • to represent longs and cubes. Children do the same on their mats. *What number do these **base-10 blocks** represent?* 34 To support English language learners, discuss the meaning of *represent.*
2. Write the number on your mat. Point out that the 3 **longs** stand for 3 tens and that the 4 **cubes** stand for 4 ones. *We say that the 3 in 34 is in the **tens place** and the 4 is in the **ones place.*** To support English language learners, discuss the everyday meaning of *place,* as well as its meaning in this context.

Repeat this routine with other numbers, as needed.

NOTE You may wish to make several copies of *Math Masters,* page 318 (Tens-and-Ones Mat) for children to use if they are having difficulty keeping their journal pages flat when working with the base-10 blocks.

Interactive whiteboard-ready ePresentations are available at www.everydaymathonline.com to help you teach the lesson.

Children place 3 longs and 4 cubes on their Tens-and-Ones-Mats (*Math Journal 1,* page 81, or *Math Masters,* page 318).

Student Page

Date

LESSON 5·1 **Tens-and-Ones Mat**

Tens 10s	Ones 1s

***Math Journal 1,* p. 81**

Ongoing Assessment: Recognizing Student Achievement

Exit Slip

Use an **Exit Slip** (*Math Masters,* page 305) to assess children's ability to name numbers represented by base-10 blocks. Put a small number of longs and cubes on your Tens-and-Ones Mat transparency, or draw them on the board. Have children write the number shown on an Exit Slip. Children are making adequate progress if they are able to correctly count the longs and the cubes.

[Number and Numeration Goal 3]

NOTE *Everyday Mathematics* uses base-10 blocks to introduce children to place-value concepts. When children add larger numbers using base-10 blocks, exchanging cubes for longs provides them with a concrete representation of the place-value concept of composing a ten from ones. Whenever children exchange cubes for longs, you may wish to remind them that they are composing a new "ten" from 10 "ones."

▶ Making Exchanges with Base-10 Blocks

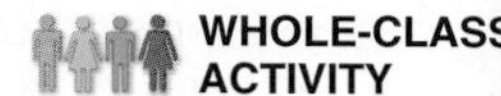

(*Math Journal 1,* p. 81)

Place 2 longs and 15 cubes on your Tens-and-Ones Mat. Children do the same on journal page 81. (Or, they can use a copy of *Math Masters,* page 318.) *What number is shown?* 35 If children do not come up with the answer right away, have them discuss the problem among themselves. Someone might suggest trading 2 longs for 20 cubes and then counting the total number of cubes. If needed, demonstrate the following exchange: Trade 10 cubes for 1 long and place the long in the tens column. As you make this trade, emphasize to children that you are composing a new ten (1 long) from 10 ones (10 cubes). Point out that there are now 3 longs and 5 cubes. *What number is shown?* 35

Repeat this routine with other combinations of longs and cubes that require an exchange.

Adjusting the Activity

Have children use pennies and dimes as another model of 10-for-1 exchanges when making two-digit numbers on their Tens-and-Ones Mats.

AUDITORY ◆ KINESTHETIC ◆ TACTILE ◆ VISUAL

Student Page

Date

LESSON 5·1 **Tens-and-Ones Riddles**

Solve the riddles. Use your base-10 blocks to help you.

Example: 2 longs and 3 cubes What am I? 23

1. 6 longs and 5 cubes What am I? 65
2. 7 longs and 2 cubes What am I? 72
3. 6 longs and 4 cubes. What am I? 64
4. 7 longs and 0 cubes. What am I? 70

Try This

Trade to find the answers.

5. 1 long and 11 cubes. What am I? 21
6. 2 longs and 14 cubes. What am I? 34
7. Make up your own riddle. Ask a friend to solve it.
   Answers vary.

Math Journal 1, p. 82

▶ Naming Numbers for Collections of Base-10 Blocks

(*Math Journal 1,* p. 82)

Children solve riddles using base-10 blocks. When most children have finished the page, volunteers can read their riddles aloud for classmates to solve.

Ongoing Assessment: Informing Instruction

Watch for children who confuse the tens and ones places when solving the riddles. Remind them that the tens digit, or the number on the left, is represented by the number of longs; and that the ones digit, or the number on the right, is represented by the number of cubes.

2 Ongoing Learning & Practice

Playing the *Digit Game*

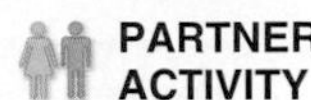
PARTNER ACTIVITY

Partners play the *Digit Game* with a set of number cards 0–9, 4 cards of each number.

Directions

1. The deck is shuffled and placed number-side down between the partners.
2. Each player draws 2 cards from the deck and uses them to make the larger 2-digit number.
3. The player with the larger number takes all 4 cards.
4. The game is over when all of the cards have been used.
5. The player with more cards wins.

Have partners play several rounds of the game.

Math Boxes 5•1

INDEPENDENT ACTIVITY

(*Math Journal 1,* p. 83)

Mixed Practice Math Boxes in this lesson are paired with Math Boxes in Lesson 5-3. The skills in Problem 4 preview Unit 6 content.

Writing/Reasoning Have children draw, write, or verbalize an answer to the following question: *How do you find a missing rule?* A reasonable answer should describe a strategy to identify the number pattern, such as skip counting or using a number grid.

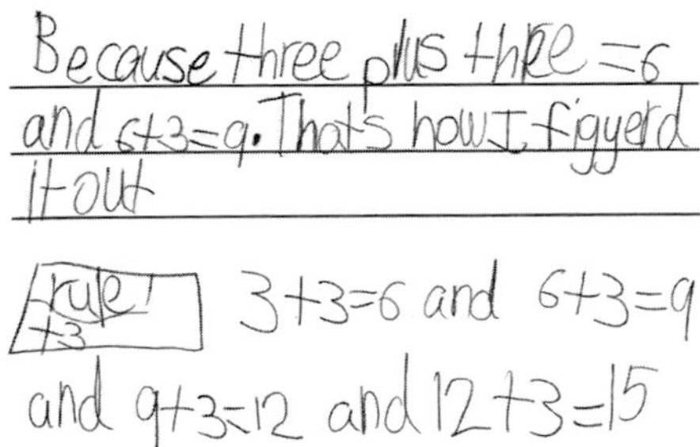

One child's work in response to the Writing/Reasoning prompt

Home Link 5•1

INDEPENDENT ACTIVITY

(*Math Masters,* p. 120)

Home Connection Children record numbers represented by base-10 blocks.

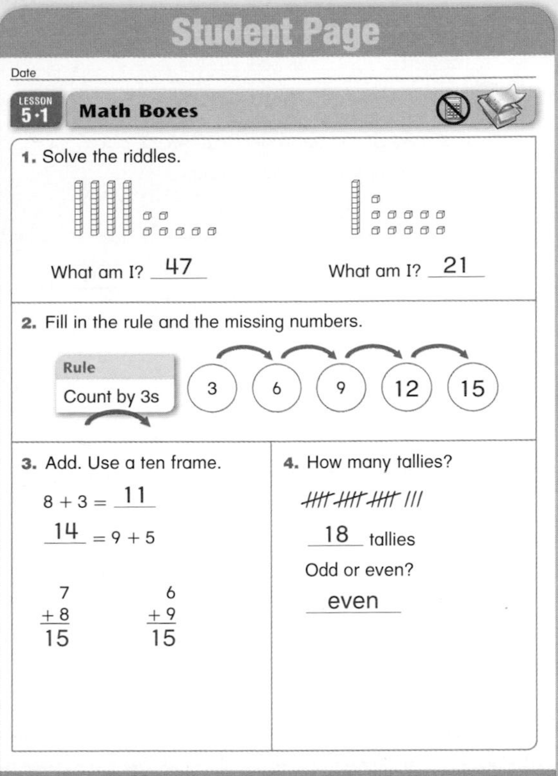

Student Page

Date

LESSON 5•1 **Math Boxes**

1. Solve the riddles.

What am I? 47

What am I? 21

2. Fill in the rule and the missing numbers.

Rule: Count by 3s

3, 6, 9, 12, 15

3. Add. Use a ten frame.

8 + 3 = 11

14 = 9 + 5

7 + 8 = 15

6 + 9 = 15

4. How many tallies?

18 tallies

Odd or even? even

Math Journal 1, p. 83

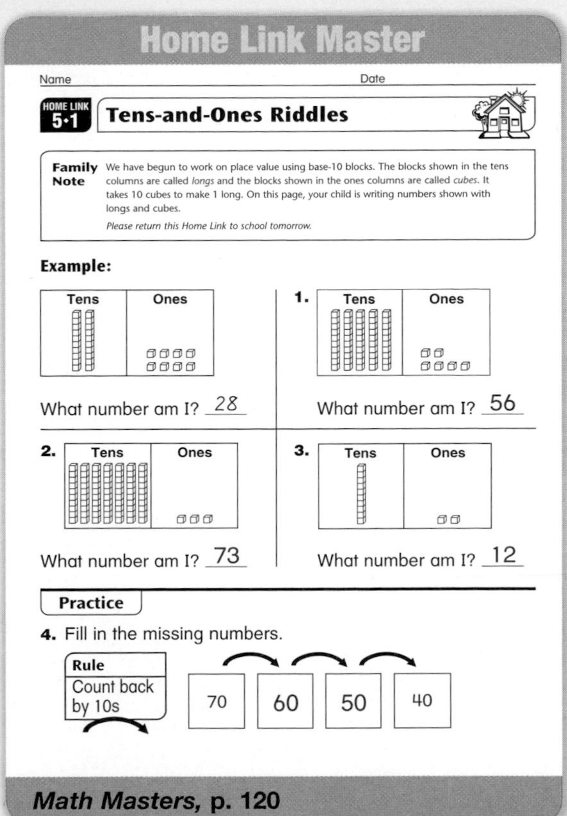

Home Link Master

Name　Date

HOME LINK 5•1 **Tens-and-Ones Riddles**

Family Note We have begun to work on place value using base-10 blocks. The blocks shown in the tens columns are called *longs* and the blocks shown in the ones columns are called *cubes.* It takes 10 cubes to make 1 long. On this page, your child is writing numbers shown with longs and cubes.

Please return this Home Link to school tomorrow.

Example:

Tens	Ones

What number am I? 28

1.

Tens	Ones

What number am I? 56

2.

Tens	Ones

What number am I? 73

3.

Tens	Ones

What number am I? 12

Practice

4. Fill in the missing numbers.

Rule: Count back by 10s

70, 60, 50, 40

Math Masters, p. 120

Teaching Master

Name Date

LESSON 5·1 **Guessing My 2-Digit Number** 

1. Think of a 2-digit number. Write it in a "secret" place.
2. Ask your partner to guess your number.
3. Record each guess.
4. Use an X to give clues about your number.

Guess	0 digits correct	1 digit correct	2 digits correct

Math Masters, p. 121

3 Differentiation Options

READINESS

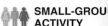

 SMALL-GROUP ACTIVITY

5–15 Min

▶ Reading and Writing Numbers to 99

To provide experience reading and writing 1- and 2-digit numbers, have children write and identify numbers to 99. Tell children to write each number you name aloud on a slate. Begin by naming 1-digit numbers and progress to 2-digit numbers. Then reverse roles. Write a number on your slate, and ask children to name the number. Again, begin with 1-digit numbers and progress to 2-digit numbers.

ENRICHMENT

 PARTNER ACTIVITY

 5–15 Min

▶ Guessing My 2-Digit Number

(*Math Masters*, p. 121)

To apply children's understanding of place-value, have one partner think of a 2-digit number and write it in a "secret place." The other partner tries to guess the number. The first partner records each guess and places an X in the column that describes the guess. The second partner uses the information in the table to continue guessing until he or she guesses the correct number. Partners switch roles and repeat the activity. Have extra copies of *Math Masters*, page 121 available for children to repeat the activity.

Example:

Guess	0 digits correct	1 digit correct	2 digits correct
37	X		
71		X	
78		X	
74			X

EXTRA PRACTICE

 SMALL-GROUP ACTIVITY

 15–30 Min

▶ Reading About Place Value

(*Math Masters*, p. 305)

Literature Link To provide practice with place-value concepts, read ***The Warlord's Beads*** by Virginia Walton Pilegard (Pelican Publishing Company, 2001). On an Exit Slip (*Math Masters,* page 305), have children draw base-10 blocks for a number they choose.

5•2 Place Value with Calculators

Objective To provide experiences investigating place-value digit patterns.

Technology Resources www.everydaymathonline.com

ePresentations

eToolkit

Algorithms Practice

EM Facts Workshop Game™

Family Letters

Assessment Management

Common Core State Standards

Curriculum Focal Points

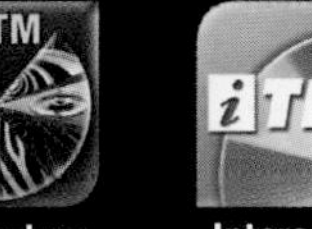

Interactive Teacher's Lesson Guide

1 Teaching the Lesson

Key Concepts and Skills

- Count forward by 1s and 10s on a calculator. [Number and Numeration Goal 1]
- Use base-10 blocks to model whole numbers; name whole numbers modeled by base-10 blocks. [Number and Numeration Goal 3]
- Exchange base-10 cubes, longs, and flats to show different representations of the same number. [Number and Numeration Goal 3]
- Recognize patterns on a number grid. [Patterns, Functions, and Algebra Goal 1]

Key Activities

Children use base-10 blocks and calculators to investigate digit patterns when 1 is added to a number with 9 in the ones place and when 10 is added to a 2-digit number. They discuss the fact that the value of a digit depends on its place in a numeral.

Key Vocabulary

flat ◆ hundreds ◆ digit

Materials

Math Journal 1, p. 84, Activity Sheet 6 (optional), and inside back cover
Home Link 5•1
Math Masters, pp. 318 and 319
transparency of *Math Masters,* p. 319 (optional) ◆ base-10 blocks (flats, longs, and cubes) ◆ slate ◆ calculator

2 Ongoing Learning & Practice

Doing Two-Fisted Penny Addition for 13 and 14
Math Masters, p. 105
tool-kit pennies
Children find complements of 13 and 14.

Ongoing Assessment: Recognizing Student Achievement
Use *Math Masters,* page 105.
[Operations and Computation Goal 1]

Math Boxes 5•2
Math Journal 1, p. 85
Children practice and maintain skills through Math Box problems.

Home Link 5•2
Math Masters, p. 122
Children practice and maintain skills through Home Link activities.

3 Differentiation Options

READINESS

Building Designs with Base-10 Blocks
Math Masters, p. 319
base-10 blocks (flats, longs, and cubes) ◆ grid paper
Children make designs with base-10 blocks and determine the value of their designs.

EXTRA PRACTICE

Minute Math+
Minute Math®+, pp. 23 and 24
Children practice identifying numbers using place-value digit patterns.

Advance Preparation

For Part 1, make a transparency of *Math Masters,* page 319 to use with overhead base-10 blocks, or draw a Place-Value Mat on the board. For children who have a difficult time keeping their journal pages flat when working with base-10 blocks, make a few extra copies of the Place-Value Mat (*Math Masters,* page 319), or have children use Activity Sheet 6.

***Teacher's Reference Manual,* Grades 1–3** pp. 70–76

Getting Started

Mental Math and Reflexes

Have children display the following numbers of longs and cubes on their Tens-and-Ones Mat. Then have them record each number represented on their slates.

●○○ *2 longs and 7 cubes* 27

●●○ *5 longs and 9 cubes* 59

●●● *8 longs and 12 cubes* 92

Remind children that 2 longs and 7 cubes stand for 2 tens and 7 ones, respectively. The 2 in 27 is in the tens place and the 7 is in the ones place. Continue with other numbers as time allows.

Math Message

What number comes after 9? After 39? After 99?

Home Link 5•1 Follow-Up

Go over the answers to the Home Link. If appropriate, model the numbers on a Tens-and-Ones Mat.

NOTE To demonstrate the concept of place value, it may be useful to display three different quantities using the same numeral and explain the difference in magnitude; for example, 1, 10, and 100.

Student Page

Date

LESSON 5•2 **Place-Value Mat**

	Hundreds
	Tens
	Ones

Math Journal 1, p. 84

NOTE This is children's first exposure to exchanges into **hundreds.** Limit the discussion to this one problem for the time being. Place value to hundreds will be revisited throughout the year.

1 Teaching the Lesson

▶ Math Message Follow-Up

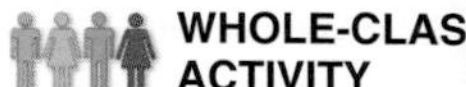

WHOLE-CLASS ACTIVITY

(*Math Journal 1,* p. 84)

As you discuss the numbers that come after 9 and 39, use your Place-Value Mat (*Math Masters,* page 319) as children follow along on their mats on journal page 84.

1. Place (or draw) 9 cubes (or dots) in the ones column.
2. Add 1 cube to the ones column. Now there are 10 cubes.
3. Exchange the 10 cubes for 1 long and put it in the tens column.

Follow the same procedure when discussing what number comes after 39. 40 The following activity discusses what number comes after 99.

▶ Adding 1 to 99

WHOLE-CLASS ACTIVITY

ELL

Ask children to use longs to completely cover one **flat**. To support English language learners, discuss the everyday meaning of the word *flat* as well as the meaning in this context. *How many longs are needed to cover a flat?* 10 longs

Have someone choose the base-10 blocks needed to show 99 and put them on your Place-Value Mat (*Math Masters,* page 319). 9 longs and 9 cubes Then add 1 cube to the ones column to show 100. *How can we make 100, using fewer base-10 blocks?* Give children time to share their ideas. Exchange 10 cubes for 1 long and put that long in the tens column. Now there are 10 longs. Exchange the 10 longs for 1 flat and put that flat in the **hundreds** column.

Write 1, 0, 0 in the appropriate columns on the Place-Value Mat. Mention that the 1 in 100 stands for 1 hundred and that it is in th hundreds place. *How many cubes are equal to 1 flat?* 100 cubes

Investigating Digit Patterns in Counts by 1s

Review how to count up by 1s on the calculator, starting at 0. (See Lesson 3-10 for programming instructions for two different types of calculators.) After children have programmed their calculators, have them do the following:

1. Press (=) repeatedly and slowly, while counting together by 1s as the numbers 1 through 9 appear in the displays. Pause at 9. *What number comes next?* 10
2. Then press (=) once, observing the change from 9 to 0 in the ones place and the appearance of a 1 in the tens place. *What does the 1 stand for?* 1 ten
3. Continue to press (=) and count aloud through 40 or 50. Pause at each number that has 9 in the ones place, and predict the next number. *What pattern do you see?* The **digit** in the tens place increases by 1, and the digit in the ones place becomes 0.
4. Clear the calculators and program them to count up by 1s, starting at 85. Press (=) to count past 100. Count aloud, pause at the 9s, and predict the next number.

If time permits, try counting past 200 from 196.

Investigating Digit Patterns in Counts by 10s

Ask someone to describe how to program the calculator to count up by 10s, starting at 0. After children have programmed their calculators, have them count aloud as they press (=) until they get to 90. *What happens to the digits in the tens place as you count by 10s?* The digit in the tens place increases by 1 with each count. *Press (=) again. What happens?* 1 appears in the hundreds place, and 0 appears in the tens place. Continue the count past 100, and observe the digit patterns.

Choose a starting number less than 100, such as 53. Program the calculator to count up by 10s. As children press (=), they observe that the tens digit increases by 1 and the ones digit does not change. Pause just before passing 100, and discuss what will happen next. Similarly, pause and discuss what will happen next just before passing 200.

Adjusting the Activity

Have children work in partnerships to do the counts by 10s. Choose a starting number and have children show it with base-10 longs and cubes. Then as one partner does the calculator count by 10s, the other partner adds a long to represent each number shown on the calculator.

AUDITORY • KINESTHETIC • TACTILE • VISUAL

Language Arts Link Review that there are 26 letters in our English alphabet. These 26 letters and a few symbols make up all of the words and sentences that we say, write, and read. Similarly, the digits 0–9 and a few other symbols make up all of the whole numbers, fractions, decimals, and negative numbers that we use.

1	2	3	4	5	6	7	8	9	10
11	12	13	14	15	16	17	18	19	20
21	22	23	24	25	26	27	28	29	30
31	32	33	34	35	36	37	38	39	40
41	42	43	44	45	46	47	48	49	50
51	52	53	54	55	56	57	58	59	60
61	62	63	64	65	66	67	68	69	70
71	72	73	74	75	76	77	78	79	80
81	82	83	84	85	86	87	88	89	90
91	92	93	94	95	96	97	98	99	100

Numbers with 5 in the ones place or 5 in the tens place

Teaching Master

Name Date

LESSON 4·8 **Two-Fisted Penny Addition Summary**

10		11		12		13		14	
Left	Right	Left	Right	Left	Right	Left	Right	Left	Right
0	10	0	11	0	12	0	13	0	14
1	9	1	10	1	11	1	12	1	13
2	8	2	9	2	10	2	11	2	12
3	7	3	8	3	9	3	10	3	11
4	6	4	7	4	8	4	9	4	10
5	5	5	6	5	7	5	8	5	9
6	4	6	5	6	6	6	7	6	8
7	3	7	4	7	5	7	6	7	7
8	2	8	3	8	4	8	5	8	6
9	1	9	2	9	3	9	4	9	5
10	0	10	1	10	2	10	3	10	4
		11	0	11	1	11	2	11	3
				12	0	12	1	12	2
						13	0	13	1
								14	0

Order of numbers may vary.

Math Masters, p. 105

▶ Discovering the Role of Place in the Value of Digits

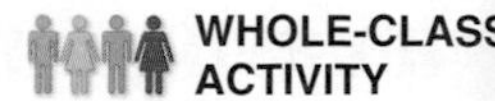
WHOLE-CLASS ACTIVITY

(*Math Journal 1,* inside back cover)

On their calculators, children enter any 2-digit number with a 5 in the ones place. Record several numbers in a column on the board, all with 5 in the ones place.

Next, children enter 2-digit numbers of their choice, each with a 5 in the tens place. Record several numbers in another column, all with 5 in the tens place. *Examples:*

45	52
95	57
25	54
35	56

Have children find each set of numbers on their number grids on the inside back covers of their journals. Point out that numbers with 5 in the ones place are all in the same column; numbers with 5 in the tens place are all in the same row.

Repeat this routine for another digit. Discuss the role of the *placement* of digits within a number, noting how the same digit can represent different values depending on the digit's place in the number.

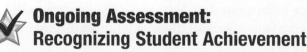

2 Ongoing Learning & Practice

▶ Doing Two-Fisted Penny Addition for 13 and 14

PARTNER ACTIVITY

FACTS PRACTICE

(*Math Masters,* p. 105)

Partners pool their pennies to find complements of the numbers 13 and 14 and record their results on *Math Masters,* page 105.

Ongoing Assessment: Recognizing Student Achievement

Math Masters Page 105

Use ***Math Masters,* page 105** to assess children's ability to find complements of numbers. Children are making adequate progress if they are able to list some of the complements of 13 and 14. Some children may be able to list all of the complements.

[Operations and Computation Goal 1]

Math Boxes 5·2

INDEPENDENT ACTIVITY

(*Math Journal 1,* p. 85)

Mixed Practice Math Boxes in this lesson are paired with Math Boxes in Lesson 5-4. The skills in Problem 4 preview Unit 6 content.

Writing/Reasoning Have children draw, write, or verbalize an answer to the following question: *How do you count base-10 blocks?* A reasonable answer should include counting by 10s and 1s.

Home Link 5·2

INDEPENDENT ACTIVITY

(*Math Masters,* p. 122)

Home Connection Children complete Frames-and-Arrows diagrams for the rules "+10," "−10," and "count back by 10s." They continue to explore changes to the digits in a numeral when counting by 10s.

3 Differentiation Options

READINESS

PARTNER ACTIVITY

Building Designs with Base-10 Blocks

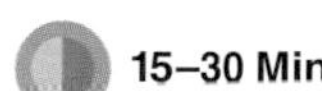
15–30 Min

(*Math Masters,* p. 319)

To review place-value exchanges with base-10 blocks, have children create designs and make exchanges to figure out the value of their designs. Have children take from 10 to 30 base-10 cubes and from 4 to 6 longs. They use their blocks to create designs. Have them record their designs on grid paper and write how many cubes and how many longs they used. Once they record their designs, have them place the blocks on Place-Value Mats and make the appropriate exchanges. Then they determine the total value of their designs and record them on the grid paper.

EXTRA PRACTICE

SMALL-GROUP ACTIVITY

Minute Math+

5–15 Min

Use *Minute Math+*, pages 23 and 24, to provide practice identifying numbers based on given place-value information and patterns.

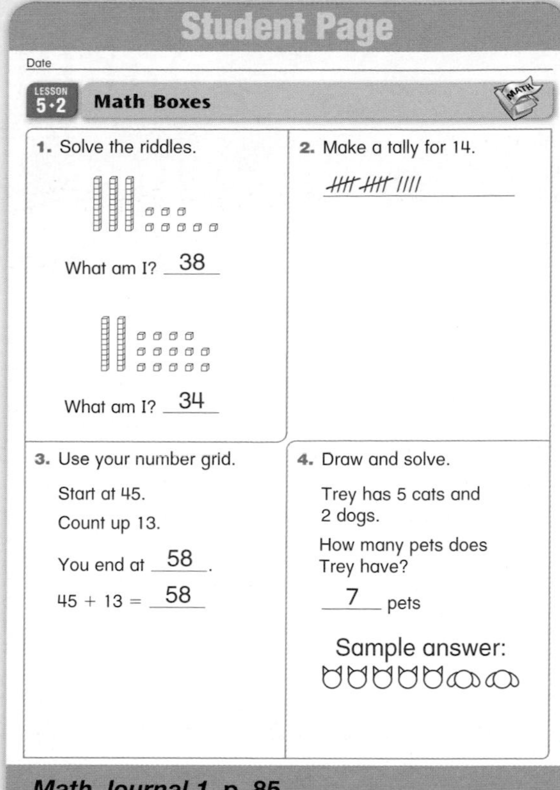

Student Page

Date

LESSON 5·2 **Math Boxes**

1. Solve the riddles.

What am I? 38

What am I? 34

2. Make a tally for 14.

3. Use your number grid.

Start at 45.

Count up 13.

You end at 58.

45 + 13 = 58

4. Draw and solve.

Trey has 5 cats and 2 dogs.

How many pets does Trey have?

7 pets

Sample answer:

Math Journal 1, p. 85

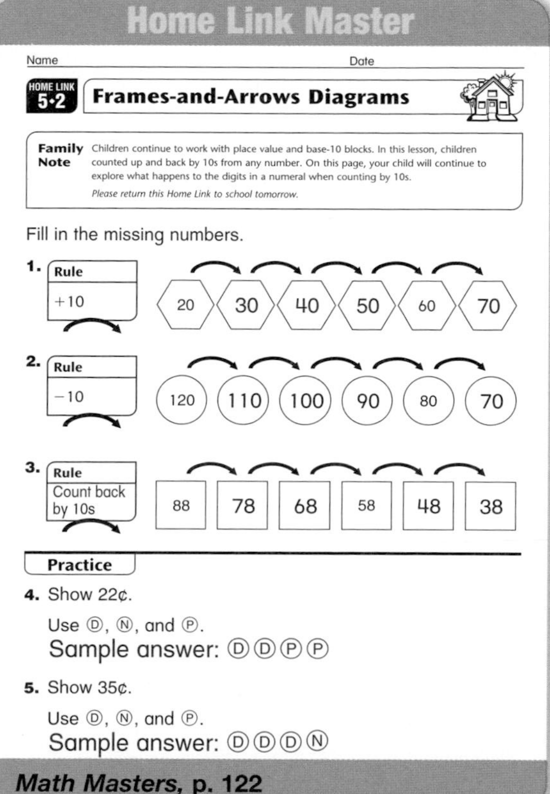

Home Link Master

Name Date

HOME LINK 5·2 **Frames-and-Arrows Diagrams**

Family Note Children continue to work with place value and base-10 blocks. In this lesson, children counted up and back by 10s from any number. On this page, your child will continue to explore what happens to the digits in a numeral when counting by 10s.

Please return this Home Link to school tomorrow.

Fill in the missing numbers.

1. Rule +10: 20, 30, 40, 50, 60, 70

2. Rule −10: 120, 110, 100, 90, 80, 70

3. Rule Count back by 10s: 88, 78, 68, 58, 48, 38

Practice

4. Show 22¢.

Use Ⓓ, Ⓝ, and Ⓟ.

Sample answer: ⒹⒹⓅⓅ

5. Show 35¢.

Use Ⓓ, Ⓝ, and Ⓟ.

Sample answer: ⒹⒹⒹⓃ

Math Masters, p. 122

5•3 Relations: Greater Than, Less Than, and Equal To

Objective To introduce the relation symbols < and >.

www.everydaymathonline.com

ePresentations

eToolkit

Algorithms Practice

EM Facts Workshop Game™

Family Letters

Assessment Management

Common Core State Standards

Curriculum Focal Points

Interactive Teacher's Lesson Guide

1 Teaching the Lesson

Key Concepts and Skills

- Compare whole numbers using <, >, and =. [Number and Numeration Goal 7]
- Calculate and compare money amounts using <, >, and =. [Patterns, Functions, and Algebra Goal 2]

Key Activities

Children discuss methods of distinguishing between the relation symbols < and >. They practice using these symbols in number models by playing a variation of *Top-It.*

Ongoing Assessment: Informing Instruction See page 371.

Key Vocabulary

is more than ◆ is less than

Materials

Math Journal 1, inside back cover (optional)
Home Link 5•2
Math Masters, pp. 320 and 321
slate ◆ tool-kit number cards

2 Ongoing Learning & Practice

Playing *Base-10 Exchange*

Math Journal 1, p. 81 or *Math Masters,* p. 318
Math Masters, p. 339
per partnership: base-10 blocks (cubes and longs), die
Children practice exchanging 10 cubes for 1 long.

Math Boxes 5•3

Math Journal 1, p. 86
Children practice and maintain skills through Math Box problems.

Ongoing Assessment: Recognizing Student Achievement
Use Math Boxes, Problem 2.
[Patterns, Functions, and Algebra Goal 1]

Home Link 5•3

Math Masters, p. 123
Children practice and maintain skills through Home Link activities.

3 Differentiation Options

READINESS

Grabbing Numbers

Math Masters, p. 311
per partnership: 40 base-10 cubes
Children compare quantities of base-10 cubes.

ENRICHMENT

Completing Number Models

Math Masters, p. 124
Children write missing relation symbols and numbers in number models.

EXTRA PRACTICE

Reading About Relations

Math Masters, p. 305
Children read *Just Enough Carrots* to practice relation symbols.

ELL SUPPORT

Building a Math Word Bank

Differentiation Handbook, p. 127
Children add the terms *equal to, greater than,* and *less than* to their Math Word Banks.

Advance Preparation

For the optional Extra Practice activity in Part 3, obtain a copy of ***Just Enough Carrots*** by Stuart J. Murphy (HarperCollins Publishers, 1997).

***Teacher's Reference Manual,* Grades 1–3** pp. 68, 69

Getting Started

Mental Math and Reflexes

Dictate the following pairs of numbers. Have children write them on their slates and circle the specified number.

●○○ *Write 0 and 15. Circle the smaller number.* 0

●●○ *Write 35 and 42. Circle the smaller number.* 35

●●● *Write 23 and 27. Circle the larger number.* 27

Continue as time allows. Have children share their strategies. Check to see if children are focusing on the tens place of each number. Remind them to think of the value of each digit.

Math Message

Henry has 2 nickels and 1-dime. Ada has 2 dimes and 1 nickel. Who has more money?

Home Link 5·2 Follow-Up

Briefly review answers.
Have volunteers describe the patterns they notice in the completed diagrams.

1 Teaching the Lesson

Math Message Follow-Up

Draw coins on the board to represent Ada's and Henry's money. Elicit from the class that Ada has *more* money than Henry because 25 cents (2 dimes and 1 nickel) *is more than* 20 cents (2 nickels and 1 dime). Write the following on the board: *25 cents is more than 20 cents.*

Explain that another way to compare Ada's and Henry's money is to say that Henry has *less* money than Ada because 20 cents *is less than* 25 cents. To support English language learners, discuss the meaning of *compare.* Write the following sentence next to the first sentence on the board: *20 cents is less than 25 cents.*

Introducing the > and < Relation Symbols

(*Math Masters,* pp. 320 and 321)

Discuss how children have been using the symbol = in number models to stand for the words *is equal to* or *equals.* Explain that they can also use symbols for the words **is more than** and **is less than.** Introduce the > symbol for *is more than* and the < symbol for *is less than.* Use the large symbols on *Math Masters,* pages 320 and 321 for display. Have children write the symbols on their slates. Then write *25¢ > 20¢* and *20¢ < 25¢* on the board under the two sentences that express the same number relations.

Ask: *Can anyone describe an easy way to tell them apart?* Mention that it takes a while to learn which symbol means *is more than* and which symbol means *is less than.* Suggest the following strategies:

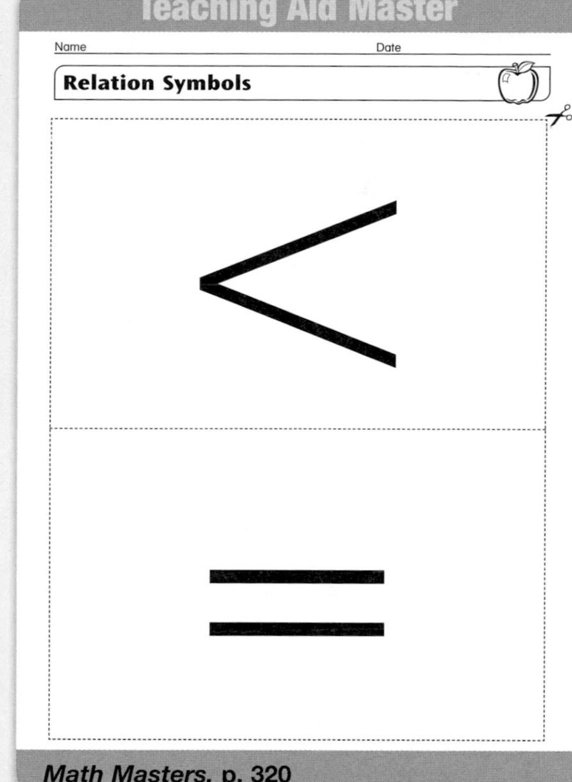

Math Masters, p. 320

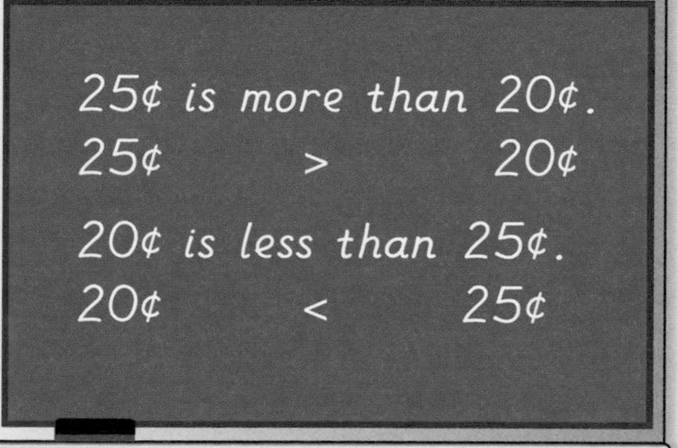

25¢ is more than 20¢.
25¢ > 20¢
20¢ is less than 25¢.
20¢ < 25¢

25 > 20

20 < 25

25 > 20

Strategy 1: Use various animal-related analogies. For example, the animal's open mouth must be larger to swallow the larger number.

Strategy 2: The < symbol for *is less than* looks like the left-hand finger and thumb.

Strategy 3: The meeting point of the two lines always points to the smaller number; the open part of the two lines always points to the larger number.

Strategy 4: Put two heavy dots next to the larger number and one heavy dot next to the smaller number. Then connect the dots to make the symbol.

Dictate pairs of numbers such as 3 and 12, 9 and 20, 24 and 18, 30 and 27, and 14 and 40. Have children write the numbers on their slates and write the symbol < or > between them.

NOTE It is okay for children to write either 3 < 12 or 12 > 3. Both are correct. Allow time for a brief class discussion about the difference between the two number sentences.

Adjusting the Activity

Encourage children to use the number grid on the inside back cover of their journals to help them determine which number is more than or less than another number.

AUDITORY ◆ KINESTHETIC ◆ TACTILE ◆ VISUAL

Links to the Future

This is the children's first exposure to relation symbols. Children should begin to understand how to use the relation symbols to compare numbers. Using and explaining the relation symbols is a Grade 2 Goal.

Teaching Aid Master

Name Date

Relation Symbols

< means "is less than."

> means "is more than."

= means "is the same as."

= means "is equal to."

Math Masters, p. 321

▶ Playing *Top-It* with Relation Symbols

PARTNER ACTIVITY

Players take out their tool-kit number cards and set aside the +, −, ×, ÷, ? cards and the two wild cards, which are not used in the game. They will need the <, >, and = cards. Players combine the number cards into a single deck, mix them, and put them in a stack facedown on the table.

Directions

1. Players sit next to each other. Each partner turns over a card from the top of the deck and places the card number-side up next to his or her partner's card with a space between them.
2. Children take turns placing the correct relation symbol ($<$, $>$, or $=$) between the cards and reading the resulting number sentence.
3. The player with the larger number takes both number cards.

When placing the two number cards on the table, players should place them in the same position each time—the first player's card on the left, the second player's card on the right.

Ongoing Assessment: Informing Instruction

Watch for children who confuse < and > symbols. Remind children that the animal's mouth opens to the larger number.

Adjusting the Activity

Have children play a variation of the game in which each child draws two cards to form a 2-digit number. The game then proceeds as described.

AUDITORY ◆ KINESTHETIC ◆ TACTILE ◆ VISUAL

Circulate to assess children's ability to determine the correct symbol and to read the number sentence. Remind children of the strategies for distinguishing between the $<$ symbol and the $>$ symbol.

2 Ongoing Learning & Practice

Playing *Base-10 Exchange*

PARTNER ACTIVITY

(*Math Journal 1,* p. 81; *Math Masters,* p. 339)

Directions:

1. Players take turns putting base-10 blocks on their Tens-and-Ones Mats (*Math Journal 1,* page 81 or *Math Masters,* page 318) according to the roll of the die. Players use *Math Masters,* page 339 to tell how many base-10 blocks correspond to each dice roll.
2. Whenever possible, they exchange 10 cubes for 1 long.
3. The first player to get 10 longs wins.

Student Page

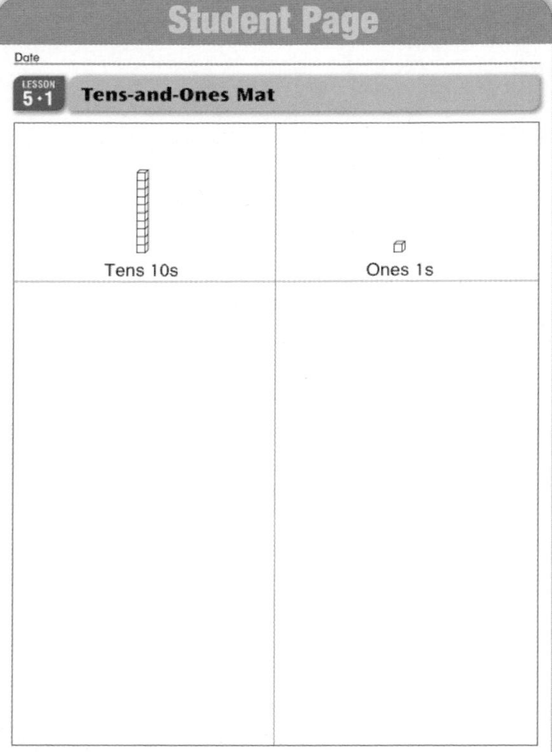
Date

LESSON 5·1 **Tens-and-Ones Mat**

Tens 10s	Ones 1s

Math Journal 1, p. 81

Game Master

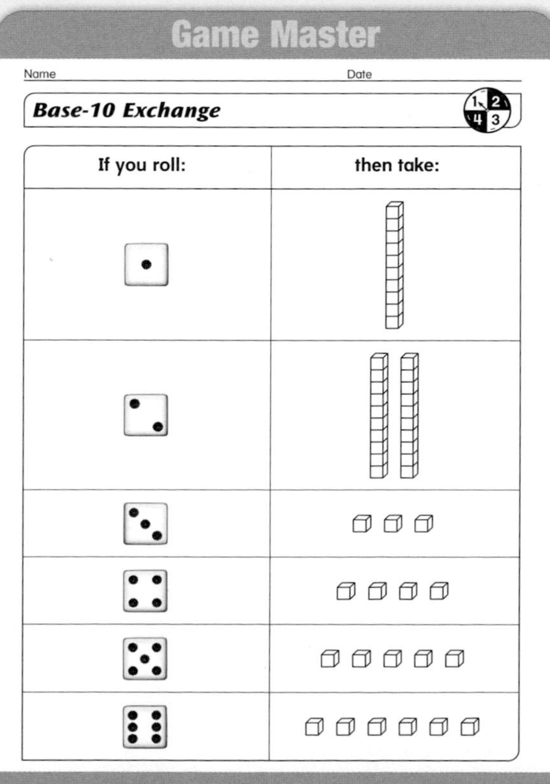
Name Date

Base-10 Exchange

If you roll:	then take:

Math Masters, p. 339

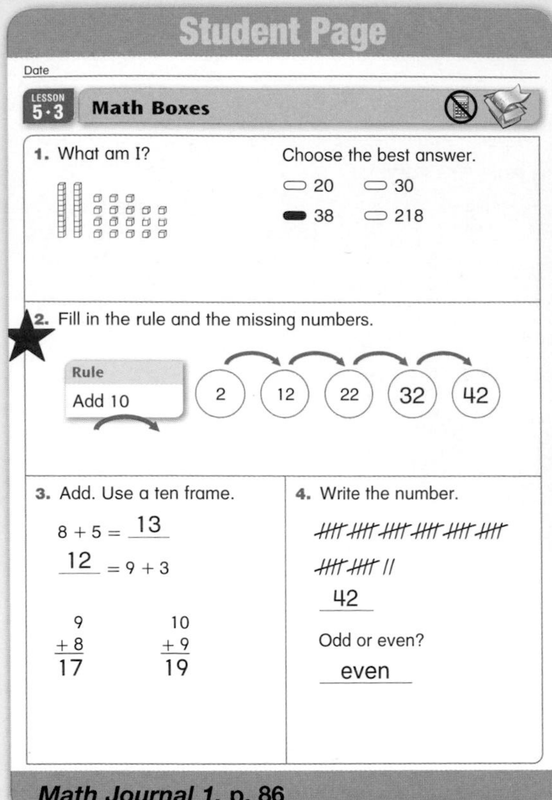

Student Page

Date

LESSON 5·3 **Math Boxes**

1. What am I?

Choose the best answer.

⬭ 20 ⬭ 30

⬬ 38 ⬭ 218

2. Fill in the rule and the missing numbers.

Rule: Add 10

2, 12, 22, 32, 42

3. Add. Use a ten frame.

8 + 5 = 13

12 = 9 + 3

9 + 8 = 17

10 + 9 = 19

4. Write the number.

42

Odd or even?

even

Math Journal 1, p. 86

NOTE Remember to reserve time every day to complete the number-line, attendance, calendar, temperature, and weather routines.

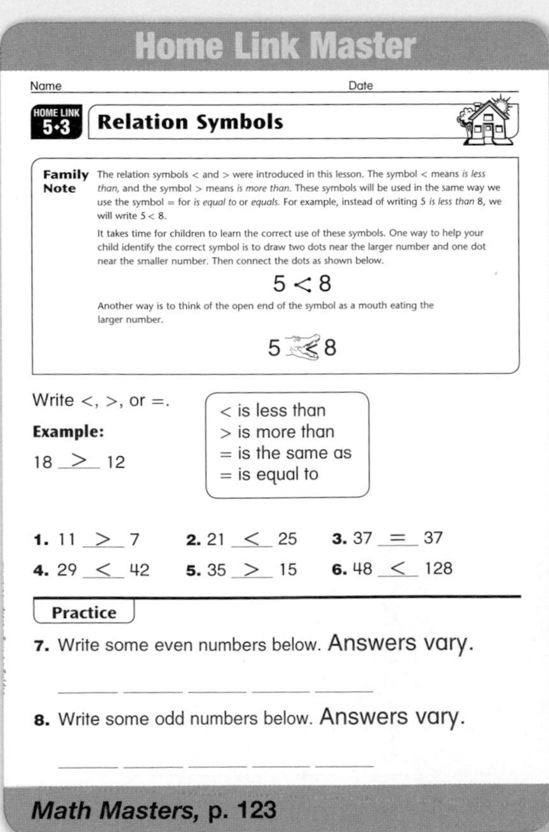

Home Link Master

Name Date

HOME LINK 5·3 **Relation Symbols**

Family Note The relation symbols < and > were introduced in this lesson. The symbol < means *is less than,* and the symbol > means *is more than.* These symbols will be used in the same way we use the symbol = for *is equal to* or *equals.* For example, instead of writing 5 *is less than* 8, we will write 5 < 8.

It takes time for children to learn the correct use of these symbols. One way to help your child identify the correct symbol is to draw two dots near the larger number and one dot near the smaller number. Then connect the dots as shown below.

5 < 8

Another way is to think of the open end of the symbol as a mouth eating the larger number.

5 < 8

Write <, >, or =.

Example:

18 > 12

< is less than
> is more than
= is the same as
= is equal to

1. 11 > 7
2. 21 < 25
3. 37 = 37
4. 29 < 42
5. 35 > 15
6. 48 < 128

Practice

7. Write some even numbers below. Answers vary.

8. Write some odd numbers below. Answers vary.

Math Masters, p. 123

▶ Math Boxes 5·3

INDEPENDENT ACTIVITY

(*Math Journal 1,* p. 86)

Mixed Practice Math Boxes in this lesson are paired with Math Boxes in Lesson 5-1. The skills in Problem 4 preview Unit 6 content.

Ongoing Assessment: Recognizing Student Achievement

Math Boxes Problem 2 ★

Use **Math Boxes, Problem 2** to assess children's ability to solve Frames-and-Arrows problems. Children are making adequate progress if they are able to tell what number comes next. Some children may be able to state the rule.

[Patterns, Functions and Algebra Goal 1]

▶ Home Link 5·3

INDEPENDENT ACTIVITY

(*Math Masters,* p. 123)

Home Connection Children enter the correct relation symbols between pairs of numbers. Strategies for helping children remember the symbols are provided for families.

3 Differentiation Options

READINESS

PARTNER ACTIVITY

▶ Grabbing Numbers

5–15 Min

(*Math Masters,* p. 311)

To provide experience comparing quantities using a concrete model, have children count two sets of base-10 cubes and determine which set is larger. Each partnership begins with 40 cubes. Each partner grabs a handful and arranges his or her cubes on the number grid so that one cube fills each square beginning with the number one. The last square each partner fills should represent the number of base-10 cubes he or she grabbed. On a half-sheet of paper, children record the number of cubes that each partner grabbed and circle the larger number. If partners grabbed the same number of cubes, they circle both numbers. If time permits, children repeat the activity.

ENRICHMENT

INDEPENDENT ACTIVITY

Completing Number Models

5–15 Min

(*Math Masters,* p. 124)

To further explore the <, >, and = symbols, have children fill in the missing numbers and relation symbols on *Math Masters,* page 124. Allow time for children to read their number models aloud to classmates.

EXTRA PRACTICE

SMALL-GROUP ACTIVITY

Reading About Relations

5–15 Min

(*Math Masters,* p. 305)

Literature Link To provide practice with relation symbols, read ***Just Enough Carrots*** by Stuart J. Murphy (HarperCollins Publishers, 1997). On an Exit Slip (*Math Masters,* page 305), have children use >, <, or = to write a number model for one of the scenarios in the story.

ELL SUPPORT

SMALL-GROUP ACTIVITY

Building a Math Word Bank

5–15 Min

(*Differentiation Handbook,* p. 127)

To provide language support for relation symbols, have children use the Word Bank Template found on *Differentiation Handbook,* page 127. Ask children to write the terms *greater than, less than,* and *equal to,* draw pictures representing the terms, and write other words that describe them. See the *Differentiation Handbook* for more information.

Planning Ahead

Starting in Lesson 5-5, each child will need his or her own set of animal cards. These cards are found on Activity Sheets 7 and 8 at the back of the journal.

Teaching Master

Name ______ Date ______

LESSON 5·3 **Completing Number Models**

Write numbers that make these number sentences true.
Answers vary.

1. 164 > ______
2. ______ < 105
3. 76 = ______
4. 132 < ______
5. ______ < 97
6. 116 > ______
7. ______ > 127
8. ______ = 85
9. 146 > ______
10. 100 > ______

Make your own.

11. ______ < ______
12. ______ > ______
13. ______ = ______

Try This

Write <, >, or =.

14. 20 + 15 __<__ 30 + 25
15. 67 __=__ 53 + 14
16. 40 + 12 __>__ 30 + 11
17. 90 __>__ 30 + 15
18. 37 __=__ 17 + 20
19. 77 __<__ 40 + 45

Math Masters, p. 124

5•4 Exploring Area, Weight, and Counting

Explorations

Objectives To develop the concept of area by counting units; to provide experiences weighing objects with a pan balance; and to provide practice with rational counting.

Technology Resources www.everydaymathonline.com

ePresentations

eToolkit

Algorithms Practice

EM Facts Workshop Game™

Family Letters

Assessment Management

Common Core State Standards

Curriculum Focal Points

Interactive Teacher's Lesson Guide

1 Teaching the Lesson

Key Concepts and Skills

- Count objects by 1s. [Number and Numeration Goal 2]
- Estimate and count objects. [Number and Numeration Goal 2]
- Compare weights of pairs of objects. [Measurement and Reference Frames Goal 1]
- Exchange pennies for nickels and dimes. [Measurement and Reference Frames Goal 2]

Key Activities

Exploration A: Following a demonstration of finding area by covering a surface with a unit, children estimate the area of a surface, cover it, and count units to check their estimates.

Exploration B: Children use a pan balance to find sets of objects that weigh about the same.

Exploration C: Children devise and carry out a plan for counting a large number of pennies.

Ongoing Assessment: Informing Instruction See page 377.

Key Vocabulary

area ◆ pan balance

Materials

Math Journal 1, pp. 81 and 84 (optional)
Home Link 5•3
Math Masters, p. 318
base-10 blocks (cubes and longs) ◆ slate

Exploration A: Per group:
Math Masters, p. 125
objects to use as units, such as blocks, index cards, or tiles

Exploration B: Per partnership:
Math Masters, pp. 126 and 127
pan balance ◆ sets of objects, including pennies, pencils, base-10 cubes, pattern blocks and dice

Exploration C: Per group:
Math Masters, pp. 128 and 129
tool-kit coins and about 50 extra pennies ◆ slate

2 Ongoing Learning & Practice

Playing the *Digit Game*
per partnership: 4 each of number cards 0–9 (from the Everything Math Deck, if available)

Math Boxes 5•4
Math Journal 1, p. 87

Ongoing Assessment: Recognizing Student Achievement
Use Math Boxes, Problem 2.
[Number and Numeration Goal 6]

Home Link 5•4
Math Masters, p. 130

3 Differentiation Options

ENRICHMENT
Comparing Weights
Math Masters, p. 131
per partnership: sets of objects including 10 pennies, base-10 cubes, dice, and square pattern blocks; pan balance

EXTRA PRACTICE
Minute Math+
Minute Math®+, pp. 29 and 31

Advance Preparation

Choose a surface and a unit for the Math Message. For Exploration C, provide groups with about 50 additional pennies.

***Teacher's Reference Manual,* Grades 1–3** pp. 158, 159, 161, 167, 168

Getting Started

Mental Math and Reflexes

Display 4 longs and 9 cubes on your Tens-and-Ones Mat.

Ask: *What number do these base-10 blocks show?* 49

Remind children that 4 longs and 9 cubes stand for 4 tens and 9 ones. The 4 is in the tens place and the 9 is in the ones place. Continue with other numbers as time allows.

Before recording the number on their slates, children model the numbers with base-10 blocks on their Tens-and-Ones Mats on journal page 81.

You may wish to try this routine with the following:

▷ base-10 block combinations that require exchanges; for example, 3 longs and 17 cubes.

▷ numbers in the hundreds using your Place-Value Mat.

Math Message

Post one of the units and indicate the surface to be covered; for example, a number card and a table. *About how many (units) would you need to cover (surface)?*

Home Link 5·3 Follow-Up

Briefly review answers.

1 Teaching the Lesson

▶ Math Message Follow-Up

WHOLE-CLASS DISCUSSION

Share answers and strategies. Explain that children can measure and compare the surfaces of objects by finding how many of a unit will cover the surface. Tell children that the unit is usually in the shape of a rectangle or a square.

▶ Covering a Surface

WHOLE-CLASS ACTIVITY

Demonstrate how the rectangular units need to lie next to each other on a surface without overlaps or gaps between them. (*See margin.*) Explain that there might be open spaces along the edges that can't be filled with whole units. Children can estimate the final count of units by adding half-units for larger spaces and ignoring smaller spaces.

Have children act out and solve the Math Message. All children (or groups) should use the same unit. Make sure children understand that the surface must be completely covered, with no overlaps and no gaps.

▶ Exploration A: Estimating and Finding the Area of a Surface

SMALL-GROUP ACTIVITY

(*Math Masters,* p. 125)

Children work in groups to cover a surface, recording their work on *Math Masters,* page 125. Before they begin, children estimate the number of units needed. Discuss how they will make their estimates. Observe as children cover the surface and count units. Tell them that the result is called the **area** of the surface.

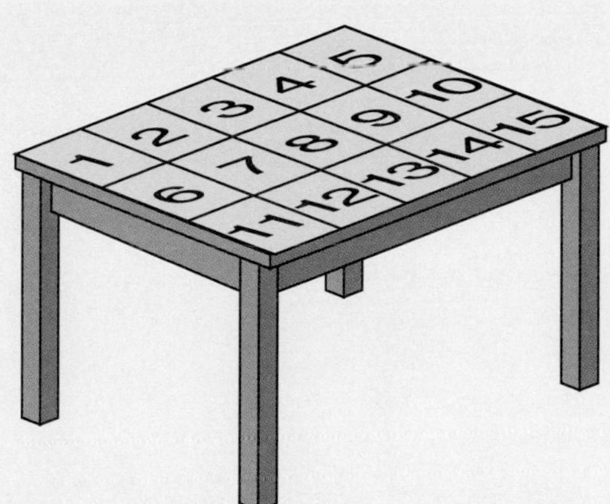

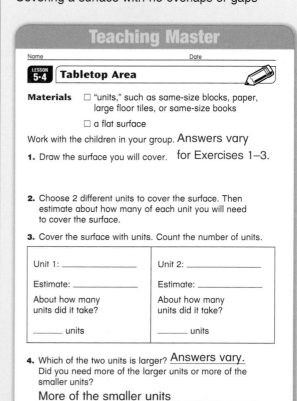

Covering a surface with no overlaps or gaps

Teaching Master

Name Date

LESSON 5·4 **Tabletop Area**

Materials ☐ "units," such as same-size blocks, paper, large floor tiles, or same-size books

☐ a flat surface

Work with the children in your group. Answers vary

1. Draw the surface you will cover. for Exercises 1–3.

2. Choose 2 different units to cover the surface. Then estimate about how many of each unit you will need to cover the surface.

3. Cover the surface with units. Count the number of units.

Unit 1: ______	Unit 2: ______
Estimate: ______	Estimate: ______
About how many units did it take? ______ units	About how many units did it take? ______ units

4. Which of the two units is larger? Answers vary.
Did you need more of the larger units or more of the smaller units?
More of the smaller units

Math Masters, p. 125

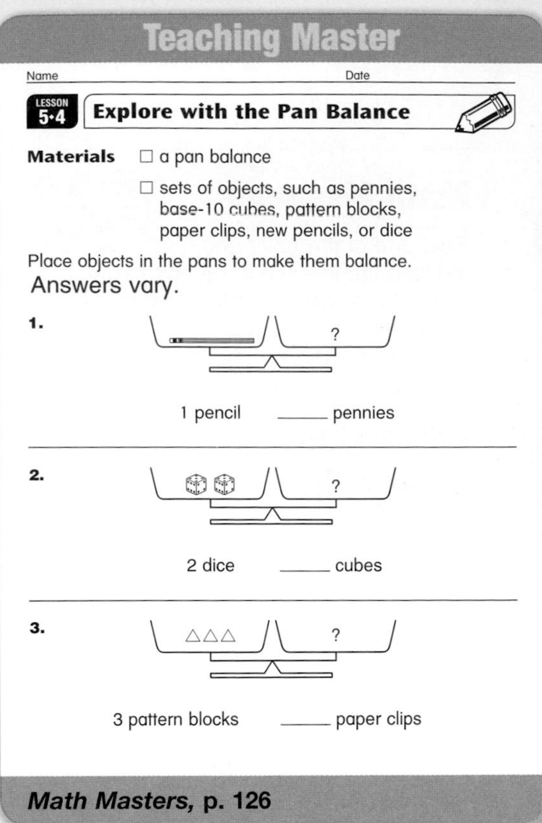
Teaching Master

Name Date

LESSON 5•4 **Explore with the Pan Balance**

Materials ☐ a pan balance

☐ sets of objects, such as pennies, base-10 cubes, pattern blocks, paper clips, new pencils, or dice

Place objects in the pans to make them balance.

Answers vary.

1. 1 pencil ____ pennies

2. 2 dice ____ cubes

3. 3 pattern blocks ____ paper clips

Math Masters, p. 126

Teaching Master

Name Date

LESSON 5•4 **Explore with the Pan Balance** *continued*

Choose your own objects.

4. ____ ____

5. ____ ____

6. ____ ____

7. ____ ____

8. ____ ____

Math Masters, p. 127

Suggestions:

▷ Use index cards, playing cards, or number cards to cover a desktop.

▷ Use pattern-block squares to cover a journal cover.

▷ Use dominoes to cover a slate.

When all of the groups have completed this Exploration, bring the class together to discuss estimates and share results.

NOTE Keep extra copies of *Math Masters,* page 125, on hand for children to repeat the activity.

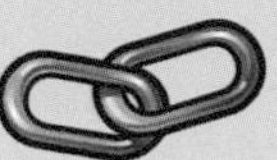

Links to the Future

This activity marks the beginning of children's work with area. Children will begin to estimate and count the number of units that cover a surface, but they should not be expected to understand the concept of area at this time. Counting unit squares to find the area of rectangular shapes is a Grade 2 Goal.

▶ Exploration B: Finding Sets of Objects that Weigh the Same

PARTNER ACTIVITY

(*Math Masters,* pp. 126 and 127)

Children use a **pan balance** to find out how many of one kind of object weigh about the same as a number of another kind of object. For example: *How many pennies weigh about the same as a pencil?* Children record their results on *Math Masters,* pages 126 and 127.

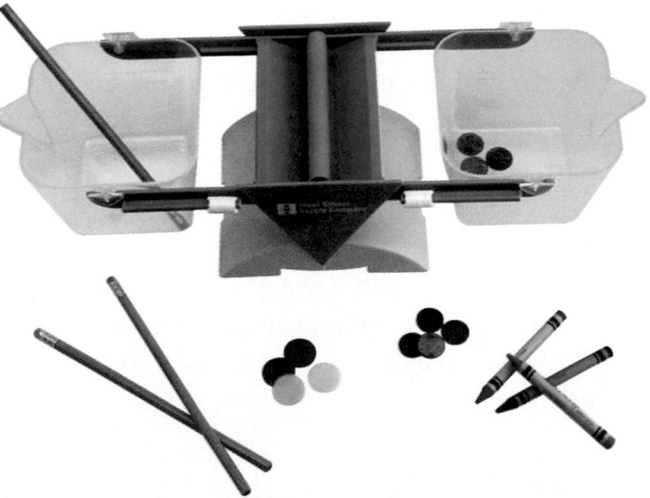

NOTE Before children begin to use the pan balance, check that the two pans balance when empty. Adjust them if necessary. (A bit of modeling clay on the lighter side usually works well.)

Exploration C: Counting Large Numbers of Pennies

SMALL-GROUP ACTIVITY

(*Math Masters,* pp. 128 and 129)

Children combine their tool-kit pennies with the extra pennies you have provided. They discuss the best way to share the work of counting the pennies and how to check the total for accuracy.

Children record the total number of pennies on a *Math Masters,* page 129, and explain, using words or pictures, how their group counted the pennies. Then they return the tool-kit pennies to their owners.

Adjusting the Activity

Have children exchange pennies for dimes and nickels and show the same amount with the fewest possible coins. They can record their work on a half-sheet of paper. *Example:*

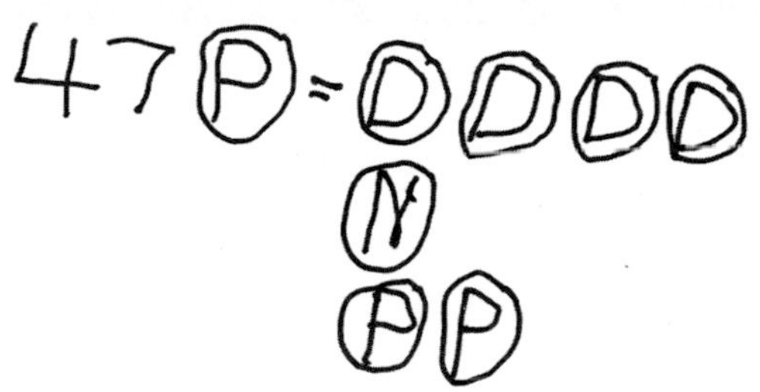

AUDITORY ♦ KINESTHETIC ♦ TACTILE ♦ VISUAL

Ongoing Assessment: Informing Instruction

Watch for groups of children who have trouble making a plan. You may want to elect one child to be the group leader.

Teaching Master

Name Date

LESSON 5•4 **Pile of Money**

Materials □ all of your pennies and about 50 extra pennies

□ slate

1. Count your pennies. Write the number on your slate.
2. Work with the children in your group. Put all of your pennies in a pile.
3. Make a plan to count all of the pennies.
   - How will you keep track of the pennies as you count?
   - Make sure everybody gets to count some pennies. How will you do that?
   - How will you check that your count is correct?
4. Record the final total on a quarter-sheet of paper.
5. Take back your pennies, and put them in your tool kit.

Math Masters, p. 128

NOTE Before children count the pennies in Exploration C, you may wish to have them estimate the number of pennies.

2 Ongoing Learning & Practice

Playing the *Digit Game*

PARTNER ACTIVITY

Children practice using place-value concepts and comparing numbers by playing the *Digit Game.* For detailed instructions, see Lesson 5-1.

Math Boxes 5•4

INDEPENDENT ACTIVITY

(*Math Journal 1,* p. 87)

Mixed Practice Math Boxes in this lesson are paired with Math Boxes in Lesson 5-2. The skills in Problem 4 preview Unit 6 content.

Student Page

Date

LESSON 5•4 **Math Boxes**

1. Use | and • to show the number 42.

   |||| ••

2. How many tallies?

   卌 卌 卌 卌 |||

   Choose the best answer.

   ○ 19
   ● 23
   ○ 25
   ○ 43

3. Use your number grid.

   Start at 48.

   Count up 15.

   You end at 63.

   48 + 15 = 63

4. Draw and solve.

   Rosa had 9 grapes.

   She ate 3 grapes.

   How many grapes does Rosa have left?

   6 grapes

   Sample answer: ⊠⊠⊠○○○○○○

Math Journal 1, p. 87

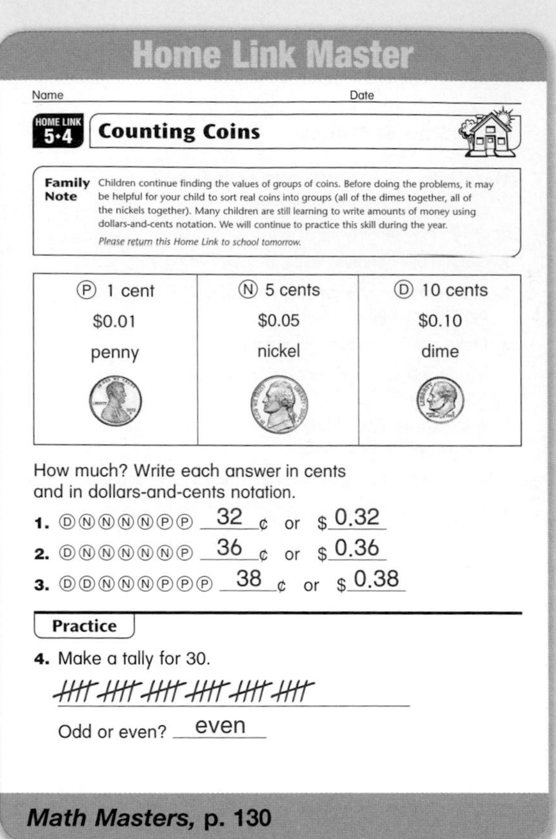

Home Link Master

Name Date

HOME LINK 5·4 **Counting Coins**

Family Note Children continue finding the values of groups of coins. Before doing the problems, it may be helpful for your child to sort real coins into groups (all of the dimes together, all of the nickels together). Many children are still learning to write amounts of money using dollars-and-cents notation. We will continue to practice this skill during the year.

Please return this Home Link to school tomorrow.

(P) 1 cent	(N) 5 cents	(D) 10 cents
$0.01	$0.05	$0.10
penny	nickel	dime

How much? Write each answer in cents and in dollars-and-cents notation.

1. (D)(N)(N)(N)(N)(P)(P) 32 ¢ or $ 0.32
2. (D)(N)(N)(N)(N)(N)(P) 36 ¢ or $ 0.36
3. (D)(D)(N)(N)(N)(P)(P)(P) 38 ¢ or $ 0.38

Practice

4. Make a tally for 30.

    HHH HHH HHH HHH HHH HHH

    Odd or even? even

Math Masters, p. 130

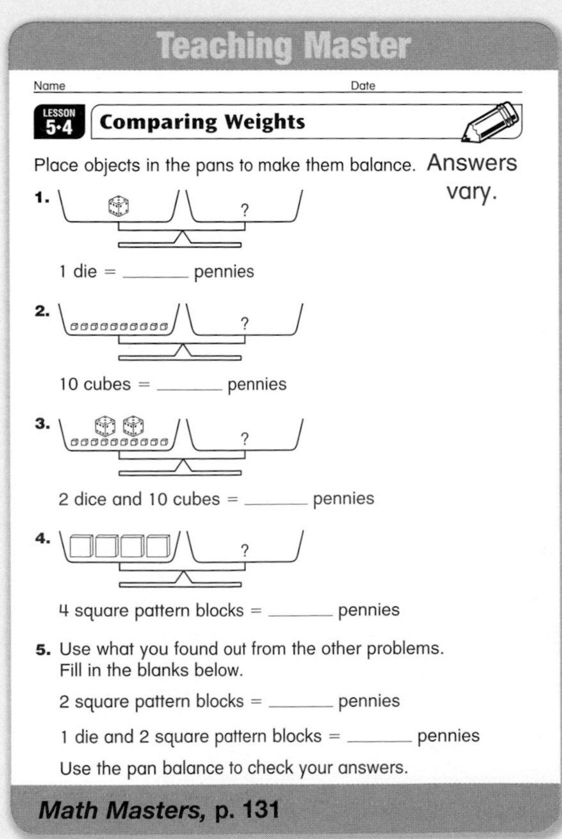

Teaching Master

Name Date

LESSON 5·4 **Comparing Weights**

Place objects in the pans to make them balance. Answers vary.

1. 1 die = ______ pennies
2. 10 cubes = ______ pennies
3. 2 dice and 10 cubes = ______ pennies
4. 4 square pattern blocks = ______ pennies
5. Use what you found out from the other problems. Fill in the blanks below.

    2 square pattern blocks = ______ pennies

    1 die and 2 square pattern blocks = ______ pennies

    Use the pan balance to check your answers.

Math Masters, p. 131

Ongoing Assessment: Recognizing Student Achievement

Math Boxes Problem 2 

Use **Math Boxes, Problem 2** to assess children's ability to find equivalent names for numbers. Children are making adequate progress if they are able to tell that there are 23 tally marks shown.

[Number and Numeration Goal 6]

▶ Home Link 5·4

INDEPENDENT ACTIVITY

(*Math Masters,* p. 130)

Home Connection Children calculate the values of combinations of pennies, nickels, and dimes.

3 Differentiation Options

ENRICHMENT

PARTNER ACTIVITY

▶ Comparing Weights

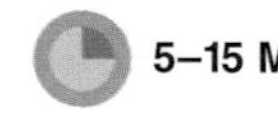

5–15 Min

(*Math Masters,* p. 131)

To further explore the concept of comparing weights, have children work with a partner to complete *Math Masters,* page 131 using the objects you provide. When children have completed the page, discuss the strategies they used to solve Problems 3 and 5.

EXTRA PRACTICE

SMALL-GROUP ACTIVITY

▶ *Minute Math+*

5–15 Min

Use *Minute Math+,* pages 29 and 31, to practice skip counting.

5•5 Animal Weights

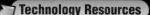

Objective To introduce addition of 2-digit numbers.

 www.everydaymathonline.com

ePresentations

eToolkit

Algorithms Practice

EM Facts Workshop Game™

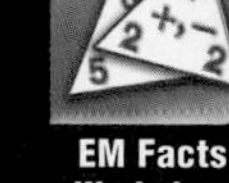
Family Letters

Assessment Management

Common Core State Standards

Curriculum Focal Points

Interactive Teacher's Lesson Guide

1 Teaching the Lesson

Key Concepts and Skills

- Use base-10 blocks to model 2- and 3-digit whole numbers.
  [Number and Numeration Goal 3]
- Exchange base-10 longs and cubes to show different representations of the same number.
  [Number and Numeration Goal 3]
- Use base-10 blocks to find sums of 2- and 3-digit numbers.
  [Operations and Computation Goal 2]
- Model parts-and-total diagrams for addition number stories.
  [Operations and Computation Goal 4]

Key Activities

Children use base-10 blocks to find the total weight of pairs of animals.

 **Ongoing Assessment: Informing Instruction** See page 381.

Materials

Math Journal 1, Activity Sheets 7 and 8
Home Link 5•4
Math Masters, pp. 132–137
Tens-and-Ones Mat (*Math Journal 1,* p. 81)
◆ slate ◆ base-10 blocks (longs and cubes)
◆ domino for overhead projector (optional)

2 Ongoing Learning & Practice

Playing *Shaker Addition Top-It*
Math Masters, p. 353
per group: 2 six-sided dice or 2 polyhedral dice marked 0–9, 20 pennies or counters
Children practice addition facts.

Math Boxes 5•5
Math Journal 1, p. 88
Children practice and maintain skills through Math Box problems.

Ongoing Assessment: Recognizing Student Achievement
Use Math Boxes, Problem 3.
[Measurement and Reference Frames Goal 1]

Home Link 5•5
Math Masters, p. 138
Children practice and maintain skills through Home Link activities.

3 Differentiation Options

READINESS

Solving Parts-and-Total Problems
Math Masters, p. 139
paper plate ◆ base-10 blocks (cubes and longs)
Children solve parts-and-total problems using base-10 blocks.

ENRICHMENT

Playing *Animal Weight Top-It*
Animal Cards (*Math Journal 1,* Activity Sheets 7 and 8)
Children explore comparing quantities, addition of 2-digit numbers, and finding differences.

Advance Preparation

For Part 1, *Math Masters,* pages 132–137 provide a set of Animal Cards for problem solving. There are 2 animals per master for a total of 12 animals. Activity Sheets 7 and 8 provide each child with a set of Animal Cards that match those on the masters. For the optional Readiness activity in Part 3, divide paper plates into parts-and-total diagrams as shown on page 383.

Getting Started

Mental Math and Reflexes

Show dominos, such as the following, on the overhead projector or draw them on the board.

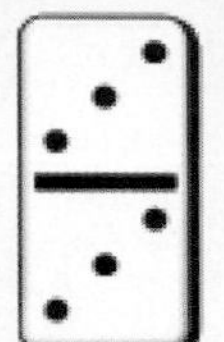

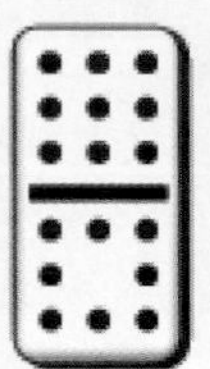

On their slates, have children write a number fact for the numbers on each of the dominoes.

Math Message

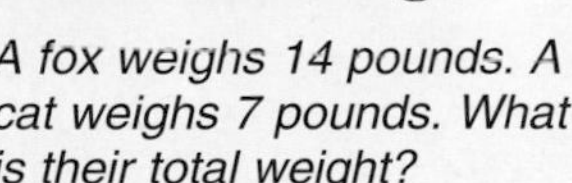

A fox weighs 14 pounds. A cat weighs 7 pounds. What is their total weight?

Home Link 5·4 Follow-Up

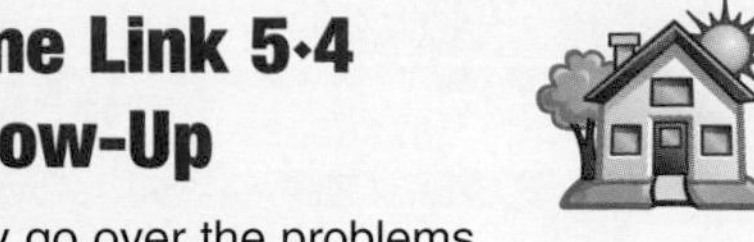
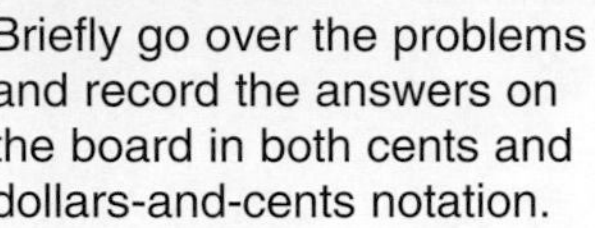

Briefly go over the problems and record the answers on the board in both cents and dollars-and-cents notation.

1 Teaching the Lesson

▶ Math Message Follow-Up

WHOLE-CLASS DISCUSSION

ELL

Algebraic Thinking Children share their solution strategies, which may include modeling with counters or with base-10 blocks or counting up on the number line or number grid. Show children ways to record their various strategies. To summarize, draw a parts-and-total diagram and write a number model on the board. Call attention to the abbreviation *lb* for *pound.* Tell children to look for the word *pound* in their math lesson today. To support English language learners, give them an object to hold that weighs about one pound. Circulate the object in the class so that others have an opportunity to hold it.

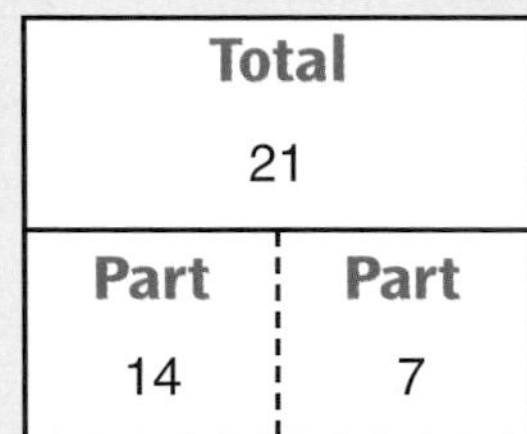

Total	
21	
Part	Part
14	7

14 lb + 7 lb = 21 lb

▶ Using Base-10 Blocks to Find Total Weight

WHOLE-CLASS ACTIVITY

PROBLEM SOLVING

(*Math Journal 1,* Activity Sheets 7 and 8)

Have children look through the set of Animal Cards from Activity Sheets 7 and 8. Point out that the same animal is shown on both sides of a card. A weight for the animal is given on one side and a height or length is given on the other side.

Student Page

Name Date

Animal Cards

First-grade girl 41 lb	7-year-old boy 50 lb
Cheetah 120 lb	Porpoise 98 lb
Penguin 75 lb	Beaver 56 lb

Math Journal 1, Activity Sheet 7 (front)

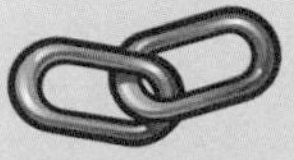

Links to the Future

This is the first lesson in which children use base-10 blocks for solving problems and number stories involving the addition of 1- and 2-digit whole numbers. Using base-10 blocks for solving number stories involving the addition and subtraction of two 2-digit numbers is a Grade 2 Goal.

Explain that the weights and heights shown on the cards are measures one might expect such an animal to have. However, weights and heights vary from animal to animal, just as different children weigh different amounts and are different heights.

Write a unit box for pounds on the board. Display your pictures of the raccoon and the fox from *Math Masters,* pages 134 and 135. Ask children to take out their base-10 blocks.

Demonstrate on the overhead projector or on the board how to use base-10 blocks to find the total weight of the raccoon (23 lb) and the fox (14 lb). On the Tens-and-Ones Mat (*Math Journal 1,* page 81), place 2 longs and 3 cubes to represent the weight of the raccoon and 1 long and 4 cubes to represent the weight of the fox. Together, there are 3 longs and 7 cubes, which represent the number 37 (pounds), the total weight of the two animals.

Display your pictures of the cat (7 lb) and the koala (19 lb) from *Math Masters,* pages 132 and 133. On their Tens-and-Ones Mats, children use their base-10 blocks to find the total weight of these animals. Ask them to describe what they did to find the answer. As a first step, they probably got a total of 1 long and 16 cubes (1 long and 9 cubes for the koala and 7 cubes for the cat). Review how to exchange the 16 cubes for 1 long and 6 cubes, for a total of 2 longs and 6 cubes, or 26. As you do so, remind children that when you have 10 cubes, you can compose a new long.

Repeat this routine for the following pairs of animals. Each time, children use their base-10 blocks to represent the weight of the animals.

▷ The boy and the girl 5 longs + 4 longs, 1 cube = 9 longs, 1 cube; or 91

▷ The raccoon and the eagle 2 longs, 3 cubes + 1 long, 5 cubes = 3 longs, 8 cubes; or 38

▷ The cat and the eagle 7 cubes + 1 long, 5 cubes = 1 long, 12 cubes = 2 longs, 2 cubes; or 22

▷ The koala and the fox 1 long, 9 cubes + 1 long, 4 cubes = 2 longs, 13 cubes = 3 longs, 3 cubes; or 33

Allow a few children to come to the board and demonstrate adding 2-digit animal weights. Encourage children to use vocabulary such as *cubes, longs,* and *pounds.* As you discuss the problems, relate children's work with cubes and longs to the place-value terms *tens* and *ones.* Emphasize that the children are adding tens to tens and ones to ones. When they have 10 cubes, or ones, they can compose a new long, or ten.

Ongoing Assessment: Informing Instruction

Watch for children who do not remember how to exchange 10 cubes for 1 long. Prompt the exchange by showing them that a line of 10 cubes is the same length as 1 long.

Student Page

Name Date

Animal Cards

Cat 7 lb	Fox 14 lb
Koala 19 lb	Raccoon 23 lb
Rabbit 6 lb	Eagle 15 lb

Math Journal 1, Activity Sheet 8 (front)

NOTE To order the weights of the animals, have children place the animal cards in weight order from lightest to heaviest.

NOTE The *Math Masters* pages picture the following:

Cheetah: 120 lb	Fox: 14 lb
Koala: 19 lb	Rabbit: 6 lb
Beaver: 56 lb	First-grade girl: 41 lb
Raccoon: 23 lb	7-year-old boy: 50 lb
Penguin: 75 lb	Eagle: 15 lb
Cat: 7 lb	Porpoise: 98 lb

Science Link Invite volunteers to tell any facts they know about the animals shown on the masters. Encourage children to name the type of covering each animal has (fur, feathers, or skin), as well as its method of movement (flying, walking/running, hopping, or swimming).

Adjusting the Activity

Have children find the total weight of the penguin and the girl. 7 longs, 5 cubes + 4 longs, 1 cube = 11 longs, 6 cubes = 1 flat, 1 long, 6 cubes = 116
You might also ask children to find the total weight of three animals.

AUDITORY ◆ KINESTHETIC ◆ TACTILE ◆ VISUAL

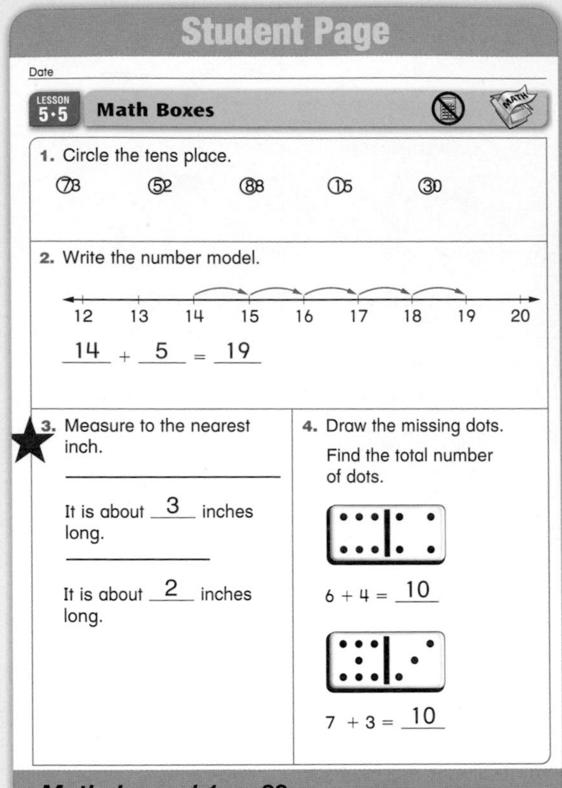
Student Page

Date

LESSON 5·5 **Math Boxes**

1. Circle the tens place.

73 52 88 15 30

2. Write the number model.

12 13 14 15 16 17 18 19 20

14 + 5 = 19

3. Measure to the nearest inch.

It is about 3 inches long.

It is about 2 inches long.

4. Draw the missing dots.

Find the total number of dots.

6 + 4 = 10

7 + 3 = 10

Math Journal 1, p. 88

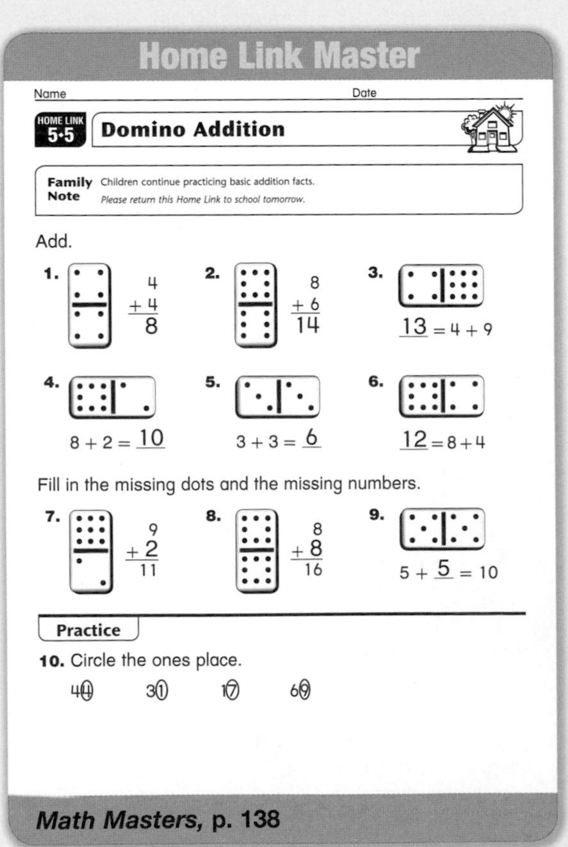
Home Link Master

Name Date

HOME LINK 5·5 **Domino Addition**

Family Note Children continue practicing basic addition facts.
Please return this Home Link to school tomorrow.

Add.

1. 4 + 4 = 8
2. 8 + 6 = 14
3. 13 = 4 + 9
4. 8 + 2 = 10
5. 3 + 3 = 6
6. 12 = 8 + 4

Fill in the missing dots and the missing numbers.

7. 9 + 2 = 11
8. 8 + 8 = 16
9. 5 + 5 = 10

Practice

10. Circle the ones place.

40 31 17 69

Math Masters, p. 138

2 Ongoing Learning & Practice

▶ Playing *Shaker Addition Top-It*

SMALL-GROUP ACTIVITY

FACTS PRACTICE

(*Math Masters,* p. 353)

Children practice addition facts by playing *Shaker Addition Top-It*. For detailed instructions, see Lesson 4-12.

NOTE To extend *Shaker Addition Top-It,* have children roll 3 dice instead of 2. Remind them that the order in which they add the numbers does not change the sum. Children need to understand the concept of the Associative Property of Addition, but do not need to memorize the term.

▶ Math Boxes 5·5

INDEPENDENT ACTIVITY

(*Math Journal 1,* p. 88)

Mixed Practice Math Boxes in this lesson are paired with Math Boxes in Lesson 5-7. The skills in Problem 4 preview Unit 6 content.

Ongoing Assessment: Recognizing Student Achievement

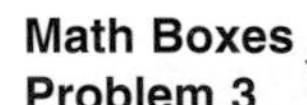
Math Boxes Problem 3

Ask children to draw a picture of one object in their classroom that is shorter than both of the line segments on **Math Boxes, Problem 3.** Use children's drawings to assess their ability to compare lengths. Children are making adequate progress if the object they choose to draw is shorter than 2 inches.

[Measurement and Reference Frames Goal 1]

Writing/Reasoning Have children draw, write, or verbalize an answer to the following question: *How do you know how many tens are in a number?* A reasonable answer should reference the digit in the tens place.

▶ Home Link 5·5

INDEPENDENT ACTIVITY

FACTS PRACTICE

(*Math Masters,* p. 138)

Home Connection Children find missing addends and sums for dominoes.

3 Differentiation Options

READINESS

▶ Solving Parts-and-Total Problems

(*Math Masters,* p. 139)

To explore solving parts-and-total problems using a concrete model, have children model number stories on a plate divided into three sections. For each number story on *Math Masters,* page 139, children put base-10 blocks in each of the Part sections of the plate, and then move the Parts into the Total section to solve the problems. Model the example for children. Allow children to work independently to complete the remaining problems.

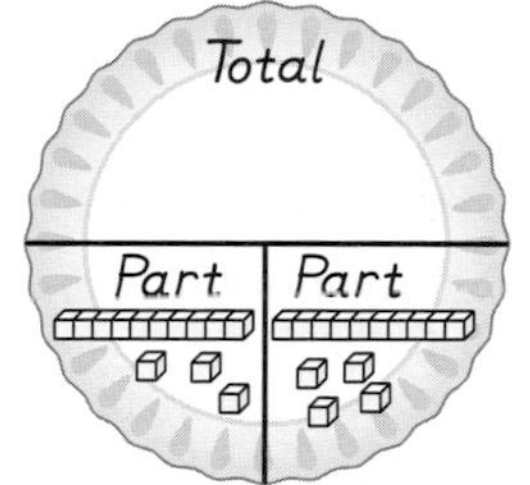

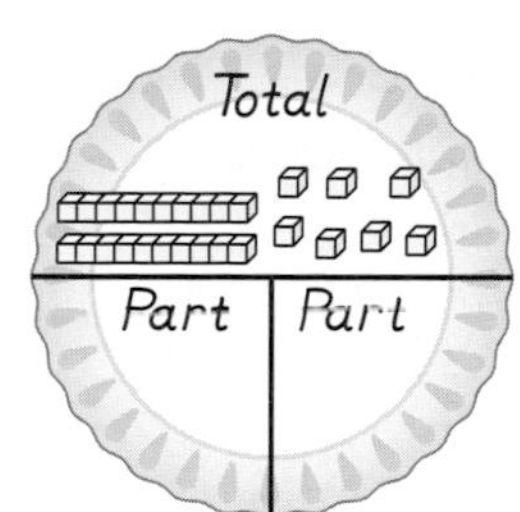

Parts-and-total diagram plates

ENRICHMENT

▶ Playing *Animal Weight Top-It*

(*Math Journal 1,* Activity Sheets 7 and 8)

To further explore comparing quantities, adding of 2-digit numbers, and finding differences, have children play a variation of *Top-It.*

Directions

To begin, players combine their decks of Animal Cards, mix them, and place them in a stack on a table, weight-side down.

1. Player A turns over the two top cards from the stack. Player B turns over the next card from the top of the stack.
2. Player A finds the total weight of the animals on his or her two cards and decides whether these two animals together weigh more or less than Player B's animal.
3. If they weigh more, Player A scores the difference between his or her total and Player B's card. If they weigh less, Player B scores the difference between his or her card and Player A's total. In case of a tie, neither player scores.
4. Players then trade roles.

The game is over when all cards from the stack have been played.

NOTE Children can use base-10 blocks and/or their number grids on the inside back covers of their journals to find the answers.

Teaching Master

Name Date

LESSON 5·5 **Solving Parts-and-Total Problems**

Solve. Record the total on the parts-and-total plate.

Example:

May had 13 marbles.
Jack had 14 marbles.
How many marbles did they have altogether?
27 marbles

1. There were 16 birds in the tree.
There were 11 birds in the pond.
How many birds were there altogether?
27 birds

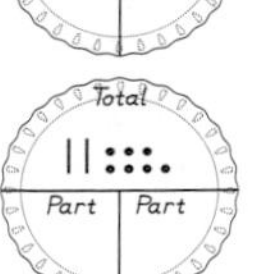

2. There are 24 red flowers.
There are 15 blue flowers.
How many flowers are there altogether?
39 flowers

3. Fred had 21 baseball cards.
Jen had 31 baseball cards.
How many cards did they have altogether?
52 cards

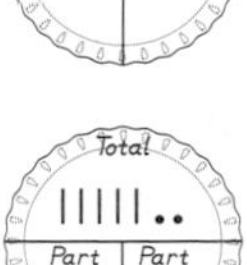

Math Masters, p. 139

5•6 More Than and Less Than Number Stories

Objectives To provide practice with *more than* and *less than* number stories; and to provide experiences with writing number models for number stories.

www.everydaymathonline.com

ePresentations

eToolkit

Algorithms Practice

EM Facts Workshop Game™

Family Letters

Assessment Management

Common Core State Standards

Curriculum Focal Points

Interactive Teacher's Lesson Guide

1 Teaching the Lesson

Key Concepts and Skills

- Compare pairs of 2-digit numbers based on meanings of the tens and ones digits.
  [Number and Numeration Goal 7]
- Use base-10 blocks to model and solve addition problems.
  [Operations and Computation Goal 2]
- Write number models using > and <.
  [Patterns, Functions, and Algebra Goal 2]

Key Activities

Children make up stories comparing the weights of animals and write number models for their number stories.

Ongoing Assessment: Informing Instruction See page 386.

Ongoing Assessment: Recognizing Student Achievement Use journal page 89.
[Patterns, Functions, and Algebra Goal 2]

Materials

Math Journal 1, pp. 84, 89, and 90
Home Link 5•5
Animal Cards (*Math Journal 1,* Activity Sheets 7 and 8; *Math Masters,* pp. 132–137) ◆ slate ◆ base-10 blocks (longs and cubes) ◆ Class Number Line or Number-Grid Poster (optional)

2 Ongoing Learning & Practice

Practicing Ordering Numbers
Math Masters, p. 140
Children practice ordering numbers.

Math Boxes 5•6
Math Journal 1, p. 91
Children practice and maintain skills through Math Box problems.

Home Link 5•6
Math Masters, p. 141
Children practice and maintain skills through Home Link activities.

3 Differentiation Options

READINESS

Comparing Cube Counts
per group: small paper cups, base-10 blocks (cubes), slates
Children compare sets of cubes and write relation number models.

ENRICHMENT

Creating Relation Number Models Using a Pan Balance
Math Masters, p. 142
per partnership: pan balance, base-10 blocks (cubes)
Children use cubes and a pan balance to write relation number models.

Advance Preparation

For the optional Readiness activity in Part 3, fill a paper cup for each child with a different quantity of cubes (20 cubes or fewer).

Getting Started

Mental Math and Reflexes

Write the number …

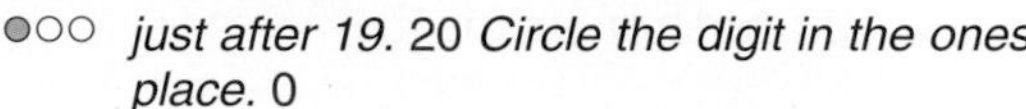

- ●○○ *just after 19.* 20 *Circle the digit in the ones place.* 0
- ●●○ *just before 30.* 29 *Circle the digit in the tens place.* 2
- ●●● *just after 49.* 50 *Circle the digit in the ones place.* 0

Adjust the numbers to suit children's abilities.

Math Message

Display pictures of four obviously different-size animals from Lesson 5-5. *Which is heaviest?*

Home Link 5·5 Follow-Up

Briefly review answers.

1 Teaching the Lesson

Math Message Follow-Up

WHOLE-CLASS DISCUSSION

Discuss which animal is heaviest. Then review the meanings of the relation symbols < and >, using the usual variations in wording.

Display pairs of animal pictures used in the Math Message activity and place a relation symbol between them. As you do, ask: *Is this correct?* As children compare pairs of two-digit weights, encourage them to compare the tens digits of each number first. Only if the tens digits are the same do they need to compare the ones digits.

Tell children that they will be learning to tell and write *more than* and *less than* relation number stories today.

NOTE For additional practice comparing weights, go to www.everydaymathonline.com.

Introducing Number Models for Relation Number Stories

WHOLE-CLASS ACTIVITY

Display two animal pictures with the correct < or > symbol between them.

Tell a number story about the animals, such as the following: *On Monday morning, the zookeeper weighed some of the animals. She found that the penguin weighed more than the beaver.*

Write a number model for the number story (75 pounds > 56 pounds). Since it is time-consuming to write "pounds" over and over in number models, draw a unit box for pounds on the board; thereafter omit the word *pounds* in your number models (75 > 56).

Have children take out their Animal Cards. Ask several children to tell number stories involving two animals of their choice. Help them illustrate the stories on the board using the appropriate animal pictures and relation symbol. You or the children write the number models for the stories; children then read them.

Language Arts Link Have children list the animals in alphabetical order.

75 pounds > 56 pounds

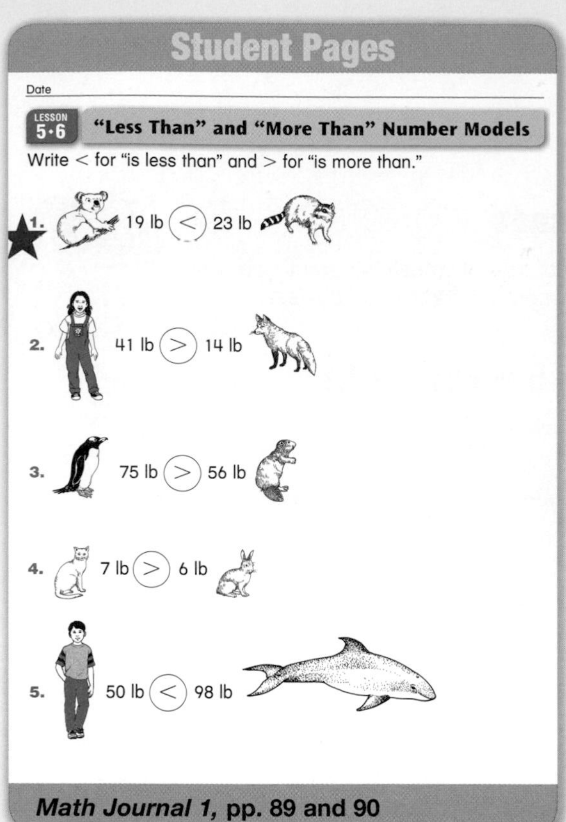
Student Pages

Date

LESSON 5·6 "Less Than" and "More Than" Number Models

Write $<$ for "is less than" and $>$ for "is more than."

1. 19 lb $<$ 23 lb
2. 41 lb $>$ 14 lb
3. 75 lb $>$ 56 lb
4. 7 lb $>$ 6 lb
5. 50 lb $<$ 98 lb

Math Journal 1, pp. 89 and 90

▶ Using $<$ and $>$ in Number Models

INDEPENDENT ACTIVITY

(*Math Journal 1*, pp. 84, 89, and 90)

In Problems 1–5 on journal page 89, children compare the weights of two animals. Problems 6–10 involve comparing the total weight of two animals to the weight of another animal.

Adjusting the Activity

To identify which number is larger, have children use the Class Number Line or the Number-Grid Poster.

AUDITORY ◆ KINESTHETIC ◆ TACTILE ◆ VISUAL

For Problems 4 and 5, have children model the problems with base-10 blocks on the Place-Value Mat on journal page 84. They should make all necessary exchanges and record the answers.

Ongoing Assessment: Informing Instruction

Watch for children who have trouble getting the $<$ and $>$ symbols pointed in the right direction. Remind children that the two dots near the larger number connect to the one dot near the smaller number.

Ongoing Assessment: Recognizing Student Achievement

Journal Page 89 Problem 1 

Use **journal page 89, Problem 1** to assess children's ability to compare numbers using $<$ and $>$. Children are making adequate progress if they are able to correctly answer Problem 1. Some children may be able to answer all of the problems on the page correctly.

[Patterns, Functions, and Algebra Goal 2]

Teaching Master

Name Date

LESSON 5·6 **Ordering Animals by Weight**

Order your animal cards from heaviest to lightest weight. Record the results below.

1st	*Cheetah*	*120*	lb
2nd	Porpoise	98	lb
3rd	Penguin	75	lb
4th	Beaver	56	lb
5th	*7-year-old boy*	*50*	lb
6th	First-grade girl	41	lb
7th	Raccoon	23	lb
8th	Koala	19	lb
9th	Eagle	15	lb
10th	*Fox*	*14*	lb
11th	Cat	7	lb
12th	Rabbit	6	lb

Math Masters, p. 140

2 Ongoing Learning & Practice

▶ Practicing Ordering Numbers

(*Math Masters*, p. 140)

Use *Math Masters*, page 140 to provide additional practice ordering numbers.

▶ Math Boxes 5·6

INDEPENDENT ACTIVITY

(*Math Journal 1,* p. 91)

Mixed Practice Math Boxes in this lesson are paired with Math Boxes in Lesson 5-8.

▶ Home Link 5·6

INDEPENDENT ACTIVITY

(*Math Masters,* p. 141)

Home Connection Children make number models by inserting a relation symbol between pairs of numbers.

3 Differentiation Options

READINESS

SMALL-GROUP ACTIVITY

▶ Comparing Cube Counts

5–15 Min

To explore comparing quantities using a concrete model, have children compare the number of cubes in a set of cups. Ask children to estimate the number of cubes in their cups and to compare cups to find classmates who have more cubes and less cubes. Then children count their cubes and check their estimates. Have children share their comparisons with the group. For example, "I have 14 cubes and Jacob has 8. I have more than Jacob." Children record the comparisons as a number model, in this case, 14 > 8, on their slates.

ENRICHMENT

PARTNER ACTIVITY

▶ Creating Relation Number Models Using a Pan Balance

5–15 Min

(*Math Masters,* p. 142)

To apply their understanding of relation number models, have children create greater-than, less-than, and equal-to situations using a pan balance. Give each partnership at least 50 cubes. Have children use their cubes and the pan balance to demonstrate each of the three relations shown on *Math Masters,* page 142, and record their work on the page. Then have children describe the numbers of cubes they used and the relationships between their quantities. Encourage children to use vocabulary from this unit.

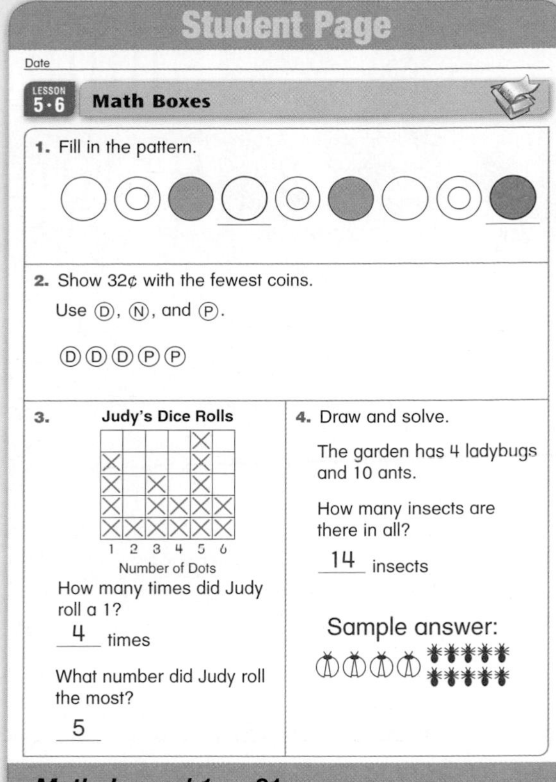

Student Page

Date

LESSON 5·6 **Math Boxes**

1. Fill in the pattern.

2. Show 32¢ with the fewest coins.
Use Ⓓ, Ⓝ, and Ⓟ.
ⒹⒹⒹⓅⓅ

3. **Judy's Dice Rolls**
Number of Dots: 1 2 3 4 5 6
How many times did Judy roll a 1?
4 times
What number did Judy roll the most?
5

4. Draw and solve.
The garden has 4 ladybugs and 10 ants.
How many insects are there in all?
14 insects
Sample answer:

Math Journal 1, p. 91

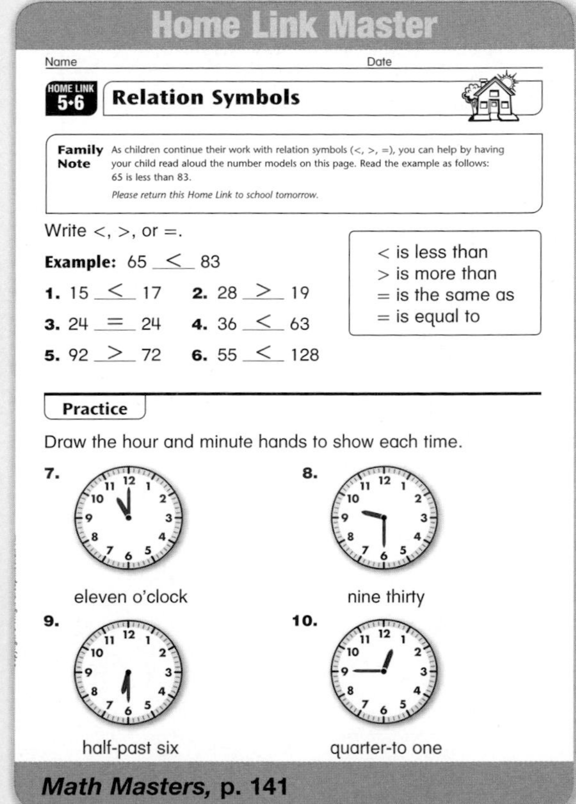

Home Link Master

Name Date

HOME LINK 5·6 **Relation Symbols**

Family Note As children continue their work with relation symbols (<, >, =), you can help by having your child read aloud the number models on this page. Read the example as follows: 65 is less than 83.

Please return this Home Link to school tomorrow.

Write <, >, or =.

Example: 65 < 83

1. 15 < 17
2. 28 > 19
3. 24 = 24
4. 36 < 63
5. 92 > 72
6. 55 < 128

< is less than
> is more than
= is the same as
= is equal to

Practice

Draw the hour and minute hands to show each time.

7. eleven o'clock
8. nine thirty
9. half-past six
10. quarter-to one

Math Masters, p. 141

5•7 Comparison Number Stories

Objective To introduce number stories that involve finding differences.

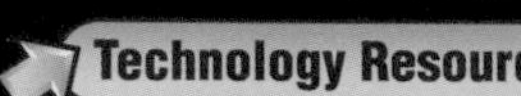

www.everydaymathonline.com

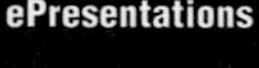

eToolkit

Algorithms Practice

EM Facts Workshop Game™

Family Letters

Assessment Management

Common Core State Standards

Curriculum Focal Points

Interactive Teacher's Lesson Guide

1 Teaching the Lesson

Key Concepts and Skills

- Count collections of objects by 1s. [Number and Numeration Goal 2]
- Compare groups of objects. [Number and Numeration Goal 7]
- Write number models to match solution strategies. [Patterns, Functions, and Algebra Goal 2]

Key Activities

Children compare two sets of pennies and determine how many more pennies there are in one set than in the other. Children play the *Difference Game* to practice finding differences.

Ongoing Assessment: Recognizing Student Achievement
Use an Exit Slip (*Math Masters,* page 305).
[Number and Numeration Goal 7]

Key Vocabulary

difference

Materials

Math Journal 1, p. 92
Home Link 5•6
Math Masters, p. 305
overhead coins (optional) ◆ per partnership: 4 each of number cards 1–10 (from the Everything Math Deck, if available) ◆ slates ◆ tool-kit coins

2 Ongoing Learning & Practice

Math Boxes 5•7
Math Journal 1, p. 93
Children practice and maintain skills through Math Box problems.

Home Link 5•7
Math Masters, p. 143
Children practice and maintain skills through Home Link activities.

3 Differentiation Options

READINESS

Finding the Distance between Numbers
Math Journal 1, inside back cover
2 clear counters ◆ slate
Children count the distance between two numbers on the number grid.

ENRICHMENT

Comparing the Values of Sets of Coins
Math Masters, p. 144
Children compare the values of sets of coins.

ELL SUPPORT

Building a Math Word Bank
Differentiation Handbook, p. 126
Children add the term *difference* to their Math Word Banks.

Getting Started

Mental Math and Reflexes

1. Draw a set of coins on the board using the Ⓟ, Ⓝ, and Ⓓ symbols. Children record the total value of the coins on their slates. Write the answer under the drawing. (Children can use their tool-kit coins to organize the combinations by type of coin.)
2. Draw a second set of coins to the right of the first set. Children record the total value of these coins on their slates.
3. Children write a < or > symbol between the two amounts. Use problems such as:
   ●○○ Ⓓ Ⓓ Ⓝ Ⓟ and Ⓓ Ⓓ Ⓓ 26¢ < 30¢
   ●●○ Ⓓ Ⓝ Ⓝ Ⓟ Ⓟ Ⓟ and Ⓝ Ⓓ Ⓝ Ⓟ Ⓟ Ⓝ 23¢ < 27¢
   ●●● Ⓝ Ⓝ Ⓟ Ⓟ Ⓝ Ⓓ Ⓓ and Ⓟ Ⓟ Ⓟ Ⓟ Ⓝ Ⓓ Ⓓ 37¢ > 29¢

Math Message

Lou saved 5 cents.
Lisa saved 8 cents.

Who saved more money? How much more money? Lisa; 3 cents more

Home Link 5·6 Follow-Up

Briefly review the answers.

1 Teaching the Lesson

Math Message Follow-Up

WHOLE-CLASS DISCUSSION

ELL

Children share solution strategies. If no one mentions the following approach, discuss it with the class. Use overhead coins or draw pennies on the board.

▷ Make rows of pennies, one to represent Lou's coins and the other to represent Lisa's coins.

▷ Pair as many pennies as possible from one set with a penny from the other set.

▷ The pennies that are not paired represent how many more pennies Lisa has than Lou.

Pose another problem: *Al has 12 cents. June has 7 cents. Who has less money?* June *How much less money?* 5 cents less

Children model the solution with their tool-kit pennies and write their answers on slates. Write $12 - 7 = 5$ on the board. Point out that the result, 5, is called the **difference** between 12 and 7. To support English language learners, discuss both the everyday and mathematical meanings of the word *difference.*

Pose several more problems, as needed. Have children model the solutions with coins. When summarizing solutions, write number models on the board that illustrate children's language. For example, some children will count up to find the difference, so the number model will have an unknown addend. To solve $12 - 7 = \square$, find the number that makes 12 when added to 7, as in $7 + \square = 12$.

NOTE This number story and the Math Message number story are examples of comparison situations. "Who has more?" and "Who has less?" are two ways of expressing comparison situations. Be sure to use both kinds of questions for comparison number stories.

Student Page

Date

LESSON 5·7 **How Much More? How Much Less?**

Find each difference.

1. John Ⓟ Ⓟ Ⓟ Ⓟ Ⓟ Ⓟ Ⓟ Ⓟ
   Nick Ⓟ Ⓟ
   Who has more? John How much more? 6 ¢

2. June Ⓟ Ⓟ Ⓟ Ⓟ Ⓟ Ⓟ Ⓟ Ⓟ Ⓟ
   Mia Ⓟ Ⓟ Ⓟ Ⓟ Ⓟ Ⓟ
   Who has less? Mia How much less? 3 ¢

3. Dante Ⓟ Ⓟ Ⓟ Ⓟ Ⓟ Ⓟ Ⓟ
   Kala Ⓟ Ⓟ Ⓟ Ⓟ Ⓟ Ⓟ Ⓟ Ⓟ Ⓟ Ⓟ Ⓟ Ⓟ Ⓟ Ⓟ Ⓟ
   Who has less? Dante How much less? 8 ¢

Try This

4. Carlos has 12 pennies.
   Mary has 20 pennies.
   Who has more? Mary
   How much more? 8 ¢

***Math Journal 1,* p. 92**

▶ Finding How Much More or Less

INDEPENDENT ACTIVITY

(*Math Journal 1,* p. 92)

PROBLEM SOLVING

Children use their tool-kit pennies to find differences.

Adjusting the Activity

Have children write number models for each of the problems. Children might record addition or subtraction number models depending on how they think of the problem. Have children draw large dots to represent pennies in Problem 4.

AUDITORY ◆ KINESTHETIC ◆ TACTILE ◆ VISUAL

▶ Playing the *Difference Game*

PARTNER ACTIVITY

Directions

1. Partners combine their tool-kit pennies (40 pennies) to create a bank.
2. They mix a deck of 1–10 number cards (four cards of each number) and put the cards number-side down in a deck.
3. In each round, each player takes 1 card from the top of the deck and takes the same number of pennies from the bank as the number shown on the card.
4. Both players then find out how many more pennies one player has than the other.
5. The player with more pennies keeps the extra pennies. The rest go back in the bank.
6. The game is over when there are not enough pennies left in the bank to play another round.
7. The player with more pennies wins the game.

NOTE To find the difference between two numbers, it is helpful to ask: *How many more do I need to add to the smaller set to have as many as there are in the larger set?* This "equalize" language encourages children to "add up to subtract."

Ongoing Assessment: Recognizing Student Achievement

Exit Slip

Portfolio Ideas

Use an **Exit Slip** to assess children's ability to solve comparison problems. On an **Exit Slip** (*Math Masters,* page 305), have children summarize one round of the game by drawing how many pennies each partner has. Have children write which partner has more pennies. Then, under the drawing, children write how many more pennies the partner has. Children are making adequate progress if they are able to tell how many more pennies the partner has. Some children might not need to draw the pennies to give an answer.
[Number and Numeration Goal 7]

Ask children to explain why, when they compare two sets of pennies, the number of extra pennies is called the "difference."

2 Ongoing Learning & Practice

Math Boxes 5•7

INDEPENDENT ACTIVITY

(*Math Journal 1,* p. 93)

Mixed Practice Math Boxes in this lesson are paired with Math Boxes in Lesson 5-5. The skills in Problem 4 preview Unit 6 content.

Home Link 5•7

INDEPENDENT ACTIVITY

(*Math Masters,* p. 143)

Home Connection Children find the difference between sets of pennies. They line up pennies in two rows and pair off as many pennies from the top row with pennies in the bottom row as possible.

3 Differentiation Options

READINESS

SMALL-GROUP ACTIVITY

Finding the Distance between Numbers

5–15 Min

(*Math Journal 1,* inside back cover)

To provide experience finding the distance between two numbers, have children count up and back on the number grid. Have them place a clear counter on the starting number and a clear counter on the ending number. Then they count up and back from one number to the other to discover that the distance is the same either way. Have children record their answers on slates.

Suggestions:

- Start at 10. Count up to 18. What is the distance between 10 and 18? 8
- Start at 22. Count up to 35. What is the distance between 22 and 35? 13
- Start at 35. Count back to 22. What is the distance between 35 and 22? 13
- Start at 62. Count back to 50. What is the distance between 62 and 50? 12
- Start at 35. Count up to 75. What is the distance between 35 and 75? 40

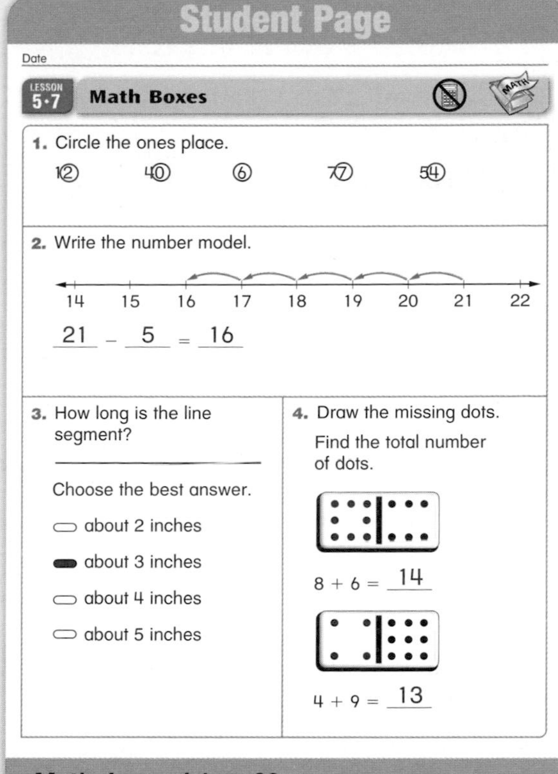

Student Page

Date

LESSON 5·7 **Math Boxes**

1. Circle the ones place.

12 40 6 77 54

2. Write the number model.

14 15 16 17 18 19 20 21 22

21 – 5 = 16

3. How long is the line segment?

Choose the best answer.

- about 2 inches
- about 3 inches
- about 4 inches
- about 5 inches

4. Draw the missing dots.

Find the total number of dots.

8 + 6 = 14

4 + 9 = 13

Math Journal 1, p. 93

NOTE Remember to reserve time during your day every day to complete the number-line, attendance, calendar, weather, and temperature routines.

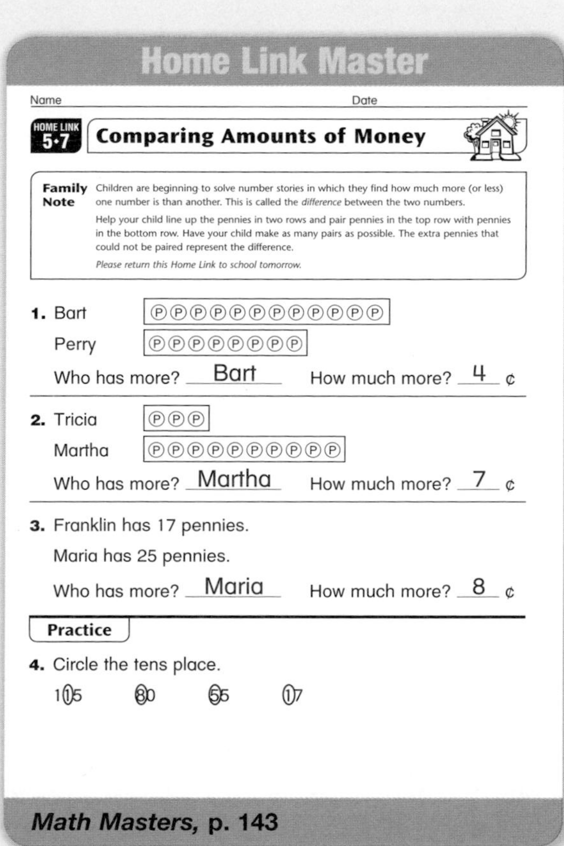

Home Link Master

Name Date

HOME LINK 5·7 **Comparing Amounts of Money**

Family Note Children are beginning to solve number stories in which they find how much more (or less) one number is than another. This is called the *difference* between the two numbers.

Help your child line up the pennies in two rows and pair pennies in the top row with pennies in the bottom row. Have your child make as many pairs as possible. The extra pennies that could not be paired represent the difference.

Please return this Home Link to school tomorrow.

1. Bart Ⓟ Ⓟ Ⓟ Ⓟ Ⓟ Ⓟ Ⓟ Ⓟ Ⓟ Ⓟ Ⓟ Ⓟ

Perry Ⓟ Ⓟ Ⓟ Ⓟ Ⓟ Ⓟ Ⓟ Ⓟ

Who has more? Bart How much more? 4 ¢

2. Tricia Ⓟ Ⓟ Ⓟ

Martha Ⓟ Ⓟ Ⓟ Ⓟ Ⓟ Ⓟ Ⓟ Ⓟ Ⓟ Ⓟ

Who has more? Martha How much more? 7 ¢

3. Franklin has 17 pennies.

Maria has 25 pennies.

Who has more? Maria How much more? 8 ¢

Practice

4. Circle the tens place.

105 80 65 07

Math Masters, p. 143

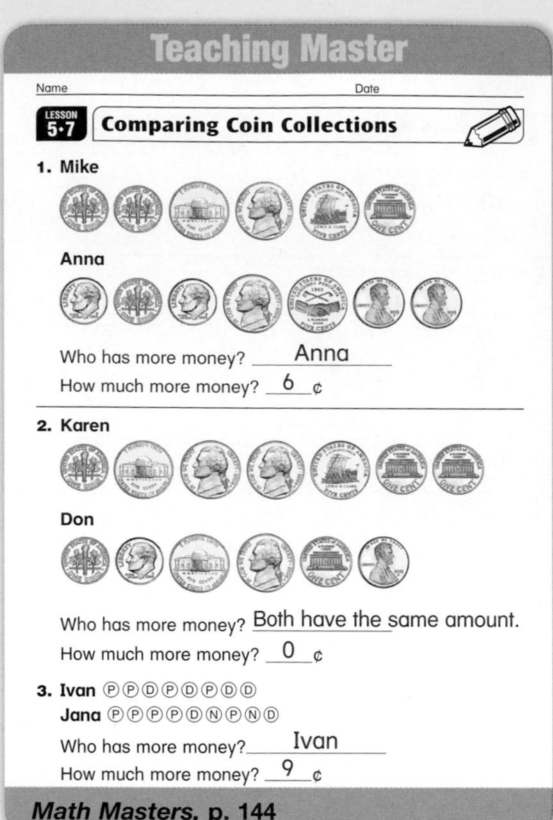
Teaching Master

Name Date

LESSON 5·7 **Comparing Coin Collections**

1. Mike

Anna

Who has more money? Anna

How much more money? 6 ¢

2. Karen

Don

Who has more money? Both have the same amount.

How much more money? 0 ¢

3. Ivan Ⓟ Ⓟ Ⓓ Ⓟ Ⓓ Ⓟ Ⓓ Ⓓ

Jana Ⓟ Ⓟ Ⓟ Ⓟ Ⓓ Ⓝ Ⓟ Ⓝ Ⓓ

Who has more money? Ivan

How much more money? 9 ¢

Math Masters, p. 144

ENRICHMENT

▶ Comparing the Values of Sets of Coins

15–30 Min

(*Math Masters,* p. 144)

To further explore comparing coin values, have children compare the values of sets of coins. They decide which set is worth more and *how much more* it is worth.

After most children have completed the first two problems, discuss solution strategies. One strategy is to count the value of each set of coins and find the difference. Another strategy involves crossing out pairs of matching coins and then comparing the values of the coins remaining, as shown:

Using this strategy, it is clear that a nickel remains in Mike's collection, and that a dime and a penny remain in Anna's collection. Now it is easy to see that Anna has 6 cents more than Mike.

ELL SUPPORT

▶ Building a Math Word Bank

5–15 Min

(*Differentiation Handbook,* p. 126)

To provide language support for subtraction, have children use the Word Bank Template found on *Differentiation Handbook,* page 126. Ask children to write the term *difference,* draw a picture representing the term, and write other words that describe it. Make sure children focus on the meaning of *difference* as it relates to subtraction. See the *Differentiation Handbook* for more information.

5•8 Solving Number Stories

Objective To provide practice making up and solving a variety of number stories involving relations, addition, and subtraction.

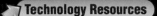

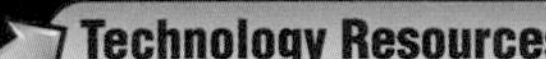 www.everydaymathonline.com

ePresentations

eToolkit

Algorithms Practice

EM Facts Workshop Game™

Family Letters

Assessment Management

Common Core State Standards

Curriculum Focal Points

Interactive Teacher's Lesson Guide

1 Teaching the Lesson

Key Concepts and Skills

- Order 1- and 2-digit whole numbers. [Number and Numeration Goal 7]
- Use number grids, base-10 blocks, and other strategies to add and subtract. [Operations and Computation Goal 2]
- Solve number stories. [Operations and Computation Goal 4]
- Generate and record number models to match solution strategies. [Patterns, Functions, and Algebra Goal 2]

Key Activities

Children solve different kinds of number stories. They make up and solve their own number stories and write number models for the stories.

Ongoing Assessment: Recognizing Student Achievement
Use Mental Math and Reflexes.
[Number and Numeration Goal 3]

Materials

Math Journal 1, p. 94
Home Link 5•7
Animal Cards (*Math Journal 1,* Activity Sheets 7 and 8; *Math Masters,* pp. 132–137)
◆ slate

2 Ongoing Learning & Practice

Practicing Finding Differences
Math Masters, p. 145
Children practice finding differences using a number line.

Math Boxes 5•8
Math Journal 1, p. 95
Children practice and maintain skills through Math Box problems.

Home Link 5•8
Math Masters, p. 146
Children practice and maintain skills through Home Link activities.

3 Differentiation Options

READINESS

Acting Out Number Stories
slate ◆ counters
Children act out and solve number stories.

ENRICHMENT

Making Thematic Number Stories
Children make up number stories based on a curricular theme.

Getting Started

Mental Math and Reflexes 

Give clues about numbers, such as the following:

●○○ *Write a 2-digit number with 3 in the ones place; with 5 in the ones place; with 8 in the ones place.*

●●○ *Write a 2-digit number with 7 in the tens place; with 4 in the tens place; with 9 in the tens place.*

●●● *Write the largest 2-digit number; the smallest 2-digit number.* 99; 10

Children write answers on slates.

Math Message

Take out your Animal Cards. How much more does the koala weigh than the eagle?

Home Link 5·7 Follow-Up

Briefly review the answers from the Home Link. Have children share strategies for solving Problem 3.

Ongoing Assessment: Recognizing Student Achievement

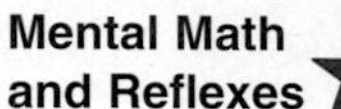

Use **Mental Math and Reflexes** to assess children's ability to identify digits in numbers. Children are making adequate progress if they are able to recognize the ones place and the tens place. Some children may be able to write the largest and smallest 2-digit numbers.

[Number and Numeration Goal 3]

1 Teaching the Lesson

▶ Math Message Follow-Up

Algebraic Thinking Briefly go over the answer. Ask how this number story is like the penny comparison stories in Lesson 5-7. Both are comparison stories; the result is called the *difference.*

Draw a comparison diagram on the board like the one shown. As you do, ask:

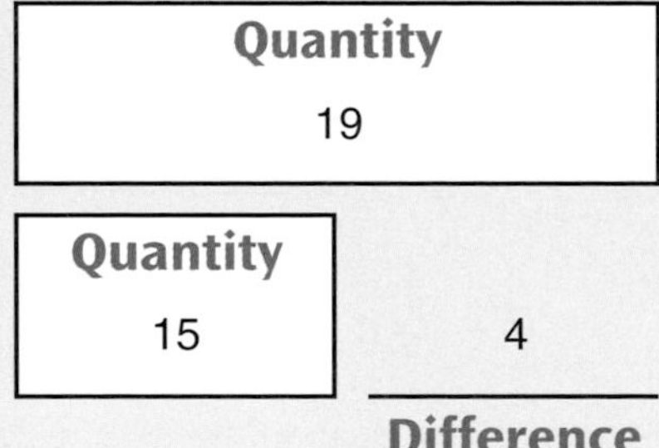

- How much does the koala weigh? 19 lb That's the larger quantity. (Write 19 in the top box.)
- How much does the eagle weigh? 15 lb That's the smaller quantity. (Write 15 in the lower left box.)
- What is the difference between 19 and 15? 4 (Write 4 on the line.)

NOTE You may wish to explain to children that finding the difference between 19 and 15 is the same as finding the unknown number that makes 19 − 15 = □ true. Remind children that they can think of subtraction as an addition problem with an unknown addend. They can solve 19 − 15 = □ by finding the number that makes 19 when added to 15, as in 15 + □ = 19.

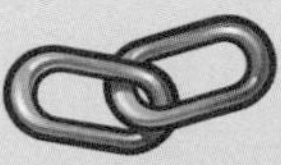

Links to the Future

This lesson demonstrates and describes change-to-less, change-to-more, comparison, and parts-and-total situations. Children will continue to be exposed to these types of number stories in first grade. Applying knowledge of these situations to solving number stories is a Grade 2 Goal.

Solving Number Stories Involving Addition and Subtraction

Algebraic Thinking By now, children have had some exposure to the following kinds of number stories:

- ▷ **Relations:** My cat weighs 7 pounds and my rabbit weighs 6 pounds. Which weighs more? My cat
- ▷ **Change-to-less:** If a 23-pound raccoon sheds 2 pounds of fur, how much will it weigh? 21 lb
- ▷ **Change-to-more:** Kareem had 3 cats. One of the cats had a litter of 6 kittens. How many cats and kittens does Kareem have in all? 9 cats and kittens
- ▷ **Parts-and-total:** A 50-pound boy holds a 7-pound cat and steps on a scale. How many pounds do they weigh together? 57 lb
- ▷ **Comparison:** How much less does a 7-pound cat weigh than a 14-pound fox? 7 lb

Have the class solve these stories or similar stories. Ask children to suggest a number model for each. You may also want to have children make up their own number stories.

If children are having difficulty getting started, suggest some of the following situations:

- ▷ Stories about dominoes: *What is the total number of dots? Which half of the domino has more dots? How many more?*
- ▷ Stories about money saved, spent, or shared
- ▷ Stories about fruit bought, eaten, or given away
- ▷ Stories about games: *Sarah played the* Difference Game. *She took 6 pennies in the first round and 3 pennies in the second round. How many more pennies did she take in the first round?*

As children solve each number story, encourage them to share a variety of solution strategies. You may wish to pose problems that allow you to highlight the following strategies:

- ▷ **Counting on from the larger addend:** How much do the rabbit and the raccoon weigh together?
  Strategy: Start with the larger weight (the raccoon's). Count up 6 from 23 to get 29 lb.
  Number model: 23 + 6 = 29
- ▷ **Counting up to subtract:** The boy stands next to the beaver. How much taller is the boy?
  Strategy: Use a number grid. Start at 30 and count up 20 to get 50. The difference is 20; the boy is 20 inches taller than the beaver.
  Number model: 30 + 20 = 50 or 50 − 30 = 20

Change-to-less

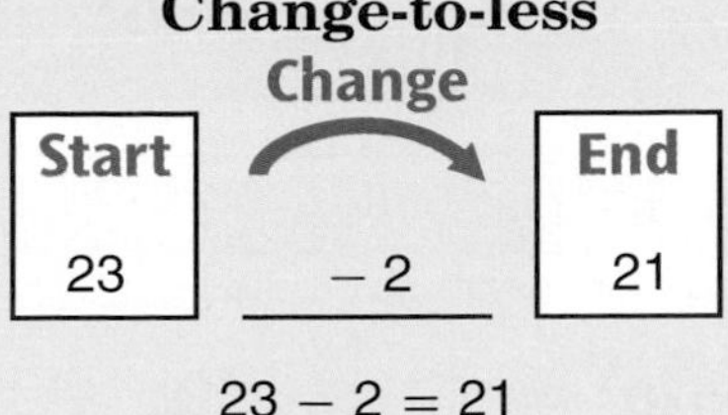

23 − 2 = 21

Change-to-more

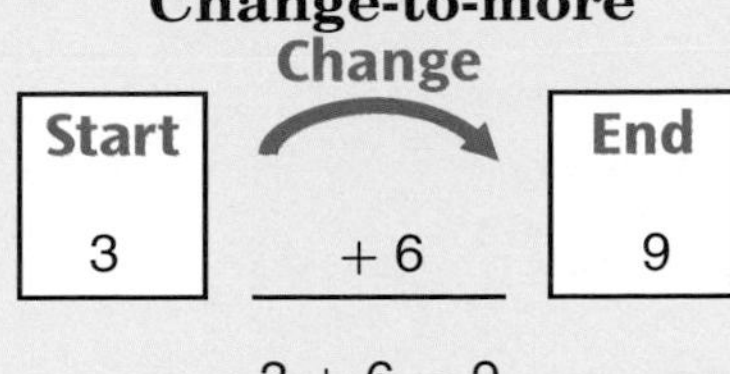

3 + 6 = 9

Parts-and-total

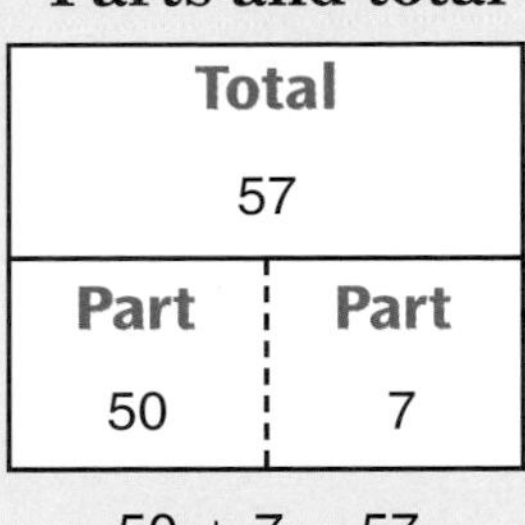

50 + 7 = 57

Comparison

Quantity
14

Quantity
7

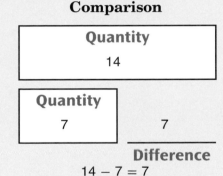

7
Difference

14 − 7 = 7

Types of number stories

NOTE The "counting on from the larger addend" strategy relies on the Commutative Property of Addition, which states that two numbers may be added in any order without affecting the sum. Children should understand that they may add large numbers in whatever order is easiest for them, but they should not be expected to know the term *Commutative Property.*

Student Page

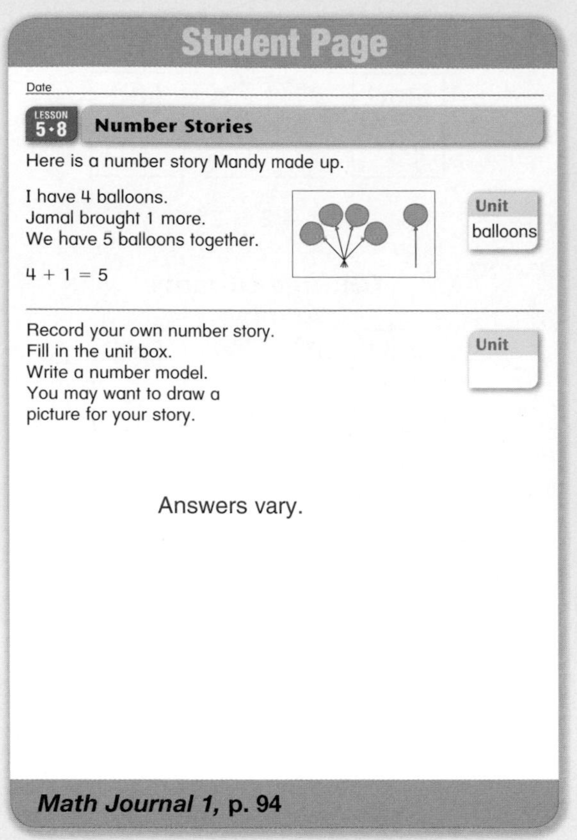
Date

LESSON 5·8 **Number Stories**

Here is a number story Mandy made up.

I have 4 balloons.
Jamal brought 1 more.
We have 5 balloons together.

4 + 1 = 5

Unit: balloons

Record your own number story.
Fill in the unit box.
Write a number model.
You may want to draw a picture for your story.

Unit

Answers vary.

Math Journal 1, p. 94

Teaching Master

Name Date

LESSON 5·8 **Comparisons**

Example:

Carlos Ⓟ Ⓟ Ⓟ

0 1 2 3 4 5 6 7 8 9

Lynn Ⓟ Ⓟ Ⓟ Ⓟ Ⓟ Ⓟ Ⓟ

Who has more money? Lynn How much more money? 4 ¢

1. Amy 13 pennies

13 14 15 16 17 18 19 20 21 22

Deon 21 pennies

Who has more money? Deon

How much more money? 8 ¢

2. Cat 7 lb

7 8 9 10 11 12 13 14 15 16

Eagle 15 lb

Which animal weighs more? Eagle

How much more? 8 lb

Try This

3. Andy has 17 crayons. Kate has 25 crayons.

Who has fewer crayons? Andy

How many fewer crayons? 8 crayons

Math Masters, p. 145

▷ **Making ten:** The cat and the koala sit on a scale at the same time. How much do they weigh altogether?
Strategy: Use base-10 blocks to represent the cat's weight (7 cubes) and the koala's weight (1 long, 9 cubes). Add the blocks together. 7 cubes + 1 long, 9 cubes = 1 long, 16 cubes. Trade 10 cubes for 1 long, leaving 6 cubes left over. 2 longs, 6 cubes = 2 tens, 6 ones = 26.
Number model: 7 + 10 + 9 = 10 + 16 = 20 + 6 = 26

▶ Making Up and Solving Number Stories

INDEPENDENT ACTIVITY

PROBLEM SOLVING

(*Math Journal 1*, p. 94)

Discuss Mandy's number story at the top of the journal page. Ask: *Can anyone suggest a different story for the picture?* Sample answer: Jean had 5 balloons. She gave 1 balloon to Jon. How many balloons does Jean have now?

Ask children to make up a number story and record it on the page along with a number model. Explain that they may write the story in words or illustrate it with counters, tallies, or pictures.

After children are finished, choose several stories for the class to act out. Make sure to include stories that involve addition and subtraction.

NOTE Remember not to force the solution to a number story into a particular mold. The diagrams used for these stories give *one* way of viewing the problems. The number models might show addition or subtraction.

2 Ongoing Learning & Practice

▶ Practicing Finding Differences

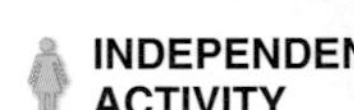

(*Math Masters*, p. 145)

Use *Math Masters,* page 145 to provide more practice finding differences using a number line.

▶ Math Boxes 5·8

(*Math Journal 1*, p. 95)

Mixed Practice Math Boxes in this lesson are paired with Math Boxes in Lesson 5-6. The skills in Problem 4 preview Unit 6 content.

Writing/Reasoning Have children draw, write, or verbalize an answer to the following question: *What is a pattern?* A reasonable answer should explain that a pattern is something that repeats.

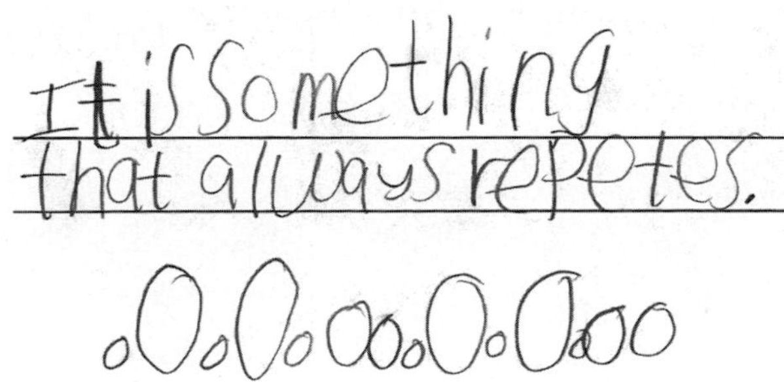
It is something
that always repetes.

One child's work in response to the Writing/Reasoning prompt

Home Link 5•8

INDEPENDENT ACTIVITY

(*Math Masters,* p. 146)

Home Connection Children find or draw a picture that illustrates a number story. They tell a number story about the picture and write a number model for the number story.

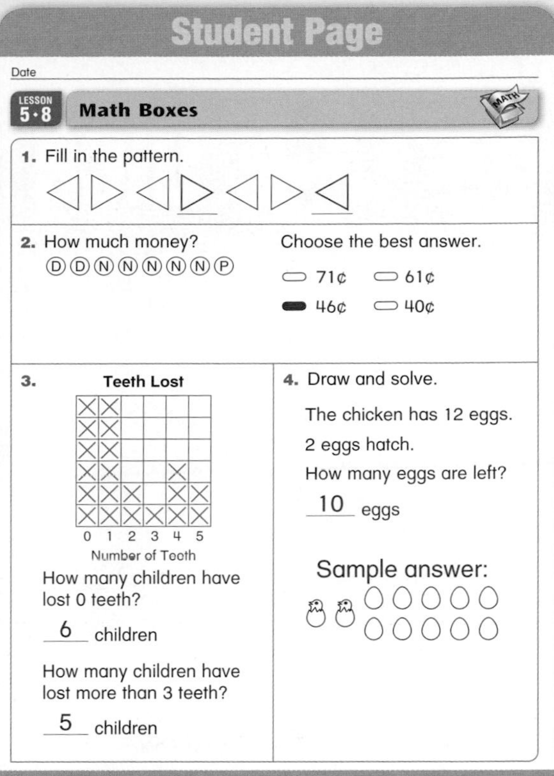

Student Page

Date

LESSON 5•8 **Math Boxes**

1. Fill in the pattern.

2. How much money? Ⓓ Ⓓ Ⓝ Ⓝ Ⓝ Ⓝ Ⓝ Ⓝ Ⓟ

Choose the best answer.
○ 71¢ ○ 61¢
● 46¢ ○ 40¢

3. Teeth Lost

Number of Teeth: 0 1 2 3 4 5

How many children have lost 0 teeth?
6 children

How many children have lost more than 3 teeth?
5 children

4. Draw and solve.

The chicken has 12 eggs.
2 eggs hatch.
How many eggs are left?
10 eggs

Sample answer:

Math Journal 1, p. 95

3 Differentiation Options

READINESS

SMALL-GROUP ACTIVITY

Acting Out Number Stories

5–15 Min

To explore creating and solving number stories, have children tell and act out number stories. Begin by telling parts-and-total, change-to-more, change-to-less, and comparison stories. Have children act out the stories using counters. For parts-and-total stories, they draw a dividing line in the middle of their slates; place the appropriate number of counters on each side of the divider; and then erase the divider to find the total. For change stories, they model the start and the change with counters to find the answer. For comparison stories, they line up the counters side-by-side to find the answer. You may wish to have children tell and act out their own stories.

ENRICHMENT

PARTNER ACTIVITY

Making Thematic Number Stories

15–30 Min

Portfolio Ideas

To apply children's understanding of number stories, select a topic from your science or social studies curriculum as a theme for children's number stories. Working with a partner, each child tells a number story using the theme. Partners then illustrate and/or write both stories in words. They write a number model for each story. Collect the stories for a classroom book or bulletin-board display.

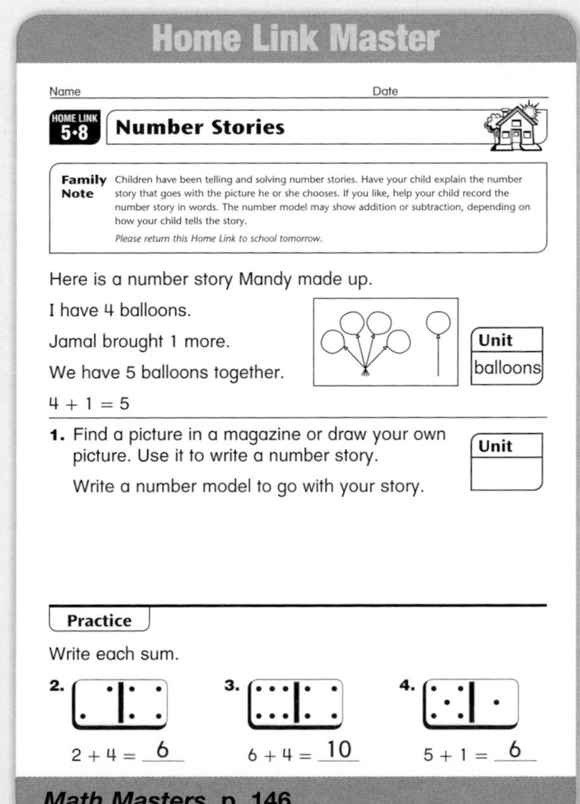

Home Link Master

Name Date

HOME LINK 5•8 **Number Stories**

Family Note Children have been telling and solving number stories. Have your child explain the number story that goes with the picture he or she chooses. If you like, help your child record the number story in words. The number model may show addition or subtraction, depending on how your child tells the story.

Please return this Home Link to school tomorrow.

Here is a number story Mandy made up.

I have 4 balloons.
Jamal brought 1 more.
We have 5 balloons together.
4 + 1 = 5

Unit: balloons

1. Find a picture in a magazine or draw your own picture. Use it to write a number story.
Write a number model to go with your story.

Unit

Practice

Write each sum.

2. 2 + 4 = 6

3. 6 + 4 = 10

4. 5 + 1 = 6

Math Masters, p. 146

5•9 Dice Sums

Objective To provide experience with sums generated by rolling pairs of dice.

Technology Resources www.everydaymathonline.com

ePresentations

eToolkit

Algorithms Practice

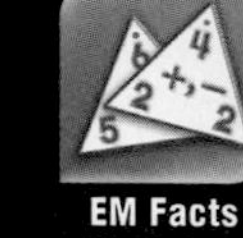
EM Facts Workshop Game™

Family Letters

Assessment Management

Common Core State Standards

Curriculum Focal Points

Interactive Teacher's Lesson Guide

1 Teaching the Lesson

Key Concepts and Skills

- Count up from the larger number to solve addition problems. [Operations and Computation Goal 1]
- Create and use a tally chart to represent data. [Data and Chance Goal 1]
- Draw conclusions about the probability of dice rolls. [Data and Chance Goal 3]

Key Activities

Children roll pairs of dice and record the sum of the dots. They observe which sums occur most often.

Ongoing Assessment: Informing Instruction See page 400.

Key Vocabulary

multiple of 10

Materials

Math Journal 1, p. 96 and inside back cover
Home Link 5•8
Number-Grid Poster ◆ per partnership: pair of dice ◆ slate

2 Ongoing Learning & Practice

Playing *Base-10 Exchange*

Math Journal 1, p. 81 or *Math Masters,* p. 318
Math Masters, p. 339
per partnership: base-10 blocks (cubes and longs), die
Children practice exchanging 10 cubes for 1 long.

Math Boxes 5•9

Math Journal 1, p. 97
Children practice and maintain skills through Math Box problems.

Ongoing Assessment: Recognizing Student Achievement

Use Math Boxes, Problem 4.
[Measurement and Reference Frames Goal 4]

Home Link 5•9

Math Masters, p. 147
Children practice and maintain skills through Home Link activities.

3 Differentiation Options

ENRICHMENT

Exploring the Roll of a Die

Math Masters, p. 148
die
Children roll a die and graph their results.

EXTRA PRACTICE

Reading about Probability

Math Masters, p. 305
Children read *Probably Pistachio* to practice probability concepts.

Advance Preparation

For the optional Extra Practice activity in Part 3, obtain a copy of ***Probably Pistachio*** by Stuart J. Murphy (HarperCollins Publishers, 2001).

***Teacher's Reference Manual,* Grades 1–3** pp. 116, 117, 127, 128, 191, 192

Getting Started

Mental Math and Reflexes

Begin to practice place-value and rounding skills. Have children write their answers on their slates.

- Is 18 closer to 10 or 20? 20
- Is 12 closer to 10 or 20? 10
- Is 19 closer to 10 or 20? 20

Explain that the numbers 10, 20, 30, ... are called **multiples of 10.** Ask someone to point to the multiples of 10 on the Number-Grid Poster. *How are they alike?* They all end in 0. They are all in the last column on the right.

Ask children to count spaces on the number grid on the inside back cover of their journal to help them answer the following questions on their slates.

- Is 27 closer to 20 or 30? 30
- Is 54 closer to 50 or 60? 50
- Is 86 closer to 80 or 90? 90

Ask: *Is there a way to solve problems like these by just looking at the numbers?* If the ones digit is less than 5, the number is closer to the smaller number. If it is more than 5, the number is closer to the larger number. If it is 5, the number is halfway between the smaller and larger number.

Math Message

FACTS PRACTICE

Add.

$1 + 6 = \boxed{7}$	$2 + 5 = \boxed{7}$
$\boxed{7} = 3 + 4$	$\boxed{7} = 4 + 3$
$5 + 2 = \boxed{7}$	$\boxed{7} = 6 + 1$

Home Link 5·8 Follow-Up

Briefly go over the answers.
Ask several volunteers to tell their number stories and have the class solve them. Share solution strategies for the problems.

1 Teaching the Lesson

Math Message Follow-Up

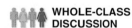

WHOLE-CLASS DISCUSSION

Briefly go over the answers. *How are these problems like the Two-Fisted Penny Addition activity with 7 pennies?* They show different ways to get 7.

> **NOTE** You may wish to discuss with children why there is no column for 1 on the record sheet (*Math Journal 1,* page 96).

Investigating Frequency of Sums from Dice Rolls

PARTNER ACTIVITY

(*Math Journal 1,* p. 96)

Partners investigate which sum is likely to come up most often when two dice are thrown. They perform the following experiment twice. The first time, they record the results in one partner's journal. The second time, they record the results in the other partner's journal.

Directions

1. One partner rolls the two dice.
2. Both partners figure out the sum of the dots on the dice.
3. The other partner marks the first empty box above the sum shown on the journal page with an X.

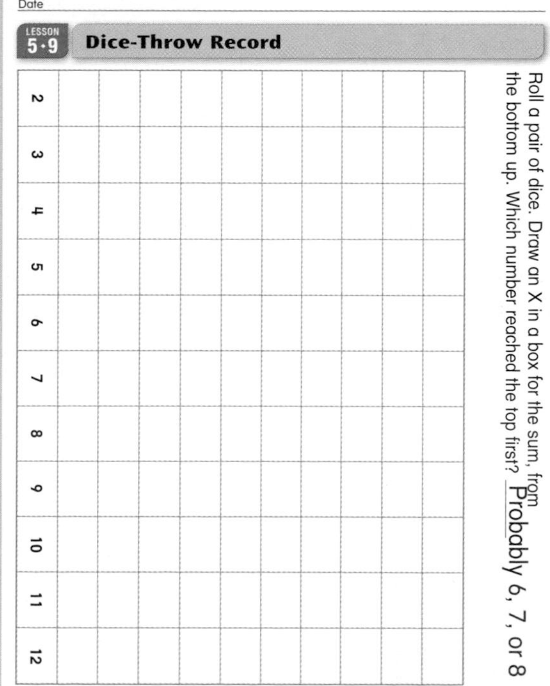
Student Page

Date

LESSON 5·9 **Dice-Throw Record**

Roll a pair of dice. Draw an X in a box for the sum, from the bottom up. Which number reached the top first? Probably 6, 7, or 8

2	3	4	5	6	7	8	9	10	11	12

Math Journal 1, p. 96

Filled Columns	
2	
3	
4	
5	/
6	~~////~~
7	~~////~~ ~~////~~
8	~~////~~ /
9	///
10	//
11	
12	

When the column for any one sum is filled to the top, partners repeat the experiment and record the results in the other partner's journal.

Circulate and talk with children about the facts they know and how they figure out a sum when they don't know the fact.

Ongoing Assessment: Informing Instruction

Watch for children who still need to count all of the dots on both dice rather than counting up from the larger number. Suggest that they use the number line to count up. For example, if the child rolls 5 and 3, put a finger at 5 and count up 3 to 8.

When children complete both tables, discuss the results with the class. Make a tally of which columns reached the top for each partnership.

- Which sum came up most often? Probably 6, 7, or 8

If the sum 7 came up most often, ask children why they think this is so. Expect answers like "7 is a lucky number" or "7 is a favorite number." Someone may bring up the fact that there are more different ways for 7 to come up than any of the other numbers, but do not expect this response. This idea will be revisited in Lesson 6-1.

- Is there a better chance of getting a 7 than of getting a 2 or a 12? yes
- Imagine we played a game. In the game, we roll two dice. If a 7 comes up, the teacher wins. If a 2 or a 12 comes up, the class wins. Is the game fair? The game is not fair. The teacher will win most of the time, since 7 comes up more often than 2 and 12 combined.

2 Ongoing Learning & Practice

▶ Playing *Base-10 Exchange*

PARTNER ACTIVITY

(*Math Masters,* p. 339)

Children practice trading base-10 blocks by playing *Base-10 Exchange.* For detailed instructions, see Lesson 5-3.

▶ Math Boxes 5·9

INDEPENDENT ACTIVITY

(*Math Journal 1,* p. 97)

Mixed Practice Math Boxes in this lesson are linked to Math Boxes in Lessons 5-11 and 5-13. The skills in Problem 4 preview Unit 6 content.

Game Master

Name Date

Base-10 Exchange

If you roll:	then take:
1	1 long
2	2 longs
3	3 cubes
4	4 cubes
5	5 cubes
6	6 cubes

Math Masters, p. 339

Writing/Reasoning Have children draw, write or verbalize an answer to the following question: *How do you use > to compare numbers?* A reasonable answer should include relational words, such as *greater* or *larger than.* Sample answer: You use it to pretend it's a duck mouth to chomp off the bigger one.

Ongoing Assessment: Recognizing Student Achievement

Math Boxes Problem 4 

Use **Math Boxes, Problem 4** to assess children's ability to show time to the quarter-hour on a clock. Children are making adequate progress if they are able to draw the minute hand in the correct place. Most children will also be able to draw the hour hand in the correct place.

[Measurement and Reference Frames Goal 4]

Home Link 5•9

(*Math Masters,* p. 147)

Home Connection Children compare the sum of the dots on pairs of die faces and dominoes.

3 Differentiation Options

ENRICHMENT

Exploring the Roll of a Die

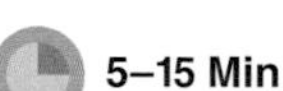

5–15 Min

(*Math Masters,* p. 148)

To further explore probability with dice, have children record results for rolling a single die. Have them record their die throws on *Math Masters,* page 148. Discuss how and why this graph differs from the graph made when rolling a pair of dice.

EXTRA PRACTICE

Reading about Probability

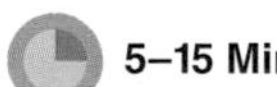

(*Math Masters,* p. 305)

Literature Link To provide practice with probability concepts, read ***Probably Pistachio*** by Stuart J. Murphy (HarperCollins Publishers, 2001). On an Exit Slip (*Math Masters,* page 305) have children tell something about their day using a probability word that Jack uses in the book.

Student Page

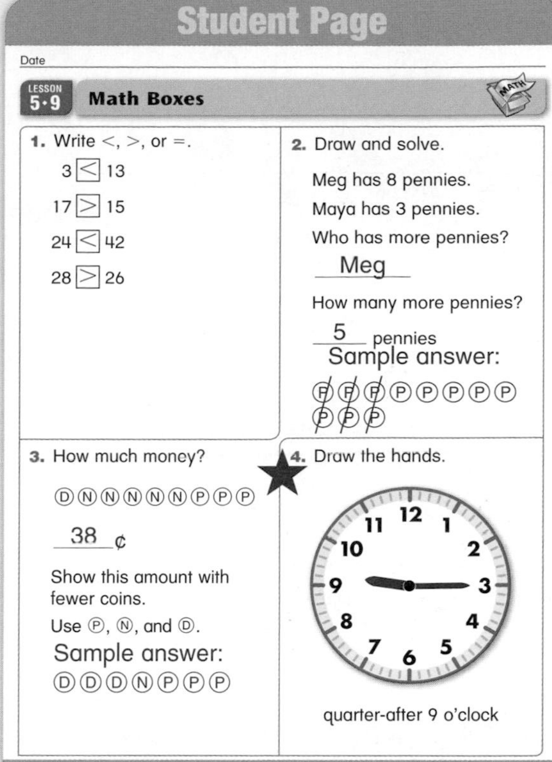

Date

LESSON 5•9 **Math Boxes**

1. Write <, >, or =.
3 < 13
17 > 15
24 < 42
28 > 26

2. Draw and solve.
Meg has 8 pennies.
Maya has 3 pennies.
Who has more pennies? Meg
How many more pennies? 5 pennies
Sample answer: ⓅⓅⓅⓅⓅⓅⓅⓅ ⓅⓅⓅ

3. How much money?
ⒹⓃⓃⓃⓃⓃⓅⓅⓅ
38 ¢
Show this amount with fewer coins.
Use Ⓟ, Ⓝ, and Ⓓ.
Sample answer: ⒹⒹⒹⓃⓅⓅⓅ

4. Draw the hands.
quarter-after 9 o'clock

Math Journal 1, p. 97

Home Link Master

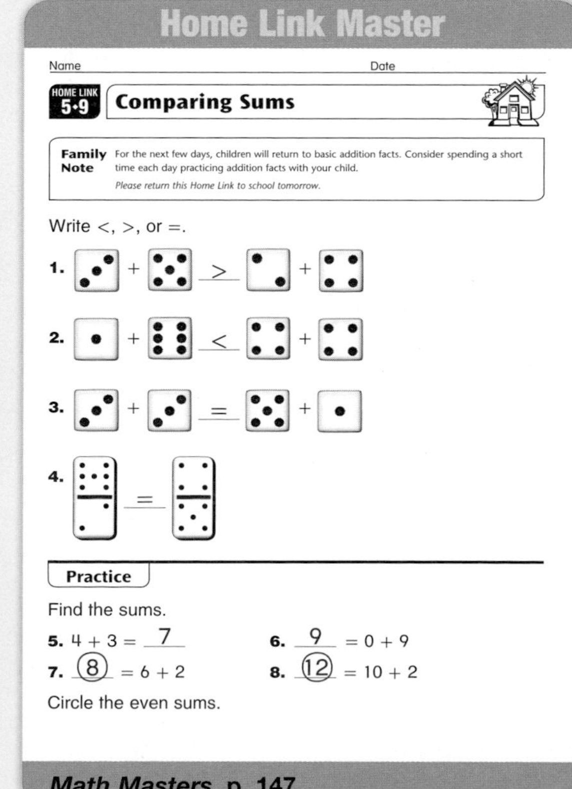

Name Date

HOME LINK 5•9 **Comparing Sums**

Family Note For the next few days, children will return to basic addition facts. Consider spending a short time each day practicing addition facts with your child.
Please return this Home Link to school tomorrow.

Write <, >, or =.

1. ⚂ + ⚄ > ⚁ + ⚃
2. ⚀ + ⚅ < ⚃ + ⚃
3. ⚂ + ⚂ = ⚄ + ⚀
4. (domino) = (domino)

Practice

Find the sums.

5. 4 + 3 = 7
6. 9 = 0 + 9
7. (8) = 6 + 2
8. (12) = 10 + 2

Circle the even sums.

Math Masters, p. 147

5•10 Facts Using Doubles

Objective To provide opportunities for children to explore and practice doubles-plus-1 and doubles-plus-2 facts, as well as review strategies for solving other addition facts.

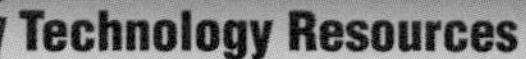

Technology Resources www.everydaymathonline.com

ePresentations

eToolkit

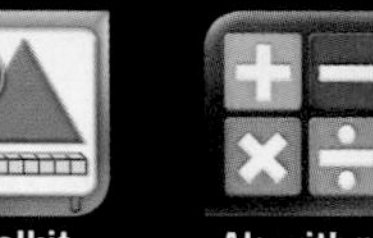
Algorithms Practice

EM Facts Workshop Game™

Family Letters

Assessment Management

Common Core State Standards

Curriculum Focal Points

Interactive Teacher's Lesson Guide

1 Teaching the Lesson

Key Concepts and Skills

- Develop and practice strategies for addition that use doubles facts.
  [Operations and Computation Goal 1]
- Use a variety of addition fact strategies for solving multi-addend addition problems.
  [Operations and Computation Goals 1 and 2]

Key Activities

Children identify and practice strategies that use doubles facts. They also practice adding 3 or more addends and discussing the strategies they use.

Ongoing Assessment: Recognizing Student Achievement Use Mental Math and Reflexes.
[Operations and Computation Goal 4]

Key Vocabulary

doubles-plus-1 fact ◆ doubles-plus-2 fact

Materials

Math Journal 1, p. 98
Home Link 5•9
counters of two colors or types ◆ 3 or 4 dice

2 Ongoing Learning & Practice

Guessing the Grab

clear plastic bag ◆ pattern blocks ◆ paper bag (optional)
Children describe the probability of grabbing a given shape from a clear bag containing different shapes.

Math Boxes 5•10

Math Journal 1, p. 99
Children practice and maintain skills through Math Box problems.

Home Link 5•10

Math Masters, p. 149
Children practice and maintain skills through Home Link activities.

3 Differentiation Options

READINESS

Exploring Doubles

number cards 0–10 (from *Math Journal 1,* Activity Sheet 1; or the Everything Math Deck, if available)
counters
Children practice with doubles facts using counters.

EXTRA PRACTICE

Playing *Domino Top-It*

dominoes
Children practice comparing quantities and finding sums.

Advance Preparation

***Teacher's Reference Manual,* Grades 1–3** pp. 196–198

Getting Started

Mental Math and Reflexes 

Tell simple number stories. Children use any strategy to solve them and then share their solution strategies. Summarize solutions with an appropriate diagram and number model. (Remember not to force the solution to a number story into a particular mold.) If children are able to do so, ask them to complete the diagrams and/or suggest a number model. Children should not be expected to do either at this time.

Number story suggestions:

●○○ Malcolm has 7 basketballs and 7 baseballs. How many balls does Malcolm have in all? 14 balls; $7 + 7 = 14$

●●○ Henrietta had 15¢. She gave the cashier 5¢ for an eraser. How much money does Henrietta have left? 10¢; $15 - 5 = 10$

●●● Raymond and Eli collect baseball cards. Raymond has 19 cards. Eli has fewer cards than Raymond. The difference between the number of cards that Raymond has and the number of cards Eli has is 10. How many cards does Eli have in all? 9 cards; $19 - 9 = 10$

Math Message

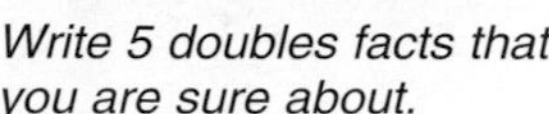

Write 5 doubles facts that you are sure about.

Home Link 5·9 Follow-Up

Briefly go over the answers.

Ongoing Assessment: Recognizing Student Achievement

Mental Math and Reflexes ★

Use **Mental Math and Reflexes** to assess children's ability to solve simple number stories. Children are making adequate progress if they are able to correctly answer the first problem. Some children might answer all three problems with relative ease.

[Operations and Computation Goal 4]

1 Teaching the Lesson

Math Message Follow-Up

WHOLE-CLASS DISCUSSION

Ask children to name the doubles facts they know. List doubles facts in a column on one side of the board until you have listed all of the facts from $1 + 1 = 2$ through $10 + 10 = 20$. Leave enough space between each doubles fact to write an additional fact later in the activity. Ask: *What do all doubles facts have in common?* Sample answers: Both addends are the same; the sums are all even. Tell them that today they will learn how to use doubles facts to solve other facts.

Introducing Doubles-Plus-1 Facts

WHOLE-CLASS ACTIVITY

Without erasing the doubles facts you listed on the board for the Math Message Follow-Up, focus children's attention on $5 + 5 = 10$. Have children use one color or type of counters to show two columns of 5 counters each. Represent this on the board with a drawing labeled $5 + 5 = 10$.

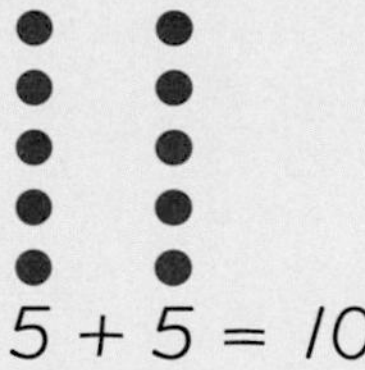

$5 + 5 = 10$

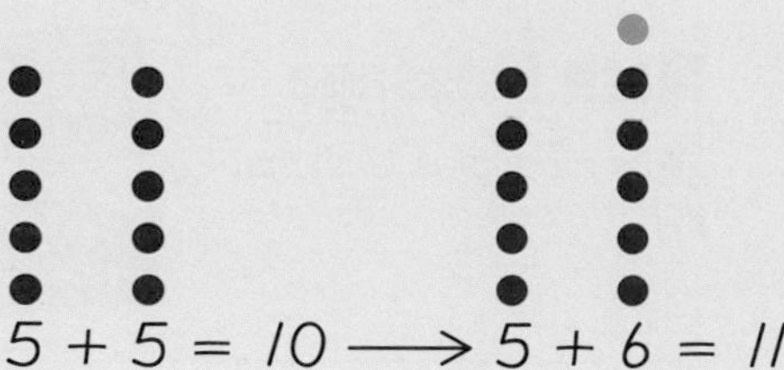

NOTE Knowledge of doubles facts is important, as this lesson focuses on strategies that assume quick recall of these facts. Daily practice of the doubles facts will help reinforce this skill.

NOTE Be sure to add Doubles-Plus-1 and Doubles-Plus-2 strategies to your Fact Strategy Wall.

Have children add one counter of a different color or type to the top of one column. Represent this on the board by drawing a counter of a different color on top of the right column. Ask: *How is this like 5 + 5 = 10? How is it different from 5 + 5 = 10?* Sample answer: It still has two sets of 5 counters, but it has 1 extra counter in one of the columns. Below the drawing, write the number model 5 + 6 = 10. Ask: *Is this number model true or false?* false Erase the 10. *How could you use doubles to solve this problem?* You can add 5 + 5 = 10 and then add one more to make 11. Write 11 to the right of the equals sign. Ask: *Is this number model true or false?* true Explain that this is called a **doubles-plus-1 fact.**

Repeat this activity with several other doubles-plus-1 facts. Then ask children to look at the list of doubles facts on the board and name some doubles-plus-1 facts that could be solved using the doubles facts. Insert these doubles-plus-1 facts next to the doubles facts in your list of facts. Point to various facts and ask how children could use doubles facts to find the sums. Once children seem to grasp the strategy, ask them to describe the strategy to put on the Fact Strategy Wall. For example, for the fact 3 + 4, children might say: You know that 3 + 3 = 6. Since 4 is one more than 3, then 3 + 4 is one more than 3 + 3. So to solve 3 + 4, you can think of the problem this way:

3 + 3 = 6
and 6 + 1 = 7
so 3 + 4 = 7.

▶ Introducing Doubles-Plus-2 Facts

Begin again with the doubles fact 5 + 5 = 10 written on the board and represented by two columns of 5 counters of the same color or type. Have children make two columns of 5 counters. Have children add two counters of a different color or type to one column. Draw two different counters at the top of one of your columns. Change the number model to 5 + 7 = 10. Ask: *Is this number model true or false?* false Erase the 10. Ask: *How can we use the doubles fact 5 + 5 = 10 to solve this problem?* Since 5 + 5 = 10 and there are 2 extra counters, add 2 to 10. Since 10 + 2 = 12, then 5 + 7 = 12. Explain that this is called a **doubles-plus-2 fact.** Write 12 to the right of the equals sign. Ask: *Is this number model true or false?* true

Ask: *Can anyone think of another doubles fact that can be used to solve this problem?* This will likely be a difficult question for children to answer. Guide children by moving one of the counters from the taller column to the shorter column. Again ask: *Can anyone think of another doubles fact that can be used to solve this problem?* Children should now be able to see that $5 + 7 = 6 + 6 = 12$.

Have children use counters to practice using both methods to solve a variety of doubles-plus-2 facts. Some children will find that one method is easier for them than the other.

Practicing Using Doubles to Add

INDEPENDENT ACTIVITY

FACTS PRACTICE

(*Math Journal 1*, p. 98)

In Problems 1–3, children solve problems that could be solved using the doubles-plus-1 strategy. In Problems 5–7, they solve problems that could be solved using the doubles-plus-2 strategies. Take care, however, not to force a particular strategy for a problem. Your most efficient strategy for solving a particular problem may not be the most efficient strategy for every child. Demonstrating a variety of strategies and allowing children to share and discuss their own strategies with the class will allow children to internalize the strategies that are most efficient for them over time. Problems 4 and 8 will give insight into what strategies children are using most comfortably.

Doing a Dice-Roll Activity

Ask a child to roll the dice and say aloud the numbers shown. Write the numbers on the board as an addition number model with an answer box for the sum. Have another child describe one strategy for adding the numbers. Show the order in which the child adds the numbers by connecting pairs of numbers and writing their sum. Write the sum of the numbers in the answer box. Refer to the Fact Strategy Wall as strategies arise (doubles, doubles-plus-1, doubles-plus-2, making ten, +10, etc.). Write the number model again and ask other children to add in a different order while you note the steps, the strategies used, and the sum.

You may wish to use this activity as an ongoing routine to practice fact strategies. As your class becomes more comfortable, try these variations: roll additional dice, roll again when a 1 appears on a die, or include one or more polyhedral die (8–20 sides). Have partnerships or individuals roll dice and record their work on slates or on paper.

Student Page

Date

LESSON 5·10 **Using Doubles Facts**

Add. Use doubles facts to help you.

1. 5 + 4 = 9
2. 15 = 8 + 7
3. 3 + 4 = 7
4. Explain how you solved 3 + 4.
   Answers vary.
5. 5 + 3 = 8
6. 16 = 7 + 9
7. 6 + 4 = 10
8. Explain how you solved 6 + 4.
   Answers vary.

***Math Journal 1*, p. 98**

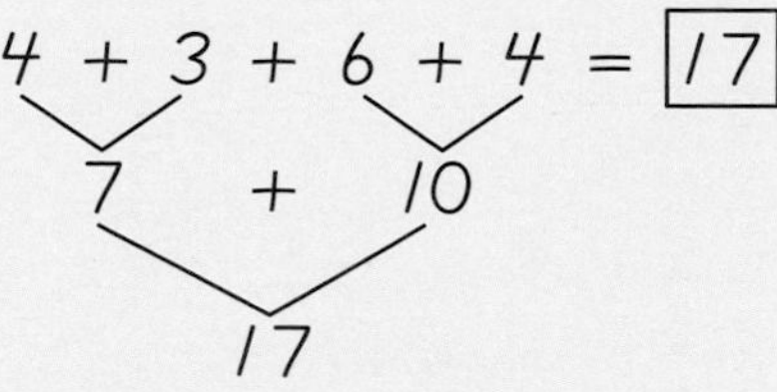

2 Ongoing Learning & Practice

▶ Guessing the Grab

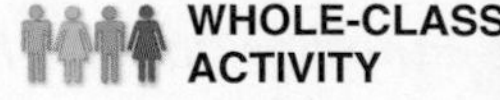

Display a large, clear plastic bag containing 3 orange squares and 5 green triangles. Explain that you are going to close your eyes, reach into the bag, and grab a shape. Ask them which shape they think you will *likely* grab. Allow them to explain their reasoning. Then grab and remove a shape. Children continue to make predictions about what shape you will remove. Continue to remove shapes from the bag until the bag is empty. Refill the bag with different shapes. Repeat the activity.

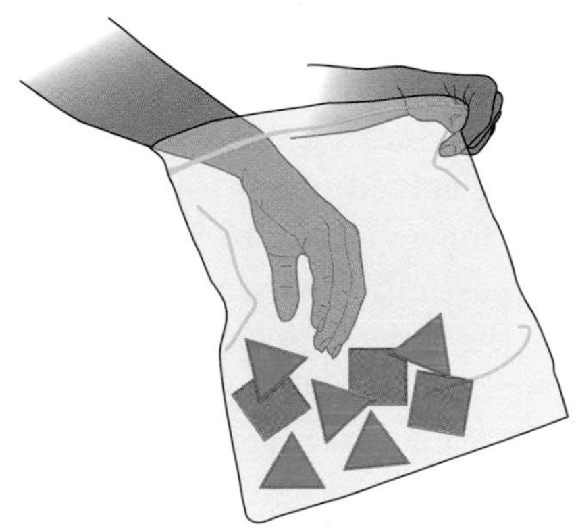

After doing this activity several times, discuss children's observations. *For example:*

- The shape with the greatest quantity is *likely* to be grabbed.
- The shape with the least quantity is *unlikely* to be grabbed.
- As you remove shapes from the original bag, the likelihood of which shape you grab will change.

Adjusting the Activity

When children start to see patterns in probability, do this activity with a brown paper bag. Show children what shapes and how many of each shape are in the bag. Then ask them which shape they think you are most likely to remove. Continue the activity as described.

AUDITORY ◆ KINESTHETIC ◆ TACTILE ◆ VISUAL

Links to the Future

"Guessing the Grab" gives children the opportunity to use the most basic language of probability. They will be exposed to this language throughout the year. Explaining the most basic language of probability is a Grade 2 Goal.

▶ Math Boxes 5•10

INDEPENDENT ACTIVITY

(*Math Journal 1,* p. 99)

Mixed Practice Math Boxes in this lesson are paired with Math Boxes in Lesson 5-12. The skills in Problem 4 preview Unit 6 content.

▶ Home Link 5•10

INDEPENDENT ACTIVITY

(*Math Masters,* p. 149)

Home Connection Children find the sums of near-doubles addition facts and solve base-10 block riddles.

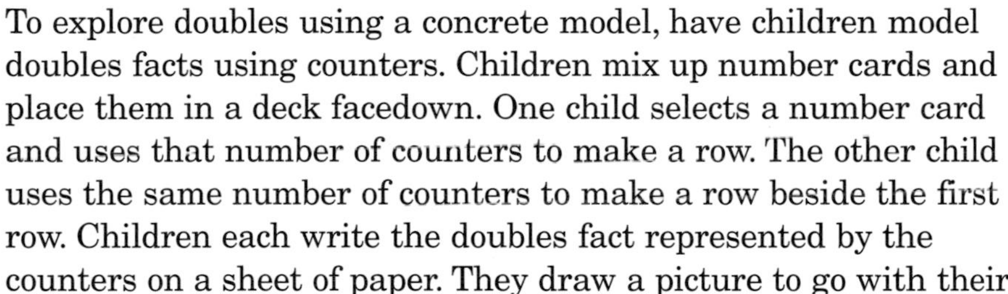

READINESS

PARTNER ACTIVITY

▶ Exploring Doubles

(*Math Journal 1,* Activity Sheet 1)

To explore doubles using a concrete model, have children model doubles facts using counters. Children mix up number cards and place them in a deck facedown. One child selects a number card and uses that number of counters to make a row. The other child uses the same number of counters to make a row beside the first row. Children each write the doubles fact represented by the counters on a sheet of paper. They draw a picture to go with their doubles fact. Children repeat this activity as time allows.

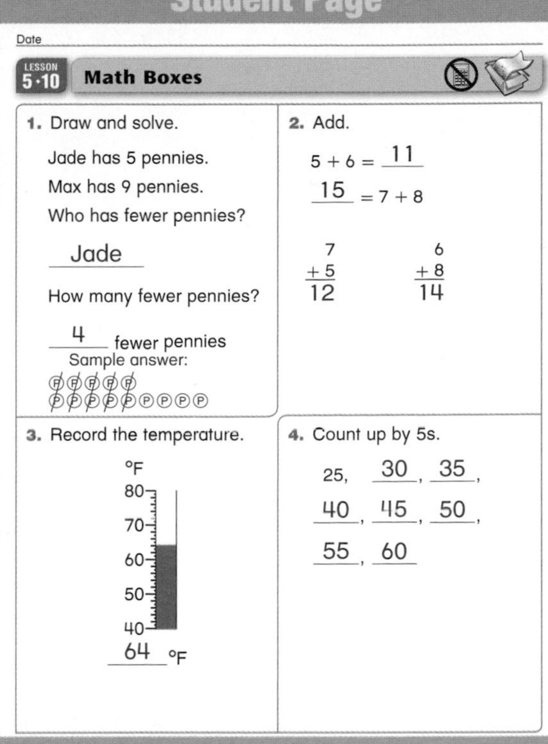

Student Page

Date

LESSON 5•10 **Math Boxes**

1. Draw and solve.
Jade has 5 pennies.
Max has 9 pennies.
Who has fewer pennies?
Jade
How many fewer pennies?
4 fewer pennies
Sample answer:

2. Add.
5 + 6 = 11
15 = 7 + 8
7 + 5 = 12
6 + 8 = 14

3. Record the temperature.
°F
80
70
60
50
40
64 °F

4. Count up by 5s.
25, 30, 35, 40, 45, 50, 55, 60

Math Journal 1, p. 99

NOTE Remember to reserve time every day to complete the number-line, attendance, calendar, weather, and temperature routines.

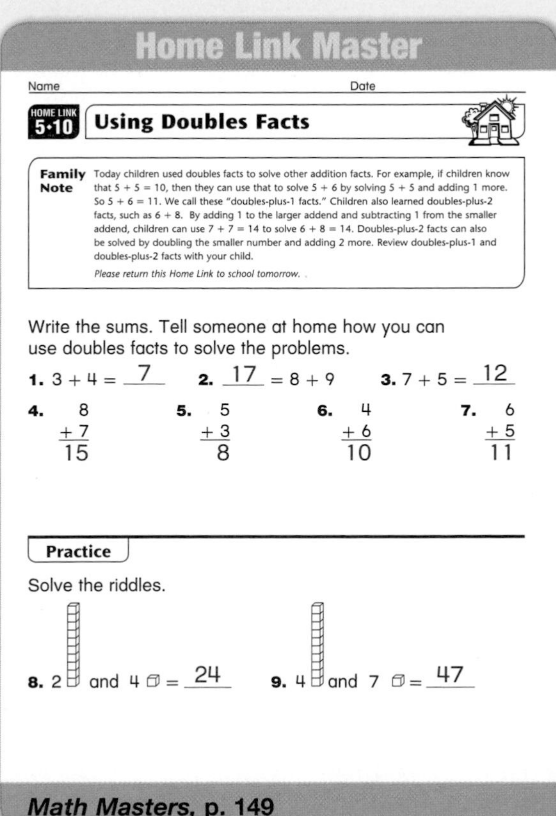

Home Link Master

Name Date

HOME LINK 5•10 **Using Doubles Facts**

Family Note Today children used doubles facts to solve other addition facts. For example, if children know that 5 + 5 = 10, then they can use that to solve 5 + 6 by solving 5 + 5 and adding 1 more. So 5 + 6 = 11. We call these "doubles-plus-1 facts." Children also learned doubles-plus-2 facts, such as 6 + 8. By adding 1 to the larger addend and subtracting 1 from the smaller addend, children can use 7 + 7 = 14 to solve 6 + 8 = 14. Doubles-plus-2 facts can also be solved by doubling the smaller number and adding 2 more. Review doubles-plus-1 and doubles-plus-2 facts with your child.

Please return this Home Link to school tomorrow.

Write the sums. Tell someone at home how you can use doubles facts to solve the problems.

1. 3 + 4 = 7
2. 17 = 8 + 9
3. 7 + 5 = 12
4. 8 + 7 = 15
5. 5 + 3 = 8
6. 4 + 6 = 10
7. 6 + 5 = 11

Practice

Solve the riddles.

8. 2 and 4 = 24
9. 4 and 7 = 47

Math Masters, p. 149

EXTRA PRACTICE

PARTNER ACTIVITY

▶ Playing *Domino Top-It*

15–30 Min

Children determine sums and compare quantities by playing *Domino Top-It*.

Directions

1. Children place the dominoes facedown on the table.
2. Each child chooses a domino and compares the total number of dots to the total number on his or her partner's domino.
3. The child with the larger total takes both dominoes. Ties are settled by another draw.
4. The game ends when time is up or when all of the dominoes have been drawn.

Planning Ahead

Provide time for children to work on the number scrolls that they began in Lesson 4-10.

5•11 Fact Strategy Review

Objectives To review various addition fact strategies; and to provide practice with addition facts with sums to 20.

Technology Resources www.everydaymathonline.com

ePresentations

eToolkit

Algorithms Practice

EM Facts Workshop Game™

Family Letters

Assessment Management

Common Core State Standards

Curriculum Focal Points

Interactive Teacher's Lesson Guide

1 Teaching the Lesson

Key Concepts and Skills

- Recite addition facts; use strategies to solve addition facts; find sums of addition facts with and without a calculator. [Operations and Computation Goal 1]
- Discuss patterns in addition facts. [Patterns, Functions, and Algebra Goal 1]
- Identify and explain turn-around facts. [Patterns, Functions, and Algebra Goal 3]

Key Activities

Children review the meaning of turn-around facts. They explore patterns in the +0 and +1 facts and identify the doubles facts and the facts whose sums are 10. Children review strategies used to solve +8, +9, and +10 facts, as well as doubles-plus-1 and doubles-plus-2 facts. Children play *Beat the Calculator.*

Ongoing Assessment: Recognizing Student Achievement
Use the Math Message.
[Patterns, Functions, and Algebra Goal 3]

Materials

Math Journal 1, pp. 100, 101, 101A, and 101B
Math Masters, p. 336 (optional)
Home Link 5•10
base-10 blocks (cubes) ◆ calculator ◆ counters (optional)

2 Ongoing Learning & Practice

Playing *Penny Plate*
per partnership: tool-kit pennies, paper plate
Children practice making sums of 10.

Math Boxes 5•11
Math Journal 1, p. 102
Children practice and maintain skills through Math Box problems.

Home Link 5•11
Math Masters, p. 150
Children practice and maintain skills through Home Link activities.

3 Differentiation Options

READINESS

Two-Fisted Penny Addition for 15 and 16
Math Masters, p. 151
tool-kit pennies
Children find and record complements of 15 and 16 in the Two-Fisted Penny Addition activity.

EXTRA PRACTICE

Solving Easy Math Facts
Math Masters, p. 317
Children review easy math facts.

Advance Preparation

Fill in *Math Masters,* page 317 with addition facts before copying it for use in the optional Extra Practice activity in Part 3.

***Teacher's Reference Manual,* Grades 1–3** pp. 195, 196

Getting Started

Mental Math and Reflexes

Set the following amounts of cubes on the overhead. Turn on the overhead for about 3 seconds; turn it off. Ask children to estimate how many longs could be exchanged for the cubes they saw on the overhead.

●○○ Show 10 cubes.

●●○ Show 19 cubes.

●●● Show 50 cubes.

Count the cubes to check.

Math Message 

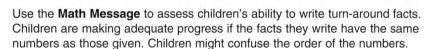

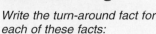

Write the turn-around fact for each of these facts:

0 + 4 = 4 *6 + 5 = 11*

8 = 3 + 5 *10 = 2 + 8*

Home Link 5·10 Follow-Up

Briefly go over the answers.

Student Page

Date

LESSON 5·11 **Facts Table**

0 + 0 0	0 + 1 1	0 + 2 2	0 + 3 3	0 + 4 4	0 + 5 5	0 + 6 6	0 + 7 7	0 + 8 8	0 + 9 9
1 + 0 1	1 + 1 2	1 + 2 3	1 + 3 4	1 + 4 5	1 + 5 6	1 + 6 7	1 + 7 8	1 + 8 9	1 + 9 10
2 + 0 2	2 + 1 3	2 + 2 4	2 + 3 5	2 + 4 6	2 + 5 7	2 + 6 8	2 + 7 9	2 + 8 10	2 + 9 11
3 + 0 3	3 + 1 4	3 + 2 5	3 + 3 6	3 + 4 7	3 + 5 8	3 + 6 9	3 + 7 10	3 + 8 11	3 + 9 12
4 + 0 4	4 + 1 5	4 + 2 6	4 + 3 7	4 + 4 8	4 + 5 9	4 + 6 10	4 + 7 11	4 + 8 12	4 + 9 13
5 + 0 5	5 + 1 6	5 + 2 7	5 + 3 8	5 + 4 9	5 + 5 10	5 + 6 11	5 + 7 12	5 + 8 13	5 + 9 14
6 + 0 6	6 + 1 7	6 + 2 8	6 + 3 9	6 + 4 10	6 + 5 11	6 + 6 12	6 + 7 13	6 + 8 14	6 + 9 15
7 + 0 7	7 + 1 8	7 + 2 9	7 + 3 10	7 + 4 11	7 + 5 12	7 + 6 13	7 + 7 14	7 + 8 15	7 + 9 16
8 + 0 8	8 + 1 9	8 + 2 10	8 + 3 11	8 + 4 12	8 + 5 13	8 + 6 14	8 + 7 15	8 + 8 16	8 + 9 17
9 + 0 9	9 + 1 10	9 + 2 11	9 + 3 12	9 + 4 13	9 + 5 14	9 + 6 15	9 + 7 16	9 + 8 17	9 + 9 18

Math Journal 1, p. 100

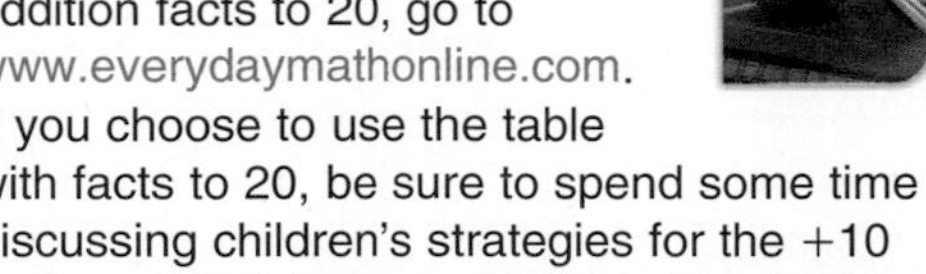

NOTE If you want children to use a Facts Table with addition facts to 20, go to www.everydaymathonline.com. If you choose to use the table with facts to 20, be sure to spend some time discussing children's strategies for the +10 facts and their turn-around facts (the bottom row and right column of the table).

1 Teaching the Lesson

▶ Math Message Follow-Up

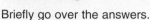

Go over the answers. *What if we had a new student who didn't know about turn-around facts? Can you explain how they work? Why does it make learning the facts easier?* You can add two numbers in a different order and get the same answer. When you learn one fact, you are really learning two facts.

Tell children that they will also be reviewing other fact strategies.

Ongoing Assessment: Recognizing Student Achievement

Math Message ★

Use the **Math Message** to assess children's ability to write turn-around facts. Children are making adequate progress if the facts they write have the same numbers as those given. Children might confuse the order of the numbers.

[Patterns, Functions, and Algebra Goal 3]

▶ +0 and +1 Fact Patterns

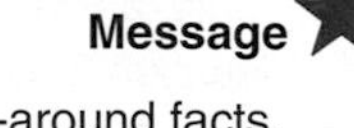

FACTS PRACTICE

(*Math Journal 1,* p. 100)

Direct children's attention to the Facts Table on journal page 100. Read and recite together the facts in the 0-column (the first column). Discuss the sums. Children should notice that the sum is always the same as the number with which the problem began. Have a volunteer tell why this is so. Ask children to lightly shade all of the + 0 facts with a crayon (the first column) and then to shade the turn-around facts for the + 0 facts (the first row).

NOTE The number zero is called the *additive identity* because the sum of zero and any number is that number.

Next, follow the same procedure for the +1 facts. Again, read and recite together the facts in the 1-column (the second column). Children should notice that the sum is always the number that comes after the number with which the problem began. Have them shade with a different color all of the +1 facts and their turn-around facts.

Pose several problems with numbers that are not in the table, such as 17 +0, 98 +0, 53 +1, and 69 +1. Have children name the sums and tell how they found them.

Doubles Facts and Facts Whose Sums Are 10

FACTS PRACTICE

(*Math Journal 1,* pp. 100 and 101)

Help children find and shade the doubles facts in the Facts Table on journal page 100. Ask children to recite them in unison. Then have them find and shade all of the facts in the table with sums of 10. Point out that these facts and the doubles facts are found on diagonals that go in opposite directions.

Next, have children solve the problems on journal page 101. Tell them to do as many problems as they can without using the Facts Table, but if they are unsure of an answer, they should look it up in the table. When they have completed the page, have partners check each other's work.

Doubles-Plus-1 and Doubles-Plus-2 Facts

FACTS PRACTICE

(*Math Journal 1,* pp. 100, 101, and 101A)

Remind children that in the last lesson, they learned how to use doubles to solve doubles-plus-1 and doubles-plus-2 facts. Have children look at the list of doubles facts on journal page 101. Help them use the facts to create a list of the doubles-plus-1 and doubles-plus-2 facts on the board. Remember to include the turn-around facts for each of these facts. Then, have children find each of these facts on the Facts Table and shade them lightly with a crayon. Ask children to review the strategy that they used for solving doubles-plus-1 and doubles-plus-2 facts.

Next, have children solve the problems on journal page 101A. Have them find as many sums as they can without using the Facts Table.

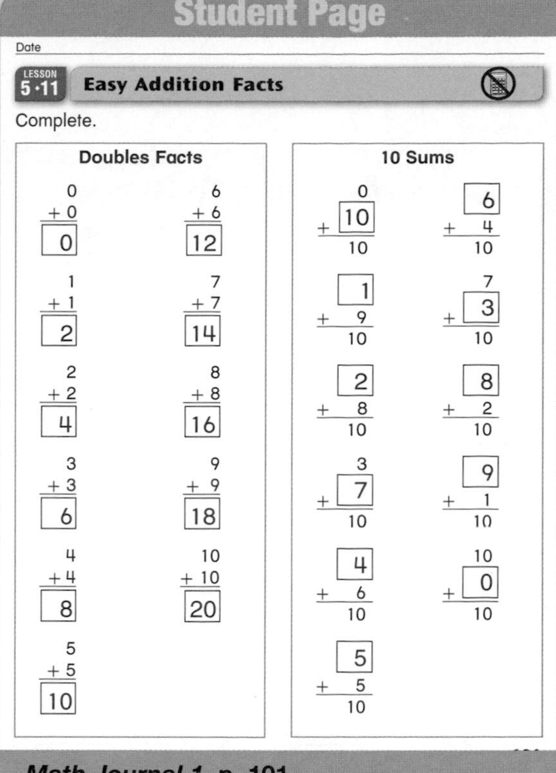

Student Page

Date

LESSON 5·11 **Easy Addition Facts**

Complete.

Doubles Facts		10 Sums	
0 + 0 = 0	6 + 6 = 12	0 + 10 = 10	6 + 4 = 10
1 + 1 = 2	7 + 7 = 14	1 + 9 = 10	7 + 3 = 10
2 + 2 = 4	8 + 8 = 16	2 + 8 = 10	8 + 2 = 10
3 + 3 = 6	9 + 9 = 18	3 + 7 = 10	9 + 1 = 10
4 + 4 = 8	10 + 10 = 20	4 + 6 = 10	10 + 0 = 10
5 + 5 = 10		5 + 5 = 10	

Math Journal 1, p. 101

NOTE It may be visually challenging for some children to navigate the Facts Table. If so, you might want to enlarge the table on the copying machine so that the numbers are bigger and less crowded, making the table more manageable.

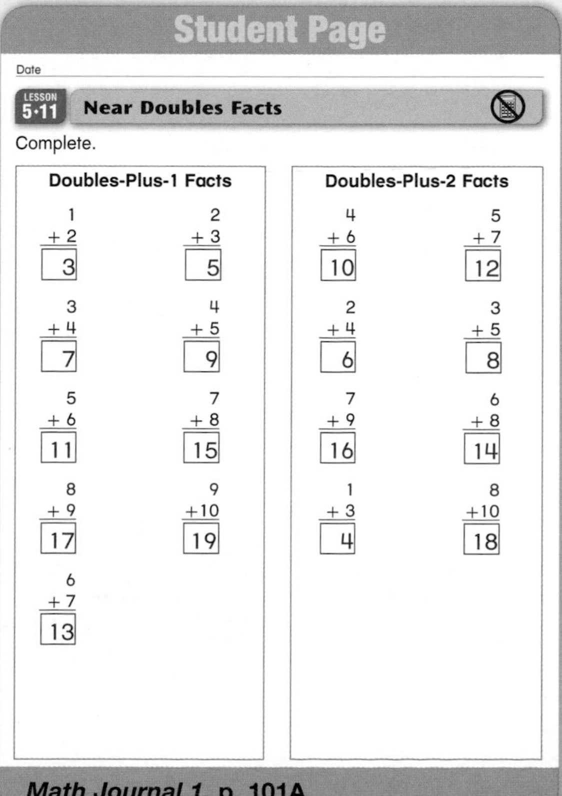

Student Page

Date

LESSON 5·11 **Near Doubles Facts**

Complete.

Doubles-Plus-1 Facts		Doubles-Plus-2 Facts	
1 + 2 = 3	2 + 3 = 5	4 + 6 = 10	5 + 7 = 12
3 + 4 = 7	4 + 5 = 9	2 + 4 = 6	3 + 5 = 8
5 + 6 = 11	7 + 8 = 15	7 + 9 = 16	6 + 8 = 14
8 + 9 = 17	9 + 10 = 19	1 + 3 = 4	8 + 10 = 18
6 + 7 = 13			

Math Journal 1, p. 101A

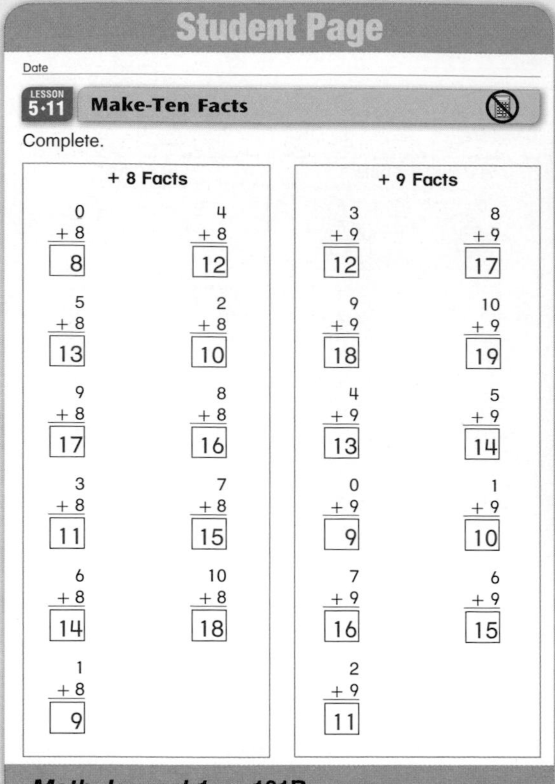
Student Page

Date

LESSON 5·11 **Make-Ten Facts**

Complete.

+ 8 Facts		+ 9 Facts	
0 + 8 = 8	4 + 8 = 12	3 + 9 = 12	8 + 9 = 17
5 + 8 = 13	2 + 8 = 10	9 + 9 = 18	10 + 9 = 19
9 + 8 = 17	8 + 8 = 16	4 + 9 = 13	5 + 9 = 14
3 + 8 = 11	7 + 8 = 15	0 + 9 = 9	1 + 9 = 10
6 + 8 = 14	10 + 8 = 18	7 + 9 = 16	6 + 9 = 15
1 + 8 = 9		2 + 9 = 11	

Math Journal 1, **p. 101B**

Adjusting the Activity

Children who play the role of the Brain in *Beat the Calculator* may use counters and fingers to help them. As your work with fact power continues, encourage children to rely on memory.

AUDITORY ◆ KINESTHETIC ◆ TACTILE ◆ VISUAL

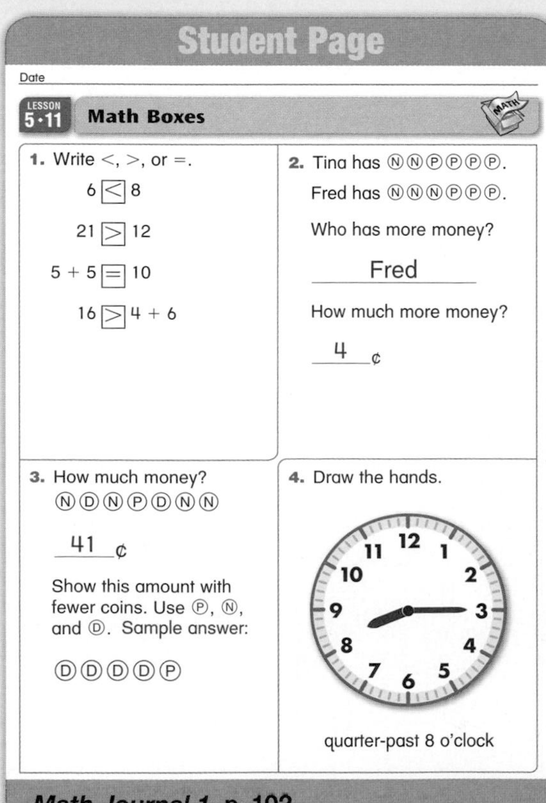
Student Page

Date

LESSON 5·11 **Math Boxes**

1. Write <, >, or =.
   6 [<] 8
   21 [>] 12
   5 + 5 [=] 10
   16 [>] 4 + 6
2. Tina has ⓃⓃⓅⓅⓅⓅ.
   Fred has ⓃⓃⓃⓅⓅⓅ.
   Who has more money?
   Fred
   How much more money?
   4 ¢
3. How much money?
   ⓃⒹⓃⓅⒹⓃⓃ
   41 ¢
   Show this amount with fewer coins. Use Ⓟ, Ⓝ, and Ⓓ. Sample answer:
   ⒹⒹⒹⒹⓅ
4. Draw the hands.
   quarter-past 8 o'clock

Math Journal 1, **p. 102**

▶ Making-Ten Facts

(*Math Journal 1,* pp. 100 and 101B; *Math Masters,* p. 336)

Remind children that they used the Making-Ten Strategy to solve addition facts in which one of the addends was an 8 or a 9. Help children find these facts on the Facts Table on journal page 100. Recite together the facts in the 8- and 9-columns (last two columns in the Facts Table).

Ask someone to summarize the Making-Ten Strategy. Have children lightly shade the +8 and +9 facts (last two columns) and then shade the turn-around facts for these facts (bottom two rows).

Next, have children solve the problems on journal page 101B. Once again, encourage children to do as many of the problems as they can without the Facts Table. They may use a ten frame (*Math Masters,* page 336) and counters if necessary.

Have children look at the Facts Table. They have reviewed strategies to solve all facts except five of the facts on the table and the related turn-around facts: 5 + 2, 6 + 2, 7 + 2, 6 + 3, and 7 + 4. Discuss possible strategies children might use to solve these.

▶ Introducing *Beat the Calculator*

Prior to playing *Beat the Calculator,* explain how to find the answer to addition facts using a calculator. Remind children to clear the calculator before entering an addition fact. Write an addition fact on the board, such as 2 + 1 = ____. Tell children to press 2 [+] 1 [=] to find the answer. Ask them what number appears on the screen. Tell children that this is the answer. Remind them to clear their calculators after each sum is found. Repeat as necessary.

Divide the class into two groups. Children in one group, the "Calculators," use their calculators to find the sum for a fact given by the "Caller." They hold up the calculator showing the answer as they call it out. Children in the other group, the "Brains," do the problem in their heads and say the answer.

For today, you be the Caller until children become comfortable with the game. Emphasize +0, +1, doubles facts, and facts with sums of 10.

Play this game every day for the next few days, then every once in a while over the next few months. The eventual goal is to beat the calculator on all of the addition facts.

Variation: Include problems that add 10 to single-digit numbers.

Discuss the fact that some problems can be solved more easily and quickly in one's head than by using a calculator.

2 Ongoing Learning & Practice

▶ Playing *Penny Plate*

Children practice with sums of 10 by playing *Penny Plate.* For detailed instructions, see Lesson 2-8.

▶ Math Boxes 5•11

INDEPENDENT ACTIVITY

(*Math Journal 1,* p. 102)

Mixed Practice Math Boxes in this lesson are linked to Math Boxes in Lesson 5-9 and Lesson 5-13. The skills in Problem 4 preview Unit 6 content.

▶ Home Link 5•11

INDEPENDENT ACTIVITY

(*Math Masters,* p. 150)

Home Connection Children ask someone at home to give them a 1-, a 2-, and a 3-digit number. They add 0 and then 1 to the numbers and tell the results.

Home Link Master

Name Date

HOME LINK 5•11 **Adding 0 and 1**

Family Note Give your child several 1-digit, 2-digit, and 3-digit numbers. Ask him or her to add 0 and 1 to each number.
Include numbers with 9 in the ones place like 9, 49, 79, 129, 359, and 789.
Also use 0 in the tens and ones places, like in 208 and 320.
Please return this Home Link to school tomorrow.

Record your answers in the table below.

1. Ask someone at home to say a 1-digit number; for example, 7. Add 0 to the number and give the answer. Then add 1 to the number and give the answer.
2. Have someone say a 2-digit number. Repeat with a 3-digit number.

Example: 25 + 0 = 25 25 + 1 = 26

Number Models

	Number	+0	+1
Example	25	25 + 0 = 25	25 + 1 = 26
1-digit number	Answers		
2-digit number	vary.		
3-digit number			

Practice

Write <, >, or =.

3. 19 < 21 **4.** 10 > 4 **5.** 2 < 11 **6.** 0 = 0

Math Masters, **p. 150**

3 Differentiation Options

READINESS

▶ Two-Fisted Penny Addition for 15 and 16

5–15 Min

(*Math Masters,* p. 151)

To provide experience with fact practice, children do the Two-Fisted Penny Addition activity. This activity is a continuation of the systematic record of complements of the numbers 5–18. Children find and record all the complements of 15 and 16 on *Math Masters,* page 151.

EXTRA PRACTICE

▶ Solving Math Facts

5–15 Min

(*Math Masters,* p. 317)

To provide practice finding sums of math facts, fill in the addends on *Math Masters,* page 317 and have children fill in the sums.

Teaching Master

Name Date

LESSON 5•11 **Two-Fisted Penny Addition**

15		16		17		18	
Left	Right	Left	Right	Left	Right	Left	Right
0	15	0	16	0	17	0	18
1	14	1	15	1	16	1	17
2	13	2	14	2	15	2	16
3	12	3	13	3	14	3	15
4	11	4	12	4	13	4	14
5	10	5	11	5	12	5	13
6	9	6	10	6	11	6	12
7	8	7	9	7	10	7	11
8	7	8	8	8	9	8	10
9	6	9	7	9	8	9	9
10	5	10	6	10	7	10	8
11	4	11	5	11	6	11	7
12	3	12	4	12	5	12	6
13	2	13	3	13	4	13	5
14	1	14	2	14	3	14	4
15	0	15	1	15	2	15	3
		16	0	16	1	16	2
				17	0	17	1
						18	0

Order of answers may vary.

Math Masters, **p. 151**

5·12 "What's My Rule?"

Objective To introduce the "What's My Rule?" routine.

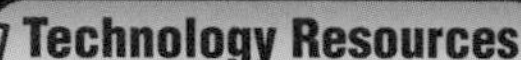

Technology Resources www.everydaymathonline.com

ePresentations

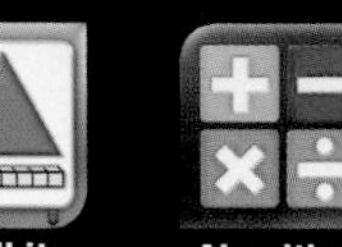
eToolkit

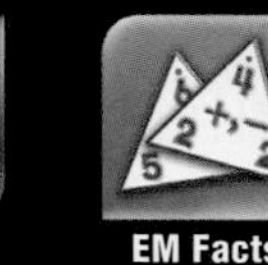
Algorithms Practice

EM Facts Workshop Game™

Family Letters

Assessment Management

Common Core State Standards

Curriculum Focal Points

Interactive Teacher's Lesson Guide

1 Teaching the Lesson

Key Concepts and Skills

- Count forward and backward from a given number.
  [Number and Numeration Goal 1]
- Use addition and subtraction to solve "What's My Rule?" problems.
  [Operations and Computation Goal 2]
- Find and describe rules in "What's My Rule?" problems.
  [Patterns, Functions, and Algebra Goal 1]

Key Activities

Children solve "What's My Rule?" problems—find and apply rules—using a function machine.

Ongoing Assessment: Informing Instruction See page 417.

Key Vocabulary

function machine ◆ rule

Materials

Math Journal 1, p. 103
Home Link 5•11
calculator ◆ paper bag ◆ craft sticks ◆ slate ◆ counters (optional)

2 Ongoing Learning & Practice

Practicing Solving "What's My Rule?" Problems

Math Masters, p. 152
Children practice solving "What's My Rule?" problems.

Math Boxes 5•12

Math Journal 1, p. 104
Children practice and maintain skills through Math Box problems.

Ongoing Assessment: Recognizing Student Achievement

Use Math Boxes, Problem 3.
[Measurement and Reference Frames Goal 3]

Home Link 5•12

Math Masters, pp. 153–155
Children practice and maintain skills through Home Link activities.

3 Differentiation Options

READINESS

Following a Rule on the Calculator

calculator ◆ overhead calculator (optional)
Children use a calculator to add and subtract by a given number.

ENRICHMENT

Making "What's My Rule?" Problems

Math Masters, p. 323
Children make up their own "What's My Rule?" problems.

ELL SUPPORT

Building a Math Word Bank

Differentiation Handbook, p. 126
Children add the term *rule* to their Math Word Banks.

Advance Preparation

***Teacher's Reference Manual,* Grades 1–3** pp. 18, 19, 209–215

Getting Started

Mental Math and Reflexes

Play *Beat the Calculator.* Emphasize + 0, + 1, sums of 10, and doubles facts. Add a few more difficult facts so that children with calculators can win some of the time.

Math Message

How are these facts alike?

1 + 1   *7 + 1*

4 + 1   *5 + 1*

Home Link 5•11 Follow-Up

Children share some of the +1 problems they recorded in their Number Models tables.

1 Teaching the Lesson

Math Message Follow-Up

WHOLE-CLASS ACTIVITY

Children may say that all of the facts are +1 facts and describe the change as "add 1," "count up by 1," or "the next number."

Tell children that you have a magic bag with the power to change whatever is put in it. Use a paper bag and craft sticks to play a guessing game. Put 1 stick in the bag, say a "magic word," and take 2 sticks out of the bag. Then put 4 sticks in and pull 5 sticks out. Repeat several times until the children can predict how many sticks will come out. Discuss the rule that fits the action of the magic bag.

Next, tell children that you are going to change the magic rule. Play the game again with "add 2." Repeat with one or two more rules like "subtract 1" or "double."

Introducing the "What's My Rule?" Routine

WHOLE-CLASS ACTIVITY

ELL

Algebraic Thinking Tell children that a new math routine called "What's My Rule?" works like the magic bag. But instead of using craft sticks, it uses numbers.

Draw a **function machine** on the board. Explain that if you put a number into the machine, it will do something to the number and a different number will come out. It will do the same thing to any number that you put in. For example, if you put in 5, 6 will come out. If you put in 12, 13 will come out. If you put in 19, 20 will come out.

- What number do you think will come out if you put in 26? 27

Ask someone to give you a number to put into the machine.

- What number will come out? The number that is 1 more than the number that was put in
- Can you figure out what the function machine does to the numbers you put in? It adds 1 to them.

A function machine

NOTE Use the words *input* and *output,* but do not expect children to use them. The concepts are more important than the words at this stage in first grade.

You say:	Record
	in → out
I put in a 4; a 14 comes out.	4 → 14
I put in a 12; a 22 comes out.	12 → 22
I put in a 20; a 30 comes out.	20 → 30
I put in a 15; what number comes out?	15 → ? 25
I put in a 56; what number comes out?	56 → ? 66
What's my rule? Add 10	

in → out	in → out
3 → 5	15 → 5
7 → 9	26 → 16
18 → 20	49 → 39
6 → ? 8	32 → ? 22
21 → ? 23	50 → ? 40
Add 2	Subtract 10

Suggested "What's My Rule?" problems

ELL

Have children use counters to explore the relationship between input and output numbers. Have children line up counters for a pair of input and output numbers in two rows, and then match pairs of counters in the two rows. The unmatched counters will give a clue to the relationship between pairs of "in" and "out" numbers.

AUDITORY • KINESTHETIC • TACTILE • VISUAL

Explain that all function machines don't work the same way. For example, one machine might subtract 2 from any number you put in and another machine might add 10. Tell children that they are going to play a guessing game called "What's My Rule?" The object of the game is to figure out what **rule** a function machine uses to change the numbers that are put in. To support English language learners, explain that *rule* has an everyday usage like classroom rules, and *rule* also has a mathematical usage.

When posing a "What's My Rule?" problem, record each number you put into the machine (the input) followed by an arrow and the number that comes out (the output). (*See margin.*)

Encourage children to describe the rule in different ways. Expect responses such as the following:

▷ The "out" number is always 10 more than the "in" number.

▷ The function machine is adding 10 to the "in" number.

▷ The "in" number gets bigger by 10.

▷ The machine adds 1 to the tens digit.

Do a few more "What's My Rule?" problems. Have children write the missing "out" numbers on their slates. For each problem, ask what the function machine does to the "in" numbers.

Function machines are not restricted to adding or subtracting the same number to the input number, as illustrated by the following problems. Try them with your class, but don't expect most children to solve them at this time.

in → out	in → out
2 → 4	16 → 8
6 → 12	2 → 1
3 → 6	12 → 6
5 → ? 10	4 → ? 2
9 → ? 18	10 → ? 5
doubles	halves

▶ Solving "What's My Rule?" Problems

INDEPENDENT ACTIVITY

(*Math Journal 1,* p. 103)

Algebraic Thinking Explain that the numbers under the headings "in" and "out" on the journal page show what numbers go *into* the function machine and what numbers come *out*. Tell children to figure out the rule that determines what numbers come out of the machine and use that rule to find the missing output numbers. You might want to do the first problem together to make sure children understand what to do.

NOTE If children have difficulty naming a rule, ask them to find the missing output numbers. Extending a pattern is often easier than stating the rule for it.

Ongoing Assessment: Informing Instruction

Watch for children who do not apply the same rule to all the numbers in a problem. Remind children that a function machine will do the same thing to any number that is put in.

2 Ongoing Learning & Practice

Practicing Solving "What's My Rule?" Problems

(*Math Masters,* p. 152)

Algebraic Thinking Use *Math Masters,* page 152, to provide more practice solving "What's My Rule?" problems.

Math Boxes 5·12

(*Math Journal 1,* p. 104)

Mixed Practice Math Boxes in this lesson are paired with Math Boxes in Lesson 5-10. The skills in Problem 4 preview Unit 6 content.

Ongoing Assessment: Recognizing Student Achievement

Math Boxes Problem 3

Use **Math Boxes, Problem 3** to assess children's ability to record temperature. Children are making adequate progress if they are able to give the temperature to the nearest 10 degrees. Some children may be able to give the temperature to the nearest two degrees.

[Measurement and Reference Frames Goal 3]

Writing/Reasoning Have children draw, write, or verbalize an answer to the following: *How do you find the temperature?* A reasonable answer should include reference to the marks between multiples of 10 degrees.

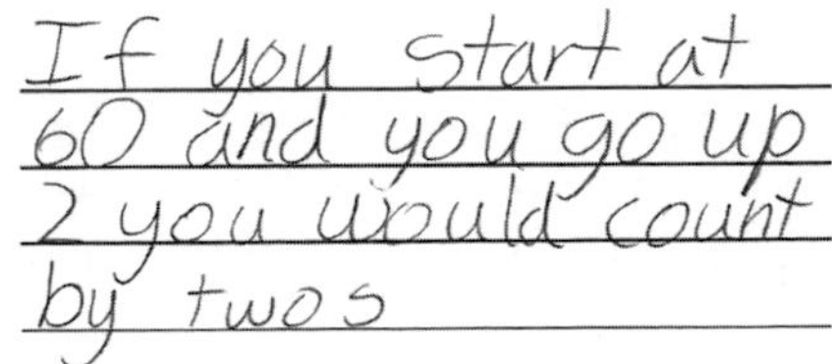

One child's work in response to the Writing/Reasoning prompt

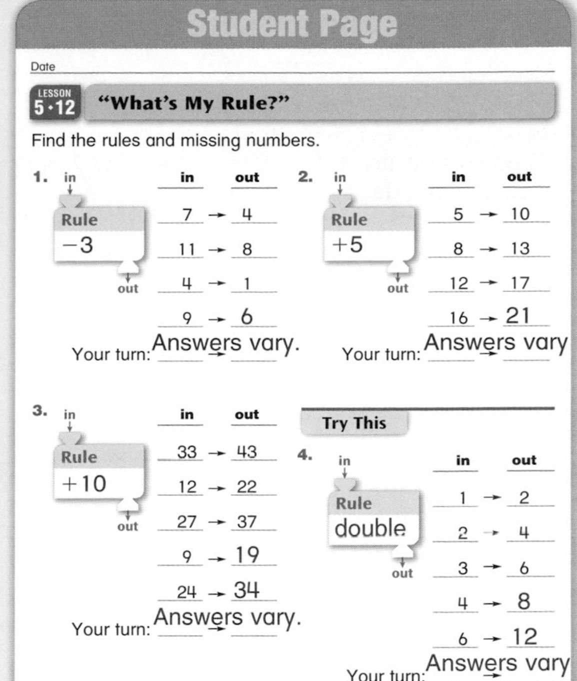

Student Page

Date

LESSON 5·12 **"What's My Rule?"**

Find the rules and missing numbers.

1. Rule −3

in	out
7	4
11	8
4	1
9	6

Your turn: Answers vary.

2. Rule +5

in	out
5	10
8	13
12	17
16	21

Your turn: Answers vary

3. Rule +10

in	out
33	43
12	22
27	37
9	19
24	34

Your turn: Answers vary.

Try This

4. Rule double

in	out
1	2
2	4
3	6
4	8
6	12

Your turn: Answers vary

Math Journal 1, p. 103

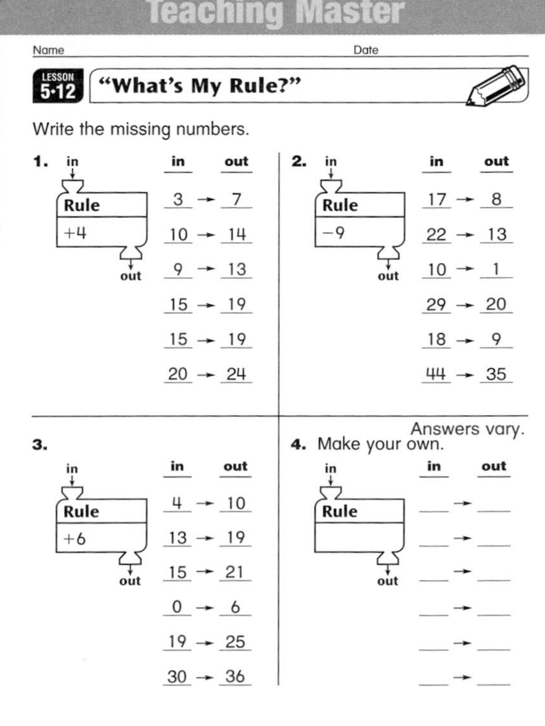

Teaching Master

Name Date

LESSON 5·12 **"What's My Rule?"**

Write the missing numbers.

1. Rule +4

in	out
3	7
10	14
9	13
15	19
15	19
20	24

2. Rule −9

in	out
17	8
22	13
10	1
29	20
18	9
44	35

3. Rule +6

in	out
4	10
13	19
15	21
0	6
19	25
30	36

4. Make your own. Answers vary.

Rule

in	out

Math Masters, p. 152

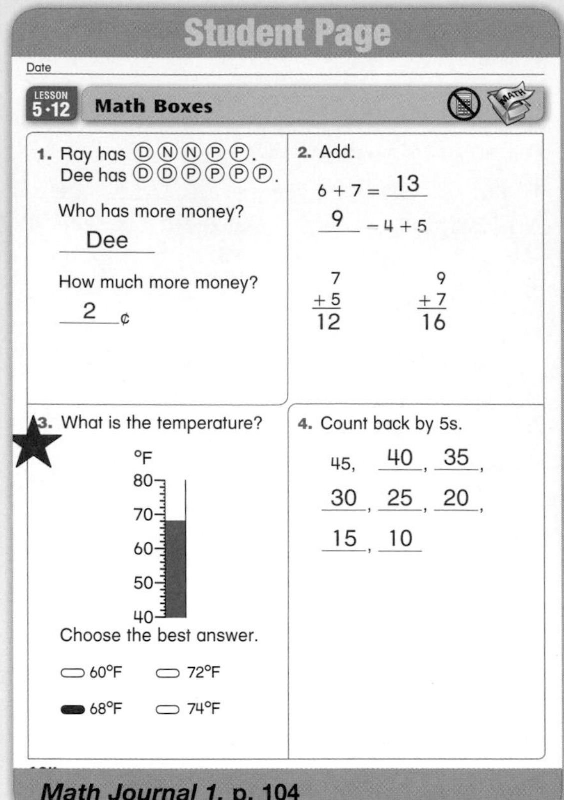

Student Page

Date

LESSON 5·12 **Math Boxes**

1. Ray has Ⓓ Ⓝ Ⓝ Ⓟ Ⓟ.
Dee has Ⓓ Ⓓ Ⓟ Ⓟ Ⓟ Ⓟ.
Who has more money? Dee
How much more money? 2 ¢

2. Add.
6 + 7 = 13
9 = 4 + 5
7 + 5 = 12
9 + 7 = 16

3. What is the temperature?
°F 80, 70, 60, 50, 40
Choose the best answer.
○ 60°F ○ 72°F
● 68°F ○ 74°F

4. Count back by 5s.
45, 40, 35, 30, 25, 20, 15, 10

Math Journal 1, p. 104

NOTE Remember to reserve time every day to complete the number-line, attendance, calendar, weather, and temperature routines.

Home Link Masters

Name Date

HOME LINK 5·12 **Family Letter**

"What's My Rule?"

Today your child learned about a kind of problem you may not have seen before. We call it "What's My Rule?" Please ask your child to explain it to you. Here is a little background information you may find useful.

Imagine a machine with a funnel at the top and a tube at the bottom—we call this a *function machine.* The function machine can be programmed so that when you drop a number into the funnel at the top, the machine changes the number according to the rule and a new number comes out of the tube at the bottom.

For example, you can program the machine to add 2 to any number that is dropped into the funnel. If you put in 3, out comes 5; if you put in 6, out comes 8.

You can show this with a table:

in 3; Rule +2; out 5

in	out
3	5
6	8
10	12

Here is another example of a function machine:

in 5; Rule +3; out 8

in	out
5	8
6	9
2	5

Math Masters, pp. 153–155

▶ Home Link 5·12

INDEPENDENT ACTIVITY

PROBLEM SOLVING

(*Math Masters,* pp. 153–155)

Home Connection Children solve "What's My Rule?" problems. Home Link 5-12 includes a two-page Family Letter explaining "What's My Rule?" problems.

3 Differentiation Options

READINESS

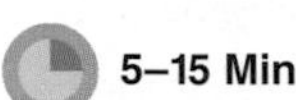

SMALL-GROUP ACTIVITY

5–15 Min

▶ Following a Rule on the Calculator

To provide experience following rules, have children solve addition and subtraction problems using a calculator. Name a rule such as "add 2" for children to follow. Using a calculator, children add 2 to any given number. Invite children to suggest numbers to enter into the calculator and share answers.

Repeat with other rules, such as "subtract 2" or "add 5." Discuss how the calculator changes any number entered according to the rule.

ENRICHMENT

INDEPENDENT ACTIVITY

15–30 Min

PROBLEM SOLVING

▶ Making "What's My Rule?" Problems

(*Math Masters,* p. 323)

Algebraic Thinking To further explore the "What's My Rule?" routine, have children make their own "What's My Rule?" problems. Have children use *Math Masters,* page 323 to make four problems and trade completed pages to check each other's work.

ELL SUPPORT

SMALL-GROUP ACTIVITY

▶ Building a Math Word Bank

(*Differentiation Handbook,* p. 126)

To provide language support for the "What's My Rule?" routine, have children use the Word Bank Template found on *Differentiation Handbook,* page 126. Ask children to write the term *rule,* draw a picture representing the term, and write other words that describe it. See the *Differentiation Handbook* for more information.

5•13 Applying Rules

Objective To provide experiences with finding the output for given rules and input numbers.

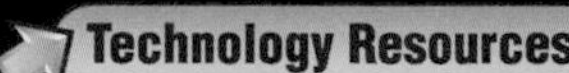

Technology Resources www.everydaymathonline.com

ePresentations

eToolkit

Algorithms Practice

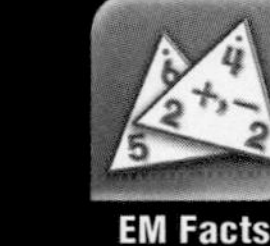
EM Facts Workshop Game™

Family Letters

Assessment Management

Common Core State Standards

Curriculum Focal Points

Interactive Teacher's Lesson Guide

1 Teaching the Lesson

Key Concepts and Skills

- Count forward and backward from a given number.
  [Number and Numeration Goal 1]
- Use addition and subtraction to solve "What's My Rule?" problems.
  [Operations and Computation Goal 2]
- Continue patterns in "What's My Rule?" problems.
  [Patterns, Functions, and Algebra Goal 1]
- Find the rule in "What's My Rule?" problems.
  [Patterns, Functions, and Algebra Goal 1]

Key Activities

Children use a rule and an input number to find an output number. They record the input and output in a table.

Materials

Math Journal 1, p. 105
Home Link 5•12
calculator

2 Ongoing Learning & Practice

Playing *Penny-Nickel-Dime Exchange*
per partnership: 20 pennies, 10 nickels, and 10 dimes; 2 dice; additional tool-kit coins (optional); 2 polyhedron dice (optional)
Children practice making exchanges between coins.

Math Boxes 5•13
Math Journal 1, p. 106
Children practice and maintain skills through Math Box problems.

Ongoing Assessment: Recognizing Student Achievement
Use Math Boxes, Problem 2.
[Operations and Computation Goal 2]

Home Link 5•13
Math Masters, p. 156
Children practice and maintain skills through Home Link activities.

Minute Math+
Minute Math®+, pp. 17 and 97
Children practice with shapes and temperature.

3 Differentiation Options

ENRICHMENT

Simulating a Function Machine on a Calculator
calculator ◆ overhead calculator (optional)
Children program their calculators to simulate function machines.

EXTRA PRACTICE

Filling In Function Machines
Math Masters, p. 323
Children solve "What's My Rule?" problems.

Advance Preparation

Fill in four rules and input numbers on *Math Masters,* page 323 before copying it for the optional Extra Practice activity in Part 3.

Getting Started

Mental Math and Reflexes

Play *Beat the Calculator.* See Lesson 5-11 for detailed instructions.

Math Message

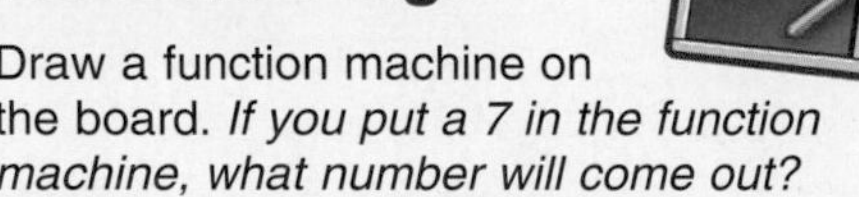

Draw a function machine on the board. *If you put a 7 in the function machine, what number will come out?*

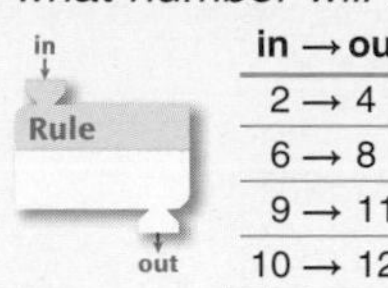

in → out
2 → 4
6 → 8
9 → 11
10 → 12

Home Link 5·12 Follow-Up

Go over the answers. Ask children to state a rule for each problem.

in
Rule
Add 2
out

1 Teaching the Lesson

▶ Math Message Follow-Up

Algebraic Thinking Review the concept of a function machine by having children describe it in their own words.

Ask what the function machine does to each number that is put in. It adds 2 to it. Write "Add 2" or "+2" on the machine on the board, and explain that this is the rule that describes what the function machine does to numbers that are put in. If you put a 7 in, a 9 will come out.

▶ Applying Rules

Algebraic Thinking Do several more function-machine problems, using the format of the Math Message problem. Write several pairs of input and output numbers, and have children find the rule and supply the missing outputs. Record the rule on the function machine. Use rules like "Add 3," "+5," "−3," "Subtract 10," and "Double."

When children are comfortable finding, stating, and applying a rule, pose a problem with just a rule and an input number. Children use the rule to find the output. For example: *If the rule is "Subtract 3," and the input is 9, what is the output?* 6

Draw a table on the board. Write a simple rule on the function machine. Write a number in the "in" column of the table. Have children name the number that goes in the "out" column. Repeat the procedure with several other input numbers.

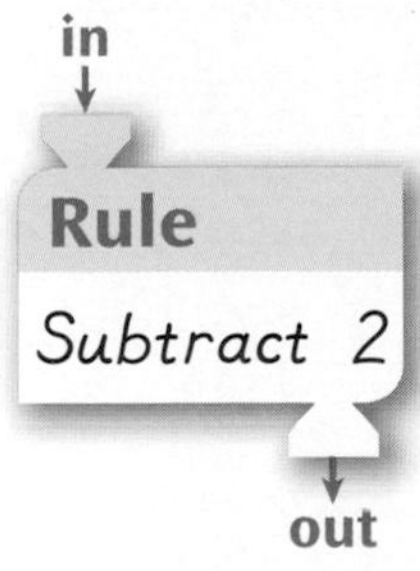

in	out
7	5
11	9
19	17
50	48

Point out that it takes time to draw an arrow for each pair of numbers and that the numbers may not always line up exactly. An easier way to keep track of the input and output numbers is to record them in a table.

Repeat this activity with other rules that are appropriate for your class. Use the table format to record inputs and outputs.

Adjusting the Activity

Instead of having children find the output for a given input, ask them to find the input for a given output. For example: *The rule is "Add 1." If I put a number in the machine and a 9 comes out, what number did I put in?* 8 *The rule is "Subtract 1." If I put a number in and a zero comes out, what number did I put in?* 1 Keep the rules simple for this variation.

AUDITORY ◆ KINESTHETIC ◆ TACTILE ◆ VISUAL

Finding and Applying Rules

(*Math Journal 1,* p. 105)

Algebraic Thinking Children complete the problems and make up problems for their partners to solve.

2 Ongoing Learning & Practice

Playing *Penny-Nickel-Dime Exchange*

Directions

1. Partners create a bank by putting 20 pennies, 10 nickels, and 10 dimes in a pile.
2. Players take turns. At each turn, a player rolls two dice and collects the amount shown on the dice from the bank. Whenever players have at least 5 pennies, they say, "Exchange," and trade 5 of their pennies for 1 nickel in the bank. Whenever players have at least 2 nickels or 5 pennies and 1 nickel, they say, "Exchange," and trade them for 1-dime.
3. The game ends when there are no more dimes in the bank. The player who has more dimes wins. If players have the same number of dimes, the player who has the greater amount of money wins.

Student Page

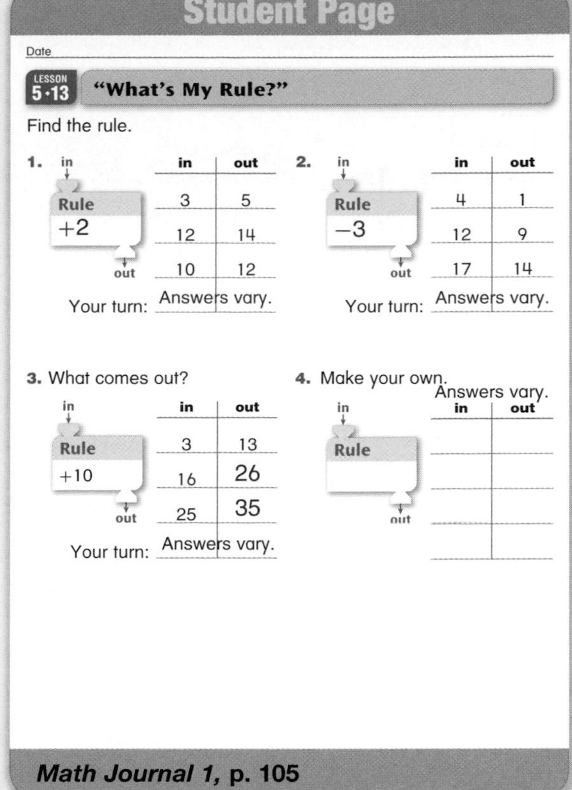

Date
LESSON 5·13 "What's My Rule?"
Find the rule.
1. in
Rule +2
out
in | out
3 | 5
12 | 14
10 | 12
Your turn: Answers vary.
2. in
Rule −3
out
in | out
4 | 1
12 | 9
17 | 14
Your turn: Answers vary.
3. What comes out?
in
Rule +10
out
in | out
3 | 13
16 | 26
25 | 35
Your turn: Answers vary.
4. Make your own.
Answers vary.
in
Rule
out
in | out

Math Journal 1, p. 105

Adjusting the Activity

Children can play the game with a larger bank and two polyhedral dice.

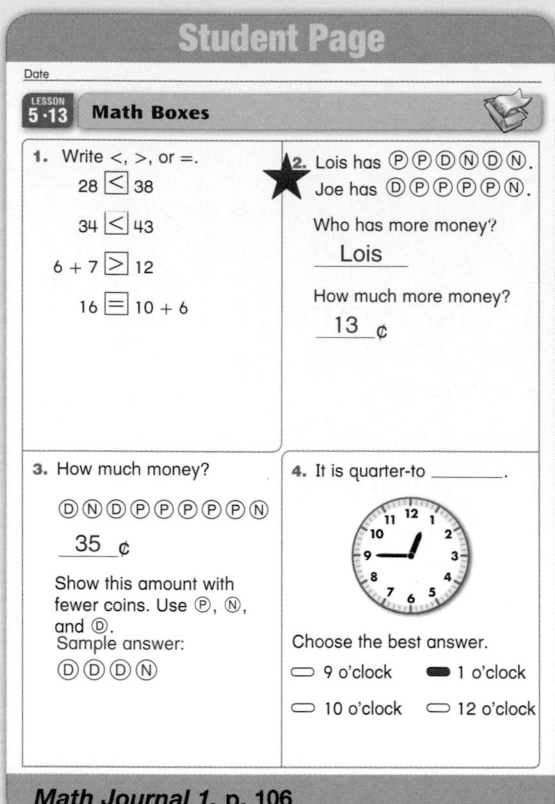

Student Page

Date

LESSON 5·13 **Math Boxes**

1. Write <, >, or =.
28 < 38
34 < 43
6 + 7 > 12
16 = 10 + 6

★ 2. Lois has Ⓟ Ⓟ Ⓓ Ⓝ Ⓓ Ⓝ.
Joe has Ⓓ Ⓟ Ⓟ Ⓟ Ⓟ Ⓝ.
Who has more money? Lois
How much more money? 13 ¢

3. How much money?
Ⓓ Ⓝ Ⓓ Ⓟ Ⓟ Ⓟ Ⓟ Ⓟ Ⓝ
35 ¢
Show this amount with fewer coins. Use Ⓟ, Ⓝ, and Ⓓ.
Sample answer: Ⓓ Ⓓ Ⓓ Ⓝ

4. It is quarter-to ______.
Choose the best answer.
◯ 9 o'clock ● 1 o'clock
◯ 10 o'clock ◯ 12 o'clock

Math Journal 1, p. 106

▶ Math Boxes 5·13

INDEPENDENT ACTIVITY

(*Math Journal 1*, p. 106)

Mixed Practice Math Boxes in this lesson are linked to Math Boxes in Lesson 5-9 and Lesson 5-11. The skills in Problem 4 preview Unit 6 content.

Ongoing Assessment: Recognizing Student Achievement

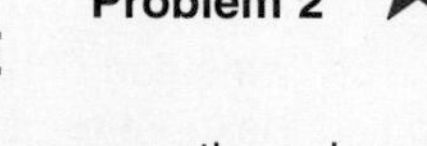

Math Boxes Problem 2 ★

Use **Math Boxes, Problem 2** to assess children's ability to compare the values of combinations of coins. Children are making adequate progress if they are able to tell who has more money. Some children will be able to tell how much more money.

[Operations and Computation Goal 2]

▶ Home Link 5·13

INDEPENDENT ACTIVITY

(*Math Masters*, p. 156)

Home Connection Children complete a page of "What's My Rule?" problems including one in which they make up their own rule.

▶ *Minute Math+*

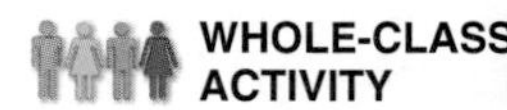

WHOLE-CLASS ACTIVITY

Use *Minute Math+*, pages 17 and 97, to provide more practice with shapes and temperature.

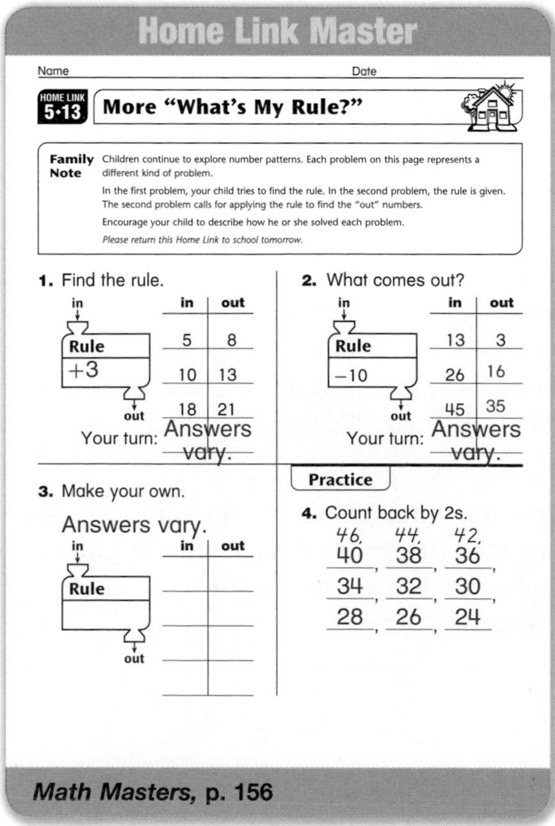

Home Link Master

Name Date

HOME LINK 5·13 **More "What's My Rule?"**

Family Note Children continue to explore number patterns. Each problem on this page represents a different kind of problem.
In the first problem, your child tries to find the rule. In the second problem, the rule is given. The second problem calls for applying the rule to find the "out" numbers.
Encourage your child to describe how he or she solved each problem.
Please return this Home Link to school tomorrow.

1. Find the rule.
Rule: +3

in	out
5	8
10	13
18	21

Your turn: Answers vary.

2. What comes out?
Rule: −10

in	out
13	3
26	16
45	35

Your turn: Answers vary.

3. Make your own.
Answers vary.

Practice

4. Count back by 2s.
46, 44, 42, 40, 38, 36, 34, 32, 30, 28, 26, 24

Math Masters, p. 156

3 Differentiation Options

ENRICHMENT

SMALL-GROUP ACTIVITY

15–30 Min

Simulating a Function Machine on a Calculator

Algebraic Thinking To apply children's understanding of function machines, have children simulate a function on a calculator. Children can use the same calculator program that was used to count up and back to simulate a function machine with an addition or subtraction rule. For example, to program the TI-108 calculator to simulate a function machine for the rule "Add 5," do the following:

▷ Clear the calculator.

▷ Enter [+] 5 [=] 0.

The display will show the number 0. The calculator is now ready to act as a function machine.

If you enter any input number and press [=], the display will show the output number. For example, if you enter the input number 9 and press [=], the display will show the output number 14. **Do not clear the calculator before entering the next input number.**

If possible, use an overhead calculator to guide children through several examples. Enter a secret rule; then ask a volunteer to enter a number and press [=]. Repeat this procedure several times. Record each input and output number in a table. Then have the group figure out the rule.

After you have done a few examples, have partners take turns programming their calculators and figuring out the rule.

NOTE To program the Casio SL-450L, press 5 (+) (+). Then enter the input numbers and press (=). The display will show the output number.

EXTRA PRACTICE

SMALL-GROUP ACTIVITY

Filling In Function Machines

(*Math Masters,* p. 323)

Algebraic Thinking Children solve "What's My Rule" problems with the given rule and input numbers on *Math Masters,* page 323.

5•14 Progress Check 5

Objective To assess children's progress on mathematical content through the end of Unit 5.

1 Looking Back: Cumulative Assessment

The **Mid-Year Assessment** in the *Assessment Handbook* is a written assessment that you may use to determine how children are progressing toward a range of Grade-Level Goals.

Input children's data from Progress Check 5 and the Mid-Year Assessment into the **Assessment Management Spreadsheets**.

Materials
- Home Link 5•13
- *Assessment Handbook,* pp. 84–91, 153–156, 181, and 216–219
- Mid-Year Assessment (*Assessment Handbook,* pp. 92, 93, 187–190)
- slate

CONTENT ASSESSED	LESSON(S)	ASSESSMENT ITEMS				
		SELF	ORAL/SLATE	WRITTEN		OPEN RESPONSE
				PART A	PART B	
Read, write, and represent whole numbers. [Number and Numeration Goal 3]	5•1–5•6, 5•9	2		1		✔
Compare whole numbers through 100. [Number and Numeration Goal 7]	5•1–5•9, 5•11–5•13			1–3	12	✔
Know addition facts. [Operations and Computation Goal 1]	5•1, 5•5, 5•9–5•11	6	1	7, 8		
Solve problems involving the addition or subtraction of whole numbers; calculate and compare the value of combinations of coins. [Operations and Computation Goal 2]	5•1–5•5, 5•7, 5•9, 5•11	4	2, 3	4		✔
Solve number stories. [Operations and Computation Goal 4]	5•5, 5•8		3			
Ask and answer questions and draw conclusions based on data representations. [Data and Chance Goal 2]	5•1, 5•6, 5•8, 5•9	3			11, 12	
Read a thermometer. [Measurement and Reference Frames Goal 3]	5•10, 5•12, 5•13	1	4		9	
Show and tell time on an analog clock. [Measurement and Reference Frames Goal 4]	5•9, 5•11, 5•13				10	
Solve problems involving simple functions. [Patterns, Functions, and Algebra Goal 1]	5•12, 5•13	5		5, 6		
Write number sentences using symbols. [Patterns, Functions, and Algebra Goal 2]	5•5–5•8		3	1–3		✔

2 Looking Ahead: Preparing for Unit 6

Math Boxes 5•14

Home Link 5•14: Unit 6 Family Letter

Materials
- *Math Journal 1,* p. 107
- *Math Masters,* pp. 157–160

Getting Started

Math Message • Self Assessment

Complete the Self Assessment (Assessment Handbook, page 153).

Home Link 5·13 Follow-Up

Briefly go over the missing numbers and missing rules. Have volunteers share problems they created.

1 Looking Back: Cumulative Assessment

Math Message Follow-Up

INDEPENDENT ACTIVITY

(Self Assessment, *Assessment Handbook*, p. 153)

The Self Assessment offers children the opportunity to reflect upon their progress.

Oral and Slate Assessments

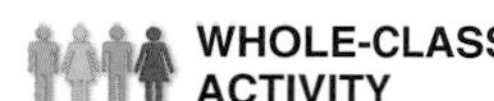

WHOLE-CLASS ACTIVITY

Problems 1 and 2 provide summative information and can be used for grading purposes. Problems 3 and 4 provide formative information that can be useful in planning future instruction.

Oral Assessment

1. Ask children to mentally find the answer to each math fact. Then ask the children to state the answers verbally.
   - $24 + 0 = 24$
   - $7 + 7 = 14$
   - $19 - 0 = 19$
   - $9 + 1 = 10$
   - $4 - 1 = 3$
   - $7 + 3 = 10$
2. Show a combination of coins by writing Ⓟ Ⓝ Ⓓ on the board. Children write the amounts on their slates.
   - Ⓟ Ⓟ Ⓟ Ⓝ Ⓝ 13¢
   - Ⓟ Ⓟ Ⓟ Ⓝ Ⓓ Ⓓ 28¢

Slate Assessment

3. Tell the following number stories. Children record a number model and the answers on their slates. Encourage children to use various strategies to solve the problems.
   - Stephen's puppy Bailey weighed 6 pounds when he brought her home. Six months later, Bailey weighed 17 pounds more. How much did Bailey weigh after six months?
     $6 + 17 = 23$ pounds
   - Myra's dad was running a 26-mile marathon. So far Myra's dad had run 20 miles. How many more miles did Myra's dad have to run? $26 - 20 = 6$ miles
4. Set the red ribbon on the Class Thermometer Poster to show various temperatures. Then have children record the temperatures. Show:
   - 90°F
   - 46°F
   - 20°F
   - 30°F
   - 62°F

Assessment Master

Name ____ Date ____

LESSON 5·14 **Self Assessment** Progress Check 5

Put a check in the box that tells how you do each skill.

Skills	I can do this by myself. I can explain how to do this.	I can do this by myself.	I can do this with help.
1. Use a thermometer.			
2. Use base 10 blocks to make numbers.			
3. Answer questions using a tally chart.			
4. Count coins.			
5. Solve "What's My Rule?" problems.			
6. Solve math facts.			

Assessment Handbook, **p. 153**

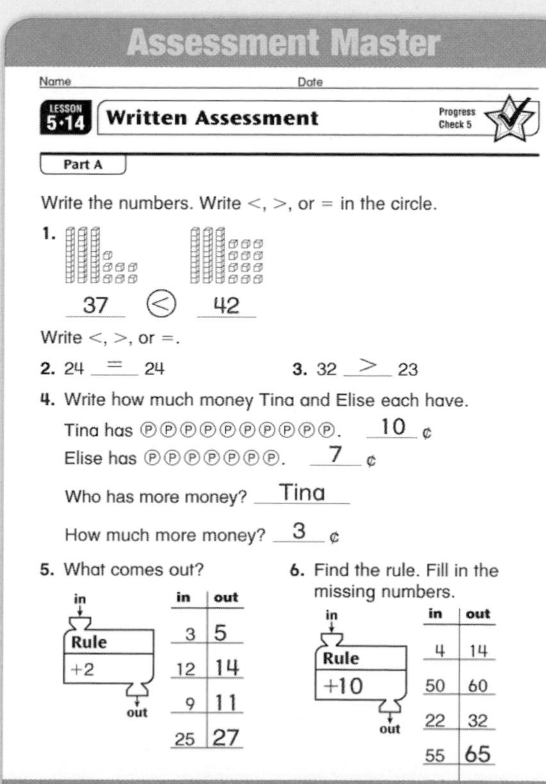

Assessment Master

Name ____ Date ____

LESSON 5·14 **Written Assessment** Progress Check 5

Part A

Write the numbers. Write <, >, or = in the circle.

1. 37 < 42

Write <, >, or =.

2. 24 = 24
3. 32 > 23
4. Write how much money Tina and Elise each have.
   Tina has ⓅⓅⓅⓅⓅⓅⓅⓅⓅⓅ. 10 ¢
   Elise has ⓅⓅⓅⓅⓅⓅⓅ. 7 ¢
   Who has more money? Tina
   How much more money? 3 ¢
5. What comes out?

   Rule +2

in	out
3	5
12	14
9	11
25	27

6. Find the rule. Fill in the missing numbers.

   Rule +10

in	out
4	14
50	60
22	32
55	65

Assessment Handbook, **p. 154**

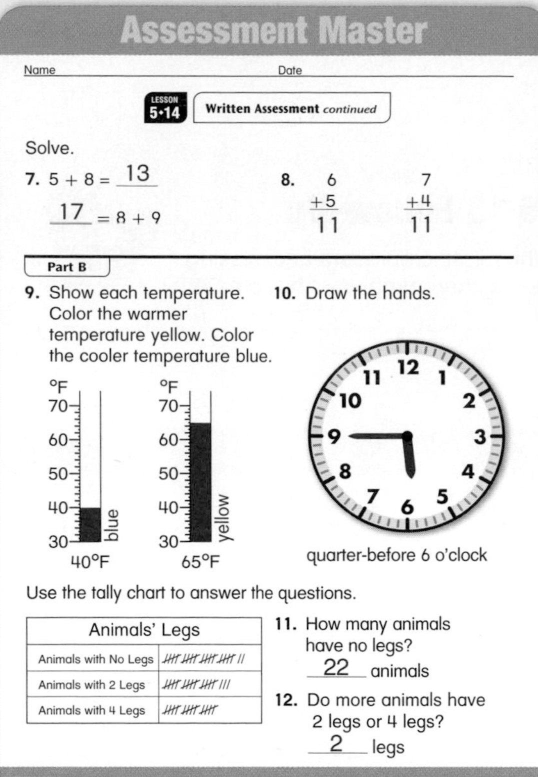

Assessment Master

Name ____ Date ____

LESSON 5·14 Written Assessment *continued*

Solve.

7. 5 + 8 = 13

17 = 8 + 9

8. 6 + 5 = 11   7 + 4 = 11

Part B

9. Show each temperature. Color the warmer temperature yellow. Color the cooler temperature blue.

40°F (blue)   65°F (yellow)

10. Draw the hands.

quarter-before 6 o'clock

Use the tally chart to answer the questions.

Animals' Legs	
Animals with No Legs	HHT HHT HHT HHT //
Animals with 2 Legs	HHT HHT HHT ///
Animals with 4 Legs	HHT HHT HHT

11. How many animals have no legs? 22 animals

12. Do more animals have 2 legs or 4 legs? 2 legs

Assessment Handbook, p. 155

Assessment Master

Name ____ Date ____

LESSON 5·14 **Open Response** Progress Check 5

Making Numbers

You found these number cards on the floor.

Circle three of the cards.

6 2 8 1 4 9 7 3 5

Use two of your circled cards. Write the largest possible 2-digit number. Answers vary.	Use two of your circled cards. Write the smallest possible 2-digit number. Answers vary.

Add your numbers together using base-10 blocks. Use base-10 block symbols (■, |, and •) to record your work.
Answers vary.

Write a number model for the problem you solved.
Answers vary.

Assessment Handbook, p. 156

▶ Written Assessment

INDEPENDENT ACTIVITY

(*Assessment Handbook,* pp. 154 and 155)

Part A Recognizing Student Achievement

Problems 1–8 provide summative information and may be used for grading purposes.

Problem(s)	Description
1	Read, write, and represent whole numbers through hundreds with base-10 blocks.
1–3	Compare whole numbers through 100.
4	Calculate and compare the values of combinations of coins.
5, 6	Solve problems involving simple functions represented as Function Machines.
7, 8	Know addition facts.

Part B Informing Instruction

Problems 9–12 provide formative information that can be useful in planning future instruction.

Problem(s)	Description
9	Recognize appropriate range of temperatures as hot or cold.
10	Show and tell time on an analog clock to the nearest quarter-hour.
11, 12	Answer questions and draw conclusions based on data representations.

Use the checklists on pages 217 and 219 of the *Assessment Handbook* to record results. Then input the data into the **Assessment Management Spreadsheets** to keep an ongoing record of children's progress toward Grade-Level Goals.

Open Response

INDEPENDENT ACTIVITY

(*Assessment Handbook,* p. 156)

Making Numbers

The open-response item requires children to apply skills and concepts from Unit 5 to solve a multistep problem. See *Assessment Handbook,* pages 87–91 for rubrics and children's work samples for this problem.

There are two options for completing this open-response problem. For both Option 1 and Option 2, children begin by working independently (or with a partner) to solve a multistep problem.

Take this time to circulate throughout the classroom.

NOTE You may wish to have number cards and base-10 blocks available for children to use in solving the problem.

Option 1:

- You found a set of cards numbered 1–9 on the floor. Choose 3 cards from the set.
- Make the largest and smallest 2-digit numbers from the cards you chose. Make the numbers with base-10 blocks.
- Add the two numbers together. Name the sum.

NOTE For Option 1, it may be helpful to work through the steps with children one at a time.

Option 2:

Distribute *Assessment Handbook,* page 156. Read the problem aloud and have children record their solutions on the page.

After children have had a chance to complete either option, invite individual children to explain their solution strategies as you record them on the board. Be sure to discuss both successful and unsuccessful strategies.

See the *Assessment Handbook* for more information.

Mid-Year Assessment

INDEPENDENT ACTIVITY

(*Assessment Handbook,* pp. 187–190)

The Mid-Year Assessment (*Assessment Handbook,* pages 187–190) provides an additional assessment opportunity that covers important concepts and skills presented in *First Grade Everyday Mathematics.* They complement the ongoing and periodic assessments that appear within lessons and at the end of units. See pages 92 and 93 in the *Assessment Handbook* for more information.

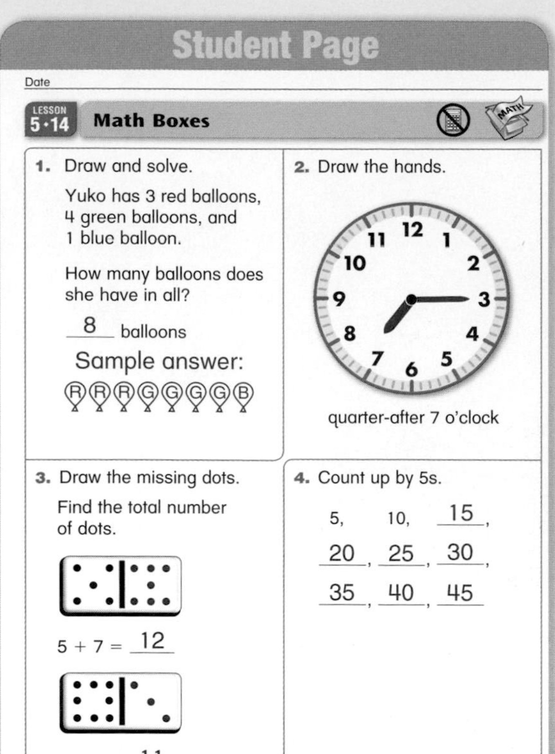
Student Page

Date

LESSON 5•14 Math Boxes

1. Draw and solve.

Yuko has 3 red balloons, 4 green balloons, and 1 blue balloon.

How many balloons does she have in all?

8 balloons

Sample answer: R R R G G G G B

2. Draw the hands.

quarter-after 7 o'clock

3. Draw the missing dots.

Find the total number of dots.

5 + 7 = 12

8 + 3 = 11

4. Count up by 5s.

5, 10, 15,

20, 25, 30,

35, 40, 45

Math Journal 1, p. 107

2 Looking Ahead: Preparing for Unit 6

▶ Math Boxes 5•14

INDEPENDENT ACTIVITY

(*Math Journal 1*, p. 107)

Mixed Practice This Math Boxes page previews Unit 6 content.

▶ Home-Link 5•14: Unit 6 Family Letter

(*Math Masters*, pp. 157–160)

Home Connection The Unit 6 Family Letter provides families with information and activities related to Unit 6 topics.

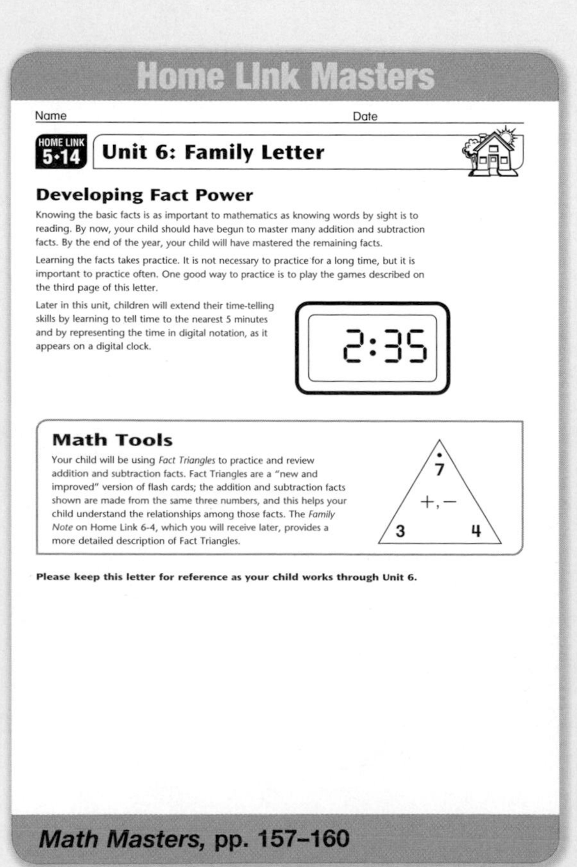
Home Link Masters

Name Date

HOME LINK 5•14 Unit 6: Family Letter

Developing Fact Power

Knowing the basic facts is as important to mathematics as knowing words by sight is to reading. By now, your child should have begun to master many addition and subtraction facts. By the end of the year, your child will have mastered the remaining facts.

Learning the facts takes practice. It is not necessary to practice for a long time, but it is important to practice often. One good way to practice is to play the games described on the third page of this letter.

Later in this unit, children will extend their time-telling skills by learning to tell time to the nearest 5 minutes and by representing the time in digital notation, as it appears on a digital clock.

2:35

Math Tools

Your child will be using *Fact Triangles* to practice and review addition and subtraction facts. Fact Triangles are a "new and improved" version of flash cards; the addition and subtraction facts shown are made from the same three numbers, and this helps your child understand the relationships among those facts. The *Family Note* on Home Link 6-4, which you will receive later, provides a more detailed description of Fact Triangles.

7 +, − 3 4

Please keep this letter for reference as your child works through Unit 6.

Math Masters, pp. 157–160

Appendices

Contents

Project 1

Geometric Gift Wrap and Greeting Cards

Objective To provide opportunities to use geometric shapes to create designs for gift wrap and greeting cards.

Technology Resources www.everydaymathonline.com

eToolkit

Algorithms Practice

EM Facts Workshop Game™

Family Letters

Assessment Management

Common Core State Standards

Curriculum Focal Points

Interactive Teacher's Lesson Guide

1 Doing the Project

Recommended Use During or after Unit 3

Key Concepts and Skills

- Use plane shapes to make designs. [Geometry Goal 1]
- Make line-symmetric designs. [Geometry Goal 2]
- Make repeating patterns. [Patterns, Functions, and Algebra Goal 1]

Key Activities

Children use pattern-block shapes to create designs. Then they print their designs to create wrapping paper or greeting cards.

Materials

- ◆ pattern blocks
- ◆ paper towels or pieces of sponge
- ◆ small paper plates
- ◆ tempera paint
- ◆ Pattern-Block Template
- ◆ plain paper for gift wrap such as newsprint is fine
- ◆ paper for greeting cards
- ◆ *A Cloak for the Dreamer* by Aileen Friedman

2 Extending the Project

Children create patterns using tangrams and letters of the alphabet; they write what they learned about geometric shapes; they discuss places where shapes are found; and they learn how to make shapes with their bodies.

Children practice skills through Home Link activities.

Materials

- ◆ sets of tangrams
- ◆ *Kente Colors*
- ◆ *The Spider Weaver: A Legend of Kente Cloth*
- ◆ *Babar's Yoga for Elephants*

Advance Preparation

For Doing the Project in Part 1, you may want to obtain ***A Cloak for the Dreamer*** by Aileen Friedman (Scholastic Inc., 1995).

You may want to obtain the following books for the optional Extension Suggestions in Part 2:

▷ ***Kente Colors*** by Debbi Chocolate (Walker and Company, 1997)

▷ ***The Spider Weaver: A Legend of Kente Cloth*** by Margaret Musgrove (Blue Sky Press, 2001)

▷ ***Babar's Yoga for Elephants*** by Laurent de Brunhoff (Harry N. Adams, Inc., 2006)

1 Doing the Project

Using Pattern-Block Shapes to Create Wrapping Paper or Greeting Cards

Working in small groups, have children use pattern-block shapes to create designs for wrapping paper or greeting cards. Encourage them to include patterns in their designs. *For example:*

▷ patterns in which two or three different shapes and colors repeat

▷ patterns in which the sizes of the shapes vary

▷ patterns that are symmetrical

Point out that new shapes can be made by combining pattern-block shapes; for example, three rhombuses form a regular hexagon (equal sides and equal angles). A regular hexagon will *tessellate*—that is, the whole paper can be covered by hexagons without gaps or overlaps.

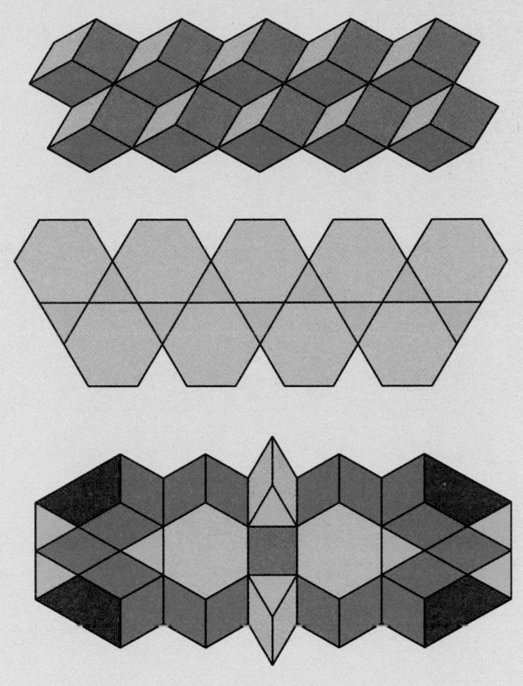

Literature Link Read ***A Cloak for the Dreamer*** by Aileen Friedman (Scholastic Inc., 1995). Discuss designs that do or do not tessellate.

NOTE Encourage children to demonstrate or explain how they used pattern blocks to create their designs using words such as *slide, flip,* or *turn.* Have them use positional words such as *above, below,* and *to the right of.*

Printing with Pattern-Block Shapes

When children complete their designs, explain one of the two suggestions for printing the designs to make wrapping paper or greeting cards:

Stenciling with the Pattern-Block Template

Show children how to use small pieces of sponge or crumpled paper towels as daubers. As they use the Pattern-Block Template as a stencil, they should hold it against the paper, and fill in an open area with paint. Tell children that this technique works best when the daubers are fairly dry.

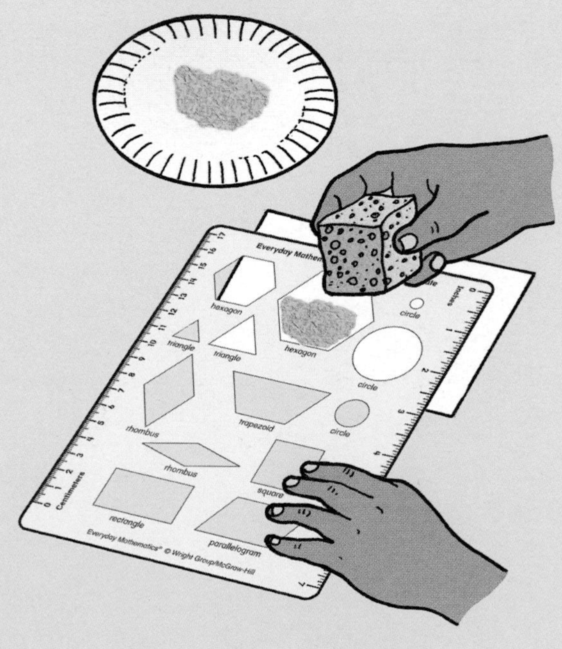

Printing with Pattern Blocks

Children can make small "stamp pads" from folded paper towels saturated with tempera paint. They need to keep these in plastic trays. Have them dip one side of a pattern block into the paint, and then press the pattern block onto the paper.

Alternatively, they may spread finger paint on plates or other waterproof surfaces, and use them as stamp pads to put paint on the blocks.

After children have made a variety of gift wrappings and greeting cards, bring them together to describe their designs. Help them name the shapes they used. If appropriate, count various shapes.

2 Extending the Project

▶ Extension Suggestions

- ▷ Have children use sets of tangrams and create repeating designs.
- ▷ Suggest that children make repeating designs with letters of the alphabet.
- ▷ Ask each child to write what they learned about geometric shapes. Display the children's writings next to their geometric designs.

Literature Link To further explore geometric patterns you may want to read: ***Kente Colors*** by Debbi Chocolate (Walker and Company, 1997) or ***The Spider Weaver: A Legend of Kente Cloth*** by Margaret Musgrove (Blue Sky Press, 2001).

Physical Education Link Read ***Babar's Yoga for Elephants*** by Laurent de Brunhoff (Harry N. Abrams, Inc., 2006). Use the book's step-by-step instructions for basic yoga techniques and positions. Ask children to do the downward-facing dog, plough, and triangle poses. Discuss how these poses are all shape-related.

Social Studies Link Tell children that Frank Lloyd Wright, an architect famous for his use of shapes in the buildings he designed, believed that geometric shapes could be found "hidden" within everyday objects that people have made. Ask children to try to find "hidden" geometric shapes in their designs.

▶ Home Link Suggestion

Many of the textile arts, such as cross-stitch, needlepoint, and quilting, use basic geometric shapes to create designs and pictures of objects. Ask children to bring in fabrics that have shapes in their patterns; for example, handmade quilts, rugs, pillows, baby blankets, tablecloths, or clothing.

Project 2

Amaryllis Plant

Objectives To provide opportunities to observe plant growth over time; and to provide opportunities to collect and graph data.

Technology Resources www.everydaymathonline.com

eToolkit

Algorithms Practice

EM Facts Workshop Game™

Family Letters

Assessment Management

Common Core State Standards

Curriculum Focal Points

Interactive Teacher's Lesson Guide

1 Doing the Project

Recommended Use During or after Unit 4

Key Concepts and Skills

- Measure height with standard measuring tools. [Measurement and Reference Frames Goal 1]
- Collect and organize data in a bar graph. [Data and Chance Goal 1]

Key Activities

Children plant an amaryllis bulb and observe and chart the growth of an amaryllis plant to maturity.

Key Vocabulary

bulb

Materials

- Class Data Pad
- 2–3 amaryllis bulbs
- container of lukewarm water
- 2–3 plant pots with a diameter slightly larger than the diameter of the bulb and with a small drainage hole
- 2–3 saucers
- potting soil
- tape measure
- magnifying lens
- strips of construction paper

2 Extending the Project

Children create a poster that identifies the needs of living things; they learn to take care of plants; they photograph plants; they draw pictures and make a timeline or journal about the growth of an amaryllis plant; they measure and record how much the plant is watered; they discuss the parts of a plant; and they compare different plants using a Venn diagram.

Children practice skills through Home Link activities.

Materials

- poster board
- camera
- photographs of amaryllis plants
- measuring tools for water
- materials for growing additional plants of any variety
- *The Empty Pot*
- *From Seed to Plant*
- *How Plants Grow*

Advance Preparation

Amaryllis bulbs are usually sold at nurseries until April. An amaryllis grows quickly. As much as 24 inches of stem growth can be observed over a period of 6 to 8 weeks. It is strongly recommended that you plant more than one bulb, as there is a possibility that one bulb may not grow. Do not discard a bulb that fails to grow; keep it for children to observe as it decomposes. *Warning:* An amaryllis bulb is poisonous if eaten.

You may want to obtain the following books for the optional Extension Suggestions in Part 2:

▷ ***The Empty Pot*** by Demi (Henry Holt and Company Inc., 1996)

▷ ***From Seed to Plant*** by Gail Gibbons (Holiday House, 1993)

▷ ***How Plants Grow*** by Angela Royston (Heineman Library, 2001)

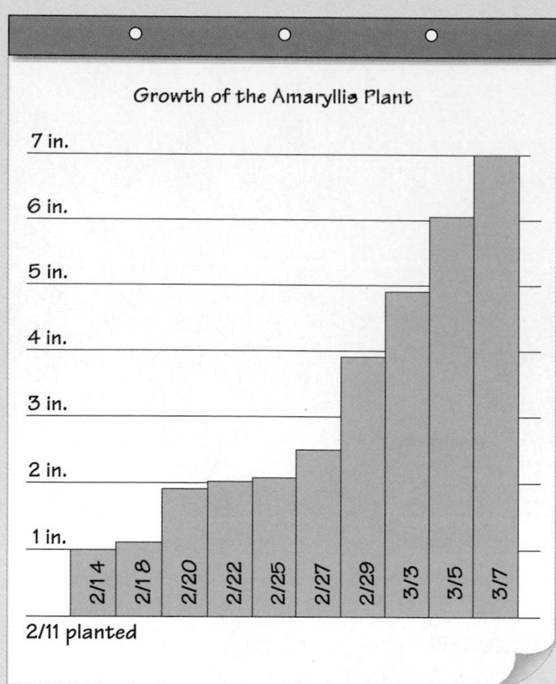

NOTE Measure 1 inch increments from the baseline of the graph to make sure the strips are accurately represented on the graph.

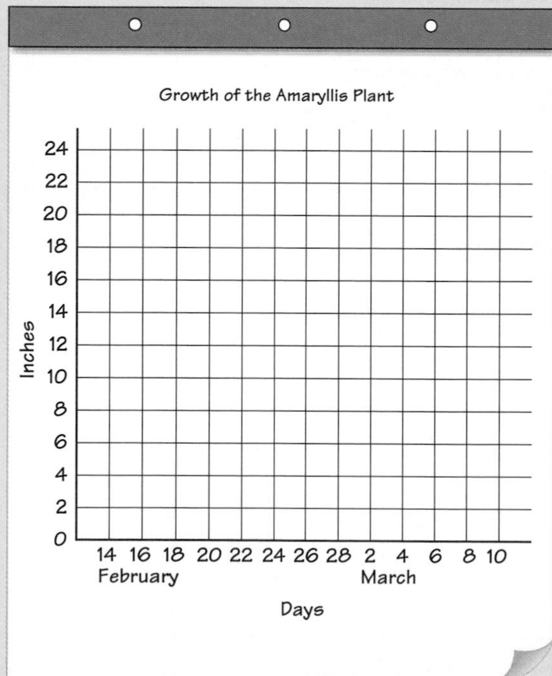

NOTE You may wish to measure and record the growth of the amaryllis using both centimeters and inches.

1 Doing the Project

▶ Planting the Amaryllis Bulb

Explain to children that a **bulb** is a type of seed that is planted underground and is often larger than most seeds. Bulbs will grow into mature plants when properly nurtured.

Soak the bulbs and roots in a container of lukewarm water for several hours before planting. Encourage children to observe and draw a picture of the bulbs before they are planted.

Plant the bulbs so that $\frac{1}{3}$ of the bulbs rise above the potting soil. Be careful not to damage the roots.

Put the pots on saucers for drainage. Place the plants in as much light as possible because direct sunlight and warm temperatures will stimulate growth. Water bulbs sparingly until green shoots begin to appear. Then add more water as needed.

▶ Graphing the Growth of the Amaryllis Plant

Have children measure the plant's height at regular intervals—daily, if you wish.

When the plant is measured, be sure the measurements are taken from the same spot at the bottom of the plant.

The following graphing methods work well:

- ▷ Have children cut strips of construction paper equal in length to the height of the plant. Date these strips and mount them from a baseline on the Class Data Pad.
- ▷ Have children find the amount of growth between two different points in time; for example, on February 14th the plant was 1 inch tall and on February 22nd the plant was 2 inches tall. The plant grew 1 inch.
- ▷ Draw a grid like the one in the margin on the Class Data Pad. Allow for 24 inches of growth over 6 to 8 weeks. Have children mark heights above the corresponding dates on the graph. It doesn't matter if measurements are skipped for some dates, but measurements should not be recorded on incorrect dates.

Have children make estimates of future growth; for example, ask them what they think the height will be on a particular date. Follow up by comparing their estimates with the actual measurement for that day.

Mark on the graph when buds and blossoms appear. Allow time for children to closely examine the large flowers using a magnifying lens.

2 Extending the Project

Extension Suggestions

▷ Discuss responsibility and respect for living things and the environment. List ways that children can respect the environment so that living things can grow. Have children create posters that identify the needs of living things (food, water, oxygen, and light) and how they can help to fulfill those needs.

Literature Link Children can learn how to take care of a plant while listening to ***The Empty Pot*** by Demi (Henry Holt and Company Inc., 1996).

▷ Photograph the amaryllis from time to time; date and display the photos with the graph. Search online for professional photographs of the amaryllis plant. Children may enjoy trying to mimic the professional perspectives they see in the images.

▷ Have children make a timeline or journal about the plant's growth. They might include pictures, poems, or stories about the plant as well as measurements and descriptions.

▷ Have children use measuring tools to measure and record the amount of water that the amaryllis receives.

▷ Discuss the parts of a plant and their functions. *(See margin.)*

▷ Grow additional plants. Keep records of their growth and changes. Compare different plants to one another using a Venn diagram.

Science Link Children may enjoy reading the following books in order to help them learn more about the parts of a plant and photosynthesis: ***From Seed to Plant*** by Gail Gibbons (Holiday House Inc., 1993); and ***How Plants Grow*** by Angela Royston (Heinemann Library, 2001).

Language Arts Link Tell children that the name *amaryllis* comes from Greek mythology. *Amaryllis* means "splendid beauty."

Home Link Suggestion

Have children draw three pictures—one of an amaryllis bulb, one of a young amaryllis plant, and one of a mature amaryllis plant. Encourage them to share the pictures with their family and challenge their family members to put the pictures in order from youngest to most mature.

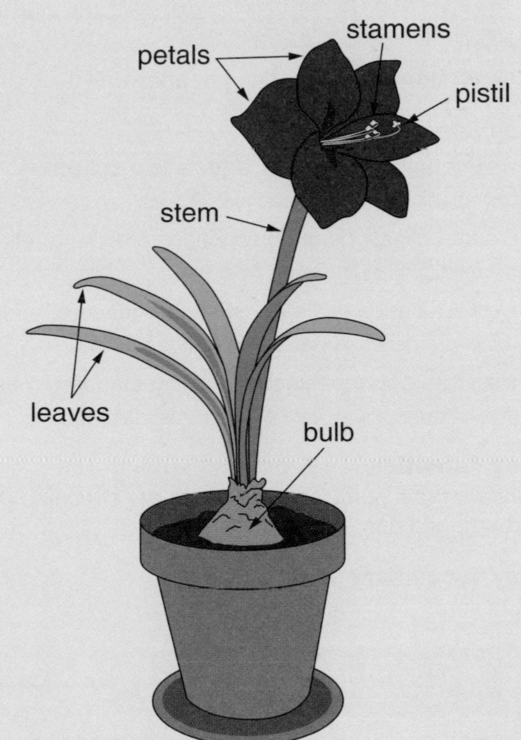

Project

3 Pumpkin Math

Objectives To provide opportunities to estimate weight and girth; compare objects; and count a large collection of objects.

Technology Resources www.everydaymathonline.com

eToolkit

Algorithms Practice

EM Facts Workshop Game™

Family Letters

Assessment Management

Common Core State Standards

Curriculum Focal Points

Interactive Teacher's Lesson Guide

1 Doing the Project

Recommended Use During or after Unit 5

Key Concepts and Skills

- Estimate the number of objects in a collection. [Number and Numeration Goal 2]
- Count collections of objects accurately and reliably. [Number and Numeration Goal 2]
- Use a balance scale to estimate, measure, and compare weight. [Measurement and Reference Frames Goal 1]
- Estimate and measure girth using standard measuring tools. [Measurement and Reference Frames Goal 1]

Key Activities

Children use pumpkins to explore the concepts of girth and weight. In addition, they group and count pumpkin seeds.

Key Vocabulary

girth

Materials

- three pumpkins
- stick-on notes
- bath scale
- ruler
- string
- note cards
- clear tape
- scissors
- knife
- colander
- newspaper
- small paper cups

2 Extending the Project

Children make pumpkin pies and describe parts of the pies using fractions; they make pumpkins with geometric faces; they read literature selections about pumpkins; and they explore the nutritional value of pumpkins.

Children practice skills through Home Link activities.

Materials

- ingredients and supplies for making and serving pumpkin pie
- construction paper
- Pattern-Block Template
- *Full House: An Invitation to Fractions*
- *Pumpkin Pumpkin*
- *Pumpkin Jack*
- *Pumpkin Circle: The Story of a Garden*
- *Pumpkins*

Advance Preparation

You will need three pumpkins of various sizes. Use stick-on notes to label the pumpkins *A, B,* and *C.* Pumpkin A should be small enough for a child to comfortably hold in his or her hand.

For the optional activities in Part 2, obtain the following books: ***Full House: An Invitation to Fractions*** by Dayle Ann Dodds (Candlewick Press, 2009); ***Pumpkin Pumpkin*** by Jeanne Titherington (Greenwillow Books, 1990); ***Pumpkin Jack*** by Will Hubbell (Albert Whitman, 2003); ***Pumpkin Circle: The Story of a Garden*** by George Levenson (Tricycle Press, 2004); ***Pumpkins*** by Jacqueline Farmer (Charlesbridge Publishing, Inc., 2004).

1 Doing the Project

Comparing Weights and Weighing Pumpkins

Label two columns on the board *Lighter than Pumpkin A* and *Heavier than Pumpkin A*. Ask children to suggest classroom items that belong in each column. Record their suggestions. After the list is complete, "check" children's comparisons by allowing them to act as pan balances. Have a child hold Pumpkin A in one hand and one of the objects from the chart in the other hand. Encourage the child to raise and lower the "hand pans" to show which object is heavier or lighter. Encourage children to state weight comparisons using language such as, "My book bag is heavier than Pumpkin A but my stapler is lighter than Pumpkin A."

After children act as pan balances, discuss weight. Explain that in the United States weight is measured in pounds (lb). Place Pumpkin A on the bath scale and record its weight. Ask children to estimate the weights of the objects in the comparison chart based on the weight of Pumpkin A.

Conclude the activity by weighing each of the three pumpkins and recording the weights. Allow a volunteer to put the pumpkins in order from lightest to heaviest.

Estimating and Measuring the Girth of Pumpkins

Divide the children into three groups; each group will work with a different pumpkin.

Explain to children that **girth** is the distance around the widest part of an object. Ask each group to cut a length of string to represent its estimate for the girth of its pumpkin. Have each group measure its string using an inch ruler and record its girth estimate, in inches, on a note card. Each group attaches its string to a note card with clear tape.

Wrap a string around each pumpkin and cut it to show the actual girth. Allow three volunteers to measure the three strings and record the actual girths on note cards. Tape the strings and note cards on the board and label them *Actual Girth of Pumpkin X*. Encourage each group to compare its estimate to the actual girth of its pumpkin.

▶ Relating Weight and Girth

Ask:

- Which pumpkin has the largest girth? Does this pumpkin weigh the most?
- Which pumpkin has the smallest girth? Does the smallest pumpkin weigh the least?

Put the pumpkins in order from lightest to heaviest. Draw them approximately to scale. Put the pumpkins in order from smallest to largest girth. Draw them approximately to scale. Is the order the same or different? Encourage children to reference the drawings when making this comparison.

▶ Counting Pumpkin Seeds

Remove the pulp of each pumpkin. Wash the seeds from each pumpkin in a separate colander. Spread the seeds on separate newspapers to dry overnight. Ask children to estimate the total number of seeds in each pumpkin. Encourage them to explain their estimates; for example, "I think there are 200 seeds in this pumpkin because I counted 100 seeds in my pumpkin, and my pumpkin is smaller than this one."

When the seeds are dry, divide the class into three groups. Give each group all of the seeds from one of the pumpkins. Children check the reasonableness of their estimates by counting the seeds. Ask each group to count its seeds by placing each group of 10 seeds in a separate small cup. Then, as a whole class, use the cups to count the seeds in each pumpkin by 10s. When you get to 100, make one tally mark on the board. Continue in this manner until all of the seeds for a pumpkin have been counted. Count the tallies to determine the total number of seeds in a pumpkin. Repeat this activity for the other two pumpkins.

Ask:

- Does the largest pumpkin have the greatest number of seeds?
- Does the smallest pumpkin have the fewest number of seeds?
- Were your estimates close to the actual number of seeds in each pumpkin?

2 Extending the Project

Extension Suggestions

▷ Make pumpkin pies. Write the recipe on the board and discuss it with the class before making the pies. Measure and mix the ingredients while pointing out the various fractions used on measuring utensils.

Literature Link Read ***Full House: An Invitation to Fractions*** by Dayle Ann Dodds (Candlewick Press, 2009) before you divide the pumpkin pies into equal parts. Then divide the pies, name fractional parts, and encourage children to describe the pies using sentences like the following: "I am eating $\frac{1}{10}$ of the pumpkin pie. Together, Jamal and I ate $\frac{2}{10}$ of the pie."

Art Link Children cut pumpkins out of construction paper. Then they use their Pattern-Block Templates to draw or cut out eyes, noses, and mouths to make geometric faces on the pumpkins.

Literature Link Children may explore books about pumpkins, such as ***Pumpkin Pumpkin*** by Jeanne Titherington (Greenwillow Books, 1990); ***Pumpkin Jack*** by Will Hubbell (Albert Whitman, 2003); and ***Pumpkin Circle: The Story of a Garden*** by George Levenson (Tricycle Press, 2004).

Social Studies Link Find out how the tradition of pumpkin pie was begun by the colonists. Read ***Pumpkins*** by Jacqueline Farmer (Charlesbridge Publishing, Inc., 2004) to learn about additional interesting pumpkin facts.

Health Link Explore the nutritional value of pumpkins.

Home Link Suggestion

Start a classroom seed collection, beginning with pumpkin seeds. Have children bring seeds from home, such as apple seeds, corn kernels, sunflower seeds, acorns, and so on. The seeds can be compared, labeled, and made into seed mosaics.

Project

All About Time

Objective To provide children with opportunities to explore time.

Technology Resources www.everydaymathonline.com

eToolkit

Algorithms Practice

EM Facts Workshop Game™

Family Letters

Assessment Management

Common Core State Standards

Curriculum Focal Points

Interactive Teacher's Lesson Guide

1 Doing the Project

Recommended Use During or after Unit 6

Key Concepts and Skills

- Count by 1s.
  [Number and Numeration Goal 1]
- Mark the passage of time in seconds.
  [Measurement and Reference Frames Goal 4]
- Make calendars to identify days, weeks, months, and dates.
  [Measurement and Reference Frames Goal 4]

Key Activities

Children explore various timepieces and use the second hand for timing tasks. Children discuss the layout of a calendar and make a personal calendar to show the passage of twelve months.

Materials

- ◆ *Math Masters,* p. 300; p. 301 (at least 12 copies per child)
- ◆ Class Data Pad
- ◆ class calendar
- ◆ stapler
- ◆ various timepieces, preferably with second hands
- ◆ green and red dots
- ◆ working analog clock with a second hand

2 Extending the Project

Children measure time using nonstandard units; they tally their weekly activities; they time five different activities and order the activities from the least amount of time an activity takes to the greatest amount of time; they count to 15 using different methods; they discuss the passage of time in relation to topics such as the seasons and tides; and they read fiction and non-fiction books about time, months, and seasons.

Children practice skills through Home Link activities.

Materials

- ◆ stopwatches
- ◆ children's personal calendars
- ◆ *Sunshine Makes the Seasons*
- ◆ *Dear Rebecca, Winter Is Here*
- ◆ *Chimp Math: Learning About Time from a Baby Chimpanzee*
- ◆ *Telling Time: How to Tell Time on Digital and Analog Clocks!*

Advance Preparation

You will need a calendar for the current or upcoming year to provide accurate information about the first day of each month.

You may want to obtain the following books for the optional Extension Suggestions in Part 2:

▷ ***Sunshine Makes the Seasons*** by Franklyn M. Branley (HarperCollins Children's Books, 2005)

▷ ***Dear Rebecca, Winter Is Here*** by Jean Craighead George (HarperCollins Children's Books, 1995)

▷ ***Chimp Math: Learning About Time from a Baby Chimpanzee*** by Ann Whitehead Nagda and Cindy Bickel (Henry Holt and Company Inc., 2002)

▷ ***Telling Time: How to Tell Time on Digital and Analog Clocks!*** by Jules Older (Charlesbridge Publishing, 2000)

1 Doing the Project

Timing in Seconds

Show children a variety of timepieces—preferably with second hands—such as a watch, an analog clock, a pocket watch, and so on. Discuss the following concepts:

- ▷ It takes 60 seconds for the second hand to move around the clock face once.
- ▷ There are 60 seconds in a minute.
- ▷ A second is shorter than a minute.
- ▷ The second hand moves faster than the minute hand.

Practice reading seconds by watching a clock and calling out 5-second intervals up to 60 seconds. Note that the 5-second intervals fall on the hour numbers displayed on the clock. It may be helpful to label the analog clock with the second counts for children to use as a reference.

Tell children that they will participate in various activities that will be timed in seconds. Explain that they will calculate the time in seconds using the second hand on an analog clock. When the second hand points straight up, they should give the "start" command. Instruct them to count the seconds, using the 5-second interval marks. For example, when the second hand points to the 1, say "5," when it points to the 2, say "10," and so on. Instruct children to say, "stop," when the correct number of seconds have passed. You may want to mark the start and stop points on the clock with green and red dots. Practice as a whole group until children are comfortable with the procedure.

Timing Activity

(*Math Masters,* p. 300)

Divide children into partnerships. Have one child be the timer and the second child count and record his or her results on *Math Masters,* page 300. Children switch roles and repeat the activity.

Encourage children to compare the collected data.

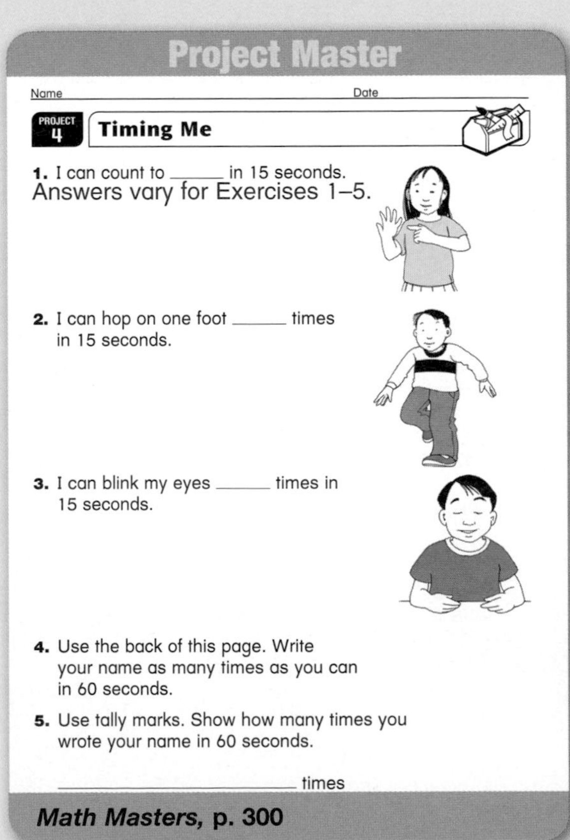

Project Master

Name ______ Date ______

PROJECT 4 **Timing Me**

1. I can count to ______ in 15 seconds.
   Answers vary for Exercises 1–5.
2. I can hop on one foot ______ times in 15 seconds.
3. I can blink my eyes ______ times in 15 seconds.
4. Use the back of this page. Write your name as many times as you can in 60 seconds.
5. Use tally marks. Show how many times you wrote your name in 60 seconds.

   ______ times

Math Masters, p. 300

Project Master

Name Date

PROJECT 4 **Calendar**

Sun.	Mon.	Tues.	Wed.	Thurs.	Fri.	Sat.

***Math Masters,* p. 301**

What are the months of the year?	On what day of the week does the month begin?	How many days are in the month?
January	Monday	31 days
February	Thursday	28 days
March	Thursday	31 days
April	Sunday	30 days
May	Tuesday	31 days
June	Friday	30 days
July	Sunday	31 days
August	Wednesday	31 days
September	Saturday	30 days
October	Monday	31 days
November	Thursday	30 days
December	Saturday	31 days

This sample chart is for the year 2007.

▶ Making Personal Calendars

(*Math Masters,* p. 301)

Discuss with children that in addition to seconds, minutes, and hours, time can be counted in days, months, and years. Help children determine how many minutes are in an hour, how many hours are in a day, how many days are in a week, and how many months are in a year. Identify the days, weeks, and months on a class calendar and recite the days and months in order.

Ask children how they think people might keep track of important events that occur during the year. Invite each child to make a personal calendar. Discuss how their personal calendars will be different from the classroom calendar; for example, size, information recorded on it, and so on. Make a chart on the Class Data Pad to help children know on which day each month begins and how many days are in each month.

Give each child 12 copies of *Math Masters*, page 301. This page provides a grid for dates and space for an illustration. Have children put their calendar pages in chronological order and staple them together.

NOTE Children may want to make additional calendars for the school staff, such as the nurse and principal.

2 Extending the Project

▶ Extension Suggestions

- ▷ Children may enjoy measuring time with nonstandard units; for example, ask: *In the amount of time it takes me to walk from one side of the room to the other, how many times can you do a jumping jack?*
- ▷ Have children tally on their personal calendars how many times they do various activities in a day, a week, or a month. *For example:*
  - ▷ brush their teeth
  - ▷ go to the park
  - ▷ read a book
- ▷ Provide stopwatches for children to use as they time themselves doing five different activities. Then have children put the activities in order from the least amount of time an activity takes to the greatest amount of time.

▷ Time children counting to 15 in several different ways such as: 1, 2, 3 ...; 1,001, 1,002, 1,003 ...; 1 Mississippi, 2 Mississippi, 3 Mississippi ...; 1, clap, clap, 2, clap, clap, 3, clap, clap ... . After trying a variety of different methods, discuss which way appears to be their most accurate method for estimating seconds. Challenge children to count using this method while you time them for 30 seconds. Compare children's counts to the actual elapsed time.

Science Link Discuss measuring the passage of time in relation to the seasons, tides, sunrise/sunset, and so on. ***Sunshine Makes the Seasons*** by Franklyn M. Branley (HarperCollins Children's Books, 2005) is a simple book that will help children understand the causes of seasonal changes.

Literature Link You might want to read aloud or allow children to explore these fiction and non-fiction books about time, months, and seasons: ***Dear Rebecca, Winter Is Here*** by Jean Craighead George (HarperCollins Children's Books, 1995); ***Chimp Math: Learning About Time from a Baby Chimpanzee*** by Ann Whitehead Nagda and Cindy Bickel (Henry Holt and Company Inc., 2002); and ***Telling Time: How to Tell Time on Digital and Analog Clocks!*** by Jules Older (Charlesbridge Publishing, 2000).

Home Link Suggestion

Have children bring their personal calendars home and ask family members to help them add upcoming family events to their calendars.

Project

5 Apple Math

Objective To provide opportunities to classify, count, compare, and measure.

Technology Resources www.everydaymathonline.com

eToolkit

Algorithms Practice

EM Facts Workshop Game™

Family Letters

Assessment Management

Common Core State Standards

Curriculum Focal Points

Interactive Teacher's Lesson Guide

1 Doing the Project

Recommended Use During or after Unit 7

Key Concepts and Skills

- Count collections of objects accurately and reliably. [Number and Numeration Goal 2]
- Tell and solve comparison number stories. [Operations and Computation Goal 4]
- Collect and organize data in a real graph and a bar graph. [Data and Chance Goal 1]
- Measure girth using standard measuring tools. [Measurement and Reference Frames Goal 1]
- Use a pan balance to measure and compare weights. [Measurement and Reference Frames Goal 1]

Key Activities

Children sort apples, gather quantitative data by counting apple seeds, and create a real graph on the floor. They also tell number comparison stories, measure the girth of apples with string, and weigh apples using a pan balance.

Materials

- *Math Masters,* p. 329
- apples (2 per partnership)
- construction paper
- scissors
- glue or transparent tape
- pan balance
- string
- ruler
- 1 plastic spoon per child
- stick-on notes
- masking tape

2 Extending the Project

Children make applesauce or baked apples; they research the life cycle of an apple tree; they take a field trip to an apple orchard or a local produce market; they find nutritional information for apple products; and they create family trees.

Children practice skills through Home Link activities.

Materials

- ingredients and items needed to make applesauce or baked apples
- *A Tree Is a Plant*
- *Tree*
- *Me and My Family Tree*

Advance Preparation

Gather apples of as many different varieties, colors, shapes, and sizes as possible. Use masking tape to make a large grid on the floor that will be used for the real graph in Part 1.

You may want to obtain the following books for the optional Extension Suggestions in Part 2:

▷ ***A Tree Is a Plant*** by Clyde Robert Bulla (HarperCollins Publisher, 2001)

▷ ***Tree*** by David Burnie (Dorling Kindersley, 2004)

▷ ***Me and My Family Tree*** by Joan Sweeney (Random House Children's Books, 2000)

1 Doing the Project

Classifying, Counting, and Comparing Apples

(*Math Masters,* p. 329)

Have children sort apples in different ways; for example, by color, shape, variety, or size. Compare their results by asking questions such as: *Are there more red apples or green apples? Are there fewer small apples or large apples? Of which variety do we have the most or fewest?*

Explain to children that they will use the results of their apple comparisons to make a graph.

Decide as a class if you will graph the apples according to color, size, shape, or variety. Have children use stick-on notes to label the axes. Children take turns placing apples on the graph. When all of the apples have been accurately placed, have each child use *Math Masters,* page 329 to make a bar graph that represents the data.

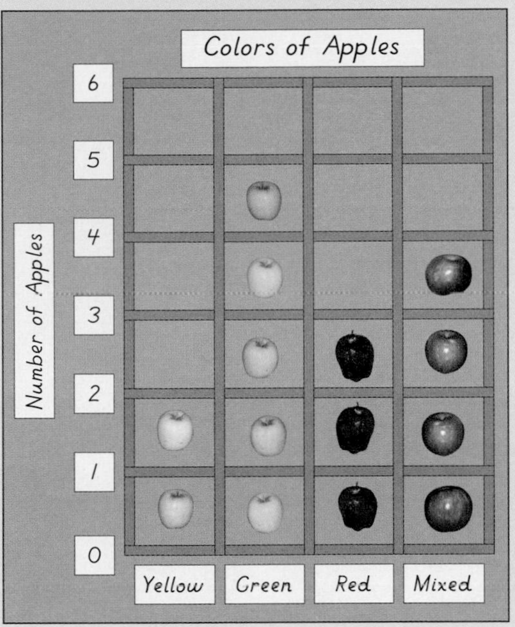

Making Apple Trees

Have children make apple trees from green and brown construction paper. Then they cut out a number of apples and fasten them onto their trees. Last, they number their apples 1, 2, and so on.

Ask partners to compare the number of apples on each other's trees and act out a comparison number story for their classmates. For example: *Al has 4 apples. Francesca has 3 apples. Who has fewer apples?* Francesca *How many fewer?* 1

Children use their apple trees to tell comparison stories.

Counting Apple Seeds

Give each partnership two halves of an apple. Have children use a plastic spoon to remove the seeds. When all of the seeds have been collected, one partner tapes or glues the seeds onto a quarter-sheet of paper and the other partner writes the total number of seeds. Have the class order the papers from the least to the greatest number of seeds.

▶ Measuring the Girth of an Apple

Remind children that girth is the distance around the widest part of an object. Ask children to measure the girth of an apple by wrapping a string around it. They should touch both ends of the string together without overlapping.

Have partners line up their strings alongside a ruler and record the measurements in inches on a quarter-sheet of paper. Remind children to label their measurements.

To arrange the apples in order from smallest girth to largest girth, ask for the child that thinks his or her apple has the smallest girth to share that measurement. Ask if anyone has an apple with a larger girth until all of the apples have been placed in order.

▶ Weighing Apples

Show children a pan balance. Remind them that it can be used for comparing the weights of objects. Direct their attention to the triangle on the pan balance that points to a line. Explain that the triangle only points to the line when the scale is balanced or has the same amount of weight on both sides. Put an apple on one side of the pan balance and point out how the triangle moves away from the line.

NOTE After items are "weighed," ask children to line them up in order by weight from lightest to heaviest.

A pan balance

Find two apples that are very close in weight. Cut one of the apples into fractional pieces. Ask which fractions the pieces represent—one-half, one-quarter, and so on. Put all of the pieces on one side of the scale and place the whole apple on the other side. Compare the weights of the apples. Ask: *Do the apple pieces and the whole apple balance the scale?* yes

Compare the weights of other items to apples such as boxes of crayons, pencils, or a drinking cup.

2 Extending the Project

Extension Suggestions

- ▷ Make applesauce or baked apples.
- ▷ Research the life cycle of an apple tree.
- ▷ Take a field trip to an apple orchard and learn about the kinds of apples grown there and how much they cost. Explain to children that one large basket of apples is sometimes referred to as a bushel.
- ▷ Have children tell about a visit to a local produce market. *What varieties of apples do they sell? How much do they cost?*

Literature Link To further explore the life cycle of a tree, have children read ***A Tree Is a Plant*** by Clyde Robert Bulla (HarperCollins Publisher, 2001) or ***Tree*** by David Burnie (Dorling Kindersley, 2004).

Health Link Have children find nutritional information for apples and apple products.

Social Studies Link Read the book ***Me and My Family Tree*** by Joan Sweeney (Random House Children's Books, 2000). Have children draw their own family trees and label them with names of family members.

Home Link Suggestion

Have children ask their families to help them look for different scales used to weigh objects. Some examples may include a bath scale, a food scale at the grocery store, or a postal scale at the post office. Have children draw pictures of the scales they find.

Project 6

Celebrate the Hundredth Day

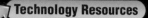

Objective To provide opportunities to explore the number 100.

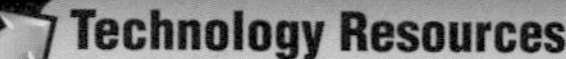

www.everydaymathonline.com

eToolkit

Algorithms Practice

EM Facts Workshop Game™

Family Letters

Assessment Management

Common Core State Standards

Curriculum Focal Points

Interactive Teacher's Lesson Guide

1 Doing the Project

Recommended Use On or around the hundredth day of school

Key Concepts and Skills

- Estimate the number of objects in a collection. [Number and Numeration Goal 2]
- Count collections of objects accurately and reliably. [Number and Numeration Goal 2]
- Use manipulatives to model equal parts of a collection. [Number and Numeration Goal 4]
- Calculate the values of combinations of coins. [Operations and Computation Goal 2]

Key Activities

Children celebrate the hundredth day of school by participating in a variety of activities involving the number 100.

Materials

Depending on your choice of activities:

- Class Thermometer Poster (°F)
- collections of small items
- transparent containers
- 100 toothpicks
- large piece of paper
- 100 pattern blocks
- 12-inch ruler
- masking tape
- classroom books
- pan balance
- 100-piece jigsaw puzzle
- tool-kit coins
- clock or watch with a second hand
- calculator
- base-10 blocks

2 Extending the Project

Children fill a name-collection box for 100; they solve number stories related to 100; they find how many centimeters are in a meter; they read literature selections related to 100; and they find out what world events happened 100 years ago and draw pictures to show their predictions for 100 years from now.

Children practice skills through Home Link activities.

Materials

- 100 base-10 cubes
- meter stick
- 12-month calendar
- *One Hundred Hungry Ants*
- *100th Day Worries*

Advance Preparation

Ask each child to collect and bring to school 100 small items. The items should be arranged in a display that is easy to count. For example, a child can glue 100 paper clips to cardboard in 10 rows of 10, or string 100 beads on 5 strings of 20. These collections will be displayed in a Hundreds Museum.

Look through the suggested activities on pages 449–450 and obtain materials for those activities you choose to do.

For the optional activities in Part 2, obtain the following books: ***One Hundred Hungry Ants*** by Elinor J. Pinczes (Houghton Mifflin Co., 1993); ***100th Day Worries*** by Margery Cuyler (Simon and Schuster Children's Publishing, 2005).

1 Doing the Project

Sharing the Hundreds Collections

Have children show and describe their collections of 100 items.

Make a class Hundreds Museum with the collections. Use some of the collections for the Suggested Celebration Activities that follow.

Suggested Celebration Activities

Following are suggestions for ways of celebrating the 100th day of first grade. Some teachers may choose to devote the whole day to doing 100th day activities; others may spend only part of the day. Choose those activities you wish, and add your own.

1. Fill transparent containers with more or less than 100 small items, such as pretzels, buttons, or erasers. Have children estimate the number of items in each container and record their estimates on the board. Reveal the exact numbers and count aloud with the children to double-check the quantities.
2. Give 100 toothpicks to small groups of 2–5 children. Ask them to estimate how many toothpicks each child would get if the toothpicks were shared equally. Children check their estimates by sharing the toothpicks and then gluing the toothpicks on a large sheet of paper in equal groups.
3. For each partnership or small group, have available 100 pattern blocks. Let children make patterns, mosaics, or designs.
4. Have children make 100 tally marks on the board.
5. With children's help, use 12-inch rulers to measure 100 feet in the hallway. Use masking tape to mark off the distance.

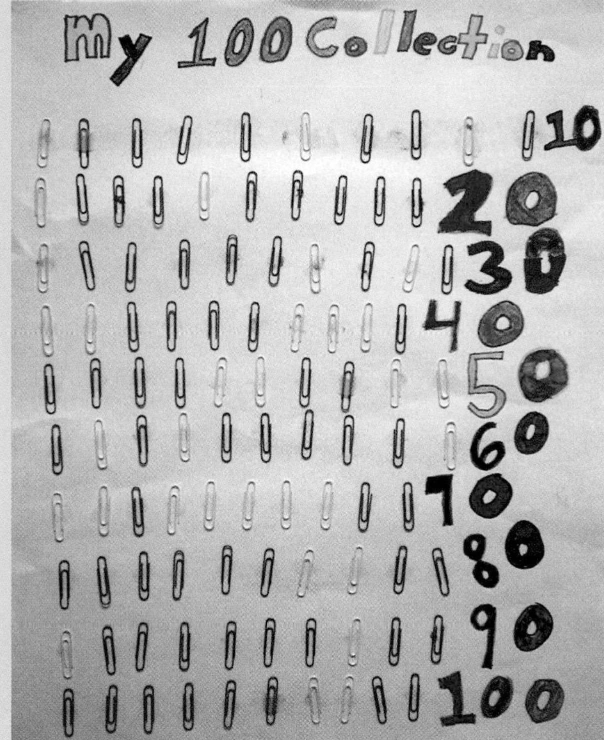

6. During a recreation time, have a 100-foot race.
7. Ask children to estimate where they would end up if they took 100 heel-to-toe steps from the start. Then have them actually take the steps and compare the distance to 100 standard feet.
8. Invite children to locate page 100 in several books.
9. Ask children to use the pan balance to weigh and compare collections of 100 small items from the Hundreds Museum.
10. Provide 100-piece jigsaw puzzles for children to work on during free time.
11. Ask children to find different ways to make $1.00 (100 cents) using their tool-kit coins. Have them record their coin combinations using Ⓠ, Ⓓ, Ⓝ, and Ⓟ.
12. Have children say when they think 100 seconds has passed while you time them. Then have them estimate how many times they can say the alphabet in 100 seconds, and then try it. Ask children how many hours are in 100 minutes. About $1\frac{1}{2}$ hours
13. Have children use their calculators. Tell them to press [ON/C] 0 [+] 10, then [=] 100 times, and report the result. 1,000
14. Ask children to list 100 words on a piece of paper.
15. Provide children with base-10 blocks and challenge them to build structures that total 100 or a multiple of 100.
16. Have children set the Classroom Thermometer Poster (°F) to 100°F. Ask children to describe what they might do or wear on a 100°F day.

Language Arts Link Invite children who speak languages other than English to teach the class how to say 100 in their languages. Use the chart below for other suggestions.

Language	100	Pronunciation
Chinese	*yibai*	(ee-by)
French	*cent*	(sahN)
German	*hundert*	(HUN-dert)
Italian	*cento*	(CHEHN-toh)
Japanese	*hyaku*	(hyah-koo)
Korean	*baek*	(bake)
Portuguese	*cem*	(say)
Russian	*sto*	(stoh)
Spanish	*cien*	(see-EHN)
Turkish	*yüz*	(yewz)

2 Extending the Project

Extension Suggestions

▷ Make a large name-collection box for 100 on the board. Have children fill in names for 100 throughout the day. Encourage children to make names using addition, subtraction, coins, base-10 blocks, tallies, and number stories. Challenge them to think of 100 different names!

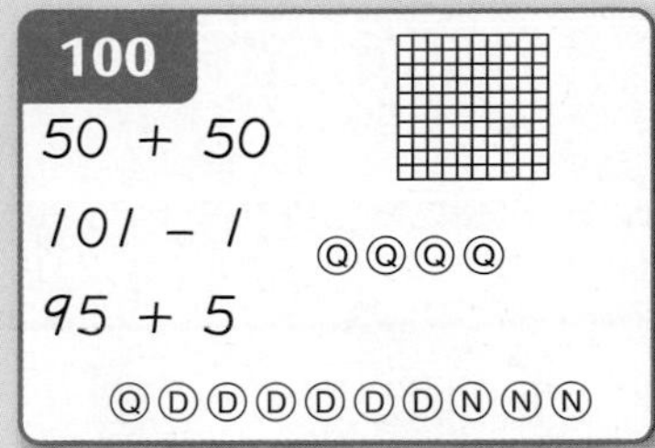

▷ Tell number stories related to 100. For example: *How many people would it take to have a total of 100 fingers?* 10 people *How many people would it take to have a total of 100 eyes?* 50 people *How many cars would it take to have a total of 100 wheels?* 25 cars

▷ Line up 100 base-10 cubes along a meterstick. Remind children that each cube measures 1 centimeter. Ask: *How many centimeters are in 1 meter?* 100 centimeters

Literature Link Read the following books related to the number 100 and the hundredth day of school: ***One Hundred Hungry Ants*** by Elinor J. Pinczes (Houghton Mifflin Co., 1993) and ***100th Day Worries*** by Margery Cuyler (Simon and Schuster Children's Publishing, 2005).

Social Studies Link Find out what major world events happened 100 years ago. Share facts about everyday life during that time. Ask children to make predictions about life 100 years from now. Children can write and illustrate their predictions.

Home Link Suggestion

Have children count 100 days from today on a calendar at home. Have them discuss with a family member what they might be doing 100 days from now and draw a picture. *What month will it be? What season of the year? Will they be celebrating a family occasion at that time?*

Project

7 Weather and Probability

Objective To introduce the basic language of probability to describe events.

Technology Resources www.everydaymathonline.com

eToolkit

Algorithms Practice

EM Facts Workshop Game™

Family Letters

Assessment Management

Common Core State Standards

Curriculum Focal Points

Interactive Teacher's Lesson Guide

1 Doing the Project

Recommended Use During or after Unit 7

Key Concepts and Skills

- Compare quantities.
  [Number and Numeration Goal 7]
- Describe events using basic probability terms.
  [Data and Chance Goal 3]

Key Activities

Children discuss probability, use weather data to make predictions, and discuss the likelihood of events. They make a class book of weather events that are likely or unlikely during different seasons.

Key Vocabulary

likely ◆ unlikely

Materials

◆ Class Data Pad

◆ Class Weather Chart

◆ *Cloudy With a Chance of Meatballs* (optional)

2 Extending the Project

Children use the Class Weather Chart to create a bar graph; they write and perform a TV news weather report; they learn about the job of a meteorologist; they learn what causes the seasons to change; and they identify different ways to describe probability terms.

Children practice skills through Home Link activities.

Materials

◆ Class Weather Chart

◆ videotaping equipment (optional)

◆ *What Will the Weather Be?*

◆ *The Reasons for Seasons*

Advance Preparation

You will need data about the weather in your area for the current month. This information can come from your Class Weather Chart or the Internet.

For Doing the Project in Part 1, you may want to obtain ***Cloudy With a Chance of Meatballs*** by Judith Barrett (Simon and Schuster Children's Publishing, 1982).

You may want to obtain the following books for the optional Extension Suggestions in Part 2:

▷ ***What Will the Weather Be?*** by Lynda Dewitt (HarperCollins Publishers, 1993)

▷ ***The Reasons for Seasons*** by Gail Gibbons (Holiday House, 1996)

1 Doing the Project

Discussing Weather Forecasts

Begin a discussion about probability by asking children about weather forecasts. Ask:

- How did you decide whether or not to wear a coat (or bring an umbrella) to school today?
- What does a weather forecast tell you?
- What words do weather reporters use to talk about the weather?
- What information does a weather reporter use to make his or her predictions?

As children share their ideas, make a list on the Class Data Pad of probability words such as ***likely, unlikely***, *chance*, *impossible*, *possible,* and *certain.*

NOTE Of all of the strands of mathematics, probability is one of the most useful in daily life. The vocabulary of qualitative probability—likely, unlikely, impossible, certain, and so on—should be introduced early as the basis for mathematical probability in *Everyday Mathematics* and beyond. Through repeated use, children will gradually make these terms part of their vocabularies.

Predicting Weather Events

Share local weather data with the class for the current month. Discuss trends in the weather. Ask:

- Have there been more sunny days or rainy (snowy) days this month?
- What kind of weather did we have on the greatest number of days? On the fewest number of days?
- Based on the weather we have had in the past few days, what do you predict the weather will be tomorrow?

List children's predictions in a column on the Class Data Pad under the heading *Likely*. Then make a new column titled *Unlikely*. Ask children to think of weather events that are unlikely to occur on the following day. Encourage children to be imaginative. Unlikely events could include raining cats and dogs or a 100°F day in the winter.

NOTE You may wish to review temperature using both the Fahrenheit and Celsius scales on page 87 of the *My Reference Book.*

Literature Link Read ***Cloudy With a Chance of Meatballs*** by Judith Barrett (Simon and Schuster Children's Publishing, 1982). In the fictional town of Chewandswallow, the weather comes in the form of food. Use this funny story to talk about weather events that are unlikely or even impossible!

▶ Making a Class Book of Weather

Ask children to name the different seasons. Fall, winter, spring, and summer Tell children that weather varies by season, changing the likelihood of weather events such as rain, snow, or fog.

Ask the class to suggest a few likely weather events—occasions of different types of weather—for each season. Then share ideas about seasonal, weather-related activities such as ice skating, raking leaves, or swimming at the beach.

Have children make a class book of weather events and weather-related activities that are likely or unlikely during different seasons. Children choose a season and record it on a page. Then they write a statement about likely weather for that season and illustrate it. They repeat the activity with a statement about unlikely weather for that season. Remind children that each statement must include the word *likely* or *unlikely*.

NOTE Adapt the discussion of seasons to fit your climate. It may be more appropriate to talk about dry and rainy seasons or other weather events such as hurricanes or tornadoes.

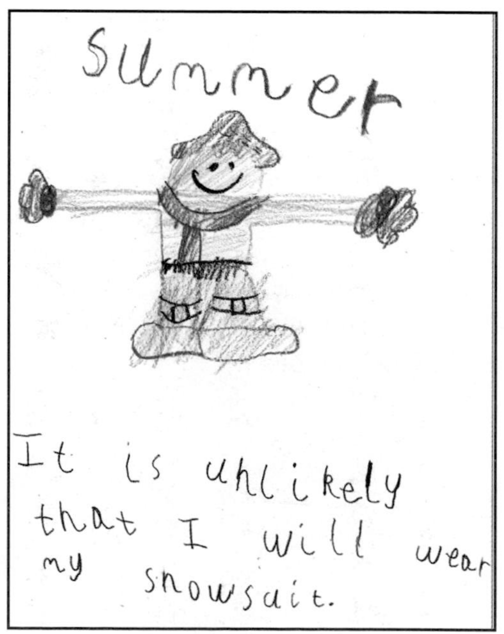

Children write and illustrate statements that describe likely and unlikely seasonal events.

2 Extending the Project

Extension Suggestions

- Ask children if weather forecasts are always accurate. Discuss the fact that weather forecasts are predictions. Explain the difference between *likely* and *certain* events.
- Use the data from the Class Weather Chart to create a weather bar graph.
- Have small groups of children write and perform a TV news weather report. You may wish to videotape the performances.

Science Link Children can learn more about the job and tools of a meteorologist by reading ***What Will the Weather Be?*** by Lynda DeWitt (HarperCollins Publishers, 1993).

Science Link Help children understand what causes the seasons to change by reading ***The Reasons for Seasons*** by Gail Gibbons (Holiday House, 1996).

Language Arts Link Ask children to think of different ways of saying *likely*, *unlikely*, *certain*, and *impossible*. Encourage children to use informal, everyday language. For example, a child might say, "no way," "never," and "definitely not" for *impossible;* or "for sure," "guaranteed," and "definitely" for *certain*.

Home Link Suggestion

Have children watch a weather forecast on TV or listen to one on the radio. Ask children to list any probability words that they hear and bring the list to school. Children can compare weather forecasts and discuss their accuracy.

Project

8 A Flea Market

Objective To provide opportunities to practice buying-and-selling situations using coins.

Technology Resources www.everydaymathonline.com

eToolkit

Algorithms Practice

EM Facts Workshop Game™

Family Letters

Assessment Management

Common Core State Standards

Curriculum Focal Points

Interactive Teacher's Lesson Guide

1 Doing the Project

Recommended Use During or after Unit 8

Key Concepts and Skills

- Calculate and compare values of combinations of coins. [Operations and Computation Goal 2]
- Use a calculator to solve subtraction problems. [Operations and Computation Goal 2]

Key Activities

Children create and work in a classroom flea market. Children practice paying for items and making change for the customers using coins and calculators. They practice adding and subtracting 1- and 2-digit prices.

Materials

- toys, books, puzzles, and other items from home and classroom
- 3" by 5" index cards
- tool-kit coins
- stick-on notes or masking tape
- calculator

2 Extending the Project

Children conduct a flea-market sale using half-off coupons; they make a tally chart to determine how to use the proceeds from the flea market; they discuss the types of markets found in their community; and they read literature selections related to stores and selling items.

Children practice skills through Home Link activities.

Materials

- handmade half-off coupons
- proceeds from class flea market
- *Grandma Went to Market: A Round-the-World Counting Rhyme*
- *Mama and Papa Have a Store*
- *Market!*

Advance Preparation

Send a letter home describing the project. Explain that items from home will not be returned to their child once they have been sold to a classmate during the flea market. Give families an option of sending 2 or 3 items or cutting pictures of items out of catalogs and gluing them to index cards. Decide on an amount of money for each child to use. Children can bring money from home or take that amount from their tool kits. Label items with prices using stick-on notes or masking tape.

You may want to obtain the following books for the optional Extension Suggestions in Part 2:

▷ ***Grandma Went to Market: A Round-the-World Counting Rhyme*** by Stella Blackstone (Houghton Mifflin Co., 1996)

▷ ***Mama and Papa Have a Store*** by Amelia Lau Carling (Dial, 1998)

▷ ***Market!*** by Ted Lewin (HarperCollins Publisher, 1996)

1 Doing the Project

Discussing the Flea Market

Explain that a flea market provides an opportunity for people to sell items they no longer want, or to exchange them for someone else's items that they might want. Tell children to talk with an adult at home about items they might bring to school for the flea market. These could include unwanted toys, books, puzzles, stuffed animals, and so on.

Set a date for the flea market. Decide whether the market will be open several consecutive days or for several chosen days in a given time period. Children should bring items to school several days before.

Pricing the Items

Set a range in which all items will be priced; 5 to 50 cents works well. Be sure children understand the idea of the price range. Children can price the items they bring to class.

Talk about money and change. Ask:

- If I have a nickel and a dime, how much money do I have? 15¢
- Suppose I bought your toy car for 5 cents and gave you a dime. How much change should you give me back? 5¢
- I have 35 cents. Can I buy a book for 10 cents and a pen for 30 cents? No, the book and pen together cost 40¢.

Give an example of bartering by sharing the following conversation:

Josephine: *I want to barter for your purse, Shawna. Can I give you my two dolls and 15¢?*

Shawna: *No, I will not accept your barter Josephine. I want your two dolls and 20¢ since my purse is priced at 50¢.*

Flea market items

Holding the Flea Market

Establish a space in the classroom to store and display the items for the flea market before it opens. Decide on the time of day that the market will be open. Have children help plan and organize “shopping times” for other classes to participate in the flea market.

▶ Making Change

Have children take turns being the cashier. You may want to write the following steps for making change with a calculator on the board. Be sure children understand that the amount the customer pays is entered into the calculator first.

1. Clear the calculator.
2. Enter the amount the customer gives you.
3. Press [−].
4. Enter the cost of the item being purchased.
5. Press [=].
6. This number is the amount of change you owe the customer.

▶ Using a Shopkeeper's Journal

Explain to children that long before cash registers and computers, shopkeepers kept records of sales by writing them down. Have children staple pieces of blank paper together to create a shopkeeper's journal. Tell them that they will record their transactions, or number stories, while working as the cashier. Encourage them to use any strategy they wish.

▶ Reviewing the Results

Have each "shift" use their shopkeeper's journals to report how much money they have made.

Children can use calculators to find the grand total. Compare the total amount received with the total amount of money at the start of the project. Ask whether all of the money was spent.

Have children talk about their experiences. For example: *Did cheaper items sell faster? Were some items overpriced?*

2 Extending the Project

Extension Suggestions

- Have children make half-off discount coupons for the flea market. Use them to conduct a half-off sale at the end of the project. You may also consider reducing items for a "quick sale" during the last few minutes or days of the sale.
- Discuss how the proceeds from the flea market should be spent. You may consider donating the proceeds to a local charity or buying something for the classroom. Have children vote for their preferences and then tally and record their votes in a chart. If children decide to buy something for the classroom, bring in school supply catalogs so that children can determine whether they have enough money to buy the items they want.

Language Arts Link You may want to read the following books aloud: ***Grandma Went to Market: A Round-the-World Counting Rhyme*** by Stella Blackstone (Houghton Mifflin Co. 1996); and ***Mama and Papa Have a Store*** by Amelia Lau Carling (Dial, 1998).

Social Studies Link Read ***Market!*** by Ted Lewin (HarperCollins Publisher, 1996). Discuss the different types of markets that can be found in your community.

NOTE If children used their tool-kit coins, have them divide the coins so that each child puts the correct coins back into his or her kit.

Home Link Suggestion

Ask families to accompany their children to a local market and give children a number of coins to spend.

Project

9

Ad Wizard

 **Objective** To practice strategies for adding and subtracting with 2-digit numbers.

 Technology Resources www.everydaymathonline.com

eToolkit

Algorithms Practice

EM Facts Workshop Game™

Family Letters

Assessment Management

Common Core State Standards

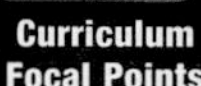
Curriculum Focal Points

Interactive Teacher's Lesson Guide

1 Doing the Project

Recommended Use During or after Unit 5

Key Concepts and Skills

- Add 2-digit numbers to 1-digit numbers and multiples of 10.
  [Operations and Computation Goal 2]
- Subtract multiples of 10.
  [Operations and Computation Goal 2]
- Use number grids, base-10 blocks, and other strategies to add and subtract.
  [Operations and Computation Goal 2]
- Write or draw to represent addition and subtraction strategies.
  [Operations and Computation Goal 2]

Key Activities

Children make advertisements to practice adding and subtracting 2-digit numbers, including multiples of 10. They review strategies for addition and subtraction. They illustrate their strategies with words and drawings.

Materials

- *Math Masters,* pp. 302–302F
- print ads children bring from home
- base-10 blocks
- number grid
- counters
- scissors
- glue sticks
- markers and craft supplies
- posterboard

See Advance Preparation

2 Extending the Project

Children make advertisements with their own items and prices; they reexamine prices in print ads they bring to class; and they read about tricks of advertising.

Materials

- *Math Masters,* p. 302G
- *The Berenstain Bears and the Trouble with Commercials* by Jan Berenstain

Advance Preparation

Ask children to bring advertisements from print materials like newspapers and magazines. You may wish to send a letter home describing the project and this request. Make one copy per child of *Math Masters,* pages 302, 302A, 302B, 302D, and 302F; make three copies per child of *Math Masters,* pages 302C and 302E.

1 Doing the Project

Learning about Ads

Discuss with children what advertisements or ads are. Ask children to describe ads they have read in newspapers or magazines, viewed on television, seen on billboards or the Internet, or heard on the radio. As children share, keep a running list of features that make ads memorable; for example, the ads have products children want, bargains or sales, eye-catching graphics, or funny or clever slogans.

Display some of the print ads children brought from home. As a class, examine these ads to make another list of features that are common to the ads. This list may include the names of the stores, lists or pictures of one or more items that the stores sell, the prices of the items, or slogans.

Tell children that today they will be making ads for items sold in their own imaginary pet stores. Remind children that good ads include features from both lists. Post the lists, along with some of the print ads children brought from home, so that children can refer to them.

Language Arts Link Discuss the difference in meaning and spelling between *ad,* as in advertisement, and *add,* as in to perform addition.

Determining the Right Price

WHOLE-CLASS ACTIVITY

(*Math Masters,* pp. 302 and 302A)

Tell children that they are going to determine prices for items and show how they determined prices as a class before they plan their own ads. Tell them that they may use base-10 blocks, number grids, counters, tally marks, or other strategies in determining prices.

Ask children to determine the combined price of the hamster and hamster wheel on *Math Masters,* page 302. Have several children explain their strategies for determining the total price. Help children write or draw to illustrate their strategies on page 302. For instance, children may need assistance with drawing tally marks, counters, or base-10 shorthand. Help children write number models on the page to correspond with the strategies they illustrate.

During the discussion, be sure to emphasize the following strategies:

▷ **Counting on from the larger addend**

Strategy: Start with the larger price, 16, and count up 8.

Number model: $16 + 8 = 24$

Math Masters, p. 302

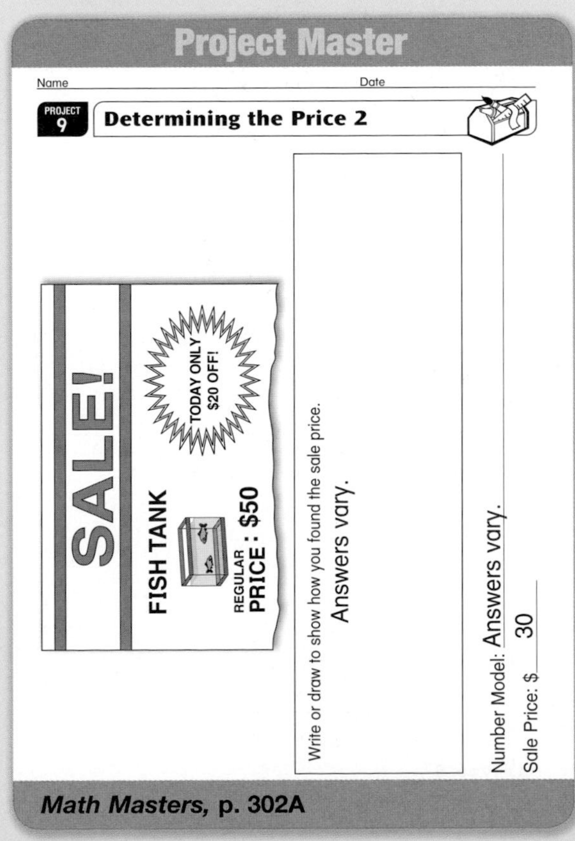

Math Masters, p. 302A

Project Master

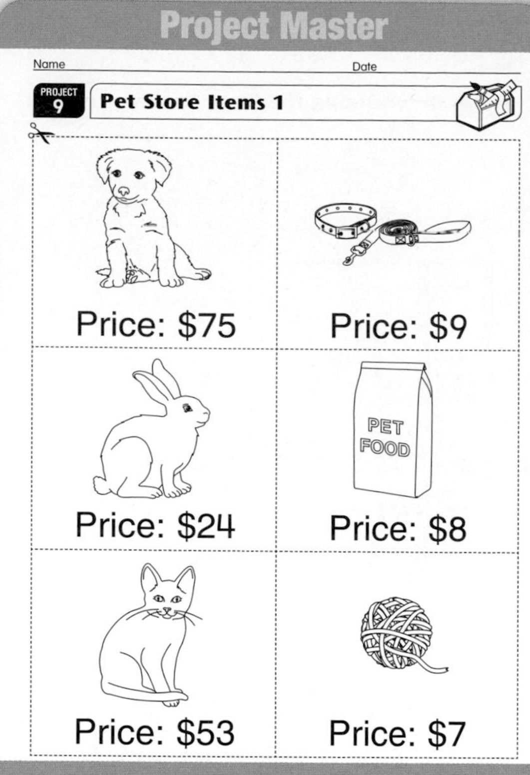
Name Date

PROJECT 9 Pet Store Items 1

Price: $75

Price: $9

Price: $24

Price: $8

Price: $53

Price: $7

Math Masters, p. 302B

Project Master

Name Date

PROJECT 9 Ad Template for Two Items

_______________'s Pet Store

Paste picture here.	Paste picture here.

Write or draw to show how you found the total price.

Number Model: ______________________

Total Price: $__________

Math Masters, p. 302C

▷ **Making ten**

Strategy: Use base-10 blocks to represent 16 (1 long, 6 cubes) and 8 (8 cubes). Add the blocks together, adding tens to tens and ones to ones: 8 cubes + 1 long, 6 cubes = 1 long, 14 cubes. Trade 10 cubes for 1 long, composing a 10 and leaving 4 cubes left over: 2 longs, 4 cubes = 2 tens, 4 ones = 24.

Number model: $16 + 8 = 10 + 6 + 8 = 10 + 14 =$
$10 + 10 + 4 = 20 + 4 = 24$

Provide children with *Math Masters,* page 302A. Ask children to determine the price of the fish tank if it is on sale for $20 off. Have several children explain their strategies for determining the price. Help them illustrate their strategies and write appropriate number models.

During the discussion, be sure to emphasize the following strategies:

▷ **Using the number grid**

Strategy: Find 50 on the number grid. To subtract 20, stay in the same column, and move up two rows to 30.

Number model: $50 - 20 = 30$

▷ **Counting up to subtract**

Strategy: Use a number grid. Start at 20 and move down rows to reach 50. Count by tens as you move down 3 rows. The difference is 30.

Number model: $20 + 30 = 50$ or $50 - 20 = 30$

▶ Making Ads

INDEPENDENT ACTIVITY

(*Math Masters,* pp. 302B–302E)

Tell children that they will start by making advertisements for which they add the prices of two items. They will then make ads for which they subtract to find the sale price of an item.

Provide children with scissors, glue sticks, and copies of *Math Masters*, pages 302B and 302C. Have children cut out the pictures of the dog and the leash on page 302B. Show children how to glue the items onto the template on page 302C to make their ads. Remind children that they are adding the prices of the two items, and review how to fill out the rest of the page as they did on *Math Masters*, page 302.

After children have made ads for the first row of items, have them independently complete two more ads. For each ad, children should match a pet with a pet accessory. Circulate and assist children until they each have made three ads.

Next, provide children with copies of *Math Masters*, pages 302D and 302E. Emphasize to children that they are now subtracting to determine the sale price of an item. Review how to fill out the rest of the template on page 302E as they did on *Math Masters*, page 302A.

As with the previous ads, you may wish to complete one ad with the whole class before having children make their own ads. To make their ads, children should match each pet or pet accessory with a sale price. Circulate and assist children until they each have made two more ads.

Provide each child with a piece of posterboard, markers, and other craft materials as needed. Have children display their six ads on the posterboard and decorate the posters. Encourage children to refer to the lists they made at the beginning of class about common and memorable features of ads to generate ideas for decorating their posters. Children may wish to add slogans, drawings, and color to their posters.

Checking the Ads

PARTNER ACTIVITY

(*Math Masters,* p. 302F)

When children are finished, display their store posters. Have pairs of children place their ads side-by-side so that they may examine them. Ask the partnerships to look closely at others' ads to make sure the prices are correct. Have the partnerships work through any questionable prices together.

After children have examined the ads, discuss the following questions:

- Did you and your partner get the correct prices for all of the items?
- If not, which prices did you change?
- What strategies did you use to determine the correct prices?
- What made the ads on your partner's store poster memorable?

Finally, have children practice explaining how they solve 2-digit addition and subtraction problems by completing *Math Masters,* page 302F.

Display the store posters for several days after the project, so that children get a chance to look at more of them.

2 Extending the Project

Extension Suggestions

▷ Have children imagine their own pet store items, draw pictures of their imagined items, and write prices for the items using *Math Masters,* page 302G. You may wish to have children determine the total prices for these items and make new ads.

▷ Have children reexamine the print ads they brought to class. Ask them to consider whether the prices on the ads are correct.

Language Arts Link Children can learn more about advertisements and being cautious consumers by reading ***The Berenstain Bears and the Trouble with Commercials*** by Jan Berenstain (HarperCollins, 2007).

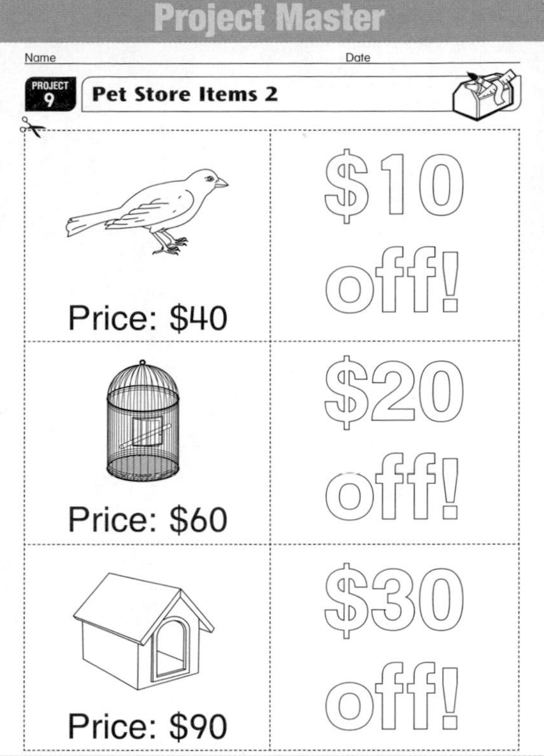

Project Master

Name Date

PROJECT 9 **Pet Store Items 2**

Math Masters, p. 302D

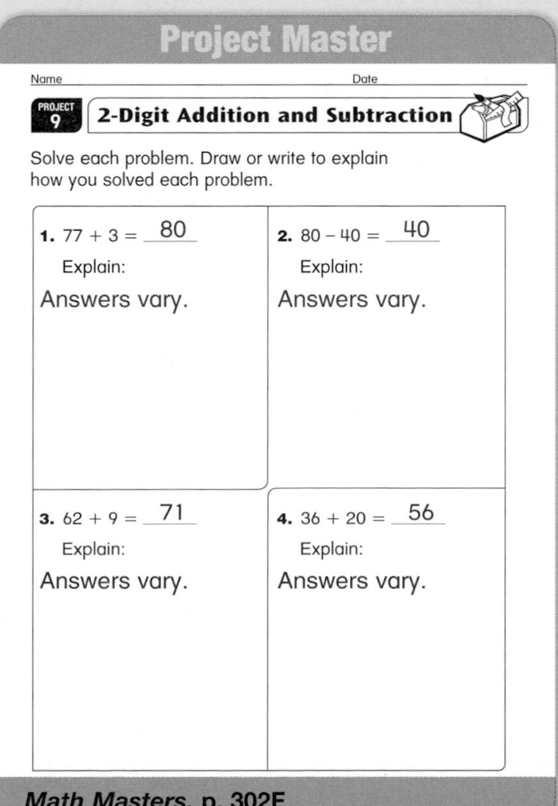

Project Master

Name Date

PROJECT 9 **2-Digit Addition and Subtraction**

Solve each problem. Draw or write to explain how you solved each problem.

1. 77 + 3 = 80
Explain:
Answers vary.

2. 80 − 40 = 40
Explain:
Answers vary.

3. 62 + 9 = 71
Explain:
Answers vary.

4. 36 + 20 = 56
Explain:
Answers vary.

Math Masters, p. 302F

Project

10 Shape City

Objective To construct composite figures from plane shapes and solid figures.

Technology Resources www.everydaymathonline.com

eToolkit

Algorithms Practice

EM Facts Workshop Game™

Family Letters

Assessment Management

Common Core State Standards

Curriculum Focal Points

Interactive Teacher's Lesson Guide

1 Doing the Project

Recommended Use During or after Unit 7

Key Concepts and Skills

- Compose plane shapes.
  [Geometry Goal 1]
- Compose solid figures.
  [Geometry Goal 1]
- Construct composite shapes from plane shapes and solid figures.
  [Geometry Goal 1]

Key Activities

Children review plane shapes, solid figures, and composite shapes. They learn about cities, including the buildings, people, animals, and objects one might find in a city. They construct models of city buildings from solid figures. They construct models of people, animals, and objects from plane shapes. They use their constructions to create a class model of a city.

Materials

- *Math Masters,* pp. 212A, 212B, 288A, 288B, 302H, 302I, 302J, and 302K
- pattern blocks
- circle blocks (from *Math Masters,* page 205A)
- solid figures collected in the Shapes Museum
- scissors
- scotch and masking tape
- glue sticks and glue
- Pattern-Block Templates
- white construction paper (5 sheets per small group)
- markers
- chart paper (optional)

***See* Advance Preparation**

2 Extending the Project

Children find plane shapes and solid figures in pictures from magazines; they combine and trace pattern blocks to make composite shapes; they make familiar shapes from other shapes; and they read about cities.

Materials

- old magazines
- pattern blocks
- *Busy, Busy Town* by Richard Scarry

Advance Preparation

Before beginning the project, clear a space (approximately 4 feet by 4 feet) in the classroom or in the hallway outside of your classroom for children to construct their city model. You may wish to use masking tape to mark this space on the floor and to mark roads within the city. On firm colored paper (the firmer, the better), copy two sets of *Math Masters,* pages 212A, 212B, 288A, and 288B for each small group. Consider cutting out some of the templates on these pages in advance. On firm white paper, copy two sets of *Math Masters,* pages 302H, 302I, and 302J for each small group. Make one copy of *Math Masters,* page 302K and cut out the building tags from this page before the lesson.

Collect (or have children collect) old magazines for the project extensions.

1 Doing the Project

Exploring Composite Shapes

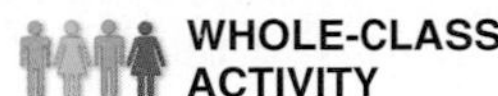
WHOLE-CLASS ACTIVITY

Tell children that they are going to be learning more about shapes. Ask children to name plane shapes they know. Make a list of plane shapes on the board or on chart paper. Be sure the list includes the following plane shapes: square, rectangle, triangle, trapezoid, hexagon, rhombus, parallelogram, circle, half-circle, and quarter-circle.

Ask children to name the solid figures they know. Make a separate list of these shapes on the board or on chart paper. Be sure the list includes the following solid figures: cube, rectangular prism, cylinder, cone, pyramid, and sphere.

Remind children that they can combine the shapes they know to make new shapes. Provide children with pattern blocks, circle blocks (introduced in Lesson 7-4), and solid figures from the Shapes Museum. Encourage them to try combining shapes to form several different composite shapes.

Circulate and monitor children as they make new shapes. Children should combine plane shapes with plane shapes and solid figures with solid figures. When children have made composite shapes they like, ask them to combine multiple composite shapes to make a new one.

NOTE Children do not need to tape or fasten their shapes together. At this point, they are simply exploring different ways to combine shapes. Later in the project, they will connect their shapes together.

After children have explored composite shapes, ask several children to share interesting shapes they constructed. As each child shares, pose the following questions to the rest of class:

- Does the new shape remind you of other shapes?
- Which shapes make up the new shape?
- Can you make the same shape?

Tell children that when they see an unfamiliar shape, they can often break it down into simpler shapes that they know.

▶ Learning about Cities

> **NOTE** In this project, the term "city" is used generically, to represent any town, village, or settlement, not just an urban or metropolitan area. You may use whichever term (village, town, or city) your class would best understand. Children should discuss and model generic buildings and people such as hospitals and doctors, not specific ones, such as the Empire State Building.

Explain that children are going to use the shapes they know to build a model of a city. Many people, including people who design buildings, make models of their constructions before they actually build them. Tell children they may have done something similar when they played with blocks. In this project, children are going to combine simple plane shapes and solid figures to design and model the things they would find in a city.

Discuss what cities are and what children may find in and around cities. Make separate lists of buildings children have seen in cities and of the people, animals, and objects they have seen in cities. You may wish to ask children the following questions:

- What is the name of the city, village, or town where you live (or nearest to where you live)? What other cities have you been to? What other cities have you heard of?
- What are some places or buildings you might visit in a city? Sample answers: House, school, store, hospital, park, library
- Who are some people you might see at a hospital? Sample answers: Patients, doctors, nurses At a school? Sample answers: Other children, teachers, maintenance staff At a store? Sample answers: Shoppers, cashiers At other places?
- What animals or other objects might you see in a city when you are outside? Sample answers: Dogs, cats, cars, stop lights, benches, signs

Tell children that today they will use what they know about cities and shapes to make models of buildings, people, animals, and things.

▶ Modeling Buildings with Solid Figures

(*Math Masters,* pp. 212A, 212B, 288A, and 288B)

Review the list children made of buildings in a city. Have each small group select its own building to model with solid figures. Some possible buildings include school, bank, library, store, police station, or hospital.

Distribute two sets of *Math Masters,* pages 212A, 212B, 288A, and 288B to each small group. Tell children that they may use these pages to make solid figures, which they will combine to make models of their buildings. If necessary, demonstrate how to cut out, fold, and tape each template into a solid (see Lessons 7-5, 7-6, and 10-5 for more on these templates). Provide children with scissors and tape, and have them work together in their groups to construct the solid figures. Each small group should construct two of each solid figure: cube, cone, rectangular prism, and cylinder.

NOTE Some children may have difficulty cutting out the templates. You may wish to pair children with strong fine-motor skills with those who have difficulty with fine-motor tasks, or you may wish to cut a few of each template before the project begins.

After children have composed their solid figures, have them work in their small groups to combine the solid figures into a model of their building. They may fasten the solid figures together using tape or glue. Remind them that the models do not have to look exactly like the buildings they represent and that they do not have to use all of their solid figures to make their composite figures. What is important is that they combine solid figures in some way to make a composite figure that resembles a building.

Modeling People, Animals, and Objects with Plane Shapes

(*Math Masters,* pp. 302H, 302I, and 302J)

Review the list of people, animals, and objects children see around a city. Tell children that they will use plane shapes to model people, animals, or objects they would see at the building they constructed. For instance, if children modeled a school with their solid figures, they could now model people with plane shapes and then color or decorate them to look like teachers and students.

Children should have their pattern blocks, circle blocks, and Pattern-Block Templates ready to compose shapes and composite shapes. Provide each small group with five sheets of white construction paper and two sets of *Math Masters,* pages 302H, 302I, and 302J. Explain that these masters give children some ideas for how to model various people, animals, and objects with plane shapes.

NOTE You may wish to discuss each item on the masters with children. The masters distinguish Block Figures, or those that can be made with pattern blocks and circle blocks, from Shape Figures, or those that can be made with other shapes not found on the Pattern-Block Template. Some of the items are modeled more realistically than others, and the items are not to scale, so that they are easier for children to construct.

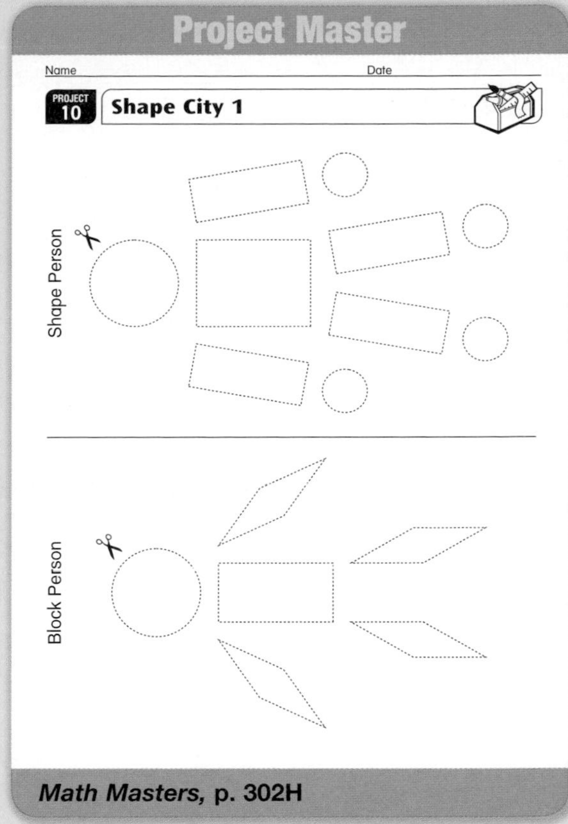

Math Masters, p. 302H

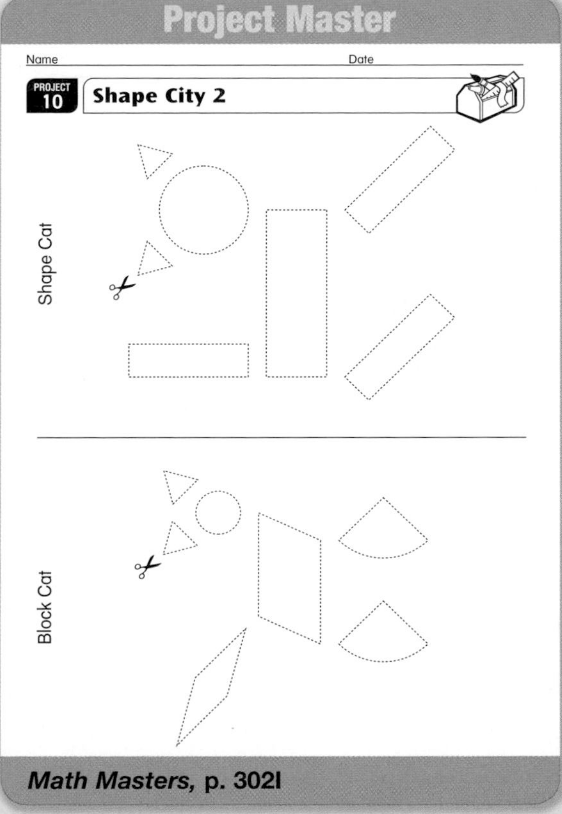

Math Masters, p. 302I

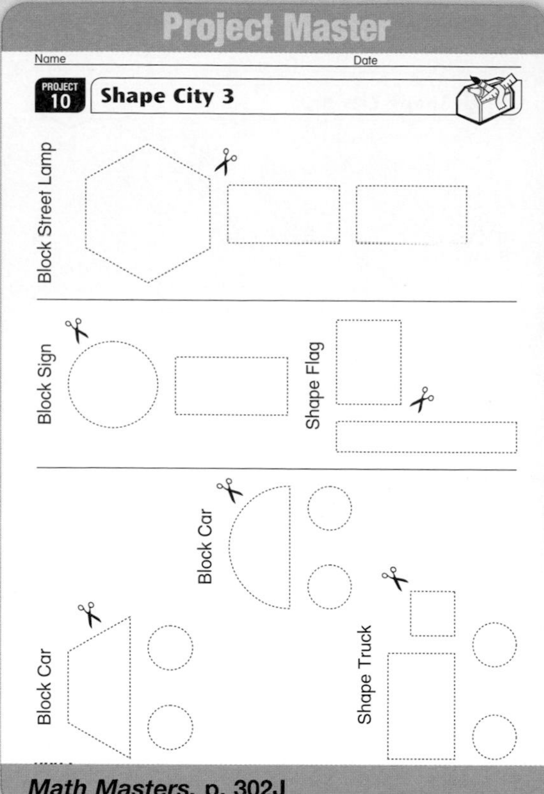

Math Masters, p. 302J

NOTE The three options presented here are ordered in terms of increasing difficulty. Depending on the skill level of your class, you may wish to introduce only Option 1 or only Options 1 and 2. You may then challenge some children to use Option 3.

NOTE Some children may try to make a stop sign with the hexagon. You may wish to remind them that stop signs are actually octagons.

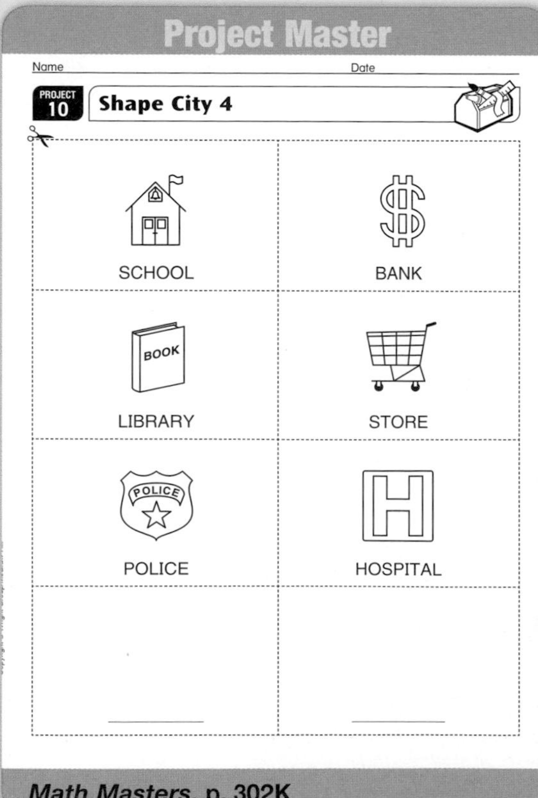

Math Masters, p. 302K

Discuss and model at least one of the three options children may use to construct their composite figures. Demonstrate the options by using the Block Person on *Math Masters,* page 302H as an example.

Option 1: Use the masters. Demonstrate this option for children by cutting out the component shapes for the Block Person from *Math Masters,* page 302H. Fold a piece of the white construction paper in half, and use a glue stick to affix the shapes, in the form of a person, to one half of the folded construction paper. Set the construction paper upright, so that the figure will stand up.

Option 2: Use pattern blocks and circle blocks. Demonstrate this option for children on the overhead by arranging pattern blocks and circle blocks so that they make the person. Trace the outline of the figure on the overhead. Tell children that they will trace the composite figure onto one half of their folded construction paper so that the figure will stand up.

Option 3: Use the Pattern-Block Template. Demonstrate this option for children on the overhead by using the Pattern-Block Template to draw each component shape for the person. Tell children that they will trace the shapes, in the form of a person, onto one half of their folded construction paper so that the figure will stand up.

After each small group has composed four or five figures, provide children with markers to color and decorate their figures. Remind them to decorate the figures based on the building where they will be placed. For instance, if they modeled a police station, they may wish to decorate one of the people they modeled in blue or black to resemble a police officer.

▶ Building the City

WHOLE-CLASS ACTIVITY

(*Math Masters,* p. 302K)

Provide each small group with the appropriate building tag from *Math Masters,* page 302K. (Use the blank tags to label buildings children create for which tags are not included.) Children color or decorate the tags using markers. Before the lesson, you should have cleared a space to house the model city. (To organize the city, you may wish to make roads within the city using masking tape or gray construction paper.) When children are finished decorating their tags, have each small group bring the tag, the building model, and the models of people, animals, and objects to this space.

Have each small group place its models in the city space. Each small group presents its models to the class by explaining what the building is and what the people, animals and objects are.

When each small group has placed its models in the city area, remind children that they used very simple shapes to make new shapes. Those new shapes allowed them to model a whole city. If they wish, they can continue making models with blocks and other toys.

Celebrate the city with children by leaving it intact for a few days after the project and allowing children to play with it. Take a photograph to remember the city before you deconstruct it.

2 Extending the Project

Extension Suggestions

- Offer children old magazines. Have children examine pictures in the magazines and circle any familiar plane shapes and solid figures they see.
- Provide pairs of children with scratch paper and pattern blocks. Have each partnership sit back to back or hide their work with folders so that children cannot see what their partners are doing. Tell children to combine several pattern blocks and trace the outline of the new shape on the paper. Then have partners switch papers. Children then place pattern blocks in their partner's figure to determine the component shapes their partners used to make the composite shapes.
- Provide each member of a partnership with the same set of four or five pattern blocks. For instance, each child may take two triangles, a square, and a fat rhombus. Have each partnership sit back to back or hide their work with folders so that children cannot see what their partners are doing. Tell children to combine the pattern blocks into a new shape. When they are finished, partners reveal their composite shape to see if they made the same shape.
- Provide children with pattern blocks and solid figures from the Shapes Museum. Challenge children to make shapes they know from the pattern blocks and solid figures. For instance, you may wish to tell children to do the following:
  - Make a hexagon from triangles or rhombuses.
  - Make a rectangular prism from cubes.
  - Make a trapezoid from triangles.

Language Arts Link To further explore the people, places, and things in cities, you may wish to read ***Busy, Busy Town*** by Richard Scarry (Golden Books, 2000).

First Grade Key Vocabulary

For a more comprehensive glossary that includes additional entries and illustrations, please refer to the *Teacher's Reference Manual.*

NOTE: In a definition, terms in italics are defined elsewhere in this glossary.

addend Any one of a set of numbers that are added. For example, in $5 + 3 + 1$, the addends are 5, 3, and 1.

addition fact Two 1-digit numbers and their *sum,* such as $9 + 7 = 16$.

A.M. The abbreviation for *ante meridiem,* meaning "before the middle of the day" in Latin. From midnight to noon.

analog clock (1) A clock that shows the time by the positions of the hour and minute hands. (2) Any device that shows time passing in a continuous manner, such as a sundial. Compare to *digital clock.*

area The amount of *surface* inside a 2-*dimensional figure.* The figure might be a *triangle* or *rectangle* in a plane, the curved *surface* of a *cylinder,* or a state or country on the Earth's surface. Commonly, area is measured in square *units* such as square miles, square *inches,* or square *centimeters.*

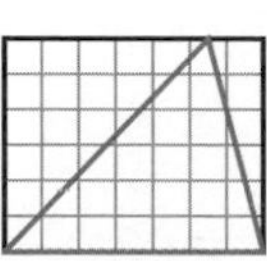

A triangle with area 21 square units

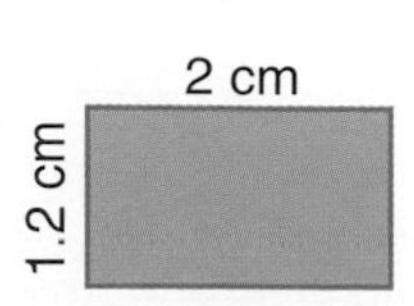

A rectangle with area $1.2 \text{ cm} \times 2 \text{ cm} = 2.4 \text{ cm}^2$

The area of the United States is about 3,800,000 square miles.

arithmetic facts The *addition facts* (whole-number *addends* 9 or less); their inverse subtraction facts; multiplication facts (whole-number factors 9 or less); and their inverse division facts, except there is no division by zero. There are

100 addition facts:	$0 + 0 = 0$ through $9 + 9 = 18$
100 subtraction facts:	$0 - 0 = 0$ through $18 - 9 = 9$
100 multiplication facts:	$0 \times 0 = 0$ through $9 \times 9 = 81$
90 division facts:	$0 / 1 = 0$ through $81 / 9 = 9$

See *fact power.*

arm span A *unit* of length equal to 6 *feet,* or 2 *yards.* It is used mainly by people who work with boats and ships to measure depths underwater and lengths of cables.

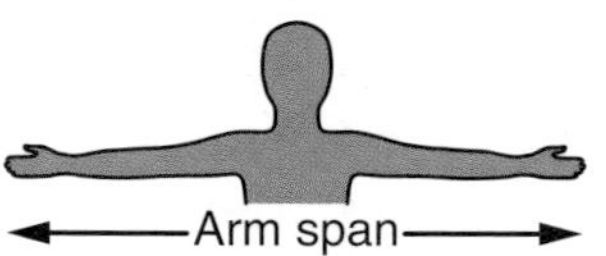

arrow rule In *Everyday Mathematics,* an operation that determines the number that goes into the next *frame* in a *Frames-and-Arrows* diagram. There may be more than one arrow rule per diagram.

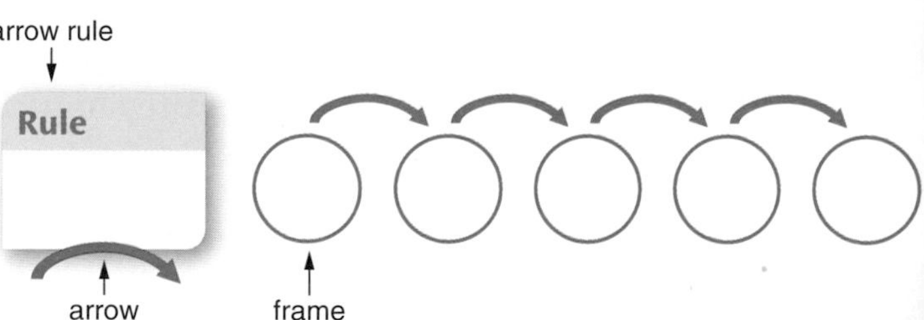

attribute A feature of an object or common feature of a *set* of objects. Examples of attributes include size, shape, color, and number of sides.

average A typical value for a set of numbers. In everyday life, average usually refers to the *mean* of the *set,* found by adding all the numbers and dividing the *sum* by the number of numbers. In statistics, several different averages, or *landmarks,* are defined, including *mean, median,* and *mode.*

B

bar graph A graph with horizontal or vertical bars that represent *data.*

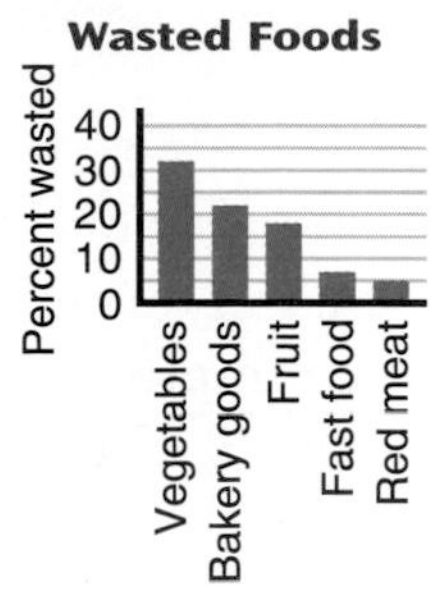

Source: The Garbage Product

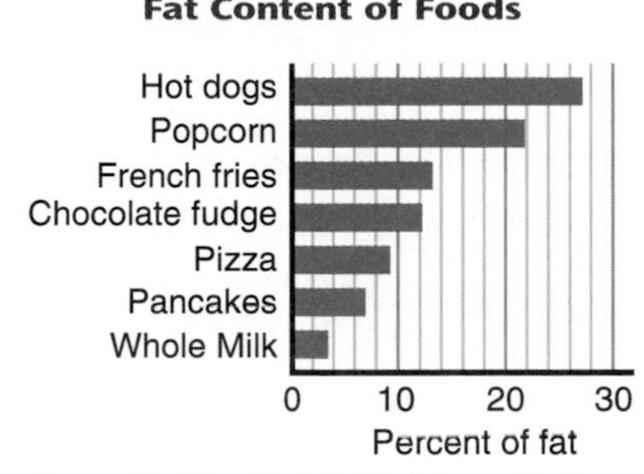

Source: The New York Public Library Desk Reference

base 10 Our system for writing numbers that uses only the 10 symbols 0, 1, 2, 3, 4, 5, 6, 7, 8, and 9, called *digits.* You can write any number using one or more of these 10 digits, and each digit has a value that depends on its place in the number (its *place value*). In the base-10 system, each place has a value 10 times that of the place to its right, and 1 tenth the value of the place to its left.

base-10 blocks A *set* of blocks to represent ones, tens, hundreds, and thousands in the *base-10 place-value* system. In *Everyday Mathematics,* the unit block, or *cube,* has 1-cm edges; the ten block, or *long,* is 10 unit blocks in length; the hundred block, or *flat,* is 10 longs in width; and the thousand block, or big cube, is 10 flats high. See *cube, long,* and *flat* for photos of the blocks. See *base-10 shorthand.*

base-10 shorthand In *Everyday Mathematics,* a written notation for *base-10 blocks.*

Name	Base-10 block	Base-10 shorthand
cube		
long		
flat		
big cube		

C

calendar (1) A *reference frame* to keep track of the passage of time. Many different calendars exist, including the Gregorian calendar currently used by most of the Western world, the Hebrew calendar and the Islamic calendar. (2) A practical model of the reference frame, such as the large, reusable Class Calendar in *First* through *Third Grade Everyday Mathematics.* (3) A schedule or listing of events.

August 2007

Sunday	Monday	Tuesday	Wednesday	Thursday	Friday	Saturday
			1 Dr.'s appt. 3:00	2	3	4
5	6	7	8	9	10	11
12	13 Mom's b-day	14	15	16	17	18
19	20	21	22	23	24	25
26	27	28	29	30	31	

capacity (1) The amount of space occupied by a *3-dimensional figure.* Same as volume. (2) Less formally, the amount a container can hold. Capacity is often measured in *units* such as quarts, gallons, cups, or liters.

Celsius A temperature scale on which pure water at sea level freezes at 0° and boils at 100°. The Celsius scale is used in the *metric system.* A less common name for this scale is centigrade, because there are 100 units between the freezing and boiling points of water. Compare to *Fahrenheit.*

cent A penny; $\frac{1}{100}$ of a dollar. From the Latin word *centesimus,* which means "a hundredth part."

centimeter (cm) A metric *unit* of length equivalent to 10 millimeters, $\frac{1}{10}$ of a decimeter, and $\frac{1}{100}$ of a *meter.*

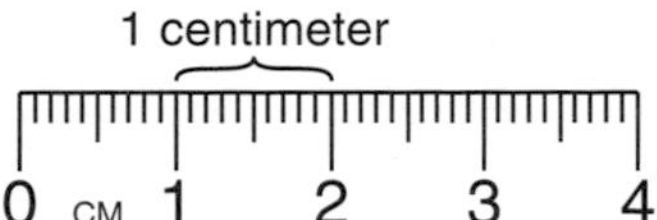

chance The possibility that an outcome will occur in an uncertain event. For example, in flipping a coin there is an equal chance of getting HEADS or TAILS.

change diagram A diagram used in *Everyday Mathematics* to model situations in which quantities are either increased or decreased by addition or subtraction. The diagram includes a starting quantity, an ending quantity, and an amount of change. See *situation diagram.*

A change diagram for 14 − 5 = 9

change-to-less story A *number story* about a change situation in which the ending quantity is less than the starting quantity. For example, a story about spending money is a change-to-less story. Compare to *change-to-more story.*

change-to-more story A *number story* about a change situation in which the ending quantity is more than the starting quantity. For example, a story about earning money is a change-to-more story. Compare to *change-to-less story.*

circle The set of all points in a plane that are equally distant from a fixed point in the plane called the center of the circle. The distance from the center to the circle is the radius of the circle. The diameter of a circle is twice its radius. Points inside a circle are not part of the circle. A circle together with its interior is called a disk or a circular region.

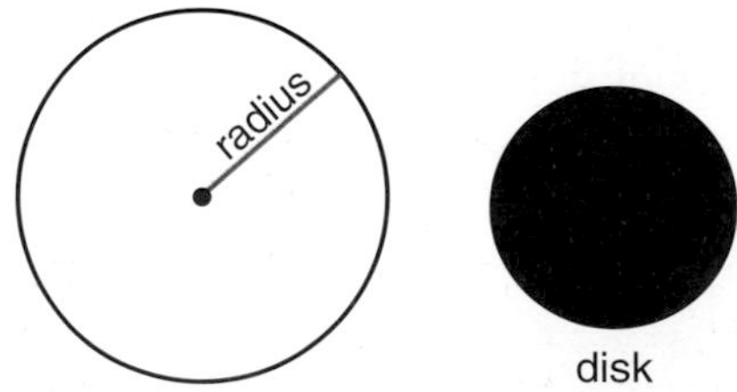

Class Data Pad In *Everyday Mathematics,* a large pad of paper used to store and recall *data* collected throughout the year. The data can be used for analysis, graphing, and generating *number stories.*

clockwise rotation The direction in which the hands move on a typical *analog clock;* a turn to the right.

column A vertical arrangement of objects or numbers in an array or a table.

Commutative Property of Addition A property of addition that two numbers can be added in either order without changing the *sum.* For example, 5 + 10 = 10 + 5. In *Everyday Mathematics,* this is called a *turn-around fact,* and the two Commutative Properties are called turn-around rules. In symbols:

For any numbers a and b, $a + b = b + a$.

Subtraction is not commutative. For example, $8 - 5 \neq 5 - 8$ because $3 \neq -3$.

comparison diagram A diagram used in *Everyday Mathematics* to model situations in which two quantities are compared by addition or subtraction. The diagram contains two quantities and their *difference.* See *situation diagram.*

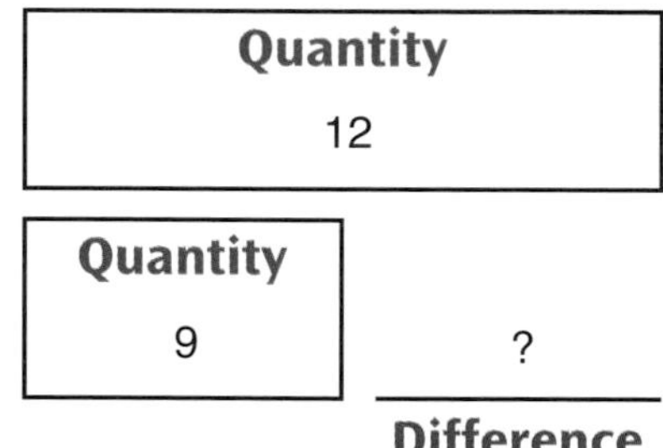

A comparison diagram for 12 = 9 + ?

comparison story A *number story* about the *difference* between two quantities. Comparison situations can lead to either addition or subtraction depending on whether one of the compared quantities or the difference between them is unknown.

cone A *geometric solid* with a circular base, a *vertex* (apex) not in the plane of the base, and all of the *line segments* with one endpoint at the apex and the other endpoint on the circumference of the base.

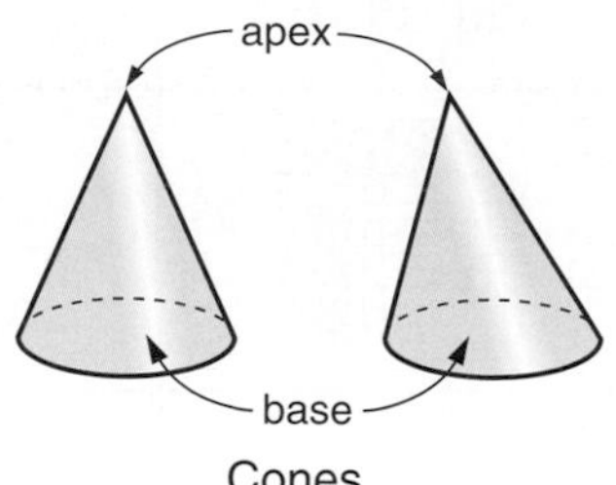

Cones

congruent figures (≅) Figures having the same size and shape. Two figures are congruent if they match exactly when one is placed on top of the other after a combination of *slides, flips,* and/or *turns.* In diagrams of congruent figures, the corresponding congruent *sides* may be marked with the same number of hash marks. The symbol ≅ means "is congruent to."

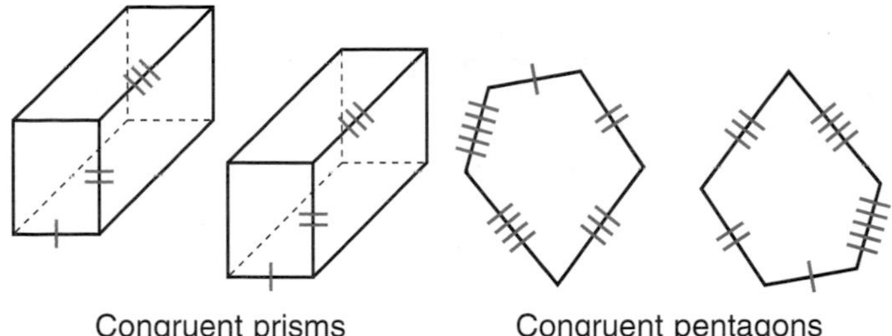
Congruent prisms Congruent pentagons

consecutive Following one after another in an uninterrupted order. For example, A, B, C, and D are four consecutive letters of the alphabet; 6, 7, 8, 9, and 10 are five consecutive whole numbers.

corner Same as *vertex.*

counting numbers The numbers used to count things. The *set* of counting numbers is {1, 2, 3, 4, . . .}. Sometimes 0 is included, but not in *Everyday Mathematics.* Counting numbers are in the sets of whole numbers, integers, *rational numbers,* and real numbers, but each of these sets include numbers that are not counting numbers.

cube (1) A *regular polyhedron* with 6 square *faces.* A cube has 8 *vertices* and 12 *edges.*

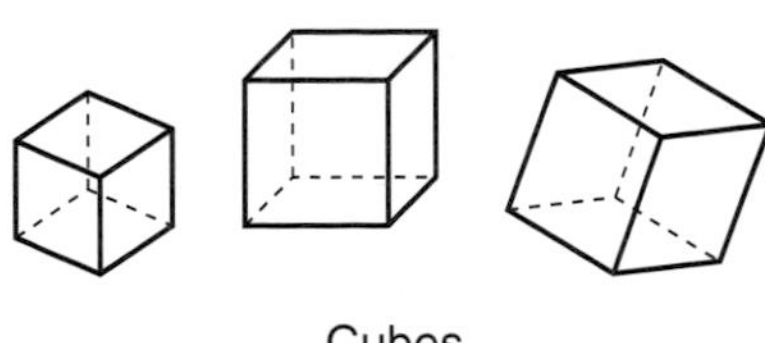
Cubes

(2) In *Everyday Mathematics,* the smaller cube of the *base-10 blocks,* measuring 1 cm on each edge.

cubit An ancient *unit* of length, measured from the point of the elbow to the end of the middle finger. The cubit has been standardized at various times between 18 and 22 *inches.* The Latin word *cubitum* means "elbow."

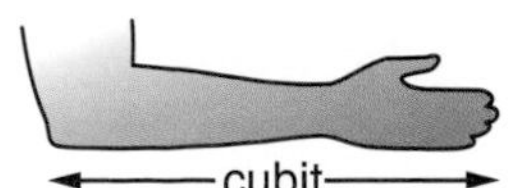

cup (c) A *U.S. customary* unit of volume or *capacity* equal to 8 fluid ounces or $\frac{1}{2}$ pint.

curved surface A *2-dimensional* surface that does not lie in a plane. *Spheres, cylinders,* and *cones* each have one curved surface.

customary system of measurement In *Everyday Mathematics,* the same as *U.S. customary system* of measurement.

cylinder A *geometric solid* with two congruent, parallel circular regions for bases and a curved face formed by all the segments with an endpoint on each *circle* that are parallel to a segment with endpoints at the centers of the circles. Also called a circular cylinder.

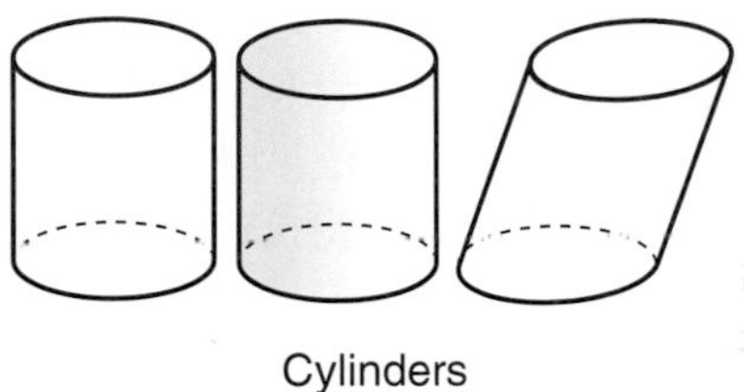
Cylinders

D

data Information that is gathered by counting, measuring, questioning, or observing. Strictly, data is the plural of *datum,* but data is often used as a singular word.

decimal point A mark used to separate the ones and tenths places in decimals. A decimal point separates dollars from cents in *dollars-and-cents notation.* The mark is a dot in the *U.S. customary system* and a comma in Europe and some other countries.

degree (°) (1) A *unit* of measure for angles based on dividing a *circle* into 360 equal parts. Lines of latitude and longitude are measured in degrees, and these degrees are based on angle measures. (2) A unit for measuring *temperature.* The symbol ° means degrees of any type.

denominator The nonzero divisor b in a *fraction* $\frac{a}{b}$ and a/b. In a part-whole fraction, the denominator is the number of equal parts into which the *whole,* or *ONE,* has been divided. Compare to *numerator.*

difference The result of subtracting one number from another. For example, the difference of 12 and 5 is $12 - 5 = 7$.

digit Any one of the symbols 0, 1, 2, 3, 4, 5, 6, 7, 8, and 9 in the *base-10* numeration system. For example, the *numeral* 145 is made up of the digits 1, 4, and 5.

digital clock A clock that shows the time with numbers of hours and minutes, usually separated by a colon. This display is discrete, not continuous, meaning that the display jumps to a new time after a minute delay. Compare to *analog clock.*

dollar The basic *unit* in the U.S. monetary system, equal to 100 *cents.*

dollars-and-cents notation The U.S. customary notation for writing amounts of money as a number of dollars and hundredths of dollars (*cents*). The decimal is preceded by the $ symbol, as in $8.98, meaning "eight dollars and 98 cents."

doubles fact The *sum* (or product) of a 1-digit number added to or multiplied by itself, such as $4 + 4 = 8$ or $3 \times 3 = 9$. A doubles fact does not have a *turn-around fact* partner.

E

edge (1) Any *side* of a polyhedron's *faces.* (2) A *line segment* or curve where two surfaces of a geometric solid meet.

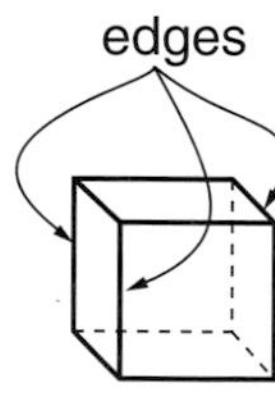

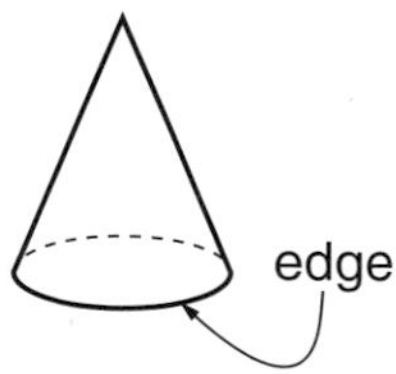

equally likely outcomes *Outcomes* of a chance experiment or situation that have the same *probability* of happening. If all of the possible outcomes are equally likely, then the probability of an event is equal to:

$$\frac{\text{number of favorable outcomes}}{\text{number of possible outcomes}}$$

equal parts Equivalent parts of a *whole.* For example, dividing a pizza into 4 equal parts means each part is $\frac{1}{4}$ of the pizza and is equal in size to the other 3 parts.

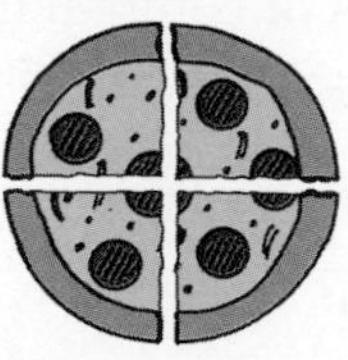

4 equal parts, each $\frac{1}{4}$ of a pizza

equation A *number sentence* that contains an equal sign. For example, $5 + 10 = 15$ and $P = 2l + 2w$ are equations.

equivalent names Different ways of naming the same number. For example, 2 + 6, 4 + 4, 12 − 4, 18 − 10, 100 − 92, 5 + 1 + 2, eight, VIII, and 𝍸 ||| are all equivalent names for 8. See *name-collection box.*

estimate (1) An answer close to, or approximating, an exact answer. (2) To make an estimate.

even number (1) A *counting number* that is divisible by 2. (2) An integer that is divisible by 2. Compare to *odd number.*

expanded notation A way of writing a number as the *sum* of the values of each *digit.* For example, 356 is 300 + 50 + 6 in expanded notation.

Explorations In *First* through *Third Grade Everyday Mathematics,* independent or small-group activities that focus on one or more of the following: concept development, manipulatives, data collection, problem solving, games, and skill reviews.

expression (1) A mathematical phrase made up of numbers, variables, operation symbols, and/or grouping symbols. An expression does not contain *relation symbols* such as =, >, and ≤. (2) Either side of an *equation* or inequality.

$9x - 2$

$2 + 3$

$\sqrt{2ab}$

πr^2

Expressions

face (1) In *Everyday Mathematics,* a flat *surface* on a *3-dimensional* shape. Some special faces are called bases. (2) More generally, any *2-dimensional surface* on a 3-dimensional shape.

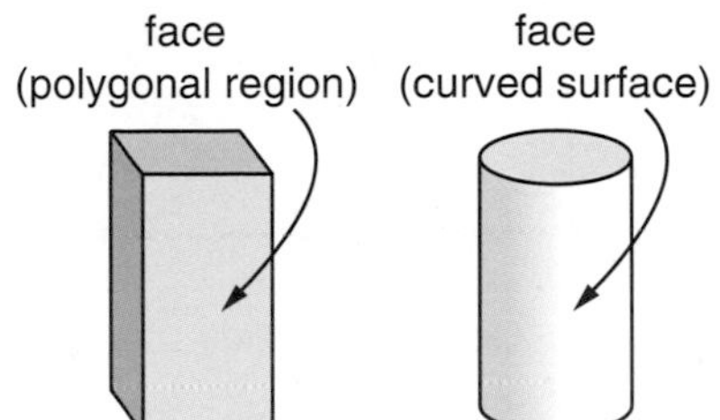

fact family A set of related *arithmetic facts* linking two inverse operations. For example,

$5 + 6 = 11, \quad 6 + 5 = 11, \quad 11 - 5 = 6, \text{ and } \quad 11 - 6 = 5$

are an addition/subtraction fact family. Similarly,

$5 \times 7 = 35, \quad 7 \times 5 = 35, \quad 35/7 = 5, \text{ and } 35/5 = 7$

are a multiplication/division fact family. Same as number family.

fact power In *Everyday Mathematics,* the ability to automatically recall basic *arithmetic facts.* Automatically knowing the facts is as important to arithmetic as knowing words by sight is to reading.

facts table A chart showing *arithmetic facts.* An addition/subtraction facts table shows addition and subtraction facts. A multiplication/division facts table shows multiplication and division facts.

Fact Triangle In *Everyday Mathematics,* a triangular flash card labeled with the numbers of a *fact family* that students may use to practice addition/subtraction and multiplication/division facts. The two 1-digit numbers and their *sum* or product (marked with a dot) appear in the corners of each *triangle.*

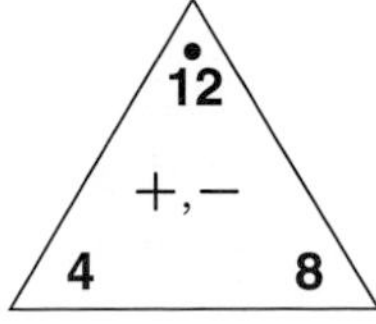

Fahrenheit A *temperature* scale on which pure water at sea level freezes at 32° and boils at 212°. The Fahrenheit scale is widely used in the U.S. but in few other places. Compare to *Celsius.*

fair Free from bias. Each side of a fair die or coin will land up about equally often. Each region of a fair spinner will be landed on in proportion to its area.

flat In *Everyday Mathematics,* the *base-10 block* consisting of one hundred 1-cm cubes.

A flat

flip An informal name for a reflection transformation.

foot (ft) A *U.S. customary* unit of length equivalent to 12 *inches,* or $\frac{1}{3}$ of a *yard.*

fraction (primary definition) A number in the form $\frac{a}{b}$ or a/b, where a and b are whole numbers and b is not 0. A fraction may be used to name part of an object or part of a collection of objects, to compare two quantities, or to represent division. For example, $\frac{12}{6}$ might mean 12 eggs divided into 6 groups of 2 eggs each, a ratio of 12 to 6, or 12 divided by 6.

fraction (other definitions) (1) A fraction that satisfies the previous definition and includes a *unit* in both the *numerator* and *denominator.* For example, the rates $\frac{50 \text{ miles}}{1 \text{ gallon}}$ and $\frac{40 \text{ pages}}{10 \text{ minutes}}$ are fractions. (2) A number written using a fraction bar, where the fraction bar is used to indicate division. For example, $\frac{2.3}{6.5}$, $\frac{1\frac{4}{5}}{12}$, and $\frac{\frac{3}{4}}{\frac{5}{8}}$.

fractional part Part of a *whole. Fractions* represent fractional parts of numbers, *sets,* or objects.

frames In *Everyday Mathematics,* the empty shapes in which numbers are written in a *Frames-and-Arrows* diagram.

Frames and Arrows In *Everyday Mathematics,* diagrams consisting of frames connected by arrows used to represent *number sequences.* Each frame contains a number, and each arrow represents a rule that determines which number goes in the next frame. There may be more than one rule, represented by different-color arrows. Frames-and-Arrows diagrams are also called "chains."

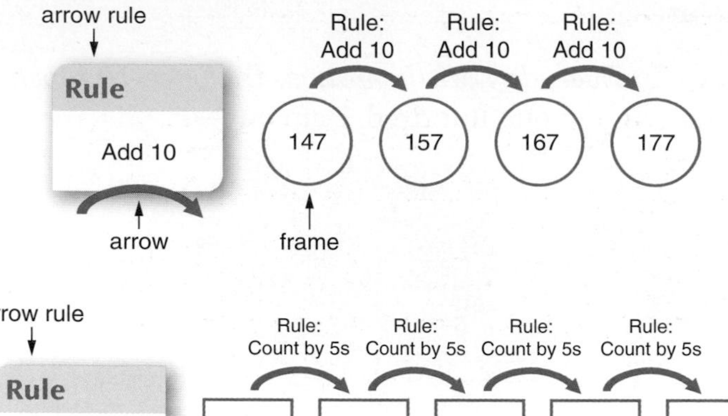

function machine In *Everyday Mathematics,* an imaginary device that receives *inputs* and pairs them with *outputs.* For example, the function machine below pairs an input number with its double.

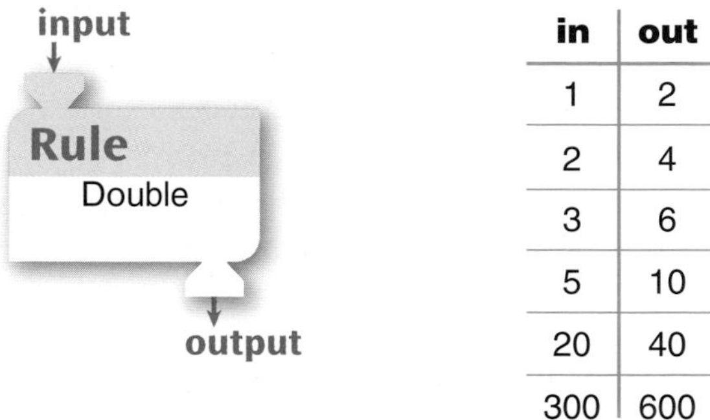

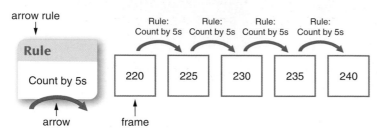

in	out
1	2
2	4
3	6
5	10
20	40
300	600

A function machine and function table

G

geoboard A manipulative *2-dimensional* coordinate system made with nails or other posts at equally-spaced intervals relative to both axes. Children loop rubber bands around the posts to make *polygons* and other shapes.

geometric solid The *surface* or surfaces that make up a *3-dimensional figure* such as a *prism, pyramid, cylinder, cone,* or *sphere.* Despite its name, a geometric solid is hollow; that is, it does not include the *points* in its interior. Informally, and in some dictionaries, a solid is defined as both the surface and its interior.

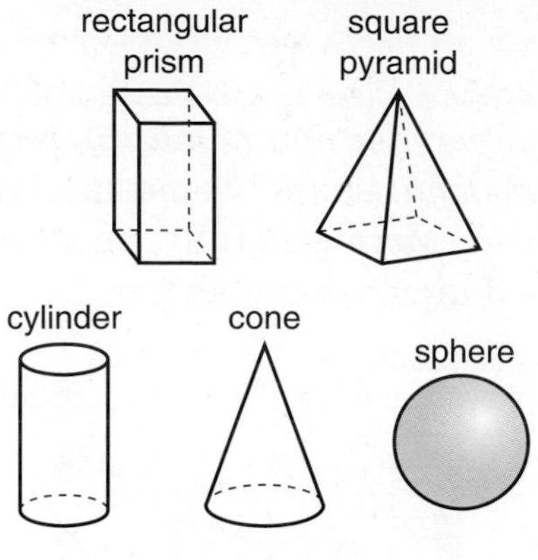

Geometric solids

girth The distance around a *3-dimensional* object.

H

half One of two *equal parts.*

hand span The distance from the tip of the thumb to the tip of the little finger (pinkie), when the hand is stretched as far as possible.

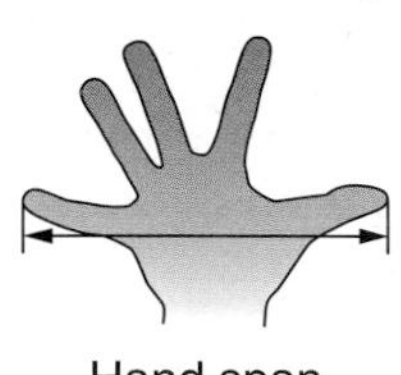

Hand span

heptagon A 7-sided *polygon.*

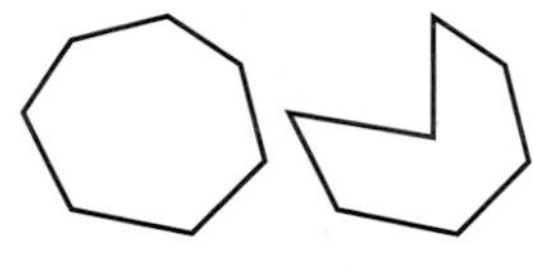

Heptagons

hexagon A 6-sided *polygon.*

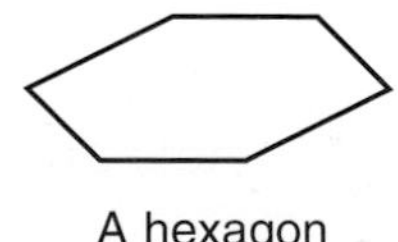

A hexagon

Home Link In *First* through *Third Grade Everyday Mathematics,* a suggested follow-up or enrichment activity to be done at home.

I

inch (in.) A *U.S. customary* unit of length equal to $\frac{1}{12}$ of a *foot* and 2.54 *centimeters.*

input (1) A number inserted into an imaginary *function machine,* which applies a rule to pair the input with an *output.* (2) The values for x in a function consisting of ordered pairs (x,y). (3) Numbers or other information entered into a calculator or computer.

kite A *quadrilateral* with two distinct pairs of adjacent sides of equal length. In *Everyday Mathematics,* the four *sides* cannot all have equal length; that is, a *rhombus* is not a kite. The diagonals of a kite are perpendicular.

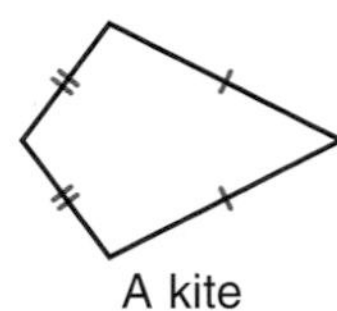

A kite

landmark In *Everyday Mathematics,* a notable feature of a *data* set. Landmarks include the *median, mode, mean, maximum, minimum,* and *range.*

length of a rectangle Typically, but not necessarily, the longer dimension of a *rectangle.*

line In *Everyday Mathematics,* a 1-dimensional straight path that extends forever in opposite directions. A line is named using two points on it or with a single, italicized lower-case letter such as *l*. In formal Euclidean geometry, a line is an undefined geometric term.

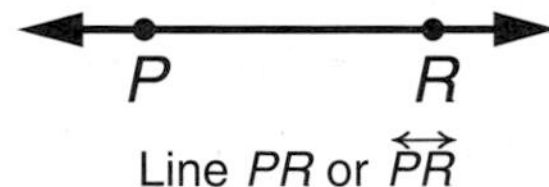

Line *PR* or $\overleftrightarrow{PR}$

line of symmetry A line that divides a figure into two parts that are reflection images of each other. A figure may have zero, one, or more lines of symmetry. For example, the numeral 2 has no lines of symmetry, a square has four lines of symmetry, and a *circle* has infinitely many lines of symmetry. Also called a symmetry line.

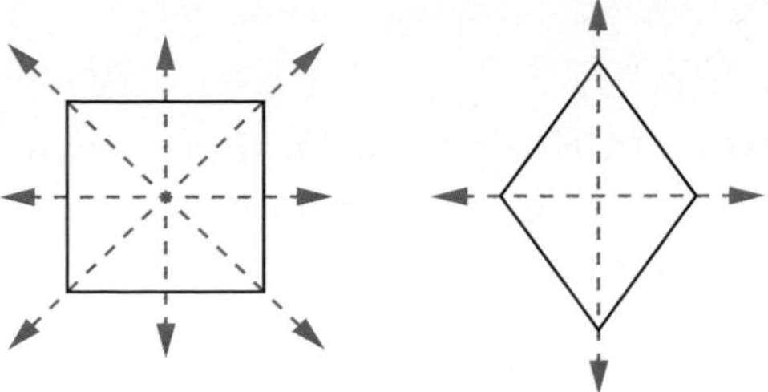

Lines of symmetry are shown in blue.

line plot A sketch of *data* in which check marks, Xs, or other symbols above a labeled line show the frequency of each value.

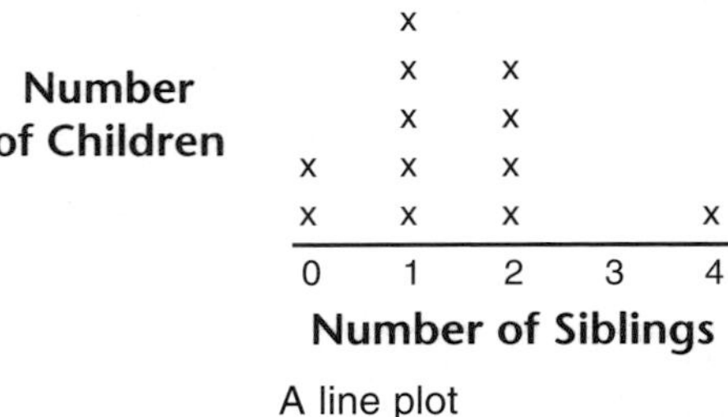

A line plot

line segment A part of a line between and including two points, called endpoints of the segment. A line segment is often named by its endpoints.

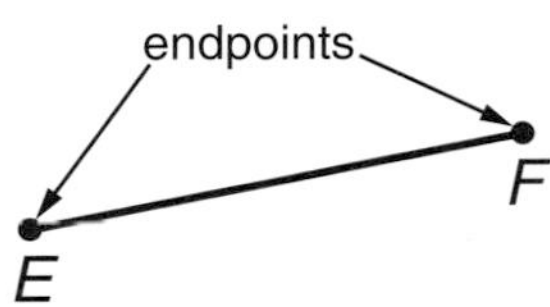

Segment *EF* or $\overline{EF}$

line symmetry A figure has line symmetry if a line can be drawn that divides it into two parts that are reflection images of each other. See *line of symmetry.*

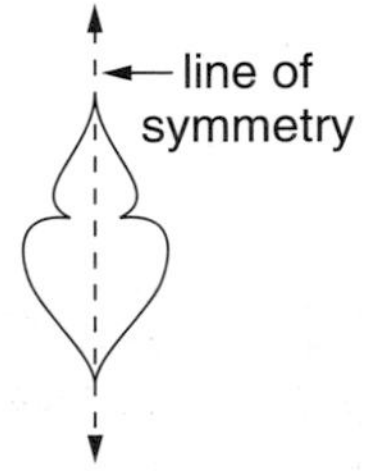

long In *Everyday Mathematics,* the *base-10 block* consisting of ten 1-cm cubes. Sometimes called a "rod."

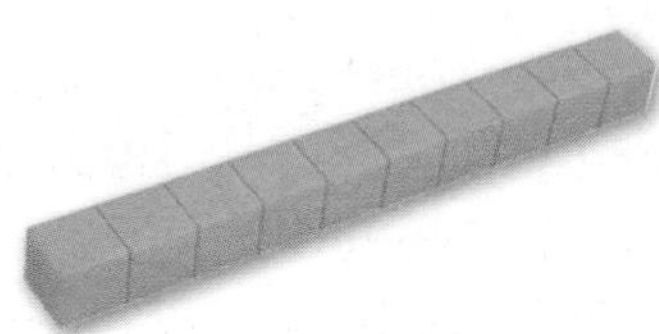

Math Boxes In *Everyday Mathematics,* a collection of problems to practice skills. Math Boxes for each lesson are in the *Math Journal.*

Math Journal In *Everyday Mathematics,* a place for students to record their mathematical discoveries and experiences. Journal pages give models for conceptual understanding, problems to solve, and directions for individual and small-group activities.

Math Master In *Everyday Mathematics,* a page ready for duplicating. Most masters support children in carrying out suggested activities. Some masters are used more than once during the school year.

Math Message In *Everyday Mathematics,* an introductory activity to the day's lesson that children complete before the lesson starts. Messages may include problems to solve, directions to follow, sentences to complete or correct, review exercises, or reading assignments.

maximum The largest amount; the greatest number in a *set* of *data.* Compare to *minimum.*

mean For a *set* of numbers, their *sum* divided by the number of numbers. Often called the *average* value of the set. Compare to other data *landmarks median* and *mode.*

median The middle value in a *set* of *data* when the data are listed in order from smallest to largest or vice versa. If there is an *even number* of data points, the median is the *mean* of the two middle values. Compare to other data *landmarks mean* and *mode.*

mental arithmetic Computation done by people "in their heads," either in whole or in part. In *Everyday Mathematics,* students learn a variety of mental-calculation strategies to develop automatic recall of basic facts and *fact power.*

Mental Math and Reflexes In *Everyday Mathematics,* exercises at three levels of difficulty at the beginning of lessons for students to get ready to think about math, warm up skills they need for the lesson, continually build mental-arithmetic skills, and help you assess individual strengths and weaknesses.

meter (m) The basic metric unit of length from which other metric units of length are derived. Originally, the meter was defined as $\frac{1}{10,000,000}$ of the distance from the North Pole to the equator along a meridian passing through Paris. From 1960 to 1983, the meter was redefined as 1,630,763.73 wavelengths of orange-red light from the element krypton. Today, the meter is defined as the distance light travels in a vacuum in $\frac{1}{299,792,458}$ second. One meter is equal to 10 decimeters, 100 *centimeters,* or 1,000 millimeters.

metric system A measurement system based on the *base-10* (decimal) numeration system that is used in most countries and by virtually all scientists around the world. *Units* for length include millimeter, *centimeter, meter,* and kilometer; units for mass and *weight* include gram and kilogram; units for volume and *capacity* include milliliter and liter; and the unit for *temperature* change is degrees *Celsius.*

middle value Same as *median.*

minimum The smallest amount; the smallest number in a *set* of *data.* Compare to *maximum.*

mode The value or values that occur most often in a *set* of *data.* Compare to other *landmarks median* and *mean.*

multiple of a number *n* (1) A product of n and a *counting number.* For example, the multiples of 7 are 7, 14, 21, 28, ... (2) A product of n and an integer. For example, the multiples of 7 are . . . , −21, −14, −7, 0, 7, 14, 21, ...

name-collection box In *Everyday Mathematics,* a diagram that is used for collecting *equivalent names* for a number.

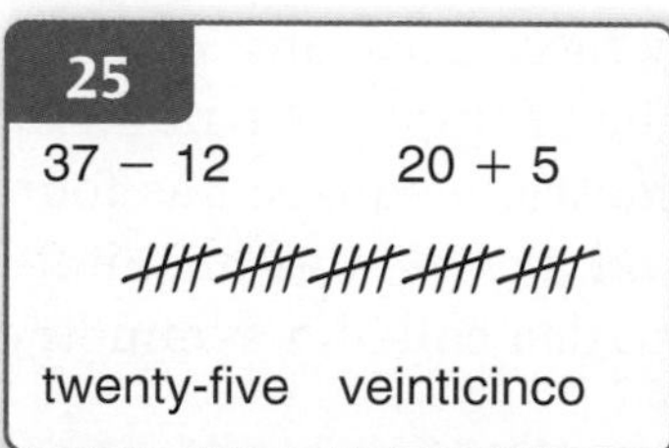

negative numbers Numbers less than 0; the opposites of the *positive numbers,* commonly written as a positive number preceded by a − or *OPP.* Negative numbers are plotted left of 0 on a horizontal *number line* or below 0 on a vertical number line.

number grid In *Everyday Mathematics,* a table in which *consecutive* numbers are arranged in *rows,* usually 10 *columns* per row. A move from one number to the next within a *row* is a change of 1; a move from one number to the next within a *column* is a change of 10.

−9	−8	−7	−6	−5	−4	−3	−2	−1	0
1	2	3	4	5	6	7	8	9	10
11	12	13	14	15	16	17	18	19	20
21	22	23	24	25	26	27	28	29	30
31	32	33	34	35	36	37	38	39	40
41	42	43	44	45	46	47	48	49	50
51	52	53	54	55	56	57	58	59	60
61	62	63	64	65	66	67	68	69	70
71	72	73	74	75	76	77	78	79	80
81	82	83	84	85	86	87	88	89	90
91	92	93	94	95	96	97	98	99	100
101	102	103	104	105	106	107	108	109	110

A number grid

number-grid puzzle In *Everyday Mathematics,* a piece of a *number grid* in which some, but not all, of the numbers are missing. Students use number-grid puzzles to practice *place-value* concepts.

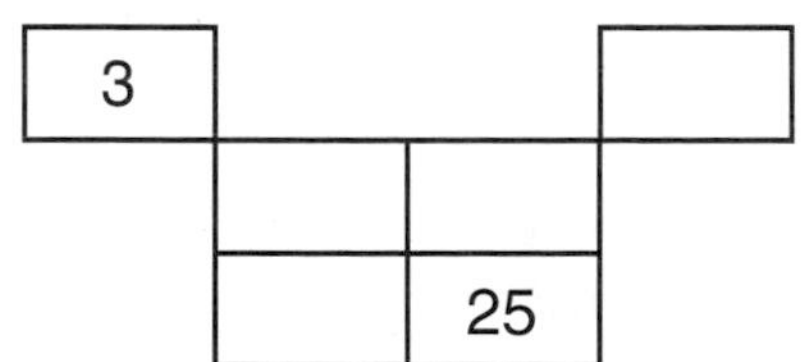

A number-grid puzzle

number line A line on which *points* are indicated by tick marks that are usually at regularly spaced intervals from a starting point called the origin, the zero point, or simply 0. Numbers are associated with the tick marks on a scale defined by the *unit* interval from 0 to 1. Every real number locates a point on the line, and every point corresponds to a real number.

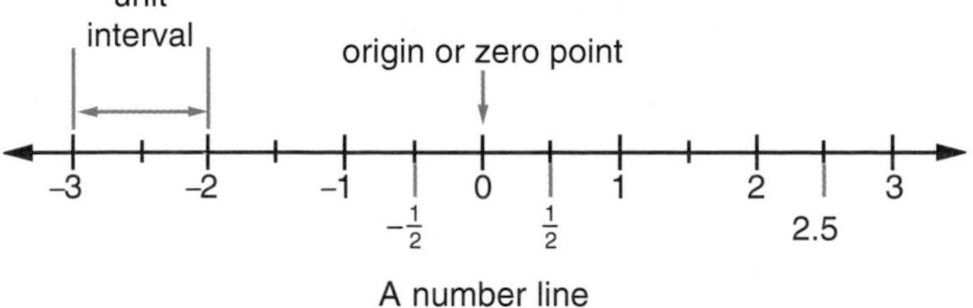

A number line

number model A *number sentence, expression,* or other representation that models a *number story* or situation. For example, the story *Sally had $5, and then she earned $8* can be modeled as the *number sentence* $5 + 8 = 13$, as the expression $5 + 8$, or by

$$\begin{array}{r} 5 \\ +\,8 \\ \hline 13 \end{array}$$

number scroll In *Everyday Mathematics,* a series of *number grids* taped together.

A number scroll

number sentence Two *expressions* with a *relation symbol.* For example,

$5 + 5 = 10$ $\qquad 16 \leq a \times b$

$2 - ? = 8$ $\qquad a^2 + b^2 = c^2$

Number sentences

number sequence A list of numbers, often generated by a rule. In *Everyday Mathematics,* students explore number sequences using *Frames-and-Arrows* diagrams.

1, 2, 3, 4, 5, . . . 1, 4, 9, 16, 25, . . .

1, 2, 1, 2, 1, . . . 1, 3, 5, 7, 9, . . .

Number sequences

number story A story that involves numbers and one or more explicit or implicit questions. For example, *I have 7 crayons in my desk. Carrie gave me 8 more crayons. Now I have 15 crayons in all* is a number story.

numeral A word, symbol, or figure that represents a number. For example, six, VI, 卌 /, and 6 are all numerals that represent the same number.

numerator The dividend a in a fraction $\frac{a}{b}$ or a/b. In a part-whole fraction, in which the *whole* (the *ONE* or unit whole) is divided into a number of equal parts, the numerator is the number of equal parts being considered. Compare to *denominator.*

octagon An 8-sided *polygon.*

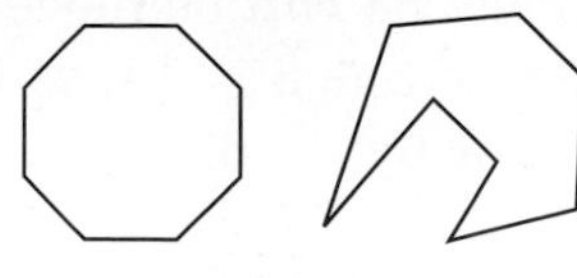

Octagons

odd number A *counting number* that is not divisible by 2. Compare to *even number.*

ONE An entire object, collection of objects, or quantity being considered in a problem situation; 100%.

ordinal number The position or order of something in a sequence, such as first, third, or tenth. Ordinal numbers are commonly used in dates, as in "May fifth" instead of "May five."

outcome A possible result of a *chance* experiment or situation. For example, HEADS and TAILS are the two possible outcomes of flipping a coin. See *equally likely outcomes.*

output (1) A number paired to an *input* by an imaginary *function machine* applying a rule. (2) The values for y in a function consisting of ordered pairs (x,y). (3) Numbers or other information displayed by calculator or computer.

pan balance A device used to weigh objects or compare their *weights.*

parallel lines *Lines* in a plane that never meet. Two parallel lines are always the same distance apart. *Line segments* or rays on parallel lines are parallel to each other.

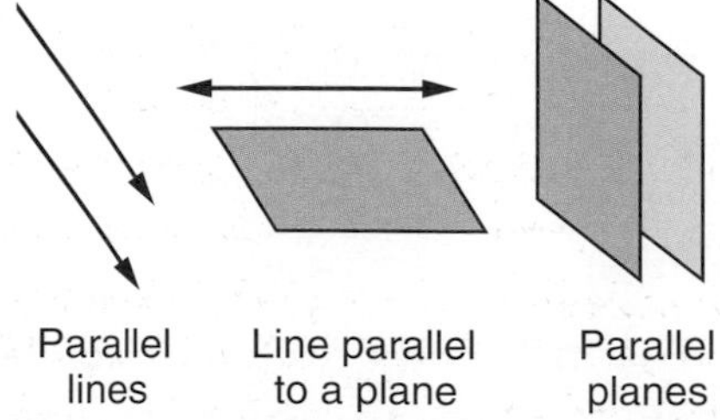

parallelogram A *quadrilateral* with two pairs of parallel sides. Opposite *sides* of a parallelogram have the same length and opposite angles have the same measure. All *rectangles* are parallelograms, but not all parallelograms are rectangles because parallelograms do not necessarily have right angles.

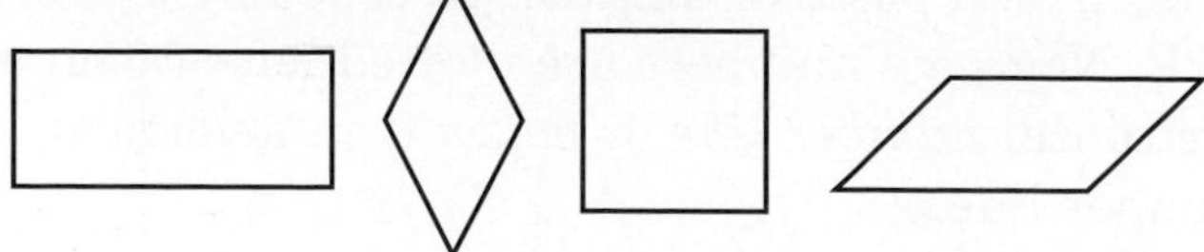

Parallelograms

parts-and-total diagram In *Everyday Mathematics,* a diagram used to model problems in which two or more quantities (parts) are combined to get a total quantity. See *situation diagram.*

Total	
13	
Part	**Part**
8	?

Parts-and-total diagram for 13 = 8 + ?

parts-and-total story A *number story* in which a *whole* is made up of distinct parts. For example, *There are 15 girls and 12 boys in Mrs. Dorn's class. How many students are there in all?* is a parts-and-total story. In other stories, the total and one or more parts may be known and the last part unknown.

pattern A repetitive order or arrangement. In *Everyday Mathematics,* students mainly explore visual and number patterns in which elements are arranged so that what comes next can be predicted.

Pattern-Block Template In *First* through *Third Grade Everyday Mathematics,* a sheet of plastic with geometric shapes cut out, used to draw patterns and designs.

pattern blocks A set of *polygon*-shaped blocks of varying sizes in which smaller blocks can be placed on larger blocks to show *fractional parts.* The blocks are used for geometric-shape identification and fraction activities.

pentagon A 5-sided *polygon.*

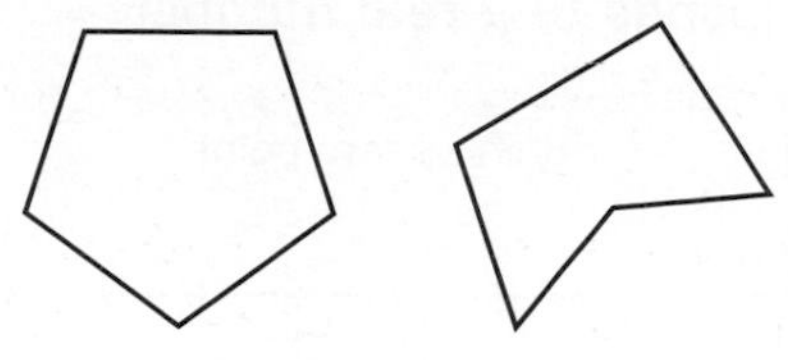

Pentagons

pictograph A graph constructed with pictures or symbols.

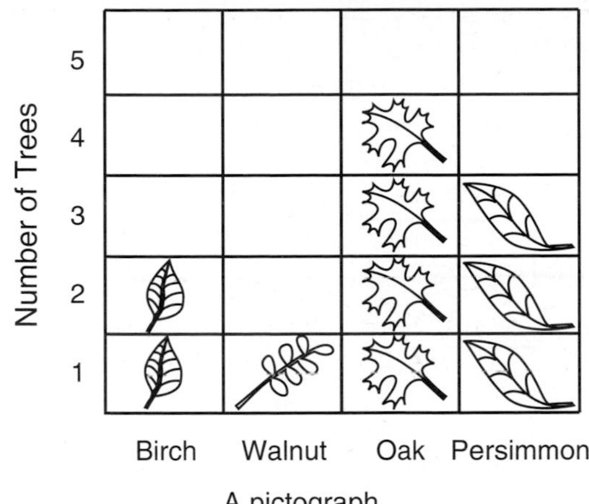

A pictograph

place value A system that gives a *digit* a value according to its position, or place, in a number. In our standard, *base-10* (decimal) system for writing numbers, each place has a value 10 times that of the place to its right and 1 tenth the value of the place to its left.

thousands	hundreds	tens	ones	.	tenths	hunderedths

A place-value chart

plane figure A *2-dimensional figure* that is entirely contained in a single plane. For example, *triangles, squares, pentagons, circles,* and parabolas are plane figures; *lines,* rays, *cones, cubes,* and *prisms* are not.

P.M. The abbreviation for *post meridiem,* meaning "after the middle of the day" in Latin. From noon to midnight.

point In *Everyday Mathematics,* an exact location in space. Points are usually labeled with capital letters. In formal Euclidean geometry, a point is an undefined geometric term.

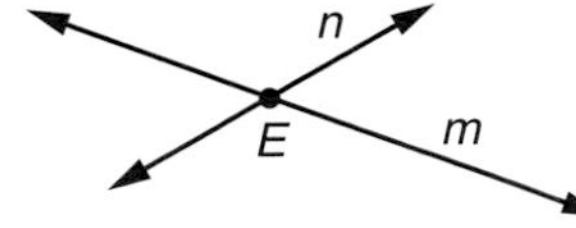

Lines *m* and *n* intersect at point *E*.

polygon A *2-dimensional figure* formed by three or more *line segments* (*sides*) that meet only at their endpoints (*vertices*) to make a closed path. The *sides* may not cross one another.

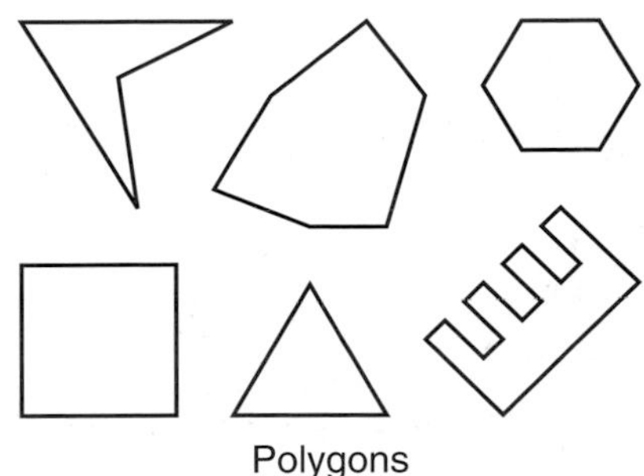

Polygons

polyhedron A *3-dimensional figure* formed by *polygons* with their interiors (*faces*) and having no holes. Plural is polyhedrons or polyhedra.

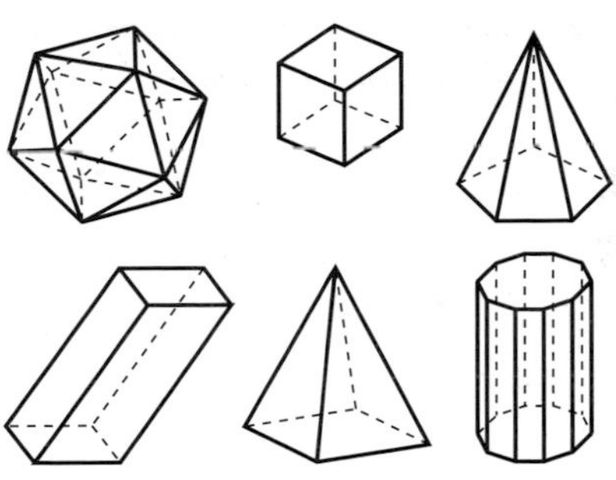

Polyhedrons

positive numbers Numbers greater than 0; the opposites of the *negative numbers.* Positive numbers are plotted to the right of 0 on a horizontal *number line* or above 0 on a vertical number line.

poster In *Everyday Mathematics,* a page displaying a collection of illustrated numerical *data.* A poster may be used as a source of data for developing *number stories.*

pound (lb) A *U.S. customary* unit of *weight* equal to 16 ounces and defined as 0.45359237 kilograms.

prism A *polyhedron* with two parallel and congruent polygonal regions for bases and lateral *faces* formed by all of the *line segments* with endpoints on corresponding edges of the bases. The lateral faces are all *parallelograms.* Lateral faces intersect at lateral edges. In a right prism, the lateral faces are rectangular. Prisms get their names from the shape of their bases.

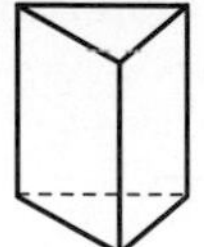

A triangular prism

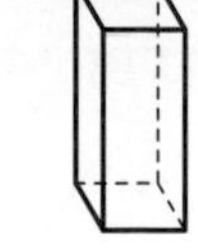

A rectangular prism

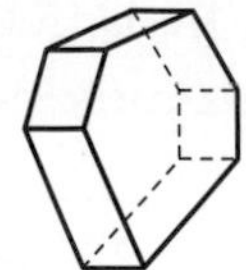

A hexagonal prism

probability A number from 0 through 1 giving the likelihood of an event happening. The closer a probability is to 1, the more likely the event is to happen. The closer a probability is to 0, the less likely the event is to happen. For example, the probability that a *fair* coin will show heads is $\frac{1}{2}$.

program a calculator To instruct a calculator to repeat a calculation using its memory instead of having the user enter a key sequence over and over. In *Everyday Mathematics,* children program their calculators to *skip count* using the machines' built-in constant operation feature.

Project In *Everyday Mathematics,* a thematic activity to be completed in one or more days by small groups or by a whole class. Projects often involve collecting and analyzing *data* and are usually cross-curricular in nature.

property (1) A generalized statement about a mathematical relationship such as the Distributive Property of Multiplication over Addition. (2) Same as *attribute.*

$$\frac{12 \text{ miles}}{1 \text{ hour}} = \frac{n \text{ miles}}{3 \text{ hours}}$$

pyramid A *polyhedron* made up of any polygonal region for a base, a *point* (apex) not in the plane of the base, and all of the *line segments* with one endpoint at the apex and the other on an *edge* of the base. All *faces* except the base are triangular. Pyramids get their name from the shape of their base.

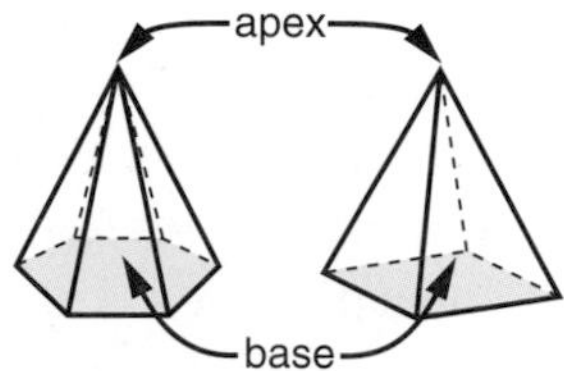

quadrangle Same as *quadrilateral.*

quadrilateral A 4-sided *polygon.* See *square, rectangle, parallelogram, rhombus, kite,* and *trapezoid.*

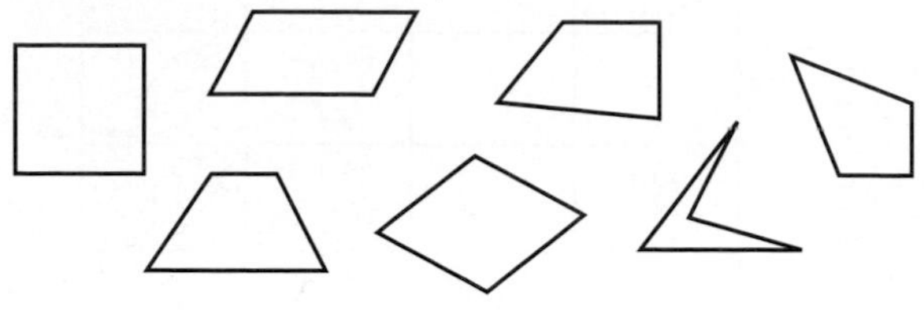

Quadrilaterals

range The *difference* between the *maximum* and the *minimum* in a *set* of *data.* Used as a measure of the spread of the data.

rational counting Counting using one-to-one matching. For example, counting a number of chairs, people, or crackers.

rational numbers Numbers that can be written in the form $\frac{a}{b}$, where a and nonzero b are integers. The decimal form of a rational number either terminates or repeats. For example, $\frac{2}{3}$, $-\frac{2}{3}$, 0.5, 20.5, and 0.333 . . . are rational numbers.

rectangle A *parallelogram* with all right angles.

rectangular prism A *prism* with rectangular bases. The four *faces* that are not bases are either *rectangles* or *parallelograms.* For example, a shoe box models a rectangular prism in which all sides are rectangles.

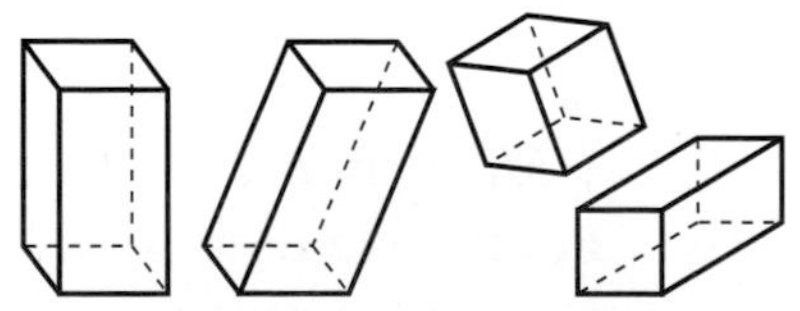

Rectangular prisms

rectangular pyramid A *pyramid* with a rectangular base.

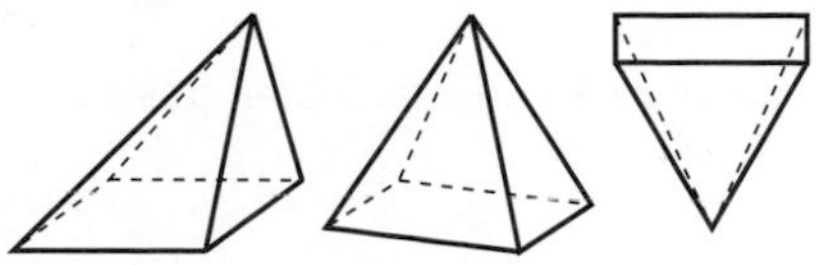

Rectangular pyramids

reference frame A system for locating numbers within a given context, usually with reference to an origin or zero point. For example, *number lines,* clocks, *calendars, temperature* scales, and maps are reference frames.

regular polygon A *polygon* in which all *sides* are the same length and all angles have the same measure.

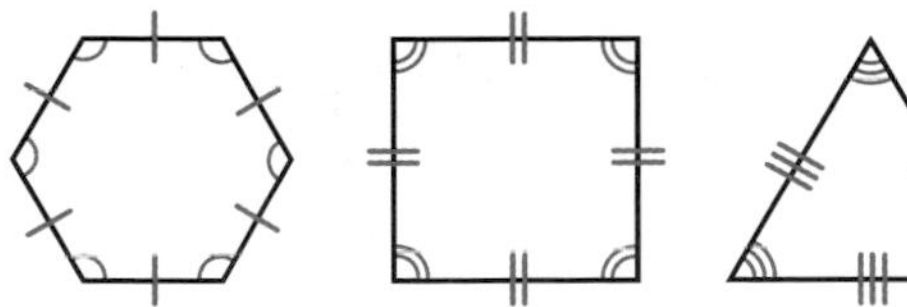

Regular polygons

regular polyhedron A *polyhedron* whose *faces* are all *congruent* regular *polygons* and in which the same number of faces meet at each *vertex.* The five regular polyhedrons, known as the Platonic solids, are shown below.

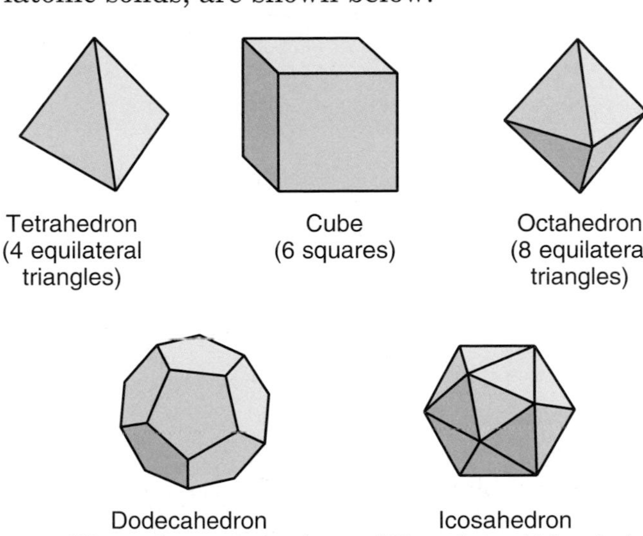

relation symbol A symbol used to express a relationship between two quantities.

Relation	Meaning
$=$	is equal to
$\neq$	is not equal to
$<$	is less than
$>$	is greater than
$\leq$	is less than or equal to
$\geq$	is greater than or equal to
$\approx$	is approximately equal to

rhombus A *parallelogram* with all *sides* the same length. All rhombuses are parallelograms. Every *square* is a rhombus, but not all rhombuses are squares. Also called a diamond. Plural is rhombuses or rhombi.

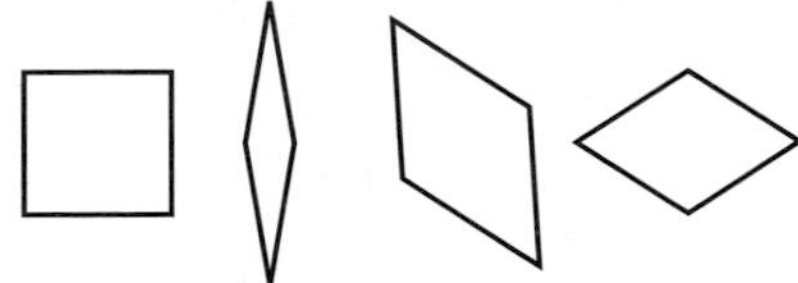

Rhombuses

rote counting Reciting a string of number words by rote, without understanding their significance. See *skip counting*.

round (1) To approximate a number to make it easier to work with, or to make it better reflect the precision of the *data.* "Rounding up" means to approximate larger than the actual value. "Rounding down" means to approximate smaller than the actual value. (2) Circular in shape.

row (1) A horizontal arrangement of objects or numbers in an array or table.

S

second (s) (1) A *unit* of time defined as $\frac{1}{31{,}556{,}925.9747}$ of the tropical year at midnight Eastern Time on New Year's Day, 1900. There are 60 seconds in a minute. (2) An *ordinal number* in the sequence *first, second, third, ...*

set A collection or group of objects, numbers, or other items.

side (1) One of the *line segments* that make up a *polygon.* (2) One of the rays or segments that form an angle. (3) One of the *faces* of a *polyhedron.*

situation diagram A diagram used to organize information in a problem situation in one of the addition/subtraction or multiplication/division use classes.

skip counting *Rote counting* by intervals, such as by twos, fives, or tens.

slate A lap-size (about 8-inch by 11-inch) chalkboard or whiteboard that children use in *Everyday Mathematics* for recording responses during group exercises and informal group assessments.

slide An informal name for a translation.

sphere The *set* of all *points* in space that are an equal distance from a fixed point called the center of the sphere. The distance from the center to the sphere is the radius of the sphere. The diameter of a sphere is twice its radius. Points inside a sphere are not part of the sphere.

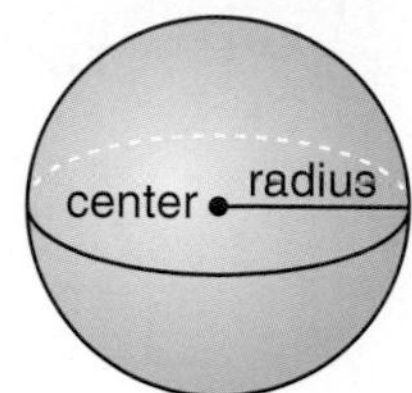

A sphere

square A *rectangle* with all sides of equal length. All angles in a square are *right angles.*

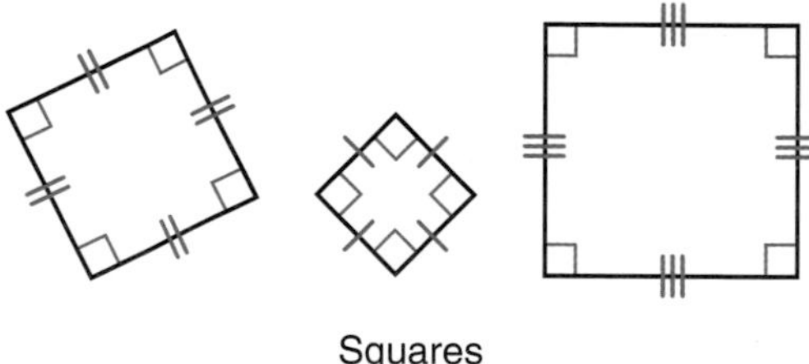

Squares

square corner A 90° angle.

standard unit A unit of measure that has been defined by a recognized authority, such as a government or a standards organization. For example, *inches, meters,* miles, *seconds, pounds,* grams, and acres are all standard units.

straightedge A tool used to draw *line segments.* Strictly speaking, a straightedge does not have a measuring scale on it, so ignore the marks if you use a ruler as a straightedge. Together, a compass and a straightedge are used to construct geometric figures.

sum The result of adding two or more numbers. For example, in 5 + 3 = 8, the sum is 8.

surface (1) The boundary of a *3-dimensional* object. The part of an object that is next to the air. Common surfaces include the top of a body of water, the outermost part of a ball, and the topmost layer of ground that covers Earth. (2) Any *2-dimensional* layer, such as a plane or a face of a *polyhedron.*

symmetry The balanced distribution of *points* over a line or around a point in a symmetric figure. See *line symmetry.*

A figure with line symmetry

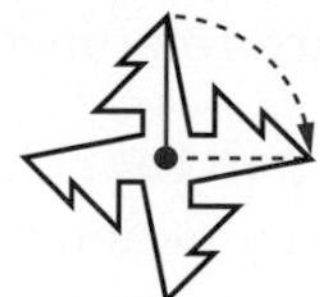

A figure with rotation symmetry

tally (1) To keep a record of a count, commonly by making a mark for each item as it is counted. (2) The mark used in a count. Also called "tally mark" and "tick mark."

tally chart A table to keep track of a *tally,* typically showing how many times each value appears in a *set* of *data.*

Number of Pull-Ups	Number of Children
0	~~////~~ /
1	~~////~~
2	////
3	//

A tally chart

temperature How hot or cold something is relative to another object or as measured on a standardized scale such as *degrees Celsius* or *degrees Fahrenheit.*

tessellation A pattern of shapes that covers a surface completely without overlaps or gaps. Same as a tiling.

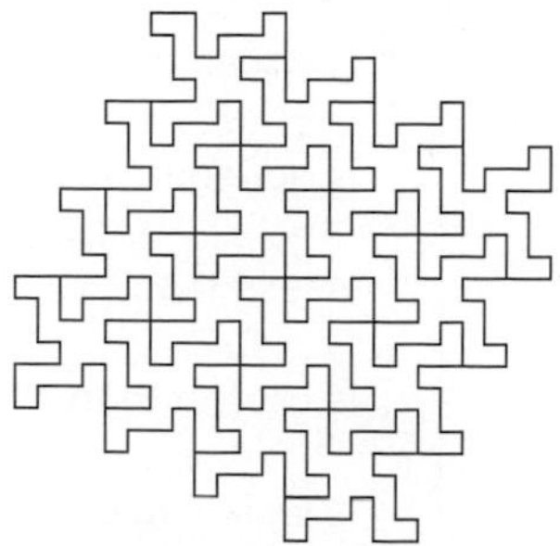

A tessellation

3-dimensional (3-D) figure A figure whose points are not all in a single plane. Examples include *prisms, pyramids,* and *spheres,* all of which have length, width, and height.

timeline A *number line* showing when events took place. In some timelines the origin is based on the context of the events being graphed, such as the birth date of the child's life graphed below. The origin can also come from another reference system, such as the year A.D. in which case the scale below might cover the years 2000 through 2005.

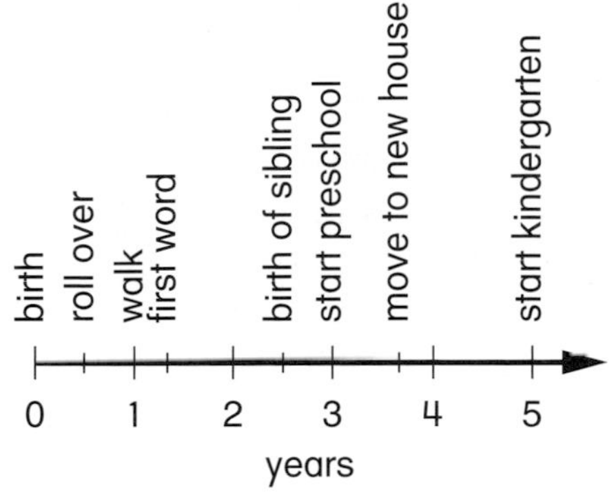

A timeline of a child's milestones

tool kit In *First* through *Third Grade Everyday Mathematics,* a bag or a box containing a calculator, measuring tools, and manipulatives often used by children in the program.

trapezoid A *quadrilateral* that has exactly one pair of parallel sides. In *Everyday Mathematics,* both pairs of sides cannot be parallel; that is, a *parallelogram* is not a trapezoid.

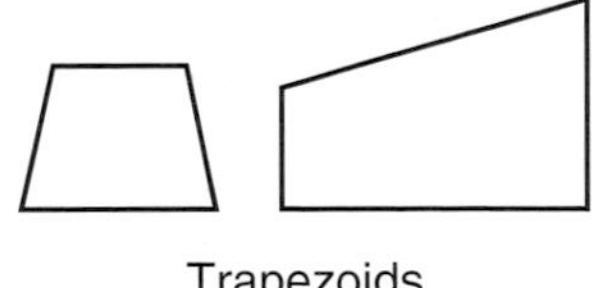
Trapezoids

triangle A 3-sided polygon.

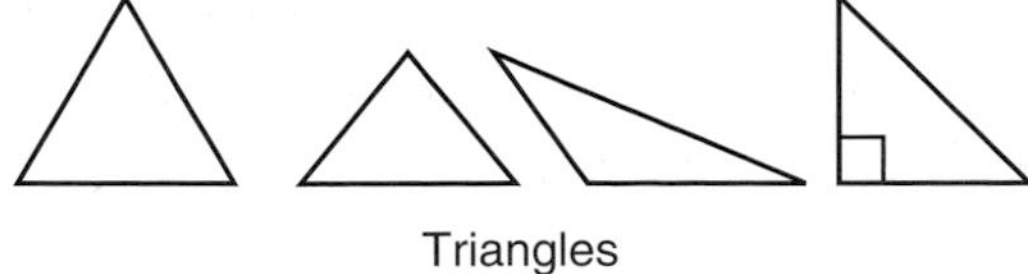
Triangles

triangular prism A *prism* whose bases are *triangles.*

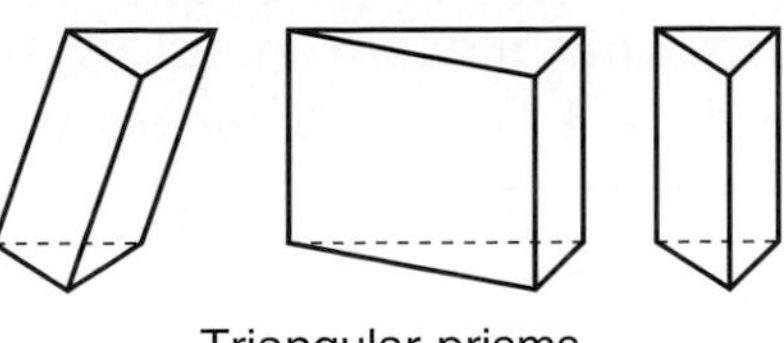
Triangular prisms

triangular pyramid A *pyramid* in which all *faces* are *triangles,* any one of which is the base. A regular tetrahedron has four equilateral *triangles,* four faces, and is one of the five regular *polyhedrons.*

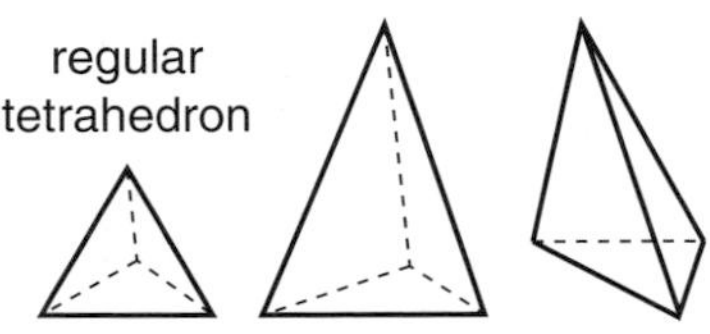

Triangular pyramids

turn An informal name for a rotation.

turn-around facts A pair of multiplication (or addition) facts in which the order of the factors (or addends) is reversed. For example, $3 \times 9 = 27$ and $9 \times 3 = 27$ are turn-around multiplication facts, and $4 + 5 = 9$ and $5 + 4 = 9$ are turn-around addition facts. There are no turn-around facts for subtraction or division. Turn-around facts are instances of the *Commutative Properties of Addition* and Multiplication.

2-dimensional (2-D) figure A figure whose points are all in one plane but not all on one *line.* Examples include *polygons* and *circles,* all of which have length and width but no height.

U

unit A label used to put a number in context. In measuring length, for example, *inches* and *centimeters* are units. In a problem about 5 apples, apple is the unit. In *Everyday Mathematics,* students keep track of units in *unit boxes.*

unit box In *Everyday Mathematics,* a box displaying the *unit* for the numbers in the problems at hand.

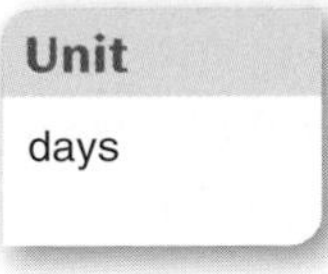

A unit box

unit fraction A *fraction* whose *numerator* is 1. For example, $\frac{1}{2}$, $\frac{1}{3}$, $\frac{1}{12}$, $\frac{1}{8}$, and $\frac{1}{20}$ are unit fractions. Unit fractions are especially useful in converting among units within measurement systems. For example, because 1 *foot* = 12 *inches* you can multiply a number of inches by $\frac{1}{12}$ to convert to feet.

U.S. customary system The measuring system used most often in the United States. *Units* for length include *inch, foot, yard,* and mile; units for *weight* include ounce and pound; units for volume or *capacity* include cup, pint, quart, gallon and cubic units; and the main unit for *temperature* change is *degrees Fahrenheit.*

Venn diagram A picture that uses *circles* or rings to show relationships between *sets.* In this diagram, 22 + 8 = 30 girls who are on the track team, and 8 girls are on both the track and the basketball teams.

Number of Girls on Sports Teams

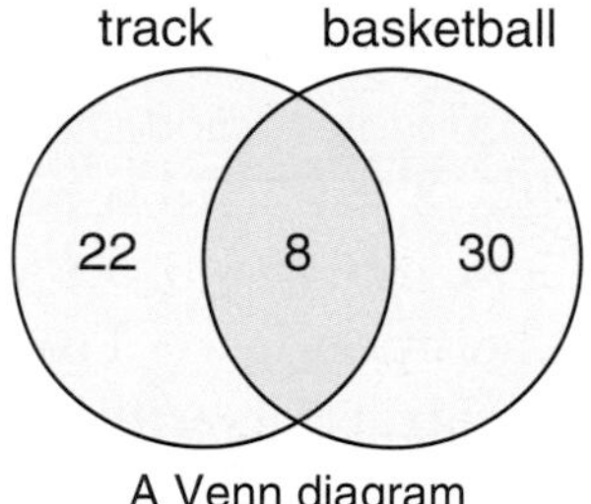

A Venn diagram

vertex The *point* at which the rays of an angle, the *sides* of a polygon, or the *edges* of a polyhedron meet. Plural is vertexes or vertices. In *Everyday Mathematics,* same as *corner.*

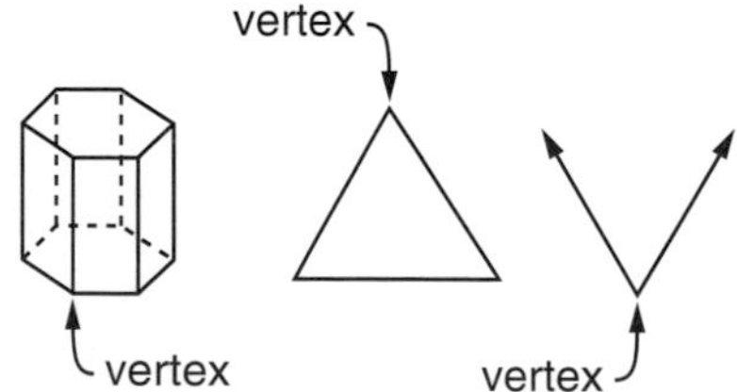

weight A measure of how heavy something is; the force of gravity on an object. An object's mass is constant, but it weighs less in weak gravity than in strong gravity. For example, a person who weighs 150 pounds in San Diego weighs about 23 pounds on the moon.

"What's My Rule?" problem In *Everyday Mathematics,* a problem in which two of the three parts of a *function* (*input, output,* and rule) are known, and the third is to be found out.

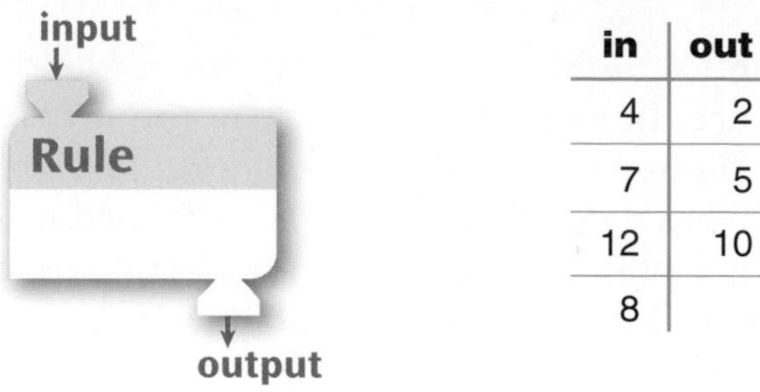

in	out
4	2
7	5
12	10
8	

A "What's My Rule?" problem

whole An entire object, collection of objects, or quantity being considered in a problem situation; 100%. Same as *ONE* and unit whole.

width of a rectangle The length of one side of a *rectangle* or rectangular object, typically the shorter side.

yard (yd) A U.S. customary unit of length equal to 3 *feet,* or 36 *inches.* To Henry I of England, a yard was the distance from the tip of the nose to the tip of the middle finger. In *Everyday Mathematics,* it is the distance from the center of the chest to the tip of the middle finger.

Grade-Level Goals

Everyday Mathematics organizes content through Program Goals and Grade-Level Goals. The Grade-Level Goals Chart shows the units in which goal content is taught and then practiced and applied. For more information, see the *Assessment Handbook.*

The Grade-Level Goals are divided according to the content strands below.

How to Read the Grade-Level Goals Chart

Each section of the chart includes Grade-Level Goals organized by content strand. The three grade-level columns divided into units indicate in which units the goals are addressed.

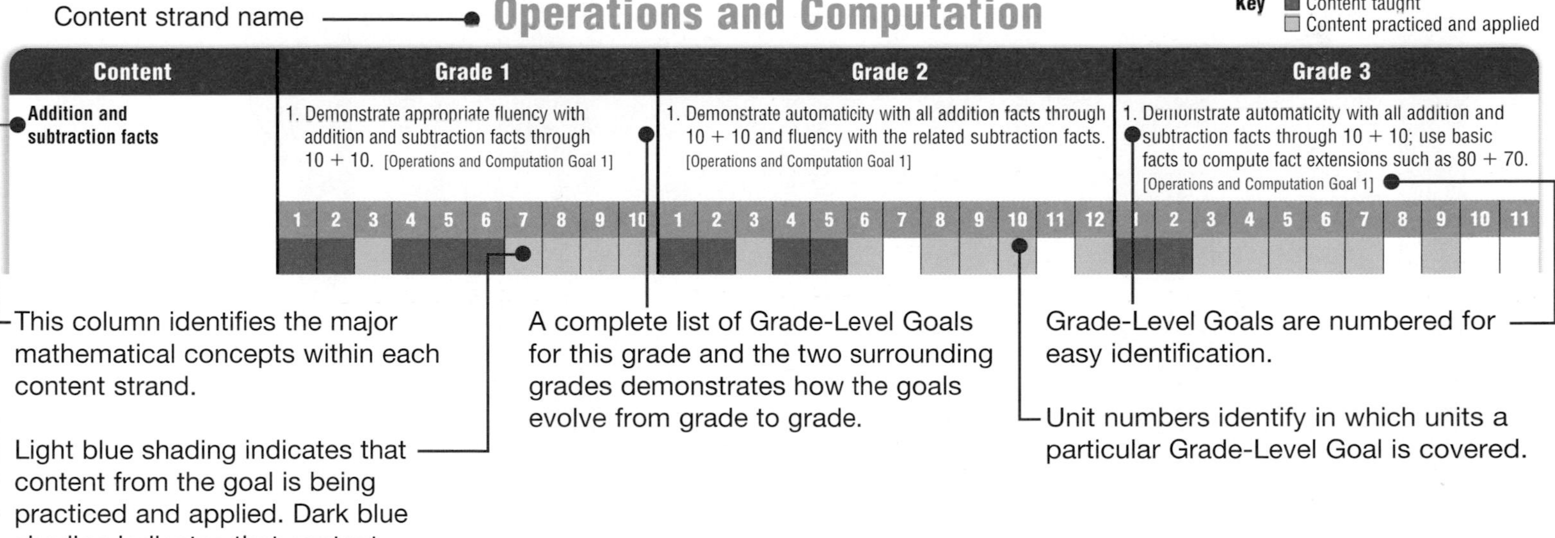

Content strand name
Operations and Computation
Key
Content taught
Content practiced and applied
Content
Grade 1
Grade 2
Grade 3
Addition and subtraction facts
1. Demonstrate appropriate fluency with addition and subtraction facts through 10 + 10. [Operations and Computation Goal 1]
1. Demonstrate automaticity with all addition facts through 10 + 10 and fluency with the related subtraction facts. [Operations and Computation Goal 1]
1. Demonstrate automaticity with all addition and subtraction facts through 10 + 10; use basic facts to compute fact extensions such as 80 + 70. [Operations and Computation Goal 1]
1 2 3 4 5 6 7 8 9 10
1 2 3 4 5 6 7 8 9 10 11 12
1 2 3 4 5 6 7 8 9 10 11
This column identifies the major mathematical concepts within each content strand.
Light blue shading indicates that content from the goal is being practiced and applied. Dark blue shading indicates that content from the goal is being taught.
A complete list of Grade-Level Goals for this grade and the two surrounding grades demonstrates how the goals evolve from grade to grade.
Grade-Level Goals are numbered for easy identification.
Unit numbers identify in which units a particular Grade-Level Goal is covered.

Number and Numeration

Key
- Content taught
- Content practiced and applied

Content	Grade 1	Grade 2	Grade 3
Rote counting	1. Count on by 1s, 2s, 5s, and 10s past 100 and back by 1s from any number less than 100 with and without number grids, number lines, and calculators. [Number and Numeration Goal 1]	1. Count on by 1s, 2s, 5s, 10s, 25s, and 100s past 1,000 and back by 1s, 10s, and 100s from any number less than 1,000 with and without number grids, number lines, and calculators. [Number and Numeration Goal 1]	
	1 2 3 4 5 6 7 8 9 10	1 2 3 4 5 6 7 8 9 10 11 12	1 2 3 4 5 6 7 8 9 10 11
Rational counting	2. Count collections of objects accurately and reliably; estimate the number of objects in a collection. [Number and Numeration Goal 2]		
	1 2 3 4 5 6 7 8 9 10	1 2 3 4 5 6 7 8 9 10 11 12	1 2 3 4 5 6 7 8 9 10 11
Place value and notation	3. Read, write, and model with manipulatives whole numbers up to 1,000; identify places in such numbers and the values of the digits in those places. [Number and Numeration Goal 3]	2. Read, write, and model with manipulatives whole numbers up to 10,000; identify places in such numbers and the values of the digits in those places; read and write money amounts in dollars-and-cents notation. [Number and Numeration Goal 2]	1. Read and write whole numbers up to 1,000,000; read, write, and model with manipulatives decimals through hundredths; identify places in such numbers and the values of the digits in those places; translate between whole numbers and decimals represented in words, in base-10 notation, and with manipulatives. [Number and Numeration Goal 1]
	1 2 3 4 5 6 7 8 9 10	1 2 3 4 5 6 7 8 9 10 11 12	1 2 3 4 5 6 7 8 9 10 11
Meanings and uses of fractions	4. Use manipulatives and drawings to model halves, thirds, and fourths as equal parts of a region or a collection; describe the model. [Number and Numeration Goal 4]	3. Use manipulatives and drawings to model fractions as equal parts of a region or a collection; describe the models and name the fractions. [Number and Numeration Goal 3]	2. Read, write, and model fractions; solve problems involving fractional parts of a region or a collection; describe strategies used. [Number and Numeration Goal 2]
	1 2 3 4 5 6 7 8 9 10	1 2 3 4 5 6 7 8 9 10 11 12	1 2 3 4 5 6 7 8 9 10 11

Key
- Content taught
- Content practiced and applied

Content	Grade 1	Grade 2	Grade 3
Number theory	5. Use manipulatives to identify and model odd and even numbers. [Number and Numeration Goal 5]	4. Recognize numbers as odd or even. [Number and Numeration Goal 4]	3. Find multiples of 2, 5, and 10. [Number and Numeration Goal 3]
	1 2 3 4 5 6 7 8 9 10	1 2 3 4 5 6 7 8 9 10 11 12	1 2 3 4 5 6 7 8 9 10 11
Equivalent names for whole numbers	6. Use manipulatives, drawings, tally marks, and numerical expressions involving addition and subtraction of 1- or 2-digit numbers to give equivalent names for whole numbers up to 100. [Number and Numeration Goal 6]	5. Use tally marks, arrays, and numerical expressions involving addition and subtraction to give equivalent names for whole numbers. [Number and Numeration Goal 5]	4. Use numerical expressions involving one or more of the basic four arithmetic operations to give equivalent names for whole numbers. [Number and Numeration Goal 4]
	1 2 3 4 5 6 7 8 9 10	1 2 3 4 5 6 7 8 9 10 11 12	1 2 3 4 5 6 7 8 9 10 11
Equivalent names for fractions, decimals, and percents		6. Use manipulatives and drawings to model equivalent names for $\frac{1}{2}$. [Number and Numeration Goal 6]	5. Use manipulatives and drawings to find and represent equivalent names for fractions; use manipulatives to generate equivalent fractions. [Number and Numeration Goal 5]
	1 2 3 4 5 6 7 8 9 10	1 2 3 4 5 6 7 8 9 10 11 12	1 2 3 4 5 6 7 8 9 10 11
Comparing and ordering numbers	7. Compare and order whole numbers up to 1,000. [Number and Numeration Goal 7]	7. Compare and order whole numbers up to 10,000; use area models to compare fractions. [Number and Numeration Goal 7]	6. Compare and order whole numbers up to 1,000,000; use manipulatives to order decimals through hundredths; use area models and benchmark fractions to compare and order fractions. [Number and Numeration Goal 6]
	1 2 3 4 5 6 7 8 9 10	1 2 3 4 5 6 7 8 9 10 11 12	1 2 3 4 5 6 7 8 9 10 11

Operations and Computation

Key
- Content taught
- Content practiced and applied

Content	Grade 1	Grade 2	Grade 3
Addition and subtraction facts	1. Demonstrate appropriate fluency with addition and subtraction facts through 10 + 10. [Operations and Computation Goal 1]	1. Demonstrate automaticity with all addition facts through 10 + 10 and fluency with the related subtraction facts. [Operations and Computation Goal 1]	1. Demonstrate automaticity with all addition and subtraction facts through 10 + 10; use basic facts to compute fact extensions such as 80 + 70. [Operations and Computation Goal 1]
	1 2 3 4 5 6 7 8 9 10	1 2 3 4 5 6 7 8 9 10 11 12	1 2 3 4 5 6 7 8 9 10 11
Addition and subtraction procedures	2. Use manipulatives, number grids, tally marks, mental arithmetic, and calculators to solve problems involving the addition and subtraction of 1-digit whole numbers with 2-digit whole numbers; calculate and compare the values of combinations of coins. [Operations and Computation Goal 2]	2. Use manipulatives, number grids, tally marks, mental arithmetic, paper & pencil, and calculators to solve problems involving the addition and subtraction of multidigit whole numbers; describe the strategies used; calculate and compare values of coin and bill combinations. [Operations and Computation Goal 2]	2. Use manipulatives, mental arithmetic, paper-and-pencil algorithms and models, and calculators to solve problems involving the addition and subtraction of whole numbers and decimals in a money context; describe the strategies used and explain how they work. [Operations and Computation Goal 2]
	1 2 3 4 5 6 7 8 9 10	1 2 3 4 5 6 7 8 9 10 11 12	1 2 3 4 5 6 7 8 9 10 11
Multiplication and division facts			3. Demonstrate automaticity with multiplication facts through 10 × 10. [Operations and Computation Goal 3]
	1 2 3 4 5 6 7 8 9 10	1 2 3 4 5 6 7 8 9 10 11 12	1 2 3 4 5 6 7 8 9 10 11
Multiplication and division procedures			4. Use arrays, mental arithmetic, paper-and-pencil algorithms and models, and calculators to solve problems involving the multiplication of 2- and 3-digit whole numbers by 1-digit whole numbers; describe the strategies used. [Operations and Computation Goal 4]
	1 2 3 4 5 6 7 8 9 10	1 2 3 4 5 6 7 8 9 10 11 12	1 2 3 4 5 6 7 8 9 10 11

* Children practice the basic facts using their Fact Triangles and record the ones they know at least once per unit.

Content	Grade 1	Grade 2	Grade 3
Computational estimation	3. Estimate reasonableness of answers to basic fact problems (e.g., Will 7 + 8 be more or less than 10?). [Operations and Computation Goal 3] 1 2 3 4 5 6 7 8 9 10	3. Make reasonable estimates for whole number addition and subtraction problems; explain how the estimates were obtained. [Operations and Computation Goal 3] 1 2 3 4 5 6 7 8 9 10 11 12	5. Make reasonable estimates for whole number addition, subtraction, multiplication, and division problems; explain how the estimates were obtained. [Operations and Computation Goal 5] 1 2 3 4 5 6 7 8 9 10 11
Models for the operations	4. Identify change-to-more, change-to-less, comparison, and parts-and-total situations. [Operations and Computation Goal 4] 1 2 3 4 5 6 7 8 9 10	4. Identify and describe change, comparison, and parts-and-total situations; use repeated addition, arrays, and skip counting to model multiplication; use equal sharing and equal grouping to model division. [Operations and Computation Goal 4] 1 2 3 4 5 6 7 8 9 10 11 12	6. Recognize and describe change, comparison, and parts-and-total situations; use repeated addition, arrays, and skip counting to model multiplication; use equal sharing and equal grouping to model division. [Operations and Computation Goal 6] 1 2 3 4 5 6 7 8 9 10 11

Data and Chance

Key
- Content taught
- Content practiced and applied

Content	Grade 1	Grade 2	Grade 3
Data collection and representation	1. Collect and organize data to create tally charts, tables, bar graphs, and line plots. [Data and Chance Goal 1] 1 2 3 4 5 6 7 8 9 10	1. Collect and organize data or use given data to create tally charts, tables, graphs, and line plots. [Data and Chance Goal 1] 1 2 3 4 5 6 7 8 9 10 11 12	1. Collect and organize data or use given data to create charts, tables, graphs, and line plots. [Data and Chance Goal 1] 1 2 3 4 5 6 7 8 9 10 11
Data analysis	2. Use graphs to answer simple questions and draw conclusions; find the maximum and minimum of a data set. [Data and Chance Goal 2] 1 2 3 4 5 6 7 8 9 10	2. Use graphs to ask and answer simple questions and draw conclusions; find the maximum, minimum, mode, and median of a data set. [Data and Chance Goal 2] 1 2 3 4 5 6 7 8 9 10 11 12	2. Use graphs to ask and answer simple questions and draw conclusions; find the maximum, minimum, range, mode, and median of a data set. [Data and Chance Goal 2] 1 2 3 4 5 6 7 8 9 10 11

Data and Chance (cont.)

Content	Grade 1	Grade 2	Grade 3
Qualitative probability	3. Describe events using *certain, likely, unlikely, impossible* and other basic probability terms. [Data and Chance Goal 3]	3. Describe events using *certain, likely, unlikely, impossible,* and other basic probability terms; explain the choice of language. [Data and Chance Goal 3]	3. Describe events using *certain, very likely, likely, unlikely, very unlikely, impossible,* and other basic probability terms; explain the choice of language. [Data and Chance Goal 3]
	1 2 3 4 5 6 7 8 9 10	1 2 3 4 5 6 7 8 9 10 11 12	1 2 3 4 5 6 7 8 9 10 11
Quantitative probability			4. Predict the outcomes of simple experiments and test the predictions using manipulatives; express the probability of an event by using "______ out of ______" language. [Data and Chance Goal 4]
	1 2 3 4 5 6 7 8 9 10	1 2 3 4 5 6 7 8 9 10 11 12	1 2 3 4 5 6 7 8 9 10 11

Measurement and Reference Frames

Key
- Content taught
- Content practiced and applied

Content	Grade 1	Grade 2	Grade 3
Length, weight, and angles	1. Use nonstandard tools and techniques to estimate and compare weight and length; measure length with standard measuring tools. [Measurement and Reference Frames Goal 1]	1. Estimate length with and without tools; measure length to the nearest inch and centimeter; use standard and nonstandard tools to measure and estimate weight. [Measurement and Reference Frames Goal 1]	1. Estimate length with and without tools; measure length to the nearest $\frac{1}{2}$ inch and $\frac{1}{2}$ centimeter; draw and describe angles as records of rotations. [Measurement and Reference Frames Goal 1]
	1 2 3 4 5 6 7 8 9 10	1 2 3 4 5 6 7 8 9 10 11 12	1 2 3 4 5 6 7 8 9 10 11
Area, perimeter, volume, and capacity		2. Partition rectangles into unit squares and count unit squares to find areas. [Measurement and Reference Frames Goal 2]	2. Describe and use strategies to measure the perimeter of polygons; find the areas of rectangles. [Measurement and Reference Frames Goal 2]
	1 2 3 4 5 6 7 8 9 10	1 2 3 4 5 6 7 8 9 10 11 12	1 2 3 4 5 6 7 8 9 10 11

Key
- ■ Content taught
- □ Content practiced and applied

Content	Grade 1	Grade 2	Grade 3
Units and systems of measurement		3. Describe relationships between days in a week and hours in a day. [Measurement and Reference Frames Goal 3]	3. Describe relationships among inches, feet, and yards; describe relationships between minutes in an hour, hours in a day, days in a week. [Measurement and Reference Frames Goal 3]
	1 2 3 4 5 6 7 8 9 10	1 2 3 4 5 6 7 8 9 10 11 12	1 2 3 4 5 6 7 8 9 10 11
Money	2. Know and compare the value of pennies, nickels, dimes, quarters, and dollar bills; make exchanges between coins. [Measurement and Reference Frames Goal 2]	4. Make exchanges between coins and bills. [Measurement and Reference Frames Goal 4]	
	1 2 3 4 5 6 7 8 9 10	1 2 3 4 5 6 7 8 9 10 11 12	1 2 3 4 5 6 7 8 9 10 11
Temperature	3. Identify a thermometer as a tool for measuring temperature; read temperatures on Fahrenheit and Celsius thermometers to the nearest 10°. [Measurement and Reference Frames Goal 3]	5. Read temperature on both the Fahrenheit and Celsius scales. [Measurement and Reference Frames Goal 5]	
	1 2 3 4 5 6 7 8 9 10	1 2 3 4 5 6 7 8 9 10 11 12	1 2 3 4 5 6 7 8 9 10 11
Time	4. Use a calendar to identify days, weeks, months, and dates; tell and show time to the nearest half and quarter hour on an analog clock. [Measurement and Reference Frames Goal 4]	6. Tell and show time to the nearest five minutes on an analog clock; tell and write time in digital notation.* [Measurement and Reference Frames Goal 6]	4. Tell and show time to the nearest minute on an analog clock; tell and write time in digital notation.* [Measurement and Reference Frames Goal 4]
	1 2 3 4 5 6 7 8 9 10	1 2 3 4 5 6 7 8 9 10 11 12	1 2 3 4 5 6 7 8 9 10 11

* Children record their start time at the top of journal pages on a daily basis.

Geometry

Content	Grade 1	Grade 2	Grade 3
Lines and angles		1. Draw line segments and identify parallel line segments. [Geometry Goal 1]	1. Identify and draw points, intersecting and parallel line segments and lines, rays, and right angles. [Geometry Goal 1]
Plane and solid figures	1. Identify and describe plane and solid figures including circles, triangles, squares, rectangles, spheres, cylinders, rectangular prisms, pyramids, cones, and cubes. [Geometry Goal 1]	2. Identify, describe, and model plane and solid figures including circles, triangles, squares, rectangles, hexagons, trapezoids, rhombuses, spheres, cylinders, rectangular prisms, pyramids, cones, and cubes. [Geometry Goal 2]	2. Identify, describe, model, and compare plane and solid figures including circles, polygons, spheres, cylinders, rectangular prisms, pyramids, cones, and cubes using appropriate geometric terms including the terms *face, edge, vertex,* and *base.* [Geometry Goal 2]
Transformations and symmetry	2. Identify shapes having line symmetry; complete line-symmetric shapes or designs. [Geometry Goal 2]	3. Create and complete two-dimensional symmetric shapes or designs. [Geometry Goal 3]	3. Create and complete two-dimensional symmetric shapes or designs; locate multiple lines of symmetry in a two-dimensional shape. [Geometry Goal 3]

Patterns, Functions, and Algebra

Key
- Content taught
- Content practiced and applied

Content	Grade 1	Grade 2	Grade 3
Patterns and functions	1. Extend, describe, and create numeric, visual, and concrete patterns; solve problems involving function machines, "What's My Rule?" tables, and Frames-and-Arrows diagrams. [Patterns, Functions, and Algebra Goal 1]	1. Extend, describe, and create numeric, visual, and concrete patterns; describe rules for patterns and use them to solve problems; use words and symbols to describe and write rules for functions involving addition and subtraction and use those rules to solve problems. [Patterns, Functions, and Algebra Goal 1]	1. Extend, describe, and create numeric patterns; describe rules for patterns and use them to solve problems; use words and symbols to describe and write rules for functions involving addition, subtraction, and multiplication and use those rules to solve problems. [Patterns, Functions, and Algebra Goal 1]

Key ■ Content taught □ Content practiced and applied

Content	Grade 1	Grade 2	Grade 3
Algebraic notation and solving number sentences	2. Read, write, and explain expressions and number sentences using the symbols +, −, and = and the symbols > and < with cues; solve equations involving addition and subtraction. [Patterns, Functions, and Algebra Goal 2]	2. Read, write, and explain expressions and number sentences using the symbols +, −, =, >, and <; solve number sentences involving addition and subtraction; write expressions and number sentences to model number stories. [Patterns, Functions, and Algebra Goal 2]	2. Read, write, and explain number sentences using the symbols +, −, ×, ÷, =, >, and <; solve number sentences; write expressions and number sentences to model number stories. [Patterns, Functions, and Algebra Goal 2]
Order of operations			3. Recognize that numeric expressions can have different values depending on the order in which operations are carried out; understand that grouping symbols can be used to affect the order in which operations are carried out. [Patterns, Functions, and Algebra Goal 3]
Properties of the arithmetic operations	3. Apply the Commutative and Associative Properties of Addition and the Additive Identity to basic addition fact problems. [Patterns, Functions, and Algebra Goal 3]	3. Describe the Commutative and Associative Properties of Addition and the Additive Identity and apply them to mental arithmetic problems. [Patterns, Functions, and Algebra Goal 3]	4. Describe and apply the Commutative and Associative Properties of Addition and Multiplication and the Multiplicative Identity; apply the Distributive Property of Multiplication over Addition. [Patterns, Functions, and Algebra Goal 4]

Scope and Sequence Chart

Throughout *Everyday Mathematics*, children repeatedly encounter skills in each of the content strands. Each exposure builds on and extends children's understanding. They study important concepts over consecutive years through a variety of formats. The Scope and Sequence Chart shows the units in which these exposures occur. The symbol ● indicates that the skill is introduced or taught. The symbol ■ indicates that the skill is revisited, practiced, or extended. These levels refer to unit content within the *K–6 Everyday Mathematics* curriculum.

The skills are divided according to the content strands below.

Content Strands **Pages**

How to Read the Scope and Sequence Chart

Each section of the chart includes a content strand title, three grade-level columns divided by units or sections, and a list of specific skills grouped by major concepts.

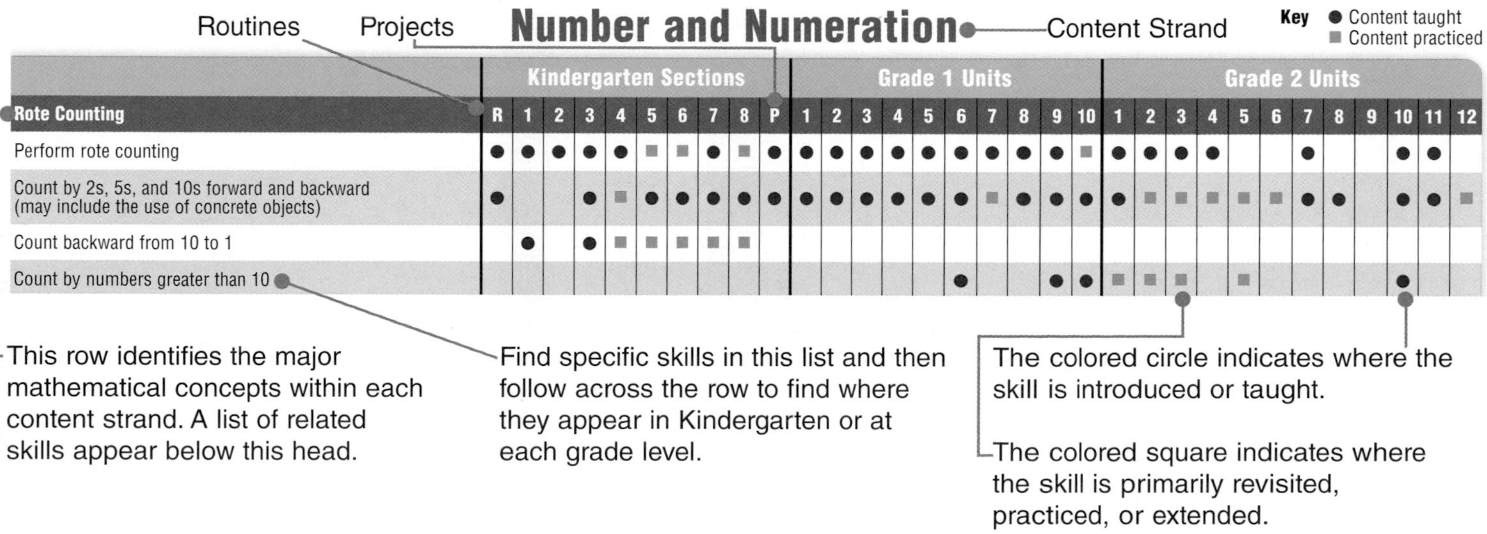

Routines
Projects
Number and Numeration
Content Strand
Key ● Content taught ■ Content practiced
Kindergarten Sections
Grade 1 Units
Grade 2 Units
Rote Counting
R 1 2 3 4 5 6 7 8 P 1 2 3 4 5 6 7 8 9 10 1 2 3 4 5 6 7 8 9 10 11 12
Perform rote counting
Count by 2s, 5s, and 10s forward and backward (may include the use of concrete objects)
Count backward from 10 to 1
Count by numbers greater than 10
This row identifies the major mathematical concepts within each content strand. A list of related skills appear below this head.
Find specific skills in this list and then follow across the row to find where they appear in Kindergarten or at each grade level.
The colored circle indicates where the skill is introduced or taught.
The colored square indicates where the skill is primarily revisited, practiced, or extended.

Number and Numeration

Key ● Content taught ■ Content practiced

	Kindergarten Sections										Grade 1 Units										Grade 2 Units											
Rote Counting	R	1	2	3	4	5	6	7	8	P	1	2	3	4	5	6	7	8	9	10	1	2	3	4	5	6	7	8	9	10	11	12
Perform rote counting	●	●	●	●	●	■	■	●	■	●	●	●	●	●	●	●	●	●	●	■	●	●	●	●			●			●	●	
Count by 2s, 5s, and 10s forward and backward (may include the use of concrete objects)	●			●	■	●	●	●	●	●	●	●	●	●	●	●	■	●	●	●	●	■	■	■	■	■	●	●		●	●	■
Count backward from 10 to 1		●		●	■	■	■	■	■																							
Count by numbers greater than 10																●			●	●	■	■	■		■					●		
Count by 25s																●			●	●			■									
Count by 100s																			●	●	●	■	■	■				●		●	●	■
Count up and back on a number grid						●	■	■				■	■	●	●		■	■	●		■	■				●	■	■	■	■		
Relate counting to addition and subtraction												●	●			●		■														
Locate numbers on a number line; count up and back on a number line; complete a number line	●			●	●		■	■			●	■	●	●					■		●	■		■		■						
Count using a calculator or calculator repeat key						●	●						●			●		●		■	●	■	■			■	●			●	■	■
Rational Counting	R	1	2	3	4	5	6	7	8	P	1	2	3	4	5	6	7	8	9	10	1	2	3	4	5	6	7	8	9	10	11	12
Perform rational counting	●	●	●	●	●	●	●	●	●	●	●	●	●	●	●	●	●	■	●	●	●	●	●	●	●	●	●	■	●	●	●	
Compare number of objects in sets of concrete objects	●	●	●	●	●	●	●	●	●																							
Estimate quantities of objects			●	■	■	■	■	■		●			■	■	●			●														
Place Value and Notation	R	1	2	3	4	5	6	7	8	P	1	2	3	4	5	6	7	8	9	10	1	2	3	4	5	6	7	8	9	10	11	12
Construct or use sets of objects to represent given quantities	●	●	●	●	●	●	●	●	●	●	●				●	■		●		■	●		●									
Read and write numbers to 20	●	●	●	●	●	●	●	●	●	●	●	●	●	●	●	●	●				●	●	■									
Read and write 2-digit numbers	●		●	●	●	■	■	■	■	●					●	■	●	●			●	●	●	●		●				●	●	
Read and write 3-digit numbers								●	●	●					●		●	●	■	●	●		●	■	■	■				●		
Read and write 4- and 5-digit numbers																				●	●		●	●						●	●	
Display and read numbers on a calculator					●	●	●		●			●	●		●	●		●		■	●	■	■			■				●		
Use multimedia and technology to explore number concepts					●	●	●		●																							
Read, write, or use ordinal numbers	●					●										●					■	■				■				●		

Key ● Content taught ■ Content practiced

Place Value and Notation (cont.)	R	1	2	3	4	5	6	7	8	P	1	2	3	4	5	6	7	8	9	10	1	2	3	4	5	6	7	8	9	10	11	12
Name the ordinal positions in a sequence and "next" and "last" positions	●																															
Identify the number that is one more or one less than a given number	●	●	■	■								■	■	■																		
Explore place value using a number grid						●		●	■	●			■		●				●											●		
Identify place value in 2-digit numbers	●							●	●				●		●	■		■	●	●	■		●	●		●				●	●	
Identify place value in 3-digit numbers																		●		●	●	■	●	●	■	■		■		●		■
Identify place value in 4-digit numbers																		●		●								■		●	■	■
Identify place value in larger numbers																							●					■	■	●		
Make exchanges among place values	●							●	●						●			●			●		●	●						●	●	
Make least and greatest numbers with randomly selected digits					●			●	■												■					■						
Write numbers in expanded notation																			■				■							●		
Use cents notation							●					●	●		■	■		■			●		●	■		●				●		
Use dollars-and-cents notation									●			●	●		■	■	●	●					●	●		●			■	●	●	
Use calculator to count/compute money amounts																		■				■								●		
Explore uses for decimals																		●												●		
Meanings and Uses of Fractions	**R**	**1**	**2**	**3**	**4**	**5**	**6**	**7**	**8**	**P**	**1**	**2**	**3**	**4**	**5**	**6**	**7**	**8**	**9**	**10**	**1**	**2**	**3**	**4**	**5**	**6**	**7**	**8**	**9**	**10**	**11**	**12**
Understand the meaning or uses of fractions							●	■	■								■	●	●	■								●	●	■	■	
Construct concrete models of fractions and equivalent fractions; identify fractions on a number line.																		●	●									●	■	■		
Identify pennies and dimes as fractional parts of a dollar																										●	■	●		●		■
Identify numerator and denominator																		●	●									●				
Shade and identify fractional parts of a region							●		■								■	●	●	■							■	●		■		
Shade and identify fractional parts of a set							●	■										●	■								■	●	●			■
Understand that the amount represented by a fraction depends on the size of the whole (ONE)																		■										●		●	■	
Use fractions in number stories																			■	■								●	■	■	■	

Number and Numeration (cont.)

Key ● Content taught ■ Content practiced

	Kindergarten Sections										Grade 1 Units										Grade 2 Units											
Number Theory	R	1	2	3	4	5	6	7	8	P	1	2	3	4	5	6	7	8	9	10	1	2	3	4	5	6	7	8	9	10	11	12
Explore or identify even and odd numbers		■					●	■					●	■	■	■	■		■		●	●	■	●	■		●		■			
Equivalent Names for Whole Numbers	R	1	2	3	4	5	6	7	8	P	1	2	3	4	5	6	7	8	9	10	1	2	3	4	5	6	7	8	9	10	11	12
Find equivalent names for numbers	●					●		●	●		●	●	■	■	●	●	■	■	■		●	●	●	●	■				●	●	●	■
Use Roman numerals																					■											
Equivalent Names for Fractions, Decimals, and Percents	R	1	2	3	4	5	6	7	8	P	1	2	3	4	5	6	7	8	9	10	1	2	3	4	5	6	7	8	9	10	11	12
Find equivalent fractions																			●								■	●	●	●		■
Comparing and Ordering Numbers	R	1	2	3	4	5	6	7	8	P	1	2	3	4	5	6	7	8	9	10	1	2	3	4	5	6	7	8	9	10	11	12
Compare and order numbers to 20	●		●	●	●	●	■	■		●	●	●	●	●	●	●				■	●		■		●		●		●			
Compare and order 2-digit numbers	●		●	●	●	●	■	●	■			●		●	●	●	■	■	■	●	●		■				●			●		●
Compare and order 3-digit numbers														●	●		■	■	■	●	●		●							●		
Compare and order 4- or 5-digit numbers												■									●									●		
Compare and order larger numbers																														●		●
Compare numbers using the symbols <, >, and =															●	■	■	■	●	■	●	■	●	■		■	■		■	■	■	■
Compare and order fractions; use manipulatives to identify/compare fractions																			●	■								●	●	●		
Compare fractions less than one																												●			■	■

Operations and Computation

	Kindergarten Sections										Grade 1 Units										Grade 2 Units											
Addition and Subtraction Facts	R	1	2	3	4	5	6	7	8	P	1	2	3	4	5	6	7	8	9	10	1	2	3	4	5	6	7	8	9	10	11	12
Find/use complements of 10		■	●	●		●	●	●	●	●		●	■	■	■	■					●				■		■	●	■			
Practice basic facts; know +/– fact families				●	●	●	■	●	●	●	●	●	■	●	●	●	●	■	■	■	●	●	■	■	■	●	■	■	■	●	■	●
Practice extensions of basic facts																			■					■								

Key ● Content taught ■ Content practiced

Addition and Subtraction Facts (cont.)	R	1	2	3	4	5	6	7	8	P	1	2	3	4	5	6	7	8	9	10	1	2	3	4	5	6	7	8	9	10	11	12
Make and solve number-grid puzzles														●					●	●	■	●										
Addition and Subtraction Procedures	**R**	**1**	**2**	**3**	**4**	**5**	**6**	**7**	**8**	**P**	**1**	**2**	**3**	**4**	**5**	**6**	**7**	**8**	**9**	**10**	**1**	**2**	**3**	**4**	**5**	**6**	**7**	**8**	**9**	**10**	**11**	**12**
Understand meaning of addition/subtraction; model addition/subtraction using concrete objects		■	●	●	●	■	■	●	●		●	●	●	●	●			■	●		●	■	●	●	●	●	●				●	
Investigate the inverse relationships between addition and subtraction			●	●	●	■	■	●	●			●		●	●	●		●		■	●	●		●							■	
Use mental arithmetic or fact strategies to add/subtract				●	●	●	■	●	●	●	●	●	●	●	●	●	●	●	■	■	●	●	■	●	■	●	■	■	■	■	■	■
Use addition to find the total number of objects in rectangular rays																								■	●	●		■			●	
Use addition/subtraction algorithms																										●	■	■	■	■	●	■
Explore calculator functions						●	●		■						●	●		■	■		●	■	■	■								
Make up and/or solve 1- or 2-step addition/subtraction number stories; determine operation needed to solve a problem	●		●	●	●	■	●	●	●		●	●	●	●	●	●	●	●	●	●	■	●	■	●	■	●	●		■	●	●	●
Use an Addition/Subtraction Facts Table															●	●						●										
Determine the value of the unknown number in an addition or subtraction problem													●	●	●	●						●	■	●	■	●				●		
Add/subtract using a number grid											●		■		●	■			●	■	●	■		■		●	●			■	■	
Add/subtract using a number line	●				●		■				●		●		■						●	●	■	●	●	●	●				■	●
Add/subtract using a calculator									●						●	●		■	■		●	●	■		■		●			■		
Add/subtract multiples of 10																			●	●	●	■		■		■				●		
Add 3 or more 1-digit numbers												●	●			●		●								●	■			■		●
Add/subtract 2-digit numbers															●	●		●	●	●	●			●	■	●	●	■	■	■	●	●
Add 3 or more 2-digit numbers																										●						●
Add/subtract 3- and 4-digit numbers																								●		●	■		●		●	●
Add/subtract money amounts/decimals; make change																●		●	●	●	●		●	●		●	●	■		●	●	■
Solve money number stories															●	●		●	●	●				■		■			■	●	●	■
Make change																		●	■	●		■		■	■				■	●	●	■

Operations and Computation (cont.)

Key ● Content taught ■ Content practiced

	Kindergarten Sections										Grade 1 Units										Grade 2 Units											
Multiplication and Division Facts	R	1	2	3	4	5	6	7	8	P	1	2	3	4	5	6	7	8	9	10	1	2	3	4	5	6	7	8	9	10	11	12
Practice multiplication/division facts																															■	●
Find complements for multiples of 10																											●					
Multiplication and Division Procedures	R	1	2	3	4	5	6	7	8	P	1	2	3	4	5	6	7	8	9	10	1	2	3	4	5	6	7	8	9	10	11	12
Use manipulatives, drawings/arrays, number sentences, repeated addition, or story problems to explain and demonstrate the meaning of multiplication/division							●							●				●							■	●	■	●		■	●	●
Understand meaning of multiplication/division and related vocabulary																									●	●	●				●	
Make up and/or solve multiplication/division number stories																										●	●				●	●
Investigate relationships between multiplication and division																										●					●	
Multiply/divide using a number line or number grid																										■					●	
Explore square numbers																															■	
Use a calculator to multiply or divide																															●	
Use a Multiplication/Division Facts Table																															●	
Use mental arithmetic to multiply/divide																															●	■
Identify factors of a number																															●	
Computational Estimation	R	1	2	3	4	5	6	7	8	P	1	2	3	4	5	6	7	8	9	10	1	2	3	4	5	6	7	8	9	10	11	12
Estimate reasonableness of answers to basic facts													●		■	■		■	●	■				■						■		
Use estimation strategies to add/subtract; make ballpark estimates													●							●				●		■	■			●	●	
Round whole numbers to the nearest ten															●		●	●	●											■		
Estimate costs																■		■						●						●	●	
Models for Operations	R	1	2	3	4	5	6	7	8	P	1	2	3	4	5	6	7	8	9	10	1	2	3	4	5	6	7	8	9	10	11	12
Solve change-to-more and change-to-less number stories/diagrams			●	●	●	■	■	●	●			●	●						●			●	●	●		●				■	●	
Solve parts-and-total number stories/diagrams			●	●	●	■	■	●	●				●	●	●	●		●					●	●		●		■	■	■		
Solve comparison number stories/diagrams							●											●		●		●			■	●				●	●	■
Solve equal-grouping and equal-sharing division problems							●																		■					■	■	

Data and Chance

Key ● Content taught ■ Content practiced

	Kindergarten Sections										Grade 1 Units										Grade 2 Units											
Data Collection and Representation	R	1	2	3	4	5	6	7	8	P	1	2	3	4	5	6	7	8	9	10	1	2	3	4	5	6	7	8	9	10	11	12
Collect data by counting	●			●		●	●	●	■	●	■							■		■			■			●	●					●
Collect data by interviewing	●						●													■						■						
Collect data by measuring														●						●							●		■	●	●	
Collect data from print sources and/or posters																										■			■	■		●
Collect data from a map																													●			
Use a weather map																				●												
Conduct a survey	●						●	■	■							■										●						
Make a tally chart or frequency table	●					●					●	●	●		●	●	■	■			■		●			●	●					■
Record data in a table/chart	●		■	●	●	■	●	●		●	●					●				●			●		■	●	●			■	■	●
Record days/events on a timeline	●					●								●											■							●
Create/interpret a bar graph, pictograph (picture graph), or Venn diagram	●	●	■	●		●	●		■					●	●	●	■	■	■	■			●		■	●	●					●
Create/interpret a line plot													●	●	■	■		■	■	●							●		■	●	●	●
Explore graphing software to make a bar graph or line plot													●	●		●				●						●						
Data Analysis	R	1	2	3	4	5	6	7	8	P	1	2	3	4	5	6	7	8	9	10	1	2	3	4	5	6	7	8	9	10	11	12
Read tables, graphs, and maps (including map scale, scale drawing)	●	●	■	●	●	●	●	●	■	●	●	●	●		●	●	■		■	●	●	●	●		■	●	●	■	●	■	■	●
Summarize and interpret data	●	●	■	●	●	●	●	●	■		●	●	●	●	●	●	■	●	●	●					■	●	●					●
Compare two sets of data; use calculator to compare data																				●			●			●	■				■	●
Make predictions about data	●	●	■	●	●	●	●	●	■		●	●				■							●			●						
Identify "more" or "less" from pictographs and bar graphs	●	●	■	●	●	●	●	●	■																							
Compare quantities from a bar graph	●	●	●	●	●	●	●	●	●				●		■	●						■	●					■				
Find the minimum/maximum of a data set																●		■	■	■		■					●			■	■	●
Find the range																●		■	■	■			●				●			■	■	●
Find the median														●				■	■	●		■	●			■	●		■	■	■	●

Data and Chance (cont.)

Key ● Content taught ■ Content practiced

	Kindergarten Sections										Grade 1 Units										Grade 2 Units											
Data Analysis (cont.)	R	1	2	3	4	5	6	7	8	P	1	2	3	4	5	6	7	8	9	10	1	2	3	4	5	6	7	8	9	10	11	12
Find the mode														●						●						■	■	■		■	■	●
Use data in problem solving	●											●	●	●		●						■				●	●			■	■	●
Qualitative and Quantitative Probability	R	1	2	3	4	5	6	7	8	P	1	2	3	4	5	6	7	8	9	10	1	2	3	4	5	6	7	8	9	10	11	12
Understand the language of probability to discuss likelihood of a given situation (using words such as certain, likely, unlikely, always, maybe, sometimes, never, possible, impossible)	●		●	●	■			■				■	■	■	●	■		■		■	■	■	■	■		■	■	■	■			
Explore equal-chance events					■										●	●		■														
Participate in games or activities based on chance			●	●	●	●	■	■	●	●																						
Predict outcomes; solve problems involving chance outcomes				●	●						●	●	■	■	■	■							●				■					
Conduct experiments; test predictions using concrete objects				●							●																■					
Find combinations (Cartesian products)	●		●	●	■			■										■									■	■				

Measurement and Reference Frames

Key ● Content taught ■ Content practiced

	Kindergarten Sections										Grade 1 Units										Grade 2 Units											
Length, Weight, and Angles	R	1	2	3	4	5	6	7	8	P	1	2	3	4	5	6	7	8	9	10	1	2	3	4	5	6	7	8	9	10	11	12
Name tools used to measure length						●	■		■			●		●										●			■		●			
Estimate, compare, and order lengths/heights of objects		●	■	●	■	●	■		■	●		●	■	●		●			●	●						■	●		●	■	■	
Compare lengths indirectly		●	●	●		●								●		●													■			
Measure lengths with nonstandard units				●	■	●	■		■	●				●										■					●			
Measure to the nearest foot						●								●															●			
Measure to the nearest inch														●	■				●					●			●	■	●			
Measure to the nearest $\frac{1}{2}$ inch														●															●			
Investigate the yard																													●			
Measure to the nearest yard																													●			
Measure to the nearest centimeter																●								●	■	■	●	■	●	■	■	
Measure to the nearest $\frac{1}{2}$ centimeter																													●			
Investigate the meter																●													●			
Measure to the nearest meter and/or decimeter																													●			
Solve length/height number stories																										●	●	■	■		■	
Investigate the mile and/or kilometer																													●		■	
Use words to describe distance										●																						
Estimate and compare distances																												■	●			
Solve distance number stories																													●		■	
Estimate, compare, and order weights				●					●										■			■		■			■	■	●			
Name tools used to measure weight				●					●	●																			●			
Order objects by weight																											■					
Use a pan balance				●		■			●						●	●					●	●										
Use a bath scale										●									■					■			●		●			
Use a spring scale																						●							●			
Choose the appropriate scale																													●			

Measurement and Reference Frames (cont.)

Key ● Content taught ■ Content practiced

	Kindergarten Sections										Grade 1 Units										Grade 2 Units											
Length, Weight, and Angles (cont.)	R	1	2	3	4	5	6	7	8	P	1	2	3	4	5	6	7	8	9	10	1	2	3	4	5	6	7	8	9	10	11	12
Solve weight number stories																								■			■		●			
Area, Perimeter, Volume, and Capacity	R	1	2	3	4	5	6	7	8	P	1	2	3	4	5	6	7	8	9	10	1	2	3	4	5	6	7	8	9	10	11	12
Investigate area															●	●								●					●			
Find the area of regular shapes concretely															●	●												■	●			■
Find the perimeter of regular shapes concretely, graphically, or with pictorial models																												■	●		■	■
Find the area of a rectangular region divided into square units																								■					●	●		
Partition rectangles into same-size squares; count to find the total																								■					●	●		
Find the area of irregular shapes concretely																												■	●	●		
Find the perimeter of irregular shapes concretely, graphically, or with pictorial models																												■	●		■	
Estimate area																													●			
Estimate perimeter																													■			
Compare perimeter and area																													●			
Name tools used to measure area																													●			
Estimate volume/capacity		●																	●									●				
Name tools used to measure volume and/or capacity										●																			●			
Find volume																												●				
Measure capacities of irregular containers																													■			
Compare and order the capacities of containers		●																	●										●			
Units and Systems of Measurement	R	1	2	3	4	5	6	7	8	P	1	2	3	4	5	6	7	8	9	10	1	2	3	4	5	6	7	8	9	10	11	12
Select and use appropriate nonstandard units to measure time							●					●																	■			
Estimate the duration of a minute									●			●																				
Investigate the duration of an hour									●			●																				
Investigate 1-minute intervals																															■	■
Identify equivalent customary units of length																													●			

Key ● Content taught ■ Content practiced

Units and Systems of Measurement (cont.)	R	1	2	3	4	5	6	7	8	P	1	2	3	4	5	6	7	8	9	10	1	2	3	4	5	6	7	8	9	10	11	12
Identify equivalent metric units of length																													●			
Identify customary and/or metric units of weight																													●			
Identify equivalent customary units of weight																													●			
Identify customary and/or metric units of capacity																			●										●			
Identify equivalent customary/metric units of capacity																													●			
Choose the appropriate unit of measure																													●			
Money	**R**	**1**	**2**	**3**	**4**	**5**	**6**	**7**	**8**	**P**	**1**	**2**	**3**	**4**	**5**	**6**	**7**	**8**	**9**	**10**	**1**	**2**	**3**	**4**	**5**	**6**	**7**	**8**	**9**	**10**	**11**	**12**
Recognize pennies and nickels		●	●	■		■	●	●	■			●	■		■			■			●	■	■	●	■	■	■	■	■	■	■	■
Recognize dimes		●	●	■		■	●	●	■				●	●			■	●	●		●	■	■	●	■	■	■	■	■	■	■	■
Recognize quarters		●		■		■		●	■							●	■	●			●	■	■	●					■	■		■
Recognize dollars									●									●			●	■		■				■	■	■		■
Calculate the value of coin combinations							●	●				●	●		■	●	●	●	■	●	●	■	●	●		■		■	■	●		
Calculate the value of bill combinations									●												●	■					■			●		
Calculate the value of coins/bills													●					●			●	■	●	●			●		■	●	■	■
Compare values of sets of coins or money amounts using <, >, and = symbols												■	■	■	●	■		■	■	■						■	■			●		
Identify equivalencies and make coin exchanges							●	■			●	●	●	■	●	●	■	●		■	■		●			●						
Identify equivalencies and make coin/bill exchanges									●									●	■	■			■			●	●		■	●		
Temperature	**R**	**1**	**2**	**3**	**4**	**5**	**6**	**7**	**8**	**P**	**1**	**2**	**3**	**4**	**5**	**6**	**7**	**8**	**9**	**10**	**1**	**2**	**3**	**4**	**5**	**6**	**7**	**8**	**9**	**10**	**11**	**12**
Compare situations or objects according to temperature	●								■																							
Use a thermometer	●								■		●		■	●	■				■	■	●	■	●	●		■						
Use the Fahrenheit temperature scale	●										●		■	●	■				■	●	●	■	●	●		■	■			■		
Use the Celsius temperature scale	●																			●			●	●						■		
Solve temperature number stories														●						●	●			●		■			■			
Time	**R**	**1**	**2**	**3**	**4**	**5**	**6**	**7**	**8**	**P**	**1**	**2**	**3**	**4**	**5**	**6**	**7**	**8**	**9**	**10**	**1**	**2**	**3**	**4**	**5**	**6**	**7**	**8**	**9**	**10**	**11**	**12**
Demonstrate an understanding of the concepts of time; estimates and measures the passage of time using words like *before, after, yesterday, today, tomorrow, morning, afternoon, hour, half-hour*	●					●	●		●		●	●		●							●			■								●

Measurement and Reference Frames (cont.)

Key ● Content taught ■ Content practiced

	Kindergarten Sections										Grade 1 Units										Grade 2 Units											
Time (cont.)	R	1	2	3	4	5	6	7	8	P	1	2	3	4	5	6	7	8	9	10	1	2	3	4	5	6	7	8	9	10	11	12
Order or compare events according to duration; calculate elapsed time	●					●	●					●		■						●	■		■				■	■				●
Name tools used to measure time	●					●	●		●												●		■									■
Relates past events to future events																●																
Investigate A.M. and P.M.	●											●									●	■	●	■	■	■	■	■	■	■	■	●
Name the seasons of the year										●																						
Use the calendar; identify today's date	●										●	■	■								●					■						●
Number and name the months in a year or days in the week	●										●	■	■	■						■	●					■		■		■		●
Investigate the second hand; compare the hour and minute hands									●			●	●								●		●									
Use an analog or digital clock to tell time on the hour	●								●			■	●	■		■		■		●	●	■	●	■	●	■	■			■		
Tell time on the half-hour													●	●	●	●	■	■		●	■	■	●	■	●					■		
Tell time on the quarter-hour														●	●	●	■	■		●		■	●	■			■			■		
Tell time to the nearest 5 minutes																●		■	●	●		■	●			■						●
Use digital notation*									●							●	■	■		●	■	■	●	■	●	■	■	■	■	■	■	■
Tell time to the nearest minute*																				●	■	■	●	■	■	■	■	■	■	■	■	■
Read time in different ways and/or identify time equivalencies									●							■												■				●
Solve time number stories																						■	●	■		■						
Coordinate Systems	R	1	2	3	4	5	6	7	8	P	1	2	3	4	5	6	7	8	9	10	1	2	3	4	5	6	7	8	9	10	11	12
Find and name locations with simple relationships on a coordinate system																			■													

*In Grade 2, children record the start time at the top of journal pages on a daily basis. In Grade 2, they use A.M. and P.M.

Geometry

Key ● Content taught ■ Content practiced

	Kindergarten Sections										Grade 1 Units										Grade 2 Units											
Lines and Angles	R	1	2	3	4	5	6	7	8	P	1	2	3	4	5	6	7	8	9	10	1	2	3	4	5	6	7	8	9	10	11	12
Identify and name line segments																									●						■	
Draw line segments with a straightedge																●									●		■	■				
Draw line segments to a specified length																■								■				■	■			
Draw designs with line segments																■																
Identify and name points																									●	■						
Model parallel lines on a geoboard																									●							
Draw parallel lines with a straightedge																									●							
Identify parallel, nonparallel, and intersecting line segments																									●							
Plane and Solid Figures	R	1	2	3	4	5	6	7	8	P	1	2	3	4	5	6	7	8	9	10	1	2	3	4	5	6	7	8	9	10	11	12
Explore shape relationships			●	■	●		●	■			●	■										■			●				●	■	■	■
Recognizes open and closed figures																	■				■	■		■								
Identify characteristics of 2-dimensional shapes; sort shapes by attributes		●	●	■	●	●	●	■			●					●	●	■	■	●	■	●		■	●							■
Distinguish between defining and non-defining attributes																■	●			●												
Explore 2-D shapes utilizing technology or multimedia resources							■										●															
Identify characteristics and use appropriate vocabulary to describe properties of 2-dimensional shapes			●	■	●	■	●	■	●		■	●			●	■	●			●					●							
Construct models of polygons using manipulatives such as straws or geoboards			●		●		●	●	●		■			●		●		●		●			●		●					●		
Match objects to outlines of shapes (on a Pattern-Block Template)		■			●					■																						
Draw 2-dimensional shapes (such as triangles and quadrilaterals); draw/describe objects in the environment that depict geometric figures		■	●		●		●	■			●	■				●	●		●	●		■		■	●			■	■	●	■	■
Create/extend designs with 2-dimensional shapes		●	●	■	■			●			■	■	●	■	■	■	●		■		●				●				■			■
Combine shapes and take them apart to form other shapes		●	●		●				●				●				●		■	●					●			●		●		
Record shapes or designs		■	●		●									●									●									
Identify and draw congruent or similar shapes																	●	■	■										■			

Geometry (cont.)

Key ● Content taught ■ Content practiced

	Kindergarten Sections										Grade 1 Units										Grade 2 Units											
Plane and Solid Figures (cont.)	R	1	2	3	4	5	6	7	8	P	1	2	3	4	5	6	7	8	9	10	1	2	3	4	5	6	7	8	9	10	11	12
Classify and name polygons											●		■	■		●									●							■
Compare 2-dimensional shapes			●	■	●	●					●	■					●	●							●							■
Compare polygons and non-polygons																	■								●							
Solve 2-dimensional shapes problems																						■		■	■							
Decompose shapes into shares																		●	●	■								●		■		
Identify/compare 3-dimensional shapes; sort shapes and/or describe attributes of each group						●	●	●	■		●					■	●	■	■	●				■	●		■			■	■	■
Construct 3-dimensional shapes								●	■											●					●				●			
Locate 2-D shapes on 3-D objects; compare 2- and 3-D shapes			●		●		●	●											■													
Explore 3-D shapes utilizing technology							■																									
Identify the number of faces, edges, vertices, and bases of prisms and pyramids																									●							
Identify the shapes of faces							●	■									■										■					
Explore slanted 3-dimensional shapes																											■					
Transformations and Symmetry	R	1	2	3	4	5	6	7	8	P	1	2	3	4	5	6	7	8	9	10	1	2	3	4	5	6	7	8	9	10	11	12
Identify symmetrical figures or symmetry in the environment			●		■		■			●							●	■	●					■	●							
Fold and cut symmetrical shapes			●		■		■			●							●	■							●							
Create/complete a symmetrical design/shape using concrete models, geoboard, and/or technology			●														●		●						●	■		■				
Identify lines of symmetry																	●		●						●	■	■		■	■		
Use objects to explore slides, flips, and turns; predict the results of changing a shape's position or orientation using slides, flips, and turns					●								●												■							
Spatial	R	1	2	3	4	5	6	7	8	P	1	2	3	4	5	6	7	8	9	10	1	2	3	4	5	6	7	8	9	10	11	12
Recognize that the quantity remains the same when the spatial arrangement changes		●		●								●																				
Arrange or describe objects by proximity, position, or direction using words such as *over, under, above, below, inside, outside, beside, in front of, behind*			●	■					■	●			●				●															

Key ● Content taught ■ Content practiced

Spatial (cont.)	R	1	2	3	4	5	6	7	8	P	1	2	3	4	5	6	7	8	9	10	1	2	3	4	5	6	7	8	9	10	11	12
Give or follow directions for finding a place or object			●							●							■		●											■		
Identify left hand and right hand			●							●																						
Identify structures from different views or match views of the same structures portrayed from different perspectives																●								■								
Use objects to explore slides, flips, and turns; predict the results of changing a shape's position or orientation using slides, flips, and turns					●																				■							

Patterns, Functions, and Algebra

	Kindergarten Sections										Grade 1 Units										Grade 2 Units											
Patterns and Functions	R	1	2	3	4	5	6	7	8	P	1	2	3	4	5	6	7	8	9	10	1	2	3	4	5	6	7	8	9	10	11	12
Identify, extend, and create patterns of sounds, physical movement, and concrete objects		●	●	●	●	●	●	●	■	●																						
Verbally describe changes in various contexts		●		■	●			●																								
Explore and extend visual patterns		●	●	●	●	●	●	●				■	●	■	■	●	●					■				■	●					
Find patterns and common attributes in objects/people in the real world	●	●	●	■	■	●	■	●	■			■		●	●	■						■		●	●	■						
Create and complete patterns with 2-dimensional shapes		●			●			●	■		■	■	●	■	■	■	■		■		■					■	●	●		●		
Identify and use patterns on a number grid			●			●	■	●					■	●	●				●	●	■	■		■	■		●			■		
Add and subtract using a number grid																			●		●	■			■					■	■	
Investigate even and odd number patterns; create, describe, extend simple number patterns/sequences			●			●	●	●	●				●	■							●	●	■									
Explore counting patterns using a calculator							●						●								●					■	●					
Solve "What's My Rule?" (e.g. function machine) problems					●			●	●						●	●		■	■	■		●	■	●			●			■	●	■
Solve Frames-and-Arrows problems with one or two rules													●	■	■	■			■	■	■	■	●	■		■		■	■	■	■	
Find patterns in addition and subtraction facts															●	●		●	■			●	■							■	■	
Explore patterns in doubling or halving numbers															●							●				■	●			■	■	
Find patterns in multiplication and division facts																											■				●	●

Patterns, Functions, and Algebra (cont.)

Key ● Content taught ■ Content practiced

	Kindergarten Sections										Grade 1 Units										Grade 2 Units											
Patterns and Functions (cont.)	**R**	**1**	**2**	**3**	**4**	**5**	**6**	**7**	**8**	**P**	**1**	**2**	**3**	**4**	**5**	**6**	**7**	**8**	**9**	**10**	**1**	**2**	**3**	**4**	**5**	**6**	**7**	**8**	**9**	**10**	**11**	**12**
Find patterns in multiples of 10, 100, and 1,000																							■							■	●	
Investigate square numbers																															■	
Algebraic Notation and Solving Number Sentences	**R**	**1**	**2**	**3**	**4**	**5**	**6**	**7**	**8**	**P**	**1**	**2**	**3**	**4**	**5**	**6**	**7**	**8**	**9**	**10**	**1**	**2**	**3**	**4**	**5**	**6**	**7**	**8**	**9**	**10**	**11**	**12**
Determine whether equations are true or false													●	■	●			■														
Use symbols ×, ÷, =																										●	●				●	●
Use symbols +, −, =; pictures; manipulatives; and models to organize, record, and communicate mathematical ideas					●	■	■	●	●			●	●	■	●	●	●	●	●	●	●	■	●	●	■	■	■		●	●	●	
Use a symbol or letter to represent the unknown number																								●		●						
Compare numbers using <, > symbols															●	■		■		■	●	■	●	■		■	■		■	■	■	■
Write/solve addition and subtraction number sentences					●	■	■	●	●			●					●	●	●	■	●	■	●	●	■	■	■		●	●	●	
Write/solve number sentences with missing addends									●						●							●				■	■		●	●	●	
Write and solve multiplication number sentences																										●	●				●	●
Write and solve division number sentences																															●	●
Write and solve number sentences with missing factors; know that symbols can be used to represent missing or unknown quantities									●															●		●					●	●
Order of Operations	**R**	**1**	**2**	**3**	**4**	**5**	**6**	**7**	**8**	**P**	**1**	**2**	**3**	**4**	**5**	**6**	**7**	**8**	**9**	**10**	**1**	**2**	**3**	**4**	**5**	**6**	**7**	**8**	**9**	**10**	**11**	**12**
Make up and/or solve number sentences involving parentheses																														●		
Properties of Arithmetic Operations	**R**	**1**	**2**	**3**	**4**	**5**	**6**	**7**	**8**	**P**	**1**	**2**	**3**	**4**	**5**	**6**	**7**	**8**	**9**	**10**	**1**	**2**	**3**	**4**	**5**	**6**	**7**	**8**	**9**	**10**	**11**	**12**
Investigate properties of addition/subtraction			●	●	●	■	■	●	●			●	●	●	●	●						●										
Investigate properties of multiplication/division																															●	●
Explore number properties (commutative, zero, and identity)		●													■							●										

Index

A

B

C

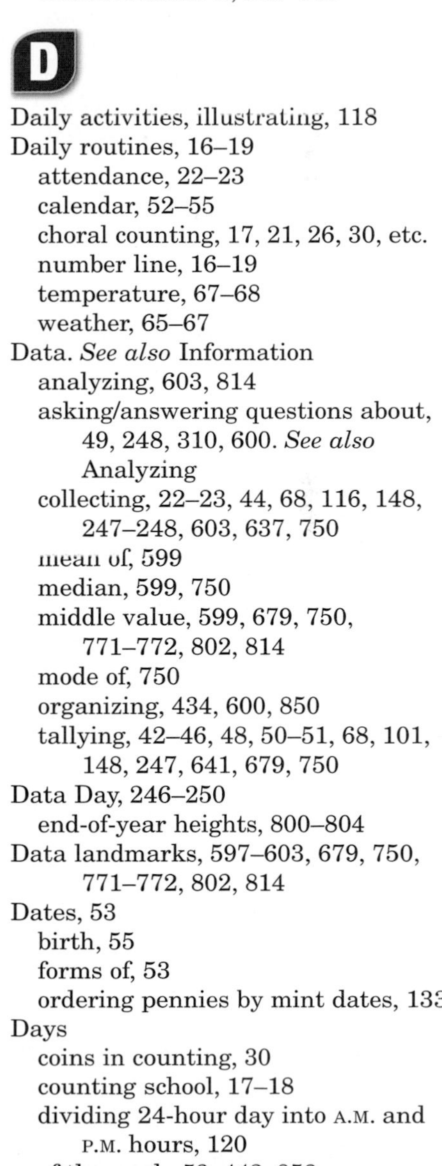

D

Q

R

T

W